BUSINESS CALCULUS I & II, 1425 & 1476

Solutions Manual to Accompany
APPLIED CALCULUS with LINEAR PROGRAMMING
For Business, Economics, Life Sciences, and Social Sciences

Taken from:

Student Solutions Manual, by Etgen
to accompany *Calculus for Business, Economics, Life Sciences,
and Social Sciences Manual*, Tenth Edition
By Raymond A. Barnett, Michael R. Ziegler, and Karl E. Byleen

Solutions Manual, by Etgen
to accompany *Applied Calculus for Business, Economics, Life Sciences,
and Social Sciences*, Fifth Edition
By Raymond A. Barnett, Michael R. Ziegler, and Karl E. Byleen

Student Solutions Manual, by Laurel Technical Services
to accompany *Finite Mathematics for Business, Economics, Life Sciences,
and Social Sciences*, Eighth Edition
By Raymond A. Barnett, Michael R. Ziegler, and Karl E. Byleen

Student Solutions Manual, by Etgen
to accompany *College Mathematics for Business, Economics, Life Sciences,
and Social Sciences*, Tenth Edition
By Raymond A. Barnett, Michael R. Ziegler, and Karl E. Byleen

PEARSON
Custom
Publishing

PEARSON
Prentice
Hall

Cover Image: *Untitled 31*, by Mark Kelly.

Taken.from:

Student Solutions Manual, by Etgen
to accompany *Calculus for Business, Economics, Life Sciences, and Social Sciences*, Tenth Edition
by Raymond A. Barnett, Michael R. Ziegler, and Karl E. Byleen
Copyright © 2005 by Pearson Education, Inc.
Published by Prentice Hall
Upper Saddle River, New Jersey 07458

Solutions Manual, by Etgen
to accompany *Applied Calculus for Business, Economics, Life Sciences, and Social Sciences*, Fifth Edition
by Raymond A. Barnett and Michael R. Ziegler
Copyright © 1994 by Prentice-Hall, Inc.
A Pearson Education Company

Student Solutions Manual, by Laurel Technical Services
to accompany *Finite Mathematics for Business, Economics, Life Sciences, and Social Sciences*, Eighth Edition
by Raymond A. Barnett, Michael R. Ziegler, and Karl E. Byleen
Copyright © 1999 by Prentice-Hall, Inc.
A Pearson Education Company

Student Solutions Manual, by Etgen
to accompany *College Mathematics for Business, Economics, Life Sciences, and Social Sciences*, Tenth Edition
by Raymond A. Barnett, Michael R. Ziegler, and Karl E. Byleen
Copyright © 2005 by Pearson Education, Inc.
Published by Prentice Hall

This special edition published in cooperation with Pearson Custom Publishing.

All trademarks, service marks, registered trademarks, and registered service marks are the property of their respective owners and are used herein for identification purposes only.

Printed in the United States of America

10 9 8 7 6 5 4 3 2 1

ISBN 0-536-97405-5

2005360638

BU

Please visit our web site at *www.pearsoncustom.com*

PEARSON CUSTOM PUBLISHING
75 Arlington Street, Suite 300, Boston, MA 02116
A Pearson Education Company

Contents

1 The Derivative

Things to remember:

1.   LIMIT

   We write
   $$\lim_{x \to c} f(x) = L \text{ or } f(x) \to L \text{ as } x \to c$$
   if the functional value $f(x)$ is close to the single real number L whenever x is close to but not equal to c (on either side of c).

   [Note: The existence of a limit at c has nothing to do with the value of the function at c. In fact, c may not even be in the domain of f. However, the function must be defined on both sides of c.]

2.   ONE-SIDED LIMITS

   We write $\lim_{x \to c^-} f(x) = K$ [$x \to c^-$ is read "x approaches c from the left" and means $x \to c$ and $x < c$] and call K the LIMIT FROM THE LEFT or LEFT-HAND LIMIT if $f(x)$ is close to K whenever x is close to c, but to the left of c on the real number line.

   We write $\lim_{x \to c^+} f(x) = L$ [$x \to c^+$ is read "x approaches c from the right" and means $x \to c$ and $x > c$] and call L the LIMIT FROM THE RIGHT or RIGHT-HAND LIMIT if $f(x)$ is close to L whenever x is close to c, but to the right of c on the real number line.

3.   EXISTENCE OF A LIMIT

   In order for a limit to exist, the limit from the left and the limit from the right must both exist, and must be equal. That is, $\lim_{x \to c} f(x) = L$ if and only if $\lim_{x \to c^-} f(x) = \lim_{x \to c^+} f(x) = L$.

4.   PROPERTIES OF LIMITS

   Let f and g be two functions and assume that
   $$\lim_{x \to c} f(x) = L \qquad \lim_{x \to c} g(x) = M$$

   where L and M are real numbers (both limits exist). Then:

   (a) $\lim_{x \to c} [f(x) + g(x)] = \lim_{x \to c} f(x) + \lim_{x \to c} g(x) = L + M.$

   (b) $\lim_{x \to c} [f(x) - g(x)] = \lim_{x \to c} f(x) - \lim_{x \to c} g(x) = L - M.$

(c) $\lim\limits_{x \to c} kf(x) = k \lim\limits_{x \to c} f(x) = kL$ for any constant k.

(d) $\lim\limits_{x \to c} [f(x)g(x)] = \left(\lim\limits_{x \to c} f(x)\right)\left(\lim\limits_{x \to c} g(x)\right) = LM$.

(e) $\lim\limits_{x \to c} \dfrac{f(x)}{g(x)} = \dfrac{L}{M}$ if $M \neq 0$; $\lim\limits_{x \to c} \dfrac{f(x)}{g(x)}$ does not exist if $L \neq 0$

and $M = 0$; $\lim\limits_{x \to c} \dfrac{f(x)}{g(x)}$ is a 0/0 INDETERMINATE FORM if $L = M = 0$.

(f) $\lim\limits_{x \to c} \sqrt[n]{f(x)} = \sqrt[n]{\lim\limits_{x \to c} f(x)} = \sqrt[n]{L}$ ($L \geq 0$ for n even).

5. LIMITS OF POLYNOMIAL AND RATIONAL FUNCTIONS

   (a) $\lim\limits_{x \to c} f(x) = f(c)$ f any polynomial function

   (b) $\lim\limits_{x \to c} r(x) = r(c)$ r any rational function with a nonzero denominator at $x = c$.

6. DIFFERENCE QUOTIENT

Let the function f be defined in an open interval containing the number a. The expression

$$\frac{f(a + h) - f(a)}{h}$$

is called the DIFFERENCE QUOTIENT. One of the most important limits in calculus is the limit of the difference quotient:

$$\lim\limits_{h \to 0} \frac{f(a + h) - f(a)}{h}$$

---

1. (A) $\lim\limits_{x \to 0^-} f(x) = 2$ (B) $\lim\limits_{x \to 0^+} f(x) = 2$ (C) $\lim\limits_{x \to 0} f(x) = 2$ (D) $f(0) = 2$

3. (A) $\lim\limits_{x \to 2^-} f(x) = 1$ (B) $\lim\limits_{x \to 2^+} f(x) = 2$ (C) $\lim\limits_{x \to 2} f(x)$ does not exist

   (D) $f(2) = 2$ (E) No, because $\lim\limits_{x \to 2^-} f(x) = 1 \neq \lim\limits_{x \to 2^+} f(x) = 2$

5. (A) $\lim\limits_{x \to 1^-} g(x) = 1$ (B) $\lim\limits_{x \to 1^+} g(x) = 2$ (C) $\lim\limits_{x \to 1} g(x) =$ does not exist

   (D) $g(1)$ does not exist   (E) No, because $\lim\limits_{x \to 1^-} f(x) = 1 \neq \lim\limits_{x \to 1^+} f(x) = 2$

7. (A) $\lim\limits_{x \to 3^-} g(x) = 1$ (B) $\lim\limits_{x \to 3^+} g(x) = 1$ (C) $\lim\limits_{x \to 3} g(x) = 1$ (D) $g(3) = 3$
   (E) Yes, define $f(3) = 1$.

9. (A) $\lim\limits_{x \to -3^+} f(x) = -2$ (B) $\lim\limits_{x \to -3^-} f(x) = -2$ (C) $\lim\limits_{x \to -3} f(x) = -2$
   (D) $f(-3) = 1$ (E) Yes, set $f(-3) = -2$.

11. (A) $\lim\limits_{x \to 0^+} f(x) = 2$ (B) $\lim\limits_{x \to 0^-} f(x) = 2$ (C) $\lim\limits_{x \to 0} f(x) = 2$

(D) $f(0)$ does not exist.   (E) Yes, define $f(0) = 2$.

13. $\lim\limits_{x \to 3} 4x = 4 \cdot 3 = 12$ (use 5)   **15.** $\lim\limits_{x \to -4} (x + 5) = -4 + 5 = 1$ (use 5)

17. $\lim\limits_{x \to 2} x(x - 4) = 2(2 - 4) = 2(-2) = -4$ (use 4c and 5)

19. $\lim\limits_{x \to -3} \dfrac{x}{x + 5} = \dfrac{-3}{-3 + 5} = -\dfrac{3}{2} = -1.5$ (use 4e and 5)

21. $\lim\limits_{x \to 1} \sqrt{5x + 4} = \sqrt{5 + 4} = \sqrt{9} = 3$ (use 4f and 5)

23. $\lim\limits_{x \to 1} -3f(x) = -3 \lim\limits_{x \to 1} f(x) = -3(-5) = 15$

25. $\lim\limits_{x \to 1} [2f(x) + g(x)] = 2 \lim\limits_{x \to 1} f(x) + \lim\limits_{x \to 1} g(x) = 2(-5) + 4 = -6$

27. $\lim\limits_{x \to 1} \dfrac{2 - f(x)}{x + g(x)} = \dfrac{\lim\limits_{x \to 1}[2 - f(x)]}{\lim\limits_{x \to 1}[x + g(x)]} = \dfrac{2 - \lim\limits_{x \to 1} f(x)}{1 + \lim\limits_{x \to 1} g(x)} = \dfrac{2 - (-5)}{1 + 4} = \dfrac{7}{5}$

29. $\lim\limits_{x \to 1} f(x)[2 - g(x)] = \lim\limits_{x \to 1} f(x) \cdot \lim\limits_{x \to 1} [2 - g(x)]$

$= (-5)(2 - 4) = 10$

31. $\lim\limits_{x \to 1} \sqrt{g(x) - f(x)} = \sqrt{\lim\limits_{x \to 1}[g(x) - f(x)]} = \sqrt{\lim\limits_{x \to 1} g(x) - \lim\limits_{x \to 1} f(x)}$

$= \sqrt{4 - (-5)} = \sqrt{9} = 3$

33. $\lim\limits_{x \to 1} [f(x) + 1]^2 = \left(\lim\limits_{x \to 1} [f(x) + 1] \right)^2 = [-5 + 1]^2 = 16$

35.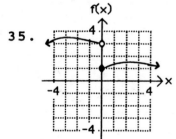

37.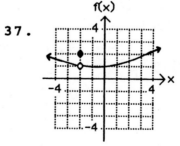

39. $f(x) = \begin{cases} 1 - x^2 & \text{if} \quad x \le 0 \\ 1 + x^2 & \text{if} \quad x > 0 \end{cases}$

(A) $\lim\limits_{x \to 0^+} f(x) = \lim\limits_{x \to 0^+} (1 + x^2) = 1$ (B) $\lim\limits_{x \to 0^-} f(x) = \lim\limits_{x \to 0^-} (1 - x^2) = 1$

(C) $\lim\limits_{x \to 0} f(x) = 1$ (D) $f(0) = 1$

41. $f(x) = \begin{cases} x^2 & \text{if} \quad x < 1 \\ 2x & \text{if} \quad x > 1 \end{cases}$

(A) $\lim\limits_{x \to 1^+} f(x) = \lim\limits_{x \to 1^+} 2x = 2$

(B) $\lim\limits_{x \to 1^-} f(x) = \lim\limits_{x \to 1^-} x^2 = 1$

(C) $\lim\limits_{x \to 1} f(x)$ does not exist

(D) $f(1)$ does not exist

43. $f(x) = \begin{cases} \dfrac{x^2 - 9}{x + 3} & \text{if} \quad x < 0 \\ \dfrac{x^2 - 9}{x - 3} & \text{if} \quad x > 0 \end{cases}$

(A) $\lim\limits_{x \to -3} f(x) = \lim\limits_{x \to -3} \dfrac{x^2 - 9}{x + 3} = \lim\limits_{x \to -3} \dfrac{(x - 3)(x + 3)}{x + 3} = \lim\limits_{x \to -3}(x - 3) = -6$

(B) $\lim\limits_{x \to 0^-} f(x) = \lim\limits_{x \to 0^-} \dfrac{x^2 - 9}{x + 3} = \dfrac{\lim\limits_{x \to 0^-}(x^2 - 9)}{\lim\limits_{x \to 0^-}(x + 3)} = \dfrac{-9}{3} = -3$

$\lim\limits_{x \to 0^+} f(x) = \lim\limits_{x \to 0^+} \dfrac{x^2 - 9}{x - 3} = \dfrac{\lim\limits_{x \to 0^+}(x^2 - 9)}{\lim\limits_{x \to 0^+}(x - 3)} = \dfrac{-9}{-3} = 3$

$\lim\limits_{x \to 0} f(x)$ does not exist

(C) $\lim\limits_{x \to 3} f(x) = \lim\limits_{x \to 3} \dfrac{x^2 - 9}{x - 3} = \lim\limits_{x \to 3} \dfrac{(x - 3)(x + 3)}{x - 3} = \lim\limits_{x \to 3}(x + 3) = 6$

45. $f(x) = \dfrac{|x - 1|}{x - 1}$

(A) For $x > 1$, $|x - 1| = x - 1$.

Thus, $\lim\limits_{x \to 1^+} \dfrac{|x - 1|}{x + 1} = \lim\limits_{x \to 1^+} \dfrac{x - 1}{x - 1} = \lim\limits_{x \to 1^+} 1 = 1$.

(B) For $x < 1$, $|x - 1| = -(x - 1)$.

Thus, $\lim\limits_{x \to 1^-} \dfrac{|x - 1|}{x - 1} = \lim\limits_{x \to 1^-} \dfrac{-(x - 1)}{x - 1} = \lim\limits_{x \to 1^-} -1 = -1$

(C) $\lim\limits_{x \to 1} f(x)$ does not exist

(D) $f(1)$ does not exist

47. $f(x) = \dfrac{x - 2}{x^2 - 2x} = \dfrac{x - 2}{x(x - 2)} = \dfrac{1}{x}$, $x \neq 2$; $f(2)$ does not exist.

(A) $\lim\limits_{x \to 0} f(x) = \lim\limits_{x \to 0} \dfrac{1}{x}$ does not exist

(B) $\displaystyle\lim_{x \to 2} f(x) = \lim_{x \to 2} \frac{1}{x} = \frac{1}{2}$

(C) $\displaystyle\lim_{x \to 4} f(x) = \lim_{x \to 4} \frac{1}{x} = \frac{1}{4}$

49. $f(x) = \dfrac{x^2 - x - 6}{x + 2} = \dfrac{(x - 3)(x + 2)}{x + 2} = x - 3,\ x \neq -2;\ f(-2)$ does not exist

    (A) $\displaystyle\lim_{x \to -2} f(x) = \lim_{x \to -2} (x - 3) = -5$

    (B) $\displaystyle\lim_{x \to 0} f(x) = \lim_{x \to 0} (x - 3) = -3$

    (C) $\displaystyle\lim_{x \to 3} f(x) = \lim_{x \to 3} (x - 3) = 0$

51. $f(x) = \dfrac{(x + 2)^2}{x^2 - 4} = \dfrac{(x + 2)^2}{(x - 2)(x + 2)} = \dfrac{x + 2}{x - 2},\ x \neq -2;\ f(-2)$ does not exist

    (A) $\displaystyle\lim_{x \to -2} f(x) = \lim_{x \to -2} \frac{x + 2}{x - 2} = \frac{0}{-4} = 0$

    (B) $\displaystyle\lim_{x \to 0} f(x) = \lim_{x \to 0} \frac{x + 2}{x - 2} = \frac{2}{-2} = -1$

    (C) $\displaystyle\lim_{x \to 2} f(x) = \lim_{x \to 2} \frac{x + 2}{x - 2}$ does not exist

53. $f(x) = \dfrac{2x^2 - 3x - 2}{x^2 + x - 6} = \dfrac{(2x + 1)(x - 2)}{(x + 3)(x - 2)} = \dfrac{2x + 1}{x + 3},\ x \neq 2;\ f(2)$ does not exist

    (A) $\displaystyle\lim_{x \to 2} f(x) = \lim_{x \to 2} \frac{2x + 1}{x + 3} = \frac{5}{5} = 1$

    (B) $\displaystyle\lim_{x \to 0} f(x) = \lim_{x \to 0} \frac{2x + 1}{x + 3} = \frac{1}{3}$

    (C) $\displaystyle\lim_{x \to 1} f(x) = \lim_{x \to 1} \frac{2x + 1}{x + 3} = \frac{3}{4}$

55. $f(x) = 3x + 1$

$\displaystyle\lim_{h \to 0} \frac{f(2 + h) - f(2)}{h} = \lim_{h \to 0} \frac{3(2 + h) + 1 - (3 \cdot 2 + 1)}{h}$

$\displaystyle = \lim_{h \to 0} \frac{6 + 3h + 1 - 7}{h} = \lim_{h \to 0} \frac{3h}{h} = \lim_{h \to 0} 3 = 3$

57. $f(x) = x^2 + 1$

$$\lim_{h \to 0} \frac{f(2 + h) - f(2)}{h} = \lim_{h \to 0} \frac{(2 + h)^2 + 1 - (2^2 + 1)}{h}$$

$$= \lim_{h \to 0} \frac{4 + 4h + h^2 + 1 - 5}{h} = \lim_{h \to 0} \frac{4h + h^2}{h}$$

$$= \lim_{h \to 0} (4 + h) = 4$$

59. $f(x) = \sqrt{x} - 2$

$$\lim_{h \to 0} \frac{f(2 + h) - f(2)}{h} = \lim_{h \to 0} \frac{\sqrt{2 + h} - 2 - (\sqrt{2} - 2)}{h} = \lim_{h \to 0} \frac{\sqrt{2 + h} - \sqrt{2}}{h}$$

$$= \lim_{h \to 0} \frac{\sqrt{2 + h} - \sqrt{2}}{h} \cdot \frac{\sqrt{2 + h} + \sqrt{2}}{\sqrt{2 + h} + \sqrt{2}} = \lim_{h \to 0} \frac{2 + h - 2}{h(\sqrt{2 + h} + \sqrt{2})}$$

$$= \lim_{h \to 0} \frac{h}{h(\sqrt{2 + h} + \sqrt{2})} = \lim_{h \to 0} \frac{1}{\sqrt{2 + h} + \sqrt{2}} = \frac{1}{2\sqrt{2}}$$

61. $f(x) = |x - 2| - 3$

$$\lim_{h \to 0} \frac{f(2 + h) - f(2)}{h} = \lim_{h \to 0} \frac{|(2 + h) - 2| - 3 - (|2 - 2| - 3)}{h}$$

$$= \lim_{h \to 0} \frac{|h| - 3 + 3}{h} = \lim_{h \to 0} \frac{|h|}{h} \text{ does not exist.}$$

63. $f(x) = \dfrac{2}{x - 1}$

$$\lim_{h \to 0} \frac{f(2 + h) - f(2)}{h} = \lim_{h \to 0} \frac{\dfrac{2}{2 + h - 1} - \dfrac{2}{2 - 1}}{h} = \lim_{h \to 0} \frac{\dfrac{2}{1 + h} - 2}{h}$$

$$= \lim_{h \to 0} \frac{\dfrac{2 - 2(1 + h)}{1 + h}}{h} = \lim_{h \to 0} \frac{-2h}{h(1 + h)}$$

$$= \lim_{h \to 0} \frac{-2}{1 + h} = -2$$

65. (A) $\displaystyle\lim_{x \to 1^-} f(x) = \lim_{x \to 1^-} (1 + x) = 2$

$\displaystyle\lim_{x \to 1^+} f(x) = \lim_{x \to 1^+} (4 - x) = 3$

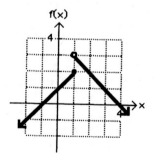

6

(B) $\lim\limits_{x \to 1^-} f(x) = \lim\limits_{x \to 1^-} (1 + 2x) = 3$

$\lim\limits_{x \to 1^+} f(x) = \lim\limits_{x \to 1^+} (4 - 2x) = 2$

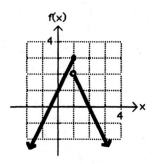

(C) $\lim\limits_{x \to 1^-} f(x) = \lim\limits_{x \to 1^-} (1 + mx) = 1 + m$

$\lim\limits_{x \to 1^+} f(x) = \lim\limits_{x \to 1^+} (4 - mx) = 4 - m$

$1 + m = 4 - m$

$2m = 3$

$m = \dfrac{3}{2}$

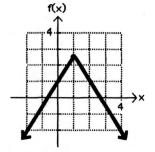

(D) The graph in (A) is broken at $x = 1$; it jumps up from $(1, 2)$ to $(1, 3)$.

The graph in (B) is also broken at $x = 1$; it jumps down from $(1, 3)$ to $(1, 2)$.

The graph in (C) is not broken; the two pieces meet at $\left(1, \dfrac{5}{2}\right)$.

67. $\lim\limits_{h \to 0} \dfrac{(a + h)^2 - a^2}{h} = \lim\limits_{h \to 0} \dfrac{a^2 + 2ah + h^2 - a^2}{h}$

$= \lim\limits_{h \to 0} \dfrac{2ah + h^2}{h} = \lim\limits_{h \to 0} (2a + h) = 2a$

69. $\lim\limits_{h \to 0} \dfrac{\sqrt{a + h} - \sqrt{a}}{h} = \lim\limits_{h \to 0} \dfrac{\sqrt{a + h} - \sqrt{a}}{h} \cdot \dfrac{\sqrt{a + h} + \sqrt{a}}{\sqrt{a + h} + \sqrt{a}} = \lim\limits_{h \to 0} \dfrac{(a + h) - a}{h(\sqrt{a + h} + \sqrt{a})}$

$= \lim\limits_{h \to 0} \dfrac{1}{\sqrt{a + h} + \sqrt{a}} = \dfrac{1}{2\sqrt{a}}$

71. (A) $F(x) = \begin{cases} 0.99 & \text{if } 0 < x \le 20 \\ 0.07(x - 20) + 0.99 & \text{if } x > 20 \end{cases}$ (B)

$= \begin{cases} 0.99 & \text{if } 0 < x \le 20 \\ 0.07x - 0.41 & \text{if } x > 20 \end{cases}$

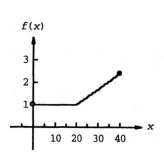

(C) $\lim\limits_{x \to 20^-} F(x) = 0.99 = \lim\limits_{x \to 20^+} F(x)$

Therefore, $\lim\limits_{x \to 20} F(x) = 0.99$

7

73. At $x = 20$ minutes, the first service charge is \$0.99 and the second service charge is \$2.70. Also, after 20 minutes, the first service charge is \$0.07 per minute versus \$0.09 per minute for the second service. The second service is much more expensive than the first.

75. (A) $D(x) = \begin{cases} x & \text{if} & 0 \le x < 300 \\ 0.97x & \text{if} & 300 \le x < 1,000 \\ 0.95x & \text{if} & 1,000 \le x < 3,000 \\ 0.93x & \text{if} & 3,000 \le x < 5,000 \\ 0.90x & \text{if} & 5,000 \le x \end{cases}$

(B) $\lim\limits_{x \to 1000^-} D(x) = \lim\limits_{x \to 1000^-} 0.97x = 970$,

$\lim\limits_{x \to 1000^+} D(x) = \lim\limits_{x \to 1000^+} 0.95x = 950$,

$\lim\limits_{x \to 1000} D(x)$ does not exist;

$\lim\limits_{x \to 3000^-} D(x) = \lim\limits_{x \to 3000^-} 0.95x = 2850$,

$\lim\limits_{x \to 3000^+} D(x) = \lim\limits_{x \to 3000^+} 0.93x = 2790$,

$\lim\limits_{x \to 3000} D(x)$ does not exist.

77. (A) $F(x) = \begin{cases} 20x & \text{if} & 0 \le x \le 4,000 \\ 80,000 & \text{if} & x > 4,000 \end{cases}$

(B) $\lim\limits_{x \to 4000^-} F(x) = \lim\limits_{x \to 4000^-} 20x = 80,000$,

$\lim\limits_{x \to 4000^+} F(x) = \lim\limits_{x \to 4000^+} 80,000 = 80,000$.

Therefore, $\lim\limits_{x \to 4000} F(x) = 80,000$.

$\lim\limits_{x \to 8000} F(x) = \lim\limits_{x \to 8000} 80,000 = 80,000$.

79. $\lim\limits_{x \to 5^-} f(x) = \lim\limits_{x \to 5^-} 0 = 0$,

$\lim\limits_{x \to 5^+} f(x) = \lim\limits_{x \to 5^+} (0.8 - 0.08x) = 0.4$.

Therefore, $\lim\limits_{x \to 5} f(x)$ does not exist.

$\lim\limits_{x \to 5^-} g(x) = \lim\limits_{x \to 5^-} 0 = 0$,

$\lim\limits_{x \to 5^+} g(x) = \lim\limits_{x \to 5^+} (0.8x - 0.04x^2 - 3) = 0$.

Therefore, $\lim\limits_{x \to 5} g(x) = 0$.

$$\lim_{x \to 10^-} f(x) = \lim_{x \to 10^-} (0.8 - 0.08x) = 0,$$

$$\lim_{x \to 10^+} f(x) = \lim_{x \to 10^+} 0 = 0.$$

Therefore, $\lim_{x \to 10} f(x) = 0.$

$$\lim_{x \to 10^-} g(x) = \lim_{x \to 10^-} (0.8x - 0.04x^2 - 3) = 1,$$

$$\lim_{x \to 10^+} g(x) = \lim_{x \to 0^+} 1 = 1.$$

Therefore, $\lim_{x \to 10} g(x) = 1.$

EXERCISE 1-2

Things to remember:

1. __CONTINUITY__

    A function f is CONTINUOUS AT THE POINT $x = c$ if:

    (a) $\lim_{x \to c} f(x)$ exists;

    (b) $f(c)$ exists;

    (c) $\lim_{x \to c} f(x) = f(c)$

    If one or more of the three conditions fails, then f is DISCONTINUOUS at $x = c$.

    A function is CONTINUOUS ON THE OPEN INTERVAL (a, b) if it is continuous at each point on the interval.

2. __ONE-SIDED CONTINUITY__

    A function f is CONTINUOUS ON THE LEFT AT $x = c$ if $\lim_{x \to c^-} f(x) = f(c)$; f is CONTINUOUS ON THE RIGHT AT $x = c$ if $\lim_{x \to c^+} f(x) = f(c)$.

    The function f is continuous on the closed interval $[a, b]$ if it is continuous on the open interval (a, b), and is continuous on the right at a and continuous on the left at b.

3. __CONTINUITY PROPERTIES OF SOME SPECIFIC FUNCTIONS__

    (a) A constant function, $f(x) = k$, is continuous for all x.

    (b) For n a positive integer, $f(x) = x^n$ is continuous for all x.

    (c) A polynomial function
    $$P(x) = a_n x^n + a_{n-1} x^{n-1} + \ldots + a_1 x + a_0$$
    is continuous for all x.

(d) A rational function
$$R(x) = \frac{P(x)}{Q(x)} ,$$
P and Q polynomial functions, is continuous for all x except those numbers $x = c$ such that $Q(c) = 0$.

(e) For n an odd positive integer, $n > 1$, $\sqrt[n]{f(x)}$ is continuous wherever f is continuous.

(f) For n an even positive integer, $\sqrt[n]{f(x)}$ is continuous wherever f is continuous and non-negative.

4. <u></u> VERTICAL ASYMPTOTES

Suppose that the limit of a function f fails to exist as x approaches c from the left because the values of $f(x)$ are becoming very large positive numbers (or very large negative numbers). This is denoted

$$\lim_{x \to c^-} f(x) = \infty \quad (\text{or } -\infty)$$

If this happens as x approaches c from the right, then

$$\lim_{x \to c^+} f(x) = \infty \quad (\text{or } -\infty)$$

If both one-sided limits exhibit the same behavior, then

$$\lim_{x \to c} f(x) = \infty \quad (\text{or } -\infty)$$

If any of the above hold, the line $x = c$ is a VERTICAL ASYMPTOTE for the graph of $y = f(x)$.

5. SIGN PROPERTIES ON AN INTERVAL (a, b)

If f is continuous or (a, b) and $f(x) \neq 0$ for all x in (a, b), then either $f(x) > 0$ for all x in (a, b) or $f(x) < 0$ for all x in (a, b).

6. CONSTRUCTING SIGN CHARTS

Given a function f:

Step 1. Find all partition numbers. That is:

(A) Find all numbers where f is discontinuous. (Rational functions are discontinuous for values of x that make a denominator 0.)

(B) Find all numbers where $f(x) = 0$. (For a rational function, this occurs where the numerator is 0 and the denominator is not 0.)

Step 2. Plot the numbers found in step 1 on a real number line, dividing the number line into intervals.

Step 3. Select a test number in each open interval determined in step 2, and evaluate $f(x)$ at each test number to determine whether $f(x)$ is positive (+) or negative (-) in each interval.

Step 4. Construct a sign chart using the real number line in step 2. This will show the sign of $f(x)$ on each open interval.

[*Note*: From the sign chart, it is easy to find the solution for the inequality $f(x) < 0$ or $f(x) > 0$.]

---

1. f is continuous at $x = 1$, since $\lim_{x \to 1} f(x) = f(1) = 2$

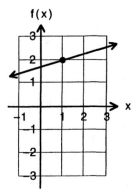

f(x)

3. f is discontinuous at $x = 1$, since $\lim_{x \to 1} f(x) \neq f(1)$

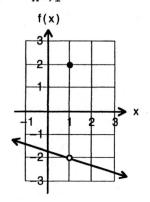

f(x)

5. $\lim_{x \to 1^-} f(x) = 2$, $\lim_{x \to 1^+} f(x) = -2$

implies $\lim_{x \to 1} f(x)$ does not exist;

f is discontinuous at $x = 1$, since $\lim_{x \to 1} f(x)$ does not exist

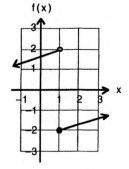

f(x)

7. (A) $\lim_{x \to 1^-} f(x) = 2$ (B) $\lim_{x \to 1^+} f(x) = 1$

(C) $\lim_{x \to 1} f(x)$ does not exist   (D) $f(1) = 1$

(E) No, because $\lim_{x \to 1} f(x)$ does not exist.

9. (A) $\lim_{x \to -2^-} f(x) = 1$ (B) $\lim_{x \to -2^+} f(x) = 1$

(C) $\lim_{x \to -2} f(x) = 1$ (D) $f(-2) = 3$

(E) No, because $\lim_{x \to -2} f(x) \neq f(-2)$.

11. (A) $\lim\limits_{x \to -3^-} g(x) = 1$ (B) $\lim\limits_{x \to -3^+} g(x) = 1$

(C) $\lim\limits_{x \to -3} g(x) = 1$ (D) $g(-3) = 3$

(E) No, because $\lim\limits_{x \to -3} g(x) \neq g(-3)$.

13. (A) $\lim\limits_{x \to 2^-} g(x) = 2$ (B) $\lim\limits_{x \to 2^+} g(x) = -1$

(C) $\lim\limits_{x \to 2} g(x)$ does not exist   (D) $g(2) = 2$

(E) No, because $\lim\limits_{x \to 2} g(x)$ does not exist.

15. $f(x) = 3x - 4$ is a polynomial function. Therefore, f is continuous for all x [$\underline{3}$(c)].

17. $g(x) = \dfrac{3x}{x + 2}$ is a rational function and the denominator $x + 2$ is 0 at $x = -2$. Thus, g is continuous for all x except $x = -2$ [$\underline{3}$(d)].

19. $m(x) = \dfrac{x + 1}{(x - 1)(x + 4)}$ is a rational function and the denominator $(x - 1)(x + 4)$ is 0 at $x = 1$ or $x = -4$. Thus, m is continuous for all x except $x = 1$, $x = -4$ [$\underline{3}$(d)].

21. $F(x) = \dfrac{2x}{x^2 + 9}$ is a rational function and the denominator $x^2 + 9 \neq 0$ for all x. Thus, F is continuous for all x.

23. $M(x) = \dfrac{x - 1}{4x^2 - 9}$ is a rational function and the denominator $4x^2 - 9 = 0$ at $x = \dfrac{3}{2}, -\dfrac{3}{2}$. Thus, M is continuous for all x except $x = \pm\dfrac{3}{2}$.

25. $f(x) = \begin{cases} 2 & \text{if } x \text{ is an integer} \\ 1 & \text{if } x \text{ is not an integer} \end{cases}$

(A) The graph of f is:

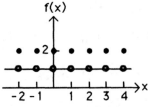

(B) $\lim\limits_{x \to 2} f(x) = 1$ (C) $f(2) = 2$

(D) f is not continuous at $x = 2$ since $\lim\limits_{x \to 2} f(x) \neq f(2)$.

(E) f is discontinuous at $x = n$ for all integers n.

12

27. $x^2 - x - 12 < 0$

Let $f(x) = x^2 - x - 12 = (x - 4)(x + 3)$. Then f is continuous for all x and $f(-3) = f(4) = 0$. Thus, $x = -3$ and $x = 4$ are partition numbers.

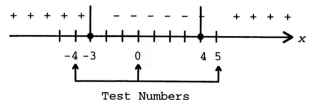

Test Numbers	
x	$f(x)$
-4	8 (+)
0	-12 (−)
5	8 (+)

Thus, $x^2 - x - 12 < 0$ for:

$-3 < x < 4$ (inequality notation)

$(-3, 4)$ (interval notation)

29. $x^2 + 21 > 10x$ or $x^2 - 10x + 21 > 0$

Let $f(x) = x^2 - 10x + 21 = (x - 7)(x - 3)$. Then f is continuous for all x and $f(3) = f(7) = 0$. Thus, $x = 3$ and $x = 7$ are partition numbers.

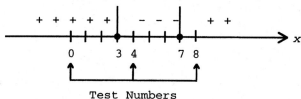

Test Numbers	
x	$f(x)$
0	21 (+)
4	-3 (−)
8	5 (+)

Thus, $x^2 - 10x + 21 > 0$ for:

$x < 3$ or $x > 7$ (inequality notation)

$(-\infty, 3) \cup (7, \infty)$ (interval notation)

31. $x^3 < 4x$ or $x^3 - 4x < 0$

Let $f(x) = x^3 - 4x = x(x^2 - 4) = x(x - 2)(x + 2)$. Then f is continuous for all x and $f(-2) = f(0) = f(2) = 0$. Thus, $x = -2$, $x = 0$ and $x = 2$ are partition numbers.

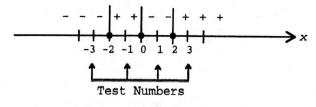

Test Numbers	
x	$f(x)$
-3	-15 (−)
-1	3 (+)
1	-3 (−)
3	15 (+)

Thus, $x^3 < 4x$ for:

$-\infty < x < -2$ or $0 < x < 2$ (inequality notation)

$(-\infty, -2) \cup (0, 2)$ (interval notation)

33. $\dfrac{x^2 + 5x}{x - 3} > 0$

Let $f(x) = \dfrac{x^2 + 5x}{x - 3} = \dfrac{x(x + 5)}{x - 3}$. Then f is discontinuous at $x = 3$ and
$f(0) = f(-5) = 0$. Thus, $x = -5$, $x = 0$, and $x = 3$ are partition numbers.

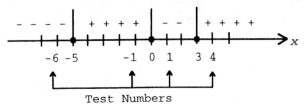

Test Numbers	
x	$f(x)$
-6	$-\frac{2}{3}\ (-)$
-1	$1\ (+)$
1	$-3\ (-)$
4	$36\ (+)$

Thus, $\dfrac{x^2 + 5x}{x - 3} > 0$ for: $-5 < x < 0$ or $x > 3$ (inequality notation)

$(-5,\ 0) \cup (3,\ \infty)$ (interval notation)

35. (A) $f(x) > 0$ on $(-4,\ -2) \cup (0,\ 2) \cup (4,\ \infty)$

(B) $f(x) < 0$ on $(-\infty,\ -4) \cup (-2,\ 0) \cup (2,\ 4)$

37. $f(x) = x^4 - 6x^2 + 3x + 5$
Partition numbers: $x_1 \approx -2.5308$, $x_2 \approx -0.7198$

(A) $f(x) > 0$ on $(-\infty,\ -2.5308) \cup (-0.7198,\ \infty)$

(B) $f(x) < 0$ on $(-2.5308,\ -0.7198)$

39. $f(x) = \dfrac{3 + 6x - x^3}{x^2 - 1}$
Partition numbers: $x_1 \approx -2.1451$, $x_2 = -1$, $x_3 \approx -0.5240$,
$\quad\quad x_4 = 1$, $x_5 \approx 2.6691$

(A) $f(x) > 0$ on $(-\infty,\ -2.1451) \cup (-1,\ -0.5240) \cup (1,\ 2.6691)$

(B) $f(x) < 0$ on $(-2.1451,\ -1) \cup (-0.5240,\ 1) \cup (2.6691,\ \infty)$

41. $f(x) = x - 6$ is continuous for all x since it is a polynomial function. Therefore, $g(x) = \sqrt{x - 6}$ is continuous for all x such that $x - 6 \geq 0$, that is, for all x in $[6,\ \infty)$ [see 3(f)].

43. $f(x) = 5 - x$ is continuous for all x since it is a polynomial function. Therefore, $F(x) = \sqrt[3]{5 - x}$ is continuous for all x, that is, for all x in $(-\infty,\ \infty)$.

45. $f(x) = x^2 - 9$ is continuous for all x since it is a polynomial function. Therefore, $g(x) = \sqrt{x^2 - 9}$ is continuous for all x such that $x^2 - 9 = (x - 3)(x + 3) \geq 0$.

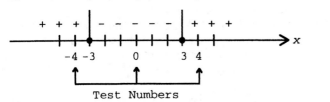

Test Numbers	
x	$f(x)$
0	-9
-4	7
4	7

Test Numbers

$\sqrt{x^2 - 9}$ is continuous on $(-\infty, -3] \cup [3, \infty)$.

47. $f(x) = x^2 + 1$ is continuous for all x since it is a polynomial function. Also $x^2 + 1 \geq 1 > 0$ for all x. Therefore, $\sqrt{x^2 + 1}$ is continuous for all x, that is, for all x in $(-\infty, \infty)$.

49. The graph of f is shown at the right. This function is discontinuous at $x = 1$. [$\lim\limits_{x \to 1} f(x)$ does not exist.]

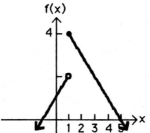

51. The graph of f is:

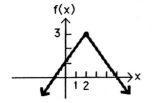

This function is continuous for all x. $\left[\lim\limits_{x \to 2} f(x) = f(2) = 3.\right]$

53. The graph of f is:

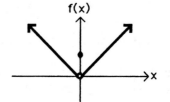

This function is discontinuous at $x = 0$. $\left[\lim\limits_{x \to 0} f(x) = 0 \neq f(0) = 1.\right]$

55. f is discontinuous at $x = 2$: f is not defined at 2, $\lim\limits_{x \to 2^-} f(x) = 0$ and $\lim\limits_{x \to 2^+} 4$.

57. f is discontinuous at $x = -1$ and $x = 1$ because f is not defined at these points. However, $\lim\limits_{x \to -1} f(x) = 2$ and $\lim\limits_{x \to 1} f(x) = 2$.

59. (A) Yes; g is continuous on $(-1, 2)$.

(B) Since $\lim\limits_{x \to -1^+} g(x) = -1 = g(-1)$, g is continuous from the right at $x = -1$

(C) Since $\lim\limits_{x \to 2^-} g(x) = 2 = g(2)$, g is continuous from the left at $x = 2$.

(D) Yes; g is continuous on the closed interval $[-1, 2]$.

15

61. (A) Since $\lim\limits_{x \to 0^+} f(x) = f(0) = 0$, f is continuous from the right at $x = 0$.

(B) Since $\lim\limits_{x \to 0^-} f(x) = -1 \neq f(0) = 0$, f is not continuous from the left at $x = 0$.

(C) f is continuous on the open interval $(0, 1)$.

(D) f is *not* continuous on the closed interval $[0, 1]$ since $\lim\limits_{x \to 1^-} f(x) = 0 \neq f(1) = 1$, i.e., f is not continuous from the left at $x = 1$.

(E) f is continuous on the half-closed interval $[0, 1)$.

63. x intercepts: $x = -5, 2$

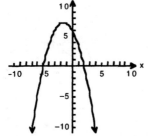

65. x intercepts: $x = -6, -1, 4$

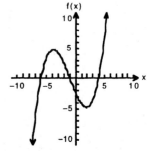

67. $f(x) = \dfrac{2}{1 - x} \neq 0$ for all x. This does not contradict Theorem 2 because f is not continuous on $(-1, 3)$; f is discontinuous at $x = 1$.

69. The following sketches illustrate that either condition is possible. Theorem 2 implies that one of these two conditions must occur.

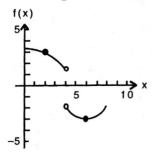
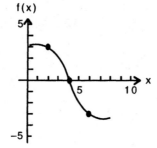

71. (A)
$$P(x) = \begin{cases} 0.37 & \text{if } 0 < x \leq 1 \\ 0.60 & \text{if } 1 < x \leq 2 \\ 0.83 & \text{if } 2 < x \leq 3 \\ 1.06 & \text{if } 3 < x \leq 4 \\ 1.29 & \text{if } 4 < x \leq 5 \end{cases}$$

(B)

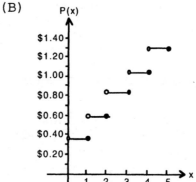

(C) P is continuous at $x = 4.5$ since P is a continuous function on $(4, 5]$; $P(x) = 1.29$ for $4 < x \leq 5$.
P is not continuous at $x = 4$ since
$$\lim\limits_{x \to 4^-} P(x) = 1.06 \neq \lim\limits_{x \to 4^+} P(x) = 1.29.$$

73. (A) Q is defined for all real numbers whereas P is defined only for $x > 0$.

(B) For each positive integer n, $P(n) = 0.37 + (n - 1)(0.23)$ while $Q(n) = 0.37 + n(0.23)$; for each positive number x, x not an integer $P(x) = Q(x)$.

75. (A) $S(x) = 5.00 + 0.63x$ if $0 \leq x \leq 50$;
$S(50) = 36.50$;
$S(x) = 36.50 + 0.45(x - 50)$
$= 14 + 0.45x$ if $x > 50$

Therefore, $S(x) = \begin{cases} 36.50 + 0.50x & \text{if} \quad 0 \leq x \leq 50 \\ 14.00 + 0.45x & \text{if} \quad x > 50 \end{cases}$

(B)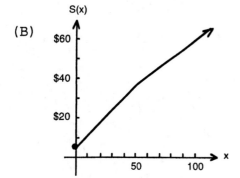

(C) $S(x)$ is continuous at $x = 50$;
$$\lim_{x \to 50^-} S(x) = \lim_{x \to 50^+} S(x)$$
$$= \lim_{x \to 50} S(x)$$
$$= S(50) = 36.5.$$

77. (A) $E(s) = \begin{cases} 1000, & 0 \leq s \leq 10{,}000 \\ 1000 + 0.05(s - 10{,}000), & 10{,}000 < s < 20{,}000 \\ 1500 + 0.05(s - 10{,}000), & s \geq 20{,}000 \end{cases}$

The graph of E is:

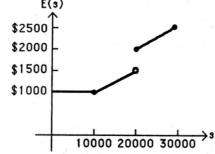

(B) From the graph, $\lim\limits_{s \to 10{,}000} E(s) = \$1000$ and $E(10{,}000) = \$1000$.

(C) From the graph, $\lim\limits_{s \to 20{,}000} E(s)$ does not exist. $E(20{,}000) = \$2000$.

(D) E is continuous at $10{,}000$; E is not continuous at $20{,}000$.

79. (A) From the graph, N is discontinuous at $t = t_2$, $t = t_3$, $t = t_4$, $t = t_6$, and $t = t_7$.

(B) From the graph, $\lim\limits_{t \to t_5} N(t) = 7$ and $N(t_5) = 7$.

(C) From the graph, $\lim\limits_{t \to t_3} N(t)$ does not exist; $N(t_3) = 4$.

Things to remember:

<u>1</u>. AVERAGE RATE OF CHANGE

For $y = f(x)$, the AVERAGE RATE OF CHANGE FROM $x = a$ TO $x = a + h$ is

$$\frac{f(a + h) - f(a)}{(a + h) - a} = \frac{f(a + h) - f(a)}{h} \qquad h \neq 0$$

The expression $\dfrac{f(a + h) - f(a)}{h}$ is called the DIFFERENCE QUOTIENT.

<u>2</u>. INSTANTANEOUS RATE OF CHANGE

For $y = f(x)$, the INSTANTANEOUS RATE OF CHANGE AT $x = a$ is

$$\lim_{h \to 0} \frac{f(a + h) - f(a)}{h}$$

if the limit exists.

<u>3</u>. SECANT LINE

A line through two points on the graph of a function is called a SECANT LINE. If $(a, f(a))$ and $((a + h), f(a + h))$ are two points on the graph of $y = f(x)$, then

$$\text{Slope of secant line} = \frac{f(a + h) - f(a)}{h} \qquad \text{[Difference quotient]}$$

<u>4</u>. SLOPE OF A GRAPH

For $y = f(x)$, the SLOPE OF THE GRAPH at the point $(a, f(a))$ is given by

$$\lim_{h \to 0} \frac{f(a + h) - f(a)}{h}$$

provided the limit exists. The slope of the graph is also the SLOPE OF THE TANGENT LINE at the point $(a, f(a))$.

<u>5</u>. THE DERIVATIVE

For $y = f(x)$, we define THE DERIVATIVE OF f AT x, denoted by $f'(x)$, to be

$$f'(x) = \lim_{h \to 0} \frac{f(x + h) - f(x)}{h} \qquad \text{if the limit exists.}$$

If $f'(x)$ exists for each x in the open interval (a, b), then f is said to be DIFFERENTIABLE OVER (a, b).

6. INTERPRETATIONS OF THE DERIVATIVE

The derivative of a function f is a new function f'. The domain of f' is a subset of the domain of f. Interpretations of the derivative are:

a. Slope of the tangent line. For each x in the domain of f', $f'(x)$ is the slope of the line tangent to the graph of f at the point $(x, f(x))$.

b. Instantaneous rate of change. For each x in the domain of f', $f'(x)$ is the instantaneous rate of change of $y = f(x)$ with respect to x.

c. Velocity. If $f(x)$ is the position of a moving object at time x, then $v = f'(x)$ is the velocity of the object at that time.

7. THE FOUR STEP PROCESS FOR FINDING THE DERIVATIVE OF A FUNCTION f.

Step 1. Find $f(x + h)$.

Step 2. Find $f(x + h) - f(x)$.

Step 3. Find $\dfrac{f(x + h) - f(x)}{h}$.

Step 4. Find $\lim\limits_{h \to 0} \dfrac{f(x + h) - f(x)}{h}$.

---

1. (A) $\dfrac{f(2) - f(1)}{2 - 1} = \dfrac{1 - 4}{1} = -3$ is the slope of the secant line through $(1, f(1))$ and $(2, f(2))$.

(B) $\dfrac{f(1 + h) - f(1)}{h} = \dfrac{5 - (1 + h)^2 - 4}{h} = \dfrac{5 - [1 + 2h + h^2] - 4}{h}$

$$= \dfrac{-2h - h^2}{h} = -2 - h;$$

slope of the secant line through $(1, f(1))$ and $(1 + h, f(1 + h))$

(C) $\lim\limits_{h \to 0} \dfrac{f(1 + h) - f(1)}{h} = \lim\limits_{h \to 0} (-2 - h) = -2;$

slope of the tangent line at $(1, f(1))$

3. $f(x) = 3x^2$

(A) Average rate of change: $\dfrac{f(4) - f(1)}{4 - 1} = \dfrac{3(4)^2 - 3(1)^2}{3} = \dfrac{48 - 3}{3} = 15.$

(B) Slope of the secant line: $\dfrac{f(4) - f(1)}{4 - 1} = 15.$

(C) $\dfrac{f(1 + h) - f(1)}{1 + h - 1} = \dfrac{3(1 + h)^2 - 3(1)^2}{h} = \dfrac{3(1 + 2h + h^2) - 3}{h}$

$$= \dfrac{6h + 3h^2}{h} = 6 + 3h.$$

(D) $\lim\limits_{h\to 0}\dfrac{f(1+h)-f(1)}{h} = \lim\limits_{h\to 0}(6+3h) = 6.$

(E) 6.

(F) 6.

(G) $f(1) = 3$, $f'(1) = 6$; tangent line: $y - 3 = 6(x - 1)$ or $y = 6x - 3$.

5. $f(x) = -5$

Step 1. Find $f(x + h)$:
$$f(x + h) = -5$$

Step 2. Find $f(x + h) - f(x)$:
$$f(x + h) - f(x) = -5 - (-5) = 0$$

Step 3. Find $\dfrac{f(x + h) - f(x)}{h}$:
$$\frac{f(x + h) - f(x)}{h} = \frac{0}{h} = 0$$

Step 4. Find $\lim\limits_{h\to 0}\dfrac{f(x + h) - f(x)}{h}$:
$$\lim\limits_{h\to 0}\frac{f(x + h) - f(x)}{h} = \lim\limits_{h\to 0}0 = 0$$
Thus, $f'(x) = 0$.
$f'(1) = 0$, $f'(2) = 0$, $f'(3) = 0$

7. $f(x) = 3x - 7$

Step 1. Find $f(x + h)$:
$$f(x + h) = 3(x + h) - 7 = \boxed{3x + 3h - 7}$$

Step 2. Find $f(x + h) - f(x)$:
$$f(x + h) - f(x) = 3x + 3h - 7 - (3x - 7) = 3h$$

Step 3. Find $\dfrac{f(x + h) - f(x)}{h}$:
$$\frac{f(x + h) - f(x)}{h} = \frac{3h}{h} = 3$$

Step 4. Find $\lim\limits_{h\to 0}\dfrac{f(x + h) - f(x)}{h}$:
$$\lim\limits_{h\to 0}\frac{f(x + h) - f(x)}{h} = \lim\limits_{h\to 0}3 = 3$$
Thus, $f'(x) = 3$.
$f'(1) = 3$, $f'(2) = 3$, $f'(3) = 3$

9. $f(x) = 2 - 3x^2$

Step 1. Find $f(x + h)$:
$$f(x + h) = 2 - 3(x + h)^2 = 2 - 3(x^2 + 2xh + h^2)$$
$$= 2 - 3x^2 - 6xh - 3h^2$$

<u>Step 2</u>. Find $f(x + h) - f(x)$:

$$f(x + h) - f(x) = 2 - 3x^2 - 6xh - 3h^2 - (2 - 3x^2) = -6xh - 3h^2$$

<u>Step 3</u>. Find $\dfrac{f(x + h) - f(x)}{h}$:

$$\frac{f(x + h) - f(x)}{h} = \frac{-6xh - 3h^2}{h} = -6x - 3h$$

<u>Step 4</u>. Find $\lim\limits_{h \to 0} \dfrac{f(x + h) - f(x)}{h}$:

$$\lim_{h \to 0} \frac{f(x + h) - f(x)}{h} = \lim_{h \to 0}(-6x - 3h) = -6x$$

Thus, $f'(x) = -6x$.

$f'(1) = -6$, $f'(2) = -12$, $f'(3) = -18$

11. $f(x) = x^2 + 6x - 10$

<u>Step 1</u>. Find $f(x + h)$:

$$f(x + h) = (x + h)^2 + 6(x + h) - 10 = x^2 + 2xh + h^2 + 6x + 6h - 10$$

<u>Step 2</u>. Find $f(x + h) - f(x)$:

$$f(x + h) - f(x) = x^2 + 2xh + h^2 + 6x + 6h - 10 - (x^2 + 6x - 10)$$
$$= 2xh + h^2 + 6h$$

<u>Step 3</u>. Find $\dfrac{f(x + h) - f(x)}{h}$:

$$\frac{f(x + h) - f(x)}{h} = \frac{2xh + h^2 + 6h}{h} = 2x + h + 6$$

<u>Step 4</u>. Find $\lim\limits_{h \to 0} \dfrac{f(x + h) - f(x)}{h}$:

$$\lim_{h \to 0} \frac{f(x + h) - f(x)}{h} = \lim_{h \to 0}(2x + h + 6) = 2x + 6$$

Thus, $f'(x) = 2x + 6$.

$f'(1) = 8$, $f'(2) = 10$, $f'(3) = 12$

13. $f(x) = 2x^2 - 7x + 3$

<u>Step 1</u>. Find $f(x + h)$:

$$f(x + h) = 2(x + h)^2 - 7(x + h) + 3$$
$$= 2(x^2 + 2xh + h^2) - 7x - 7h + 3$$
$$= 2x^2 + 4xh + 2h^2 - 7x - 7h + 3$$

<u>Step 2</u>. Find $f(x + h) - f(x)$:

$$f(x + h) - f(x) = 2x^2 + 4xh + 2h^2 - 7x - 7h + 3 - (2x^2 - 7x + 3)$$
$$= 4xh + 2h^2 - 7h$$

Step 3. Find $\dfrac{f(x + h) - f(x)}{h}$:

$$\frac{f(x + h) - f(x)}{h} = \frac{4xh + 2h^2 - 7h}{h} = 4x + 2h - 7$$

Step 4. Find $\displaystyle\lim_{h \to 0} \dfrac{f(x + h) - f(x)}{h}$:

$$\lim_{h \to 0} \frac{f(x + h) - f(x)}{h} = \lim_{h \to 0} (4x + 2h - 7) = 4x - 7$$

Thus, $f'(x) = 4x - 7$.

$f'(1) = -3$, $f'(2) = 1$, $f'(3) = 5$

15. $f(x) = -x^2 + 4x - 9$

Step 1. Find $f(x + h)$:

$$\begin{aligned}
f(x + h) &= -(x + h)^2 + 4(x + h) - 9 \\
&= -(x^2 + 2xh + h^2) + 4x + 4h - 9 \\
&= -x^2 - 2xh - h^2 + 4x + 4h - 9
\end{aligned}$$

Step 2. Find $f(x + h) - f(x)$:

$$\begin{aligned}
f(x + h) - f(x) &= -x^2 - 2xh - h^2 + 4x + 4h - 9 - (-x^2 + 4x - 9) \\
&= -2xh - h^2 + 4h
\end{aligned}$$

Step 3. Find $\dfrac{f(x + h) - f(x)}{h}$:

$$\frac{f(x + h) - f(x)}{h} = \frac{-2xh - h^2 + 4h}{h} = -2x - h + 4$$

Step 4. Find $\displaystyle\lim_{h \to 0} \dfrac{f(x + h) - f(x)}{h}$:

$$\lim_{h \to 0} \frac{f(x + h) - f(x)}{h} = \lim_{h \to 0} (-2x - h + 4) = -2x + 4$$

Thus, $f'(x) = -2x + 4$.

$f'(1) = 2$, $f'(2) = 0$, $f'(3) = -2$

17. $f(x) = 2x^3 + 1$

Step 1. Find $f(x + h)$:

$$\begin{aligned}
f(x + h) &= 2(x + h)^3 + 1 = 2(x^3 + 3x^2h + 3xh^2 + h^3) + 1 \\
&= 2x^3 + 6x^2h + 6xh^2 + 2h^3 + 1
\end{aligned}$$

Step 2. Find $f(x + h) - f(x)$:

$$\begin{aligned}
f(x + h) - f(x) &= 2x^3 + 6x^2h + 6xh^2 + 2h^3 + 1 - (2x^3 + 1) \\
&= 6x^2h + 6xh^2 + 2h^3
\end{aligned}$$

Step 3. Find $\dfrac{f(x + h) - f(x)}{h}$:

$$\frac{f(x + h) - f(x)}{h} = \frac{6x^2h + 6xh^2 + 2h^3}{h} = 6x^2 + 6xh + 2h^2$$

Step 4. Find $\lim\limits_{h \to 0} \dfrac{f(x + h) - f(x)}{h}$:

$$\lim_{h \to 0} \frac{f(x + h) - f(x)}{h} = \lim_{h \to 0}(6x^2 + 6xh + 2h^2) = 6x^2$$

Thus, $f'(x) = 6x^2$.

$f'(1) = 6, \quad f'(2) = 24, \quad f'(3) = 54$

19. $f(x) = 4 + \dfrac{4}{x}$

Step 1. Find $f(x + h)$:

$$f(x + h) = 4 + \frac{4}{x + h}$$

Step 2. Find $f(x + h) - f(x)$:

$$f(x + h) - f(x) = 4 + \frac{4}{x + h} - \left(4 + \frac{4}{x}\right) = \frac{4}{x + h} - \frac{4}{x}$$

$$= \frac{4x - 4(x + h)}{x(x + h)} = -\frac{4h}{x(x + h)}$$

Step 3. Find $\dfrac{f(x + h) - f(x)}{h}$:

$$\frac{f(x + h) - f(x)}{h} = \frac{-\dfrac{4h}{x(x + h)}}{h} = -\frac{4}{x(x + h)}$$

Step 4. Find $\lim\limits_{h \to 0} \dfrac{f(x + h) - f(x)}{h}$:

$$\lim_{h \to 0} \frac{f(x + h) - f(x)}{h} = \lim_{h \to 0} -\frac{4}{x(x + h)} = -\frac{4}{x^2}$$

Thus, $f'(x) = -\dfrac{4}{x^2}$.

$$f'(1) = -4, \quad f'(2) = -1, \quad f'(3) = -\frac{4}{9}$$

21. $f(x) = 5 + 3\sqrt{x}$

Step 1. Find $f(x + h)$:

$$f(x + h) = 5 + 3\sqrt{x + h}$$

Step 2. Find $f(x + h) - f(x)$:

$$f(x + h) - f(x) = 5 + 3\sqrt{x + h} - (5 + 3\sqrt{x})$$
$$= 3(\sqrt{x + h} - \sqrt{x})$$

Step 3. Find $\dfrac{f(x + h) - f(x)}{h}$:

$$\frac{f(x + h) - f(x)}{h} = \frac{3(\sqrt{x + h} - \sqrt{x})}{h} = \frac{3(\sqrt{x + h} - \sqrt{x})}{h} \cdot \frac{(\sqrt{x + h} + \sqrt{x})}{(\sqrt{x + h} + \sqrt{x})}$$

$$= \frac{3(x + h - x)}{h(\sqrt{x + h} + \sqrt{x})} = \frac{3h}{h(\sqrt{x + h} + \sqrt{x})} = \frac{3}{\sqrt{x + h} + \sqrt{x}}$$

Step 4. Find $\lim\limits_{h \to 0} \dfrac{f(x + h) - f(x)}{h}$:

$$\lim_{h \to 0} \frac{f(x + h) - f(x)}{h} = \lim_{h \to 0} \frac{3}{\sqrt{x + h} + \sqrt{x}} = \frac{3}{2\sqrt{x}}$$

Thus, $f'(x) = \dfrac{3}{2\sqrt{x}}$.

$$f'(1) = \frac{3}{2}, \quad f'(2) = \frac{3}{2\sqrt{2}} = \frac{3\sqrt{2}}{4}, \quad f'(3) = \frac{3}{2\sqrt{3}} = \frac{\sqrt{3}}{2}$$

23. $f(x) = 10\sqrt{x + 5}$

Step 1. Find $f(x + h)$:
$$f(x + h) = 10\sqrt{x + h + 5}$$

Step 2. Find $f(x + h) - f(x)$:
$$f(x + h) - f(x) = 10\sqrt{x + h + 5} - 10\sqrt{x + 5}$$
$$= 10\left(\sqrt{x + h + 5} - \sqrt{x + 5}\right)$$

Step 3. Find $\dfrac{f(x + h) - f(x)}{h}$:

$$\frac{f(x + h) - f(x)}{h} = \frac{10\left(\sqrt{x + h + 5} - \sqrt{x + 5}\right)}{h}$$

$$= \frac{10\left(\sqrt{x + h + 5} - \sqrt{x + 5}\right)}{h} \cdot \frac{\left(\sqrt{x + h + 5} + \sqrt{x + 5}\right)}{\left(\sqrt{x + h + 5} + \sqrt{x + 5}\right)}$$

$$= \frac{10[x + h + 5 - (x + 5)]}{h\left(\sqrt{x + h + 5} + \sqrt{x + 5}\right)} = \frac{10h}{h\left(\sqrt{x + h + 5} + \sqrt{x + 5}\right)}$$

$$= \frac{10}{\sqrt{x + h + 5} + \sqrt{x + 5}}$$

Step 4. Find $\lim\limits_{h \to 0} \dfrac{f(x + h) - f(x)}{h}$:

$$\lim_{h \to 0} \frac{f(x + h) - f(x)}{h} = \lim_{h \to 0} \frac{10}{\sqrt{x + h + 5} + \sqrt{x + 5}} = \frac{10}{2\sqrt{x + 5}} = \frac{5}{\sqrt{x + 5}}$$

Thus, $f'(x) = \dfrac{5}{\sqrt{x + 5}}$.

$$f'(1) = \frac{5}{\sqrt{6}} = \frac{5\sqrt{6}}{6}, \quad f'(2) = \frac{5}{\sqrt{7}} = \frac{5\sqrt{7}}{7}, \quad f'(3) = \frac{5}{\sqrt{8}} = \frac{5}{2\sqrt{2}} = \frac{5\sqrt{2}}{4}$$

25. $f(x) = \dfrac{3x}{x + 2}$

Step 1. Find $f(x + h)$:
$$f(x + h) = \frac{3(x + h)}{x + h + 2}$$

Step 2. Find $f(x + h) - f(x)$:

$$f(x + h) - f(x) = \frac{3(x + h)}{x + h + 2} - \frac{3x}{x + 2}$$

$$= \frac{3(x + h)(x + 2) - 3x(x + h + 2)}{(x + h + 2)(x + 2)}$$

$$= \frac{3x^2 + 3xh + 6x + 6h - 3x^2 - 3xh - 6x}{(x + h + 2)(x + 2)}$$

$$= \frac{6h}{(x + h + 2)(x + 2)}$$

Step 3. Find $\dfrac{f(x + h) - f(x)}{h}$:

$$\frac{f(x + h) - f(x)}{h} = \frac{\dfrac{6h}{(x + h + 2)(x + 2)}}{h} = \frac{6}{(x + h + 2)(x + 2)}$$

Step 4. Find $\lim\limits_{h \to 0} \dfrac{f(x + h) - f(x)}{h}$:

$$\lim_{h \to 0} \frac{f(x + h) - f(x)}{h} = \lim_{h \to 0} \frac{6}{(x + h + 2)(x + 2)} = \frac{6}{(x + 2)^2}$$

Thus, $f'(x) = \dfrac{6}{(x + 2)^2}$.

$$f'(1) = \frac{2}{3}, \quad f'(2) = \frac{3}{8}, \quad f'(3) = \frac{6}{25}$$

27. $y = f(x) = x^2 + x$

(A) $f(1) = 1^2 + 1 = 2$, $f(3) = 3^2 + 3 = 12$

Slope of secant line: $\dfrac{f(3) - f(1)}{3 - 1} = \dfrac{12 - 2}{2} = 5$

(B) $f(1) = 2$, $f(1 + h) = (1 + h)^2 + (1 + h) = 1 + 2h + h^2 + 1 + h$
$$= 2 + 3h + h^2$$

Slope of secant line: $\dfrac{f(1 + h) - f(1)}{h} = \dfrac{2 + 3h + h^2 - 2}{h} = 3 + h$

(C) Slope of tangent line at $(1, f(1))$:
$$\lim_{h \to 0} \frac{f(1 + h) - f(1)}{h} = \lim_{h \to 0} (3 + h) = 3$$

(D) Equation of tangent line at $(1, f(1))$:
$y - f(1) = f'(1)(x - 1)$ or $y - 2 = 3(x - 1)$ and $y = 3x - 1$.

29. $f(x) = x^2 + x$

(A) Average velocity: $\dfrac{f(3) - f(1)}{3 - 1} = \dfrac{3^2 + 3 - (1^2 + 1)}{2} = \dfrac{12 - 2}{2}$
$$= 5 \text{ meters/sec.}$$

(B) Average velocity: $\dfrac{f(1 + h) - f(1)}{h} = \dfrac{(1 + h)^2 + (1 + h) - (1^2 + 1)}{h}$

$$= \dfrac{1 + 2h + h^2 + 1 + h - 2}{h}$$

$$= \dfrac{3h + h^2}{h} = 3 + h \text{ meters/sec.}$$

(C) Instantaneous velocity: $\lim\limits_{h \to 0} \dfrac{f(1 + h) - f(1)}{h} = \lim\limits_{h \to 0}(3 + h) = 3$ m/sec.

31. $F'(x)$ does exist at $x = a$.

33. $F'(x)$ does not exist at $x = c$; the graph has a vertical tangent line at $(c, F(c))$.

35. $F'(x)$ does exist at $x = e$; $F'(e) = 0$.

37. $F'(x)$ does exist at $x = g$.

39. $f(x) = x^2 - 4x$

    (A) <u>Step 1</u>. Find $f(x + h)$:

$$f(x + h) = (x + h)^2 - 4(x + h) = x^2 + 2xh + h^2 - 4x - 4h$$

        <u>Step 2</u>. Find $f(x + h) - f(x)$:

$$f(x + h) - f(x) = x^2 + 2xh + h^2 - 4x - 4h - (x^2 - 4x)$$
$$= 2xh + h^2 - 4h$$

        <u>Step 3</u>. Find $\dfrac{f(x + h) - f(x)}{h}$:

$$\dfrac{f(x + h) - f(x)}{h} = \dfrac{2xh + h^2 - 4h}{h} = 2x + h - 4$$

        <u>Step 4</u>. Find $\lim\limits_{h \to 0} \dfrac{f(x + h) - f(x)}{h}$:

$$\lim\limits_{h \to 0} \dfrac{f(x + h) - f(x)}{h} = \lim\limits_{h \to 0}(2x + h - 4) = 2x - 4$$

        Thus, $f'(x) = 2x - 4$.

    (B) $f'(0) = -4$, $f'(2) = 0$,
        $f'(4) = 4$

    (C) Since f is a quadratic
        function, the graph of f is
        a parabola.

        y intercept: $y = 0$
        x intercepts: $x = 0$, $x = 4$
        Vertex: $(2, -4)$

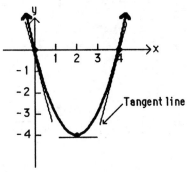

Tangent line

41. To find $v = f'(x)$, use the four-step process on the position function $f(x) = 4x^2 - 2x$.

Step 1. Find $f(x + h)$:
$$f(x + h) = 4(x + h)^2 - 2(x + h) = 4(x^2 + 2xh + h^2) - 2x - 2h$$
$$= 4x^2 + 8xh + 4h^2 - 2x - 2h$$

Step 2. Find $f(x + h) - f(x)$:
$$f(x + h) - f(x) = 4x^2 + 8xh + 4h^2 - 2x - 2h - (4x^2 - 2x)$$
$$= 8xh + 4h^2 - 2h$$

Step 3. Find $\dfrac{f(x + h) - f(x)}{h}$:
$$\frac{f(x + h) - f(x)}{h} = \frac{8xh + 4h^2 - 2h}{h} = 8x + 4h - 2$$

Step 4. Find $\lim\limits_{h \to 0} \dfrac{f(x + h) - f(x)}{h}$:
$$\lim_{h \to 0} \frac{f(x + h) - f(x)}{h} = \lim_{h \to 0}(8x + 4h - 2) = 8x - 2$$

Thus, the velocity, $v(x) = f'(x) = 8x - 2$

$f'(1) = 8 \cdot 1 - 2 = 6$ ft/sec
$f'(3) = 8 \cdot 3 - 2 = 22$ ft/sec
$f'(5) = 8 \cdot 5 - 2 = 38$ ft/sec

43. (A) The graphs of g and h are vertical translations of the graph of f. All three functions should have the same derivative.

(B) $m(x) = x^2 + C$

Step 1. Find $m(x + h)$:
$$m(x + h) = (x + h)^2 + C$$

Step 2. Find $m(x + h) - m(x)$:
$$m(x + h) - m(x) = (x + h)^2 + C - (x^2 + C)$$
$$= x^2 + 2xh + h^2 + C - x^2 + C$$
$$= 2xh + h^2$$

Step 3. Find $\dfrac{m(x + h) - m(x)}{h}$:
$$\frac{m(x + h) - m(x)}{h} = \frac{2xh + h^2}{h} = 2x + h$$

Step 4. $\lim\limits_{h \to 0} \dfrac{m(x + h) - m(x)}{h}$:
$$\lim_{h \to 0} \frac{m(x + h) - m(x)}{h} = \lim_{h \to 0}(2x + h) = 2x$$

Thus, $m'(x) = 2x$.

45. (A) The graph of $f(x) = C$, C a constant, is a horizontal line C units above or below the x axis depending on the sign of C. At any given point on the graph, the slope of the tangent line is 0.

(B) $f(x) = C$

Step 1. Find $f(x + h)$:
$$f(x + h) = C$$

Step 2. Find $f(x + h) - f(x)$:
$$f(x + h) - f(x) = C - C = 0$$

Step 3. Find $\dfrac{f(x + h) - f(x)}{h}$:
$$\frac{f(x + h) - f(x)}{h} = \frac{0}{h} = 0$$

Step 4. Find $\displaystyle\lim_{h \to 0} \dfrac{f(x + h) - f(x)}{h}$:
$$\lim_{h \to 0} \frac{f(x + h) - f(x)}{h} = \lim_{h \to 0} 0 = 0$$

Thus, $f'(x) = 0$.

47. The graph of $f(x) = \begin{cases} 2x, & x < 1 \\ 2, & x \geq 1 \end{cases}$ is:

f is not differentiable at $x = 1$ because the graph of f has a sharp corner at this point.

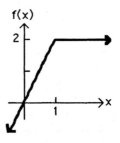

49. $f(x) = \begin{cases} x^2 + 1 & \text{if } x < 0 \\ 1 & \text{if } x \geq 0 \end{cases}$

It is clear that $f'(x) = \begin{cases} 2x & \text{if } x < 0 \\ 0 & \text{if } x > 0 \end{cases}$

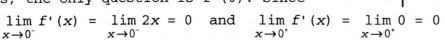

Thus, the only question is $f'(0)$. Since

$$\lim_{x \to 0^-} f'(x) = \lim_{x \to 0^-} 2x = 0 \quad \text{and} \quad \lim_{x \to 0^+} f'(x) = \lim_{x \to 0^+} 0 = 0$$

f is differentiable at 0 as well; f is differentiable for real numbers.

51. $f(x) = |x|$

$$\lim_{h \to 0} \frac{f(0 + h) - f(0)}{h} = \lim_{h \to 0} \frac{|0 + h| - |0|}{h} = \lim_{h \to 0} \frac{|h|}{h}$$

The limit does not exist. Thus, f is not differentiable at $x = 0$.

53. $f(x) = \sqrt[3]{x} = x^{1/3}$

$$\lim_{h \to 0} \frac{f(0 + h) - f(0)}{h} = \lim_{h \to 0} \frac{(0 + h)^{1/3} - 0^{1/3}}{h} = \lim_{h \to 0} \frac{h^{1/3}}{h} = \lim_{h \to 0} \frac{1}{h^{2/3}}$$

The limit does not exist. Thus, f is not differentiable at $x = 0$.

55. $f(x) = \sqrt{1 - x^2}$

$$\frac{f(0 + h) - f(0)}{h} = \frac{\sqrt{1 - h^2} - 1}{h} = \frac{\sqrt{1 - h^2} - 1}{h} \cdot \frac{\sqrt{1 - h^2} + 1}{\sqrt{1 - h^2} + 1}$$

$$= \frac{1 - h^2 - 1}{h\left(\sqrt{1 - h^2} + 1\right)} = \frac{-h}{\sqrt{1 - h^2} + 1}$$

$$\lim_{h \to 0} \frac{f(0 + h) - f(0)}{h} = \lim_{h \to 0} \frac{-h}{\sqrt{1 - h^2} + 1} = 0$$

f is differentiable at 0; $f'(0) = 0$.

57. The height of the ball at x seconds is $h(x) = 576 - 16x^2$. To find when the ball hits the ground, we solve:

$$576 - 16x^2 = 0$$
$$16x^2 = 576$$
$$x^2 = 36$$
$$x = 6 \text{ seconds}$$

The velocity of the ball is given by $h'(x) = -32x$. The velocity at impact is $h'(6) = -32(6) = -192$; the ball hits the ground at 192 ft/sec.

59. $R(x) = 60x - 0.025x^2 \qquad 0 \le x \le 2,400$.
  (A) Average rate of change:

$$\frac{R(1,050) - R(1,000)}{1,050 - 1,000}$$

$$= \frac{60(1,050) - 0.025(1,050)^2 - [60(1,000) - 0.025(1,000)^2]}{50}$$

$$= \frac{35,437.50 - 35,000}{50} = \$8.75$$

  (B) Step 1. Find $R(x + h)$:

$$R(x + h) = 60(x + h) - 0.025(x + h)^2$$
$$= 60x + 60h - 0.025(x^2 + 2xh + h^2)$$
$$= 60x + 60h - 0.025x^2 - 0.050xh - 0.025h^2$$

  Step 2. Find $R(x + h) - R(x)$:

$$R(x + h) - R(x) = 60x + 60h - 0.025x^2 - 0.050xh - 0.025h^2$$
$$- (60x - 0.025x^2)$$
$$= 60h - 0.050xh - 0.025h^2$$

  Step 3. Find $\dfrac{R(x + h) - R(x)}{h}$:

$$\frac{R(x + h) - R(x)}{h} = \frac{60h - 0.050xh - 0.025h^2}{h}$$
$$= 60 - 0.050x - 0.025h$$

Step 4. Find $\lim\limits_{h \to 0} \dfrac{R(x + h) - R(x)}{h}$:

$$\lim_{h \to 0} \frac{R(x + h) - R(x)}{h} = \lim_{h \to 0} (60 - 0.050x - 0.025h)$$
$$= 60 - 0.050x$$

Thus, $R'(x) = 60 - 0.050x$.

(C) $R(1,000) = 60(1,000) - 0.025(1,000)^2 = \$35,000;$
$R'(1,000) = 60 - 0.05(1,000) = \$10;$
at a production level of 1,000 car seats, the revenue is $35,000 and is increasing at the rate of $10 per seat.

61. (A) $S(t) = 2\sqrt{t + 10}$

Step 1. Find $S(t + h)$:
$$S(t + h) = 2\sqrt{t + h + 10}$$

Step 2. Find $S(t + h) - S(t)$:
$$S(t + h) - S(t) = 2\sqrt{t + h + 10} - 2\sqrt{t + 10}$$
$$= 2\left(\sqrt{t + h + 10} - \sqrt{t + 10}\right)$$

Step 3. Find $\dfrac{S(t + h) - S(t)}{h}$:
$$\frac{S(t + h) - S(t)}{h} = \frac{2\left(\sqrt{t + h + 10} - \sqrt{t + 10}\right)}{h}$$
$$= \frac{2\left(\sqrt{t + h + 10} - \sqrt{t + 10}\right)}{h} \cdot \frac{\left(\sqrt{t + h + 10} + \sqrt{t + 10}\right)}{\left(\sqrt{t + h + 10} + \sqrt{t + 10}\right)}$$
$$= \frac{2[t + h + 10 - (t + 10)]}{h\left(\sqrt{t + h + 10} + \sqrt{t + 10}\right)} = \frac{2h}{h\left(\sqrt{t + h + 10} + \sqrt{t + 10}\right)}$$
$$= \frac{2}{\sqrt{t + h + 10} + \sqrt{t + 10}}$$

Step 4. Find $\lim\limits_{h \to 0} \dfrac{S(t + h) - S(t)}{h}$:

$$\lim_{h \to 0} \frac{S(t + h) - S(t)}{h} = \lim_{h \to 0} \frac{2}{\sqrt{t + h + 10} + \sqrt{t + 10}} = \frac{1}{\sqrt{t + 10}}$$

Thus, $S'(t) = \dfrac{1}{\sqrt{t + 10}}$.

(B) $S(15) = 2\sqrt{15 + 10} = 2\sqrt{25} = 10;$
$$S'(15) = \frac{1}{\sqrt{15 + 10}} = \frac{1}{\sqrt{25}} = \frac{1}{5} = 0.2$$

After 15 months, the total sales are $10 million and are INCREASING at the rate of $0.2 million = $200,000 per month.

(C) The estimated total sales are $10.2 million after 16 months and $10.4 million after 17 months.

63. $p(t) = 14t^2 - 6.6t + 602.4$

    (A) <u>Step 1</u>. Find $p(t + h)$:
$$p(t + h) = 14(t + h)^2 - 6.6(t + h) + 602.4$$

        <u>Step 2</u>. Find $p(t + h) - p(t)$:
$$p(t + h) - p(t) = 14(t + h)^2 - 6.6(t + h) + 602.4$$
$$- (14t^2 - 6.6t + 602.4)$$
$$= 28th + 14h^2 - 6.6h$$

        <u>Step 3</u>. Find $\dfrac{p(t + h) - p(t)}{h}$:
$$\frac{p(t + h) - p(t)}{h} = \frac{28th + 14h^2 - 6.6h}{h} = 28t + 14h - 6.6$$

        <u>Step 4</u>. Find $\lim\limits_{h \to 0} \dfrac{p(t + h) - p(t)}{h}$:
$$\lim_{h \to 0} \frac{p(t + h) - p(t)}{h} = \lim_{h \to 0}(28t + 14h - 6.6) = 28t - 6.6$$

        Thus, $p'(t) = 28t - 6.6$.

    (B) The year 2010 corresponds to $t = 15$.
        $p(15) = 14(15)^2 - 6.6(15) + 602.4 = 3,653.4$ thousand tons;
        $p'(t) = 28t - 6.6$,
        $p'(15) = 28(15) - 6.6 = 413.4$;
        in 2010 the US will produce 3,653.4 thousand tons of zinc and this
        quantity is increasing at the rate of 413.4 thousand tons per year.

65. (A)
```
QuadReg
 y=ax²+bx+c
 a=.5303030303
 b=20.68181818
 c=921.0181818
```
    (B) $R(20) \approx 1,546.8$; $R'(20) \approx 41.9$
        Interpretation: In 2010, retail sales will be
        1,546.8 billion kilowatt hours and will be
        INCREASING at the rate of 41.9 billion
        kilowatt hours per year.

67. (A) $P(t) = 80 + 12t - t^2$

    <u>Step 1</u>. Find $P(t + h)$:
$$P(t + h) = 80 + 12(t + h) - (t + h)^2$$
$$= 80 + 12t + 12h - (t + h)^2$$

    <u>Step 2</u>. Find $P(t + h) - P(t)$:
$$P(t + h) - P(t) = 80 + 12t + 12h - (t + h)^2 - (80 + 12t - t^2)$$
$$= 12h - 2th - h^2$$

    <u>Step 3</u>. Find $\dfrac{P(t + h) - P(t)}{h}$:
$$\frac{P(t + h) - P(t)}{h} = \frac{12h - 2th - h^2}{h} = 12 - 2t - h$$

Step 4. Find $\lim\limits_{h \to 0} \dfrac{P(t + h) - P(t)}{h}$:

$$\lim_{h \to 0} \frac{P(t + h) - P(t)}{h} = \lim_{h \to 0}(12 - 2t - h) = 12 - 2t$$

Thus, $P'(t) = 12 - 2t$.

(B) $P(3) = 80 + 12(3) - (3)^2 = 107$; $P'(3) = 12 - 2(3) = 6$

After 3 hours, the ozone level is 107 ppb and is INCREASING at the rate of 6 ppb per hour.

69. (A) $f(t) = 0.011t^2 - t + 29.8$

Step 1. Find $f(t + h)$:
$$f(t + h) = 0.011(t + h)^2 - (t + h) + 29.8$$

Step 2. Find $f(t + h) - f(t)$:
$$f(t + h) - f(t) = 0.011(t + h)^2 - t - h + 29.8$$
$$- (0.011t^2 - t + 29.8)$$
$$= 0.022th + 0.011h^2 - h$$

Step 3. Find $\dfrac{f(t + h) - f(t)}{h}$:
$$\frac{f(t + h) - f(t)}{h} = \frac{0.022th + 0.011h^2 - h}{h}$$
$$= 0.022t + 0.011h - 1$$

Step 4. Find $\lim\limits_{h \to 0} \dfrac{f(t + h) - f(t)}{h}$:
$$\lim_{h \to 0} \frac{f(t + h) - f(t)}{h} = \lim_{h \to 0}(0.022t + 0.011h - 1) = 0.022t - 1$$
Thus, $f'(t) = 0.022t - 1$.

(B) The year 2000 corresponds to $t = 40$.
$f(40) = 0.011(40)^2 - 40 + 29.8 = 7.4$;
$f'(t) = 0.022t - 1$, $f'(40) = 0.022(40) - 1 = -0.12$;

The number of infant male deaths per 100,000 births was 7.4 and was decreasing at the rate of 0.12 deaths per 100,000 births per year.

EXERCISE 1-4

Things to remember:

1. DERIVATIVE NOTATION

    Given $y = f(x)$, then

    $$f'(x), \quad y', \quad \frac{dy}{dx}$$

    all represent the derivative of f at x.

2. CONSTANT FUNCTION RULE
   If $f(x) = C$, C a constant, then $f'(x) = 0$. Also
   $y' = 0$ and $\dfrac{dy}{dx} = 0$.

3. POWER RULE
   If $f(x) = x^n$, n any real number, then

   $f'(x) = nx^{n-1}$.

   Also, $y' = nx^{n-1}$ and $\dfrac{dy}{dx} = nx^{n-1}$

4. CONSTANT MULTIPLE PROPERTY
   If $y = f(x) = ku(x)$, where k is a constant, then
   $f'(x) = ku'(x)$.
   Also,

   $y' = ku'$ and $\dfrac{dy}{dx} = k\dfrac{du}{dx}$.

5. SUM AND DIFFERENCE PROPERTY
   If $y = f(x) = u(x) \pm v(x)$, then
   $f'(x) = u'(x) \pm v'(x)$.
   Also,

   $y' = u' \pm v'$ and $\dfrac{dy}{dx} = \dfrac{du}{dx} \pm \dfrac{dv}{dx}$

   [Note: This rule generalizes to the sum and difference of any given number of functions.]

---

1. $f(x) = 7$; $f'(x) = 0$ (using 2)

3. $y = x^9$; $\dfrac{dy}{dx} = 9x^8$ (using 3)

5. $\dfrac{d}{dx}x^3 = 3x^2$ (using 3)

7. $y = x^{-4}$; $y' = -4x^{-5}$ (using 3)

9. $g(x) = x^{8/3}$; $g'(x) = \dfrac{8}{3}x^{5/3}$ (using 3)

11. $y = \dfrac{1}{x^{10}}$; $\dfrac{dy}{dx} = -10x^{-11} = \dfrac{-10}{x^{11}}$

13. $f(x) = 5x^2$; $f'(x) = 5(2x) = 10x$ (using 4)

15. $y = 0.4x^7$; $y' = 0.4(7x^6) = 2.8x^6$

17. $\dfrac{d}{dx}\left(\dfrac{x^3}{18}\right) = \dfrac{1}{18}(3x^2) = \dfrac{1}{6}x^2$

19. $h(x) = 4f(x)$; $h'(2) = 4 \cdot f'(2) = 4(3) = 12$

21. $h(x) = f(x) + g(x)$; $h'(2) = f'(2) + g'(2) = 3 + (-1) = 2$

23. $h(x) = 2f(x) - 3g(x) + 7$; $h'(2) = 2f'(2) - 3g'(2)$
$$= 2(3) - 3(-1) = 9$$

25. $\dfrac{d}{dx}(2x - 5) = \dfrac{d}{dx}(2x) - \dfrac{d}{dx}(5) = 2$

27. $f(t) = 2t^2 - 3t + 1$; $f'(t) = (2t^2)' - (3t)' + (1)' = 4t - 3$

29. $y = 5x^{-2} + 9x^{-1}$; $y' = -10x^{-3} - 9x^{-2}$

31. $\dfrac{d}{du}(5u^{0.3} - 4u^{2.2}) = \dfrac{d}{du}(5u^{0.3}) - \dfrac{d}{du}(4u^{2.2}) = 1.5u^{-0.7} - 8.8u^{1.2}$

33. $h(t) = 2.1 + 0.5t - 1.1t^3$; $h'(t) = 0.5 - (1.1)3t^2 = 0.5 - 3.3t^2$

35. $y = \dfrac{2}{5x^4} = \dfrac{2}{5}x^{-4}$; $y' = \dfrac{2}{5}(-4x^{-5}) = -\dfrac{8}{5}x^{-5} = \dfrac{-8}{5x^5}$

37. $\dfrac{d}{dx}\left(\dfrac{3x^2}{2} - \dfrac{7}{5x^2}\right) = \dfrac{d}{dx}\left(\dfrac{3}{2}x^2\right) - \dfrac{d}{dx}\left(\dfrac{7}{5}x^{-2}\right) = 3x - \dfrac{14}{5}x^{-3} = 3x - \dfrac{14}{5x^3}$

39. $G(w) = \dfrac{5}{9w^4} + 5\sqrt[3]{w} = \dfrac{5}{9}w^{-4} + 5w^{1/3}$;

$G'(w) = -\dfrac{20}{9}w^{-5} + \dfrac{5}{3}w^{-2/3} = \dfrac{-20}{9w^5} + \dfrac{5}{3w^{2/3}}$

41. $\dfrac{d}{du}(3u^{2/3} - 5u^{1/3}) = \dfrac{d}{du}(3u^{2/3}) - \dfrac{d}{du}(5u^{1/3})$

$$= 2u^{-1/3} - \dfrac{5}{3}u^{-2/3} = \dfrac{2}{u^{1/3}} - \dfrac{5}{3u^{2/3}}$$

43. $h(t) = \dfrac{3}{t^{3/5}} - \dfrac{6}{t^{1/2}} = 3t^{-3/5} - 6t^{-1/2}$;

$h'(t) = 3\left(-\dfrac{3}{5}t^{-8/5}\right) - 6\left(-\dfrac{1}{2}t^{-3/2}\right) = -\dfrac{9}{5}t^{-8/5} + 3t^{-3/2} = \dfrac{-9}{5t^{8/5}} + \dfrac{3}{t^{3/2}}$

45. $y = \dfrac{1}{\sqrt[3]{x}} = \dfrac{1}{x^{1/3}} = x^{-1/3}$; $y' = -\dfrac{1}{3}x^{-4/3} = \dfrac{-1}{3x^{4/3}}$

47. $\dfrac{d}{dx}\left(\dfrac{1.2}{\sqrt{x}} - 3.2x^{-2} + x\right) = \dfrac{d}{dx}(1.2x^{-1/2} - 3.2x^{-2} + x)$

$$= \dfrac{d}{dx}(1.2x^{-1/2}) - \dfrac{d}{dx}(3.2x^{-2}) + \dfrac{d}{dx}(x)$$

$$= -0.6x^{-3/2} + 6.4x^{-3} + 1 = \dfrac{-0.6}{x^{3/2}} + \dfrac{6.4}{x^3} + 1$$

49. $f(x) = 6x - x^2$

(A) $f'(x) = 6 - 2x$

(B) Slope of the graph of f at $x = 2$: $f'(2) = 6 - 2(2) = 2$
Slope of the graph of f at $x = 4$: $f'(4) = 6 - 2(4) = -2$

(C) Tangent line at $x = 2$: $y - y_1 = m(x - x_1)$
$x_1 = 2$
$y_1 = f(2) = 6(2) - 2^2 = 8$
$m = f'(2) = 2$
Thus, $y - 8 = 2(x - 2)$ or $y = 2x + 4$.
Tangent line at $x = 4$: $y - y_1 = m(x - x_1)$
$x_1 = 4$
$y_1 = f(4) = 6(4) - 4^2 = 8$
$m = f'(4) = -2$
Thus, $y - 8 = -2(x - 4)$ or $y = -2x + 16$

(D) The tangent line is horizontal at the values $x = c$ such that $f'(c) = 0$. Thus, we must solve the following:
$f'(x) = 6 - 2x = 0$
$2x = 6$
$x = 3$

51. $f(x) = 3x^4 - 6x^2 - 7$
(A) $f'(x) = 12x^3 - 12x$

(B) Slope of the graph of $x = 2$: $f'(2) = 12(2)^3 - 12(2) = 72$
Slope of the graph of $x = 4$: $f'(4) = 12(4)^3 - 12(4) = 720$

(C) Tangent line at $x = 2$: $y - y_1 = m(x - x_1)$, where $x_1 = 2$,
$y_1 = f(2) = 3(2)^4 - 6(2)^2 - 7 = 17$, $m = 72$.
$y - 17 = 72(x - 2)$ or $y = 72x - 127$

Tangent line at $x = 4$: $y - y_1 = m(x - x_1)$, where $x_1 = 4$,
$y_1 = f(4) = 3(4)^4 - 6(4)^2 - 7 = 665$, $m = 720$.
$y - 665 = 720(x - 4)$ or $y = 720x - 2215$

(D) Solve $f'(x) = 0$ for x:
$12x^3 - 12x = 0$
$12x(x^2 - 1) = 0$
$12x(x - 1)(x + 1) = 0$
$x = -1, x = 0, x = 1$

53. $f(x) = 176x - 16x^2$

  (A) $v = f'(x) = 176 - 32x$ (B) $v\big|_{x=0} = f'(0) = 176$ ft/sec.

  $v\big|_{x=3} = f'(3) = 176 - 32(3) = 80$ ft/sec.

  (C) Solve $v = f'(x) = 0$
      for x:
      $176 - 32x = 0$
      $32x = 176$
      $x = 5.5$ sec.

55. $f(x) = x^3 - 9x^2 + 15x$

  (A) $v = f'(x) = 3x^2 - 18x + 15$

  (B) $v\big|_{x=0} = f'(0) = 15$ feet/sec.

  $v\big|_{x=3} = f'(3) = 3(3)^2 - 18(3) + 15 = -12$ feet/sec.

  (C) Solve $v = f'(x) = 0$ for x:
      $3x^2 - 18x + 15 = 0$
      $3(x^2 - 6x + 5) = 0$
      $3(x - 5)(x - 1) = 0$
      $x = 1, \ x = 5$

57. $f(x) = x^2 - 3x - 4\sqrt{x} = x^2 - 3x - 4x^{1/2}$

  $f'(x) = 2x - 3 - 2x^{-1/2}$

  The graph of f has a horizontal tangent line at the value(s) of x where $f'(x) = 0$. Thus, we need to solve the equation
  $$2x - 3 - 2x^{-1/2} = 0$$
  By graphing the function $y = 2x - 3 - 2x^{-1/2}$, we see that there is one zero. To four decimal places, it is $x = 2.1777$.

59. $f(x) = 3\sqrt[3]{x^4} - 1.5x^2 - 3x = 3x^{4/3} - 1.5x^2 - 3x$

  $f'(x) = 4x^{1/3} - 3x - 3$

  The graph of f has a horizontal tangent line at the value(s) of x where $f'(x) = 0$. Thus, we need to solve the equation
  $$4x^{1/3} - 3x - 3 = 0$$
  Graphing the function $y = 4x^{1/3} - 3x - 3$, we see that there is one zero. To four decimal places, it is $x = -2.9018$.

61. $f(x) = 0.05x^4 - 0.1x^3 - 1.5x^2 - 1.6x + 3$

  $f'(x) = 0.2x^3 + 0.3x^2 - 3x - 1.6$

  The graph of f has a horizontal tangent line at the value(s) of x where $f'(x) = 0$. Thus, we need to solve the equation
  $$0.2x^3 + 0.3x^2 - 3x - 1.6 = 0$$
  By graphing the function $y = 0.2x^3 + 0.3x^2 - 3x - 1.6$ we see that there are three zeros. To four decimal places, they are
  $$x_1 = -4.4607, \ x_2 = -0.5159, \ x_3 = 3.4765$$

63. $f(x) = 0.2x^4 - 3.12x^3 + 16.25x^2 - 28.25x + 7.5$

$f'(x) = 0.8x^3 - 9.36x^2 + 32.5x - 28.25$

The graph of f has a horizontal tangent line at the value(s) of x where $f'(x) = 0$. Thus, we need to solve the equation

$$0.8x^3 - 9.36x^2 + 32.5x - 28.25 = 0$$

Graphing the function $y = 0.8x^3 - 9.36x^2 + 32.5x - 28.25$, we see that there is one zero. To four decimal places, it is $x = 1.3050$.

65. $f(x) = ax^2 + bx + c$; $f'(x) = 2ax + b$.

The derivative is 0 at the vertex of the parabola:

$$2ax + b = 0$$
$$x = -\frac{b}{2a}$$

67. (A) $f(x) = x^3 + x$ (B) $f(x) = x^3$ (C) $f(x) = x^3 - x$

69. $f(x) = (2x - 1)^2 = 4x^2 - 4x + 1$

$f'(x) = 8x - 4$

71. $\dfrac{d}{dx}\left(\dfrac{10x + 20}{x}\right) = \dfrac{d}{dx}\left(10 + \dfrac{20}{x}\right) = \dfrac{d}{dx}(10) + \dfrac{d}{dx}(20x^{-1}) = -20x^{-2} = -\dfrac{20}{x^2}$

73. $y = \dfrac{3x - 4}{12x^2} = \dfrac{3x}{12x^2} - \dfrac{4}{12x^2} = \dfrac{1}{4}x^{-1} - \dfrac{1}{3}x^{-2}$

$\dfrac{dy}{dx} = -\dfrac{1}{4}x^{-2} + \dfrac{2}{3}x^{-3} = -\dfrac{1}{4x^2} + \dfrac{2}{3x^3}$

75. $y = \dfrac{x^4 - 3x^3 + 5}{x^2} = x^2 - 3x + 5x^{-2}$; $y' = 2x - 3 - 10x^{-3} = 2x - 3 - \dfrac{10}{x^3}$

77. $f(x) = x^3$

Step 1. Find $f(x + h)$:
$$f(x + h) = (x + h)^3 = x^3 + 3x^2h + 3xh^2 + h^3$$

Step 2. Find $f(x + h) - f(x)$:
$$f(x + h) - f(x + h) = x^3 + 3x^3h + 3xh^2 + h^3 - x^3$$
$$= 3x^2h + 3xh^2 + h^3$$

Step 3. Find $\dfrac{f(x + h) - f(x)}{h}$:
$$\frac{f(x + h) - f(x)}{h} = \frac{3x^2h + 3xh^2 + h^3}{h} = 3x^2 + 3xh + h^2$$

Step 4. Find $\lim\limits_{h \to 0} \dfrac{f(x + h) - f(x)}{h}$:
$$\lim_{h \to 0} \frac{f(x + h) - f(x)}{h} = \lim_{h \to 0}(3x^2 + 3xh + h^2) = 3x^2$$

Thus, $\dfrac{d}{dx}(x^3) = 3x^2$.

79. $f(x) = x^{1/3}$; $f'(x) = \dfrac{1}{3}x^{-2/3} = \dfrac{1}{3x^{2/3}}$

The domain of f' is the set of all real numbers except $x = 0$. The graph of f is smooth, but it has a vertical tangent line at $(0, 0)$.

81. (A) $S(t) = 0.03t^3 + 0.5t^2 + 2t + 3$

$S'(t) = 0.09t^2 + t + 2$

(B) $S(5) = 0.03(5)^3 + 0.5(5)^2 + 2(5) + 3 = 29.25$

$S'(5) = 0.09(5)^2 + 5 + 2 = 9.25$

After 5 months, sales are \$29.25 million and are increasing at the rate of \$9.25 million per month.

(C) $S(10) = 0.03(10)^3 + 0.5(10)^2 + 2(10) + 3 = 103$

$S'(10) = 0.09(10)^2 + 10 + 2 = 21$

After 10 months, sales are \$103 million and are increasing at the rate of \$21 million per month.

83. (A) $N(x) = 1,000 - \dfrac{3,780}{x} = 1,000 - 3,780x^{-1}$

$N'(x) = 3,780x^{-2} = \dfrac{3,780}{x^2}$

(B) $N'(10) = \dfrac{3,780}{(10)^2} = 37.8$

At the \$10,000 level of advertising, sales are INCREASING at the rate of 37.8 boats per \$1000 spent on advertising.

$N'(20) = \dfrac{3,780}{(20)^2} = 9.45$

At the \$20,000 level of advertising, sales are INCREASING at the rate of 9.45 boats per \$1000 spent on advertising.

85. (A)

```
CubicReg
y=ax³+bx²+cx+d
a=6.266666667
b=-194.5714286
c=1544.761905
d=2571.428571
```

(B) $L(12) \approx 3,919.09$ or $3,900$ rounded to the nearest hundred; $L'(12) = -417.75$ or -400. Interpretation: In 1992, 3,900 limousines were produced and limousine production was DECREASING at the rate of 400 limousines per year.

(C) $L(18) \approx 3,883.2$ or $3,900$ rounded to the nearest hundred; $L'(18) \approx 631.39$ or 600.

Interpretation: In 1998, 3,900 limousines were produced and limousine production was INCREASING at the rate of 600 limousines per year.

87. $y = 590x^{-1/2}$, $30 \leq x \leq 75$

First, find $\dfrac{dy}{dx} = \dfrac{d}{dx} 590x^{-1/2} = -295x^{-3/2} = \dfrac{-295}{x^{3/2}}$, the instantaneous rate

of change of pulse when a person is x inches tall.

(A) The instantaneous rate of change of pulse rate at $x = 36$ is:

$\dfrac{-295}{(36)^{3/2}} = \dfrac{-295}{216} = -1.37$ (1.37 decrease in pulse rate)

(B) The instantaneous rate of change of pulse rate at $x = 64$ is:

$\dfrac{-295}{(64)^{3/2}} = \dfrac{-295}{512} = -0.58$ (0.58 decrease in pulse rate)

89. $y = 50\sqrt{x}$, $0 \leq x \leq 9$

First, find $y' = (50\sqrt{x})' = (50x^{1/2})' = 25x^{-1/2}$

$= \dfrac{25}{\sqrt{x}}$, the rate of learning at the end of x hours.

(A) Rate of learning at the end of 1 hour: $\dfrac{25}{\sqrt{1}} = 25$ items/hr

(B) Rate of learning at the end of 9 hours: $\dfrac{25}{\sqrt{9}} = \dfrac{25}{3} = 8.33$ items/hr

---

EXERCISE 1-5
_____

Things to remember:

1. PRODUCT RULE

   If
   $$y = f(x) = F(x)S(x)$$
   and if $F'(x)$ and $S'(x)$ exist, then
   $$f'(x) = F(x)S'(x) + S(x)F'(x).$$

   Also,
   $$y' = FS' + SF';$$
   $$\dfrac{dy}{dx} = F\dfrac{dS}{dx} + S\dfrac{dF}{dx}.$$

2. QUOTIENT RULE

   If
   $$y = f(x) = \dfrac{T(x)}{B(x)}$$
   and if $T'(x)$ and $B'(x)$ exist, then
   $$f'(x) = \dfrac{B(x)T'(x) - T(x)B'(x)}{[B(x)]^2}.$$

   Also,
   $$y' = \dfrac{BT' - TB'}{B^2};$$
   $$\dfrac{dy}{dx} = \dfrac{B\left(\dfrac{dT}{dx}\right) - T\left(\dfrac{dB}{dx}\right)}{B^2}.$$

1. $f(x) = 2x^3(x^2 - 2)$

$\begin{aligned}
f'(x) &= 2x^3(x^2 - 2)' + (x^2 - 2)(2x^3)' \quad \text{[using \underline{1} with } F(x) = 2x^3, \\
&= 2x^3(2x) + (x^2 - 2)(6x^2) \qquad\qquad\qquad S(x) = x^2 - 2\text{]} \\
&= 4x^4 + 6x^4 - 12x^2 \\
&= 10x^4 - 12x^2
\end{aligned}$

3. $f(x) = (x - 3)(2x - 1)$

$\begin{aligned}
f'(x) &= (x - 3)(2x - 1)' + (2x - 1)(x - 3)' \quad \text{(using \underline{1})} \\
&= (x - 3)(2) + (2x - 1)(1) \\
&= 2x - 6 + 2x - 1 \\
&= 4x - 7
\end{aligned}$

5. $f(x) = \dfrac{x}{x - 3}$

$\begin{aligned}
f'(x) &= \frac{(x - 3)(x)' - x(x - 3)'}{(x - 3)^2} \quad \text{[using \underline{2} with } T(x) = x, \; B(x) = x - 3\text{]} \\
&= \frac{(x - 3)(1) - x(1)}{(x - 3)^2} = \frac{-3}{(x - 3)^2}
\end{aligned}$

7. $f(x) = \dfrac{2x + 3}{x - 2}$

$\begin{aligned}
f'(x) &= \frac{(x - 2)(2x + 3)' - (2x + 3)(x - 2)'}{(x - 2)^2} \quad \text{(using \underline{2})} \\
&= \frac{(x - 2)(2) - (2x + 3)(1)}{(x - 2)^2} = \frac{2x - 4 - 2x - 3}{(x - 2)^2} = \frac{-7}{(x - 2)^2}
\end{aligned}$

9. $f(x) = (x^2 + 1)(2x - 3)$

$\begin{aligned}
f'(x) &= (x^2 + 1)(2x - 3)' + (2x - 3)(x^2 + 1)' \quad \text{(using \underline{1})} \\
&= (x^2 + 1)(2) + (2x - 3)(2x) \\
&= 2x^2 + 2 + 4x^2 - 6x \\
&= 6x^2 - 6x + 2
\end{aligned}$

11. $f(x) = (0.4x + 2)(0.5x - 5)$

$\begin{aligned}
f'(x) &= (0.4x + 2)(0.5x - 5)' + (0.5x - 5)(0.4x + 2)' \\
&= (0.4x + 2)(0.5) + (0.5x - 5)(0.4) \\
&= 0.2x + 1 + 0.2x - 2 = 0.4x - 1
\end{aligned}$

13. $f(x) = \dfrac{x^2 + 1}{2x - 3}$

$\begin{aligned}
f'(x) &= \frac{(2x - 3)(x^2 + 1)' - (x^2 + 1)(2x - 3)'}{(2x - 3)^2} \quad \text{(using \underline{2})} \\
&= \frac{(2x - 3)(2x) - (x^2 + 1)(2)}{(2x - 3)^2} \\
&= \frac{4x^2 - 6x - 2x^2 - 2}{(2x - 3)^2} = \frac{2x^2 - 6x - 2}{(2x - 3)^2}
\end{aligned}$

15. $f(x) = (x^2 + 2)(x^2 - 3)$

$\quad f'(x) = (x^2 + 2)(x^2 - 3)' + (x^2 - 3)(x^2 + 2)'$

$\qquad\quad = (x^2 + 2)(2x) + (x^2 - 3)(2x)$

$\qquad\quad = 2x^3 + 4x + 2x^3 - 6x$

$\qquad\quad = 4x^3 - 2x$

17. $f(x) = \dfrac{x^2 + 2}{x^2 - 3}$

$\quad f'(x) = \dfrac{(x^2 - 3)(x^2 + 2)' - (x^2 + 2)(x^2 - 3)'}{(x^2 - 3)^2}$

$\qquad\quad = \dfrac{(x^2 - 3)(2x) - (x^2 + 2)(2x)}{(x^2 - 3)^2} \;=\; \dfrac{2x^3 - 6x - 2x^3 - 4x}{(x^2 - 3)^2} \;=\; \dfrac{-10x}{(x^2 - 3)^2}$

19. $h(x) = xf(x);\; h'(x) = xf'(x) + f(x)$

21. $h(x) = x^3 f(x);\; h'(x) = x^3 f'(x) + f(x)(3x^2) = x^3 f'(x) + 3x^2 f(x)$

23. $h(x) = \dfrac{f(x)}{x^2};\; h'(x) = \dfrac{x^2 f'(x) - f(x)(2x)}{(x^2)^2} = \dfrac{x^2 f'(x) - 2xf(x)}{x^4} = \dfrac{xf'(x) - 2f(x)}{x^3}$

$\quad$ or $h(x) = x^{-2} f(x);\; h'(x) = x^{-2} f'(x) + f(x)(-2x^{-3}) = \dfrac{xf'(x) - 2f(x)}{x^3}$

25. $h(x) = \dfrac{x}{f(x)};\; h'(x) = \dfrac{f(x) - xf'(x)}{[f(x)]^2}$

27. $f(x) = (2x + 1)(x^2 - 3x)$

$\quad f'(x) = (2x + 1)(x^2 - 3x)' + (x^2 - 3x)(2x + 1)'$

$\qquad\quad = (2x + 1)(2x - 3) + (x^2 - 3x)(2)$

$\qquad\quad = 6x^2 - 10x - 3$

29. $y = (2.5t - t^2)(4t + 1.4)$

$\quad \dfrac{dy}{dx} = (2.5t - t^2)\dfrac{d}{dt}(4t + 1.4) + (4t + 1.4)\dfrac{d}{dt}(2.5t - t^2)$

$\qquad\; = (2.5t - t^2)(4) + (4t + 1.4)(2.5 - 2t)$

$\qquad\; = 10t - 4t^2 + 10t - 2.8t + 3.5 - 8t^2$

$\qquad\; = -12t^2 + 17.2t + 3.5$

31. $y = \dfrac{5x - 3}{x^2 + 2x}$

$\quad y' = \dfrac{(x^2 + 2x)(5x - 3)' - (5x - 3)(x^2 + 2x)'}{(x^2 + 2x)^2}$

$\qquad = \dfrac{(x^2 + 2x)(5) - (5x - 3)(2x + 2)}{(x^2 + 2x)^2} \;=\; \dfrac{-5x^2 + 6x + 6}{(x^2 + 2x)^2}$

33. $\dfrac{d}{dw}\left[\dfrac{w^2 - 3w + 1}{w^2 - 1}\right] = \dfrac{(w^2 - 1)\dfrac{d}{dw}(w^2 - 3w + 1) - (w^2 - 3w + 1)\dfrac{d}{dw}(w^2 - 1)}{(w^2 - 1)^2}$

$$= \dfrac{(w^2 - 1)(2w - 3) - (w^2 - 3w + 1)(2w)}{(w^2 - 1)^2}$$

$$= \dfrac{3w^2 - 4w + 3}{(w^2 - 1)^2}$$

35. $f(x) = (1 + 3x)(5 - 2x)$

First find $f'(x)$:

$f'(x) = (1 + 3x)(5 - 2x)' + (5 - 2x)(1 + 3x)'$
$= (1 + 3x)(-2) + (5 - 2x)(3)$
$= -2 - 6x + 15 - 6x$
$= 13 - 12x$

An equation for the tangent line at $x = 2$ is:

$y - y_1 = m(x - x_1)$

where $x_1 = 2$, $y_1 = f(x_1) = f(2) = 7$, and $m = f'(x_1) = f'(2) = -11$.

Thus, we have:

$y - 7 = -11(x - 2)$ or $y = -11x + 29$

37. $f(x) = \dfrac{x - 8}{3x - 4}$

First find $f'(x)$:

$f'(x) = \dfrac{(3x - 4)(x - 8)' - (x - 8)(3x - 4)'}{(3x - 4)^2}$

$= \dfrac{(3x - 4)(1) - (x - 8)(3)}{(3x - 4)^2} = \dfrac{20}{(3x - 4)^2}$

An equation for the tangent line at $x = 2$ is: $y - y_1 = m(x - x_1)$
where $x_1 = 2$, $y_1 = f(x_1) = f(2) = -3$, and $m = f'(x_1) = f'(2) = 5$.
Thus, we have: $y - (-3) = 5(x - 2)$ or $y = 5x - 13$

39. $f(x) = (2x - 15)(x^2 + 18)$
$f'(x) = (2x - 15)(x^2 + 18)' + (x^2 + 18)(2x - 15)'$
$= (2x - 15)(2x) + (x^2 + 18)(2)$
$= 6x^2 - 30x + 36$

To find the values of x where $f'(x) = 0$, set: $f'(x) = 6x^2 - 30x + 36 = 0$
$$\text{or} \qquad x^2 - 5x + 6 = 0$$
$$(x - 2)(x - 3) = 0$$

Thus, $x = 2$, $x = 3$.

41. $f(x) = \dfrac{x}{x^2 + 1}$

$f'(x) = \dfrac{(x^2 + 1)(x)' - x(x^2 + 1)'}{(x^2 + 1)^2} = \dfrac{(x^2 + 1)(1) - x(2x)}{(x^2 + 1)^2} = \dfrac{1 - x^2}{(x^2 + 1)^2}$

Now, set $f'(x) = \dfrac{1 - x^2}{(x^2 + 1)^2} = 0$

or $\qquad 1 - x^2 = 0$

$\qquad (1 - x)(1 + x) = 0$

Thus, $x = 1, \; x = -1$.

43. $f(x) = x^3(x^4 - 1)$

First, we use the product rule:

$f'(x) = x^3(x^4 - 1)' + (x^4 - 1)(x^3)'$

$\qquad = x^3(4x^3) + (x^4 - 1)(3x^2)$

$\qquad = 7x^6 - 3x^2$

Next, simplifying $f(x)$, we have $f(x) = x^7 - x^3$. Thus, $f'(x) = 7x^6 - 3x^2$.

45. $f(x) = \dfrac{x^3 + 9}{x^3}$

First, we use the quotient rule:

$f'(x) = \dfrac{x^3(x^3 + 9)' - (x^3 + 9)(x^3)'}{(x^3)^2} = \dfrac{x^3(3x^2) - (x^3 + 9)(3x^2)}{x^6}$

$\qquad = \dfrac{-27x^2}{x^6} = \dfrac{-27}{x^4}$

Next, simplifying $f(x)$, we have $f(x) = \dfrac{x^3 + 9}{x^3} = 1 + \dfrac{9}{x^3} = 1 + 9x^{-3}$

Thus, $f'(x) = -27x^{-4} = -\dfrac{27}{x^4}$.

47. $f(w) = (3w^2 - 1)^2 = (3w^2 - 1)(3w^2 - 1)$

$f'(w) = (3w^2 - 1)(6w) + (3w^2 - 1)(6w)$

$\qquad = 12w(3w^2 - 1) = 36w^3 - 12w$

49. $\dfrac{d}{dx} \dfrac{3x^2 - 2x + 3}{4x^2 + 5x - 1}$

$= \dfrac{(4x^2 + 5x - 1)\dfrac{d}{dx}(3x^2 - 2x + 3) - (3x^2 - 2x + 3)\dfrac{d}{dx}(4x^2 + 5x - 1)}{(4x^2 + 5x - 1)^2}$

$= \dfrac{(4x^2 + 5x - 1)(6x - 2) - (3x^2 - 2x + 3)(8x + 5)}{(4x^2 + 5x - 1)^2}$

$= \dfrac{24x^3 + 30x^2 - 6x - 8x^2 - 10x + 2 - 24x^3 + 16x^2 - 24x - 15x^2 + 10x - 15}{(4x^2 + 5x - 1)^2}$

$= \dfrac{23x^2 - 30x - 13}{(4x^2 + 5x - 1)^2}$

51. $y = 9x^{1/3}(x^3 + 5)$

$\dfrac{dy}{dx} = 9x^{1/3}\dfrac{d}{dx}(x^3 + 5) + (x^3 + 5)\dfrac{d}{dx}(9x^{1/3})\dfrac{d}{dx}(9x^{1/3})$

$= 9x^{1/3}(3x^2) + (x^3 + 5)\left(9 \cdot \dfrac{1}{3}x^{-2/3}\right) = 27x^{7/3} + (x^3 + 5)(3x^{-2/3})$

$= 27x^{7/3} + \dfrac{3x^3 + 15}{x^{2/3}} = \dfrac{30x^3 + 15}{x^{2/3}}$

53. $f(x) = \dfrac{6\sqrt[3]{x}}{x^2 - 3} = \dfrac{6x^{1/3}}{x^2 - 3}$

$f'(x) = \dfrac{(x^2 - 3)(6x^{1/3})' - 6x^{1/3}(x^2 - 3)'}{(x^2 - 3)^2}$

$= \dfrac{(x^2 - 3)\left(6 \cdot \dfrac{1}{3}x^{-2/3}\right) - 6x^{1/3}(2x)}{(x^2 - 3)^2} = \dfrac{(x^2 - 3)(2x^{-2/3}) - 12x^{4/3}}{(x^2 - 3)^2}$

$\dfrac{2}{3} \quad \dfrac{4}{3} = \dfrac{6}{3} = \dfrac{\dfrac{2(x^2 - 3)}{x^{2/3}} - 12x^{4/3}}{(x^2 - 3)^2} = \dfrac{2x^2 - 6 - 12x^2}{(x^2 - 3)^2 x^{2/3}} = \dfrac{-10x^2 - 6}{(x^2 - 3)^2 x^{2/3}}$

55. $g(t) = \dfrac{0.2t}{3t^2 - 1}$; $g'(t) = \dfrac{(3t^2 - 1)(0.2) - (0.2t)(6t)}{(3t^2 - 1)^2} = \dfrac{-0.6t^2 - 0.2}{(3t^2 - 1)^2}$

57. $\dfrac{d}{dx}\dfrac{x^3 - 2x^2}{\sqrt[3]{x^2}} = \dfrac{d}{dx}\dfrac{x^3 - 2x^2}{x^{2/3}}$

$= \dfrac{x^{2/3}\dfrac{d}{dx}(x^3 - 2x^2) - (x^3 - 2x^2)\dfrac{d}{dx}(x^{2/3})}{(x^{2/3})^2}$

$= \dfrac{x^{2/3}(3x^2 - 4x) - (x^3 - 2x^2)\left(\dfrac{2}{3}x^{-1/3}\right)}{x^{4/3}}$

$= x^{-2/3}(3x^2 - 4x) - \dfrac{2}{3}x^{-5/3}(x^3 - 2x^2)$

$= 3x^{4/3} - 4x^{1/3} - \dfrac{2}{3}x^{4/3} + \dfrac{4}{3}x^{1/3}$

$= -\dfrac{8}{3}x^{1/3} + \dfrac{7}{3}x^{4/3}$

59. $f(x) = \dfrac{(2x^2 - 1)(x^2 + 3)}{x^2 + 1}$

$f'(x) = \dfrac{(x^2 + 1)[(2x^2 - 1)(x^2 + 3)]' - (2x^2 - 1)(x^2 + 3)(x^2 + 1)'}{(x^2 + 1)^2}$

$= \dfrac{(x^2 + 1)[(2x^2 - 1)(x^2 + 3)' + (x^2 + 3)(2x^2 - 1)'] - (2x^2 - 1)(x^2 + 3)(2x)}{(x^2 + 1)^2}$

$= \dfrac{(x^2 + 1)[(2x^2 - 1)(2x) + (x^2 + 3)(4x)] - (2x^2 - 1)(x^2 + 3)(2x)}{(x^2 + 1)^2}$

$$= \frac{(x^2 + 1) [4x^3 - 2x + 4x^3 + 12x] - [2x^4 + 5x^2 - 3] (2x)}{(x^2 + 1)^2}$$

$$= \frac{(x^2 + 1) (8x^3 + 10x) - 4x^5 - 10x^3 + 6x}{(x^2 + 1)^2}$$

$$= \frac{8x^5 + 10x^3 + 8x^3 + 10x - 4x^5 - 10x^3 + 6x}{(x^2 + 1)^2}$$

$$= \frac{4x^5 + 8x^3 + 16x}{(x^2 + 1)^2}$$

61. $f(x) = (x^2 + 4) (x^2 - 2x)$
$f'(x) = (x^2 + 4) (2x - 2) + (x^2 - 2x) 2x = 4x^3 - 6x^2 + 8x - 8$

Set $f'(x) = 4x^3 - 6x^2 + 8x - 8 = 0$ and solve using a root-approximation routine on a graphing utility: $f'(x) = 0$ at $x = 1.2117$.

63. $f(x) = \frac{x^3 + 17x - 2}{x^2 + 1}$

$f'(x) = \frac{(x^2 + 1) (3x^2 + 17) - (x^3 + 17x - 2) (2x)}{(x^2 + 1)^2} = \frac{x^4 - 14x^2 + 4x + 17}{(x^2 + 1)^2};$

$f'(x) = 0$ implies $x^4 - 14x^2 + 4x + 17 = 0$.

Solve using a root-approximation routine on a graphing utility: $f'(x) = 0$ at $x = -3.7212$, $x = -1$, $x = 1.3586$, $x = 3.3626$.

65. $S(t) = \frac{90t^2}{t^2 + 50}$

(A) $S'(t) = \frac{(t^2 + 50) (180t) - 90t^2 (2t)}{(t^2 + 50)^2} = \frac{9000t}{(t^2 + 50)^2}$

(B) $S(10) = \frac{90(10)^2}{(10)^2 + 50} = \frac{9000}{150} = 60;$

$S'(10) = \frac{9000(10)}{[(10)^2 + 50]^2} = \frac{90,000}{22,500} = 4$

After 10 months, the total sales are 60,000 CD's and the sales are INCREASING at the rate of 4,000 CD's per month.

(C) The total sales after 11 months will be approximately 64,000 CD's.

67. $x = \frac{4,000}{0.1p + 1}$, $10 \le p \le 70$

(A) $\frac{dx}{dp} = \frac{(0.1p + 1) (0) - 4,000(0.1)}{(0.1p + 1)^2} = \frac{-400}{(0.1p + 1)^2}$

(B) $x(40) = \dfrac{4,000}{0.1(40) + 1} = \dfrac{4,000}{5} = 800;$

$\dfrac{dx}{dp} = \dfrac{-400}{[0.1(40) + 1]^2} = \dfrac{-400}{25} = -16$

At a price level of \$40, the demand is 800 CD players and the demand is DECREASING at the rate of 16 CD players per dollar.

(C) At a price of \$41, the demand will be approximately 784 CD players.

69. $C(t) = \dfrac{0.14t}{t^2 + 1}$

(A) $C'(t) = \dfrac{(t^2 + 1)(0.14t)' - (0.14t)(t^2 + 1)'}{(t^2 + 1)^2}$

$= \dfrac{(t^2 + 1)(0.14) - (0.14t)(2t)}{(t^2 + 1)^2} = \dfrac{0.14 - 0.14t^2}{(t^2 + 1)^2} = \dfrac{0.14(1 - t^2)}{(t^2 + 1)^2}$

(B) $C'(0.5) = \dfrac{0.14(1 - [0.5]^2)}{([0.5]^2 + 1)^2} = \dfrac{0.14(1 - 0.25)}{(1.25)^2} = 0.0672$

Interpretation: At $t = 0.5$ hours, the concentration is increasing at the rate of 0.0672 units per hour.

$C'(3) = \dfrac{0.14(1 - 3^2)}{(3^2 + 1)^2} = \dfrac{0.14(-8)}{100} = -0.0112$

Interpretation: At $t = 3$ hours, the concentration is decreasing at the rate of 0.0112 units per hour.

71. $N(x) = \dfrac{100x + 200}{x + 32}$

(A) $N'(x) = \dfrac{(x + 32)(100x + 200)' - (100x + 200)(x + 32)'}{(x + 32)^2}$

$= \dfrac{(x + 32)(100) - (100x + 200)(1)}{(x + 32)^2}$

$= \dfrac{100x + 3200 - 100x - 200}{(x + 32)^2} = \dfrac{3000}{(x + 32)^2}$

(B) $N'(4) = \dfrac{3000}{(36)^2} = \dfrac{3000}{1296} \approx 2.31;$ $N'(68) = \dfrac{3000}{(100)^2} = \dfrac{3000}{10,000} = \dfrac{3}{10} = 0.30$

Things to remember:

<u>1</u>. GENERAL POWER RULE

If $u(x)$ is a differentiable function, n is any real number, and

$$y = f(x) = [u(x)]^n$$

then

$$f'(x) = n[u(x)]^{n-1} u'(x)$$

This rule is often written more compactly as

$$y' = nu^{n-1}u' \quad \text{or} \quad \frac{d}{dx}u^n = nu^{n-1}\frac{du}{dx}, \quad u = u(x)$$

1. 3; $\dfrac{d}{dx}(3x + 4)^4 = 4(3x + 4)^3 (3) = 12(3x + 4)^3$

3. $-4x$; $\dfrac{d}{dx}(4 - 2x^2)^3 = 3(4 - 2x^2)^2 (-4x) = -12x(4 - 2x^2)^2$

5. $2 + 6x$; $\dfrac{d}{dx}(1 + 2x + 3x^2)^7 = 7(1 + 2x + 3x^2)^6 (2 + 6x)$

$$= 7(2 + 6x)(1 + 2x + 3x^2)^6$$

7. $f(x) = (2x + 5)^3$
$f'(x) = 3(2x + 5)^2(2x + 5)'$
$\quad\quad = 3(2x + 5)^2(2)$
$\quad\quad = 6(2x + 5)^2$

9. $f(x) = (5 - 2x)^4$
$f'(x) = 4(5 - 2x)^3(5 - 2x)'$
$\quad\quad = 4(5 - 2x)^3(-2)$
$\quad\quad = -8(5 - 2x)^3$

11. $f(x) = (4 + 0.2x)^5$
$f'(x) = 5(4 + 0.2x)^4 (4 + 0.2x)' = 5(4 + 0.2x)^4 (0.2)$
$$= (4 + 0.2x)^4$$

13. $f(x) = (3x^2 + 5)^5$
$f'(x) = 5(3x^2 + 5)^4(3x^2 + 5)'$
$\quad\quad = 5(3x^2 + 5)^4(6x)$
$\quad\quad = 30x(3x^2 + 5)^4$

15. $f(x) = (x^3 - 2x^2 + 2)^8$
$f'(x) = 8(x^3 - 2x^2 + 2)^7(x^3 - 2x^2 + 2)'$
$\quad\quad = 8(x^3 - 2x^2 + 2)^7(3x^2 - 4x)$

17. $f(x) = (2x - 5)^{1/2}$
$f'(x) = \dfrac{1}{2}(2x - 5)^{-1/2}(2x - 5)'$

$\quad\quad = \dfrac{1}{2}(2x - 5)^{-1/2}(2) = \dfrac{1}{(2x - 5)^{1/2}}$

19. $f(x) = (x^4 + 1)^{-2}$

$\quad f'(x) = -2(x^4 + 1)^{-3}(x^4 + 1)\,'$

$\qquad\quad = -2(x^4 + 1)^{-3}(4x^3)$

$\qquad\quad = -8x^3(x^4 + 1)^{-3} = \dfrac{-8x^3}{(x^4 + 1)^3}$

21. $f(x) = (2x - 1)^3$

$\quad f'(x) = 3(2x - 1)^2(2) = 6(2x - 1)^2$

Tangent line at $x = 1$: $y - y_1 = m(x - x_1)$ where $x_1 = 1$, $y_1 = f(1) =$

$(2(1) - 1)^3 = 1$, $m = f'(1) = 6[2(1) - 1]^2 = 6$. Thus, $y - 1 = 6(x - 1)$

or $y = 6x - 5$.

The tangent line is horizontal at the value(s) of x such that $f'(x) = 0$:

$6(2x - 1)^2 = 0$

$\qquad 2x - 1 = 0$

$\qquad\qquad x = \dfrac{1}{2}$

23. $f(x) = (4x - 3)^{1/2}$

$\quad f'(x) = \dfrac{1}{2}(4x - 3)^{-1/2}(4) = \dfrac{2}{(4x - 3)^{1/2}}$

Tangent line at $x = 3$: $y - y_1 = m(x - x_1)$ where $x_1 = 3$, $y_1 = f(3) =$

$(4 \cdot 3 - 3)^{1/2} = 3$, $f'(3) = \dfrac{2}{(4 \cdot 3 - 3)^{1/2}} = \dfrac{2}{3}$. Thus, $y - 3 = \dfrac{2}{3}(x - 3)$ or

$y = \dfrac{2}{3}x + 1$.

The tangent line is horizontal at the value(s) of x such that $f'(x) = 0$.

Since $\dfrac{2}{(4x - 3)^{1/2}} \neq 0$ for all x $\left(x \neq \dfrac{3}{4}\right)$, there are no values of x where

the tangent line is horizontal.

25. $y = 3(x^2 - 2)^4$

$\quad \dfrac{dy}{dx} = 3 \cdot 4(x^2 - 2)^3(2x) = 24x(x^2 - 2)^3$

27. $\dfrac{d}{dt}[2(t^2 + 3t)^{-3}] = 2(-3)(t^2 + 3t)^{-4}(2t + 3) = \dfrac{-6(2t + 3)}{(t^2 + 3t)^4}$

29. $h(w) = \sqrt{w^2 + 8} = (w^2 + 8)^{1/2};$

$\quad h'(w) = \dfrac{1}{2}(w^2 + 8)^{-1/2}(2w) = \dfrac{w}{(w^2 + 8)^{1/2}} = \dfrac{w}{\sqrt{w^2 + 8}}.$

31. $g(x) = \sqrt[3]{3x + 4} = (3x + 4)^{1/3}$

$\quad g'(x) = \dfrac{1}{3}(3x + 4)^{-2/3}(3) = \dfrac{1}{(3x + 4)^{2/3}} = \dfrac{1}{\sqrt[3]{(3x + 4)^2}}.$

33. $\dfrac{d}{dx} = (\sqrt[4]{0.8x + 3.6}) = \dfrac{d}{dx}[(0.8x + 3.6)^{1/4}]$

$$= \frac{1}{4}(0.8x + 3.6)^{-3/4}(0.8)$$

$$= \frac{0.2}{(0.8x + 3.6)^{3/4}} = \frac{0.2}{\sqrt[4]{(0.8x + 3.6)^3}}$$

35. $F(t) = (t^2 - 4t + 2)^{1/2}$; $F'(t) = \dfrac{1}{2}(t^2 - 4t + 2)^{-1/2}(2t - 4)$

$$= \frac{t - 2}{(t^2 - 4t + 2)^{1/2}} = \frac{t - 2}{\sqrt{t^2 - 4t + 2}}.$$

37. $y = \dfrac{1}{2x + 4} = (2x + 4)^{-1}$; $y' = -1(2x + 4)^{-2}(2) = \dfrac{-2}{(2x + 4)^2}.$

39. $\dfrac{d}{dw}\left[\dfrac{1}{(w^3 + 4)^5}\right] = \dfrac{d}{dw}[(w^3 + 4)^{-5}]$

$$= -5(w^3 + 4)^{-6}(3w^2) = \frac{-15w^2}{(w^3 + 4)^6}.$$

41. $y = (3\sqrt{x} - 1)^5 = (3x^{1/2} - 1)^5$;

$\dfrac{dy}{dx} = 5(3x^{1/2} - 1)^4(3)\left(\dfrac{1}{2}x^{-1/2}\right) = \dfrac{15(3x^{1/2} - 1)^4}{2x^{1/2}} = \dfrac{15(3\sqrt{x} - 1)^4}{2\sqrt{x}}.$

43. $f(t) = \dfrac{4}{\sqrt{t^2 - 3t}} = 4(t^2 - 3t)^{-1/2}$;

$f'(t) = 4\left(-\dfrac{1}{2}\right)(t^2 - 3t)^{-3/2}(2t - 3) = \dfrac{-2(2t - 3)}{(t^2 - 3t)^{3/2}} = \dfrac{-2(2t - 3)}{\sqrt{(t^2 - 3t)^3}}$

45. $f(x) = x(4 - x)^3$

$f'(x) = x[(4 - x)^3]' + (4 - x)^3(x)'$

$\quad = x(3)(4 - x)^2(-1) + (4 - x)^3(1)$

$\quad = (4 - x)^3 - 3x(4 - x)^2 = (4 - x)^2[4 - x - 3x] = 4(4 - x)^2(1 - x)$

An equation for the tangent line to the graph of f at $x = 2$ is:
$y - y_1 = m(x - x_1)$ where $x_1 = 2$, $y_1 = f(x_1) = f(2) = 16$, and
$m = f'(x_1) = f'(2) = -16$. Thus, $y - 16 = -16(x - 2)$ or $y = -16x + 48$.

47. $f(x) = \dfrac{x}{(2x - 5)^3}$

$f'(x) = \dfrac{(2x - 5)^3(1) - x(3)(2x - 5)^2(2)}{[(2x - 5)^3]^2}$

$\quad = \dfrac{(2x - 5)^3 - 6x(2x - 5)^2}{(2x - 5)^6} = \dfrac{(2x - 5) - 6x}{(2x - 5)^4} = \dfrac{-4x - 5}{(2x - 5)^4}$

An equation for the tangent line to the graph of f at $x = 3$ is:
$y - y_1 = m(x - x_1)$ where $x_1 = 3$, $y_1 = f(x_1) = f(3) = 3$, and
$m = f'(x_1) = f'(3) = -17$. Thus, $y - 3 = -17(x - 3)$ or $y = -17x + 54$.

49. $f(x) = x\sqrt{2x + 2} = x(2x + 2)^{1/2}$

$f'(x) = x[(2x + 2)^{1/2}]' + (2x + 2)^{1/2}(x)'$

$\quad = x\left(\dfrac{1}{2}\right)(2x + 2)^{-1/2}(2) + (2x + 2)^{1/2}(1) = \dfrac{x}{(2x + 2)^{1/2}} + (2x + 2)^{1/2}$

$\qquad\qquad\qquad\qquad\qquad\qquad\qquad\qquad\qquad = \dfrac{3x + 2}{(2x + 2)^{1/2}}$

An equation for the tangent line to the graph of f at $x = 1$ is:

$y - y_1 = m(x - x_1)$ where $x_1 = 1$, $y_1 = f(x_1) = f(1) = 2$, and

$m = f'(x_1) = f'(1) = \dfrac{5}{2}$. Thus, $y - 2 = \dfrac{5}{2}(x - 1)$ or $y = \dfrac{5}{2}x - \dfrac{1}{2}$.

51. $f(x) = x^2(x - 5)^3$

$f'(x) = x^2[(x - 5)^3]' + (x - 5)^3(x^2)'$

$\quad = x^2(3)(x - 5)^2(1) + (x - 5)^3(2x)$

$\quad = 3x^2(x - 5)^2 + 2x(x - 5)^3 = 5x(x - 5)^2(x - 2)$

The tangent line to the graph of f is horizontal at the values of x such that $f'(x) = 0$. Thus, we set $5x(x - 5)^2(x - 2) = 0$ and $x = 0$, $x = 2$, $x = 5$.

53. $f(x) = \dfrac{x}{(2x + 5)^2}$

$f'(x) = \dfrac{(2x + 5)^2(x)' - x[(2x + 5)^2]'}{[(2x + 5)^2]^2}$

$\quad = \dfrac{(2x + 5)^2(1) - x(2)(2x + 5)(2)}{(2x + 5)^4} = \dfrac{2x + 5 - 4x}{(2x + 5)^3} = \dfrac{5 - 2x}{(2x + 5)^3}$

The tangent line to the graph of f is horizontal at the values of x such that $f'(x) = 0$. Thus, we set

$\dfrac{5 - 2x}{(2x + 5)^3} = 0$

$5 - 2x = 0$

and $x = \dfrac{5}{2}$.

55. $f(x) = \sqrt{x^2 - 8x + 20} = (x^2 - 8x + 20)^{1/2}$

$f'(x) = \dfrac{1}{2}(x^2 - 8x + 20)^{-1/2}(2x - 8)$

$\quad = \dfrac{x - 4}{(x^2 - 8x + 20)^{1/2}}$

The tangent line to the graph of f is horizontal at the values of x such that $f'(x) = 0$. Thus, we set

$\dfrac{x - 4}{(x^2 - 8x + 20)^{1/2}} = 0$

$x - 4 = 0$

and $x = 4$.

57. $f(x) = x(x - 1)(x^2 - 5) = x(x^3 - x^2 - 5x + 5) = x^4 - x^3 - 5x^2 + 5x$

$f'(x) = 4x^3 - 3x^2 - 10x + 5$

The tangent line to the graph of f is horizontal at the values of x where $f'(x) = 0$. Solve this equation using a root-approximation routine on a graphing utility:

$f'(x) = 0$ at $x = -1.4903$, $x = 0.4752$, $x = 1.7651$.

59. $f(x) = (x^3 - 2x^2)(x^2 + 1)$

$f'(x) = (x^3 - 2x^2)2x + (x^2 + 1)(3x^2 - 4x)$

$\qquad = 5x^4 - 8x^3 + 3x^2 - 4x$

The tangent line to the graph of f is horizontal at the values of x where $f'(x) = 0$. Solve this equation using a root-approximation routine on a graphing utility:

$f'(x) = 0$ at $x = 0$, $x = 1.5465$.

61. $f(x) = \sqrt{x^4 - 6x^2 + x + 12} = (x^4 - 6x^2 + x + 12)^{1/2}$

$f'(x) = \dfrac{1}{2}(x^4 - 6x^2 + x + 12)^{-1/2}(4x^3 - 12x + 1)$

$\qquad = \dfrac{4x^3 - 12x + 1}{2\sqrt{x^4 - 6x^2 + x + 12}}$

The tangent line to the graph of f is horizontal at the values of x where $f'(x) = 0$, that is at the values of x where $4x^3 - 12x + 1 = 0$. Solve this equation using a root-approximation routine on a graphing utility:

$f'(x) = 0$ at $x = -1.7723$, $x = 0.0835$, $x = 1.6888$.

63. $\dfrac{d}{dx}[3x(x^2 + 1)^3] = 3x\dfrac{d}{dx}(x^2 + 1)^3 + (x^2 + 1)^3\dfrac{d}{dx}3x$

$\qquad\qquad = 3x \cdot 3(x^2 + 1)^2(2x) + (x^2 + 1)^3(3)$

$\qquad\qquad = 18x^2(x^2 + 1)^2 + 3(x^2 + 1)^3$

$\qquad\qquad = (x^2 + 1)^2[18x^2 + 3(x^2 + 1)]$

$\qquad\qquad = (x^2 + 1)^2(21x^2 + 3)$

$\qquad\qquad = 3(x^2 + 1)^2(7x^2 + 1)$

65. $\dfrac{d}{dx}\dfrac{(x^3 - 7)^4}{2x^3} = \dfrac{2x^3\dfrac{d}{dx}(x^3 - 7)^4 - (x^3 - 7)^4\dfrac{d}{dx}2x^3}{(2x^3)^2}$

$\qquad = \dfrac{2x^3 \cdot 4(x^3 - 7)^3(3x^2) - (x^3 - 7)^46x^2}{4x^6}$

$\qquad = \dfrac{3(x^3 - 7)^3x^2[8x^3 - 2(x^3 - 7)]}{4x^6}$

$\qquad = \dfrac{3(x^3 - 7)^3(6x^3 + 14)}{4x^4} = \dfrac{3(x^3 - 7)^3(3x^3 + 7)}{2x^4}$

67. $\dfrac{d}{dx}[(2x - 3)^2(2x^2 + 1)^3]$

$$= (2x - 3)^2 \dfrac{d}{dx}(2x^2 + 1)^3 + (2x^2 + 1)^3 \dfrac{d}{dx}(2x - 3)^2$$

$$= (2x - 3)^2 3(2x^2 + 1)^2(4x) + (2x^2 + 1)^3 2(2x - 3)(2)$$

$$= 12x(2x - 3)^2(2x^2 + 1)^2 + 4(2x^2 + 1)^3(2x - 3)$$

$$= 4(2x - 3)(2x^2 + 1)^2[3x(2x - 3) + (2x^2 + 1)]$$

$$= 4(2x - 3)(2x^2 + 1)^2(6x^2 - 9x + 2x^2 + 1)$$

$$= 4(2x - 3)(2x^2 + 1)^2(8x^2 - 9x + 1)$$

69. $\dfrac{d}{dx}[4x^2\sqrt{x^2 - 1}] = \dfrac{d}{dx}[\sqrt{16x^4(x^2 - 1)}] = \dfrac{d}{dx}[(16x^6 - 16x^4)^{1/2}]$

$$= \dfrac{1}{2}(16x^6 - 16x^4)^{-1/2}(96x^5 - 64x^3)$$

$$= \dfrac{96x^5 - 64x^3}{2(16x^6 - 16x^4)^{1/2}} = \dfrac{8x^2(12x^3 - 8x)}{2 \cdot 4x^2(x^2 - 1)^{1/2}} = \dfrac{12x^3 - 8x}{(x^2 - 1)^{1/2}}$$

or $\dfrac{d}{dx}[4x^2\sqrt{x^2 - 1}] = \dfrac{d}{dx}[4x^2(x^2 - 1)^{1/2}]$

$$= 4x^2 \cdot \dfrac{1}{2}(x^2 - 1)^{-1/2}(2x) + (x^2 - 1)^{1/2}(8x)$$

$$= \dfrac{4x^3}{(x^2 - 1)^{1/2}} + 8x(x^2 - 1)^{1/2}$$

$$= \dfrac{4x^3 + 8x(x^2 - 1)}{(x^2 - 1)^{1/2}} = \dfrac{4x^3 + 8x^3 - 8x}{(x^2 - 1)^{1/2}} = \dfrac{12x^3 - 8x}{(x^2 - 1)^{1/2}}$$

71. $\dfrac{d}{dx}\dfrac{2x}{\sqrt{x - 3}} = \dfrac{(x - 3)^{1/2}(2) - 2x \cdot \dfrac{1}{2}(x - 3)^{-1/2}}{(x - 3)}$

$$= \dfrac{2(x - 3)^{1/2} - \dfrac{x}{(x - 3)^{1/2}}}{(x - 3)} = \dfrac{2(x - 3) - x}{(x - 3)(x - 3)^{1/2}}$$

$$= \dfrac{2x - 6 - x}{(x - 3)^{3/2}} = \dfrac{x - 6}{(x - 3)^{3/2}}$$

73. $\dfrac{d}{dx}\sqrt{(2x - 1)^3(x^2 + 3)^4} = \dfrac{d}{dx}[(2x - 1)^3(x^2 + 3)^4]^{1/2}$

$$= \dfrac{d}{dx}(2x - 1)^{3/2}(x^2 + 3)^2$$

$$= (2x - 1)^{3/2}\dfrac{d}{dx}(x^2 + 3)^2 + (x^2 + 3)^2 \dfrac{d}{dx}(2x - 1)^{3/2}$$

$$= (2x - 1)^{3/2}2(x^2 + 3)(2x) + (x^2 + 3)^2 \cdot \dfrac{3}{2}(2x - 1)^{1/2}(2)$$

$$= (2x - 1)^{1/2}(x^2 + 3)[4x(2x - 1) + 3(x^2 + 3)]$$

$$= (2x - 1)^{1/2}(x^2 + 3)(8x^2 - 4x + 3x^2 + 9)$$

$$= (2x - 1)^{1/2}(x^2 + 3)(11x^2 - 4x + 9)$$

75. $C(x) = 10 + \sqrt{2x + 16} = 10 + (2x + 16)^{1/2}, \quad 0 \le x \le 50$

(A) $C'(x) = \dfrac{1}{2}(2x + 16)^{-1/2}(2) = \dfrac{1}{(2x + 16)^{1/2}}$

(B) $C'(24) = \dfrac{1}{[2(24) + 16]^{1/2}} = \dfrac{1}{(64)^{1/2}} = \dfrac{1}{8}$ or $12.50; at a production

level of 24 calculators, total costs are INCREASING at the rate of $12.50 per calculator; also, the cost of producing the 25th calculator is approximately $12.50.

$C'(42) = \dfrac{1}{[2(42) + 16]^{1/2}} = \dfrac{1}{(100)^{1/2}} = \dfrac{1}{10}$ or $10.00; at a production

level of 42 calculators, total costs are INCREASING at the rate of $10.00 per calculator; also the cost of producing the 43rd calculator is approximately $10.00.

77. $x = 80\sqrt{p + 25} - 400 = 80(p + 25)^{1/2} - 400, \quad 20 \le p \le 100$

(A) $\dfrac{dx}{dp} = 80\left(\dfrac{1}{2}\right)(p + 25)^{-1/2}(1) = \dfrac{40}{(p + 25)^{1/2}}$

(B) At $p = 75$, $x = 80\sqrt{75 + 25} - 400 = 400$ and

$\dfrac{dx}{dp} = \dfrac{40}{(75 + 25)^{1/2}} = \dfrac{40}{(100)^{1/2}} = 4.$

At a price of $75, the supply is 400 speakers, and the supply is INCREASING at a rate of 4 speakers per dollar.

79. $A = 1000\left(1 + \dfrac{1}{12}r\right)^{48}$

$\dfrac{dA}{dr} = 1000(48)\left(1 + \dfrac{1}{12}r\right)^{47}\left(\dfrac{1}{12}\right) = 4000\left(1 + \dfrac{1}{12}r\right)^{47}$

81. $y = (3 \times 10^6)\left[1 - \dfrac{1}{\sqrt[3]{(x^2 - 1)^2}}\right] = (3 \times 10^6)[1 - (x^2 - 1)^{-2/3}]$

$\dfrac{dy}{dx} = -(3 \times 10^6)\left(-\dfrac{2}{3}\right)(x^2 - 1)^{-5/3}(2x) = \dfrac{(4 \times 10^6)x}{(x^2 - 1)^{5/3}}$

83. $T = f(n) = 2n\sqrt{n - 2} = 2n(n - 2)^{1/2}$

(A) $f'(n) = 2n[(n - 2)^{1/2}]' + (n - 2)^{1/2}(2n)'$

$= 2n\left(\dfrac{1}{2}\right)(n - 2)^{-1/2}(1) + (n - 2)^{1/2}(2)$

$= \dfrac{n}{(n - 2)^{1/2}} + 2(n - 2)^{1/2}$

$= \dfrac{n + 2(n - 2)}{(n - 2)^{1/2}} = \dfrac{3n - 4}{(n - 2)^{1/2}}$

(B) $f'(11) = \dfrac{29}{3} = 9.67$; when the list contains 11 items, the learning time is increasing at the rate of 9.67 minutes per item;

$f'(27) = \dfrac{77}{5} = 15.4$; when the list contains 27 items, the learning time is increasing at the rate of 15.4 minutes per item.

EXERCISE 1-7

Things to remember:

1. MARGINAL COST, REVENUE, AND PROFIT

   If x is the number of units of a product produced in some time interval, then:

   Total Cost $= C(x)$
   Marginal Cost $= C'(x)$
   Total Revenue $= R(x)$
   Marginal Revenue $= R'(x)$
   Total Profit $= P(x) = R(x) - C(x)$
   Marginal Profit $= P'(x) = R'(x) - C'(x)$
   $\qquad\qquad\qquad = $ (Marginal Revenue) $-$ (Marginal Cost)

   Marginal cost (or revenue or profit) is the instantaneous rate of change of cost (or revenue or profit) relative to production at a given production level.

2. MARGINAL COST AND EXACT COST

   If $C(x)$ is the cost of producing x items, then the marginal cost function approximates the exact cost of producing the $(x + 1)$st item:

Marginal Cost		Exact Cost
$C'(x)$	$\approx$	$C(x + 1) - C(x)$

   Similar interpretations can be made for total revenue and total profit functions.

3. BREAK-EVEN POINTS

   The BREAK-EVEN POINTS are the points where total revenue equals total cost.

4. MARGINAL AVERAGE COST, REVENUE, AND PROFIT

   If x is the number of units of a product produced in some time interval, then:

   Average Cost $= \overline{C}(x) = \dfrac{C(x)}{x}$ Cost per unit
   Marginal Average Cost $= \overline{C}'(x)$
   Average Revenue $= \overline{R}(x) = \dfrac{R(x)}{x}$ Revenue per unit
   Marginal Average Revenue $= \overline{R}'(x)$
   Average Profit $= \overline{P}(x) = \dfrac{P(x)}{x}$ Profit per unit
   Marginal Average Profit $= \overline{P}'(x)$

1. $C(x) = 2000 + 50x - 0.5x^2$

    (A) The exact cost of producing the 21st food processor is:

$$C(21) - C(20) = 2000 + 50(21) - \frac{(21)^2}{2} - \left[2000 + 50(20) - \frac{(20)^2}{2}\right]$$

$$= 2829.50 - 2800$$
$$= 29.50 \text{ or } \$29.50$$

    (B) $C'(x) = 50 - x$
        $C'(20) = 50 - 20 = 30 \text{ or } \$30$

3. $C(x) = 60,000 + 300x$

    (A) $\overline{C}(x) = \dfrac{60,000 + 300x}{x} = \dfrac{60,000}{x} + 300 = 60,000x^{-1} + 300$

        $\overline{C}(500) = \dfrac{60,000 + 300(500)}{500} = \dfrac{210,000}{500} = 420 \text{ or } \$420$

    (B) $\overline{C}'(x) = -60,000x^{-2} = \dfrac{-60,000}{x^2}$

        $\overline{C}'(500) = \dfrac{-60,000}{(500)^2} = -0.24 \text{ or } \$0.24$

        Interpretation: At a production level of 500 frames, average cost is decreasing at the rate of 24¢ per frame.

    (C) The average cost per frame if 501 frames are produced is approximately $420 - $0.24 = $419.76.

5. $P(x) = 30x - 0.3x^2 - 250, \ 0 \le x \le 100$

    (A) The exact profit from the sale of the 26th skateboard is:

$$P(26) - P(25) = 30(26) - 0.3(26)^2 - 250 - [30(25) - 0.3(25)^2 - 250]$$
$$= 327.20 - 312.50 = \$14.70$$

    (B) Marginal profit: $P'(x) = 30 - 0.6x$
        $P'(25) = \$15$

7. $P(x) = 5x - \dfrac{x^2}{200} - 450$

    $P'(x) = 5 - \dfrac{x}{100}$

    (A) $P'(450) = 5 - \dfrac{450}{100} = 0.5 \text{ or } \$0.50$

        Interpretation: At a production level of 450 cassettes, profit is increasing at the rate of 50¢ per cassette.

    (B) $P'(750) = 5 - \dfrac{750}{100} = -2.5 \text{ or } -\$2.50$

        Interpretation: At a production level of 750 cassettes, profit is decreasing at the rate of $2.50 per cassette.

9. $P(x) = 30x - 0.03x^2 - 750$

Average profit: $\overline{P}(x) = \dfrac{P(x)}{x} = 30 - 0.03x - \dfrac{750}{x} = 30 - 0.03x - 750x^{-1}$

(A) At $x = 50$, $\overline{P}(50) = 30 - (0.03)50 - \dfrac{750}{50} = 13.50$ or $\$13.50$.

(B) $\overline{P}'(x) = -0.03 + 750x^{-2} = -0.03 + \dfrac{750}{x^2}$

$\overline{P}'(50) = -0.03 + \dfrac{750}{(50)^2} = -0.03 + 0.3 = 0.27$ or $\$0.27$; at a

production level of 50 mowers, the average profit per mower is INCREASING at the rate of $\$0.27$ per mower.

(C) The average profit per mower if 51 mowers are produced is approximately $\$13.50 + \$0.27 = \$13.77$.

11. $x = 4,000 - 40p$

(A) Solving the given equation for p, we get

$40p = 4,000 - x$

and $p = 100 - \dfrac{1}{40}x$ or $p = 100 - 0.025x$

Since $p \geq 0$, the domain is: $0 \leq x \leq 4,00$

(B) $R(x) = xp = 100x - 0.025x^2$, $0 \leq x \leq 4,000$

(C) $R'(x) = 100 - 0.05x$; $R'(1,600) = 100 - 80 = 20$
At a production level of 1,600 radios, revenue is INCREASING at the rate of $\$20$ per radio.

(D) $R'(2,500) = 100 - 125 = -25$
At a production level of 2,500 radios, revenue is DECREASING at the rate of $\$25$ per radio.

13. Price-demand equation: $x = 6,000 - 30p$
Cost function: $C(x) = 72,000 + 60x$

(A) Solving the price-demand equation for p, we get

$p = 200 - \dfrac{1}{30}x$; domain: $0 \leq x \leq 6,000$

(B) Marginal cost: $C'(x) = 60$

(C) Revenue function: $R(x) = 200x - \dfrac{1}{30}x^2$; domain: $0 \leq x \leq 6,000$

(D) Marginal revenue: $R'(x) = 200 - \dfrac{1}{15}x$

(E) $R'(1,500) = 100$; at a production level of 1,500 saws, revenue is INCREASING at the rate of $\$100$ per saw.

$R'(4,500) = -100$; at a production level of 4,500 saws, revenue is DECREASING at the rate of $\$100$ per saw.

(F)

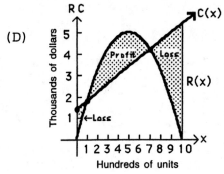

(G) Profit function: $P(x) = R(x) - C(x)$
$$= 200x - \frac{1}{30}x^2 - [72{,}000 + 60x]$$
$$= 140x - \frac{1}{30}x^2 - 72{,}000$$

(H) Marginal profit: $P'(x) = 140 - \frac{1}{15}x$

(I) $P'(1{,}500) = 140 - 100 = 40$; at a production level of 1,500 saws, profit is INCREASING at the rate of $40 per saw.

$P'(3000) = 140 - 200 = -60$; at a production level of 3,000 saws, profit is DECREASING at the rate of $60 per saw.

15. (A) Assume $p = mx + b$. We are given
$$16 = m \cdot 200 + b$$
$30 = 560m + 2b$
and $14 = m \cdot 300 + b$

Subtracting the second equation from the first, we get
$$-100m = 2 \quad \text{so} \quad m = -\frac{1}{50} = -0.02$$

Substituting this value into either equation yields $b = 20$. Therefore,
$P = 20 - 0.02x$; domain: $0 \le x \le 1{,}000$

(B) Revenue function: $R(x) = xp = 20x - 0.02x^2$, domain: $0 \le x \le 1{,}000$.

(C) $C(x) = mx + b$. From the finance department's estimates, $m = 4$ and $b = 1{,}400$. Thus, $C(x) = 4x + 1{,}400$.

(D)

(E) Profit function: $P(x) = R(x) - C(x)$
$$= 20x - 0.02x^2 - [4x + 1{,}400]$$
$$= 16x - 0.02x^2 - 1{,}400$$

(F) Marginal profit: $P'(x) = 16 - 0.04x$

   $P'(250) = 16 - 10 = 6$; at a production level of 250 toasters, profit is INCREASING at the rate of $6 per toaster.

   $P'(475) = 16 - 19 = -3$; at a production level of 475 toasters, profit is DECREASING at the rate of $3 per toaster.

17. Total cost: $C(x) = 24x + 21,900$

   Total revenue: $R(x) = 200x - 0.2x^2$, $0 \leq x \leq 1,000$

   (A) $R'(x) = 200 - 0.4x$

   The graph of R has a horizontal tangent line at the value(s) of x where $R'(x) = 0$, i.e.,

   $$200 - 0.4x = 0$$
   $$\text{or } x = 500$$

   (B) $P(x) = R(x) - C(x) = 200x - 0.2x^2 - (24x + 21,900)$
   $$= 176x - 0.2x^2 - 21,900$$

   (C) $P'(x) = 176 - 0.4x$. Setting $P'(x) = 0$, we have
   $$176x - 0.4x = 0$$
   $$\text{or } x = 440$$

   (D) The graphs of C, R and P are shown below.

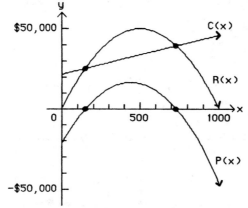

   Break-even points: $R(x) = C(x)$
   $$200x - 0.2x^2 = 24x + 21,900$$
   $$0.2x^2 - 176x + 21,900 = 0$$
   $$x = \frac{176 \pm \sqrt{(176)^2 - (4)(0.2)(21,900)}}{2(0.2)} \quad \text{(quadratic formula)}$$
   $$= \frac{176 \pm \sqrt{30,976 - 17,520}}{0.4}$$
   $$= \frac{176 \pm \sqrt{13,456}}{0.4} = \frac{176 \pm 116}{0.4} = 730, \ 150$$

   Thus, the break-even points are: (730, 39,420) and (150, 25,500).

   x-intercepts for P: $-0.2x^2 + 17.6x - 21,900 = 0$
   $$\text{or } 0.2x^2 - 176x + 21,900 = 0$$
   which is the same as the equation above.

   Thus, $x = 150$ and $x = 730$.

19. Demand equation: $p = 20 - \sqrt{x} = 20 - x^{1/2}$
Cost equation: $C(x) = 500 + 2x$

(A) Revenue $R(x) = xp = x(20 - x^{1/2})$
 or $R(x) = 20x - x^{3/2}$

(B) The graphs for R and C for $0 \le x \le 400$
 are shown at the right.

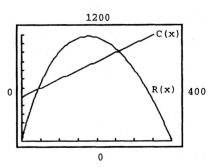

Break-even points $(44, 588)$
and $(258, 1,016)$.

21. (A)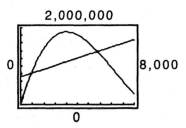
QuadReg
y=ax²+bx+c
a=1.4101002ᴇ-5
b=-.2732556676
c=1320.924694

(B) Fixed costs $\approx \$721,680$; variable costs $\approx \$121$
LinReg
y=ax+b
a=120.7047281
b=721680.1282
r=.9934384133

(C) Let $y = p(x)$ be the quadratic regression
 equation found in part (A) and let $y = C(x)$
 be the linear regression equation found in
 part (B). Then revenue $R(x) = xp(x)$, and
 the break-even points are the points where
 $R(x) = C(x)$.
 break-even points: $(713, 807,703)$,
                    $(5,423, 1,376,227)$

(D) The company will make a profit when $713 \le x \le 5,423$. From part (A),
 $p(713) \approx 1,133$ and $p(5,423) \approx 254$. Thus, the company will make a
 profit for the price range $\$254 \le p \le \$1,133$.

CHAPTER 1 REVIEW

1. (A) $f(3) - f(1) = 2(3)^2 + 5 - [2(1)^2 + 5] = 16$

(B) Average rate of change: $\dfrac{f(3) - f(1)}{3 - 1} = \dfrac{16}{2} = 8$

(C) Slope of secant line: $\dfrac{f(3) - f(1)}{3 - 1} = \dfrac{16}{2} = 8$

(D) Instantaneous rate of change at $x = 1$:

 Step 1. $\dfrac{f(1 + h) - f(1)}{h} = \dfrac{2(1 + h)^2 + 5 - [2(1)^2 + 5]}{h}$

$= \dfrac{2(1 + 2h + h^2) + 5 - 7}{h} = \dfrac{4h + 2h^2}{h} = 4 + 2h$

 Step 2. $\lim\limits_{h \to 0} \dfrac{f(1 + h) - f(1)}{h} = \lim\limits_{h \to 0} (4 + 2h) = 4$

(E) Slope of the tangent line at $x = 1$: 4

(F) $f'(1) = 4$ $(3-1, \ 3-3, \ 3-4)$

2. $f(x) = -3x + 2$

    <u>Step 1</u>. Simplify $\dfrac{f(x + h) - f(x)}{h}$

$$\frac{f(x + h) - f(x)}{h} = \frac{-3(x + h) + 2 - (-3x + 2)}{h}$$

$$= \frac{-3x - 3h + 2 + 3x - 2}{h} = -3$$

    <u>Step 2</u>. Evaluate $\lim\limits_{h \to 0} \dfrac{f(x + h) - f(x)}{h}$.

$$\lim_{h \to 0} \frac{f(x + h) - f(x)}{h} = \lim_{h \to 0} (-3) = -3 \tag{3-3}$$

3. (A) $\lim\limits_{x \to 1} (5f(x) + 3g(x)) = 5 \lim\limits_{x \to 1} f(x) + 3 \lim\limits_{x \to 1} g(x) = 5 \cdot 2 + 3 \cdot 4 = 22$

    (B) $\lim\limits_{x \to 1} [f(x) g(x)] = [\lim\limits_{x \to 1} f(x)][\lim\limits_{x \to 1} g(x)] = 2 \cdot 4 = 8$

    (C) $\lim\limits_{x \to 1} \dfrac{g(x)}{f(x)} = \dfrac{\lim\limits_{x \to 1} g(x)}{\lim\limits_{x \to 1} f(x)} = \dfrac{4}{2} = 2$

    (D) $\lim\limits_{x \to 1} [5 + 2x - 3g(x)] = \lim\limits_{x \to 1} 5 + \lim\limits_{x \to 1} 2x - 3 \lim\limits_{x \to 1} g(x)$

$$= 5 + 2 - 3(4) = -5 \tag{3-2}$$

4. (A) $\lim\limits_{x \to 1^-} f(x) = 1$ (B) $\lim\limits_{x \to 1^+} f(x) = 1$ (C) $\lim\limits_{x \to 1} f(x) = 1$

    (D) $f(1) = 1$ $\tag{3-2}$

5. (A) $\lim\limits_{x \to 2^-} f(x) = 2$ (B) $\lim\limits_{x \to 2^+} f(x) = 3$ (C) $\lim\limits_{x \to 2} f(x)$ does not exist

    (D) $f(2) = 3$ $\tag{3-2}$

6. (A) $\lim\limits_{x \to 3^-} f(x) = 4$ (B) $\lim\limits_{x \to 3^+} f(x) = 4$ (C) $\lim\limits_{x \to 3} f(x) = 4$

    (D) $f(3)$ does not exist $\tag{3-2}$

7. (A) From the graph, $\lim\limits_{x \to 1} f(x)$ does not exist since

        $\lim\limits_{x \to 1^-} f(x) = 2 \neq \lim\limits_{x \to 1^+} f(x) = 3$.

    (B) $f(1) = 3$

    (C) f is NOT continuous at $x = 1$, since $\lim\limits_{x \to 1} f(x)$ does not exist. $\tag{3-2}$

8. (A) $\lim\limits_{x \to 2} f(x) = 2$ (B) $f(2)$ is not defined

    (C) f is NOT continuous at $x = 2$ since $f(2)$ is not defined. $\tag{3-2}$

9. (A) $\lim\limits_{x \to 3} f(x) = 1$ (B) $f(3) = 1$

(C) f is continuous at $x = 3$ since $\lim\limits_{x \to 3} f(x) = f(3)$. (3-2)

10. $f(x) = 5x^2$

Step 1. Simplify $\dfrac{f(x + h) - f(x)}{h}$.

$$\frac{f(x + h) - f(x)}{h} = \frac{5(x + h)^2 - 5x^2}{h} = \frac{5(x^2 + 2xh + h^2) - 5x^2}{h}$$

$$= \frac{10xh + 5h^2}{h} = 10x + 5h$$

Step 2. Evaluate $\lim\limits_{h \to 0} \dfrac{f(x + h) - f(x)}{h}$.

$$\lim\limits_{h \to 0} \frac{f(x + h) - f(x)}{h} = \lim\limits_{h \to 0}(10x + 5h) = 10x \qquad (3\text{-}3)$$

11. (A) $h(x) = 2f(x) + 3g(x)$; $h'(5) = 2f'(5) + 3g'(5) = 2(-1) + 3(-3) = -11$

(B) $h(x) = f(x)g(x)$; $h'(5) = f(5)g'(5) + g(5)f'(5) = 4(-3) + 2(-1) = -14$

(C) $h(x) = \dfrac{f(x)}{g(x)}$; $h'(5) = \dfrac{g(5)f'(5) - f(5)g'(5)}{[g(5)]^2} = \dfrac{2(-1) - 4(-3)}{2^2} = \dfrac{10}{4} = \dfrac{5}{2}$

(D) $h(x) = [f(x)]^2$; $h'(5) = 2f(5)f'(5) = 2(4)(-1) = -8$

(E) $h(x) = x^2 f(x)$; $h'(x) = x^2 f'(x) + f(x)(2x)$;
$h'(5) = 25f'(5) + f(5)(10) = 25(-1) + 4(10) = 15$

(F) $h(x) = \dfrac{g(x)}{x + 2}$; $h'(x) = \dfrac{(x + 2)g'(x) - g(x)(1)}{(x + 2)^2}$;

$h'(5) = \dfrac{7(-3) - 2(1)}{7^2} = \dfrac{-23}{49}$ (3-4, 3-5, 3-6)

12. $6x + 4$; $\dfrac{d}{dx}(3x^2 + 4x + 1)^5 = 5(3x^2 + 4x + 1)^4(6x + 4)$ (3-6)

13. $f(x) = \dfrac{1}{3}x^3 - 5x^2 + 1$; $f'(x) = x^2 - 10x$ (3-4)

14. $f(x) = 2x^{1/2} - 3x$
$f'(x) = 2 \cdot \dfrac{1}{2}x^{-1/2} - 3 = \dfrac{1}{x^{1/2}} - 3$ (3-4)

15. $f(x) = 5$
$f'(x) = 0$
(3-4)

16. $f(x) = \dfrac{3}{2x} + \dfrac{5x^3}{4} = \dfrac{3}{2}x^{-1} + \dfrac{5}{4}x^3$;

$f'(x) = -\dfrac{3}{2}x^{-2} + \dfrac{15}{4}x^2 = -\dfrac{3}{2x^2} + \dfrac{15}{4}x^2$ (3-4)

17. $f(x) = \dfrac{0.5}{x^4} + 0.25x^4 = 0.5x^{-4} + 0.25x^4$

$f'(x) = 0.5(-4)x^{-5} + 0.25(4x^3) = -2x^{-5} + x^3 = -\dfrac{2}{x^5} + x^3$ (3-4)

18. $f(x) = (2x - 1)(3x + 2)$
$f'(x) = (2x - 1)(3) + (3x + 2)(2)$
$= 6x - 3 + 6x + 4$
$= 12x + 1$ (3-5)

19. $f(x) = (x^2 - 1)(x^3 - 3)$
$f'(x) = (x^2 - 1)(3x^2) + (x^3 - 3)(2x) = 3x^4 - 3x^2 + 2x^4 - 6x = 5x^4 - 3x^2 - 6x$
       (3-5)

20. $f(x) = (0.2x - 1.5)(0.5x + 0.4)$
$f'(x) = (0.2x - 1.5)(0.5x + 0.4)' + (0.5x + 0.4)(0.2x - 1.5)'$
$= (0.2x - 1.5)(0.5) + (0.5x + 0.4)(0.2)$
$= 0.1x - 0.75 + 0.1x + 0.08 = 0.2x - 0.67$ (3-5)

21. $f(x) = \dfrac{2x}{x^2 + 2}$

$f'(x) = \dfrac{(x^2 + 2)(2) - 2x(2x)}{(x^2 + 2)^2} = \dfrac{2x^2 + 4 - 4x^2}{(x^2 + 2)^2} = \dfrac{4 - 2x^2}{(x^2 + 2)^2}$ (3-5)

22. $f(x) = \dfrac{1}{3x + 2} = (3x + 2)^{-1}$

$f'(x) = -1(3x + 2)^{-2}(3) = \dfrac{-3}{(3x + 2)^2}$ (3-6)

23. $f(x) = (2x - 3)^3$
$f'(x) = 3(2x - 3)^2(2) = 6(2x - 3)^2$ (3-6)

24. $f(x) = (x^2 + 2)^{-2}$
$f'(x) = -2(x^2 + 2)^{-3}(2x) = \dfrac{-4x}{(x^2 + 2)^3}$ (3-6)

25. From the graph:
  (A) $\lim\limits_{x \to 2^-} f(x) = 4$ (B) $\lim\limits_{x \to 2^+} f(x) = 6$

  (C) $\lim\limits_{x \to 2} f(x)$ does not exist since $\lim\limits_{x \to 2^-} f(x) \neq \lim\limits_{x \to 2^+} f(x)$

  (D) $f(2) = 6$ (E) No, since $\lim\limits_{x \to 2} f(x)$ does not exist.   (3-2)

26. From the graph:
  (A) $\lim\limits_{x \to 5^-} f(x) = 3$ (B) $\lim\limits_{x \to 5^+} f(x) = 3$ (C) $\lim\limits_{x \to 5} f(x) = 3$ (D) $f(5) = 3$

  (E) Yes, since $\lim\limits_{x \to 5} f(x) = f(5) = 3$.   (3-2)

27. (A) $f(x) < 0$ on $(8, \infty)$
  (B) $f(x) \geq 0$ on $[0, 8]$ (3-2)

28. $x^2 - x < 12$ or $x^2 - x - 12 < 0$

Let $f(x) = x^2 - x - 12 = (x + 3)(x - 4)$. Then f is continuous for all x and $f(-3) = f(4) = 0$. Thus, $x = -3$ and $x = 4$ are partition numbers.

Test Numbers	
x	$f(x)$
-4	8 (+)
0	-12 (-)
5	8 (+)

Thus, $x^2 - x < 12$ for: $-3 < x < 4$ or $(-3, 4)$.　　　　　　(3-2)

29. $\dfrac{x - 5}{x^2 + 3x} > 0$ or $\dfrac{x - 5}{x(x + 3)} > 0$

Let $f(x) = \dfrac{x - 5}{x(x + 3)}$. Then f is discontinuous at $x = 0$ and $x = -3$, and $f(5) = 0$. Thus, $x = -3$, $x = 0$, and $x = 5$ are partition numbers.

Test Numbers	
x	$f(x)$
-4	$-\frac{9}{4}$ (−)
-1	3 (+)
1	−1 (−)
6	$\frac{1}{54}$ (+)

Thus, $\dfrac{x - 5}{x^2 + 3x} > 0$ for $-3 < x < 0$ or $x > 5$

or $(-3, 0) \cup (5, \infty)$.　　　　　　(3-2)

30. $x^3 + x^2 - 4x - 2 > 0$

Let $f(x) = x^3 + x^2 - 4x - 2$. The f is continuous for all x and $f(x) = 0$ at $x = -2.3429, -0.4707$ and 1.8136.

Thus, $x^3 + x^2 - 4x - 2 > 0$ for $-2.3429 < x < -0.4707$ or $1.8136 < x < \infty$, or $(-2.3429, -0.4707) \cup (1.8136, \infty)$.　　　　　　(3-2)

31. $f(x) = 0.5x^2 - 5$

(A) $\dfrac{f(4) - f(2)}{4 - 2} = \dfrac{0.5(4)^2 - 5 - [0.5(2)^2 - 5]}{2} = \dfrac{8 - 2}{2} = 3$

(B) $\dfrac{f(2 + h) - f(2)}{h} = \dfrac{0.5(2 + h)^2 - 5 - [0.5(2)^2 - 5]}{h}$

$= \dfrac{0.5(4 + 4h + h^2) - 5 + 3}{h}$

$= \dfrac{2h + 0.5h^2}{h} = \dfrac{h(2 + 0.5h)}{h} = 2 + 0.5h$

(C) $\lim\limits_{h \to 0} \dfrac{f(2 + h) - f(2)}{h} = \lim\limits_{h \to 0} (2 + 0.5h) = 2$ (3-3)

32. $y = \dfrac{1}{3}x^{-3} - 5x^{-2} + 1; \quad \dfrac{dy}{dx} = -x^{-4} + 10x^{-3}$ (3-4)

33. $y = (2x^2 - 3x + 2)(x^2 + 2x - 1)$

$y' = (2x^2 - 3x + 2)(2x + 2) + (x^2 + 2x - 1)(4x - 3)$

$= 4x^3 - 6x^2 + 4x + 4x^2 - 6x + 4 + 4x^3 + 8x^2 - 4x - 3x^2 - 6x + 3$

$= 8x^3 + 3x^2 - 12x + 7$ (3-5)

34. $f(x) = \dfrac{2x - 3}{(x - 1)^2}$

$f'(x) = \dfrac{(x - 1)^2 2 - (2x - 3)2(x - 1)}{(x - 1)^4} = \dfrac{(x - 1)[2(x - 1) - 4x + 6]}{(x - 1)^4}$

$= \dfrac{(2x - 2 - 4x + 6)}{(x - 1)^3} = \dfrac{4 - 2x}{(x - 1)^3}$ (3-5)

35. $y = \dfrac{3\sqrt{x}}{2} + \dfrac{5}{3\sqrt{x}} = \dfrac{3}{2}x^{1/2} + \dfrac{5}{3}x^{-1/2};$

$y' = \dfrac{3}{2}\left(\dfrac{1}{2}x^{-1/2}\right) + \dfrac{5}{3}\left(-\dfrac{1}{2}x^{-3/2}\right) = \dfrac{3}{4x^{1/2}} - \dfrac{5}{6x^{3/2}} = \dfrac{3}{4\sqrt{x}} - \dfrac{5}{6\sqrt{x^3}}$ (3-4)

36. $g(x) = 1.8\sqrt[3]{x} + \dfrac{0.9}{\sqrt[3]{x}} = 1.8x^{1/3} + 0.9x^{-1/3}$

$g'(x) = 1.8\left(\dfrac{1}{3}x^{-2/3}\right) + 0.9\left(-\dfrac{1}{3}x^{-4/3}\right)$

$= 0.6x^{-2/3} - 0.3x^{-4/3} = \dfrac{0.6}{x^{2/3}} - \dfrac{0.3}{x^{4/3}}$ (3-4)

37. $\dfrac{d}{dx}[(x^2 - 1)(2x + 1)^2] = (x^2 - 1)\dfrac{d}{dx}(2x + 1)^2 + (2x + 1)^2 \dfrac{d}{dx}(x^2 - 1)$

$= (x^2 - 1)[2(2x + 1)(2)] + (2x + 1)^2(2x)$

$= 2(2x + 1)[2(x^2 - 1) + x(2x + 1)]$

$= 2(2x + 1)(2x^2 - 2 + 2x^2 + x)$

$= 2(2x + 1)(4x^2 + x - 2)$ (3-5, 3-6)

38. $\dfrac{d}{dx}(x^3 - 5)^{1/3} = \dfrac{1}{3}(x^3 - 5)^{-2/3}(3x^2) = \dfrac{x^2}{(x^3 - 5)^{2/3}}$ (3-6)

39. $y = \dfrac{2x^3 - 3}{5x^3} = \dfrac{2}{5} - \dfrac{3}{5}x^{-3}; \quad y' = -\dfrac{3}{5}(-3x^{-4}) = \dfrac{9}{5x^4}$ (3-4)

40. $\dfrac{d}{dx}\dfrac{(x^2 + 2)^4}{2x - 3} = \dfrac{(2x - 3)4(x^2 + 2)^3(2x) - (x^2 + 2)^4(2)}{(2x - 3)^2}$

$\qquad\qquad\qquad\quad = \dfrac{2(x^2 + 2)^3[4x(2x - 3) - (x^2 + 2)]}{(2x - 3)^2}$

$\qquad\qquad\qquad\quad = \dfrac{2(x^2 + 2)^3(8x^2 - 12x - x^2 - 2)}{(2x - 3)^2} = \dfrac{2(x^2 + 2)^3(7x^2 - 12x - 2)}{(2x - 3)^2}$

$\hfill$ (3-5, 3-6)

41. $f(x) = x^2 + 4$
$f'(x) = 2x$

(A) The slope of the graph at $x = 1$ is $m = f'(1) = 2$.

(B) $f(1) = 1^2 + 4 = 5$
The tangent line at $(1, 5)$, where the slope $m = 2$, is:
$(y - 5) = 2(x - 1)$ $\qquad$ [Note: $(y - y_1) = m(x - x_1)$.]

$\qquad\qquad y = 5 + 2x - 2$
$\qquad\qquad y = 2x + 3$ $\hfill$ (3-3, 3-4)

42. $f(x) = x^3(x + 1)^2$
$f'(x) = x^3(2)(x + 1)(1) + (x + 1)^2(3x^2)$
$\qquad\quad = 2x^3(x + 1) + 3x^2(x + 1)^2$

(A) The slope of the graph of f at $x = 1$ is:
$\quad f'(1) = 2 \cdot 1^3(1 + 1) + 3 \cdot 1^2(1 + 1)^2 = 16$

(B) $f(1) = 1^3(1 + 1)^2 = 4$

An equation for the tangent line to the graph of f at $x = 1$ is
$\quad y - 4 = 16(x - 1)$ $\quad$ or $\quad$ $y = 16x - 12$. $\hfill$ (3-3, 3-5)

43. $f(x) = 10x - x^2$
$f'(x) = 10 - 2x$
The tangent line is horizontal at the values of x such that $f'(x) = 0$:
$10 - 2x = 0$
$\qquad x = 5$ $\hfill$ (3-4)

44. $f(x) = (x + 3)(x^2 - 45)$
$f'(x) = (x + 3)(2x) + (x^2 - 45)(1) = 3x^2 + 6x - 45$
Set $f'(x) = 0$:
$3x^2 + 6x - 45 = 0$
$x^2 + 2x - 15 = 0$
$(x - 3)(x + 5) = 0$
$\qquad\qquad x = 3, x = -5$ $\hfill$ (3-5)

45. $f(x) = \dfrac{x}{x^2 + 4}$

$f'(x) = \dfrac{(x^2 + 4)(1) - x(2x)}{(x^2 + 4)^2} = \dfrac{4 - x^2}{(x^2 + 4)^2}$

Set $f'(x) = 0$: $\dfrac{4 - x^2}{(x^2 + 4)^2} = 0$

$\qquad\qquad\qquad 4 - x^2 = 0$
$\qquad\qquad (2 - x)(2 + x) = 0$
$\qquad\qquad\qquad\qquad x = 2, x = -2$ $\hfill$ (3-5)

46. $f(x) = x^2(2x - 15)^3$

$f'(x) = x^2(3)(2x - 15)^2(2) + (2x - 15)^3(2x)$

$\quad\quad = (2x - 15)^2[6x^2 + 4x^2 - 30x]$

$\quad\quad = (2x - 15)^2 10x(x - 3)$

Set $f'(x) = 0$:

$10x(x - 3)(2x - 15)^2 = 0$
$$x = 0, \quad x = 3, \quad x = \frac{15}{2}$$
(3-5)

47. $f(x) = x^4 - 2x^3 - 5x^2 + 7x$

$f'(x) = 4x^3 - 6x^2 - 10x + 7$

Set $f'(x) = 4x^3 - 6x^2 - 10x + 7 = 0$ and solve for x using a root-approximation routine on a graphing utility:

$f'(x) = 0$ at $x = -1.34$, $x = 0.58$, $x = 2.26$ (3-4)

48. $f(x) = \dfrac{x^3 - 5x + 10}{x^2 + 2}$

$f'(x) = \dfrac{(x^2 + 2)(3x^2 - 5) - (x^3 - 5x + 10)2x}{(x^2 + 2)^2} = \dfrac{x^4 + 11x^2 - 20x - 10}{(x^2 + 2)^2}$

Set $f'(x) = 0$: $\dfrac{x^4 + 11x^2 - 20x - 10}{(x^2 + 2)^2} = 0$ implies $x^4 + 11x^2 - 20x - 10 = 0$

Use a root-approximation routine on a graphing utility:

$f'(x) = 0$ at $x = -0.41$, $x = 1.80$. (3-5)

49. $f(x) = \dfrac{5x^4 - 40x^2}{(x^2 + 1)^2}$

$f'(x) = \dfrac{(x^2 + 1)^2(20x^3 - 80x) - (5x^4 - 40x^2)(2)(x^2 + 1)2x}{(x^2 + 1)^4}$

$\quad = \dfrac{(x^2 + 1)(20x^3 - 80x) - 4x(5x^4 - 40x^2)}{(x^2 + 1)^3}$

$\quad = \dfrac{100x^3 - 80x}{(x^2 + 1)^3} = \dfrac{20x(5x^2 - 4)}{(x^2 + 1)^3}$

$f'(x) = 0$ implies $20x(5x^2 - 4) = 0$ and $x = 0$, $\pm\dfrac{2}{\sqrt{5}}$ or $x = -0.89$, $x = 0$,

$x = 0.89$ to two decimal places. (3-5, 3-6)

50. $y = f(x) = 8x^2 - 4x + 1$

(A) Instantaneous velocity function; $v(x) = f'(x) = 16x - 4$.

(B) $v(3) = 16(3) - 4 = 44$ ft/sec. (3-4)

51. $y = f(x) = -5x^2 + 16x + 3$

    (A) Instantaneous velocity function: $v(x) = f'(x) = -10x + 16$.

    (B) $v(x) = 0$ when $-10x + 16 = 0$

$$10x = 16$$
$$x = 1.6 \text{ sec}$$

(3-4)

52. (A) $f(x) = x^3$, $g(x) = (x - 4)^3$, $h(x) = (x + 3)^3$

    The graph of g is the graph of f shifted 4 units to the right; the graph of h is the graph of f shifted 3 units to the left.

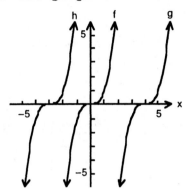

    (B) $f'(x) = 3x^2$, $g'(x) = 3(x - 4)^2$, $h'(x) = 3(x + 3)^2$

    The graph of g' is the graph of f' shifted 4 units to the right; the graph of h' is the graph of f' shifted 3 units to the left.

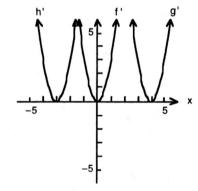

(1-2, 3-6)

53. (A) $g(x) = f(x + k)$; $g'(x) = f'(x + k)(1) = f'(x + k)$

    The graph of g is a horizontal translation of the graph of f.
    The graph of g' is a horizontal translation of the graph of f'.

    (B) $g(x) = f(x) + k$, $g'(x) = f'(x)$

    The graph of g is a vertical translation of the graph of f (up k units if $k > 0$, down k units if $k < 0$). The graph of g' is the same as the graph of f'.

(1-2, 3-6)

54. $f(x) = x^2 - 4$ is a polynomial function; f is continuous on $(-\infty, \infty)$.

(3-2)

55. $f(x) = \dfrac{x + 1}{x - 2}$ is a rational function and the denominator $x - 2$ is 0 at $x = 2$. Thus f is continuous for all x such that $x \neq 2$, i.e., on $(-\infty, 2) \cup (2, \infty)$. (3-2)

56. $f(x) = \dfrac{x + 4}{x^2 + 3x - 4}$ is a rational function and the denominator $x^2 + 3x - 4 = (x + 4)(x - 1)$ is 0 at $x = -4$ and $x = 1$. Thus, f is continuous for all x except $x = -4$ and $x = 1$, i.e., on $(-\infty, -4) \cup (-4, 1) \cup (1, \infty)$. (3-2)

57. $f(x) = \sqrt[3]{4 - x^2}$; $g(x) = 4 - x^2$ is continuous for all x since it is a polynomial function. Therefore, $f(x) = \sqrt[3]{g(x)}$ is continuous for all x, i.e., on $(-\infty, \infty)$. (3-2)

58. $f(x) = \sqrt{4 - x^2}$; $g(x) = 4 - x^2$ is continuous for all x and $g(x)$ is nonnegative for $-2 \leq x \leq 2$. Therefore, $f(x) = \sqrt{g(x)}$ is continuous for $-2 \leq x \leq 2$, i.e., on $[-2, 2]$. (3-2)

59. $f(x) = \dfrac{2x}{x^2 - 3x} = \dfrac{2x}{x(x - 3)} = \dfrac{2}{x - 3}$, $x \neq 0$

   (A) $\displaystyle\lim_{x \to 1} f(x) = \lim_{x \to 1} \dfrac{2}{x - 3} = \dfrac{\displaystyle\lim_{x \to 1} 2}{\displaystyle\lim_{x \to 1}(x - 3)} = \dfrac{2}{-2} = -1$

   (B) $\displaystyle\lim_{x \to 3} f(x) = \lim_{x \to 3} \dfrac{2}{x - 3}$ does not exist since $\displaystyle\lim_{x \to 3} 2 = 2$ and $\displaystyle\lim_{x \to 3}(x - 3) = 0$

   (C) $\displaystyle\lim_{x \to 0} f(x) = \lim_{x \to 0} \dfrac{2}{x - 3} = -\dfrac{2}{3}$ (3-1)

60. $f(x) = \dfrac{x + 1}{(3 - x)^2}$

   (A) $\displaystyle\lim_{x \to 1} \dfrac{x + 1}{(3 - x)^2} = \dfrac{\displaystyle\lim_{x \to 1}(x + 1)}{\displaystyle\lim_{x \to 1}(3 - x)^2} = \dfrac{2}{2^2} = \dfrac{1}{2}$

   (B) $\displaystyle\lim_{x \to -1} \dfrac{x + 1}{(3 - x)^2} = \dfrac{\displaystyle\lim_{x \to -1}(x + 1)}{\displaystyle\lim_{x \to -1}(3 - x)^2} = \dfrac{0}{4^2} = 0$

   (C) $\displaystyle\lim_{x \to 3} \dfrac{x + 1}{(3 - x)^2}$ does not exist since $\displaystyle\lim_{x \to 3}(x + 1) = 4$ and $\displaystyle\lim_{x \to 3}(3 - x)^2 = 0$ (3-1)

61. $f(x) = \dfrac{|x - 4|}{x - 4} = \begin{cases} -1 & \text{if } x < 4 \\ 1 & \text{if } x > 4 \end{cases}$

    (A) $\lim\limits_{x \to 4^-} f(x) = -1$ (B) $\lim\limits_{x \to 4^+} f(x) = 1$

    (C) $\lim\limits_{x \to 4} f(x)$ does not exist.   (3-1)

62. $f(x) = \dfrac{x - 3}{9 - x^2} = \dfrac{x - 3}{(3 + x)(3 - x)} = \dfrac{-(3 - x)}{(3 + x)(3 - x)} = \dfrac{-1}{3 + x},\ \ x \neq 3$

    (A) $\lim\limits_{x \to 3} f(x) = \lim\limits_{x \to 3} \dfrac{-1}{3 + x} = -\dfrac{1}{6}$

    (B) $\lim\limits_{x \to -3} f(x) = \lim\limits_{x \to -3} \dfrac{-1}{3 + x}$ does not exist

    (C) $\lim\limits_{x \to 0} f(x) = \lim\limits_{x \to 0} \dfrac{-1}{3 + x} = -\dfrac{1}{3}$ (3-1)

63. $f(x) = \dfrac{x^2 - x - 2}{x^2 - 7x + 10} = \dfrac{(x - 2)(x + 1)}{(x - 2)(x - 5)} = \dfrac{x + 1}{x - 5},\ \ x \neq 2$

    (A) $\lim\limits_{x \to -1} f(x) = \lim\limits_{x \to -1} \dfrac{x + 1}{x - 5} = 0$

    (B) $\lim\limits_{x \to 2} f(x) = \lim\limits_{x \to 2} \dfrac{x + 1}{x - 5} = \dfrac{3}{-3} = -1$

    (C) $\lim\limits_{x \to 5} f(x) = \lim\limits_{x \to 5} \dfrac{x + 1}{x - 5}$ does not exist   (3-1)

64. $f(x) = x^2 + 4$

$$\lim\limits_{h \to 0} \dfrac{f(2 + h) - f(2)}{h} = \lim\limits_{h \to 0} \dfrac{[(2 + h)^2 + 4] - [2^2 + 4]}{h}$$

$$= \lim\limits_{h \to 0} \dfrac{4 + 4h + h^2 + 4 - 8}{h} = \lim\limits_{h \to 0} \dfrac{4h + h^2}{h}$$

$$= \lim\limits_{h \to 0}(4 + h) = 4 \qquad\qquad (3\text{-}1)$$

65. Let $f(x) = \dfrac{1}{x + 2}$

$$\lim\limits_{h \to 0} \dfrac{f(x + h) - f(x)}{h} = \lim\limits_{h \to 0} \dfrac{\dfrac{1}{(x + h) + 2} - \dfrac{1}{x + 2}}{h}$$

$$= \lim\limits_{h \to 0} \dfrac{x + 2 - (x + h + 2)}{h(x + h + 2)(x + 2)}$$

$$= \lim\limits_{h \to 0} \dfrac{-h}{h(x + h + 2)(x + 2)}$$

$$= \lim\limits_{h \to 0} \dfrac{-1}{(x + h + 2)(x - 2)} = \dfrac{-1}{(x + 2)^2} \qquad (3\text{-}1)$$

66. (A) $\lim\limits_{x \to -2^-} f(x) = -6$, $\lim\limits_{x \to -2^+} f(x) = 6$; $\lim\limits_{x \to -2} f(x)$ does not exist

(B) $\lim\limits_{x \to 0} f(x) = 4$

(C) $\lim\limits_{x \to 2^-} f(x) = 2$, $\lim\limits_{x \to 2^+} f(x) = -2$; $\lim\limits_{x \to 2} f(x)$ does not exist

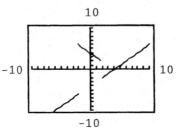

(3-1)

67. $f(x) = x^2 - x$

Step 1. Simplify $\dfrac{f(x + h) - f(x)}{h}$.

$$\frac{f(x + h) - f(x)}{h} = \frac{[(x + h)^2 - (x + h)] - (x^2 - x)}{h}$$

$$= \frac{x^2 + 2xh + h^2 - x - h - x^2 + x}{h}$$

$$= \frac{2xh + h^2 - h}{h} = 2x + h - 1$$

Step 2. Evaluate $\lim\limits_{h \to 0} \dfrac{f(x + h) - f(x)}{h}$.

$$\lim\limits_{h \to 0} \frac{f(x + h) - f(x)}{h} = \lim\limits_{h \to 0}(2x + h - 1) = 2x - 1$$

Thus, $f'(x) = 2x - 1$. (3-3)

68. $f(x) = \sqrt{x} - 3$

Step 1. Simplify $\dfrac{f(x + h) - f(x)}{h}$.

$$\frac{f(x + h) - f(x)}{h} = \frac{[\sqrt{x + h} - 3] - (\sqrt{x} - 3)}{h}$$

$$= \frac{\sqrt{x + h} - \sqrt{x}}{h} \cdot \frac{\sqrt{x + h} + \sqrt{x}}{\sqrt{x + h} + \sqrt{x}} = \frac{x + h - x}{h[\sqrt{x + h} + \sqrt{x}]}$$

$$= \frac{1}{\sqrt{x + h} + \sqrt{x}}$$

Step 2. Evaluate $\lim\limits_{h \to 0} \dfrac{f(x + h) - f(x)}{h}$.

$$\lim\limits_{h \to 0} \frac{f(x + h) - f(x)}{h} = \lim\limits_{h \to 0} \frac{1}{\sqrt{x + h} + \sqrt{x}} = \frac{1}{2\sqrt{x}}$$

(3-3)

69. f is not differentiable at $x = 0$, since f is not continuous at 0. (3-3)

70. f is not differentiable at $x = 1$; the curve has a vertical tangent line at this point. (3-3)

71. f is not differentiable at $x = 2$; the curve has a "corner" at this point. (3-3)

72. f is differentiable at $x = 3$. In fact, $f'(3) = 0$. (3-3)

73. $f(x) = (x - 4)^4 (x + 3)^3$

$$f'(x) = (x - 4)^4 (3)(x + 3)^2 (1) + (x + 3)^3 (4)(x - 4)^3 (1)$$
$$= (x - 4)^3 (x + 3)^2 [3(x - 4) + 4(x + 3)]$$
$$= 7x(x - 4)^3 (x + 3)^2 \qquad (3\text{-}5, \ 3\text{-}6)$$

74. $f(x) = 5x^3 (x^2 - 1)^2; \quad f'(x) = 5x^3 (2)(x^2 - 1)(2x) + (x^2 - 1)^2 (15x^2)$
$$= 5x^2 (x^2 - 1)[4x^2 + 3(x^2 - 1)]$$
$$= 5x^2 (x^2 - 1)(7x^2 - 3) \qquad (3\text{-}5, \ 3\text{-}6)$$

75. $f(x) = \dfrac{x^5}{(2x + 1)^4}$

$$f'(x) = \frac{(2x + 1)^4 (5x^4) - x^5 (4)(2x + 1)^3 (2)}{[(2x + 1)^4]^2}$$

$$= \frac{(2x + 1)(5x^4) - 8x^5}{(2x + 1)^5} = \frac{2x^5 + 5x^4}{(2x + 1)^5} = \frac{x^4 (2x + 5)}{(2x + 1)^5} \qquad (3\text{-}5, \ 3\text{-}6)$$

76. $f(x) = \dfrac{\sqrt{x^2 - 1}}{x} = \dfrac{(x^2 - 1)^{1/2}}{x}$

$$f'(x) = \frac{x\left(\dfrac{1}{2}\right)(x^2 - 1)^{-1/2}(2x) - (x^2 - 1)^{1/2}(1)}{x^2} = \frac{\dfrac{x^2}{(x^2 - 1)^{1/2}} - (x^2 - 1)^{1/2}}{x^2}$$

$$= \frac{1}{x^2 (x^2 - 1)^{1/2}} = \frac{1}{x^2 \sqrt{x^2 - 1}} \qquad (3\text{-}5, \ 3\text{-}6)$$

77. $f(x) = \dfrac{x}{\sqrt{x^2 + 4}} = \dfrac{x}{(x^2 + 4)^{1/2}}$

$$f'(x) = \frac{(x^2 + 4)^{1/2}(1) - x\left(\dfrac{1}{2}\right)(x^2 + 4)^{-1/2}(2x)}{[(x^2 + 4)^{1/2}]^2}$$

$$= \frac{(x^2 + 4)^{1/2} - \dfrac{x^2}{(x^2 + 4)^{1/2}}}{(x^2 + 4)} = \frac{4}{(x^2 + 4)^{3/2}} \qquad (3\text{-}5, \ 3\text{-}6)$$

78. $f(x) = x^{1/5}$; $f'(x) = \dfrac{1}{5}x^{-4/5} = \dfrac{1}{5x^{4/5}}$

The domain of f' is all real numbers except $x = 0$. At $x = 0$, the graph of f is smooth, but the tangent line to the graph at $(0, 0)$ is vertical.

(3-3)

79. $f(x) = \begin{cases} x^2 - m & \text{if } x \le 1 \\ -x^2 + m & \text{if } x > 1 \end{cases}$

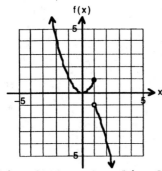
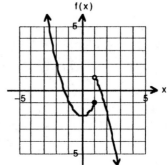

$$\lim_{x \to 1^-} f(x) = 1, \quad \lim_{x \to 1^+} f(x) = -1 \qquad \lim_{x \to 1^-} f(x) = -1, \quad \lim_{x \to 1^+} f(x) = 1$$

(C) $\displaystyle\lim_{x \to 1^-} f(x) = 1 - m, \quad \lim_{x \to 1^+} f(x) = -1 + m$

We want $1 - m = -1 + m$ which implies $m = 1$.

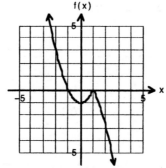

(D) The graphs in (A) and (B) have jumps at $x = 1$; the graph in (C) does not.

(3-1)

80. $f(x) = 1 - |x - 1|$, $0 \le x \le 2$

(A) $\displaystyle\lim_{h \to 0^-} \frac{f(1 + h) - f(1)}{h} = \lim_{h \to 0^-} \frac{1 - |1 + h - 1| - 1}{h} = \lim_{h \to 0^-} \frac{-|h|}{h}$

$$= \lim_{h \to 0^-} \frac{h}{h} = 1 \quad (|h| = -h \text{ if } h < 0)$$

(B) $\displaystyle\lim_{h \to 0^+} \frac{f(1 + h) - f(1)}{h} = \lim_{h \to 0^+} \frac{1 - |1 + h - 1| - 1}{h} = \lim_{h \to 0^+} \frac{-|h|}{h}$

$$= \lim_{h \to 0^+} \frac{-h}{h} = -1 \quad (|h| = h \text{ if } h > 0)$$

(C) $\displaystyle\lim_{h \to 0} \frac{f(1 + h) - f(1)}{h}$ does not exist, since the left limit and the right limit are not equal.

(D) $f'(1)$ does not exist.

(3-3)

81. (A) $S(x) = 7.47 + 0.4000x$ for $0 \le x \le 90$;

$S(90) = 43.47$;

$S(x) = 43.47 + 0.2076 (x - 90)$
$= 24.786 + 0.2076x, \ x > 90$

Therefore,

$$S(x) = \begin{cases} 7.47 + 0.4000x & \text{if} \quad 0 \le x \le 90 \\ 24.786 + 0.2076x & \text{if} \quad x > 90 \end{cases}$$

(B)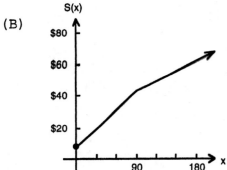

(C) $\lim\limits_{x \to 90^-} S(x) = \lim\limits_{x \to 90^+} S(x) = 43.47 = S(90)$;
$S(x)$ is continuous at $x = 90$.

(3-2)

82. $C(x) = 10,000 + 200x - 0.1x^2$

(A) $C(101) - C(100) = 10,000 + 200(101) - 0.1(101)^2$
$\qquad\qquad\qquad\qquad\quad - [10,000 + 200(100) - 0.1(100)^2]$
$\qquad\qquad\quad = 29,179.90 - 29,000$
$\qquad\qquad\quad = \$179.90$

(B) $C'(x) = 200 - 0.2x$
$C'(100) = 200 - 0.2(100)$
$\qquad\qquad = 200 - 20$
$\qquad\qquad = \$180$

(3-7)

83. $C(x) = 5,000 + 40x + 0.05x^2$

(A) Cost of producing 100 bicycles:

$C(100) = 5,000 + 40(100) + 0.05(100)^2$
$\qquad\quad = 9000 + 500 = 9500$

Marginal cost:
$C'(x) = 40 + 0.1x$
$C'(100) = 40 + 0.1(100) = 40 + 10 = 50$

Interpretation: At a production level of 100 bicycles, the total cost is \$9,500 and is increasing at the rate of \$50 per additional bicycle.

(B) Average cost: $\bar{C}(x) = \dfrac{C(x)}{x} = \dfrac{5000}{x} + 40 + 0.05x$

$\bar{C}(100) = \dfrac{5000}{100} + 40 + 0.05(100) = 50 + 40 + 5 = 95$

Marginal average cost: $\bar{C}'(x) = -\dfrac{5000}{x^2} + 0.05$

and $\bar{C}'(100) = -\dfrac{5000}{(100)^2} + 0.05 = -0.5 + 0.05 = -0.45$

Interpretation: At a production level of 100 bicycles, the average cost is \$95 and the marginal average cost is decreasing at a rate of \$0.45 per additional bicycle.

(3-7)

84. The approximate cost of producing the 201st printer is greater than that of producing the 601st printer (the slope of the tangent line at $x = 200$ is greater than the slope of the tangent line at $x = 600$). Since the marginal costs are decreasing, the manufacturing process is becoming more efficient.

(3-7)

85. $p = 25 - 0.1x$, $C(x) = 2x + 9,000$

(A) Marginal cost: $C'(x) = 2$

Average cost: $\overline{C}(x) = \dfrac{C(x)}{x} = 2 + \dfrac{9,000}{x}$

Marginal cost: $\overline{C}'(x) = -\dfrac{9,000}{x^2}$

(B) Revenue: $R(x) = xp = 25x - 0.01x^2$

Marginal revenue: $R'(x) = 25 - 0.02x$

Average revenue: $\overline{R}(x) = \dfrac{R(x)}{x} = 25 - 0.01x$

Marginal average revenue: $\overline{R}'(x) = -0.01$

(C) Profit: $P(x) = R(x) - C(x) = 25x - 0.01x^2 - (2x + 9,000)$

$\qquad\qquad\qquad\qquad = 23x - 0.01x^2 - 9,000$

Marginal profit: $P'(x) = 23 - 0.02x$

Average profit: $\overline{P}(x) = \dfrac{P(x)}{x} = 23 - 0.01x - \dfrac{9,000}{x}$

Marginal average profit: $\overline{P}'(x) = -0.01 + \dfrac{9,000}{x^2}$

(D) Break-even points: $R(x) = C(x)$

$$25x - 0.01x^2 = 2x + 9,000$$
$$0.01x^2 - 23x + 9,000 = 0$$
$$x^2 - 2,300x + 900,000 = 0$$
$$(x - 500)(x - 1,800) = 0$$

Thus, the break-even points are: $x = 500$, $x = 1,800$.

(E) $P'(1,000) = 23 - 0.02(1000) = 3$; profit is increasing at the rate of \$3 per umbrella.

$P'(1,150) = 23 - 0.02(1,150) = 0$; profit is flat.

$P'(1,400) = 23 - 0.02(1,400) = -5$; profit is decreasing at the rate of \$5 per umbrella.

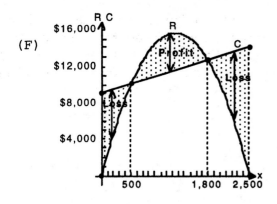

(F)

$16,000

$12,000

$8,000

$4,000

R C

R

Profit

C

Loss

Loss

500   1,800 2,500   x

(3-7)

86. $N(t) = \dfrac{40t}{t + 2}$

(A) Average rate of change from $t = 3$ to $t = 6$:

$$\dfrac{N(6) - N(3)}{6 - 3} = \dfrac{\dfrac{40 \cdot 6}{6 + 2} - \dfrac{40 \cdot 3}{3 + 2}}{3} = \dfrac{30 - 24}{3} = 2 \text{ components per day}$$

(B) $N'(t) = \dfrac{(t + 2)(40) - 40t(1)}{(t + 2)^2} = \dfrac{80}{(t + 2)^2}$

$N'(3) = \dfrac{80}{25} = 3.2$ components per day   (3-5)

87. $N(t) = t\sqrt{4 + t} = t(4 + t)^{1/2}$

$N'(t) = t\left(\dfrac{1}{2}\right)(4 + t)^{-1/2} + (4 + t)^{1/2} = \dfrac{t}{2(4 + t)^{1/2}} + \dfrac{(4 + t)^{1/2}}{1}$

$\qquad\qquad = \dfrac{t + 2(4 + t)}{2(4 + t)^{1/2}} = \dfrac{8 + 3t}{2(4 + t)^{1/2}}$

$N(5) = 5\sqrt{4 + 5} = 15; \quad N'(t) = \dfrac{8 + 3(5)}{2(4 + 5)^{1/2}} = \dfrac{23}{6} = 3.833;$

After 5 months, the total sales are 15,000 pools and sales are
INCREASING at the rate of 3,833 pools per month.   (3-6)

88. (A)
```
CubicReg
y=ax³+bx²+cx+d
a=.001225
b=-.0819285714
c=1.564642857
d=12.08428571
```

(B) $N(50) \approx 38.6$, $N'(50) \approx 2.6$; in 1020, natural
gas consumption will be 38.6 trillion cubic
feet and will be INCREASING at the rate of
2.6 trillion cubic feet per year.   (3-3)

89. (A)
```
LinReg
y=ax+b
a=-.0384180791
b=13.59887006
r=-.9897782666
```

(B) Fixed costs: $484.21; variable cost per
kringle: $2.11.
```
LinReg
y=ax+b
a=2.107344633
b=484.2090395
r=.9939318704
```

(C) Let $p(x)$ be the linear regression equation found in part (A) and let $C(x)$ be the linear regression equation found in part (B). Then revenue $R(x) = xp(x)$ and the break-even points are the points where $R(x) = C(x)$.

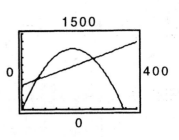

Using an intersection routine on a graphing utility, the break-even points are: (51, 591.15) and (248, 1,007.62).

(D) The bakery will make a profit when $51 < x < 248$. From the regression equation in part (A), $p(51) = 11.64$ and $p(248) = 4.07$. Thus, the bakery will make a profit for the price range $\$4.07 < p < \$11.64$.

(3-7)

90. $C(x) = 500(x + 1)^{-2}$

The instantaneous rate of change of concentration at x meters is:

$C'(x) = 500(-2)(x + 1)^{-3}$

$\quad = -1000(x + 1)^{-3} = \dfrac{-1000}{(x + 1)^3}$

The rate of change of concentration at 9 meters is:

$C'(9) = \dfrac{-1000}{(9 + 1)^3} = \dfrac{-1000}{10^3} \doteq -1$ part per million per meter

The rate of change of concentration at 99 meters is:

$C'(99) = \dfrac{-1000}{(99 + 1)^3} = \dfrac{-1000}{100^3} = \dfrac{-10^3}{10^6} = -10^{-3}$ or $= -\dfrac{1}{1000}$

$\quad = -0.001$ parts per million per meter   (3-4)

91. $F(t) = 98 + \dfrac{4}{\sqrt{t + 1}} = 98 + 4(t + 1)^{-1/2}$,

$F'(t) = 4\left(-\dfrac{1}{2}\right)(t + 1)^{-3/2} = \dfrac{-2}{(t + 1)^{3/2}}$

$F(3) = 98 + \dfrac{4}{\sqrt{3 + 1}} = 100$; $F'(3) = \dfrac{-2}{(3 + 1)^{3/2}} = -\dfrac{1}{4} = -0.25$

After 3 hours, the body temperature of the patient is 100° and is DECREASING at the rate of 0.25° per hour.   (3-6)

92. $N(t) = 20\sqrt{t} = 20t^{1/2}$

The rate of learning is $N'(t) = 20\left(\dfrac{1}{2}\right)t^{-1/2} = 10t^{-1/2} = \dfrac{10}{\sqrt{t}}$.

(A) The rate of learning after one hour is $N'(1) = \dfrac{10}{\sqrt{1}}$

$\quad = 10$ items per hour.

(B) The rate of learning after four hours is $N'(4) = \dfrac{10}{\sqrt{4}} = \dfrac{10}{2}$

$\quad = 5$ items per hour.

(3-4)

2 Graphing & Optimization

Things to remember:

1.   INCREASING AND DECREASING FUNCTIONS

   For the interval (a, b):

$f'(x)$	$f(x)$	Graph of f	Examples
+	Increases ↗	Rises ↗	
-	Decreases ↘	Falls ↘	

2.   CRITICAL VALUES

   The values of x in the domain of f where $f'(x) = 0$ or where $f'(x)$ does not exist are called the CRITICAL VALUES of f.

   The critical values of f are always in the domain of f and are also partition numbers for f', but f' may have partition numbers that are not critical values.

   If f is a polynomial, then both the partition numbers for f' and the critical values of f are the solutions of $f'(x) = 0$.

3.   LOCAL EXTREMA

   Given a function f. The value $f(c)$ is a LOCAL MAXIMUM of f if there is an interval (m, n) containing c such that $f(x) \leq f(c)$ for all x in (m, n). The value $f(e)$ is a LOCAL MINIMUM of f if there is an interval (p, q) containing e such that $f(x) \geq f(e)$ for all x in (p, q). Local maxima and local minima are called LOCAL EXTREMA.

   A point on the graph where a local extremum occurs is also called a TURNING POINT.

4.   FIRST DERIVATIVE TEST FOR LOCAL EXTREMA

   Let c be a critical value of f [$f(c)$ is defined and either $f'(c) = 0$ or $f'(c)$ is not defined.]

   Construct a sign chart for $f'(x)$ close to and on either side of c.

Sign Chart	$f(c)$
$f'(x)$ $\xrightarrow{\quad(\quad\underset{m}{\ \ }\ \ \underset{c}{---\,}\begin{smallmatrix}\vdots\end{smallmatrix}\underset{n}{+++}\ \ )\quad} x$ $f(x)$ Decreasing $\vdots$ Increasing	$f(c)$ is a local minimum. If $f'(x)$ changes from negative to positive at c, then $f(c)$ is a local minimum.
$f'(x)$ $\xrightarrow{\quad(\quad\underset{m}{\ \ }\ \ \underset{c}{+++\,}\begin{smallmatrix}\vdots\end{smallmatrix}\underset{n}{---}\ \ )\quad} x$ $f(x)$ Increasing $\vdots$ Decreasing	$f(c)$ is a local maximum. If $f'(x)$ changes from positive to negative at c, then $f(c)$ is a local maximum.
$f'(x)$ $\xrightarrow{\quad(\quad\underset{m}{\ \ }\ \ \underset{c}{---\,}\begin{smallmatrix}\vdots\end{smallmatrix}\underset{n}{---}\ \ )\quad} x$ $f(x)$ Decreasing $\vdots$ Decreasing	$f(c)$ is not a local extremum. If $f'(x)$ does not change sign at c, then $f(c)$ is neither a local maximum nor a local minimum.
$f'(x)$ $\xrightarrow{\quad(\quad\underset{m}{\ \ }\ \ \underset{c}{+++\,}\begin{smallmatrix}\vdots\end{smallmatrix}\underset{n}{+++}\ \ )\quad} x$ $f(x)$ Increasing $\vdots$ Increasing	$f(c)$ is not a local extremum. If $f'(x)$ does not change sign at c, then $f(c)$ is neither a local maximum nor a local minimum.

$\underline{5}$. INTERCEPTS AND LOCAL EXTREMA FOR POLYNOMIAL FUNCTIONS
If $f(x) = a_n x^n + a_{n-1} x^{n-1} + \ldots + a_1 x + a_0$, $a_n \neq 0$ is an nth degree polynomial then f has at most n x intercepts and at most $n-1$ local extrema.

1. (a, b), (d, f), (g, h) **3.** (b, c), (c, d), (f, g)

5. $x = c, d, f$ **7.** $x = b, f$

9. f has a local maximum at $x = a$, and a local minimum at $x = c$; f does not have a local extremum at $x = b$ or at $x = d$.

11. e **13.** d **15.** f **17.** c

19. $f(x) = 2x^2 - 4x$; domain of f: $(-\infty, \infty)$
$f'(x) = 4x - 4$; f' is continuous for all x.
$f'(x) = 4x - 4 = 0$
$\quad\quad\quad\quad x = 1$
Thus, $x = 1$ is a partition number for f', and since 1 is in the domain of f, $x = 1$ is a critical value of f.
Sign chart for f':

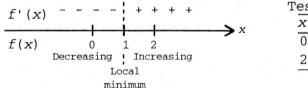

Test Numbers	
x	$f'(x)$
0	$-4\ (-)$
2	$4\ (+)$

Therefore, f is decreasing on $(-\infty, 1)$; f is increasing on $(1, \infty)$; $f(1) = -2$ is a local minimum.

21. $f(x) = -2x^2 - 16x - 25$; domain of f: $(-\infty, \infty)$
$f'(x) = -4x - 16$; f' is continuous for all x and
$$f'(x) = -4x - 16 = 0$$
$$x = -4$$
Thus, $x = -4$ is a partition number for f', and since -4 is in the domain of f, $x = -4$ is a critical value for f.
Sign chart for f':

Test Numbers	
x	$f'(x)$
-5	$4\ (+)$
0	$-16\ (-)$

f'(x) + + + +｜- - - - -

f(x) -5 -4 0

Increasing ｜ Decreasing

Therefore, f is increasing on $(-\infty, -4)$; f is decreasing on $(-4, \infty)$; f has a local maximum at $x = -4$.

23. $f(x) = x^3 + 4x - 5$; domain of f: $(-\infty, \infty)$
$f'(x) = 3x^2 + 4 \geq 4 > 0$ for all x; f is increasing on $(-\infty, \infty)$; f has no local extrema.

25. $f(x) = x^3 - 6x^2 + 1$; domain of f: $(-\infty, \infty)$
$f'(x) = 3x^2 - 12x$; f' is continuous for all x.
$$f'(x) = 3x^2 - 12x = 0$$
$$3x(x - 4) = 0$$
$$x = 0, 4$$
The partition numbers for f' are $x = 0$ and $x = 4$. Since 0 and 4 are in the domain of f, $x = 0$, $x = 4$ are critical values of f.
Sign chart for f':

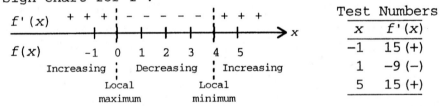

Test Numbers	
x	$f'(x)$
-1	$15\ (+)$
1	$-9\ (-)$
5	$15\ (+)$

Therefore, f is increasing on $(-\infty, 0)$ and $(4, \infty)$; f is decreasing on $(0, 4)$; $f(0) = 1$ is a local maximum, $f(4) = -31$ is a local minimum.

27. $f(x) = 2x^3 - 3x^2 - 36x$; domain of f: $(-\infty, \infty)$
$f'(x) = 6x^2 - 6x - 36$; f' is continuous for all x and
$$f'(x) = 6(x^2 - x - 6) = 0$$
$$6(x - 3)(x + 2) = 0$$
$$x = -2, 3$$
The partition numbers for f are $x = -2$ and $x = 3$. Since -2 and 3 are in the domain of f, $x = -2$, $x = 3$ are critical values for f.
Sign chart for f':

Test Numbers	
x	$f'(x)$
-3	$36\ (+)$
0	$-36\ (-)$
4	$36\ (+)$

f'(x) + + +｜- - - - -｜+ + +

f(x) -3 -2 0 3 4

Increasing ｜ Decreasing ｜ Increasing

Therefore, f is increasing on $(-\infty, -2)$ and $(3, \infty)$; f is decreasing on $(-2, 3)$; f has a local maximum at $x = -2$ and a local minimum at $x = 3$.

29. $f(x) = 3x^4 - 4x^3 + 5$; domain of f: $(-\infty, \infty)$
$f'(x) = 12x^3 - 12x^2$; f' is continuous for all x.
$f'(x) = 12x^3 - 12x^2 = 0$
$\qquad\quad 12x^2(x - 1) = 0$
$\qquad\qquad\qquad x = 0, 1$
The partition numbers for f' are $x = 0$ and $x = 1$. Since 0 and 1 are in the domain of f, $x = 0$, $x = 1$ are critical values of f.

Sign chart for f':

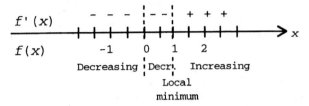

Test Numbers	
x	$f'(x)$
-1	$-24\,(-)$
$\frac{1}{2}$	$-\frac{3}{2}\,(-)$
2	$48\,(+)$

Therefore, f is decreasing on $(-\infty, 1)$; f is increasing on $(1, \infty)$; $f(1) = 4$ is a local minimum.

31. $f(x) = -x^4 + 32x$; domain of f: $(-\infty, \infty)$
$f'(x) = -4x^3 + 32$; f' is continuous for all x and
$\qquad f'(x) = -4x^3 + 32 = 0$
$\qquad\qquad\qquad x^3 = 8$
$\qquad\qquad\qquad x = 2$
$x = 2$ is a partition number for f' and since 2 is in the domain of f, $x = 2$ is a critical value for f.
Sign chart for f':

Test Numbers	
x	$f'(x)$
0	$32\,(+)$
3	$-76\,(-)$

Therefore, f is increasing on $(-\infty, 2)$ and decreasing on $(2, \infty)$; f has a local maximum at $x = 2$.

33. $f(x) = x^4 + x^2 + x$; domain of f: $(-\infty, \infty)$
$f'(x) = 4x^3 + 2x + 1$; f' is continuous for all x, so we must solve
$f'(x) = 4x^3 + 2x + 1 = 0$ using a root-approximation routine, $f'(x) = 0$
at $x = -0.39$ (to two decimal places); critical value.
Sign chart for f':

Test Numbers	
x	$f'(x)$
-1	$-5\,(-)$
0	$1\,(+)$

f is decreasing on $(-\infty, -0.39)$; increasing on $(-0.39, \infty)$; f has a local minimum at $x = -0.39$.

35. $f(x) = x^4 - 4x^3 + 9x$; domain of f: $(-\infty, \infty)$

$f'(x) = 4x^3 - 12x^2 + 9$; f is continuous for all x. Using a root-approximation routine, $f'(x) = 0$ at $x = -0.77$, $x = 1.08$, and $x = 2.69$; critical values.

Sign chart for f':

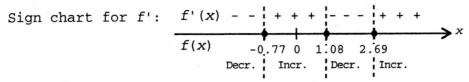

f is decreasing on $(-\infty, -0.77)$ and $(1.08, 2.69)$; increasing on $(-0.77, 1.08)$ and $(2.69, \infty)$; f has a local minima at $x = -0.77$ and $x = 2.69$, f has a local maximum at $x = 1.08$.

37. $f(x) = x^4 - 2x^3 - 5x^2 + 4x$; domain of f: $(-\infty, \infty)$

$f'(x) = 4x^3 - 6x^2 - 10x + 4$; f is continuous for all x. Using a root-approximation routine, $f'(x) = 0$ at $x = -1.22$, $x = 0.35$, and $x = 2.38$; critical values.

Sign chart for f':

```
           f'(x)   - - ¦ + + + ¦- - - ¦+ + +
         ───────────●───┼───●───┼───●──────────→ x
           f(x)      -1.22  0 0.35  2.38
                  Decr. ¦ Incr. ¦Decr. ¦ Incr.
```

f is decreasing on $(-\infty, -1.22)$ and $(0.35, 2.38)$; f is increasing on $(-1.22, 0.35)$ and $(2.38, \infty)$; f has local minima at $x = -1.22$ and $x = 2.38$, f has a local maximum at $x = 0.35$.

39. $f(x) = 4 + 8x - x^2$

$f'(x) = 8 - 2x$

f' is continuous for all x and

$f'(x) = 8 - 2x = 0$

$\qquad x = 4$

Thus, $x = 4$ is a partition number for f'.

The sign chart for f' is:

```
 f'(x)          + + + + 0 - - - -
       ──────────┼┼┼┼┼●┼┼──────────→ x
                 0     4 5

 f(x)        Increasing ¦ Decreasing
```

Test Numbers	
x	$f'(x)$
0	8 (+)
5	−2 (−)

Therefore, f is increasing on $(-\infty, 4)$ and decreasing on $(4, \infty)$; f has a local maximum at $x = 4$.

x	$f'(x)$	f	GRAPH OF f
$(-\infty, 4)$	+	Increasing	Rising
$x = 4$	0	Local maximum	Horizontal tangent
$(4, \infty)$	−	Decreasing	Falling

x	$f(x)$
0	4
4	20

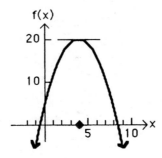

41. $f(x) = x^3 - 3x + 1$

$f'(x) = 3x^2 - 3$

f' is continuous for all x and

$f'(x) = 3x^2 - 3 = 0$

$3(x^2 - 1) = 0$

$3(x + 1)(x - 1) = 0$

Thus, $x = -1$ and $x = 1$ are partition numbers for f'.

The sign chart for f' is:

$f'(x)$ + + + + + 0 − − − − − − 0 + + + + +

-2   -1   0   1   2 $\rightarrow x$

$f(x)$ Increasing ¦ Decreasing ¦ Increasing

Test Numbers

x	$f'(x)$
-2	9 (+)
0	-3 (−)
2	9 (+)

Therefore, f is increasing on $(-\infty, -1)$ and on $(1, \infty)$, f is decreasing on $(-1, 1)$; f has a local maximum at $x = -1$ and a local minimum at $x = 1$.

x	$f'(x)$	f	GRAPH OF f
$(-\infty, -1)$	+	Increasing	Rising
$x = -1$	0	Local maximum	Horizontal tangent
$(-1, 1)$	−	Decreasing	Falling
$x = 1$	0	Local minimum	Horizontal tangent
$(1, \infty)$	+	Increasing	Rising

x	$f(x)$
-1	3
0	1
1	-1

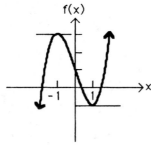

43. $f(x) = 10 - 12x + 6x^2 - x^3$

$f'(x) = -12 + 12x - 3x^2$

f' is continuous for all x and

$f'(x) = -12 + 12x - 3x^2 = 0$

$-3(x^2 - 4x + 4) = 0$

$-3(x - 2)^2 = 0$

Thus, $x = 2$ is a partition number for f'.

The sign chart for f' is:

f'(x)   - - - - - 0 - - - - -

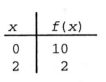

f(x)   Decreasing ¦ Decreasing

Test Numbers	
x	f'(x)
0	−12 (−)
3	−3 (−)

Therefore, f is decreasing for all x, i.e., on $(-\infty, \infty)$, and there is a horizontal tangent line at $x = 2$.

x	f'(x)	f	GRAPH of f
$(-\infty, 2)$	−	Decreasing	Falling
$x = 2$	0		Horizontal tangent
$x > 2$	−	Decreasing	Falling

x	f(x)
0	10
2	2

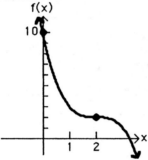

45. $f(x) = x^4 - 18x^2$

$f'(x) = 4x^3 - 36x$

f' is continuous for all x and

$f'(x) = 4x^3 - 36x = 0$

$\qquad 4x(x^2 - 9) = 0$

$4x(x - 3)(x + 3) = 0$

Thus, $x = -3$, $x = 0$, and $x = 3$ are partition numbers for f'.

Sign chart for f':

f'(x)   - - - 0 + + + 0 - - - 0 + + +

f(x)   -3   0   3

        Decr.¦ Incr. ¦ Decr. ¦ Incr.

Test Numbers	
x	f'(x)
−4	−196 (−)
−1	32 (+)
1	−32 (−)
4	196 (+)

Therefore, f is increasing on $(-3, 0)$ and on $(3, \infty)$; f is decreasing on $(-\infty, -3)$ and on $(0, 3)$; f has a local maximum at $x = 0$ and local minima at $x = -3$ and $x = 3$.

x	f'(x)	f	GRAPH of f
$(-\infty, -3)$	−	Decreasing	Falling
$x = -3$	0	Local minimum	Horizontal tangent
$(-3, 0)$	+	Increasing	Rising
$x = 0$	0	Local maximum	Horizontal tangent
$(0, 3)$	−	Decreasing	Falling
$x = 3$	0	Local minimum	Horizontal tangent
$(3, \infty)$	+	Increasing	Rising

x	$f(x)$
0	0
-3	-81
3	-81

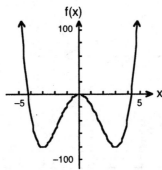

47.

x	$f'(x)$	$f(x)$	GRAPH OF f
$(-\infty,\ -1)$	+	Increasing	Rising
$x = -1$	0	Neither local maximum nor local minimum	Horizontal tangent
$(-1,\ 1)$	+	Increasing	Rising
$x = 1$	0	Local maximum	Horizontal tangent
$(1,\ \infty)$	–	Decreasing	Falling

Using this information together with the points $(-2, -1)$, $(-1, 1)$, $(0, 2)$, $(1, 3)$, $(2, 1)$ on the graph, we have

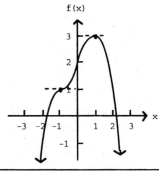

49.

x	$f'(x)$	$f(x)$	GRAPH OF $f(x)$
$(-\infty,\ -1)$	–	Decreasing	Falling
$x = -1$	0	Local minimum	Horizontal tangent
$(-1,\ 0)$	+	Increasing	Rising
$x = 0$	Not defined	Local maximum	Vertical tangent line
$(0,\ 2)$	–	Decreasing	Falling
$x = 2$	0	Neither local maximum nor local minimum	Horizontal tangent
$(2,\ \infty)$	–	Decreasing	Falling

Using this information together with the points $(-2, 2)$, $(-1, 1)$, $(0, 2)$, $(2, 1)$, $(4, 0)$ on the graph, we have

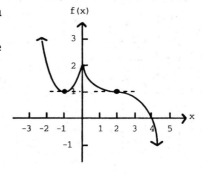

51.

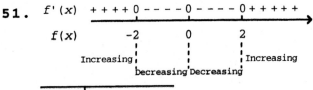

x	-2	0	2
$f(x)$	4	0	-4

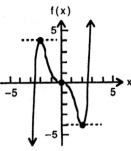

53.

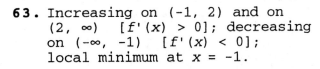

x	-1	0	1
$f(x)$	2	0	2

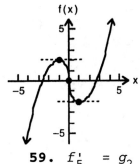

55. $f_1' = g_4$ **57.** $f_3' = g_6$ **59.** $f_5' = g_2$

61. Increasing on $(-1, 2)$ $[f'(x) > 0]$; decreasing on $(-\infty, -1)$ and on $(2, \infty)$ $[f'(x) < 0]$; local minimum at $x = -1$; local maximum at $x = 2$.

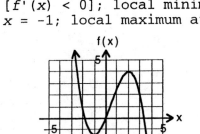

63. Increasing on $(-1, 2)$ and on $(2, \infty)$ $[f'(x) > 0]$; decreasing on $(-\infty, -1)$ $[f'(x) < 0]$; local minimum at $x = -1$.

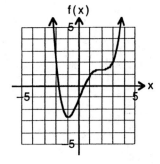

65. Increasing on $(-2, 0)$ and $(3, \infty)$ $[f'(x) > 0]$; decreasing on $(-\infty, -2)$ and $(0, 3)$ $[f'(x) < 0]$; local minima at $x = -2$ and $x = 3$, local maximum at $x = 0$.

67. $f'(x) > 0$ on $(-\infty, -1)$ and on $(3, \infty)$; $f'(x) < 0$ on $(-1, 3)$; $f'(x) = 0$ at $x = -1$ and $x = 3$.

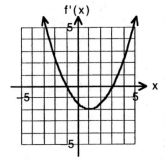

69. $f'(x) > 0$ on $(-2, 1)$ and on $(3, \infty)$; $f'(x) < 0$ on $(-\infty, -2)$ and on $(1, 3)$: $f'(x) = 0$ at $x = -2$, $x = 1$, and $x = 3$.

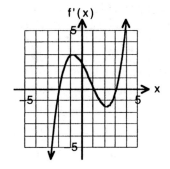

71. $f(x) = x + \dfrac{4}{x}$ [Note: f is not defined at $x = 0$.]

$f'(x) = 1 - \dfrac{4}{x^2}$

Critical values: $x = 0$ is *not* a critical value of f since 0 is not in the domain of f, but $x = 0$ is a partition number for f'.

$f'(x) = 1 - \dfrac{4}{x^2} = 0$

$x^2 - 4 = 0$

$(x + 2)(x - 2) = 0$

Thus, the critical values are $x = -2$ and $x = 2$; $x = -2$ and $x = 2$ are also partition numbers for f'.

The sign chart for f' is:

$f'(x)$ + + 0 - - ND - - 0 + +

$f(x)$ -3 -2 -1   0   1   2   3

Increasing | Decreasing | Increasing

Test Numbers

x	$f'(x)$
-3	$\frac{5}{9}$ (+)
-1	-3 (−)
1	-3 (−)
3	$\frac{5}{9}$ (+)

Therefore, f is increasing on $(-\infty, -2)$ and on $(2, \infty)$, f is decreasing on $(-2, 0)$ and on $(0, 2)$; f has a local maximum at $x = -2$ and a local minimum at $x = 2$.

73. $f(x) = 1 + \dfrac{1}{x} + \dfrac{1}{x^2}$ [Note: f is not defined at $x = 0$.]

$f'(x) = -\dfrac{1}{x^2} - \dfrac{2}{x^3}$

Critical values: $x = 0$ is not a critical value of f since 0 is not in the domain of f; $x = 0$ is a partition number for f'.

$f'(x) = -\dfrac{1}{x^2} - \dfrac{2}{x^3} = 0$

$-x - 2 = 0$

$x = -2$

Thus, the critical value is $x = -2$; -2 is also a partition number for f'.

The sign chart for f' is:

$f'(x)$ - - - - - 0 + + + + + ND - - - - -

$f(x)$ -3   -2   -1   0   1

Decreasing | Increasing | Decreasing

Test Numbers

x	$f'(x)$
-3	$-\frac{1}{27}$ (−)
-1	1 (+)
1	-3 (−)

Therefore, f is increasing on $(-2, 0)$ and f is decreasing on $(-\infty, -2)$ and on $(0, \infty)$; f has a local minimum at $x = -2$.

75. $f(x) = \dfrac{x^2}{x - 2}$ [Note: f is not defined at $x = 2$.]

$$f'(x) = \frac{(x - 2)(2x) - x^2(1)}{(x - 2)^2} = \frac{x^2 - 4x}{(x - 2)^2}$$

Critical values: $x = 2$ is *not* a critical value of f since 2 is not in the domain of f; $x = 2$ is a partition number for f'.

$$f'(x) = \frac{x^2 - 4x}{(x - 2)^2} = 0$$
$$x^2 - 4x = 0$$
$$x(x - 4) = 0$$

Thus, the critical values are $x = 0$ and $x = 4$; 0 and 4 are also partition numbers for f'.

The sign chart for f' is:

Test Numbers	
x	$f'(x)$
-1	$\frac{5}{9}$ $(+)$
1	-3 $(-)$
3	-3 $(-)$
5	$\frac{5}{9}$ $(+)$

Therefore, f is increasing on $(-\infty, 0)$ and on $(4, \infty)$, f is decreasing on $(0, 2)$ and on $(2, 4)$; f has a local maximum at $x = 0$ and a local minimum at $x = 4$.

77. $f(x) = x^4(x - 6)^2$

$$\begin{aligned}
f'(x) &= x^4(2)(x - 6)(1) + (x - 6)^2(4x^3)\\
&= 2x^3(x - 6)[x + 2(x - 6)]\\
&= 2x^3(x - 6)(3x - 12)\\
&= 6x^3(x - 4)(x - 6)
\end{aligned}$$

Thus, the critical values of f are $x = 0$, $x = 4$, and $x = 6$.

Now we construct the sign chart for f' ($x = 0$, $x = 4$, $x = 6$ are partition numbers).

Test Numbers	
x	$f'(x)$
-1	-210 $(-)$
1	90 $(+)$
5	-750 $(-)$
7	$+$

Therefore, f is increasing on $(0, 4)$ and on $(6, \infty)$, f is decreasing on $(-\infty, 0)$ and on $(4, 6)$; f has a local maximum at $x = 4$ and local minima at $x = 0$ and $x = 6$.

79. $f(x) = 3(x - 2)^{2/3} + 4$

$f'(x) = 3\left(\dfrac{2}{3}\right)(x - 2)^{-1/3} = \dfrac{2}{(x - 2)^{1/3}}$

Critical values: f' is not defined at $x = 2$. [Note: $f(2)$ is defined, $f(2) = 4$.] $f'(x) \neq 0$ for all x. Thus, the critical value for f is $x = 2$; $x = 2$ is also a partition number for f'.

	Test Numbers
	x $f'(x)$
	1 $-2\,(-)$
	3 $2\,(+)$

$f'(x)$ $- - - -$ ND $+ + + + + +$

               0 1 2 3 x

$f(x)$ Decreasing $\vert$ Increasing

Therefore, f is increasing on $(2, \infty)$ and decreasing on $(-\infty, 2)$; f has a local minimum at $x = 2$.

81. $f(x) = \dfrac{2x^2}{x^2 + 1}$; domain of f: $(-\infty, \infty)$

$f'(x) = \dfrac{(x^2 + 1)4x - 2x^2(2x)}{(x^2 + 1)^2} = \dfrac{4x}{(x^2 + 1)^2}$

Critical values:

$f'(x) = \dfrac{4x}{(x^2 + 1)^2} = 0$

$4x = 0$

$x = 0$

Thus, the critical value is $x = 0$.

The sign chart for f' is:

	Test Numbers
	x $f'(x)$
	-1 $-1\,(-)$
	1 $1\,(+)$

$f'(x)$ $- - - - $ 0 $+ + + +$

              -1 0 1 x

$f(x)$ Decreasing $\vert$ Increasing

            Local
           minimum

Therefore, f is increasing on $(0, \infty)$; f is decreasing on $(-\infty, 0)$; $f(0) = 0$ is a local minimum.

83. Let $f(x) = x^3 + kx$

(A) $k > 0$

$f'(x) = 3x^2 + k > 0$ for all x.
There are no critical values and no local extrema; f is increasing on $(-\infty, \infty)$.

(B) $k < 0$

$f'(x) = 3x^2 + k$; $3x^2 + k = 0$

$x^2 = -\dfrac{k}{3}$

$x = \pm\sqrt{-\dfrac{k}{3}}$

Critical values: $x = -\sqrt{-\dfrac{k}{3}}$, $x = \sqrt{-\dfrac{k}{3}}$;

$f'(x)$ $+++++0---------0+++++$

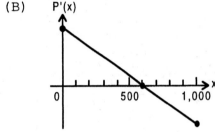

f is increasing on $\left(-\infty, -\sqrt{-\dfrac{k}{3}}\right)$ and on $\left(\sqrt{-\dfrac{k}{3}}, \infty\right)$; f is decreasing on $\left(-\sqrt{-\dfrac{k}{3}}, \sqrt{-\dfrac{k}{3}}\right)$; f has a local maximum at $x = -\sqrt{-\dfrac{k}{3}}$ and a local minimum at $x = \sqrt{-\dfrac{k}{3}}$.

(C) The only critical value is $x = 0$. There are no extrema, the function is increasing for all x.

85. (A) The marginal profit function, P', is positive on $(0, 600)$, zero at $x = 600$, and negative on $(600, 1,000)$.

(B)

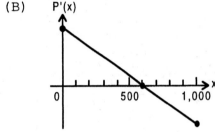

87. (A) The price function, $B(t)$, decreases for the first 15 months to a local minimum, increases for the next 40 months to a local maximum, and then decreases for the remaining 15 months.

(B)

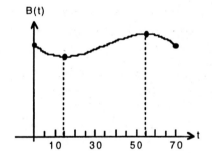

89. $C(x) = \dfrac{x^2}{20} + 20x + 320$

(A) $\overline{C}(x) = \dfrac{C(x)}{x} = \dfrac{x}{20} + 20 + \dfrac{320}{x}$

(B) Critical values:

$$\overline{C}'(x) = \dfrac{1}{20} - \dfrac{320}{x^2} = 0$$
$$x^2 - 320(20) = 0$$
$$x^2 - 6400 = 0$$
$$(x - 80)(x + 80) = 0$$

Thus, the critical value of $\overline{C}$ on the interval $(0, 150)$ is $x = 80$.

Next, construct the sign chart for $\overline{C}'$ ($x = 80$ is a partition number for $\overline{C}'$).

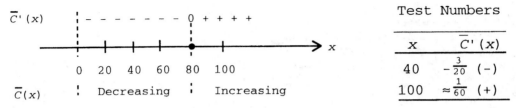

Test Numbers	
x	$\overline{C}'(x)$
40	$-\frac{3}{20}$ (–)
100	$\approx \frac{1}{60}$ (+)

Therefore, $\overline{C}$ is increasing for $80 < x < 150$ and decreasing for $0 < x < 80$; $\overline{C}$ has a local minimum at $x = 80$.

91. $P(x) = R(x) - C(x)$
$P'(x) = R'(x) - C'(x)$
Thus, if $R'(x) > C'(x)$ on the interval (a, b), then $P'(x) = R'(x) - C'(x) > 0$ on this interval and P is increasing.

93. $C(t) = \dfrac{0.28t}{t^2 + 4}$, $0 < t < 24$

$C'(t) = \dfrac{(t^2 + 4)(0.28) - 0.28t(2t)}{(t^2 + 4)^2} = \dfrac{0.28(4 - t^2)}{(t^2 + 4)^2}$

Critical values: C' is continuous for all t on the interval $(0, 24)$.

$C'(t) = \dfrac{0.28(4 - t^2)}{(t^2 + 4)^2} = 0$

$4 - t^2 = 0$

$(2 - t)(2 + t) = 0$

Thus, the critical value of C on the interval $(0, 24)$ is $t = 2$.
The sign chart for C' ($t = 2$ is a partition number) is:

$C'(t)$ $+ + + \ 0 \ - - -$

$C(t)$ 0   1   2   3 t

Increasing | Decreasing
Local
maximum

Test Numbers	
t	$C'(t)$
1	(+)
3	(–)

Therefore, C is increasing on $(0, 2)$ and decreasing on $(2, 24)$; $C(2) = 0.07$ is a local maximum.

95. $P(t) = \dfrac{8.4t}{t^2 + 49} + 0.1$, $0 < t < 24$

$P'(t) = \dfrac{(t^2 + 49)(8.4) - 8.4t(2t)}{(t^2 + 49)^2} = \dfrac{8.4(49 - t^2)}{(t^2 + 49)^2}$

Critical values: P is continuous for all t on the interval $(0, 24)$:

$P'(t) = \dfrac{8.4(49 - t^2)}{(t^2 + 49)^2} = 0$

$49 - t^2 = 0$

$(7 - t)(7 + t) = 0$

Thus, the critical value of P on $(0, 24)$ is $t = 7$.

90

The sign chart for P' (t = 7 is a partition number for P') is:

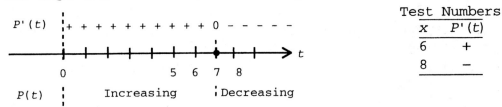

Test Numbers	
x	P'(t)
6	+
8	−

Therefore, P is increasing for 0 < t < 7 and decreasing for 7 < t < 24; P has a local maximum at t = 7.

EXERCISE 2-2
_____

Things to remember:

1. CONCAVITY

    The graph of a function f is concave upward on the interval (a, b) if f'(x) is *increasing* on (a, b) and is concave downward on the interval (a, b) if f'(x) is *decreasing* on (a, b).

    For the interval (a, b):

$f''(x)$	$f'(x)$	Graph of $y = f(x)$	Example
+	Increasing	Concave upward	⌣
−	Decreasing	Concave downward	⌢

2. SECOND DERIVATIVE

    For y = f(x), the SECOND DERIVATIVE of f, provided it exists, is:
    $$f''(x) = \frac{d}{dx}f'(x)$$
    Other notations for f''(x) are:
    $$\frac{d^2y}{dx^2} \quad \text{and} \quad y''.$$

3. INFLECTION POINT

    An INFLECTION POINT is a point on the graph of a function where the concavity changes (from upward to downward, or from downward to upward).

STRATEGY FOR GRAPHING A POLYNOMIAL

Step 1. Analyze $f(x)$.

Find the intercepts. The x intercepts are the solutions to $f(x) = 0$, if they exist, and the y intercept is $f(0)$.

Step 2. Analyze $f'(x)$.

Find the zeros of $f'(x)$. Construct a sign chart for $f'(x)$, determine the intervals where $f(x)$ is increasing and decreasing, and find local maxima and minima.

Step 3. Analyze $f''(x)$.

Find the zeros of $f''(x)$. Construct a sign chart for $f''(x)$, determine where the graph of f is concave upward and concave downward, and find any inflection points.

Step 4. Sketch the graph of f.

---

1. (A) The graph of f is concave upward on (a, c), (c, d), and (e, g).
(B) The graph of f is concave downward on (d, e) and (g, h).
(C) $f''(x) < 0$ on (d, e) and (g, h).
(D) $f''(x) > 0$ on (a, c), (c, d), and (e, g).
(E) $f'(x)$ is increasing on (a, c), (c, d), and (e, g).
(F) $f'(x)$ is decreasing on (d, e) and (g, h).
(G) Inflection points occur at $x = d$, $x = e$, and $x = g$.
(H) The local extrema occur at $x = b$, $x = c$, and $x = f$.

3. $f'(x) > 0$, $f''(x) > 0$; (c)

5. $f'(x) < 0$, $f''(x) > 0$; (d)

7. $f(x) = 2x^3 - 4x^2 + 5x - 6$
$f'(x) = 6x^2 - 8x + 5$
$f''(x) = 12x - 8$

9. $h(x) = 2x^{-1} - 3x^{-2}$
$h'(x) = -2x^{-2} + 6x^{-3}$
$h''(x) = 4x^{-3} - 18x^{-4}$

11. $y = x^2 - 18x^{1/2}$
$\dfrac{dy}{dx} = 2x - 9x^{-1/2}$
$\dfrac{d^2y}{dx^2} = 2 + \dfrac{9}{2}x^{-3/2}$

13. $y = (x^2 + 9)^4$
$y' = 4(x^2 + 9)^3(2x) = 8x(x^2 + 9)^3$
$y'' = 24x(x^2 + 9)^2(2x) + 8(x^2 + 9)^3$
$\quad = 48x^2(x^2 + 9)^2 + 8(x^2 + 9)^3 = 8(x^2 + 9)^2(7x^2 + 9)$

15. $f(x) = x^4 + 6x^2$
$f'(x) = 4x^3 + 12x$
$f''(x) = 12x^2 + 12 \geq 12 > 0$
The graph of f is concave upward for all x; there are no inflection points.

17. $f(x) = x^3 - 4x^2 + 5x - 2$
$f'(x) = 3x^2 - 8x + 5$
$f''(x) = 6x - 8$
$f''(x) = 0: 6x - 8 = 0$
$$x = \frac{4}{3}$$

Sign chart for f'' $\left(\text{partition number is } \dfrac{4}{3}\right)$:

$f''(x)$ − − − − − 0 + + + + +

0   1 $\frac{4}{3}$ 2   → x

Test Numbers	
x	$f''(x)$
0	−8 (−)
2	4 (+)

Graph   Concave   ⋮ Concave
of f Downward ⋮ Upward

Therefore, the graph of f is concave downward on $\left(-\infty, \dfrac{4}{3}\right)$ and concave upward on $\left(\dfrac{4}{3}, \infty\right)$; there is an inflection point at $x = \dfrac{4}{3}$.

19. $f(x) = -x^4 + 12x^3 - 12x + 24$

$f'(x) = -4x^3 + 36x^2 - 12$

$f''(x) = -12x^2 + 72x$

$f''(x) = 0:\ -12x^2 + 72x = 0$

$\qquad\qquad -12x(x - 6) = 0$

$\qquad\qquad\qquad x = 0,\ 6$

Sign chart for f'' (partition numbers 0, 6):

$f''(x)$ − − − 0 + + + + + 0 − − −

-1 0 1   6 7   → x

Graph Concave   ⋮ Concave ⋮ Concave
of f Downward ⋮ Upward   ⋮ Downward

Test Numbers	
x	$f''(x)$
−1	−84 (−)
1	60 (+)
7	−84 (−)

Therefore, the graph of f is concave downward on $(-\infty, 0)$ and $(6, \infty)$; concave upward on $(0, 6)$; there are inflection points at $x = 0$ and $x = 6$.

21.

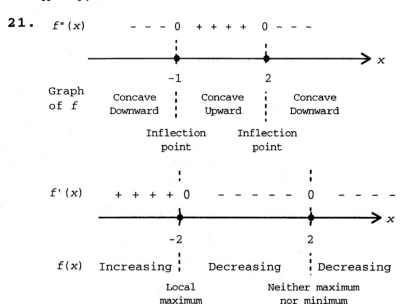

$f''(x)$ − − − 0 + + + + 0 − − −

-1   2   → x

Graph   Concave   ⋮ Concave   ⋮ Concave
of f Downward   ⋮ Upward   ⋮ Downward

                Inflection   Inflection
                 point   point

$f'(x)$ + + + + 0 − − − − − 0 − − − −

-2   2   → x

$f(x)$ Increasing ⋮ Decreasing ⋮ Decreasing

            Local   Neither maximum
           maximum   nor minimum

Using this information together with the points $(-4, 0)$, $(-2, 3)$, $(-1, 1.5)$, $(0, 0)$, $(2, -1)$, $(4, -3)$ on the graph, we have

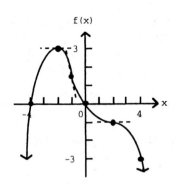

23.

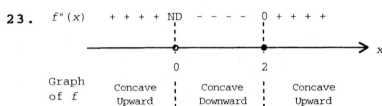

$f''(x)$ $+ + + +$ ND $- - - -$ 0 $+ + + +$

             0   2 x

Graph of f Concave Upward | Concave Downward | Concave Upward

        Point of Inflection   Point of Inflection

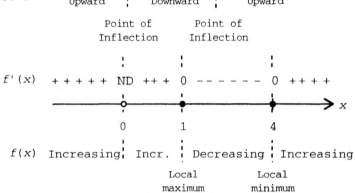

$f'(x)$ $+ + + + +$ ND $+ + +$ 0 $- - - - - -$ 0 $+ + + +$

            0   1   4 x

$f(x)$ Increasing | Incr. | Decreasing | Increasing

                    Local maximum   Local minimum

Using this information together with the points $(-3, -4)$, $(0, 0)$, $(1, 2)$, $(2, 1)$, $(4, -1)$, $(5, 0)$ on the graph, we have

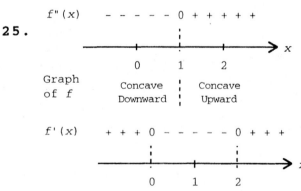

$f''(x)$ $- - - - - -$ 0 $+ + + + +$

25.

        0   1   2 x

Graph of f Concave Downward | Concave Upward

$f'(x)$ $+ + + 0 - - - - - - 0 + + +$

        0   1   2 x

$f(x)$ Increasing | Decreasing | Increasing

           Local maximum   Local minimum

x	0	1	2
$f(x)$	2	0	-2

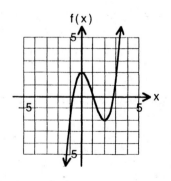

27.

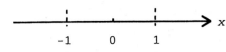

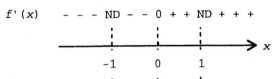

Graph of f: Concave downward (left of -1) | Concave upward (between -1 and 1) | Concave downward (right of 1)

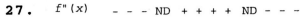

f'(x)   - - - ND - - 0 + + ND + + +

           -1   0   1

f(x)   Decreasing | Decr. | Incr. | Increasing

x	-1	0	1
$f(x)$	0	-2	0

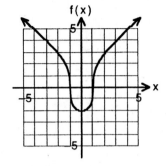

29. $f(x) = x^3 - 6x^2 + 16$

Step 1. Analyze $f(x)$.

x-intercept(s): $f(x) = 0$

$$x^3 - 6x^2 + 16 = 0$$
$$(x - 2)(x^2 - 4x - 8) = 0$$
$$x = 2, \ 2 \pm 2\sqrt{3}$$

y-intercept: $f(0) = 16$

Step 2. Analyze $f'(x)$. $f'(x) = 3x^2 - 12x = 3x(x - 4)$
Zeros for $f'(x)$: 0 and 4.
Sign chart for $f'(x)$:

f'(x)   + + + 0 - - - - - 0 + + +

f(x)   -1 0 1 2 3 4 5

        Increasing | Decreasing | Increasing

              Local   Local
            maximum   minimum

Test Numbers	
x	$f'(x)$
-1	10 (+)
2	-12 (-)
5	15 (+)

Thus, $f(x)$ is increasing on $(-\infty, 0)$ and on $(4, \infty)$; $f(x)$ is decreasing on $(0, 4)$; f has a local maximum at $x = 0$ and a local minimum at $x = 4$.

Step 3. Analyze $f''(x)$. $f''(x) = 6x - 12 = 6(x - 2)$
Partition numbers for $f''(x)$: $x = 2$
Sign chart for $f''(x)$:

f"(x)   - - - - - 0 + + + +

               0   1   2   3

Graph   Concave | Concave
of f   Downward | Upward

Test Numbers	
x	$f''(x)$
0	-12 (-)
3	6 (+)

The graph of f is concave upward on $(2, \infty)$, concave downward on $(-\infty, 2)$; and has an inflection point at $x = 2$.

Step 4. Sketch the graph of f.

x	f(x)
0	16
2	0
4	-16

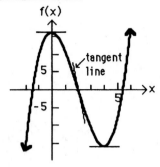

31. $f(x) = x^3 + x + 2$

Step 1. Analyze f(x):
x-intercept(s): $f(x) = 0$
$$x^3 + x + 2 = 0$$
$$(x + 1)(x^2 - x + 2) = 0$$
$$x = -1 \text{ (the quadratic factor does not have real roots)}$$
y-intercept: $f(0) = 2$

Step 2. Analyze f'(x): $f'(x) = 3x^2 + 1 > 0$ for all x.
Zeros of f'(x): f'(x) does not have any zeros.
Sign chart for f'(x):

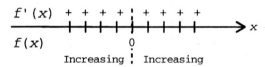

Thus, f(x) is increasing on (-∞, ∞).

Step 3. Analyze f"(x): $f"(x) = 6x$
Partition numbers for f"(x): $x = 0$
Sign chart for f"(x):

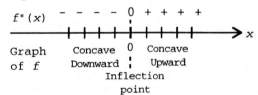

Test Numbers	
x	f"(x)
-1	-6 (-)
1	6 (+)

Thus, the graph of f is concave upward on (0, ∞) and concave downward on (-∞, 0); the graph has an inflection point at $x = 0$.

Step 4. Sketch the graph of f:

x	f(x)
-1	0
0	2
1	4

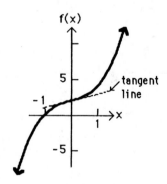

33. $f(x) = -0.25x^4 + x^3 = -\dfrac{1}{4}x^4 + x^3$

<u>Step 1. Analyze $f(x)$</u>:
x-intercept(s): $f(x) = 0$
$$-\frac{1}{4}x^4 + x^3 = 0$$
$$x^3\left(-\frac{1}{4}x + 1\right) = 0$$
$$x = 0,\ 4$$
y-intercept: $f(0) = 0$

<u>Step 2. Analyze $f'(x)$</u>: $f'(x) = -x^3 + 3x^2 = -x^2(x - 3)$
Zeros of $f'(x)$: $x = 0,\ 3$
Sign chart for $f'(x)$:

Test Numbers	
x	$f'(x)$
-1	$4\ (+)$
2	$4\ (+)$
4	$-16\ (-)$

```
         + + + 0 + + + + + 0 - - -
f'(x) ──┼───┼───┼───┼───┼──→ x
f(x)    0   1   2   3   4
     Increasing ¦ Increasing ¦ Decreasing
```

Thus, f is increasing on $(-\infty, 3)$; f is decreasing on $(3, \infty)$; f has a local maximum at $x = 3$.

<u>Step 3. Analyze $f''(x)$</u>: $f''(x) = -3x^2 + 6x = -3x(x - 2)$
Partition numbers for $f''(x)$: $x = 0,\ 2$
Sign chart for $f''(x)$:

Test Numbers	
x	$f''(x)$
-1	$-9\ (-)$
1	$3\ (+)$
3	$-9\ (-)$

```
          - - - 0 + + + 0 - - -
f''(x) ──┼───┼───┼───┼───┼──→ x
Graph    -1  0   1   2   3   4
of f   Concave ¦ Concave ¦ Concave
       Downward¦ Upward  ¦ Downward
         Inflection  Inflection
            point       point
```

Thus, the graph of f is concave downward on $(-\infty, 0)$ and on $(2, \infty)$; concave upward on $(0, 2)$, and has inflection points at $x = 0, 2$.

<u>Step 4. Sketch the graph of f</u>:

x	$f(x)$
0	0
2	4
3	$\dfrac{27}{4}$
4	0

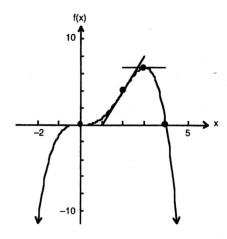

35. $f(x) = 16x(x - 1)^3$

Step 1. Analyze $f(x)$:

x-intercept(s): $f(x) = 0$

$$16x(x - 1)^3 = 0$$
$$x = 0, 1$$

y-intercept: $f(0) = 0$

Step 2. Analyze $f'(x)$: $f'(x) = 16x(3)(x - 1)^2 + 16(x - 1)^3$

$$= 16(x - 1)^2(3x + x - 1)$$
$$= 16(x - 1)^2(4x - 1)$$

Zeros of $f'(x)$: $x = 0, \frac{1}{4}$

Sign chart for $f'(x)$:

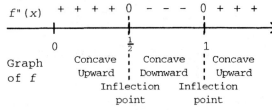

Test Numbers	
x	$f'(x)$
0	$-16\ (-)$
$\frac{1}{2}$	$4\ (+)$
$\frac{3}{2}$	$20\ (+)$

Thus, f is increasing on $\left(\frac{1}{4}, \infty\right)$; decreasing on $\left(-\infty, \frac{1}{4}\right)$; and has a local minimum at $x = \frac{1}{4}$.

Step 3. Analyze $f''(x)$: $f''(x) = 16(x - 1)^2 4 + 32(x - 1)(4x - 1)$

$$= 32(x - 1)[2(x - 1) + 4x - 1]$$
$$= 32(x - 1)(6x - 3) \cdot$$

Partition numbers for $f''(x)$: $x = 1, \frac{1}{2}$

Sign chart for $f''(x)$:

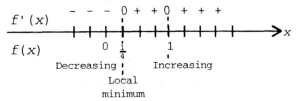

Test Numbers	
x	$f''(x)$
0	$96\ (+)$
$\frac{3}{4}$	$-12\ (-)$
$\frac{3}{2}$	$96\ (+)$

Thus, the graph of f is concave upward on $\left(-\infty, \frac{1}{2}\right)$ and on $(1, \infty)$, concave downward on $\left(\frac{1}{2}, 1\right)$, and has inflection points at $x = \frac{1}{2}, 1$.

Step 4. Sketch the graph of f:

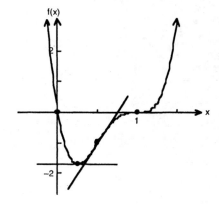

37. $f(x) = (x^2 + 3)(9 - x^2)$

Step 1. Analyze $f(x)$:

Intercepts: y-intercept: $f(0) = 3(9) = 27$

x-intercepts: $(x^2 + 3)(9 - x^2) = 0$

$(3 - x)(3 + x) = 0$

$x = 3, -3$

Step 2. Analyze $f'(x)$:

$f'(x) = (x^2 + 3)(-2x) + (9 - x^2)(2x)$

$= 2x[9 - x^2 - (x^2 + 3)]$

$= 2x(6 - 2x^2)$

$= 4x(\sqrt{3} + x)(\sqrt{3} - x)$

Zeros of $f'(x)$: $x = 0$, $x = -\sqrt{3}$, $x = \sqrt{3}$

Sign chart for f':

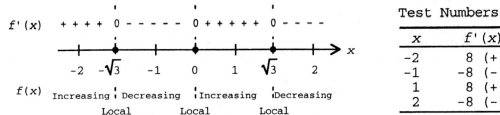

Test Numbers	
x	$f'(x)$
-2	8 $(+)$
-1	-8 $(-)$
1	8 $(+)$
2	-8 $(-)$

Thus, f is increasing on $(-\infty, -\sqrt{3})$ and on $(0, \sqrt{3})$; f is decreasing on $(-\sqrt{3}, 0)$ and on $(\sqrt{3}, \infty)$; f has local maxima at $x = -\sqrt{3}$ and $x = \sqrt{3}$ and a local minimum at $x = 0$.

Step 3. Analyze $f''(x)$:

$f''(x) = 2x(-4x) + (6 - 2x^2)(2) = 12 - 12x^2 = -12(x - 1)(x + 1)$

Partition numbers for f'': $x = 1$, $x = -1$

Sign chart for f'':

Test Numbers	
x	$f''(x)$
-2	-36 $(-)$
0	12 $(+)$
2	-36 $(-)$

Thus, the graph of f is concave downward on $(-\infty, -1)$ and on $(1, \infty)$; the graph of f is concave upward on $(-1, 1)$; the graph has inflection points at $x = -1$ and $x = 1$.

Step 4. Sketch the graph of f:

x	$f(x)$
$-\sqrt{3}$	36
-1	32
0	27
1	32
$\sqrt{3}$	36

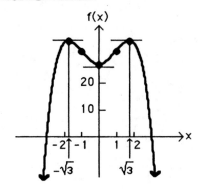

39. $f(x) = (x^2 - 4)^2$

Step 1. Analyze $f(x)$:

Intercepts: y-intercept: $f(0) = (-4)^2 = 16$

x-intercepts: $(x^2 - 4)^2 = 0$

$$[(x - 2)(x + 2)]^2 = 0$$
$$(x - 2)^2(x + 2)^2 = 0$$
$$x = 2, -2$$

Step 2. Analyze $f'(x)$:

$f'(x) = 2(x^2 - 4)(2x) = 4x(x - 2)(x + 2)$
Zeros of $f'(x)$: $x = 0$, $x = 2$, $x = -2$
Sign chart for f':

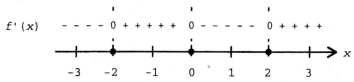

Test Numbers	
x	$f'(x)$
-3	-60 $(-)$
-1	12 $(+)$
1	-12 $(-)$
3	60 $(+)$

Thus, f is decreasing on $(-\infty, -2)$ and on $(0, 2)$; f is increasing on $(-2, 0)$ and on $(2, \infty)$; f has local minima at $x = -2$ and $x = 2$ and a local maximum at $x = 0$.

Step 3. Analyze $f''(x)$:

$$f''(x) = 4x(2x) + (x^2 - 4)(4) = 12x^2 - 16 = 12\left(x^2 - \frac{4}{3}\right)$$

$$= 12\left(x - \frac{2\sqrt{3}}{3}\right)\left(x + \frac{2\sqrt{3}}{3}\right)$$

Partition numbers for f'': $x = \dfrac{2\sqrt{3}}{3}$, $x = \dfrac{-2\sqrt{3}}{3}$

Sign chart for f'':

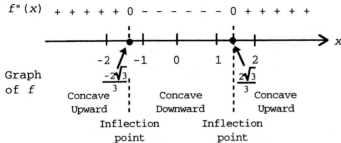

Thus, the graph of f is concave upward on $\left(-\infty, \dfrac{-2\sqrt{3}}{3}\right)$ and on $\left(\dfrac{2\sqrt{3}}{3}, \infty\right)$;

the graph of f is concave downward on $\left(\dfrac{-2\sqrt{3}}{3}, \dfrac{2\sqrt{3}}{3}\right)$; the graph has

inflection points at $x = \dfrac{-2\sqrt{3}}{3}$ and $x = \dfrac{2\sqrt{3}}{3}$.

Step 4. Sketch the graph of f:

x	$f(x)$
-2	0
$-\dfrac{2\sqrt{3}}{3}$	$\dfrac{64}{9}$
0	16
$\dfrac{2\sqrt{3}}{3}$	$\dfrac{64}{9}$
2	0

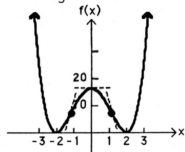

41. $f(x) = 2x^6 - 3x^5$

Step 1. Analyze $f(x)$:

Intercepts: y-intercept: $f(0) = 2 \cdot 0^6 - 3 \cdot 0^5 = 0$

              x-intercepts: $2x^6 - 3x^5 = 0$

$$x^5(2x - 3) = 0$$
$$x = 0, \ \frac{3}{2}$$

Step 2. Analyze $f'(x)$:

$$f'(x) = 12x^5 - 15x^4 = 12x^4\left(x - \frac{5}{4}\right)$$

Zeros of $f'(x)$: $x = 0$, $x = \dfrac{5}{4}$

Sign chart for f':

	Test Numbers	
x	$f'(x)$	
-1	-27	$(-)$
1	-3	$(-)$
2	144	$(+)$

$f'(x)$ $- - - - 0 - - - - - - - 0 + + + +$

$f(x)$ Decreasing ⋮ Decreasing ⋮ Increasing

Local
minimum

Thus, f is decreasing on $(-\infty, 0)$ and $\left(0, \dfrac{5}{4}\right)$; f is increasing on $\left(\dfrac{5}{4}, \infty\right)$;

f has a local minimum at $x = \dfrac{5}{4}$.

101

Step 3. Analyze $f''(x)$:

$f''(x) = 60x^4 - 60x^3 = 60x^3(x - 1)$

Partition numbers for f'': $x = 0$, $x = 1$

Sign chart for f'':

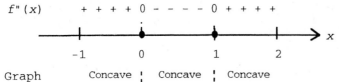

	Test Numbers	
x		$f''(x)$
-1		120 $(+)$
$\frac{1}{2}$		$-\frac{15}{4}$ $(-)$
2		480 $(+)$

Thus, the graph of f is concave upward on $(-\infty, 0)$ and on $(1, \infty)$; the graph of f is concave downward on $(0, 1)$; the graph has inflection points at $x = 0$ and $x = 1$.

Step 4. Sketch the graph of f:

x	$f(x)$
0	0
1	-1
$\frac{5}{4}$	≈ -1.5

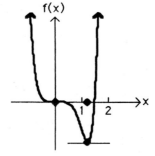

43.

x	$f'(x)$	$f(x)$
$-\infty < x < -1$	Positive and decreasing	Decreasing and concave downward
$x = -1$	x-intercept	Local maximum
$-1 < x < 0$	Negative and decreasing	Decreasing and concave downward
$x = 0$	Local minimum	Inflection point
$0 < x < 2$	Negative and increasing	Decreasing and concave upward
$x = 2$	Local maximum	Inflection point
$2 < x < \infty$	Negative and decreasing	Decreasing and concave downward

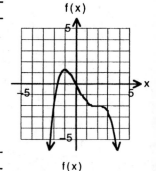

45.

x	$f'(x)$	$f(x)$
$-\infty < x < -2$	Negative and increasing	Decreasing and concave upward
$x = -2$	Local maximum	Inflection point
$-2 < x < 0$	Negative and decreasing	Decreasing and concave downward
$x = 0$	Local minimum	Inflection point
$0 < x < 2$	Negative and increasing	Decreasing and concave upward
$x = 2$	Local maximum	Inflection point
$2 < x < \infty$	Negative and decreasing	Decreasing and concave downward

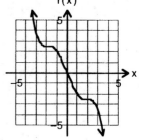

47. $f(x) = x^4 - 5x^3 + 3x^2 + 8x - 5$

Step 1. Analyze $f(x)$:

Intercepts: y-intercept: $f(0) = -5$

x-intercepts: $x \approx -1.18$, 0.61, 1.87, 3.71

Step 2. Analyze $f'(x)$: $f'(x) = 4x^3 - 15x^2 + 6x + 8$
Zeros of $f'(x)$: $x \approx -0.53, 1.24, 3.04$
f is decreasing on $(-\infty, -0.53)$ and $(1.24, 3.04)$; f is increasing on $(-0.53, 1.24)$ and $(3.04, \infty)$; f has local minima at $x = -0.53$ and 3.04; f has a local maximum at $x = 1.24$

Step 3. Analyze $f''(x)$: $f''(x) = 12x^2 - 30x + 6$
The graph of f is concave upward on $(-\infty, 0.22)$ and $(2.28, \infty)$; the graph of f is concave downward on $(0.22, 2.28)$; the graph has inflection points at $x = 0.22$ and 2.28.

49. $f(x) = x^4 - 21x^3 + 100x^2 + 20x + 100$

Part 1. Analyze $f(x)$:
Intercepts: y-intercept: $f(0) = 100$
$\qquad\qquad$ x-intercept: $x \approx 8.01, 13.36$

Part 2. Analyze $f'(x)$: $f'(x) = 4x^3 - 63x^2 + 200x + 20$
Zeros of $f'(x)$:
$\qquad x \approx -0.10, 4.57, 11.28$

f is increasing on $(-0.10, 4.57)$ and $(11.28, \infty)$;
f is decreasing on $(-\infty, -0.10)$ and $(4.57, 11.28)$;
f has a local maximum at $x = 4.57$; f has local minima at $x = -0.10$ and 11.28.

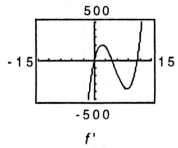

f'

Part 3. Analyze $f''(x)$: $f''(x) = 12x^2 - 126x + 200$
The graph of f is concave upward on $(-\infty, 1.95)$ and $(8.55, \infty)$; the graph of f is concave downward on $(1.95, 8.55)$; the graph has inflection points at $x = 1.95$ and $x = 8.55$.

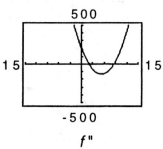

f''

51. $f(x) = -x^4 - x^3 + 2x^2 - 2x + 3$
Step 1. Analyze $f(x)$:

Intercepts: y-intercept: $f(0) = 3$
$\qquad\qquad$ x-intercepts: $x \approx -2.40, 1.16$

Step 2. Analyze $f'(x)$: $f'(x) = -4x^3 - 3x^2 + 4x - 2$
Zeros of $f'(x)$: $x \approx -1.58$
f is increasing on $(-\infty, -1.58)$; f is decreasing on $(-1.58, \infty)$; f has a local maximum at $x = -1.58$

Step 3. Analyze $f''(x)$: $f''(x) = -12x^2 - 6x + 4$
The graph of f is concave downward on $(-\infty, -0.88)$ and $(0.38, \infty)$; the graph of f is concave upward on $(-0.88, 0.38)$; the graph has inflection points at $x = -0.88$ and $x = 0.38$.

53. $f(x) = 0.1x^5 + 0.3x^4 - 4x^3 - 5x^2 + 40x + 30$

Part 1. Analyze $f(x)$:

Intercepts: y-intercept: $f(0) = 3$

x-intercepts: $x \approx -6.68, -3.64, -0.72$

Part 2. Analyze $f'(x)$:

$f'(x) = 0.5x^4 + 1.2x^3 - 12x^2 - 10x + 40$

Zeros of $f'(x)$: $x \approx -5.59, -2.27, 1.65, 3.82$

f is increasing on $(-\infty, -5.59)$, $(-2.27, 1.65)$, and $(3.82, \infty)$; f is decreasing on $(-5.59, -2.27)$ and $(1.65, 3.82)$; f has local minima at $x = -2.27$ and 3.82; f has local maxima at $x = -5.59$ and 1.65

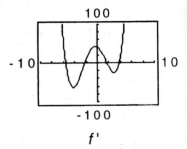

f'

Part 3. Analyze $f''(x)$: $f''(x) = 2x^3 + 3.6x^2 - 24x - 10$
The graph of f is concave downward on $(-\infty, -4.31)$ and $(-0.40, 2.91)$; the graph of f is concave upward on $(-4.31, -0.40)$ and $(2.91, \infty)$; the graph has inflection points at $x = -4.31, -0.40$ and 2.91.

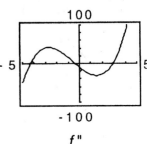

f''

55. If $f'(x)$ has a local extremum at $x = c$, then $f'(x)$ must change from increasing to decreasing, or from decreasing to increasing at $x = c$. It follows from this that the graph of f must change its concavity at $x = c$ and so there must be an inflection point at $x = c$.

57. If there is an inflection point on the graph of f at $x = c$, then the graph changes its concavity at $x = c$. Consequently, f' must change from increasing to decreasing, or from decreasing to increasing at $x = c$ and so $x = c$ is a local extremum of f'.

59. The graph of the CPI is concave up.

61. The graph of C is increasing and concave down. Therefore, the graph of C' is positive and decreasing. Since the marginal costs are decreasing, the production process is becoming more efficient.

63. $R(x) = xp = 1296x - 0.12x^3$, $0 < x < 80$

$R'(x) = 1296 - 0.36x^2$

Critical values: $R'(x) = 1296 - 0.36x^2 = 0$

$$x^2 = \frac{1296}{0.36} = 3600$$

$$x = \pm 60$$

Thus, $x = 60$ is the only critical value on the interval $(0, 80)$.

$R''(x) = -0.72x$

$R''(60) = -43.2 < 0$

(A) R has a local maximum at $x = 60$.

(B) Since $R''(x) = -0.72x < 0$ for $0 < x < 80$, R is concave downward on this interval.

65. $T(x) = -0.25x^4 + 5x^3 = -\dfrac{1}{4}x^4 + 5x^3$, $0 \le x \le 15$

$T'(x) = -x^3 + 15x^2$

$T''(x) = -3x^2 + 30x = -3x(x - 10)$

Partition numbers for $T''(x)$: $x = 10$

Sign chart for $T''(x)$:

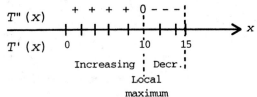

Test Numbers	
x	$T''(x)$
9	27 (+)
11	−33 (−)

Thus, T' is increasing on $(0, 10)$ and decreasing on $(10, 15)$; the point of diminishing returns is $x = 10$; the maximum rate of change is $T'(10) = 500$.

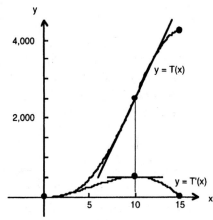

67. $N(x) = -0.25x^4 + 23x^3 - 540x^2 + 80{,}000$, $24 \le x \le 45$

$N'(x) = -x^3 + 69x^2 - 1080x$

$N''(x) = -3x^2 + 138x - 1080 = -3(x^2 - 46x + 360)$
$\qquad\qquad\qquad\qquad\qquad\;\; = -3(x - 10)(x - 36)$

Partition numbers for $N''(x)$: $x = 36$

Sign chart for $N''(x)$:

Test Numbers	
x	$N''(x)$
35	75 (+)
37	−111 (−)

Thus, N' is increasing on $(24, 36)$ and decreasing on $(36, 45)$; the point of diminishing returns is $x = 36$; the maximum rate of change is

$N'(36) = -(36)^3 + 69(36)^2 - 1080(36)$
$\qquad\quad = 3888.$

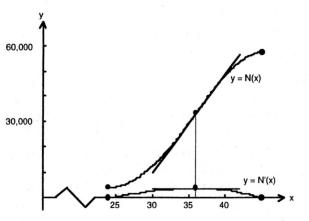

69. (A)
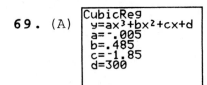

(B) From part (A),
$$y(x) = -0.005x^3 + 0.485x^2 - 1.85x + 300$$
so $y'(x) = -0.015x^2 + 0.970x - 1.85$

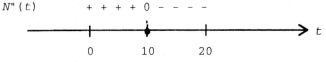

The graph of $y'(x)$ is shown at the right and the maximum value of y' occurs at $x \approx 32$; and $y(32) \approx 574$.

The manager should place 32 ads each month to maximize the rate of change of sales; the manager can expect to sell 574 cars.

71. $N(t) = 1000 + 30t^2 - t^3,\ 0 \le t \le 20$

$N'(t) = 60t - 3t^2$

$N''(t) = 60 - 6t$

(A) To determine when N' is increasing or decreasing, we must solve the inequalities $N''(t) > 0$ and $N''(t) < 0$, respectively. Now
$$N''(t) = 60 - 6t = 0$$
$$t = 10$$

The sign chart for N'' (partition number is 10) is:

	Test Numbers
	t $\quad$ $N''(t)$
	0 $\quad$ 60 (+)
	20 $\quad$ −60 (−)

$N''(t)$ $\qquad$ + + + + 0 − − − −

$N'(t)$ $\qquad$ Increasing ⋮ Decreasing

Thus, N' is increasing on $(0, 10)$ and decreasing on $(10, 20)$.

(B) From the results in (A), the graph of N has an inflection point at $t = 10$.

(C)
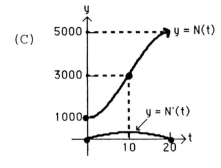

(D) Using the results in (A), N' has a local maximum at $t = 10$:
$$N'(10) = 300$$

73. $T(n) = 0.08n^3 - 1.2n^2 + 6n,\ n \ge 0$

$T'(n) = 0.24n^2 - 2.4n + 6,\ \ n \ge 0$

$T''(n) = 0.48n - 2.4$

(A) To determine when the rate of change of T, i.e., T', is increasing or decreasing, we must solve the inequalities $T''(n) > 0$ and $T''(n) < 0$, respectively. Now
$$T''(n) = 0.48n - 2.4 = 0$$
$$n = 5$$

The sign chart for T'' (partition number is 5) is:

$T''(n)$ $- - - - 0 + + + +$

$\xrightarrow{\hspace{8cm}} n$

     1   5   10

$T'(n)$ Decreasing ¦ Increasing

Test Numbers	
t	$N''(t)$
1	-1.92 $(-)$
10	2.4 $(+)$

Thus, T' is increasing on $(5, \infty)$ and decreasing on $(0, 5)$.

(B) Using the results in (A), the graph of T has an inflection point at $n = 5$. The graphs of T and T' are shown at the right.

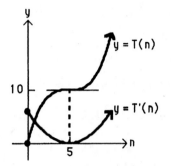

(C) Using the results in (A), T' has a local minimum at $n = 5$:

$T'(5) = 0.24(5)^2 - 2.4(5) + 6 = 0$

EXERCISE 2-3

Things to remember:

1. RATIONAL FUNCTIONS

A RATIONAL FUNCTION is any function that can be written in the form

$$f(x) = \frac{n(x)}{d(x)} \qquad d(x) \neq 0$$

where $n(x)$ and $d(x)$ are polynomials. The DOMAIN of f is the set of all real numbers such that $d(x) \neq 0$.

2. VERTICAL ASYMPTOTES

The vertical line $x = a$ is a VERTICAL ASYMPTOTE for the graph of $y = f(x)$ if

$$f(x) \to \infty \text{ or } f(x) \to -\infty \text{ as } x \to a^+ \text{ or } x \to a^-$$

(that is, if $f(x)$ either increases or decreases without bound as x approaches a from the right or from the left).

3. LOCATING VERTICAL ASYMPTOTES OF RATIONAL FUNCTIONS

If $f(x) = \dfrac{n(x)}{d(x)}$ is a rational function, $d(c) = 0$ and $n(c) \neq 0$,

then the line $x = c$ is a vertical asymptote of the graph of f.

4. HORIZONTAL ASYMPTOTES

The line $y = b$ is a HORIZONTAL ASYMPTOTE for the graph of $y = f(x)$ if

$$\lim_{x \to \infty} f(x) = b \quad \text{or} \quad \lim_{x \to -\infty} f(x) = b$$

5. HORIZONTAL ASYMPTOTES FOR RATIONAL FUNCTIONS

Let $f(x) = \dfrac{a_m x^m + a_{m-1}x^{m-1} + \ldots + a_1 x + a_0}{b_n x^n + b_{n-1}x^{n-1} + \ldots + b_1 x + b_0}$

1. If $m < n$, then $y = 0$ (the x axis) is a horizontal asymptote for $f(x)$.

2. If $m = n$, then the line $y = \dfrac{a_m}{b_n}$ is a horizontal asymptote for $f(x)$.

3. If $m > n$, then $f(x)$ does not have a horizontal asymptote.

6. STRATEGY FOR GRAPHING A RATIONAL FUNCTION

Step 1. Analyze $f(x)$.
(A) Find the domain of f.
(B) Find intercepts.
(C) Find asymptotes.

Step 2. Analyze $f'(x)$.
Find the zeros of $f'(x)$. Construct a sign chart for $f'(x)$, determine the intervals where $f(x)$ is increasing and decreasing, and find local maxima and minima.

Step 3. Analyze $f''(x)$.
Find the zeros of $f''(x)$. Construct a sign chart for $f''(x)$, determine where the graph of f is concave upward and concave downward, and find any inflection points.

Step 4. Sketch the graph of f.
Draw asymptotes and locate intercepts, local maxima and minima, and inflection points. Sketch in what you know from steps 1–3. In regions of uncertainty, use point-by-point plotting to complete the graph.

---

1. (A) $f'(x) < 0$ on $(-\infty,\ b)$, $(0,\ e)$, $(e,\ g)$
   (B) $f'(x) > 0$ on $(b,\ d)$, $(d,\ 0)$, $(g,\ \infty)$
   (C) $f(x)$ is increasing on $(b,\ d)$, $(d,\ 0)$, $(g,\ \infty)$
   (D) $f(x)$ is decreasing on $(-\infty,\ b)$, $(0,\ e)$, $(e,\ g)$
   (E) $f(x)$ has a local maximum at $x = 0$
   (F) $f(x)$ has local minima at $x = b$ and $x = g$
   (G) $f''(x) < 0$ on $(-\infty,\ a)$, $(d,\ e)$, $(h,\ \infty)$
   (H) $f''(x) > 0$ on $(a,\ c)$, $(e,\ h)$
   (I) The graph of f is concave upward on $(a,\ c)$ and $(e,\ h)$.
   (J) The graph of f is concave downward on $(-\infty,\ a)$, $(d,\ e)$, and $(h,\ \infty)$.
   (K) Inflection points at $x = a$, $x = h$
   (L) Horizontal asymptote: $y = L$
   (M) Vertical asymptotes: $x = d$, $x = e$

3. $f(x) = \dfrac{3x - 4}{x}$

Horizontal asymptote: $\dfrac{a_m x^m}{b_n x^n} = \dfrac{3x}{x} = 3$

$\qquad\qquad\qquad y = 3$ is a horizontal asymptote [4b].

Vertical asymptotes: Let $n(x) = 3x - 4$, $d(x) = x$; $d(0) = 0$ and $n(0) = 4 \neq 0$. Therefore, $x = 0$ is a vertical asymptote [5].

5. $f(x) = \dfrac{x^2 - 4}{x^2 + 4}$

Horizontal asymptote: $\dfrac{a_m x^m}{b_n x^n} = \dfrac{x^2}{x^2} = 1$

$\qquad\qquad\qquad y = 1$ is a horizontal asymptote [4b].

Vertical asymptotes: Let $n(x) = x^2 - 4$, $d(x) = x^2 + 4$.
Since $x^2 + 4 \geq 4 > 0$ for all x, $d(x) \neq 0$ for all x; there are no vertical asymptotes [5].

7. $f(x) = \dfrac{x}{x^2 - 1}$

Horizontal asymptote: $\dfrac{a_m x^m}{b_n x^n} = \dfrac{x}{x^2} = \dfrac{1}{x}$

$\qquad\qquad\qquad y = 0$ is a horizontal asymptote [4a].

Vertical asymptotes: Let $n(x) = x$, $d(x) = x^2 - 1 = (x - 1)(x + 1)$.
Since $d(1) = 0$ and $n(1) = 1 \neq 0$, $x = 1$ is a vertical asymptote; since $d(-1) = 0$ and $n(-1) = -1 \neq 0$, $x = -1$ is a vertical asymptote [5].

9. $f(x) = \dfrac{x^3}{x^2 - 16}$

Horizontal asymptote: $\dfrac{a_m x^m}{b_n x^n} = \dfrac{x^3}{x^2} = x;$

$\qquad\qquad\qquad$ there is no horizontal asymptote [4c].

Vertical asymptotes: Let $n(x) = x^3$, $d(x) = x^2 - 16 = (x - 4)(x + 4)$.
Since $d(4) = 0$ and $n(4) = 64 \neq 0$, $x = 4$ is a vertical asymptote; since $d(-4) = 0$ and $n(-4) = -64 \neq 0$, $x = -4$ is a horizontal asymptote [5].

11. $f(x) = \dfrac{2x^2 + x - 3}{x^2 - 2x + 1}$

Horizontal asymptote: $\dfrac{a_m x^m}{b_n x^n} = \dfrac{2x^2}{x^2} = 2;$

$\qquad\qquad\qquad y = 2$ is a horizontal asymptote.

Vertical asymptotes: Let $n(x) = 2x^2 + x - 3 = (2x + 3)(x - 1)$ and $d(x) = x^2 - 2x + 1 = (x - 1)^2$. Then $\dfrac{n(x)}{d(x)} = \dfrac{(2x + 3)(x - 1)}{(x - 1)^2} = \dfrac{2x + 3}{x - 1}$
The denominator is 0 at $x = 1$, the numerator is nonzero. Therefore, $x = 1$ is a vertical asymptote.

13. $f(x) = \dfrac{3x^2 + 2x + 5}{2x^2 + 3x - 20}$

<u>Horizontal asymptote</u>: $\dfrac{a_m x^m}{b_n x^n} = \dfrac{3x^2}{2x^2} = \dfrac{3}{2}$;

$y = \dfrac{3}{2}$ is a horizontal asymptote.

<u>Vertical asymptotes</u>: Let $n(x) = 3x^2 + 2x + 5$ and $d(x) = 2x^2 + 3x - 20 =$ $(2x - 5)(x + 4)$. Since $d\left(\dfrac{5}{2}\right) = 0$ and $d(-4) = 0$, and $n\left(\dfrac{5}{2}\right) \neq 0$, $n(-4) \neq 0$, $x = \dfrac{5}{2}$ and $x = -4$ are vertical asymptotes.

15. <u>Step 1. Analyze $f(x)$</u>:

(A) Domain: All real numbers

(B) Intercepts: y-intercept: 0
$\qquad\qquad\qquad\quad$ x-intercepts: -4, 0, 4

(C) Asymptotes: Horizontal asymptote: $y = 2$

<u>Step 2. Analyze $f'(x)$</u>:

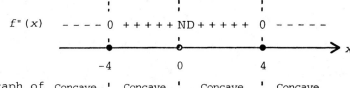

<u>Step 3. Analyze $f''(x)$</u>:

<u>Step 4. Sketch the graph of f</u>:

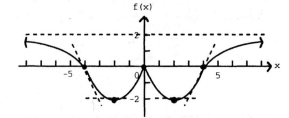

17. <u>Step 1. Analyze $f(x)$</u>:

(A) Domain: All real numbers except $x = -2$

(B) Intercepts: y-intercept: 0
$\qquad\qquad\qquad\quad$ x-intercepts: -4, 0

(C) Asymptotes: Horizontal asymptote: $y = 1$
$\qquad\qquad\qquad\quad$ Vertical asymptote: $x = -2$

110

<u>Step 2.</u>   <u>Analyze $f'(x)$</u>:

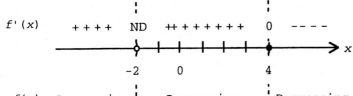

$f'(x)$ $+ + + +$ ND $+ + + + + + +$ 0 $- - - -$

-2   0   4

$f(x)$ Increasing   Increasing   Decreasing

Local
maximum

<u>Step 3.</u>   <u>Analyze $f''(x)$</u>:

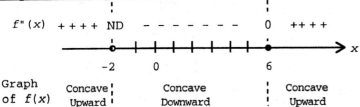

$f''(x)$ $+ + + +$ ND $- - - - - - - -$ 0 $+ + + +$

-2   0   6

Graph   Concave   Concave   Concave
of $f(x)$ Upward   Downward   Upward

<u>Step 4.</u>   <u>Sketch the graph of f</u>:

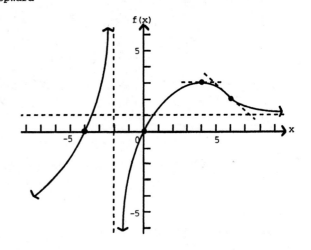

19. <u>Step 1.</u>   <u>Analyze $f(x)$</u>:

(A) Domain: All real numbers except
$x = -1$

(B) Intercepts: y-intercept: -1
                        x-intercept: 1

(C) Asymptotes: Horizontal asymptote: $y = 1$
                        Vertical asymptote: $x = -1$

<u>Step 2.</u>   <u>Analyze $f'(x)$</u>:

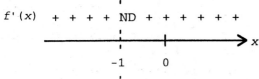

$f'(x)$ $+ + + +$ ND $+ + + + + +$

-1   0

$f(x)$ Increasing   Increasing

Step 3. Analyze $f''(x)$:

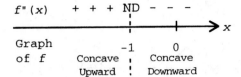

$f''(x)$ + + + ND - - -

Graph
of f -1 0
         Concave   Concave
         Upward   Downward

Step 4. Sketch the graph of f:

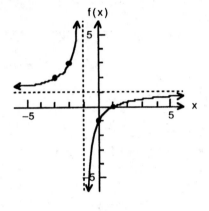

21. Step 1. Analyze $f(x)$:

(A) Domain: All real numbers except $x = -2$, $x = 2$

(B) Intercepts: y-intercept: 0
                x-intercept: 0

(C) Asymptotes: Horizontal asymptote: $y = 0$
                   Vertical asymptotes: $x = -2$, $x = 2$

Step 2. Analyze $f'(x)$:

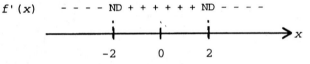

$f'(x)$ - - - - ND + + + + + + ND - - - -

          -2 0 2

$f(x)$ Decreasing   Increasing   Decreasing

Step 3. Analyze $f''(x)$:

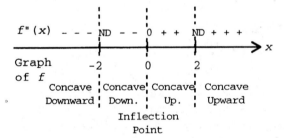

$f''(x)$ - - - ND - - 0 + + ND + + +

Graph -2 0 2
of f
     Concave Concave Concave Concave
     Downward Down.   Up.   Upward
            Inflection
            Point

Step 4. Sketch the graph of f:

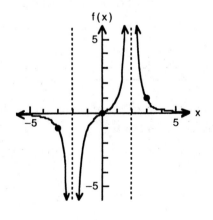

23. $f(x) = \dfrac{x + 3}{x - 3}$

Step 1. Analyze $f(x)$:

(A) Domain: All real numbers except $x = 3$.

(B) Intercepts: y-intercept: $f(0) = \dfrac{3}{-3} = -1$

x-intercepts: $\dfrac{x + 3}{x - 3} = 0$

$x + 3 = 0$

$x = -3$

(C) Asymptotes:

Horizontal asymptote: $\displaystyle\lim_{x \to \infty} \frac{x + 3}{x - 3} = \lim_{x \to \infty} \frac{x\left(1 + \frac{3}{x}\right)}{x\left(1 - \frac{3}{x}\right)} = 1.$

Thus, $y = 1$ is a horizontal asymptote.

Vertical asymptote: The denominator is 0 at $x = 3$ and the numerator is not 0 at $x = 3$. Thus, $x = 3$ is a vertical asymptote.

Step 2. Analyze $f'(x)$:

$f'(x) = \dfrac{(x - 3)(1) - (x + 3)(1)}{(x - 3)^2} = \dfrac{-6}{(x - 3)^2} = -6(x - 3)^{-2}$

Critical values: None

Partition number: $x = 3$

Sign chart for f':

	Test Numbers	
	x	$f'(x)$
	2	-6 $(-)$
	4	-6 $(-)$

$f'(x)$: $- - - - -$ ND $- - - -$

$f(x)$: Decreasing | Decreasing

(0 1 2 3 4)

Thus, f is decreasing on $(-\infty, 3)$ and on $(3, \infty)$; there are no local extrema.

Step 3. Analyze $f''(x)$:

$f''(x) = 12(x - 3)^{-3} = \dfrac{12}{(x - 3)^3}$

Partition number for f'': $x = 3$

Sign chart for f'':

	Test Numbers	
	x	$f''(x)$
	2	-12 $(-)$
	4	12 $(+)$

$f''(x)$: $- - - - -$ ND $+ + + +$

Graph of f : Concave Downward | Concave Upward

(0 1 2 3 4)

Thus, the graph of f is concave downward on $(-\infty, 3)$ and concave upward on $(3, \infty)$.

Step 4. Sketch the graph of f:

x	$f(x)$
-3	0
0	-1
5	4

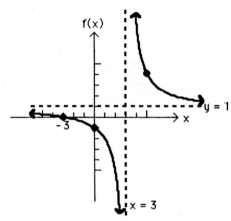

25. $f(x) = \dfrac{x}{x - 2}$

Step 1. Analyze $f(x)$:

(A) Domain: All real numbers except $x = 2$.

(B) Intercepts: y-intercept: $f(0) = \dfrac{0}{-2} = 0$

$\qquad\qquad$ x-intercepts: $\dfrac{x}{x - 2} = 0$

$\qquad\qquad\qquad\qquad\qquad$ $x = 0$

(C) Asymptotes:

<u>Horizontal asymptote</u>: $\lim\limits_{x \to \infty} \dfrac{x}{x - 2} = \lim\limits_{x \to \infty} \dfrac{x}{x\left(1 - \frac{2}{x}\right)} = 1$.

Thus, $y = 1$ is a horizontal asymptote.

<u>Vertical asymptote</u>: The denominator is 0 at $x = 2$ and the numerator is not 0 at $x = 2$. Thus, $x = 2$ is a vertical asymptote.

Step 2. Analyze $f'(x)$:

$f'(x) = \dfrac{(x - 2)(1) - x(1)}{(x - 2)^2} = \dfrac{-2}{(x - 2)^2} = -2(x - 2)^{-2}$

Critical values: None
Partition number: $x = 2$
Sign chart for f':

Test Numbers	
x	$f'(x)$
0	$-\frac{1}{2}$ (−)
3	-2 (−)

$f'(x)$ $\qquad\qquad$ $- \ - \ - \ -$ ND $- \ - \ - \ -$

$\qquad\qquad\qquad$ 0 $\quad$ 1 $\quad$ 2 $\quad$ 3 $\qquad\qquad$ → x

$f(x)$ $\qquad\qquad$ Decreasing $\vdots$ Decreasing

Thus, f is decreasing on $(-\infty, 2)$ and on $(2, \infty)$; there are no local extrema.

Step 3. Analyze $f''(x)$:

$$f''(x) = 4(x - 2)^{-3} = \frac{4}{(x - 2)^3}$$

Partition number for f'': $x = 2$

Sign chart for f'':

	Test Numbers

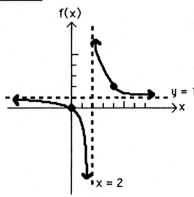

x	$f''(x)$
0	$-\frac{1}{2}$ (−)
3	4 (+)

Thus, the graph of f is concave downward on $(-\infty, 2)$ and concave upward on $(2, \infty)$.

Step 4. Sketch the graph of f:

x	$f(x)$
0	0
4	2

27. $f(x) = \dfrac{x}{x^2 - 4} = \dfrac{x}{(x - 2)(x + 2)}$

Step 1. Analyze $f(x)$:

(A) Domain: All real numbers except $x = 2$, $x = -2$.

(B) Intercepts: y-intercept: $f(0) = \dfrac{0}{-4} = 0$

x-intercept: $\dfrac{x}{x^2 - 4} = 0$

$x = 0$

(C) Asymptotes:
   Horizontal asymptote:

$$\lim_{x \to \infty} \frac{x}{x^2 - 4} = \lim_{x \to \infty} \frac{x}{x^2\left(1 - \frac{4}{x^2}\right)} = \lim_{x \to \infty} \frac{1}{x}\left(\frac{1}{1 - \frac{4}{x^2}}\right) = 0$$

   Thus, $y = 0$ (the x axis) is a horizontal asymptote.

   Vertical asymptotes: The denominator is 0 at $x = 2$ and $x = -2$. The numerator is nonzero at each of these points. Thus, $x = 2$ and $x = -2$ are vertical asymptotes.

<u>Step 2. Analyze $f'(x)$</u>:

$$f'(x) = \frac{(x^2 - 4)(1) - x(2x)}{(x^2 - 4)^2} = \frac{-(x^2 + 4)}{(x^2 - 4)^2}$$

Critical values: None ($x^2 + 4 \neq 0$ for all x)
Partition numbers: $x = 2$, $x = -2$
Sign chart for f':

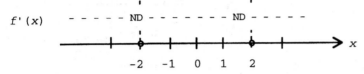

$f(x)$ Decreasing ┊ Decreasing ┊ Decreasing

Thus, f is decreasing on $(-\infty, -2)$, on $(-2, 2)$, and on $(2, \infty)$; f has no local extrema.

<u>Step 3. Analyze $f''(x)$</u>:

$$f''(x) = \frac{(x^2 - 4)^2(-2x) - [-(x^2 + 4)](2)(x^2 - 4)(2x)}{(x^2 - 4)^4}$$

$$= \frac{(x^2 - 4)(-2x) + 4x(x^2 + 4)}{(x^2 - 4)^3} = \frac{2x^3 + 24x}{(x^2 - 4)^3} = \frac{2x(x^2 + 12)}{(x^2 - 4)^3}$$

Partition numbers for f'': $x = 0$, $x = 2$, $x = -2$
Sign chart for f'':

$f''(x)$ - - - ND + + + + 0 - - - - ND + + +

Graph of f Concave ┊ Concave ┊ Concave ┊ Concave
Downward ┊ Upward ┊ Downward ┊ Upward
Inflection
point

Test Numbers	
x	$f''(x)$
-3	$-\frac{126}{125}$ $(-)$
-1	$\frac{26}{27}$ $(+)$
1	$-\frac{26}{27}$ $(-)$
3	$\frac{126}{127}$ $(+)$

Thus, the graph of f is concave downward on $(-\infty, -2)$ and on $(0, 2)$; the graph of f is concave upward on $(-2, 0)$ and on $(2, \infty)$; the graph has an inflection point at $x = 0$.

<u>Step 4. Sketch the graph of f</u>:

x	$f(x)$
0	0
1	$-\frac{1}{3}$
-1	$\frac{1}{3}$
3	$\frac{3}{5}$
-3	$-\frac{3}{5}$

29. $f(x) = \dfrac{1}{1 + x^2}$

<u>Step 1. Analyze $f(x)$</u>:

(A) Domain: All real numbers $(1 + x^2 \neq 0$ for all $x)$.

(B) Intercepts: y-intercept: $f(0) = 1$

               x-intercept: $\dfrac{1}{1 + x^2} \neq 0$ for all x; no x intercepts

(C) Asymptotes:

   <u>Horizontal asymptote</u>: $\lim\limits_{x \to \infty} \dfrac{1}{1 + x^2} = 0$

   Thus, $y = 0$ (the x-axis) is a horizontal asymptote.

   <u>Vertical asymptotes</u>: Since $1 + x^2 \neq 0$ for all x, there are no vertical asymptotes.

<u>Step 2. Analyze $f'(x)$</u>:

$f'(x) = \dfrac{(1 + x^2)(0) - 1(2x)}{(1 + x^2)^2} = \dfrac{-2x}{(1 + x^2)^2}$

Critical values: $x = 0$
Partition numbers: $x = 0$

Sign chart for f':

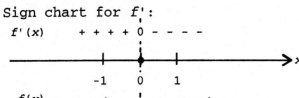

Test Numbers	
x	$f'(x)$
-1	$\frac{1}{2}$ (+)
1	$-\frac{1}{2}$ (−)

Thus, f is increasing on $(-\infty, 0)$; f is decreasing on $(0, \infty)$; f has a local maximum at $x = 0$.

<u>Step 3. Analyze $f''(x)$</u>:

$f''(x) = \dfrac{(1 + x^2)^2(-2) - (-2x)(2)(1 + x^2)2x}{(1 + x^2)^4} = \dfrac{(-2)(1 + x^2) + 8x^2}{(1 + x^2)^3}$

$\quad\quad = \dfrac{6x^2 - 2}{(1 + x^2)^3} = \dfrac{6\left(x + \frac{\sqrt{3}}{3}\right)\left(x - \frac{\sqrt{3}}{3}\right)}{(1 + x^2)^3}$

Partition numbers for f'': $x = -\dfrac{\sqrt{3}}{3}$, $x = \dfrac{\sqrt{3}}{3}$

Sign chart for f'':

Test Numbers	
x	$f''(x)$
-1	$\frac{1}{2}$ (+)
0	-2 (−)
1	$\frac{1}{2}$ (+)

Thus, the graph of f is concave upward on $\left(-\infty, \dfrac{-\sqrt{3}}{3}\right)$ and on $\left(\dfrac{\sqrt{3}}{3}, \infty\right)$; the graph of f is concave downward on $\left(\dfrac{-\sqrt{3}}{3}, \dfrac{\sqrt{3}}{3}\right)$; the graph has inflection points at $x = \dfrac{-\sqrt{3}}{3}$ and $x = \dfrac{\sqrt{3}}{3}$.

Step 4. Sketch the graph of f:

x	$f(x)$
$-\dfrac{\sqrt{3}}{3}$	$\dfrac{3}{4}$
0	1
$\dfrac{\sqrt{3}}{3}$	$\dfrac{3}{4}$

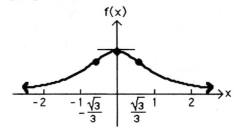

31. $f(x) = \dfrac{2x}{1 - x^2}$

Step 1. Analyze $f(x)$:

(A) Domain: All real numbers except $x = -1$ and $x = 1$.

(B) Intercepts: y-intercept: $f(0) = \dfrac{0}{1} = 0$

$\qquad\qquad x$-intercepts: $\dfrac{2x}{1 - x^2} = 0$

$\qquad\qquad\qquad\qquad\qquad x = 0$

(C) Asymptotes:

$\quad$ Horizontal asymptote: $\lim\limits_{x\to\infty} \dfrac{2x}{1 - x^2} = \lim\limits_{x\to\infty} \dfrac{\frac{2}{x}}{\frac{1}{x^2} - 1} = 0$. Thus, $y = 0$

$\qquad\qquad\qquad\qquad\qquad$ (the x-axis) is a horizontal asymptote.

$\quad$ Vertical asymptotes: The denominator is 0 at $x = \pm 1$ and the numerator is not 0 at $x = \pm 1$. Thus, $x = -1$, $x = 1$ are vertical asymptotes.

Step 2. Analyze $f'(x)$:

$f'(x) = \dfrac{(1 - x^2)2 - 2x(-2x)}{(1 - x^2)^2} = \dfrac{4x^2 + 2}{(1 - x^2)^2}$

Critical values: none
Partition numbers: $x = -1$, $x = 1$
Sign chart for f':

$$+ + + \text{ ND } + + \text{ ND } + + +$$

$f'(x)$				
$f(x)$	-2 -1	0	1 2	
	Increasing	Incr.	Increasing	

Test Numbers	
x	$f'(x)$
-2	$2\ (+)$
0	$2\ (+)$
2	$2\ (+)$

Thus, f is increasing on $(-\infty, -1)$, $(-1, 1)$, and $(1, \infty)$.

Step 3. Analyze $f''(x)$:

$$f''(x) = \frac{(1 - x^2)^2 8x - (4x^2 + 2)(2)(1 - x^2)(-2x)}{(1 - x^2)^4} = \frac{8x(x^2 + 2)}{(1 - x^2)^3}$$

Partition numbers for $f''(x)$: $x = -1$, $x = 0$, $x = 1$

Sign chart for f'':

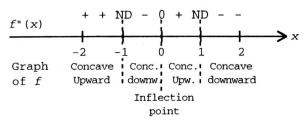

Test Numbers	
x	$f''(x)$
-2	$\frac{32}{3}$ (+)
$-\frac{1}{2}$	$-\frac{16}{3}$ (−)
$\frac{1}{2}$	$\frac{16}{3}$ (+)
2	$-\frac{32}{3}$ (−)

Thus, the graph of f is concave upward on $(-\infty, -1)$ and $(0, 1)$, concave downward on $(-1, 0)$ and $(1, \infty)$, and has an inflection point at $x = 0$.

Step 4. Sketch the graph of f:

x	$f(x)$
0	0

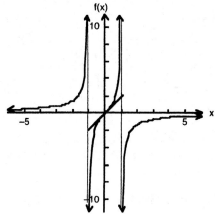

33. $f(x) = \dfrac{-5x}{(x - 1)^2} = \dfrac{-5x}{x^2 - 2x + 1}$

Step 1. Analyze $f(x)$:

(A) Domain: All real numbers except $x = 1$.

(B) Intercepts: y-intercept: $f(0) = 0$

x-intercepts: $\dfrac{-5x}{(x - 1)^2} = 0$

$x = 0$

(C) Asymptotes:

Horizontal asymptote: $\lim\limits_{x \to \infty} \dfrac{-5x}{x^2 - 2x + 1} = \lim\limits_{x \to \infty} \dfrac{-\frac{5}{x}}{1 - \frac{2}{x} + \frac{1}{x^2}} = 0$. Thus,

$y = 0$ (the x-axis) is a horizontal asymptote.

Vertical asymptotes: The denominator is 0 at $x = 1$ and the numerator is not 0 at $x = 1$. Thus, $x = 1$ is a vertical asymptote.

Step 2. Analyze $f'(x)$:

$$f'(x) = \frac{(x - 1)^2(-5) + 5x(2)(x - 1)}{(x - 1)^4} = \frac{5(x + 1)}{(x - 1)^3}$$

Critical values: $x = -1$

Partition numbers: $x = -1$, $x = 1$

Sign chart for f':

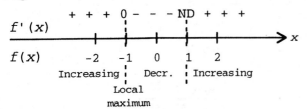

Test Numbers	
x	$f'(x)$
-2	$\frac{5}{27}$ (+)
0	-5 (−)
2	15 (+)

Thus, f is increasing on $(-\infty, -1)$, $(1, \infty)$, decreasing on $(-1, 1)$, and has a local maximum at $x = -1$.

Step 3. Analyze $f''(x)$:

$$f''(x) = \frac{(x - 1)^3 5 - 5(x + 1)(3)(x - 1)^2}{(x - 1)^6} = \frac{-10(x + 2)}{(x - 1)^4}$$

Partition numbers for $f''(x)$: $x = -2$, $x = 1$

Sign chart for f'':

$f''(x)$	+ + 0 − − − − − ND − −

$$\xrightarrow{} x$$

$-3 \quad -2 \quad -1 \quad 0 \quad 1 \quad 2$

Graph of f: Concave Upward | Concave downward | Concave downward

Test Numbers	
x	$f''(x)$
-3	(+)
0	-10 (−)
2	-40 (−)

Thus, the graph of f is concave upward on $(-\infty, -2)$, concave downward on $(-2, 1)$ and $(1, \infty)$, and has an inflection point at $x = -2$.

Step 4. Sketch the graph of f:

x	$f(x)$
-2	$\frac{10}{9}$
-1	$\frac{5}{4}$
0	0

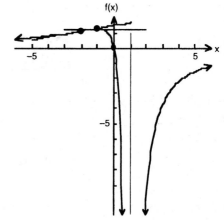

35. $f(x) = \dfrac{x^2 + 2}{x}$

Step 1. Analyze $f(x)$:

(A) Domain: All real numbers except $x = 0$.

(B) Intercepts: y-intercept: $f(0)$ not defined; no y-intercept

x-intercepts: $\dfrac{x^2 + 2}{x} = 0$; no solutions; no x-intercepts

(C) Asymptotes:

Horizontal asymptote: no horizontal asymptote.

Vertical asymptotes: $x = 0$ (the y-axis)

Step 2. Analyze $f'(x)$:

$$f'(x) = \frac{x(2x) - (x^2 + 2)}{x^2} = \frac{x^2 - 2}{x^2} = 1 - \frac{2}{x^2}$$

Critical values: $x = -\sqrt{2}$, $x = \sqrt{2}$

Partition numbers: $x = -\sqrt{2}$, $x = 0$, $x = \sqrt{2}$

Sign chart for f':

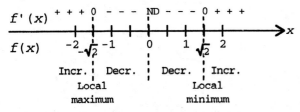

Test Numbers	
x	$f'(x)$
-2	$2\ (+)$
-1	$-1\ (-)$
1	$1\ (-)$
2	$2\ (+)$

Thus, f is increasing on $(-\infty, -\sqrt{2})$ and $(\sqrt{2}, \infty)$, decreasing on $(-\sqrt{2}, 0)$ and $(0, \sqrt{2})$, and has a local maximum at $x = -\sqrt{2}$ and a local minimum at $x = \sqrt{2}$.

Step 3. Analyze $f''(x)$:

$$f''(x) = \frac{4}{x^3}$$

Partition numbers for $f''(x)$: $x = 0$

Sign chart for f'':

Test Numbers	
x	$f''(x)$
-1	$-4\ (-)$
1	$4\ (+)$

The graph of f is concave upward on $(0, \infty)$ and concave downward on $(-\infty, 0)$.

Step 4. Sketch the graph of f:

x	$f(x)$
$-\sqrt{2}$	$-2\sqrt{2}$
$\sqrt{2}$	$2\sqrt{2}$

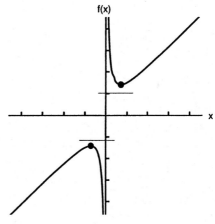

37. $f(x) = \dfrac{x^2 + x - 2}{x^2} = \dfrac{(x + 2)(x - 1)}{x^2}$

Step 1. Analyze $f(x)$:

(A) Domain: All real numbers except $x = 0$.

(B) Intercepts: y-intercept: $f(0)$ not defined; no y-intercept

x-intercepts: $\dfrac{(x + 2)(x - 1)}{x^2} = 0$

$x = -2$, $x = 1$

(C) Asymptotes:

Horizontal asymptote: $\lim\limits_{x\to\infty} \dfrac{x^2 + x - 2}{x^2} = \lim\limits_{x\to\infty} \dfrac{1 + \frac{1}{x} - \frac{2}{x^2}}{1} = 1.$

Thus, $y = 1$ is a horizontal asymptote.

Vertical asymptotes: $x = 0$ (the x-axis)

Step 2. Analyze $f'(x)$:

$$f'(x) = \frac{x^2(2x + 1) - (x^2 + x - 2)(2x)}{x^4} = \frac{4 - x}{x^3}$$

Critical values: $x = 4$

Partition numbers: $x = 0$, $x = 4$

Sign chart for f':

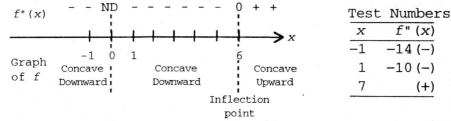

x	f'(x)
−1	−5 (−)
1	3 (+)
5	(−)

Test Numbers

Thus, f is increasing on $(0, 4)$, decreasing on $(-\infty, 0)$ and $(4, \infty)$, and has a local maximum at $x = 4$.

Step 3. Analyze $f''(x)$:

$$f''(x) = \frac{x^3(-1) - (4 - x)(3x^2)}{x^6} = \frac{2x - 12}{x^4} = \frac{2(x - 6)}{x^4}$$

Partition numbers for $f''(x)$: $x = 0$, $x = 6$

Sign chart for f'':

Test Numbers

x	f''(x)
−1	−14 (−)
1	−10 (−)
7	(+)

Thus, the graph of f is concave upward on $(6, \infty)$, concave downward on $(-\infty, 0)$ and $(0, 6)$, and has an inflection point at $x = 6$.

Step 4. Sketch the graph of f:

x	f(x)
4	$\frac{9}{8}$
6	$\frac{10}{9}$

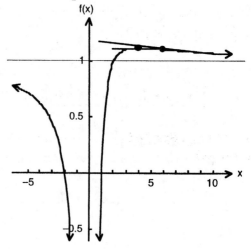

39. $f(x) = \dfrac{x^2}{x - 1}$

Step 1. Analyze $f(x)$:

(A) Domain: All real numbers except $x = 1$.

(B) Intercepts: y-intercept: $f(0) = 0$

$$x\text{-intercepts:} \quad \frac{x^2}{x - 1} = 0$$
$$x = 0$$

(C) Asymptotes:

Horizontal asymptote: $\dfrac{x^2}{x} = x$; no horizontal asymptote

Vertical asymptote: $x = 1$

Step 2. Analyze $f'(x)$:

$$f'(x) = \frac{(x - 1)(2x) - x^2}{(x - 1)^2} = \frac{x^2 - 2x}{(x - 1)^2} = \frac{x(x - 2)}{(x - 1)^2}$$

Critical values: $x = 0$, $x = 2$

Partition numbers: $x = 0$, $x = 1$, $x = 2$

Sign chart for f':

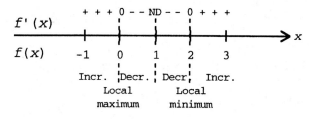

Test Numbers

x	$f'(x)$
-1	$\frac{3}{4}$ (+)
$\frac{1}{2}$	-3 (−)
$\frac{3}{2}$	-3 (−)
3	$\frac{3}{4}$ (+)

Thus, f is increasing on $(-\infty, 0)$ and $(2, \infty)$, decreasing on $(0, 1)$ and $(1, 2)$, and has a local maximum at $x = 0$ and a local minimum at $x = 2$.

Step 3. Analyze $f''(x)$:

$$f''(x) = \frac{(x - 1)^2(2x - 2) - (x^2 - 2x)(2)(x - 1)}{(x - 1)^4} = \frac{2}{(x - 1)^3}$$

Partition numbers for $f''(x)$: $x = 1$

Sign chart for f'':

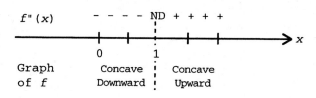

Thus, the graph of f is concave upward on $(1, \infty)$ and concave downward on $(-\infty, 1)$.

123

Step 4. Sketch the graph of f:

x	$f(x)$
0	0
2	4

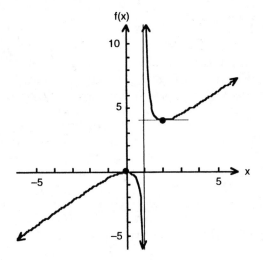

41. $f(x) = \dfrac{3x^2 + 2}{x^2 - 9}$

Step 1. Analyze $f(x)$:

(A) Domain: All real numbers except $x = -3$, $x = 3$.

(B) Intercepts: y-intercept: $f(0) = -\dfrac{2}{9}$

x-intercepts: $3x^2 + 2 \neq 0$ for all x; no x-intercepts

(C) Asymptotes:

<u>Horizontal asymptote</u>: $\dfrac{3x^2}{x^2} = 3$; $y = 3$ is a horizontal asymptote

<u>Vertical asymptote</u>: $x = -3$, $x = 3$

Step 2. Analyze $f'(x)$:

$$f'(x) = \frac{(x^2 - 9)(6x) - (3x^2 + 2)(2x)}{(x^2 - 9)^2} = \frac{-58x}{(x^2 - 9)^2}$$

Critical values: $x = 0$

Partition numbers: $x = -3$, $x = 0$, $x = 3$

Sign chart for f':

```
              + + + ND + + + 0 - - - ND - - -
f'(x)                                              → x
              |         |          |
f(x)         -3         0          3
           Incr.     Incr.     Decr.    Decr.
                      Local
                     maximum
```

Test Numbers	
x	$f'(x)$
-4	$(+)$
-2	$(+)$
2	$(-)$
4	$(-)$

Thus, f is increasing on $(-\infty, -3)$ and $(-3, 0)$, decreasing on $(0, 3)$ and $(3, \infty)$, and has a local maximum at $x = 0$.

Step 3. Analyze $f''(x)$:

$$f''(x) = \frac{(x^2 - 9)^2(-58) + 58x(2)(x^2 - 9)(2x)}{(x^2 - 9)^4} = \frac{174(x^2 + 3)}{(x^2 - 9)^3}$$

Partition numbers for $f''(x)$: $x = -3$, $x = 3$

Sign chart for f'':

$f''(x)$ $+ + +$ ND $- - - - - - - -$ ND $+ + +$

$$\xrightarrow{\hspace{6cm}} x$$

$\qquad\quad$ -3 $\qquad$ 0 $\qquad$ 3

Graph $\quad$ Concave $\quad$ Concave $\quad$ Concave
of f $\quad$ Upward $\quad$ Downward $\quad$ Upward

Test Numbers

x	$f''(x)$
-4	$(+)$
0	$(-)$
4	$(+)$

Thus, the graph of f is concave upward on $(-\infty, -3)$ and $(3, \infty)$, and concave downward on $(-3, 3)$.

<u>Step 4. Sketch the graph of f</u>:

x	$f(x)$
0	$-\frac{2}{9}$

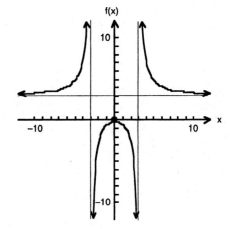

43. $f(x) = \dfrac{x^3}{x - 2}$

<u>Step 1. Analyze $f(x)$</u>:

(A) Domain: All real numbers except $x = 2$.

(B) Intercepts: y-intercept: $f(0) = 0$

$\qquad\qquad\qquad$ x-intercepts: $\dfrac{x^3}{x - 2} = 0$

$\qquad\qquad\qquad\qquad\qquad\qquad$ $x = 0$

(C) Asymptotes:

$\quad$ <u>Horizontal asymptote</u>: $\dfrac{x^3}{x} = x^2$; no horizontal asymptote

$\quad$ <u>Vertical asymptote</u>: $x = 2$

<u>Step 2. Analyze $f'(x)$</u>:

$$f'(x) = \frac{(x - 2)(3x^2) - x^3}{(x - 2)^2} = \frac{2x^2(x - 3)}{(x - 2)^2}$$

Critical values: $x = 0$, $x = 3$
Partition numbers: $x = 0$, $x = 2$, $x = 3$
Sign chart for f':

$f'(x)$ $\qquad$ $- - 0 - - - -$ ND $- 0 + +$

$$\xrightarrow{\hspace{6cm}} x$$

$f(x)$ $\quad$ -1 $\quad$ 0 $\quad$ 1 $\quad$ 2 $\quad$ 3 $\quad$ 4

$\qquad$ Decreasing $\quad$ Decr. $\quad$ Dec. $\quad$ Increasing

$\qquad\qquad\qquad\qquad\qquad$ Local
$\qquad\qquad\qquad\qquad\qquad$ minimum

Test Numbers

x	$f'(x)$
-1	$-\frac{8}{9}$ $(-)$
1	-4 $(-)$
$\frac{5}{2}$	-25 $(-)$
4	8 $(+)$

Thus, f is increasing on $(3, \infty)$, decreasing on $(-\infty, 2)$ and $(2, 3)$, and has a local minimum at $x = 3$.

Step 3. Analyze $f''(x)$:

$$f''(x) = \frac{(x-2)^2[2x^2 + 4x(x-3)] - 2x^2(x-3)(2)(x-2)}{(x-2)^4} = \frac{2x(x^2 - 6x + 12)}{(x-2)^3}$$

Partition numbers for $f''(x)$: $x = 0$, $x = 2$ ($x^2 - 6x + 12$ has no real roots)

Sign chart for f'':

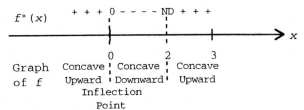

Test Numbers	
x	$f''(x)$
-1	$\frac{38}{9}$ (+)
1	-14 (−)
3	18 (+)

Thus, the graph of f is concave upward on $(-\infty, 0)$ and $(2, \infty)$, concave downward on $(0, 2)$, and has an inflection point at $x = 0$.

Step 4. Sketch the graph of f:

x	$f(x)$
0	0
3	27

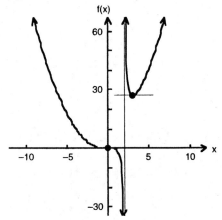

45. $f(x) = \dfrac{1}{x^2 + 2x - 8} = \dfrac{1}{(x+4)(x-2)}$

Step 1. Analyze $f(x)$:

(A) Domain: All real numbers except $x = -4$, $x = 2$.

(B) Intercepts: y-intercept: $f(0) = -\dfrac{1}{8}$

x-intercepts: no x-intercept

(C) Asymptotes:

Horizontal asymptote: $\dfrac{1}{x^2}$; $y = 0$ (the x-axis) is a horizontal asymptote

Vertical asymptote: $x = -4$, $x = 2$

Step 2. Analyze $f'(x)$:

$$f'(x) = \frac{-(2x+2)}{(x^2 + 2x - 8)^2} = \frac{-2(x+1)}{(x^2 + 2x - 8)^2}$$

Critical values: $x = -1$

Partition numbers: $x = -4$, $x = -1$, $x = 2$

Sign chart for f':

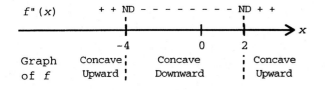

Test Numbers	
x	$f'(x)$
-5	$(+)$
-2	$(+)$
0	$-\frac{1}{32}\,(-)$
3	$(-)$

Thus, f is increasing on $(-\infty, -4)$ and $(-4, -1)$, decreasing on $(-1, 2)$ and $(2, \infty)$, and has a local maximum at $x = -1$.

Step 3. Analyze $f''(x)$:

$$f''(x) = \frac{(x^2 + 2x - 8)^2(-2) + (2x + 2)(2)(x^2 + 2x - 8)(2x + 2)}{(x^2 + 2x - 8)^4} = \frac{6(x^2 + 2x + 4)}{(x^2 + 2x - 8)^3}$$

Partition numbers for $f''(x)$: $x = -4$, $x = 2$ ($x^2 + 2x + 4$ has no real roots)

Sign chart for f'':

		$f''(x)$			$+\ +$ ND $-\ -\ -\ -\ -\ -\ -\ -$ ND $+\ +$			

Test Numbers	
x	$f''(x)$
-5	$(+)$
0	$(-)$
3	$(+)$

$$\begin{array}{ccc} & -4 & 0 & 2 \\ \text{Graph} & \text{Concave} & \text{Concave} & \text{Concave} \\ \text{of } f & \text{Upward} & \text{Downward} & \text{Upward} \end{array}$$

Thus, the graph of f is concave upward on $(-\infty, -4)$ and $(2, \infty)$, and concave downward on $(-4, 2)$.

Step 4. Sketch the graph of f:

x	$f(x)$
-1	$-\frac{1}{9}$
0	$-\frac{1}{8}$

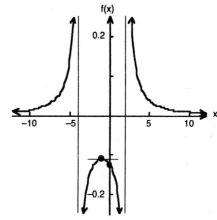

47. $f(x) = \dfrac{x}{x^2 - 4}$

Step 1. Analyze $f(x)$:

(A) Domain: All real numbers except $x = -2$, $x = 2$.

(B) Intercepts: y-intercept: $f(0) = 0$

x-intercepts: $\dfrac{x}{x^2 - 4} = 0$, $x = 0$

(C) Asymptotes:

Horizontal asymptotes: $\dfrac{x}{x^2} = \dfrac{1}{x}$; $y = 0$ (the x-axis) is a horizontal asymptote

Vertical asymptotes: $x = -2$, $x = 2$

$$f'(x) = \frac{(x^2 - 4)(1) - x(2x)}{(x^2 - 4)^2} = \frac{-x^2 - 4}{(x^2 - 4)^2} = -\frac{(x^2 + 4)}{(x^2 - 4)^2}$$

Critical values: No critical values
Partition numbers: $x = -2$, $x = 2$
Sign chart for f':

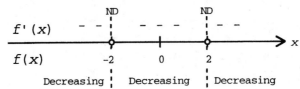

Thus, f is decreasing on $(-\infty, -2)$, $(-2, 2)$ and $(2, \infty)$.

Step 3. Analyze $f''(x)$:

$$f''(x) = \frac{(x^2 - 4)^2(-2x) + (x^2 + 4)2(x^2 - 4)2x}{(x^2 - 4)^4} = \frac{2x^3 + 16x}{(x^2 - 4)^3} = \frac{2x(x^2 + 8)}{(x^2 - 4)^3}$$

Partition numbers for $f''(x)$: $x = -2$, $x = 0$, $x = 2$
Sign chart for f'':

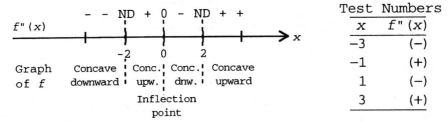

Test Numbers	
x	$f''(x)$
-3	$(-)$
-1	$(+)$
1	$(-)$
3	$(+)$

Thus, the graph of f is concave upward on $(-2, 0)$ and $(2, \infty)$, concave downward on $(-\infty, -2)$ and $(0, 2)$, and has an inflection point at $x = 0$.

Step 4. Sketch the graph of f:

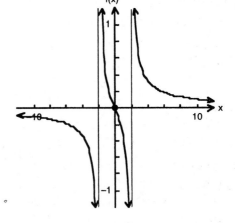

49. $f(x) = \dfrac{x^3}{(x - 4)^2}$

Step 1. Analyze $f(x)$:
(A) Domain: All real numbers except $x = 4$.
(B) Intercepts: y-intercept: $f(0) = 0$

$\qquad\qquad\quad$ x-intercepts: $\dfrac{x^3}{(x - 4)^2} = 0$, $x = 0$

(C) Asymptotes:

    <u>Horizontal asymptote</u>: $\dfrac{x^3}{x^2} = x$; no horizontal asymptote

    <u>Vertical asymptote</u>: $x = 4$

<u>Step 2. Analyze $f'(x)$</u>:

$$f'(x) = \frac{(x-4)^2(3x^2) - x^3(2)(x-4)}{(x-4)^4} = \frac{x^2(x-12)}{(x-4)^3}$$

Critical values: $x = 0$, $x = 12$
Partition numbers: $x = 0$, $x = 4$, $x = 12$
Sign chart for f':

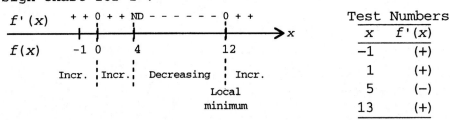

Test Numbers	
x	$f'(x)$
-1	$(+)$
1	$(+)$
5	$(-)$
13	$(+)$

Thus, f is increasing on $(-\infty, 0)$, $(0, 4)$, and $(12, \infty)$, decreasing on $(4, 12)$, and has a local minimum at $x = 12$.

<u>Step 3. Analyze $f''(x)$</u>:

$$f''(x) = \frac{(x-4)^3(3x^2 - 24x) - x^2(x-12)(3)(x-4)^2}{(x-4)^6} = \frac{96x}{(x-4)^4}$$

Partition numbers for $f''(x)$: $x = 0$, $x = 4$
Sign chart for f'':

$f''(x)$	$-$ $-$ 0 $+$ $+$ $+$ $+$ ND $+$ $+$			Test Numbers	
				x	$f''(x)$
	-1 0 1 4 5			-1	$(-)$
Graph	Concave	Concave	Concave	1	$(+)$
of f	Downward	Upward	Upward	5	$(+)$
	Inflection point				

Thus, the graph of f is concave upward on $(0, 4)$ and $(4, \infty)$, concave downward on $(-\infty, 0)$, and has an inflection point at $x = 0$.

<u>Step 4. Sketch the graph of f</u>:

x	$f(x)$
0	0
12	27

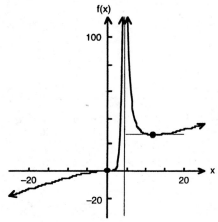

51. $f(x) = \dfrac{x^3}{3 - x^2}$

Step 1. Analyze $f(x)$:

(A) Domain: All real numbers except $x = -\sqrt{3}$, $x = \sqrt{3}$.

(B) Intercepts: y-intercept: $f(0) = 0$

$\quad\quad\quad\quad\quad x$-intercepts: $\dfrac{x^3}{3 - x^2} = 0$, $x = 0$

(C) Asymptotes:

Horizontal asymptote: $\dfrac{x^3}{-x^2} = -x$; no horizontal asymptote

Vertical asymptote: $x = -\sqrt{3}$, $x = \sqrt{3}$

Step 2. Analyze $f'(x)$:

$f'(x) = \dfrac{(3 - x^2)(3x^2) - x^3(-2x)}{(3 - x^2)^2} = \dfrac{x^2(9 - x^2)}{(3 - x^2)^2}$

Critical values: $x = -3$, $x = 0$, $x = 3$

Partition numbers: $x = -3$, $x = -\sqrt{3}$, $x = 0$, $x = \sqrt{3}$, $x = 3$

Sign chart for f':

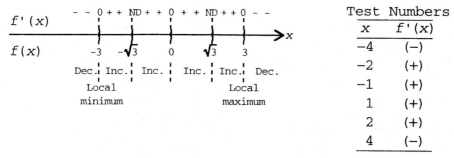

Test Numbers	
x	$f'(x)$
-4	$(-)$
-2	$(+)$
-1	$(+)$
1	$(+)$
2	$(+)$
4	$(-)$

Thus, f is increasing on $(-3, -\sqrt{3})$, $(-\sqrt{3}, \sqrt{3})$, $(\sqrt{3}, 3)$, decreasing on $(-\infty, -3)$ and $(3, \infty)$, and has a local minimum at $x = -3$ and a local maximum at $x = 3$.

Step 3. Analyze $f''(x)$:

$f''(x) = \dfrac{(3 - x^2)^2(18x - 4x^3) - x^2(9 - x^2)2(3 - x^2)(-2x)}{(3 - x^2)^4} = \dfrac{6x(9 + x^2)}{(3 - x^2)^3}$

Partition numbers for $f''(x)$: $x = -\sqrt{3}$, $x = 0$, $x = \sqrt{3}$

Sign chart for f'':

```
f"(x)        + + ND - - - 0 + + + ND - -
 ─────────────┼─────────┼─────────┼──────────→ x
            -√3        0        √3
Graph    Concave ¦ Concave ¦ Concave ¦ Concave
of f     Upward ¦Downward¦ Upward ¦ Downward
                    Inflection
                      point
```

Test Numbers	
x	$f''(x)$
-2	$(+)$
-1	$(-)$
1	$(+)$
2	$(-)$

Thus, the graph of f is concave upward on $(-\infty, -\sqrt{3})$ and $(0, \sqrt{3})$, concave downward on $(-\sqrt{3}, 0)$ and $(\sqrt{3}, \infty)$, and has an inflection point at $x = 0$.

Step 4. Sketch the graph of f:

x	$f(x)$
-3	$\frac{9}{2}$
0	0
3	$-\frac{9}{2}$

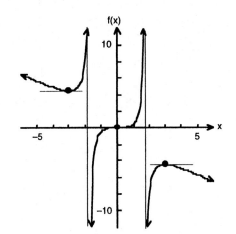

53. $f(x) = x + \dfrac{4}{x} = \dfrac{x^2 + 4}{x}$

Step 1. Analyze $f(x)$:

(A) Domain: All real numbers except $x = 0$.

(B) Intercepts: y-intercept: no y-intercept

                    x-intercepts: no x-intercepts

(C) Asymptotes:

<u>Horizontal asymptote</u>: $\dfrac{x^2}{x} = x$; no horizontal asymptote

<u>Vertical asymptote</u>: $x = 0$ (the y-axis) is a vertical asymptote

<u>Oblique asymptote</u>: $\displaystyle\lim_{x \to \infty}\left(x + \dfrac{4}{x}\right) = x$; $y = x$ is an oblique asymptote.

Step 2. Analyze $f'(x)$:

$f'(x) = 1 - \dfrac{4}{x^2} = \dfrac{x^2 - 4}{x^2}$

Critical values: $x = -2$, $x = 2$

Partition numbers: $x = -2$, $x = 0$, $x = 2$

Sign chart for f':

Test Numbers	
x	$f'(x)$
-3	$\frac{5}{9}$ (+)
-1	-3 (−)
1	-3 (−)
3	$\frac{5}{9}$ (+)

$f'(x)$: $+\ +\ +\ 0\ -\ -\ ND\ -\ -\ 0\ +\ +$

$f(x)$: -3 -2 $\quad 0 \quad$ 2 3

Incr. | Decr. | Decr. | Incr.

Local   Local

maximum   minimum

Thus, f is increasing on $(-\infty,\ -2)$ and $(2,\ \infty)$, decreasing on $(-2,\ 0)$ and $(0,\ 2)$, and has a local maximum at $x = -2$ and a local minimum at $x = 2$.

Step 3. Analyze $f''(x)$:

$f''(x) = \dfrac{8}{x^3}$

Partition numbers for $f''(x)$: $x = 0$

Sign chart for f'': $\quad f''(x)$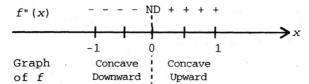

Thus, the graph of f is concave upward on $(0, \infty)$ and concave downward on $(-\infty, 0)$.

Step 4. Sketch the graph of f:

x	$f(x)$
-2	-4
2	4

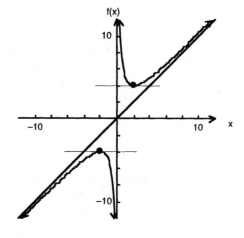

55. $f(x) = x - \dfrac{4}{x^2} = \dfrac{x^3 - 4}{x^2}$

Step 1. Analyze $f(x)$:

(A) Domain: All real numbers except $x = 0$.

(B) Intercepts: y-intercept: no y-intercept

$\qquad\qquad$ x-intercepts: $\dfrac{x^3 - 4}{x} = 0,\ x = \sqrt[3]{4}$

(C) Asymptotes:

$\quad$ <u>Horizontal asymptote</u>: $\dfrac{x^3}{x^2} = x$; no horizontal asymptote

$\quad$ <u>Vertical asymptote</u>: $x = 0$ (the y-axis) is a vertical asymptote

$\quad$ <u>Oblique asymptote</u>: $\lim\limits_{x \to \infty}\left(x - \dfrac{4}{x^2}\right) = x$; $y = x$ is an oblique asymptote

Step 2. Analyze $f'(x)$:

$f'(x) = 1 + \dfrac{8}{x^3} = \dfrac{x^3 + 8}{x^3}$

Critical values: $x = -2$
Partition numbers: $x = -2,\ x = 0$
Sign chart for f':

Test Numbers	
x	$f'(x)$
-3	$\frac{19}{27}$ (+)
-1	-7 (−)
1	9 (+)

$f'(x)$ $\quad + + + 0 - - - \text{ND} + + +$

$f(x)$ $\qquad\qquad -2 \qquad 0$

Increasing | Decr. | Increasing
Local
maximum

Thus, f is increasing on $(-\infty, -2)$ and $(0, \infty)$, decreasing on $(-2, 0)$; f has a local maximum at $x = -2$.

$$f''(x) = -\frac{24}{x^4}$$

Partition numbers for $f''(x)$: $x = 0$

Sign chart for f'':

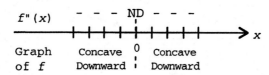

Thus, the graph of f is concave downward on $(-\infty, 0)$ and $(0, \infty)$.

Step 4. Sketch the graph of f:

x	$f(x)$
-2	-3

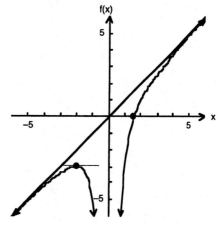

57. $f(x) = x - \dfrac{9}{x^3} = \dfrac{x^4 - 9}{x^3} = \dfrac{(x^2 - 3)(x^2 + 3)}{x^3}$

Step 1. Analyze $f(x)$:

(A) Domain: All real numbers except $x = 0$.

(B) Intercepts: y-intercept: no y-intercept

                   x-intercepts: $x = -\sqrt{3}$, $x = \sqrt{3}$

(C) Asymptotes:

    <u>Horizontal asymptote</u>: $\dfrac{x^4}{x^3} = x$; no horizontal asymptote

    <u>Vertical asymptote</u>: $x = 0$ (the y-axis) is a vertical asymptote

    <u>Oblique asymptote</u>: $\lim\limits_{x \to \infty}\left(x + \dfrac{9}{x^3}\right) = x$; $y = x$ is an oblique asymptote

Step 2. Analyze $f'(x)$:

$$f'(x) = 1 + \frac{27}{x^4} = \frac{x^4 + 27}{x^4}$$

Critical values: none

Partition numbers: $x = 0$

Sign chart for f':

Thus, f is increasing on $(-\infty, 0)$ and $(0, \infty)$.

Step 3. Analyze $f''(x)$:

$$f''(x) = -\frac{108}{x^5}$$

Partition numbers for $f''(x)$: $x = 0$

Sign chart for f'':

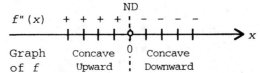

Thus, the graph of f is concave upward on $(-\infty, 0)$ and concave downward on $(0, \infty)$.

Step 4. Sketch the graph of f:

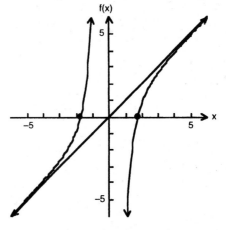

x	$f(x)$
$-\sqrt{3}$	0
$\sqrt{3}$	0

59. $f(x) = x + \dfrac{1}{x} + \dfrac{4}{x^3} = \dfrac{x^4 + x^2 + 4}{x^3}$

Step 1. Analyze $f(x)$:

(A) Domain: All real numbers except $x = 0$.

(B) Intercepts: y-intercept: no y-intercept

                 x-intercepts: no x-intercepts

(C) Asymptotes:

Horizontal asymptote: $\dfrac{x^4}{x^3} = x$; no horizontal asymptote

Vertical asymptote: $x = 0$ (the y-axis) is a vertical asymptote

Oblique asymptote: $\displaystyle\lim_{x \to \infty}\left(x + \frac{1}{x} + \frac{4}{x^3}\right) = x$; $y = x$ is an oblique asymptote

Step 2. Analyze $f'(x)$:

$$f'(x) = 1 - \frac{1}{x^2} - \frac{12}{x^4} = \frac{x^4 - x^2 - 12}{x^4} = \frac{(x^2 - 4)(x^2 + 3)}{x^4}$$

Critical values: $x = -2$, $x = 2$

Partition numbers: $x = -2$, $x = 0$, $x = 2$

Sign chart for f':

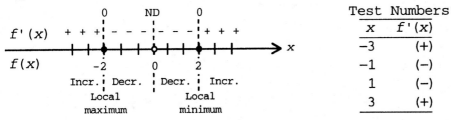

	Test Numbers	
	x	$f'(x)$
	-3	$(+)$
	-1	$(-)$
	1	$(-)$
	3	$(+)$

Thus, f is increasing on $(-\infty, -2)$ and $(2, \infty)$, decreasing on $(-2, 0)$ and $(0, 2)$; f has a local maximum at $x = -2$ and a local minimum at $x = 2$.

Step 3. Analyze $f''(x)$:

$$f''(x) = \frac{2}{x^3} + \frac{48}{x^5} = \frac{2x^2 + 48}{x^5}$$

Partition numbers for $f''(x)$: $x = 0$

Sign chart for f'':

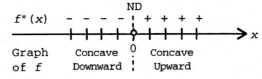

Thus, the graph of f is concave upward on $(0, \infty)$ and concave downward on $(-\infty, 0)$.

Step 4. Sketch the graph of f:

x	$f(x)$
-2	-3
2	3

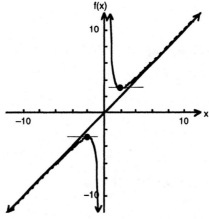

61. $f(x) = \dfrac{x^2 + x - 6}{x^2 - 6x + 8} = \dfrac{(x + 3)(x - 2)}{(x - 4)(x - 2)} = \dfrac{x + 3}{x - 4}, \quad x \neq 2$

Step 1. Analyze $f(x)$:

(A) Domain: All real numbers except $x = 2$, $x = 4$.

(B) Intercepts: y-intercept: $f(0) = -\dfrac{3}{4}$

$\qquad\qquad\quad$ x-intercepts: $x = -3$

(C) Asymptotes:

$\quad$ <u>Horizontal asymptote</u>: $\dfrac{x^2}{x^2} = 1$, $y = 1$ is a horizontal asymptote

$\quad$ <u>Vertical asymptote</u>: $x = 4$ is a vertical asymptote

Step 2. Analyze $f'(x)$:

$$f'(x) = \frac{x - 4 - (x + 3)}{(x - 4)^2} = -\frac{7}{(x - 4)^2}$$

Critical values: None

Partition numbers: $x = 4$

Sign chart for f':

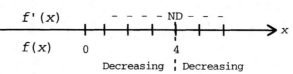

Thus, f is decreasing on $(-\infty, 4)$ and $(4, \infty)$.

Step 3. Analyze $f''(x)$:

$$f''(x) = \frac{14}{(x - 4)^3}$$

Partition numbers for $f''(x)$: $x = 4$

Sign chart for f'':

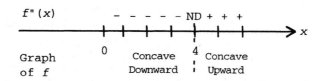

The graph of f is concave upward on $(4, \infty)$ and concave downward on $(-\infty, 4)$.

Step 4. Sketch the graph of f:

x	$f(x)$
-3	0
0	$-\frac{3}{4}$

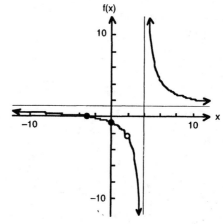

63. $f(x) = \dfrac{2x^2 + x - 15}{x^2 - 9} = \dfrac{(2x - 5)(x + 3)}{(x - 3)(x + 3)} = \dfrac{2x - 5}{x - 3}$, $x \neq -3$

Step 1. Analyze $f(x)$:

(A) Domain: All real numbers except $x = -3$, $x = 3$.

(B) Intercepts: y-intercept: $f(0) = \dfrac{5}{3}$

x-intercepts: $x = \dfrac{5}{2}$

(C) Asymptotes:

Horizontal asymptote: $\dfrac{2x^2}{x^2} = 2$, $y = 2$ is a horizontal asymptote

Vertical asymptote: $x = 3$ is a vertical asymptote

Step 2. Analyze $f'(x)$:

$$f'(x) = \frac{(x - 3)2 - (2x - 5)}{(x - 3)^2} = \frac{-1}{(x - 3)^2}$$

Critical values: None

Partition numbers: $x = 3$

Sign chart for f':

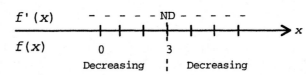

Thus, f is decreasing on $(-\infty, 3)$ and $(3, \infty)$.

Step 3. Analyze $f''(x)$:

$$f''(x) = \frac{2}{(x - 3)^3}$$

Partition numbers for $f''(x)$: $x = 3$

Sign chart for f'':

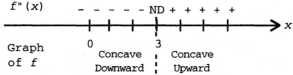

The graph of f is concave upward on $(3, \infty)$ and concave downward on $(-\infty, 3)$.

Step 4. Sketch the graph of f:

x	$f(x)$
$\frac{5}{2}$	0
0	$\frac{5}{3}$

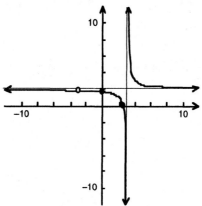

65. $f(x) = \dfrac{x^3 - 5x^2 + 6x}{x^2 - x - 2} = \dfrac{x(x - 3)(x - 2)}{(x - 2)(x + 1)} = \dfrac{x(x - 3)}{x + 1}, \quad x \neq 2$

Step 1. Analyze $f(x)$:

(A) Domain: All real numbers except $x = -1$, $x = 2$.

(B) Intercepts: y-intercept: $f(0) = 0$
x-intercepts: $x = 0$, $x = 3$

(C) Asymptotes:

Horizontal asymptote: $\dfrac{x^3}{x^2} = x$; no horizontal asymptote

Vertical asymptote: $x = -1$ is a vertical asymptote

Step 2. Analyze $f'(x)$:

$$f'(x) = \frac{(x + 1)(2x - 3) - (x^2 - 3x)}{(x + 1)^2} = \frac{x^2 + 2x - 3}{(x + 1)^2} = \frac{(x + 3)(x - 1)}{(x + 1)^2}$$

Critical values: $x = -3$, $x = 1$

Partition numbers: $x = -3$, $x = -1$, $x = 1$

Sign chart for f':

$f'(x)$: $+ + 0 - - ND - - 0 + +$

$f(x)$: $-3 \quad -1 \quad 0 \quad 1$

Incr. | Decr. | Decr. | Incr.

Local maximum   Local minimum

Test Numbers

x	$f'(x)$
-4	$\frac{5}{9}$ (+)
-2	-3 (−)
0	-3 (−)
2	$\frac{5}{9}$ (+)

Thus, f is increasing on $(-\infty, -3)$ and $(1, \infty)$, f is decreasing on $(-3, -1)$ and $(-1, 1)$; f has a local maximum at $x = -3$ and a local minimum at $x = 1$.

Step 3. Analyze $f''(x)$:

$$f''(x) = \frac{(x + 1)^2(2x + 2) - (x^2 + 2x - 3)(2)(x + 1)}{(x + 1)^4} = \frac{8}{(x + 1)^3}$$

Partition numbers for $f''(x)$: $x = -1$

Sign chart for f'':

$f''(x)$: $- - - - - ND + + + + +$

x

Graph of f : $-1 \quad 0$

Concave Downward | Concave Upward

The graph of f is concave upward on $(-1, \infty)$ and concave downward on $(-\infty, -1)$.

Step 4. Sketch the graph of f:

x	$f(x)$
-3	-9
0	0
1	-1
3	0

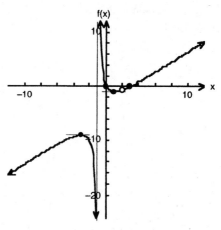

67. $f(x) = \dfrac{x^2 + x - 2}{x^2 - 2x + 1} = \dfrac{(x + 2)(x - 1)}{(x - 1)^2} = \dfrac{x + 2}{x - 1}$, $x \neq 1$

Step 1. Analyze $f(x)$:

(A) Domain: All real numbers except $x = 1$.

(B) Intercepts: y-intercept: $f(0) = -2$

x-intercepts: $x = -2$

(C) Asymptotes:

Horizontal asymptote: $\dfrac{x^2}{x^2} = 1$; $y = 1$ is a horizontal asymptote

Vertical asymptote: $x = 1$ is a vertical asymptote

138

Step 2. Analyze $f'(x)$:

$$f'(x) = \frac{(x - 1) - (x + 2)}{(x - 1)^2} = \frac{-3}{(x - 1)^2}$$

Critical values: None

Partition numbers: $x = 1$

Sign chart for f':

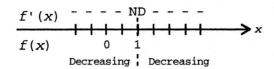

Thus, f is decreasing on $(-\infty, 1)$ and $(1, \infty)$.

Step 3. Analyze $f''(x)$:

$$f''(x) = \frac{6}{(x - 1)^3}$$

Partition numbers for $f''(x)$: $x = 1$

Sign chart for f'':

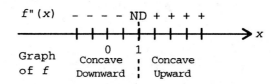

The graph of f is concave upward on $(1, \infty)$ and concave downward on $(-\infty, 1)$.

Step 4. Sketch the graph of f:

x	$f(x)$
-2	0
0	-2

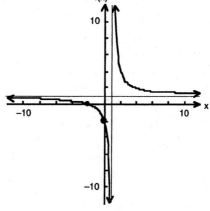

71. $P(x) = \dfrac{2x}{1 - x}$, $0 \le x < 1$

(A) $P'(x) = \dfrac{(1 - x)(2) - 2x(-1)}{(1 - x)^2} = \dfrac{2}{(1 - x)^2}$

$P'(x) > 0$ for $0 \le x < 1$. Thus, P is increasing on $(0, 1)$.

(B) From (A), $P'(x) = 2(1 - x)^{-2}$. Thus,

$P''(x) = -4(1 - x)^{-3}(-1) = \dfrac{4}{(1 - x)^3}$.

$P''(x) > 0$ for $0 \le x < 1$, and the graph of P is concave upward on $(0, 1)$.

(C) Since the domain of P is $[0, 1)$, there are no horizontal asymptotes. The denominator is 0 at $x = 1$ and the numerator is nonzero there. Thus, $x = 1$ is a vertical asymptote.

(D) $P(0) = \dfrac{2 \cdot 0}{1 - 0} = 0$.

Thus, the origin is both an x and a y intercept of the graph.

(E) The graph of P is:

x	$P(x)$
0	0
$\frac{1}{2}$	2
$\frac{3}{4}$	6

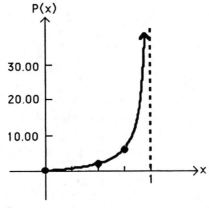

73. $C(n) = 3200 + 250n + 50n^2$, $0 < n < \infty$

(A) Average cost per year:
$$\overline{C}(n) = \frac{C(n)}{n} = \frac{3200}{n} + 250 + 50n, \quad 0 < n < \infty$$

(B) Graph $\overline{C}(n)$:

Step 1. Analyze $\overline{C}(n)$:

Domain: $0 < n < \infty$

Intercepts: C intercept: None $(n > 0)$

n intercepts: $\frac{3200}{n} + 250 + 50n > 0$ on $(0, \infty)$;

there are no n intercepts.

Asymptotes: For large n, $\overline{C}(n) = \frac{3200}{n} + 250 + 50n \approx 250 + 50n$.

Thus, $y = 250 + 50n$ is an oblique asymptote. As $n \to 0$, $\overline{C}(n) \to \infty$; thus, $n = 0$ is a vertical asymptote.

Step 2. Analyze $\overline{C}'(n)$:
$$\overline{C}'(n) = -\frac{3200}{n^2} + 50 = \frac{50n^2 - 3200}{n^2} = \frac{50(n^2 - 64)}{n^2}$$
$$= \frac{50(n - 8)(n + 8)}{n^2}, \quad 0 < n < \infty$$

Critical value: $n = 8$

Sign chart for $\overline{C}'$:

$\overline{C}'(n)$ $- - - - \; 0 \; + + + +$

```
        +--------------+---------------------->  n
        0              8
```

$\overline{C}(n)$ Decreasing : Increasing

Local
minimum

Test Numbers	
n	$\overline{C}(n)$
7	$(-)$
9	$(+)$

Thus, $\overline{C}$ is decreasing on $(0, 8)$ and increasing on $(8, \infty)$; $n = 8$ is a local minimum.

Step 3: Analyze $\overline{C}''(n)$:
$$\overline{C}''(n) = \frac{6400}{n^3}, \quad 0 < n < \infty$$

$\overline{C}''(n) > 0$ on $(0, \infty)$. Thus, the graph of $\overline{C}$ is concave upward on $(0, \infty)$.

Step 4.   Sketch the graph of $\overline{C}$:

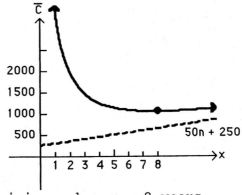

(C) The average cost per year is a minimum when $n = 8$ years.

75. $C(x) = 1000 + 5x + 0.1x^2$, $0 < x < \infty$.

(A) The average cost function is: $\overline{C}(x) = \dfrac{1000}{x} + 5 + 0.1x$.

Now, $\overline{C}'(x) = -\dfrac{1000}{x^2} + \dfrac{1}{10} = \dfrac{x^2 - 10,000}{10x^2} = \dfrac{(x + 100)(x - 100)}{10x^2}$

Sign chart for $\overline{C}'$:

$\overline{C}'(x)$ - - - - - - 0 + + + + +

⟶ x

0   100

$\overline{C}(x)$ Decreasing   Increasing

Local
minimum

Test Numbers		
x		$\overline{C}'(x)$
1	$\approx$	$-1000\,(-)$
101	$\approx$	$\frac{1}{500}\,(+)$

Thus, $\overline{C}$ is decreasing on $(0, 100)$ and increasing on $(100, \infty)$; $\overline{C}$ has a minimum at $x = 100$.

Since $\overline{C}''(x) = \dfrac{2000}{x^3} > 0$ for $0 < x < \infty$, the graph of $\overline{C}$ is concave upward on $(0, \infty)$. The line $x = 0$ is a vertical asymptote and the line $y = 5 + 0.1x$ is an oblique asymptote for the graph of $\overline{C}$.

The marginal cost function is $C'(x) = 5 + 0.2x$.

The graphs of $\overline{C}$ and C' are:

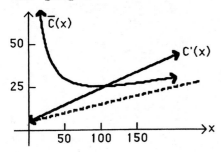

(B) The minimum average cost is:

$$\overline{C}(100) = \dfrac{1000}{100} + 5 + \dfrac{1}{10}(100) = 25$$

141

77. (A)

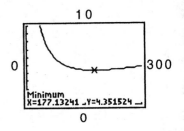

```
QuadReg
y=ax²+bx+c
a=.0100714286
b=.7835714286
c=316
```

(B) The average cost function $\overline{y} = \dfrac{y(x)}{x}$ where

$y(x)$ is the regression equation found in part (A).

The minimum average cost is \$4.35 when 177 pizzas are produced.

10

0 ⌐ ┐ 300

```
Minimum
X=177.13241  Y=4.351524
```

0

79. $C(t) = \dfrac{0.14t}{t^2 + 1}$

Step 1. Analyze $C(t)$:

Domain: $t \geq 0$, i.e., $[0, \infty)$

Intercepts: y intercept: $C(0) = 0$

         t intercepts: $\dfrac{0.14t}{t^2 + 1} = 0$

                  $t = 0$

Asymptotes:

Horizontal asymptote: $\displaystyle\lim_{t \to \infty} \dfrac{0.14t}{t^2 + 1} = \lim_{t \to \infty} \dfrac{0.14t}{t^2\left(1 + \frac{1}{t^2}\right)} = \lim_{t \to \infty} \dfrac{0.14}{t\left(1 + \frac{1}{t^2}\right)} = 0$

Thus, $y = 0$ (the t axis) is a horizontal asymptote.

Vertical asymptotes: Since $t^2 + 1 > 0$ for all t, there are no vertical asymptotes.

Step 2. Analyze $C'(t)$:

$C'(t) = \dfrac{(t^2 + 1)(0.14) - 0.14t(2t)}{(t^2 + 1)^2} = \dfrac{0.14(1 - t^2)}{(t^2 + 1)^2} = \dfrac{0.14(1 - t)(1 + t)}{(t^2 + 1)^2}$

Critical values on $[0, \infty)$: $t = 1$

Sign chart for C':

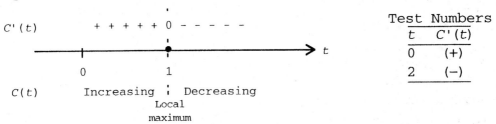

Test Numbers	
t	$C'(t)$
0	(+)
2	(−)

Thus, C is increasing on $(0, 1)$ and decreasing on $(1, \infty)$; C has a maximum value at $t = 1$.

Step 3. Analyze $C''(t)$:

$$C''(t) = \frac{(t^2 + 1)^2(-0.28t - 0.14(1 - t^2)(2)(t^2 + 1)(2t)}{(t^2 + 1)^4}$$

$$= \frac{(t^2 + 1)(-0.28t) - 0.56t(1 - t^2)}{(t^2 + 1)^3} = \frac{0.28t^3 - 0.84t}{(t^2 + 1)^3}$$

$$= \frac{0.28t(t^2 - 3)}{(t^2 + 1)^3} = \frac{0.28t(t - \sqrt{3})(t + \sqrt{3})}{(t^2 + 1)^3}, \quad 0 \le t < \infty$$

Partition numbers for C'' on $[0, \infty)$: $t = \sqrt{3}$

Sign chart for C'':

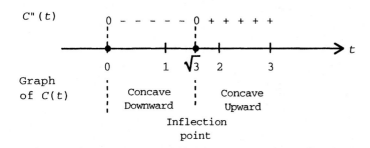

Test Numbers	
t	$C''(t)$
1	$-0.07 \, (-)$
2	$\approx 0.005 \, (+)$

Thus, the graph of C is concave downward on $(0, \sqrt{3})$ and concave upward on $(\sqrt{3}, \infty)$; the graph has an inflection point at $t = \sqrt{3}$.

Step 4. Sketch the graph of $C(t)$:

t	$C(t)$
0	0
1	0.07
$\sqrt{3}$	≈ 0.06

81. $N(t) = \dfrac{5t + 20}{t} = 5 + 20t^{-1}, \quad 1 \le t \le 30$

Step 1. Analyze $N(t)$:

Domain: $1 \le t \le 30$, or $[1, 30]$.
Intercepts: There are no t or N intercepts.
Asymptotes: Since N is defined only for $1 \le t \le 30$, there are no horizontal asymptotes. Also, since $t \ne 0$ on $[1, 30]$, there are no vertical asymptotes.

Step 2. Analyze $N'(t)$:

$$N'(t) = -20t^{-2} = \frac{-20}{t^2}, \quad 1 \le t \le 30$$

Since $N'(t) < 0$ for $1 \le t \le 30$, N is decreasing on $(1, 30)$; N has no local extrema.

$$N''(t) = \frac{40}{t^3}, \quad 1 \leq t \leq 30$$

Since $N''(t) > 0$ for $1 \leq t \leq 30$, the graph of N is concave upward on $(1, 30)$.

Step 4. Sketch the graph of N:

t	$N(t)$
1	25
5	9
10	7
30	5.67

EXERCISE 2-4

Things to remember:

1. ABSOLUTE MAXIMA AND MINIMA

    If $f(c) \geq f(x)$ for all x in the domain of f, then $f(c)$ is called the ABSOLUTE MAXIMUM VALUE of f.

    If $f(c) \leq f(x)$ for all x in the domain of f, then $f(x)$ is called the ABSOLUTE MINIMUM VALUE of f.

2. A function f continuous on a closed interval $[a, b]$ has both an absolute maximum and an absolute minimum on that interval. Absolute extrema (if they exist) must always occur at critical values or at endpoints.

3. PROCEDURE FOR FINDING ABSOLUTE EXTREMA ON A CLOSED INTERVAL

    Step 1. Check to make certain that f is continuous over $[a, b]$.

    Step 2. Find the critical values in the interval (a, b).

    Step 3. Evaluate f at the endpoints a and b and at the critical values found in step 2.

    Step 4. The absolute maximum $f(x)$ on $[a, b]$ is the largest of the values found in step 3.

    Step 5. The absolute minimum $f(x)$ on $[a, b]$ is the smallest of the values found in step 3.

4. SECOND DERIVATIVE TEST

Let c be a critical value for $f(x)$.

$f'(c)$	$f''(c)$	GRAPH OF f IS:	$f(c)$	EXAMPLE
0	+	Concave upward	Local minimum	
0	−	Concave downward	Local maximum	
0	0	?	Test does not apply	

5. SECOND DERIVATIVE TEST FOR ABSOLUTE EXTREMUM

Let f be continuous on an interval I with only one critical value c on I:

If $f'(c) = 0$ and $f''(c) > 0$, then $f(c)$ is the absolute minimum of f on I.

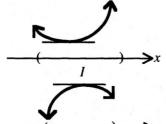

If $f'(c) = 0$ and $f''(c) < 0$, then $f(c)$ is the absolute maximum of f on I.

1. Interval $[0, 10]$; absolute minimum: $f(0) = 0$; absolute maximum: $f(10) = 14$

3. Interval $[0, 8]$; absolute minimum: $f(0) = 0$; absolute maximum: $f(3) = 9$

5. Interval $[1, 10]$; absolute minimum: $f(1) = f(7) = 5$; absolute maximum: $f(10) = 14$

7. Interval $[1, 9]$; absolute minimum: $f(1) = f(7) = 5$; absolute maximum: $f(4) = f(9) = 9$

9. Interval $[2, 5]$; absolute minimum: $f(5) = 7$; absolute maximum: $f(3) = 9$

11. $f(x) = x^2 - 2x + 3$, $I = (-\infty, \infty)$
$f'(x) = 2x - 2 = 2(x - 1)$
$f'(x) = 0$: $2(x - 1) = 0$
$\qquad\qquad\qquad x = 1$

$x = 1$ is the ONLY critical value on I, and $f(1) = 1^2 - 2(1) + 3 = 2$
$f''(x) = 2$ and $f''(1) = 2 > 0$. Therefore, $f(1) = 2$ is the absolute minimum. The function does not have an absolute maximum since $\lim_{x \to \pm\infty} f(x) = \infty$.

13. $f(x) = -x^2 - 6x + 9$, $I = (-\infty, \infty)$
$f'(x) = -2x - 6 = -2(x + 3)$
$f'(x) = 0$: $-2(x + 3) = 0$
$\qquad\qquad\qquad x = -3$
$x = -3$ is the ONLY critical value on I, and
$f(-3) = -(-3)^2 - 6(-3) + 9 = 18$
$f''(x) = -2$ and $f''(-3) = -2 < 0$. Therefore, $f(-3) = 18$ is the absolute maximum. The function does not have an absolute minimum since $\lim_{x \to \pm\infty} f(x) = -\infty$.

15. $f(x) = x^3 + x$, $I = (-\infty, \infty)$

$f'(x) = 3x^2 + 1 \geq 1$ on I; f is increasing on I and $\lim\limits_{x \to -\infty} f(x) = -\infty$,

$\lim\limits_{x \to \infty} f(x) = \infty$. Therefore, f does not have any absolute extrema.

17. $f(x) = 8x^3 - 2x^4$; domain: all real numbers

$f'(x) = 24x^2 - 8x^3 = 8x^2(3 - x)$

$f''(x) = 48x - 24x^2 = 24x(2 - x)$

Critical values: $x = 0$, $x = 3$

$f''(0) = 0$ (second derivative test fails)

$f''(3) = -72$ f has a local maximum at $x = 3$.

Sign chart for $f'(x) = 8x^2(3 - x)$
(0 and 3 are partition numbers)

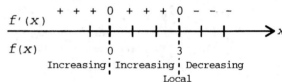

From the sign chart, f does not have a local extremum at $x = 0$; f has a local maximum at $x = 3$ which must be an absolute maximum since f is increasing on $(-\infty, 3)$ and decreasing on $(3, \infty)$; $f(3) = 54$ is the absolute maximum of f. f does not have an absolute minimum since $\lim\limits_{x \to \infty} f(x) = \lim\limits_{x \to -\infty} f(x) = -\infty$.

19. $f(x) = x + \dfrac{16}{x}$; domain: all real numbers except $x = 0$.

$f'(x) = 1 - \dfrac{16}{x^2} = \dfrac{x^2 - 16}{x^2} = \dfrac{(x - 4)(x + 4)}{x^2}$

$f''(x) = \dfrac{32}{x^3}$

Critical values: $x = -4$, $x = 4$

$f''(-4) = -\dfrac{1}{2} < 0$; f has a local maximum at $x = -4$

$f''(4) = \dfrac{1}{2} > 0$; f has a local minimum at $x = 4$

$\lim\limits_{x \to \infty} f(x) = \lim\limits_{x \to \infty}\left(x + \dfrac{16}{x}\right) = \infty$; $\lim\limits_{x \to -\infty} f(x) = \lim\limits_{x \to -\infty}\left(x + \dfrac{16}{x}\right) = -\infty$;

f has no absolute extrema.

21. $f(x) = \dfrac{x^2}{x^2 + 1}$; domain: all real numbers

$f'(x) = \dfrac{(x^2 + 1)2x - x^2(2x)}{(x^2 + 1)^2} = \dfrac{2x}{(x^2 + 1)^2}$

$f''(x) = \dfrac{(x^2 + 1)^2(2) - 2x(2)(x^2 + 1)(2x)}{(x^2 + 1)^4} = \dfrac{2 - 6x^2}{(x^2 + 1)^3}$

Critical value: $x = 0$

Since f has only one critical value and $f''(0) = 2 > 0$, $f(0) = 0$ is the absolute minimum of f. Since $\lim\limits_{x \to \infty} f(x) = \lim\limits_{x \to \infty} \dfrac{x^2}{x^2 + 1} = 1$, f has no absolute maximum; $y = 1$ is a horizontal asymptote for the graph of f.

23. $f(x) = \dfrac{2x}{x^2 + 1}$; domain: all real numbers

$$f'(x) = \frac{(x^2 + 1)2 - 2x(2x)}{(x^2 + 1)^2} = \frac{2 - 2x^2}{(x^2 + 1)^2} = \frac{2(1 - x^2)}{(x^2 + 1)^2}$$

$$f''(x) = \frac{(x^2 + 1)^2(-4x) - 2(1 - x^2)(2)(x^2 + 1)(2x)}{(x^2 + 1)^4} = \frac{4x(x^2 - 3)}{(x^2 + 1)^3}$$

Critical values: $x = -1$, $x = 1$

$f''(-1) = 8 > 0$; f has a local minimum at $x = -1$

$f''(1) = -8 < 0$; f has a local maximum at $x = 1$

Sign chart for $f'(x)$
(partition numbers are -1 and 1)

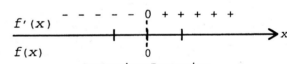

$$\lim_{x \to \pm\infty} f(x) = \lim_{x \to \pm\infty} \frac{2x}{x^2 + 1} = 0$$
(the x-axis is a horizontal asymptote)

We can now conclude that $f(1) = 1$ is the absolute maximum of f and $f(-1) = -1$ is the absolute minimum of f.

25. $f(x) = \dfrac{x^2 - 1}{x^2 + 1}$; domain: all real numbers

$$f'(x) = \frac{(x^2 + 1)(2x) - (x^2 - 1)(2x)}{(x^2 + 1)^2} = \frac{4x}{(x^2 + 1)^2}$$

$$f''(x) = \frac{(x^2 + 1)^2(4) - 4x(2)(x^2 + 1)2x}{(x^2 + 1)^4} = \frac{4(3 - x^2)}{(x^2 + 1)^3}$$

Critical value: $x = 0$

$f''(0) = 12 > 0$; f has a local minimum at $x = 0$

Sign chart for $f'(x) = \dfrac{4x}{(x^2 + 1)^2}$

(0 is the partition number)

$$\lim_{x \to \pm\infty} f(x) = \lim_{x \to \pm\infty} \frac{x^2 - 1}{x^2 + 1} = 1$$
($y = 1$ is a horizontal asymptote)

We can now conclude that $f(0) = -1$ is the absolute minimum and f does not have an absolute maximum.

27. $f(x) = 2x^2 - 8x + 6$ on $I = [0, \infty)$

$f'(x) = 4x - 8 = 4(x - 2)$

$f''(x) = 4$

Critical value: $x = 2$

$f''(2) = 4 > 0$; f has a local minimum at $x = 2$

Since $x = 2$ is the only critical value of f on I, $f(2) = -2$ is the absolute minimum of f on I.

29. $f(x) = 3x^2 - x^3$ on $I = [0, \infty)$

$f'(x) = 6x - 3x^2 = 3x(2 - x)$

$f''(x) = 6 - 6x$

Critical value (in $(0, \infty)$): $x = 2$

$f''(2) = -6 < 0$; f has a local maximum at $x = 2$

Since $f(0) = 0$ and $x = 2$ is the only critical value of f in $(0, \infty)$, $f(2) = 4$ is the absolute maximum value of f on I.

31. $f(x) = (x + 4)(x - 2)^2$ on $I = [0, \infty)$

$f'(x) = (x + 4)(2)(x - 2) + (x - 2)^2 = (x - 2)[2x + 8 + x - 2]$
$= (x - 2)(3x + 6)$
$= 3x^2 - 12$

$f''(x) = 6x$

Critical value in I: $x = 2$

$f''(2) = 12 > 0$; f has a local minimum at $x = 2$

Since $f(0) = 16$ and $x = 2$ is the only critical value of f in $(0, \infty)$, $f(2) = 0$ is the absolute minimum of f on I.

33. $f(x) = 2x^4 - 8x^3$ on $I = (0, \infty)$

Since $\lim\limits_{x \to \infty} f(x) = \lim\limits_{x \to \infty} (2x^4 - 8x^3) = \infty$, f does not have an absolute maximum on I.

35. $f(x) = 20 - 3x - \dfrac{12}{x}$, $x > 0$; $I = (0, \infty)$

$f'(x) = -3 + \dfrac{12}{x^2}$

$f'(x) = 0$: $-3 + \dfrac{12}{x^2} = 0$

$3x^2 = 12$

$x^2 = 4$

$x = 2$ (-2 is not in I)

$x = 2$ is the only critical value of f on I, and

$f(2) = 20 - 3(2) - \dfrac{12}{2} = 8.$

$f''(x) = -\dfrac{24}{x^2}$; $f''(2) = -\dfrac{24}{4} = -6 < 0$. Therefore, $f(2) = 8$ is the absolute

maximum of f. The function does not have an absolute minimum since $\lim\limits_{x \to \infty} f(x) = -\infty$. (Also, $\lim\limits_{x \to 0^+} f(x) = -\infty$.)

37. $f(x) = 10 + 2x + \dfrac{64}{x^2}$, $x > 0$; $I = (0, \infty)$

$f'(x) = 2 - \dfrac{128}{x^3}$

$f'(x) = 0$: $2 - \dfrac{128}{x^3} = 0$

$$2x^3 = 128$$
$$x^3 = 64$$
$$x = 4$$

$x = 4$ is the only critical value of f on I and

$f(4) = 10 + 2(4) + \dfrac{64}{4^2} = 22$

$f''(x) = \dfrac{384}{x^4}$; $f''(4) = \dfrac{384}{4^4} = \dfrac{3}{2} > 0$. Therefore, $f(4) = 22$ is the absolute

minimum of f. The function does not have an absolute maximum since $\lim\limits_{x \to \infty} f(x) = \infty$. (Also, $\lim\limits_{x \to 0^+} f(x) = \infty$.)

39. $f(x) = x + \dfrac{1}{x} + \dfrac{30}{x^3}$ on $I = (0, \infty)$

$f'(x) = 1 - \dfrac{1}{x^2} - \dfrac{90}{x^4} = \dfrac{x^4 - x^2 - 90}{x^4} = \dfrac{(x^2 - 10)(x^2 + 9)}{x^4}$

$f''(x) = \dfrac{2}{x^3} + \dfrac{360}{x^5}$

Critical value (in $(0, \infty)$): $x = \sqrt{10}$

$f''(\sqrt{10}) = \dfrac{2}{(10)^{3/2}} + \dfrac{360}{(10)^{5/2}} > 0$; f has a local minimum at $x = \sqrt{10}$

Since $\sqrt{10}$ is the only critical value of f on I, $f(\sqrt{10}) = \dfrac{14}{\sqrt{10}}$ is the

absolute minimum of f on I.

41. $f(x) = x^3 - 6x^2 + 9x - 6$

$f'(x) = 3x^2 - 12x + 9 = 3(x^2 - 4x + 3) = 3(x - 3)(x - 1)$
Critical values: $x = 1, 3$

(A) On the interval $[-1, 5]$: $f(-1) = -1 - 6 - 9 - 6 = -22$
$\qquad\qquad\qquad\qquad\qquad\;\; f(1) = 1 - 6 + 9 - 6 = -2$
$\qquad\qquad\qquad\qquad\qquad\;\; f(3) = 27 - 54 + 27 - 6 = -6$
$\qquad\qquad\qquad\qquad\qquad\;\; f(5) = 125 - 150 + 45 - 6 = 14$

Thus, the absolute maximum of f is $f(5) = 14$, and the absolute minimum of f is $f(-1) = -22$.

(B) On the interval $[-1, 3]$: $f(-1) = -22$
$\qquad\qquad\qquad\qquad\qquad\;\; f(1) = -2$
$\qquad\qquad\qquad\qquad\qquad\;\; f(3) = -6$

Absolute maximum of f: $f(1) = -2$
Absolute minimum of f: $f(-1) = -22$

(C) On the interval $[2, 5]$: $f(2) = 8 - 24 + 18 - 6 = -4$
$\qquad\qquad\qquad\qquad\qquad\;\; f(3) = -6$
$\qquad\qquad\qquad\qquad\qquad\;\; f(5) = 14$

Absolute maximum of f: $f(5) = 14$
Absolute minimum of f: $f(3) = -6$

43. $f(x) = (x - 1)(x - 5)^3 + 1$

$f'(x) = (x - 1)3(x - 5)^2 + (x - 5)^3$

$\qquad = (x - 5)^2(3x - 3 + x - 5)$

$\qquad = (x - 5)^2(4x - 8)$

Critical values: $x = 2, 5$

(A) Interval $[0, 3]$: $f(0) = (-1)(-5)^3 + 1 = 126$

$\qquad\qquad\qquad\quad f(2) = (2 - 1)(2 - 5)^3 + 1 = -26$

$\qquad\qquad\qquad\quad f(3) = (3 - 1)(3 - 5)^3 + 1 = -15$

Absolute maximum of f: $f(0) = 126$
Absolute minimum of f: $f(2) = -26$

(B) Interval $[1, 7]$: $f(1) = 1$

$\qquad\qquad\qquad\quad f(2) = -26$

$\qquad\qquad\qquad\quad f(5) = 1$

$\qquad\qquad\qquad\quad f(7) = (7 - 1)(7 - 5)^3 + 1 = 6 \cdot 8 + 1 = 49$

Absolute maximum of f: $f(7) = 49$
Absolute minimum of f: $f(2) = -26$

(C) Interval $[3, 6]$: $f(3) = (3 - 1)(3 - 5)^3 + 1 = -15$

$\qquad\qquad\qquad\quad f(5) = 1$

$\qquad\qquad\qquad\quad f(6) = (6 - 1)(6 - 5)^3 + 1 = 6$

Absolute maximum of f: $f(6) = 6$
Absolute minimum of f: $f(3) = -15$

45. $f(x) = x^4 - 4x^3 + 5$

$f'(x) = 4x^3 - 12x^2 = 4x^2(x - 3)$
Critical values: $x = 0, x = 3$

(A) On the interval $[-1, 2]$: $f(-1) = 10$

$\qquad\qquad\qquad\qquad\quad f(0) = 5$

$\qquad\qquad\qquad\qquad\quad f(2) = -11$

Thus, the absolute maximum of f is $f(-1) = 10$; the absolute minimum of f is $f(2) = -11$.

(B) On the interval $[0, 4]$: $f(0) = 5$

$\qquad\qquad\qquad\qquad\quad f(3) = -22$

$\qquad\qquad\qquad\qquad\quad f(4) = 5$

Absolute maximum of f: $f(0) = f(4) = 5$
Absolute minimum of f: $f(3) = -22$

(C) On the interval $[-1, 1]$: $f(-1) = 10$

$\qquad\qquad\qquad\qquad\quad f(0) = 5$

$\qquad\qquad\qquad\qquad\quad f(1) = 2$

Absolute maximum of f: $f(-1) = 10$
Absolute minimum of f: $f(1) = 2$

47. f has a local minimum at $x = 2$.

49. Unable to determine from the given information ($f'(-3) = f''(-3) = 0$).

51. Neither a local maximum nor a local minimum at $x = 6$; $x = 6$ is not a critical value of f.

53. f has a local maximum at $x = 2$.

Things to remember:

STRATEGY FOR SOLVING OPTIMIZATION PROBLEMS

<u>Step 1</u>. Introduce variables, look for relationships among these variables, and construct a mathematical model of the form: Maximize (or minimize) $f(x)$ on the interval I

<u>Step 2</u>. Find the critical values of $f(x)$.

<u>Step 3</u>. Use the procedures developed in Section 4-4 to find the absolute maximum (or minimum) value of $f(x)$ on the interval I and the value(s) of x where this occurs.

<u>Step 4</u>. Use the solution to the mathematical model to answer all the questions asked in the problem.

---

1. Let one length = x and the other = $10 - x$.
Since neither length can be negative, we have $x \geq 0$ and $10 - x \geq 0$, or $x \leq 10$. We want the maximum value of the product $x(10 - x)$, where $0 \leq x \leq 10$.

Let $f(x) = x(10 - x) = 10x - x^2$; domain $I = [0, 10]$
  $f'(x) = 10 - 2x$; $x = 5$ is the only critical value
  $f''(x) = -2$
  $f''(5) = -2 < 0$
Thus, $f(5) = 25$ is the absolute maximum; divide the line in half.

3. Let one number = x. Then the other number = $x + 30$.
  $f(x) = x(x + 30) = x^2 + 30x$; domain $I = (-\infty, \infty)$
  $f'(x) = 2x + 30$; $x = -15$ is the only critical value
  $f''(x) = 2$
  $f''(-15) = 2 > 0$
Thus, the absolute minimum of f occurs at $x = -15$. The numbers, then, are -15 and $-15 + 30 = 15$.

5. Let x = the length of the rectangle and y = the width of the rectangle.
Then, $2x + 2y = 100$
  $x + y = 50$
  $y = 50 - x$
We want to find the maximum of the area:
$A(x) = x \cdot y = x(50 - x) = 50x - x^2$.

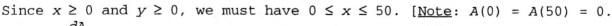

Since $x \geq 0$ and $y \geq 0$, we must have $0 \leq x \leq 50$. [<u>Note</u>: $A(0) = A(50) = 0$.
$A'(x) = \dfrac{dA}{dx} = 50 - 2x$; $x = 25$ is the only critical value.
Now, $A'' = -2$ and $A''(25) = -2 < 0$. Thus, $A(25)$ is the absolute maximum.
The maximum area is $A(25) = 25(50 - 25) = 625$ cm^2, which means that the rectangle is actually a square with sides measuring 25 cm each.

7. Let the rectangle of fixed area A have dimensions x and y. Then $A = xy$ and $y = \dfrac{A}{x}$.

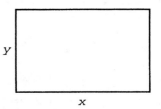

The cost of the fence is

$$C = 2Bx + 2By = 2Bx + \frac{2AB}{x}, \quad x > 0$$

Thus, we want to find the absolute minimum of

$$C(x) = 2Bx + \frac{2AB}{x}, \quad x > 0$$

Since $\lim\limits_{x \to 0} C(x) = \lim\limits_{x \to \infty} C(x) = \infty$, and $C(x) > 0$ for all $x > 0$, we can conclude that C has an absolute minimum on $(0, \infty)$. This agrees with our intuition that there should be a cheapest way to build the fence.

9. Let x and y be the dimensions of the rectangle and let C be the fixed amount which can be spent. Then

$$C = 2Bx + 2By \quad \text{and} \quad y = \frac{C - 2Bx}{2B}$$

The area enclosed by the fence is:

$$A = xy = x\left[\frac{C - 2Bx}{2B}\right]$$

Thus, we want to find the absolute maximum value of

$$A(x) = \frac{C}{2B}x - x^2, \quad 0 \le x \le \frac{C}{2B}$$

Since $A(x)$ is a continuous function on the closed interval $\left[0, \dfrac{C}{2B}\right]$, it has an absolute maximum value. This agrees with our intuition that there should be a largest rectangular area that can be enclosed with a fixed amount of fencing.

11. Price-demand: $p(x) = 500 - 0.5x$; cost: $C(x) = 20,000 + 135x$

(A) Revenue: $R(x) = x \cdot p(x) = 500x - 0.5x^2, \quad 0 \le x < \infty$
$R'(x) = 500 - x$
$R'(x) = 500 - x = 0$ implies $x = 500$
$R''(x) = -1; \quad R''(500) = -1 < 0$
R has an absolute maximum at $x = 500$.
$p(500) = 500 - 0.5(500) = 250; \quad R(500) = (500)^2 - 0.5(500)^2 = 125,000$
The company should produce 500 phones each week at a price of \$250 per phone to maximize their revenue. The maximum revenue is \$125,000

(B) Profit: $P(x) = R(x) - C(x) = 500x - 0.5x^2 - (20,000 + 135x)$
$$= 365x - 0.5x^2 - 20,000$$
$P'(x) = 365 - x$
$P'(x) = 365 - x = 0$ implies $x = 365$
$P''(x) = -1; \quad P''(365) = -1 < 0$
P has an absolute maximum at $x = 365$
$p(365) = 500 - 0.5(365) = 317.50;$
$P(365) = (365)^2 - 0.5(365)^2 - 20,000 = 46,612.50$
To maximize profit, the company should produce 365 phones each week at a price of \$317.50 per phone. The maximum profit is \$46,612.50.

13. (A) Revenue $R(x) = x \cdot p(x) = x\left(200 - \dfrac{x}{30}\right) = 200x - \dfrac{x^2}{30}$, $0 \le x \le 6{,}000$

$R'(x) = 200 - \dfrac{2x}{30} = 200 - \dfrac{x}{15}$

Now $R'(x) = 200 - \dfrac{x}{15} = 0$ implies $x = 3000$.

$R''(x) = -\dfrac{1}{15} < 0$.

Thus, $R''(3000) = -\dfrac{1}{15} < 0$ and we conclude that R has an absolute maximum at $x = 3000$. The maximum revenue is

$R(3000) = 200(3000) - \dfrac{(3000)^2}{30} = \$300{,}000$

(B) Profit $P(x) = R(x) - C(x) = 200x - \dfrac{x^2}{30} - (72{,}000 + 60x)$

$\qquad = 140x - \dfrac{x^2}{30} - 72{,}000$

$P'(x) = 140 - \dfrac{x}{15}$

Now $140 - \dfrac{x}{15} = 0$ implies $x = 2{,}100$.

$P''(x) = -\dfrac{1}{15}$ and $P''(2{,}100) = -\dfrac{1}{15} < 0$. Thus, the maximum profit occurs when $2{,}100$ television sets are produced. The maximum profit is

$\qquad P(2{,}100) = 140(2{,}100) - \dfrac{(2{,}100)^2}{30} - 72{,}000 = \$75{,}000$

the price that the company should charge is

$\qquad p(2{,}100) = 200 - \dfrac{2{,}100}{30} = \$130$ for each set.

(C) If the government taxes the company $5 for each set, then the profit $P(x)$ is given by

$\qquad P(x) = 200x - \dfrac{x^2}{30} - (72{,}000 + 60x) - 5x$

$\qquad = 135x - \dfrac{x^2}{30} - 72{,}000.$

$P'(x) = 135 - \dfrac{x}{15}.$

Now $135 - \dfrac{x}{15} = 0$ implies $x = 2{,}025$.

$P''(x) = -\dfrac{1}{15}$ and $P''(2{,}025) = -\dfrac{1}{15} < 0$. Thus, the maximum profit in this case occurs when $2{,}025$ television sets are produced. The maximum profit is

$\qquad P(2{,}025) = 135(2{,}025) - \dfrac{(2{,}025)^2}{30} - 72{,}000 = \$64{,}687.50$

and the company should charge $p(2{,}025) = 200 - \dfrac{2{,}025}{30} = \$132.50/\text{set}.$

15. (A)

```
QuadReg
 y=ax²+bx+c
 a=-2.352941ᴇ-5
 b=-.0325964781
 c=288.9535407
```

(B)

```
LinReg
 y=ax+b
 a=53.50318471
 b=82245.22293
```

(C) The revenue at the demand level x is:
$$R(x) = xp(x)$$
where $p(x)$ is the quadratic regression equation in (A).

The cost at the demand level x is $C(x)$ given by the linear regression equation in (B). The profit $P(x) = R(x) - C(x)$.

The maximum profit is \$118,996 at the demand level $x = 1422$.

The price per saw at the demand level $x = 1422$ is \$195.

17. (A) Let x = number of 10¢ reductions in price. Then
$640 + 40x$ = number of sandwiches sold at x 10¢ reductions
$8 - 0.1x$ = price per sandwich $\quad 0 \le x \le 80$
Revenue: $R(x) = (640 + 40x)(8 - 0.1x)$
$$= 5120 + 256x - 4x^2, \ 0 \le x \le 80$$
$R'(x) = 256 - 8x$
$R'(x) = 256 - 8x = 0$ implies $x = 32$
$R(0) = 5120, \ R(32) = 9216, \ R(80) = 0$

Thus, the deli should charge $8 - 3.20 = \$4.80$ per sandwich to realize a maximum revenue of \$9216.

(B) Let x = number of 20¢ reductions in price. Then
$640 + 15x$ = number of sandwiches sold
$8 - 0.2x$ = price per sandwich $\quad 0 \le x \le 40$
Revenue: $R(x) = (640 + 15x)(8 - 0.2x)$
$$= 5120 - 8x - 3x^2, \ 0 \le x \le 40$$
$R'(x) = -8 - 6x$
$R'(x) = -8 - 6x = 0$ has no solutions in $(0, 40)$
Now, $R(0) = 640 \cdot 8 = \$5120$
$\quad\quad R(40) = 0$

Thus, the deli should charge \$8 per sandwich to maximize their revenue under these conditions.

19. Let x = number of dollar increases in the rate per day. Then
$200 - 5x$ = total number of cars rented and $30 + x$ = rate per day.
Total income = (total number of cars rented)(rate)
$$y(x) = (200 - 5x)(30 + x), \ 0 \le x \le 40$$
$$y'(x) = (200 - 5x)(1) + (30 + x)(-5)$$
$$= 200 - 5x - 150 - 5x$$
$$= 50 - 10x$$
$$= 10(5 - x)$$
Thus, $x = 5$ is the only critical value and
$y(5) = (200 - 25)(30 + 5) = 6125$.
$y''(x) = -10$
$y''(5) = -10 < 0$
Therefore, the absolute maximum income is $y(5) = \$6125$ when the rate is \$35 per day.

21. Let x = number of additional trees planted per acre. Then
$30 + x$ = total number of trees per acre and $50 - x$ = yield per tree.
Yield per acre = (total number of trees per acre)(yield per tree)
$$y(x) = (30 + x)(50 - x), \quad 0 \leq x \leq 20$$
$$y'(x) = (30 + x)(-1) + (50 - x)$$
$$= 20 - 2x$$
$$= 2(10 - x)$$
The only critical value is $x = 10$, $y(10) = 40(40) = 1600$ pounds per acre
$y''(x) = -2$
$y''(10) = -2 < 0$
Therefore, the absolute maximum yield is $y(10) = 1600$ pounds per acre
when the number of trees per acre is 40.

23. Volume = $V(x) = (12 - 2x)(8 - 2x)x, \quad 0 \leq x \leq 4$
$$= 96x - 40x^2 + 4x^3$$
$$V'(x) = 96 - 80x + 12x^2$$
$$= 4(24 - 20x + 3x^2)$$
We solve $24 - 20x + 3x^2 = 0$ by using the
quadratic formula:
$$x = \frac{20 \pm \sqrt{400 - 4 \cdot 24 \cdot 3}}{6} = \frac{10 \pm 2\sqrt{7}}{3}$$

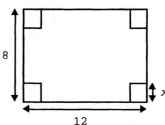

Thus, $x = \dfrac{10 - 2\sqrt{7}}{3} \approx 1.57$ is the only critical value on the interval
$[0, 4]$.
$V''(x) = -80 + 24x$
$V''(1.57) = -80 + 24(1.57) < 0$
Therefore, a square with a side of length $x = 1.57$ inches should be cut
from each corner to obtain the maximum volume.

25. Area = 800 square feet = xy $\quad$ (1)
Cost = $18x + 6(2y + x)$
From (1), we have $y = \dfrac{800}{x}$.

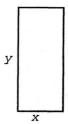

Hence, cost $C(x) = 18x + 6\left(\dfrac{1600}{x} + x\right)$, or

$$C(x) = 24x + \frac{9600}{x}, \quad x > 0,$$

$$C'(x) = 24 - \frac{9600}{x^2} = \frac{24(x^2 - 400)}{x^2} = \frac{24(x - 20)(x + 20)}{x^2}.$$
Therefore, $x = 20$ is the only critical value.
$$C''(x) = \frac{19,200}{x^3}$$

$$C''(20) = \frac{19,200}{8000} > 0. \quad \text{Therefore, } x = 20 \text{ for the}$$

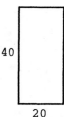

40

20
(Expensive
side)

minimum cost.
The dimensions of the fence are shown in the
diagram at the right.

27. Let x = number of cans of paint produced in each production run. Then, number of production runs: $\dfrac{16,000}{x}$, $1 \le x \le 16,000$

Cost: $C(x)$ = cost of storage + cost of set up

$$= \dfrac{x}{2}(4) + \dfrac{16,000}{x}(500)$$

[Note: $\dfrac{x}{2}$ is the average number of cans of paint in storage per day.]

Thus,

$$C(x) = 2x + \dfrac{8,000,000}{x}, \quad 1 \le x \le 16,000$$

$$C'(x) = 2 - \dfrac{8,000,000}{x^2} = \dfrac{2x^2 - 8,000,000}{x^2} = \dfrac{2(x^2 - 4,000,000)}{x^2}$$

Critical value: $x = 2000$

$$C''(x) = \dfrac{16,000,000}{x^3}; \quad C''(2000) > 0$$

Thus, the minimum cost occurs when $x = 2000$ and the number of production runs is $\dfrac{16,000}{2,000} = 8$.

29. Let x = number of books produced each printing. Then, the number of printings = $\dfrac{50,000}{x}$.

Cost = $C(x)$ = cost of storage + cost of printing

$$= \dfrac{x}{2} + \dfrac{50,000}{x}(1000), \quad x > 0$$

[Note: $\dfrac{x}{2}$ is the average number in storage each day.]

$$C'(x) = \dfrac{1}{2} - \dfrac{50,000,000}{x^2} = \dfrac{x^2 - 100,000,000}{2x^2} = \dfrac{(x + 10,000)(x - 10,000)}{2x^2}$$

Critical value: $x = 10,000$

$$C''(x) = \dfrac{100,000,000}{x^3}$$

$$C''(10,000) = \dfrac{100,000,000}{(10,000)^3} > 0$$

Thus, the minimum cost occurs when $x = 10,000$ and the number of printings is $\dfrac{50,000}{10,000} = 5$.

31. (A) Let the cost to lay the pipe on the land be 1 unit; then the cost to lay the pipe in the lake is 1.4 units.

$$C(x) = \text{total cost} = (1.4)\sqrt{x^2 + 25} + (1)(10 - x), \quad 0 \le x \le 10$$

$$= (1.4)(x^2 + 25)^{1/2} + 10 - x$$

$$C'(x) = (1.4)\dfrac{1}{2}(x^2 + 25)^{-1/2}(2x) - 1$$

$$= (1.4)x(x^2 + 25)^{-1/2} - 1$$

$$= \dfrac{1.4x - \sqrt{x^2 + 25}}{\sqrt{x^2 + 25}}$$

$C'(x) = 0$ when $1.4x - \sqrt{x^2 + 25} = 0$ or $1.96x^2 = x^2 + 25$

$$.96x^2 = 25$$
$$x^2 = \frac{25}{.96} = 26.04$$
$$x = \pm 5.1$$

Thus, the critical value is $x = 5.1$.

$$C''(x) = (1.4)(x^2 + 25)^{-1/2} + (1.4)x\left(-\frac{1}{2}\right)(x^2 + 25)^{-3/2}2x$$

$$= \frac{1.4}{(x^2 + 25)^{1/2}} - \frac{(1.4)x^2}{(x^2 + 25)^{3/2}} = \frac{35}{(x^2 + 25)^{3/2}}$$

$$C''(5.1) = \frac{35}{[(5.1)^2 + 25]^{3/2}} > 0$$

Thus, the cost will be a minimum when $x = 5.1$.

Note that: $C(0) = (1.4)\sqrt{25} + 10 = 17$
$C(5.1) = (1.4)\sqrt{51.01} + (10 - 5.1) = 14.9$
$C(10) = (1.4)\sqrt{125} = 15.65$

Thus, the absolute minimum occurs when $x = 5.1$ miles.

(B) $C(x) = (1.1)\sqrt{x^2 + 25} + (1)(10 - x)$, $0 \leq x \leq 10$

$$C'(x) = \frac{(1.1)x - \sqrt{x^2 + 25}}{\sqrt{x^2 + 25}}$$

$C'(x) = 0$ when $1.1x - \sqrt{x^2 + 25} = 0$ or $(1.21)x^2 = x^2 + 25$

$$.21x^2 = 25$$
$$x^2 = \frac{25}{.21} = 119.05$$
$$x = \pm 10.91$$

Critical value: $x = 10.91 > 10$, i.e., there are no critical values on the interval $[0, 10]$. Now,

$C(0) = (1.1)\sqrt{25} + 10 = 15.5,$
$C(10) = (1.1)\sqrt{125} \approx 12.30.$

Therefore, the absolute minimum occurs when $x = 10$ miles.

33. $C(t) = 30t^2 - 240t + 500$, $0 \leq t \leq 8$
$C'(t) = 60t - 240$; $t = 4$ is the only critical value.
$C''(t) = 60$
$C''(4) = 60 > 0$
Now, $C(0) = 500$
$C(4) = 30(4)^2 - 240(4) + 500 = 20,$
$C(8) = 30(8)^2 - 240(8) + 500 = 500.$

Thus, 4 days after a treatment, the concentration will be minimum; the minimum concentration is 20 bacteria per cm^3.

35. Let x = the number of mice ordered in each order. Then the number of

orders = $\dfrac{500}{x}$.

$C(x) = \text{Cost} = \dfrac{x}{2} \cdot 4 + \dfrac{500}{x}(10)$ [Note: Cost = cost of feeding + cost of order, $\dfrac{x}{2}$ is the average number of mice at any one time.

$C(x) = 2x + \dfrac{5000}{x}$, $0 < x \le 500$

$C'(x) = 2 - \dfrac{5000}{x^2} = \dfrac{2x^2 - 5000}{x^2} = \dfrac{2(x^2 - 2500)}{x^2} = \dfrac{2(x + 50)(x - 50)}{x^2}$

Critical value: $x = 50$ (-50 is not a critical value, since the domain
of C is $x > 0$.

$C''(x) = \dfrac{10,000}{x^3}$ and $C''(50) = \dfrac{10,000}{50^3} > 0$

Therefore, the minimum cost occurs when 50 mice are ordered each time.

The total number of orders is $\dfrac{500}{50} = 10$.

37. $H(t) = 4t^{1/2} - 2t$, $0 \le t \le 2$

$H'(t) = 2t^{-1/2} - 2$

Thus, $t = 1$ is the only critical value.

Now, $H(0) = 4 \cdot 0^{1/2} - 2(0) = 0$,

$\quad\quad H(1) = 4 \cdot 1^{1/2} - 2(1) = 2$,

$\quad\quad H(2) = 4 \cdot 2^{1/2} - 4 \approx 1.66$.

Therefore, $H(1)$ is the absolute maximum, and after one month the maximum
height will be 2 feet.

39. $N(t) = 30 + 12t^2 - t^3$, $0 \le t \le 8$

The rate of increase = $R(t) = N'(t) = 24t - 3t^2$, and

$R'(t) = N''(t) = 24 - 6t$.

Thus, $t = 4$ is the only critical value of $R(t)$.

Now, $R(0) = 0$,

$\quad\quad R(4) = 24 \cdot 4 - 3 \cdot 4^2 = 48$,

$\quad\quad R(8) = 24 \cdot 8 - 3 \cdot 8^2 = 0$.

Therefore, the absolute maximum value of R occurs when $t = 4$; the
maximum rate of increase will occur four years from now.

CHAPTER 2 REVIEW

1. The function f is increasing on (a, c_1), (c_3, c_6). (4-1, 4-2)

2. $f'(x) < 0$ on (c_1, c_3), (c_6, b). (4-1, 4-2)

3. The graph of f is concave downward on (a, c_2), (c_4, c_5), (c_7, b).

(4-1, 4-2)

4. A local minimum occurs at $x = c_3$. (4-1)

5. The absolute maximum occurs at $x = c_6$. (4-4)

6. $f'(x)$ appears to be zero at $x = c_1$, c_3, c_5. (4-1)

7. $f'(x)$ does not exist at $x = c_6$. (4-1)

8. $x = c_2$, c_4, c_5, c_7 are inflection points. (4-2)

9.

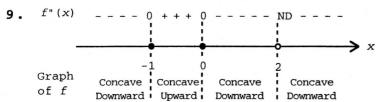

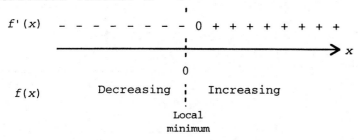

Using this information together with the points $(-3, 0)$, $(-2, 3)$, $(-1, 2)$, $(0, 0)$, $(2, -3)$, $(3, 0)$ on the graph, we have

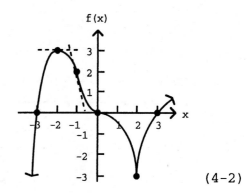

10. Domain: all real numbers
Intercepts: y-intercept: $f(0) = 0$
            x-intercepts: $x = 0$
Asymptotes: Horizontal asymptote: $y = 2$
            no vertical asymptotes
Critical values: $x = 0$

(4-2)

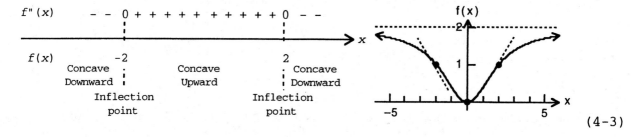

(4-3)

11. $f(x) = x^4 + 5x^3$

$f'(x) = 4x^3 + 15x^2$

$f''(x) = 12x^2 + 30x$ (4-2)

12. $y = 3x + \dfrac{4}{x}$

$y' = 3 - \dfrac{4}{x^2}$

$y'' = \dfrac{8}{x^3}$ (4-2)

13. $f(x) = x^3 - 18x^2 + 81x$

Step 1. Analyze $f(x)$:

Intercepts: y-intercept: $f(0) = 0^3 - 18(0)^2 + 81(0) = 0$

$\quad\quad\quad\quad\quad$ x-intercepts: $x^3 - 18x^2 + 81x = 0$

$$x(x^2 - 18x + 81) = 0$$
$$x(x - 9)^2 = 0$$
$$x = 0, 9$$

Step 2. Analyze $f'(x)$:

$f'(x) = 3x^2 - 36x + 81 = 3(x^2 - 12x + 27) = 3(x - 3)(x - 9)$

zeros of $f'(x)$: $x = 3$, $x = 9$

Sign chart for f':

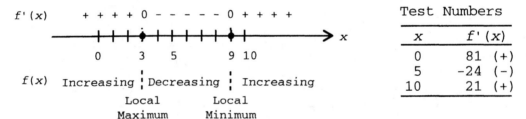

Test Numbers	
x	$f'(x)$
0	81 (+)
5	-24 (-)
10	21 (+)

Thus, f is increasing on $(-\infty, 3)$ and on $(9, \infty)$; f is decreasing on $(3, 9)$. There is a local maximum at $x = 3$ and a local minimum at $x = 9$.

Step 3. Analyze $f''(x)$:

$f''(x) = 6x - 36 = 6(x - 6)$

Thus, $x = 6$ is a partition number for f''.

Sign chart for f'':

Test Numbers	
x	$f''(x)$
0	-36 (-)
7	6 (+)

Thus, the graph of f is concave downward on $(-\infty, 6)$ and concave upward on $(6, \infty)$. The point $x = 6$ is an inflection point.

Step 4. Sketch the graph of f:

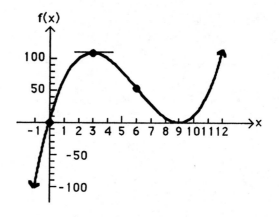

(4-2)

14. $f(x) = (x + 4)(x - 2)^2$

Step 1. Analyze $f(x)$:

(A) Domain: All real numbers, $(-\infty, \infty)$.

(B) Intercepts: y intercept: $f(0) = 4(-2)^2 = 16$
    x intercepts: $(x + 4)(x - 2)^2 = 0$
    $x = -4, 2$

(C) Asymptotes: Since f is a polynomial, there are no horizontal or vertical asymptotes.

Step 2. Analyze $f'(x)$:

$f'(x) = (x + 4)2(x - 2)(1) + (x - 2)^2(1)$
$\quad = (x - 2)[2(x + 4) + (x - 2)]$
$\quad = (x - 2)(3x + 6)$
$\quad = 3(x - 2)(x + 2)$

Critical values: $x = -2$, $x = 2$
Partition numbers: $x = -2$, $x = 2$
Sign chart for f':

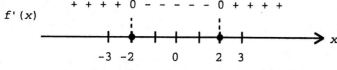

Test Numbers	
x	$f'(x)$
-3	15 (+)
0	-12 (-)
3	15 (+)

Thus, f is increasing on $(-\infty, -2)$ and on $(2, \infty)$; f is decreasing on $(-2, 2)$; f has a local maximum at $x = -2$ and a local minimum at $x = 2$.

Step 3. Analyze $f''(x)$:

$f''(x) = 3(x + 2)(1) + 3(x - 2)(1) = 6x$
Partition number for f'': $x = 0$

Sign chart for f'':

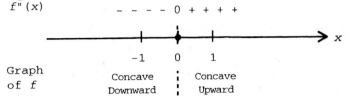

$f''(x)$ - - - - 0 + + + +

-1   0   1

Graph of f

Concave Downward   Concave Upward

Inflection Point

Test Numbers	
x	$f''(x)$
1	-6 (-)
1	6 (+)

Thus, the graph of f is concave downward on $(-\infty, 0)$ and concave upward on $(0, \infty)$; there is an inflection point at $x = 0$.

Step 4.   Sketch the graph of f:

x	$f(x)$
-2	32
0	16
2	0

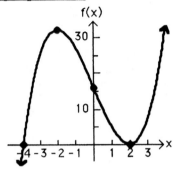

(4-2)

15. $f(x) = 8x^3 - 2x^4$

Step 1.   Analyze $f(x)$:

(A) Domain: All real numbers, $(-\infty, \infty)$.

(B) Intercepts: y intercept: $f(0) = 0$

                x intercepts: $8x^3 - 2x^4 = 0$

$$2x^3(4 - x) = 0$$
$$x = 0, 4$$

(C) Asymptotes: No horizontal or vertical asymptotes.

Step 2.   Analyze $f'(x)$:

$f'(x) = 24x^2 - 8x^3 = 8x^2(3 - x)$

Critical values: $x = 0$, $x = 3$

Partition numbers: $x = 0$, $x = 3$

Sign chart for f':

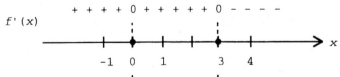

$f'(x)$ + + + + 0 + + + + + 0 - - - -

-1   0   1   3   4

$f(x)$ Increasing   Increasing   Decreasing

Local Maximum

Test Numbers	
x	$f'(x)$
-1	32 (+)
1	16 (+)
4	-128 (-)

Thus, f is increasing on $(-\infty, 3)$ and decreasing on $(3, \infty)$; f has a local maximum at $x = 3$.

$f''(x) = 48x - 24x^2 = 24x(2 - x)$

Partition numbers for f'': $x = 0$, $x = 2$

Sign chart for f'':

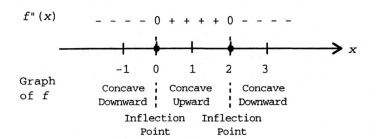

Test Numbers

x	$f''(x)$
-1	-72 (-)
1	24 (+)
3	-72 (-)

Thus, the graph of f is concave downward on $(-\infty, 0)$ and on $(2, \infty)$; the graph is concave upward on $(0, 2)$; there are inflection points at $x = 0$ and $x = 2$.

Step 4. Sketch the graph of f:

x	$f(x)$
0	0
2	32
3	54

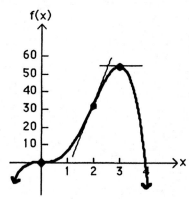

(4-2)

16. $f(x) = (x - 1)^3(x + 3)$

Step 1. Analyze $f(x)$:

(A) Domain: All real numbers.

(B) Intercepts: y intercept: $f(0) = (-1)^3(3) = -3$

x intercepts: $(x - 1)^3(x + 3) = 0$

$x = 1, -3$

(C) Asymptotes: Since f is a polynomial (of degree 4), the graph of f has no asymptotes.

Step 2. Analyze $f'(x)$:

$f'(x) = (x - 1)^3(1) + (x + 3)(3)(x - 1)^2(1)$

$= (x - 1)^2[(x - 1) + 3(x + 3)]$

$= 4(x - 1)^2(x + 2)$

Critical values: $x = -2$, $x = 1$

Partition numbers: $x = -2$, $x = 1$

Sign chart for f':

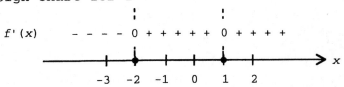

Thus, f is decreasing on $(-\infty, -2)$; f is increasing on $(-2, 1)$ and $(1, \infty)$; f has a local minimum at $x = -2$.

Step 3.   Analyze $f''(x)$:

$$f''(x) = 4(x - 1)^2(1) + 4(x + 2)(2)(x - 1)(1)$$
$$= 4(x - 1)[(x - 1) + 2(x + 2)]$$
$$= 12(x - 1)(x + 1)$$

Partition numbers for f'': $x = -1$, $x = 1$.
Sign chart for f'':

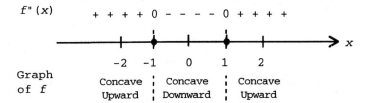

Thus, the graph of f is concave upward on $(-\infty, -1)$ and on $(1, \infty)$; the graph of f is concave downward on $(-1, 1)$; the graph has inflection points at $x = -1$ and at $x = 1$.

Step 4.   Sketch the graph of f:

x	$f(x)$
-2	-27
0	-3
1	0

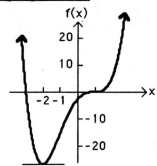

(4-2)

17. $f(x) = \dfrac{3x}{x + 2}$

Step 1. Analyze $f(x)$:
The domain of f is all real numbers except $x = -2$.

Intercepts: y-intercept: $f(0) = \dfrac{3(0)}{0 + 2} = 0$

x-intercepts: $\dfrac{3x}{x + 2} = 0$

$3x = 0$

$x = 0$

Asymptotes:

Horizontal asymptotes: $\dfrac{a_n x^n}{b_m x^m} = \dfrac{3x}{x} = 3$

Thus, the line $y = 3$ is a horizontal asymptote.

Vertical asymptote(s): The denominator is 0 at $x = -2$ and the numerator is nonzero at $x = -2$. Thus, the line $x = -2$ is a vertical asymptote.

Step 2. Analyze $f'(x)$:

$$f'(x) = \dfrac{(x + 2)(3) - 3x(1)}{(x + 2)^2} = \dfrac{6}{(x + 2)^2}$$

Critical values: $f'(x) = \dfrac{6}{(x + 2)^2} \neq 0$ for all x $(x \neq -2)$.

Thus, f does not have any critical values.

Partition numbers: $x = -2$ is a partition number for f'.

Sign chart for f':

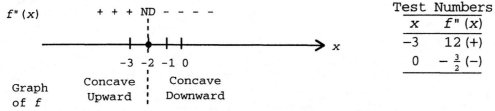

Test Numbers	
x	$f'(x)$
-3	$6\ (+)$
0	$\frac{3}{2}\ (+)$

Thus, f is increasing on $(-\infty, -2)$ and on $(-2, \infty)$; f does not have any local extrema.

Step 3. Analyze $f''(x)$:

$$f''(x) = -12(x + 2)^{-3} = \dfrac{-12}{(x + 2)^3}$$

Partition numbers for f'': $x = -2$

Sign chart for f'':

Test Numbers	
x	$f''(x)$
-3	$12\ (+)$
0	$-\frac{3}{2}\ (-)$

The graph of f is concave upward on $(-\infty, -2)$ and concave downward on $(-2, \infty)$. The graph of f does not have any inflection points.

165

Step 4. Sketch the graph of f:

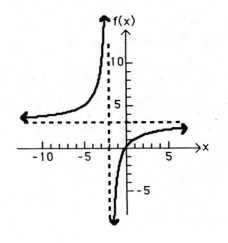

(4-3)

18. $f(x) = \dfrac{x^2}{x^2 + 27}$

Step 1. Analyze $f(x)$:

(A) Domain: All real numbers.
(B) Intercepts: y-intercepts: $f(0) = 0$

$\qquad\qquad\qquad$ x-intercepts: $\dfrac{x^2}{x^2 + 27} = 0$, $x = 0$

(C) Asymptotes

$\qquad$ Horizontal asymptote: $\dfrac{x^2}{x^2} = 1$; $y = 1$ is a horizontal asymptote

$\qquad$ Vertical asymptote: no vertical asymptotes

Step 2. Analyze $f'(x)$:

$$f'(x) = \frac{(x^2 + 27)(2x) - x^2(2x)}{(x^2 + 27)^2} = \frac{54x}{(x^2 + 27)^2}$$

Critical values: $x = 0$
Partition numbers: $x = 0$

Sign chart for f':

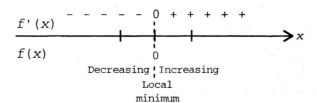

Thus, f is decreasing on $(-\infty, 0)$ and increasing on $(0, \infty)$; f has a local minimum at $x = 0$.

Step 3. Analyze $f''(x)$:

$$f''(x) = \frac{(x^2 + 27)^2(54) - 54x(2)(x^2 + 27)2x}{(x^2 + 27)^4} = \frac{162(9 - x^2)}{(x^2 + 27)^3}$$

Partition numbers for $f''(x)$: $x = -3$, $x = 3$

Sign chart for f'':

$$f''(x) \quad - - \ 0 \ + + + + \ 0 \ - -$$

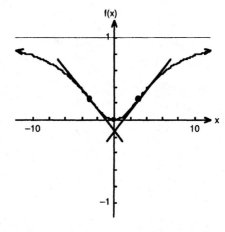

| Graph of f | Concave Downward | Concave Upward | Concave Downward |

Inflection point   Inflection point

Test Numbers

x	$f''(x)$
-4	$(-)$
0	$(+)$
4	$(-)$

The graph of f is concave upward on $(-3, 3)$ and concave downward on $(-\infty, -3)$ and $(3, \infty)$; the graph has inflection points at $x = -3$ and $x = 3$.

Step 4. Sketch the graph of f:

x	$f(x)$
-3	$\frac{1}{4}$
0	0
3	$\frac{1}{4}$

19. $f(x) = \dfrac{x}{(x + 2)^2}$

(4-3)

Step 1. Analyze $f(x)$:

(A) Domain: All real numbers except $x = -2$.

(B) Intercepts: y-intercepts: $f(0) = 0$

x-intercepts: $\dfrac{x}{(x + 2)^2} = 0$, $x = 0$

(C) Asymptotes

Horizontal asymptote: $\dfrac{x}{x^2} = \dfrac{1}{x} = 1$; $y = 0$ (the x-axis) is a horizontal asymptote.

Vertical asymptote: $x = -2$ is a vertical asymptote

Step 2. Analyze $f'(x)$:

$$f'(x) = \frac{(x + 2)^2 - x(2)(x + 2)}{(x + 2)^4} = \frac{2 - x}{(x + 2)^3}$$

Critical values: $x = 2$

Partition numbers: $x = -2$, $x = 2$

Sign chart for f':

$$f'(x) \quad - - \ \text{ND} + + + + + \ 0 \ - -$$

| $f(x)$ | Decreasing | Increasing | Decreasing |

Local maximum

Test Numbers

x	$f'(x)$
-3	$-5 \ (-)$
0	$\frac{1}{4} \ (+)$
3	$-\frac{1}{125} \ (-)$

Thus, f is increasing on $(-2, 2)$ and decreasing on $(-\infty, -2)$ and $(2, \infty)$; f has a local maximum at $x = 2$.

Step 3. Analyze $f''(x)$:

$$f''(x) = \frac{(x + 2)^3(-1) - (2 - x)(3)(x + 2)^2}{(x + 2)^6} = \frac{2(x - 4)}{(x + 2)^4}$$

Partition numbers for $f''(x)$: $x = -2$, $x = 4$
Sign chart for f'':

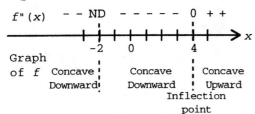

Test Numbers	
x	$f''(x)$
-3	$-14 \ (-)$
0	$-\frac{1}{2} \ (-)$
5	$(+)$

The graph of f is concave upward on $(4, \infty)$ and concave downward on $(-\infty, -2)$ and $(-2, 4)$; the graph has an inflection point at $x = 4$.

Step 4. Sketch the graph of f:

x	$f(x)$
0	0
2	$\frac{1}{8}$
4	$\frac{1}{9}$

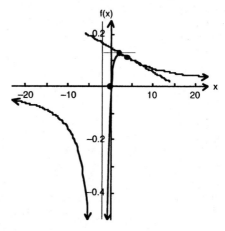

$(4-3)$

20. $f(x) = \dfrac{x^3}{x^2 + 3}$

Step 1. Analyze $f(x)$:

(A) Domain: All real numbers.

(B) Intercepts: y-intercepts: $f(0) = 0$

$\qquad\qquad\qquad\quad$ x-intercepts: $\dfrac{x^3}{x^2 + 3} = 0$, $x = 0$

(C) Asymptotes

$\quad$ Horizontal asymptote: $\dfrac{x^3}{x^2} = x$; no horizontal asymptote.

$\quad$ Vertical asymptote: no vertical asymptotes

Step 2. Analyze $f'(x)$:

$$f'(x) = \frac{(x^2 + 3)(3x^2) - x^3(2x)}{(x^2 + 3)^2} = \frac{x^2(x^2 + 9)}{(x^2 + 3)^2}$$

Critical values: $x = 0$
Partition numbers: $x = 0$

168

Sign chart for f':

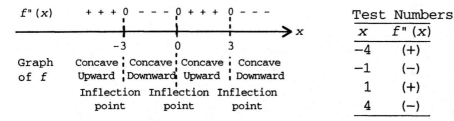

f is increasing on $(-\infty, \infty)$.

Step 3. Analyze $f''(x)$:

$$f''(x) = \frac{(x^2 + 3)(4x^3 + 18x) - x^2(x^2 + 9)(2)(x^2 + 3)2x}{(x^2 + 3)^4} = \frac{6x(9 - x^2)}{(x^2 + 3)^3}$$

Partition numbers for $f''(x)$: $x = -3$, $x = 0$, $x = 3$
Sign chart for f'':

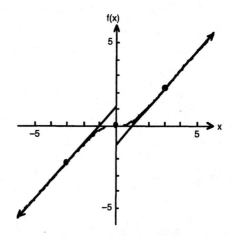

Test Numbers	
x	$f''(x)$
-4	$(+)$
-1	$(-)$
1	$(+)$
4	$(-)$

The graph of f is concave upward on $(-\infty, -3)$ and $(0, 3)$, and concave downward on $(-3, 0)$ and $(3, \infty)$; the graph has inflection points at $x = -3$, $x = 0$, $x = 3$.

Step 4. Sketch the graph of f:

x	$f(x)$
-3	$-\frac{9}{4}$
0	0
3	$\frac{9}{4}$

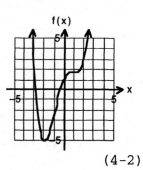

(4-3)

21.

x	$f'(x)$	$f(x)$
$-\infty < x < -2$	Negative and increasing	Decreasing and concave upward
$x = -2$	x-intercept	Local minimum
$-2 < x < -1$	Positive and increasing	Increasing and concave upward
$x = -1$	Local maximum	Inflection point
$-1 < x < 1$	Positive and decreasing	Increasing and concave downward
$x = 1$	Local minimum	Inflection point
$1 < x < \infty$	Positive and increasing	Increasing and concave upward

(4-2)

22. The graph in (C) could be the graph of $y = f''(x)$.

(4-2)

23. $f(x) = x^3 - 6x^2 - 15x + 12$

$\quad f'(x) = 3x^2 - 12x - 15$

$\quad\ 3x^2 - 12x - 15 = 0$

$\quad\ 3(x^2 - 4x - 5) = 0$

$\quad 3(x - 5)(x + 1) = 0$

Thus, $x = -1$ and $x = 5$ are critical values of f.

$\qquad f''(x) = 6x - 12$

Now, $f''(-1) = 6(-1) - 12 = -18 < 0$.

Thus, f has a local maximum at $x = -1$.

Also, $f''(5) = 6(5) - 12 = 18 > 0$ and f has a local minimum at $x = 5$.

$\hfill$ (4-2)

24. $y = f(x) = x^3 - 12x + 12$, $-3 \le x \le 5$

$\quad f'(x) = 3x^2 - 12$

Critical values: f' is defined for all x:

$\quad f'(x) = 3x^2 - 12 = 0$

$\qquad\quad 3(x^2 - 4) = 0$

$\quad\ 3(x - 2)(x + 2) = 0$

Thus, the critical values of f are: $x = -2$, $x = 2$.

$\quad f(-3) = (-3)^3 - 12(-3) + 12 = 21$

$\quad f(-2) = (-2)^3 - 12(-2) + 12 = 28$

$\quad\ f(2) = 2^3 - 12(2) + 12 = -4$ Absolute minimum

$\quad\ f(5) = 5^3 - 12(5) + 12 = 77$ Absolute maximum

$\hfill$ (4-4)

25. $y = f(x) = x^2 + \dfrac{16}{x^2}$, $x > 0$

$\quad f'(x) = 2x - \dfrac{32}{x^3} = \dfrac{2x^4 - 32}{x^3} = \dfrac{2(x^4 - 16)}{x^3} = \dfrac{2(x - 2)(x + 2)(x^2 + 4)}{x^3}$

$\quad f''(x) = 2 + \dfrac{96}{x^4}$

The only critical value of f in the interval $(0, \infty)$ is $x = 2$. Since

$\quad f''(2) = 2 + \dfrac{96}{2^4} = 8 > 0$,

$\quad f(2) = 8$ is the absolute minimum of f on $(0, \infty)$.

$\hfill$ (4-4)

26. Yes. Consider f on the interval $[a, b]$. Since f is a polynomial, f is continuous on $[a, b]$. Therefore, f has an absolute maximum on $[a, b]$. Since f has a local minimum at $x = a$ and $x = b$, the absolute maximum of f on $[a, b]$ must occur at some point c in (a, b); f has a local maximum at $x = c$.

$\hfill$ (4-4)

27. No, increasing/decreasing properties are stated in terms of intervals in the domain of f. A correct statement is: $f(x)$ is decreasing on $(-\infty, 0)$ and $(0, \infty)$.

$\hfill$ (4-1)

28. A critical value for $f(x)$ is a partition number for $f'(x)$ that is also in the domain of f. However, $f'(x)$ may have partition numbers that are not in the domain of f and hence are not critical values for $f(x)$. For example, let $f(x) = \dfrac{1}{x}$. Then $f'(x) = -\dfrac{1}{x^2}$ and 0 is a partition number for $f'(x)$, but 0 is NOT a critical value for $f(x)$ since it is not in the domain of f.

(4-1)

29. $f(x) = 6x^2 - x^3 + 8$, $0 \le x \le 4$

$f'(x) = 12x - 3x^2$
$f''(x) = 12 - 6x$

Now, $f''(x)$ is defined for all x and $f''(x) = 12 - 6x = 0$ implies $x = 2$. Thus, f' has a critical value at $x = 2$. Since this is the only critical value of f' and $(f'(x))'' = f'''(x) = -6$ so that $f'''(2) = -6 < 0$, it follows that $f'(2) = 12$ is the absolute maximum of f'. The graph is shown at the right.

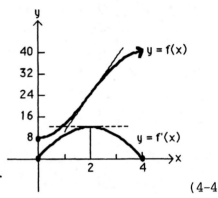

(4-4

30. Let $x > 0$ be one of the numbers. Then $\dfrac{400}{x}$ is the other number. Now, we have:

$$S(x) = x + \frac{400}{x}, \quad x > 0,$$

$$S'(x) = 1 - \frac{400}{x^2} = \frac{x^2 - 400}{x^2} = \frac{(x - 20)(x + 20)}{x^2}$$

Thus, $x = 20$ is the only critical value of S on $(0, \infty)$.

$$S''(x) = \frac{800}{x^3} \quad \text{and} \quad S''(20) = \frac{800}{8000} = \frac{1}{10} > 0$$

Therefore, $S(20) = 20 + \dfrac{400}{20} = 40$ is the absolute minimum sum, and this occurs when each number is 20.

(4-4)

31. $f(x) = x^4 + x^3 + 4x^2 - 3x + 4$.
Step 1. Analyze $f(x)$:
(A) Domain: All real numbers (f is a polynomial function)
(B) Intercepts: y-intercept: $f(0) = 4$
               x-intercepts: $x \approx 0.79, 1.64$
(C) Asymptotes: Since f is a polynomial function (of degree 4), the graph of f has no asymptotes.

Step 2. Analyze $f'(x)$:
    $f'(x) = 4x^3 + 3x^2 - 8x - 3$
Critical values: $x \approx -1.68, -0.35, 1.28$;
f is increasing on $(-1.68, -0.35)$ and $(1.28, \infty)$; f is decreasing on $(-\infty, -1.68)$ and $(-0.35, 1.28)$. f has local minima at $x = -1.68$ and $x = 1.28$. f has a local maximum at $x = -0.35$.

Step 3. Analyze $f''(x)$:

   $f''(x) = 12x^2 + 6x - 8$

The graph of f is concave downward on $(-1.10, 0.60)$; the graph of f is concave upward on $(-\infty, -1.10)$ and $(0.60, \infty)$; the graph has inflection points at $x \approx -1.10$ and 0.60.

(4-2)

32. $f(x) = 0.25x^4 - 5x^3 + 31x^2 - 70x$

Step 1. Analyze $f(x)$:

(A) Domain: all real numbers

(B) Intercepts: y-intercept: $f(0) = 0$
                x-intercepts: $x = 0$, 11.10

(C) Asymptotes: since f is a polynomial function (of degree 4), the graph of f has no asymptotes; $\lim\limits_{x \to \pm\infty} f(x) = \infty$

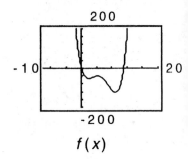

$f(x)$

Step 2. Analyze $f'(x)$:

$f'(x) = x^3 - 15x^2 + 62x - 70$

Critical values: $x \approx 1.87$, 4.19, 8.94

Sign chart for f':

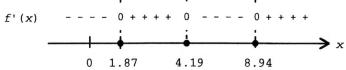

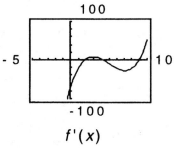

$f'(x)$

f is increasing on $(1.87, 4.19)$ and $(8.94, \infty)$;
f is decreasing on $(-\infty, 1.87)$ and $(4.19, 8.94)$;
f has local minima at $x = 1.87$ and $x = 8.94$;
f has a local maximum at $x = 4.19$

Step 3. Analyze f'':

$f''(x) = 3x^2 - 30x + 62$
Partition numbers for f'': $x \approx 2.92$, 7.08
Sign chart for f'':

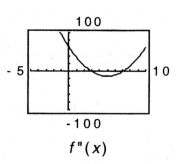

$f''(x)$

The graph of f is concave downward on $(2.92, 7.08)$ and concave upward on $(-\infty, 2.92)$ and $(7.08, \infty)$; the graph has inflection points at $x = 2.92$ and $x = 7.08$.

(4-2)

33. (A) For the first 15 months, the price is increasing and concave down, with a local maximum at $t = 15$. For the next 15 months, the price is decreasing and concave down, with an inflection point at $t = 30$. For the next 15 months, the price is decreasing and concave up, with a local minimum at $t = 45$. For the remaining 15 months, the price is increasing and concave up.

(B)

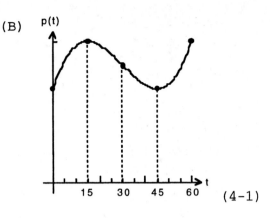

(4-1)

34. (A) $R(x) = xp(x) = 500x - 0.025x^2$, $0 \le x \le 20,000$
$R'(x) = 500 - 0.05x$; $500 - 0.05x = 0$
$$x = 10,000$$
Thus, $x = 10,000$ is a critical value.

Now, $R(0) = 0$
$R(10,000) = 2,500,000$
$R(20,000) = 0$

Thus, $R(10,000) = \$2,500,000$ is the absolute maximum of R.

(B) $P(x) = R(x) - C(x) = 500x - 0.025x^2 - (350x + 50,000)$
$$= 150x - 0.025x^2 - 50,000, \ 0 \le x \le 20,000$$
$P'(x) = 150 - 0.05x$; $150 - 0.05x = 0$
$$x = 3,000$$

Now, $P(0) = -50,000$
$P(3,000) = 175,000$
$P(20,000) = -7,050,000$

Thus, the maximum profit is \$175,000 when 3000 stoves are manufactured and sold at $p(3,000) = \$425$ each.

(C) If the government taxes the company \$20 per stove, then the cost equation is:
$$C(x) = 370x + 50,000$$
and
$$P(x) = 500x - 0.025x^2 - (370x + 50,000)$$
$$= 130x - 0.025x^2 - 50,000, \ 0 \le x \le 20,000$$
$$P'(x) = 130 - 0.05x; \ 130 - 0.05x = 0$$
$$x = 2,600$$

The maximum profit is $P(2,600) = \$119,000$ when 2,600 stoves are produced and sold for $p(2,600) = \$435$ each. (4-5)

35.

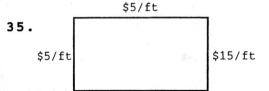

Let x be the length and y the width of the rectangle.

173

(A) $C(x, y) = 5x + 5x + 5y + 15y = 10x + 20y$

Also, Area $A = xy = 5000$, so $y = \dfrac{5000}{x}$

and $C(x) = 10x + \dfrac{100,000}{x}$, $x \geq 0$

Now, $C'(x) = 10 - \dfrac{100,000}{x^2}$ and

$10 - \dfrac{100,000}{x^2} = 0$ implies $10x^2 = 100,000$

$$x^2 = 10,000$$
$$x = \pm 100$$

Thus, $x = 100$ is the critical value.

Now, $C''(x) = \dfrac{200,000}{x^3}$ and $C''(100) = \dfrac{200,000}{1,000,000} = 0.2 > 0$

and the most economical (i.e. least cost) fence will have dimensions: length $x = 100$ feet and width $y = \dfrac{5000}{100} = 50$ feet.

(B) We want to maximize $A = xy$ subject to
$C(x, y) = 10x + 20y = 3000$ or $x = 300 - 2y$
Thus, $A = y(300 - 2y) = 300y - 2y^2$, $0 \leq y \leq 150$.

Now, $A'(y) = 300 - 4y$ and
$300 - 4y = 0$ implies $y = 75$.

Therefore, $y = 75$ is the critical value.

Now, $A''(y) = -4$ and $A''(75) = -4 < 0$. Thus, A has an absolute maximum when $y = 75$. Therefore the dimensions of the rectangle that will enclose maximum area are:
length $x = 300 - 2(75) = 150$ feet and width $y = 75$ feet. (4-5)

36. Let x = the number of dollars increase in the nightly rate, $x \geq 0$. Then $200 - 4x$ rooms will be rented at $(40 + x)$ dollars per room. [Note: Since $200 - 4x \geq 0$, $x \leq 50$.] The cost of service for $200 - 4x$ rooms at \$8 per room is $8(200 - 4x)$. Thus:

Gross profit: $P(x) = (200 - 4x)(40 + x) - 8(200 - 4x)$
$= (200 - 4x)(32 + x)$
$= 6400 + 72x - 4x^2$, $0 \leq x \leq 50$

$P'(x) = 72 - 8x$
Critical value: $72 - 8x = 0$
$x = 9$

Now, $P(0) = 6400$
$P(9) = 6724$ Absolute maximum
$P(50) = 0$

Thus, the maximum gross profit is \$6724 and this occurs at $x = 9$, i.e., the rooms should be rented at \$49 per night. (4-5)

37. Let x = number of times the company should order. Then, the number of disks per order = $\dfrac{7200}{x}$. The average number of unsold disks is given by:

$$\frac{7200}{2x} = \frac{3600}{x}$$

Total cost: $C(x) = 5x + 0.2\left(\dfrac{3600}{x}\right)$, $x > 0$

$$C(x) = 5x + \dfrac{720}{x}$$

$$C'(x) = 5 - \dfrac{720}{x^2} = \dfrac{5x^2 - 720}{x^2} = \dfrac{5(x^2 - 144)}{x^2}$$

$$= \dfrac{5(x + 12)(x - 12)}{x^2}$$

Critical value: $x = 12$ [Note: $x > 0$, so $x = -12$ is not a critical value.]

$C''(x) = \dfrac{1440}{x^3}$ and $C''(12) = \dfrac{1440}{12^3} > 0$

Therefore, $C(x)$ is a minimum when $x = 12$. (4-5)

38. $C(x) = 4000 + 10x + 0.1x^2$, $x > 0$

Average cost $= \overline{C}(x) = \dfrac{4000}{x} + 10 + 0.1x$

Marginal cost $= C'(x) = 10 + \dfrac{2}{10}x = 10 + 0.2x$

The graph of $C'(x)$ is a straight line with slope $\dfrac{1}{5}$ and y intercept 10.

$\overline{C}'(x) = \dfrac{-4000}{x^2} + \dfrac{1}{10} = \dfrac{-40,000 + x^2}{10x^2} = \dfrac{(x + 200)(x - 200)}{10x^2}$

Thus, $\overline{C}'(x) < 0$ on $(0, 200)$ and $\overline{C}'(x) > 0$ on $(200, \infty)$. Therefore, $\overline{C}(x)$ is decreasing on $(0, 200)$, increasing on $(200, \infty)$, and a minimum occurs at $x = 200$.

Min $\overline{C}(x) = \overline{C}(200) = \dfrac{4000}{200} + 10 + \dfrac{1}{10}(200) = 50$

$\overline{C}''(x) = \dfrac{8000}{x^3} > 0$ on $(0, \infty)$.

Therefore, the graph of $\overline{C}(x)$ is concave upward on $(0, \infty)$.

Using this information and point-by-point plotting (use a calculator), the graphs of $C(x)$ and $\overline{C}(x)$ are as shown in the diagram at the right.

The line $y = 0.1x + 10$ is an oblique asymptote for $y = \overline{C}(x)$.

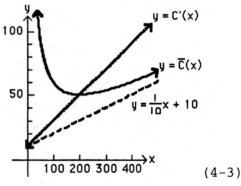

(4-3)

39. $N(x) = -0.25x^4 + 11x^3 - 108x^2 + 3,000$, $9 \le x \le 24$

$N'(x) = -x^3 + 33x^2 - 216x$

$N''(x) = -3x^2 + 66x - 216 = -3(x^2 - 22x + 72)$

$\qquad\qquad\qquad = -3(x - 4)(x - 18)$

Partition numbers for $N''(x)$: $x = 18$

Sign chart for $N''(x)$:

$$N''(x) \quad + + + + \; 0 \; - - - - \; \circ$$

$$N'(x) \quad 9 \qquad\qquad 18 \qquad 24$$

Increasing ┊ Decreasing

Test Numbers

x	$N''(x)$
17	39 (+)
19	−45 (−)

Thus, N' is increasing on (9, 18) and decreasing on (18, 24); the point of diminishing returns is $x = 18$; the maximum rate of change is $N'(18) = 972$.

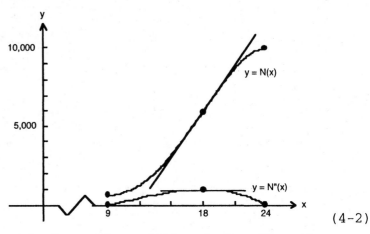

$(4-2)$

40. Let x be the length of the vertical portion of the chain. Then the length of each of the "arms" of the "Y" is $\sqrt{(10 - x)^2 + 36} = \sqrt{x^2 - 20x + 136}$. Thus, the total length is given by:

$$L(x) = x + 2\sqrt{x^2 - 20x + 136} \quad 0 \le x \le 10$$

Now,

$$L'(x) = 1 + 2\left(\frac{1}{2}\right)(x^2 - 20x + 136)^{-1/2}(2x - 20)$$

$$= 1 + \frac{2x - 20}{(x^2 - 20x + 136)^{1/2}}$$

$$L'(x) = 0: \quad 1 + \frac{2x - 20}{(x^2 - 20x + 136)^{1/2}} = 0$$

$$(x^2 - 20x + 136)^{1/2} + 2x - 20 = 0$$

$$(x^2 - 20x + 136)^{1/2} = 2(10 - x)$$

$$x^2 - 20x + 136 = 4(100 - 20x + x^2)$$

$$-3x^2 + 60x - 264 = 0$$

$$x = \frac{20 \pm \sqrt{48}}{2} = 10 \pm 2\sqrt{3}$$

Critical value (in (0, 10)): $x = 10 - 2\sqrt{3} \approx 6.54$

Sign chart for $L'(x)$:

$$L'(x) \quad - - - - \; 0 \; + + + +$$

$$L(x) \quad 0 \qquad 6.54 \qquad 10$$

Decreasing ┊ Increasing
Local
minimum

Test Numbers

x	$L'(x)$
0	(−)
10	1 (+)

Thus, to minimize the length of the chain, the vertical portion should be 6.54 feet long. The total length of the chain will be $L(6.54) = 20.39$ feet.

$(4-5)$

41. (A)

```
QuadReg
 y=ax²+bx+c
 a=.0061285714
 b=.1224285714
 c=102.2
```

(B) Let $C(x)$ be the regression equation from part (A). The average cost function $\overline{C}(x) = \dfrac{C(x)}{x}$.

Using the "find the minimum" routine on the graphing utility, we find that
$$\min \overline{C}(x) = \overline{C}(129) = 1.71$$

The minimum average cost is \$1.71 at a production level of 129 dozen cookies. (4-5)

42. (A)

```
CubicReg
 y=ax³+bx²+cx+d
 a=-.01
 b=.83
 c=-2.3
 d=221
```

(B) The regression equation found in (A) is:
$$y(x) = -0.01x^3 + 0.83x^2 - 2.3x + 221$$

The rate of change of sales with respect to the number of ads is:

$$y'(x) = -0.03x^2 + 1.66x - 2.3$$
$$y''(x) = -0.06x + 1.66$$

Critical value: $-0.06x + 1.66 = 0$
$$x \approx 27.667$$

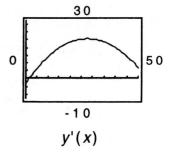

$y'(x)$

From the graph, the absolute maximum of $y'(x)$ occurs at $x \approx 27.667$. Thus, 28 ads should be placed each month. The expected number of sales is: $y(28) \approx 588$ (4-5)

43. $C(t) = 20t^2 - 120t + 800, \ 0 \le t \le 9$

$C'(t) = 40t - 120 = 40(t - 3)$

Critical value: $t = 3$

$C''(t) = 40$ and $C''(3) = 40 > 0$

Therefore, a local minimum occurs at $t = 3$.

$C(3) = 20(3^2) - 120(3) + 800 = 620$ Absolute minimum

$C(0) = 800$

$C(9) = 20(81) - 120(9) + 800 = 1340$

Therefore, the bacteria count will be at a minimum three days after a treatment. (4-5)

44. $N = 10 + 6t^2 - t^3, \ 0 \le t \le 5$

$\dfrac{dN}{dt} = 12t - 3t^2$

Now, find the critical values of the rate function $R(t)$:

$R(t) = \dfrac{dN}{dt} = 12t - 3t^2$

$R'(t) = \dfrac{dR}{dt} = \dfrac{d^2N}{dt^2} = 12 - 6t$

Critical value: $t = 2$

$R''(t) = -6$ and $R''(2) = -6 < 0$

$R(0) = 0$

$R(2) = 12$ Absolute maximum

$R(5) = -15$

Therefore, $R(t)$ has an absolute maximum at $t = 2$. The rate of increase will be a maximum after two years. (4-4)

3 Additional Derivative Topics

Things to remember:

1. THE NUMBER e

   The irrational number e is defined by
   $$e = \lim_{n \to \infty} \left(1 + \frac{1}{n}\right)^n$$
   or alternatively,
   $$e = \lim_{s \to 0} (1 + s)^{1/s}$$
   $$e = 2.7182818\ldots$$

2. CONTINUOUS COMPOUND INTEREST

   $$A = Pe^{rt}$$
   where P = Principal
   r = Annual nominal interest rate compounded continuously
   t = Time in years
   A = Amount at time t

---

1. $A = \$1000e^{0.1t}$
When $t = 2$, $A = \$1000e^{(0.1)2} = \$1000e^{0.2} = \$1221.40$.
When $t = 5$, $A = \$1000e^{(0.1)5} = \$1000e^{0.5} = \$1628.72$.
When $t = 8$, $A = \$1000e^{(0.1)8} = \$1000e^{0.8} = \$2225.54$

3.

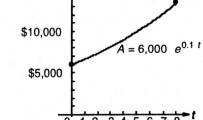

5. $2 = e^{0.06t}$
Take the natural log of both sides of this equation
$$\ln(e^{0.06t}) = \ln 2$$
$$0.06t \ln e = \ln 2$$
$$0.06t = \ln 2 \qquad (\ln e = 1)$$
$$t = \frac{\ln 2}{0.06} \approx 11.55$$

7. $3 = e^{0.1t}$
$$\ln(e^{0.1t}) = \ln 3$$
$$0.1t = \ln 3$$
$$t = \frac{\ln 3}{0.1} \approx 10.99$$

9. $2 = e^{5r}$
$$\ln(e^{5r}) = \ln 2$$
$$5r = \ln 2$$
$$r = \frac{\ln 2}{5} \approx 0.14$$

11.

n	$\left(1 + \dfrac{1}{n}\right)^n$
10	2.59374
100	2.70481
1000	2.71692
10,000	2.71815
100,000	2.71827
1,000,000	2.71828
10,000,000	2.71828
$\downarrow$	$\downarrow$
∞	$e = 2.7182818\ldots$

13.

n	4	16	64	256	1024	4096
$(1 + n)^{1/n}$	1.495349	1.193722	1.067399	1.021913	1.006793	1.002033

$$\lim_{n \to \infty} (1 + n)^{1/n} = 1$$

15. The graphs of $y_1 = \left(1 + \dfrac{1}{n}\right)^n$,

$y_2 = 2.718281828 \approx e$, and

$y_3 = \left(1 + \dfrac{1}{n}\right)^{n+1}$ for $0 \le n \le 20$

are given at the right.

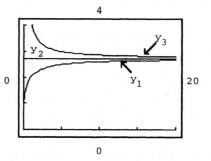

17. (A) $A = Pe^{rt}$; $P = \$10,000$, $r = 5.51\% = 0.0551$, $t = 10$:

$A = 10,000e^{(0.0551)10} = 10,000e^{0.551} = \$17,349.87$

(B) $A = \$15,000$, $P = \$10,000$, $r = 0.0551$:

$15,000 = 10,000e^{0.0551t}$

$e^{0.0551t} = 1.5$

$0.0551t = \ln(1.5)$

$t = \dfrac{\ln(1.5)}{0.0551} \approx 7.36$ years

19. $A = Pe^{rt}$; $A = \$20,000$, $r = 0.052$, $t = 10$:

$20,000 = Pe^{(0.052)10} = Pe^{0.52}$

$P = \dfrac{20,000}{e^{0.52}} = 20,000e^{-0.52} \approx \$11,890.41$

21. $30,000 = 20,000e^{5r}$

$e^{5r} = 1.5$

$5r = \ln(1.5)$

$r = \dfrac{\ln(1.5)}{5} \approx 0.0811$ or 8.11%

23. $P = 10,000e^{-0.08t}$, $0 \le t \le 50$

(A)

t	0	10	20	30	40	50
P	10,000	4493.30	2019	907.18	407.62	183.16

The graph of P is shown at the right.

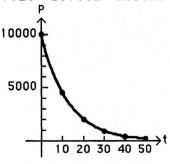

(B) $\lim\limits_{t\to\infty} 10,000e^{-0.08t} = 0$

25.
$$2P = Pe^{0.07t}$$
$$e^{0.07t} = 2$$
$$0.07t = \ln 2$$
$$t = \frac{\ln 2}{0.07} \approx 9.9 \text{ years}$$

27.
$$2P = Pe^{r(8)}$$
$$e^{8r} = 2$$
$$8r = \ln 2$$
$$r = \frac{\ln 2}{8} \approx 0.0866 \text{ or } 8.66\%$$

29. The total investment in the two accounts is given by
$$A = 10,000e^{0.072t} + 10,000(1 + 0.084)^t$$
$$= 10,000[e^{0.072t} + (1.084)^t]$$

On a graphing utility, locate the intersection point of
$$y_1 = 10,000[e^{0.072x} + (1.084)^x]$$
and $y_2 = 35,000$.

The result is: $x = t \approx 7.3$ years.

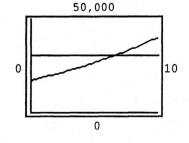

31. (A) $A = Pe^{rt}$; set $A = 2P$

(B)
$$2P = Pe^{rt}$$
$$e^{rt} = 2$$
$$rt = \ln 2$$
$$t = \frac{\ln 2}{r}$$

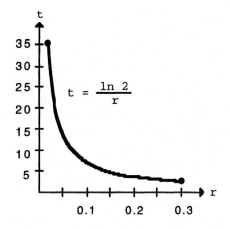

In theory, r could be any positive number. However, the restrictions on r are reasonable in the sense that most investments would be expected to earn between 2% and 30%.

(C) $r = 5\%$; $\quad t = \dfrac{\ln 2}{0.05} \approx 13.86$ years

$\qquad r = 10\%$; $\quad t = \dfrac{\ln 2}{0.10} \approx 6.93$ years

$\qquad r = 15\%$; $\quad t = \dfrac{\ln 2}{0.15} \approx 4.62$ years

$\qquad r = 20\%$; $\quad t = \dfrac{\ln 2}{0.20} \approx 3.47$ years

$\qquad r = 25\%$; $\quad t = \dfrac{\ln 2}{0.25} \approx 2.77$ years

$\qquad r = 30\%$; $\quad t = \dfrac{\ln 2}{0.30} \approx 2.31$ years

33.
$$Q = Q_0 e^{-0.0004332t}$$
$$\tfrac{1}{2} Q_0 = Q_0 e^{-0.0004332t}$$
$$e^{-0.0004332t} = \tfrac{1}{2}$$
$$\ln(e^{-0.0004332t}) = \ln\left(\tfrac{1}{2}\right) = \ln 1 - \ln 2$$
$$-0.0004332t = -\ln 2 \quad (\ln 1 = 0)$$
$$t = \dfrac{\ln 2}{0.0004332}$$
$$\approx \dfrac{0.6931}{0.0004332} \approx 1599.95$$

Thus, the half-life of radium is approximately 1600 years.

35.
$$Q = Q_0 e^{rt} \quad (r < 0)$$
$$\tfrac{1}{2} Q_0 = Q_0 e^{r(30)}$$
$$e^{30r} = \tfrac{1}{2}$$
$$\ln(e^{30r}) = \ln\left(\tfrac{1}{2}\right) = \ln 1 - \ln 2$$
$$30r = -\ln 2 \quad (\ln 1 = 0)$$
$$r = \dfrac{-\ln 2}{30} \approx \dfrac{-0.6931}{30}$$
$$\approx -0.0231$$

Thus, the continuous compound rate of decay of the cesium isotope is approximately -0.0231.

37. $2P_0 = P_0 e^{0.013t}$
$$e^{0.013t} = 2$$
$$0.013t = \ln 2$$
$$t = \dfrac{\ln 2}{0.013} \approx 53.3$$

It will take approximately 53.3 years.

39. $2P_0 = P_0 e^{r(50)}$
$$e^{50r} = 2$$
$$50r = \ln 2$$
$$r = \dfrac{\ln 2}{50} \approx 0.0139$$

$\qquad\qquad\qquad$ or 1.39%

Things to remember:

<u>1</u>. COMPOSITE FUNCTIONS

A function m is a COMPOSITE of functions f and g if
$$m(x) = f[g(x)]$$
The domain of m is the set of all numbers x such that x is in the domain of g and $g(x)$ is in the domain of f.

<u>2</u>. EXPONENTIAL DERIVATIVE FORMULAS

(a) $\dfrac{d}{dx}e^x = e^x$

(b) If $u = u(x)$ is a differentiable function of x, then
$$\frac{d}{dx}e^u = e^u \frac{d}{dx}u = e^{u(x)}u'(x)$$

---

1. $f(u) = u^3$, $g(x) = 3x^2 + 2$
$f[g(x)] = (3x^2 + 2)^3$

3. $f(u) = e^u$, $g(x) = -x^2$
$f[g(x)] = e^{-x^2}$

5. Let $u = g(x) = 3x^2 - x + 5$ and $f(u) = u^4$. Then $y = f(u) = u^4$.

7. Let $u = g(x) = 1 + x + x^2$ and $f(u) = e^u$. Then $y = f(u) = e^u$.

9. $f(x) = 4x^3 + 5e^x$
$f'(x) = 12x^2 + 5e^x$

11. $y = 4e^x - 3x^e$
$\dfrac{dy}{dx} = 4e^x - 3ex^{e-1}$
[<u>Note</u>: e is a constant so we use the power rule on the second term.]

13. $y = -3e^{-x} + 2e^x$
$y' = -3e^{-x}(-1) + 2e^x = 3e^{-x} + 2e^x$

15. $f(x) = x^3 e^x$
$f'(x) = x^3 \dfrac{d}{dx}e^x + e^x \dfrac{d}{dx}x^3$ (Product rule)
$\qquad = x^3 e^x + e^x 3x^2 = x^2 e^x (x + 3)$

17. $f(x) = 3e^{2x}$
$f'(x) = 3e^{2x}(2) = 6e^{2x}$

19. $f(x) = 5e^{-3x}$
$f'(x) = 5e^{-3x}(-3) = -15e^{-3x}$

21. $f(x) = 200e^{-0.5x}$

$\quad f'(x) = 200e^{-0.5x}(-0.5)$

$\qquad\quad = -100e^{-0.5x}$

23. $f(x) = xe^{-2x}$

$\quad f'(x) = x\dfrac{d}{dx}e^{-2x} + e^{-2x}\dfrac{d}{dx}x$

$\qquad\quad = xe^{-2x}(-2) + e^{-2x}(1)$

$\qquad\quad = -2xe^{-2x} + e^{-2x} = e^{-2x}(1 - 2x)$

25. $f(x) = \dfrac{e^x}{x^2 + 9}$

$\quad f'(x) = \dfrac{(x^2 + 9)\dfrac{d}{dx}e^x - e^x\dfrac{d}{dx}(x^2 + 9)}{(x^2 + 9)^2}$ (Quotient rule)

$\qquad\quad = \dfrac{(x^2 + 9)e^x - e^x(2x)}{(x^2 + 9)^2} = \dfrac{e^x(x^2 - 2x + 9)}{(x^2 + 9)^2}$

27. $\dfrac{d}{dx}e^{3x^2-2x} = e^{3x^2-2x}(6x - 2) = (6x - 2)e^{3x^2-2x}$

29. $\dfrac{d}{dx}(e^{2x} - 1)^4 = 4(e^{2x} - 1)^3[e^{2x}(2)] = 8e^{2x}(e^{2x} - 1)^3$

31. $f(x) = \dfrac{x^2 + 1}{e^x}$

$\quad f'(x) = \dfrac{e^x\dfrac{d}{dx}(x^2 + 1) - (x^2 + 1)\dfrac{d}{dx}e^x}{(e^x)^2} = \dfrac{e^x(2x) - (x^2 + 1)e^x}{e^{2x}} = \dfrac{2x - x^2 - 1}{e^x}$

33. $\dfrac{d}{dx}(x^2 + 1)e^{-x} = (x^2 + 1)\dfrac{d}{dx}e^{-x} + e^{-x}\dfrac{d}{dx}(x^2 + 1)$

$\qquad\qquad = (x^2 + 1)e^{-x}(-1) + e^{-x}(2x) = e^{-x}(2x - x^2 - 1)$

35. $f(x) = xe^x - e^x$

$\quad f'(x) = x\dfrac{d}{dx}e^x + e^x\dfrac{d}{dx}x - \dfrac{d}{dx}e^x = xe^x + e^x - e^x = xe^x$

37. An equation for the tangent line to the graph of $f(x) = e^x$ at the point $(3, f(3)) = (3, e^3)$ is:

$\qquad y - e^3 = e^3(x - 3)$

$\quad$ or $\qquad y = xe^3 - 2e^3 = e^3(x - 2)$

Clearly, $y = 0$ when $x = 2$, that is the tangent line passes through the point $(2, 0)$.

In general, an equation for the tangent line to the graph of $f(x) = e^x$ at the point $(c, f(c)) = (c, e^c)$ is:

$\qquad y - e^c = e^c(x - c)$

$\quad$ or $\qquad y = e^c(x - [c - 1])$

Thus, the tangent line at the point (c, e^c) passes through $(c - 1, 0)$; then tangent line at the point $(4, e^4)$ passes through $(3, 0)$.

39. $f(x) = \dfrac{e^x}{x^2}$, $x > 0$

$f'(x) = \dfrac{x^2 \dfrac{d}{dx} e^x - e^x \dfrac{d}{dx} x^2}{x^4} = \dfrac{x^2 e^x - 2x e^x}{x^4} = \dfrac{x e^x (x - 2)}{x^4} = \dfrac{e^x (x - 2)}{x^3}$

Critical values: $f'(x) = \dfrac{e^x (x - 2)}{x^3} = 0$

$$e^x (x - 2) = 0$$

$$x = 2 \quad [\underline{\text{Note}}:\ e^x \neq 0 \text{ for all } x.]$$

Thus, $x = 2$ is the only critical value of f on $(0, \infty)$.
Sign chart for f' [$\underline{\text{Note}}$: This approach is a little easier than calculating $f''(x)$]:

Test Numbers	
x	$f'(x)$
1	$-e$ $(-)$
3	$\dfrac{e^3}{27}$ $(+)$

By the first derivative test, f has a minimum value at $x = 2$;
$f(2) = \dfrac{e^2}{2^2} = \dfrac{e^2}{4} \approx 1.847$ is the absolute minimum value of f.

41. $f(x) = \dfrac{x^3}{e^x}$

$f'(x) = \dfrac{\left(\dfrac{d}{dx} x^3\right) e^x - \left(\dfrac{d}{dx} e^x\right) x^3}{(e^x)^2}$

$ = \dfrac{3x^2 e^x - x^3 e^x}{e^{2x}} = \dfrac{x^2 (3 - x) e^x}{e^{2x}} = \dfrac{x^2 (3 - x)}{e^x}$

Critical values: $f'(x) = \dfrac{x^2 (3 - x)}{e^x} = 0$

$$x^2 (3 - x) = 0$$
$$x = 0 \text{ and } x = 3$$

Sign chart for f' [$\underline{\text{Note}}$: This approach is a little easier than calculating $f''(x)$]:

Test Numbers	
x	$f'(x)$
-1	$\dfrac{4}{e^{-1}}$ $(+)$
1	$\dfrac{2}{e}$ $(+)$
4	$-\dfrac{16}{e^4}$ $(-)$

By the first derivative test, f has a maximum value at $x = 3$;
$f(3) = \dfrac{27}{e^3} \approx 1.344$ is the absolute maximum value of f.

43. $f(x) = 1 - e^{-x}$

Step 1. Analyze $f(x)$:

(A) Domain: All real numbers, $(-\infty, \infty)$.

(B) Intercepts: y-intercept: $f(0) = 1 - e^{-0} = 0$

x-intercept: $1 - e^{-x} = 0$

$$e^{-x} = 1$$
$$x = 0$$

(C) Asymptotes:

Horizontal asymptote: $\lim\limits_{x \to \infty} (1 - e^{-x}) = \lim\limits_{x \to \infty} \left(1 - \dfrac{1}{e^x}\right) = 1$

$\lim\limits_{x \to \infty} (1 - e^{-x})$ does not exist.

$y = 1$ is a horizontal asymptote.

Vertical asymptotes: There are no vertical asymptotes.

Step 2. Analyze $f'(x)$:

$f'(x) = -e^{-x}(-1) = e^{-x}$

Since $e^{-x} > 0$ for all x, f is increasing on $(-\infty, \infty)$; there are no local extrema.

Step 3. Analyze $f''(x)$:

$f''(x) = e^{-x}(-1) = -e^{-x}$

Since $-e^{-x} < 0$ for all x, the graph of f is concave downward on $(-\infty, \infty)$.

Step 4. Sketch the graph of f:

x	$f(x)$
0	0
−1	≈ −1.72
1	≈ 0.63

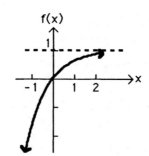

45. $f(x) = 5 + 5e^{-0.1x}$

Step 1. Analyze $f(x)$:

(A) Domain: All real numbers.

(B) Intercepts: y-intercept: $f(0) = 5 + 5e^0 = 10$

x-intercept: $5 + 5e^{-0.1x} = 0$

$$e^{-0.1x} = -1; \text{ no solutions}$$
$$e^{-0.1x} > 0 \text{ for all } x$$

(C) Asymptotes:

Vertical asymptotes: None

Horizontal asymptotes: $\lim\limits_{x \to \infty} (5 + 5e^{-0.1x}) = \lim\limits_{x \to \infty} \left(5 + \dfrac{5}{e^{0.1x}}\right) = 5$

$\lim\limits_{x \to -\infty} (5 + 5e^{-0.1x})$ does not exist

$y = 5$ is a horizontal asymptote.

Step 2. Analyze $f'(x)$:

$f'(x) = 5e^{-0.1x}(-0.1) = -0.5e^{-0.1x}$

Critical values: None

Partition numbers: None

Sign chart for f':

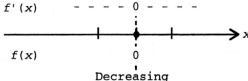

Thus, f decreases on $(-\infty, \infty)$.

Step 3. Analyze $f''(x)$:

$f''(x) = -0.5e^{-0.1x}(-0.1) = 0.05e^{-0.1x}$

Partition numbers for $f''(x)$: None

Sign chart for f':

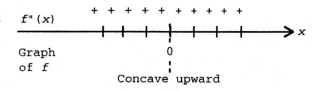

Thus, the graph of f is concave upward on $(-\infty, \infty)$.

Step 4. Sketch the graph of f:

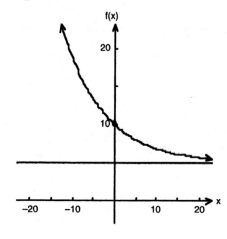

47. $f(x) = 5xe^{-0.2x}$

Step 1. Analyze $f(x)$:

(A) Domain: All real numbers.

(B) Intercepts: y-intercept: $f(0) = 5(0)e^0 = 0$

x-intercept: $5xe^{-0.2x} = 0$

$x = 0$

(C) Asymptotes:

Vertical asymptotes: None

Horizontal asymptotes:

x	10	20	30	40	$\to \infty$
$f(x)$	6.77	1.83	0.37	0.067	$\to 0$

x	-10	-20	$\to -\infty$
$f(x)$	-369.45	-5458.01	$\to -\infty$

$y = 0$ is a horizontal asymptote

187

Step 2. Analyze $f'(x)$:

$f'(x) = 5xe^{-0.2x}(-0.2) + e^{-0.2x}5 = 5e^{-0.2x}[1 - 0.2x]$
Critical values: $x = 5$
Partition numbers: $x = 5$
Sign chart for f':

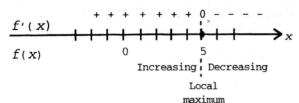

Test Numbers

x	$f'(x)$
0	5 (+)
6	$-e^{-1.2}$ (−)

Thus, $f(x)$ increases on $(-\infty, 5)$, has a local maximum at $x = 5$, and decreases on $(5, \infty)$.

Step 3. Analyze $f''(x)$:

$f''(x) = 5e^{-0.2x}(-0.2) + [1 - 0.2x]5e^{-0.2x}(-0.2)$
$\qquad = -e^{-0.2x}[2 - 0.2x]$
Partition numbers for $f''(x)$: $x = 10$
Sign chart for f'':

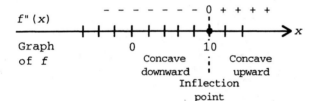

Test Numbers

x	$f''(x)$
0	-2 (−)
20	$2e^{-4}$ (+)

Step 4. Sketch the graph of f:

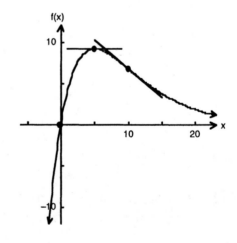

49. $f(x) = (3 - x)e^{x}$

Step 1. Analyze $f(x)$:

(A) Domain: All real numbers, $(-\infty, \infty)$.

(B) Intercepts: y-intercept: $f(0) = (3 - 0)e^{0} = 3$

x-intercept: $(3 - x)e^{x} = 0$
$\qquad\qquad\qquad 3 - x = 0$
$\qquad\qquad\qquad\qquad x = 3$

(C) Asymptotes:

Horizontal asymptote: Consider the behavior of f as $x \to \infty$ and as $x \to -\infty$.

Using the following tables,

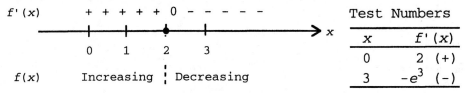

x	-1	-10	-20
$f(x)$	1.47	0.00059	0.000000047

x	5	10
$f(x)$	-296.83	-154,185.26

we conclude that $\lim\limits_{x \to -\infty} f(x) = 0$ and $\lim\limits_{x \to \infty} f(x)$ does not exist. Because of the first limit, $y = 0$ is a horizontal asymptote.

Vertical asymptotes: There are no vertical asymptotes.

Step 2. Analyze $f'(x)$:

$f'(x) = (3 - x)e^x + e^x(-1) = (2 - x)e^x$

Critical values: $(2 - x)e^x = 0$

$x = 2$ [Note: $e^x > 0$]

Partition numbers: $x = 2$

Sign chart for f':

```
f'(x)        + + + + + 0 - - - - -
        ————+———+———●———+————————————> x
            0   1   2   3
f(x)         Increasing ┊ Decreasing
```

Test Numbers	
x	$f'(x)$
0	2 (+)
3	$-e^3$ (-)

Thus, f is increasing on $(-\infty, 2)$ and decreasing on $(2, \infty)$; f has a local maximum at $x = 2$.

Step 3. Analyze $f''(x)$:

$f''(x) = (2 - x)e^x + e^x(-1) = (1 - x)e^x$

Partition number for f'': $x = 1$

Sign chart for f'':

```
f''(x)         + + + + 0 - - - -
         ————————+———●———+————————————> x
                 0   1   2
Graph         Concave ┊ Concave
of f          Upward  ┊ Downward
```

Test Numbers	
x	$f''(x)$
0	1 (+)
2	$-e^2$ (-)

Thus, the graph of f is concave upward on $(-\infty, 1)$ and concave downward on $(1, \infty)$; the graph has an inflection point at $x = 1$.

Step 4. Sketch the graph of f:

x	$f(x)$
0	3
2	$e^2 \approx 7.4$
3	0

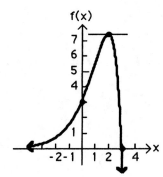

51. $f(x) = e^{-(1/2)x^2}$

Step 1. Analyze $f(x)$:

(A) Domain: All real numbers, $(-\infty, \infty)$.

(B) Intercepts: y-intercept: $f(0) = e^{-(1/2)0} = e^0 = 1$

x-intercepts: Since $e^{-(1/2)x^2} \neq 0$ for all x, there are no x-intercepts.

(C) Asymptotes: $\lim\limits_{x \to \infty} f(x) = \lim\limits_{x \to \infty} e^{-(1/2)x^2} = \lim\limits_{x \to \infty} \dfrac{1}{e^{(1/2)x^2}} = 0$

$\lim\limits_{x \to -\infty} f(x) = \lim\limits_{x \to -\infty} e^{-(1/2)x^2} = \lim\limits_{x \to -\infty} \dfrac{1}{e^{(1/2)x^2}} = 0$

Thus, $y = 0$ is a horizontal asymptote.

Since $f(x) = e^{-(1/2)x^2} = \dfrac{1}{e^{(1/2)x^2}}$ and $g(x) = e^{(1/2)x^2} \neq 0$ for all x,

there are no vertical asymptotes.

Step 2. Analyze $f'(x)$:

$f'(x) = e^{-(1/2)x^2}(-x) = -xe^{-(1/2)x^2}$

Critical values: $-xe^{-(1/2)x^2} = 0$
$$x = 0$$

Partition numbers: $x = 0$
Sign chart for f':

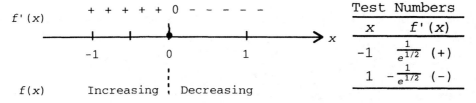

Test Numbers	
x	$f'(x)$
-1	$\frac{1}{e^{1/2}}$ (+)
1	$-\frac{1}{e^{1/2}}$ (−)

Thus, f is increasing on $(-\infty, 0)$ and decreasing on $(0, \infty)$; f has a local maximum at $x = 0$.

Step 3. Analyze $f''(x)$:

$f''(x) = -xe^{-(1/2)x^2}(-x) - e^{-(1/2)x^2}$
$\qquad = e^{-(1/2)x^2}(x^2 - 1) = e^{-(1/2)x^2}(x - 1)(x + 1)$

Partition numbers for f'': $e^{-(1/2)x^2}(x - 1)(x + 1) = 0$
$$(x - 1)(x + 1) = 0$$
$$x = -1, 1$$

Sign chart for f'':

Test Numbers	
x	$f''(x)$
-2	$\frac{3}{e^2}$ (+)
0	-1 (−)
2	$\frac{3}{e^2}$ (+)

Thus, the graph of f is concave upward on $(-\infty, -1)$ and on $(1, \infty)$; the graph of f is concave downward on $(-1, 1)$; the graph has inflection points at $x = -1$ and at $x = 1$.

Step 4. Sketch the graph of f:

x	$f(x)$
0	1
-1	$\approx$ 0.61
1	$\approx$ 0.61

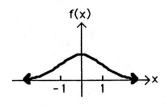

53. $f(x) = e^x - 2x^2 \qquad -\infty < x < \infty$

$f'(x) = e^x - 4x$

Critical values:

   Solve $f'(x) = e^x - 4x = 0$

To two decimal places, $x = 0.36$ and $x = 2.15$

Increasing/Decreasing: $f(x)$ is increasing on $(-\infty, 0.36)$ and on $(2.15, \infty)$; $f(x)$ is decreasing on $(0.36, 2.15)$

Local extrema: $f(x)$ has a local maximum at $x = 0.36$ and a local minimum at $x = 2.15$

55. On a graphing utility, graph $y_1 = e^x$ and $y_2 = x^4$. Rounded off to two decimal places, the points of intersection are: $(-0.82, 0.44)$, $(1.43, 4.18)$, $(8.61, 5503.66)$.

57. Demand: $p = 10e^{-x}$, $0 \leq x \leq 2$

(A) $p'(x) = -10e^{-x}$; $p'(0.8) = -10e^{-0.8} \approx -4.49$

At the demand level of 800 (= 0.8 thousand) lipsticks per week, the price is DECREASING at the rate of $4.49.

(B) The sign chart for R' is:

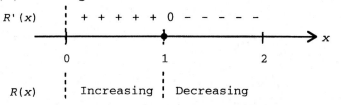

Test Numbers	
x	$f'(x)$
0	10 (+)
2	$-\dfrac{10}{e^2}$ (−)

Thus, R is increasing on $(0, 1)$ and decreasing on $(1, 2)$; the maximum value of R occurs at $x = 1$, as noted in (A).

$R''(x) = 10e^{-x}(x - 2) < 0$ on $(0, 2)$
Thus, the graph of R is concave downward on $(0, 2)$. The graph is shown at the right.

x	$R(x)$
0	0
1	3.68
2	2.71

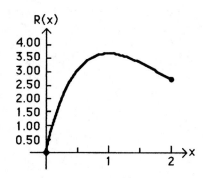

59. Price: $p = 100e^{-0.05x}$, $x \geq 0$
Revenue: $R(x) = xp = 100xe^{-0.05x}$
$$R'(x) = 100xe^{-0.05x}(-0.05) + 100e^{-0.05x}$$
$$= 100e^{-0.05x}(1 - 0.05x)$$

Critical value(s): $R'(x) = 100e^{-0.05x}(1 - 0.05x) = 0$
$$1 - 0.05x = 0$$
$$x = 20$$

$$R''(x) = 100e^{-0.05x}(-0.05) + (1 - 0.05x)100e^{-0.05x}(-0.05)$$
$$= 100e^{-0.05x}(0.0025x - 0.1)$$
$$R''(20) = -100e^{-1}(0.05) = \frac{-5}{e} < 0$$

Since $x = 20$ is the only critical value and $R''(20) < 0$, the production level that maximizes the revenue is 20 units. The maximum revenue is $R(20) = 20(36.79) = 735.80$ or \$735.80, and the price is $p(20) = 36.79$ or \$36.79 each.

61. The cost function $C(x)$ is given by
$$C(x) = 400 + 6x$$
and the revenue function $R(x)$ is
$$R(x) = xp = 100xe^{-0.05x}$$
The profit function $P(x)$ is
$$P(x) = R(x) - C(x)$$
$$= 100xe^{-0.05x} - 400 - 6x$$
and $P'(x) = 100e^{-0.05x} - 5xe^{-0.05x} - 6$
We graph $y = P(x)$ and $y = P'(x)$ in the viewing rectangle $0 \leq x \leq 50$, $-400 \leq y \leq 300$

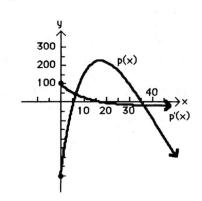

Critical value: Solve $P'(x) = (100 - 5x)e^{-0.05x} - 6 = 0$
To the nearest integer, $x = 17$.
$P(x)$ is increasing on $(0, 17)$ and decreasing on $(17, \infty)$; $P(x)$ has a maximum at $x = 17$. Thus, the maximum profit $P(17) = \$224.61$ is realized at a production level of 17 units at a price of \$42.74 per unit.

63. $S(t) = 300,000e^{-0.1t}$, $t \geq 0$
$S'(t) = 300,000e^{-0.1t}(-0.1) = -30,000e^{-0.1t}$
The rate of depreciation after one year is:
$S'(1) = -30,000e^{-0.1} \approx -\$27,145.12$ per year.
The rate of depreciation after five years is:
$S'(5) = -30,000e^{-0.5} \approx -\$18,195.92$ per year.
The rate of depreciation after ten years is:
$S'(10) = -30,000e^{-1} \approx -\$11,036.38$ per year.

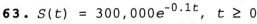

65. Revenue: $R(t) = 200{,}000(1 - e^{-0.03t})$, $t \geq 0$

Cost: $C(t) = 4000 + 3000t$, $t \geq 0$

Profit: $P(t) = R(t) - C(t) = 200{,}000(1 - e^{-0.03t}) - (4000 + 3000t)$
$$= 200{,}000(1 - e^{-0.03t}) - 3000t - 4000$$

(A) $P'(t) = -200{,}000e^{-0.03t}(-0.03) - 3000 = 6000e^{-0.03t} - 3000$

Critical value(s): $P'(t) = 6000e^{-0.03t} - 3000 = 0$

$$e^{-0.03t} = \frac{1}{2}$$

$$-0.03t = \ln\left(\frac{1}{2}\right) = -\ln 2$$

$$t = \frac{\ln 2}{0.03} \approx 23$$

$$P''(t) = 6000e^{-0.03t}(-0.03) = -180e^{-0.03t}$$

$$P''(23) = -180e^{-0.69} < 0$$

Since $t = 23$ is the only critical value and $P''(23) < 0$, 23 days of TV promotion should be used to maximize profits. The maximum profit is: $P(23) = 200{,}000(1 - e^{-0.03(23)}) - 3000(23) - 4000 \approx \$26{,}685$

The proportion of people buying the disk after t days is:

$p(t) = 1 - e^{-0.03t}$

Thus, $p(23) = 1 - e^{-0.03(23)} \approx 0.50$ or approximately 50%.

(B) From A, the sign chart for P' is:

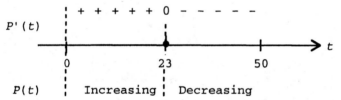

Test Numbers	
t	$P'(t)$
0	3000 (+)
50	−1661.22 (−)

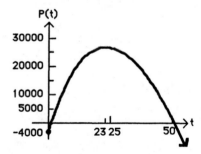

Thus, P is increasing on $(0, 23)$ and decreasing on $(23, \infty)$; P has a maximum at $t = 23$.

Since $P''(t) = -180e^{-0.03t} < 0$ on $(0, \infty)$, the graph of P is concave downward on $(0, \infty)$; $P(0) = -4000$ and $P(50) \approx 0$.

The graph of P is shown at the right.

67. $C(t) = 4.35e^{-t} = \dfrac{4.35}{e^t}$, $0 \leq t \leq 5$

(A) $C'(t) = \dfrac{-4.35e^t}{e^{2t}} = \dfrac{-4.35}{e^t} = -4.35e^{-t}$

$C'(1) = -4.35e^{-1} \approx -1.60$

$C'(4) = -4.35e^{-4} \approx -0.08$

Thus, after one hour, the concentration is decreasing at the rate of 1.60 mg/ml per hour; after four hours, the concentration is decreasing at the rate of 0.08 mg/ml per hour.

(B) $C'(t) = -4.35e^{-t} < 0$ on $(0, 5)$
Thus, C is decreasing on $(0, 5)$; there are no local extrema.

$$C''(t) = \frac{4.35e^t}{e^{2t}} = \frac{4.35}{e^t} = 4.35e^{-t} > 0 \text{ on } (0, 5)$$

Thus, the graph of C is concave upward on $(0, 5)$. The graph of C is shown at the right.

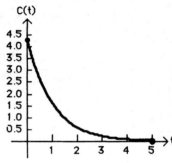

t	$C(t)$
0	4.35
1	1.60
4	0.08
5	0.03

69. $N(n) = 1,000,000e^{-0.09(n-1)}$, $1 \le n \le 20$
There are no asymptotes and no intercepts.
Using the first derivative:
$$N'(n) = 1,000,000e^{-0.09(n-1)}(-0.09)$$
$$= -90,000e^{-0.09(n-1)} < 0, \ 1 \le n \le 20$$
Thus, N is decreasing on $(0, 20)$.
Using the second derivative:
$$N''(n) = -90,000e^{-0.09(n-1)}(-0.09)$$
$$= 8100e^{-0.09(n-1)} > 0, \ 1 \le n \le 20$$
Thus, the graph of N is concave upward on $(0, 20)$.
The graph of N is:

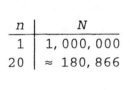

n	N
1	$1,000,000$
20	$\approx 180,866$

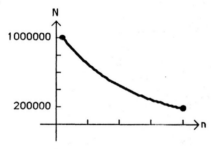

EXERCISE 3-3

Things to remember:

1. LOGARITHMIC FUNCTIONS

   The inverse of an exponential function is called a LOGARITHMIC FUNCTION. For $b > 0$, $b \ne 1$,

Logarithmic form	Exponential form
$y = \log_b x$ is equivalent to	$x = b^y$
Domain: $(0, \infty)$	Domain: $(-\infty, \infty)$
Range: $(-\infty, \infty)$	Range: $(0, \infty)$

   The graphs of $y = \log_b x$ and $y = b^x$ are symmetric with respect to the line $y = x$.

2. DERIVATIVE FORMULAS FOR LOGARITHMIC FUNCTIONS

(a) $\dfrac{d}{dx}\ln x = \dfrac{1}{x}$

(b) If $u = u(x)$ is a differentiable function of x, then

$\dfrac{d}{dx}\ln u = \dfrac{1}{u}\dfrac{d}{dx}u = \dfrac{1}{u(x)}\cdot u'(x) = \dfrac{u'(x)}{u(x)}$

(c) Other bases: For $b > 0$, $b \neq 1$,

$\dfrac{d}{dx}\log_b x = \dfrac{1}{\ln b}\cdot\dfrac{1}{x}$ and $\dfrac{d}{dx}b^x = b^x \ln b$

---

1. $\dfrac{d}{dx}\ln(x - 3) = \dfrac{1}{x - 3}(1)$ (using 3b)

$\phantom{\dfrac{d}{dx}\ln(x - 3)} = \dfrac{1}{x - 3}$

3. $\dfrac{d}{dt}\ln(3 - 2t) = \dfrac{1}{3 - 2t}(-2)$ (using 3b)

$\phantom{\dfrac{d}{dt}\ln(3 - 2t)} = \dfrac{-2}{3 - 2t}$

5. $y = \ln x^3$ or $y = \ln x^3 = 3 \ln x$ [Using logarithm properties]

$y' = \dfrac{1}{x^3}\cdot 3x^2 = \dfrac{3}{x}$ $y' = \dfrac{3}{x}$

7. $\dfrac{d}{dx}(\ln x)^6 = 6(\ln x)^5\cdot\dfrac{1}{x} = \dfrac{6(\ln x)^5}{x}$

9. $f(x) = x^4 \ln x$

$f'(x) = x^4\dfrac{d}{dx}\ln x + \ln x\dfrac{d}{dx}x^4$ (Product rule)

$ = x^4\left(\dfrac{1}{x}\right) + (\ln x)4x^3 = x^3 + 4x^3 \ln x = x^3(1 + 4 \ln x)$

11. $\dfrac{d}{dx}\ln(x + 1)^4 = \dfrac{d}{dx}4 \ln(x + 1) = 4\dfrac{d}{dx}\ln(x + 1) = 4\dfrac{1}{x + 1}(1) = \dfrac{4}{x + 1}$

13. $f(x) = \dfrac{\ln x}{x^4}$

$f'(x) = \dfrac{x^4\dfrac{d}{dx}\ln x - \ln x\dfrac{d}{dx}x^4}{(x^4)^2}$ (Quotient rule)

$ = \dfrac{x^4\left(\dfrac{1}{x}\right) - (\ln x)4x^3}{x^8} = \dfrac{x^3 - 4x^3 \ln x}{x^8} = \dfrac{1 - 4 \ln x}{x^5}$

15. $f(x) = (x + 2)^3 \ln x$

$$f'(x) = (x + 2)^3 \frac{d}{dx} \ln x + (\ln x) \frac{d}{dx} (x + 2)^3$$

$$= (x + 2)^3 \left(\frac{1}{x}\right) + (\ln x)[3(x + 2)^2(1)]$$

$$= 3(x + 2)^2 \ln x + \frac{(x + 2)^3}{x} = (x + 2)^2 \left[3 \ln x + \frac{x + 2}{x}\right]$$

17. $f(x) = \ln(x^2 + 1)$

$$f'(x) = \frac{1}{x^2 + 1} \frac{d}{dx}(x^2 + 1) = \frac{2x}{x^2 + 1}$$

19. $\dfrac{d}{dx} \ln(x^2 + 1)^{1/2} = \dfrac{d}{dx} \dfrac{1}{2} \ln(x^2 + 1) = \dfrac{1}{2} \dfrac{d}{dx} \ln(x^2 + 1)$

$$= \frac{1}{2}\left(\frac{1}{x^2 + 1}\right)(2x) = \frac{x}{x^2 + 1}$$

21. $f(x) = [\ln(x^2 + 1)]^{1/2}$

$$f'(x) = \frac{1}{2}[\ln(x^2 + 1)]^{-1/2} \frac{d}{dx}[\ln(x^2 + 1)] = \frac{1}{2}[\ln(x^2 + 1)^{-1/2} \frac{2x}{x^2 + 1}$$

$$= \frac{x}{(x^2 + 1)[\ln(x^2 + 1)]^{1/2}}$$

23. $f(x) = x(\ln x)^3$

$$f'(x) = x \frac{d}{dx}(\ln x)^3 + (\ln x)^3 \frac{d}{dx} x$$

$$= x(3)(\ln x)^2 \left(\frac{1}{x}\right) + (\ln x)^3(1) = (\ln x)^2[3 + \ln x]$$

25. $f(x) = \sqrt{1 + \ln x} = (1 + \ln x)^{1/2}$

$$f'(x) = \frac{1}{2}(1 + \ln x)^{-1/2}\left(\frac{1}{x}\right)$$

$$= \frac{1}{2x(1 + \ln x)^{1/2}} = \frac{1}{2x\sqrt{1 + \ln x}}$$

27. $f(x) = 2x^2 \ln x - x^2$

$$f'(x) = 2x^2 \frac{d}{dx} \ln x + \ln x \frac{d}{dx} 2x^2 - \frac{d}{dx} x^2 = 2x^2\left(\frac{1}{x}\right) + 4x \ln x - 2x$$

$$= 4x \ln x$$

29. $\dfrac{d}{dx} e^{-x} \ln x = e^{-x} \dfrac{d}{dx} \ln x + \ln x \dfrac{d}{dx} e^{-x} = e^{-x}\left(\dfrac{1}{x}\right) + (\ln x)(e^{-x})(-1)$

$$= \frac{e^{-x}}{x} - e^{-x} \ln x = \frac{e^{-x}[1 - x \ln x]}{x}$$

31. $\dfrac{d}{dx} \dfrac{1}{\ln(1 + x^2)} = \dfrac{d}{dx}[\ln(1 + x^2)]^{-1} = -1[\ln(1 + x^2)]^{-2} \dfrac{d}{dx} \ln(1 + x^2)$

$$= -[\ln(1 + x^2)]^{-2} \frac{1}{1 + x^2}(2x) = \frac{-2x}{(1 + x^2)[\ln(1 + x^2)]^2}$$

33. $\dfrac{d}{dx}\sqrt[3]{\ln(1-x^2)} = \dfrac{d}{dx}[\ln(1-x^2)]^{1/3} = \dfrac{1}{3}[\ln(1-x^2)]^{-2/3}\dfrac{d}{dx}\ln(1-x^2)$

$$= \dfrac{1}{3}[\ln(1-x^2)]^{-2/3}\dfrac{1}{1-x^2}(-2x) = \dfrac{-2x}{3(1-x^2)[\ln(1-x^2)]^{2/3}}$$

35. $f(x) = \ln x$

$f'(x) = \dfrac{d}{dx}(\ln x) = \dfrac{1}{x}$

The tangent line at $x = e$ has an equation of the form
$y - y_1 = m(x - x_1)$

where $x_1 = e$, $y_1 = f(e) = \ln e = 1$, and $m = f'(e) = \dfrac{1}{e}$. Thus, we have:

$y - 1 = \dfrac{1}{e}(x - e)$ or $y = \dfrac{1}{e}x$

37. $f(x) = \ln(2 - x^2)$

$f'(x) = \dfrac{1}{(2-x^2)}\dfrac{d}{dx}(2-x^2) = \dfrac{-2x}{2-x^2}$

The tangent line at $x = 1$ has an equation of the form
$y - y_1 = m(x - x_1)$
where $x_1 = 1$, $y_1 = f(1) = \ln(1) = 0$ and $m = f'(1) = -2$
Thus, we have $y = -2(x - 1)$ or $y = -2x + 2$.

39. An equation for the tangent line to the graph of $g(x) = \ln x$ at the
point $(3, g(3)) = (3, \ln 3)$ is:
$\qquad y - \ln 3 = m(x - 3)$ where $m = g'(3)$
$g'(x) = \dfrac{d}{dx}\ln x = \dfrac{1}{x}$; $g'(3) = \dfrac{1}{3}$. Thus,

$y - \ln 3 = \dfrac{1}{3}(x - 3)$

For $x = 0$, $y = \ln 3 - 1$, so this tangent line does not pass through the
origin. In fact, for any real number c, the tangent line to $g(x) = \ln x$
at the point $(c, \ln c)$ has equation $y - \ln c = \dfrac{1}{c}(x - c)$, and thus the
only tangent line which passes through the origin is the tangent line at
$(e, 1)$.

41. $f(x) = \ln(1 - x)$

Step 1. Analyze $f(x)$:
(A) Domain: All real numbers x such that $1 - x > 0$, i.e., $x < 1$
or $(-\infty, 1)$.

(B) Intercepts: y-intercept: $f(0) = \ln(1 - 0) = \ln 1 = 0$
$\qquad\qquad\qquad x$-intercepts: $\ln(1 - x) = 0$
$\qquad\qquad\qquad\qquad\qquad 1 - x = 1$
$\qquad\qquad\qquad\qquad\qquad\qquad x = 0$

(C) Asymptotes:
Horizontal asymptote: $\lim\limits_{x \to -\infty} f(x) = \lim\limits_{x \to -\infty} \ln(1 - x)$ does not exist.
$\qquad\qquad\qquad\qquad$ Thus, there are no horizontal asymptotes.
Vertical asymptote: From the table,

x	0.9	0.99	0.99999	0.9999999	$\to 1$
$f(x)$	-2.30	-4.61	-11.51	-16.12	$\to -\infty$

We conclude that $x = 1$ is a vertical asymptote.

Step 2. Analyze $f'(x)$:

$$f'(x) = \frac{1}{1-x}(-1), \quad x < 1$$

$$= \frac{1}{x-1}$$

Now, $f'(x) = \dfrac{1}{x-1} < 0$ on $(-\infty, 1)$.

Thus, f is decreasing on $(-\infty, 1)$; there are no critical values and no local extrema.

Step 3. Analyze $f''(x)$:

$$f'(x) = (x-1)^{-1}$$

$$f''(x) = -1(x-1)^{-2} = \frac{-1}{(x-1)^2}$$

Since $f''(x) = \dfrac{-1}{(1-x)^2} < 0$ on $(-\infty, 1)$, the graph of f is concave

downward on $(-\infty, 1)$; there are no inflection points.

Step 4. Sketch the graph of f:

x	$f(x)$
0	0
-2	≈ 1.10
.9	≈ -2.30

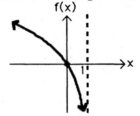

43. $f(x) = x - \ln x$

Step 1. Analyze $f(x)$:

(A) Domain: All positive real numbers, $(0, \infty)$.
   [Note: $\ln x$ is defined only for positive numbers.]

(B) Intercepts: y-intercept: There is no y intercept; $f(0) = 0 - \ln(0)$
   is not defined.

$$x\text{-intercept: } x - \ln x = 0$$
$$\ln x = x$$

Since the graph of $y = \ln x$ is below the graph of $y = x$, there are no solutions to this equation; there are no x-intercepts.

(C) Asymptotes:

Horizontal asymptote: None

Vertical asymptotes: Since $\lim\limits_{x \to 0^+} \ln x = -\infty$, $\lim\limits_{x \to 0^+} (x - \ln x) = \infty$.
Thus, $x = 0$ is a vertical asymptote for $f(x) = x - \ln x$.

Step 2. Analyze $f'(x)$:

$$f'(x) = 1 - \frac{1}{x} = \frac{x-1}{x}, \quad x > 0$$

Critical values: $\dfrac{x-1}{x} = 0$

$$x = 1$$

Partition numbers: $x = 1$

Sign chart for $f'(x) = \dfrac{x-1}{x}$:

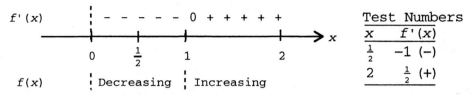

$$f'(x) \qquad \begin{array}{ccccc} & - - - - - & 0 & + + + + + \\ \hline & & & & \end{array}$$

Test Numbers

x	$f'(x)$
$\frac{1}{2}$	-1 (−)
2	$\frac{1}{2}$ (+)

$f(x)$ Decreasing   Increasing

Thus, f is decreasing on $(0, 1)$ and increasing on $(1, \infty)$; f has a local minimum at $x = 1$.

<u>Step 3. Analyze $f''(x)$</u>:

$$f''(x) = \frac{1}{x^2}, \quad x > 0$$

Thus, $f''(x) > 0$ and the graph of f is concave upward on $(0, \infty)$.

<u>Step 4. Sketch the graph of f</u>:

x	$f(x)$
0.1	≈ 2.4
1	1
10	≈ 7.7

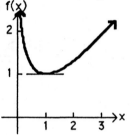

45. $f(x) = x^2 \ln x$.

<u>Step 1. Analyze $f(x)$</u>:

(A) Domain: All positive numbers, $(0, \infty)$.

(B) Intercepts: y-intercept: There is no y intercept.

                x-intercept: $x^2 \ln x = 0$

$$\ln x = 0$$
$$x = 1$$

(C) Asymptotes: Consider the behavior of f as $x \to \infty$ and as $x \to 0$. It is clear that $\lim\limits_{x \to \infty} f(x)$ does not exist; f is unbounded as x approaches ∞

The following table indicates that f approaches 0 as x approaches 0.

x	1	0.1	0.01	0.001
$f(x)$	0	-0.023	-0.00046	-0.000007

Thus, there are no vertical or horizontal asymptotes.

<u>Step 2. Analyze $f'(x)$</u>:

$$f'(x) = x^2\left(\frac{1}{x}\right) + (\ln x)(2x) = x(1 + 2 \ln x)$$

Critical values: $x(1 + 2 \ln x) = 0$

$$1 + 2 \ln x = 0 \quad [\underline{\text{Note}}:\ x > 0]$$
$$\ln x = -\frac{1}{2}$$
$$x = e^{-1/2} = \frac{1}{\sqrt{e}} \approx 0.6065$$

Partition number: $x = \dfrac{1}{\sqrt{e}} \approx 0.6065$

Sign chart for f':

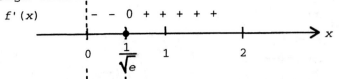

Test Numbers	
x	$f'(x)$
$\frac{1}{2}$	$\approx\ -0.19\ (-)$
1	$1\ (+)$

Thus, f is decreasing on $(0,\ e^{-1/2})$ and increasing on $(e^{-1/2},\ \infty)$; f has a local minimum at $x = e^{-1/2}$.

Step 3. Analyze $f''(x)$:

$$f''(x) = x\left(\frac{2}{x}\right) + (1 + 2\ln x) = 3 + 2\ln x$$

Partition number for f'': $3 + 2\ln x = 0$

$$\ln x = -\frac{3}{2}$$

$$x = e^{-3/2} \approx 0.2231$$

Sign chart for f'':

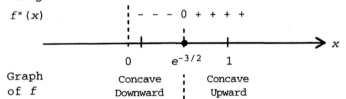

Test Numbers	
x	$f''(x)$
$\frac{1}{10}$	$\approx\ -1.61\ (-)$
1	$3\ (+)$

Thus, the graph of f is concave downward on $(0,\ e^{-3/2})$ and concave upward on $(e^{-3/2},\ \infty)$; the graph has an inflection point at $x = e^{-3/2}$.

Step 4. Sketch the graph of f:

x	$f(x)$
$e^{-3/2}$	$\approx\ -0.075$
$e^{-1/2}$	$\approx\ -0.18$
1	0

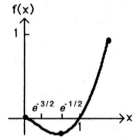

47. $f(x) = (\ln x)^2$

Step 1. Analyze $f(x)$:

(A) Domain: All positive numbers, $(0,\ \infty)$.

(B) Intercepts: y-intercept: There is no y-intercept.

$$x\text{-intercept: } (\ln x)^2 = 0$$
$$\ln x = 0$$
$$x = 1$$

(C) Asymptotes:

Vertical asymptotes: Consider the behavior of f as $x \to \infty$ and as $x \to 0$. It is clear that $\lim\limits_{x \to \infty} f(x)$ does not exist; $f(x) \to \infty$ as $x \to \infty$. Thus, there is no horizontal asymptote. The following table indicates that $f(x) \to \infty$ as $x \to 0$.

$x = 0$ (the y-axis) is a vertical asymptote.

x	1	0.01	0.0001	0.000001
$f(x)$	0	21.21	84.83	190.89

Step 2. Analyze $f(x)$:

$$f'(x) = 2(\ln x)\frac{d}{dx}\ln x = \frac{2\ln x}{x}$$

Critical values: $\dfrac{2\ln x}{x} = 0$

$$\ln x = 0$$
$$x = 1$$

Partition numbers: $x = 1$

Sign chart for f':

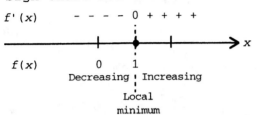

Test Numbers	
x	$f'(x)$
0.5	−2.77 (−)
2	2.77 (+)

Thus, f is decreasing on $(0, 1)$ and increasing on $(1, \infty)$; f has a local minimum at $x = 1$.

Step 3. Analyze $f''(x)$:

$$f''(x) = \frac{x\left(\frac{2}{x}\right) - 2\ln x}{x^2} = \frac{2(1 - \ln x)}{x^2}$$

Partition numbers for $f''(x)$: $\dfrac{2(1 - \ln x)}{x^2} = 0$

$$\ln x = 1$$
$$x = e$$

Sign chart for f'':

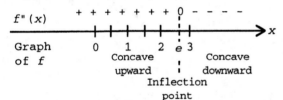

Test Numbers	
x	$f''(x)$
1	2 (+)
4	−0.48 (−)

Thus, the graph of f is concave upward on $(0, e)$ and concave downward on (e, ∞); the graph has an inflection point at $x = e$.

Step 4. Sketch the graph of f:

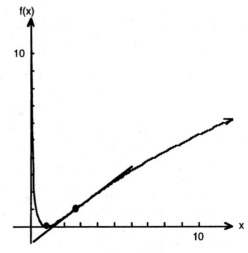

49. $f(x) = 5x - 2x \ln x, \quad x > 0$

$$f'(x) = 5 - 2x \frac{d}{dx}(\ln x) - \ln x \frac{d}{dx}(2x)$$

$$= 5 - 2x\left(\frac{1}{x}\right) - 2 \ln x = 3 - 2 \ln x, \quad x > 0$$

Critical values: $f'(x) = 3 - 2 \ln x = 0$

$$\ln x = \frac{3}{2} = 1.5; \quad x = e^{1.5}$$

Thus, $x = e^{1.5}$ is the only critical value of f on $(0, \infty)$.

Now, $f''(x) = \frac{d}{dx}(3 - 2 \ln x) = -\frac{2}{x}$

and $f''(e^{1.5}) = -\frac{2}{e^{1.5}} < 0.$

Therefore, f has a maximum value at $x = e^{1.5}$, and
$f(e^{1.5}) = 5e^{1.5} - 2e^{1.5} \ln(e^{1.5}) = 5e^{1.5} - 2(1.5)e^{1.5} = 2e^{1.5}$
is the absolute maximum of f.

51. $f(x) = x^2(3 - \ln x), \quad x > 0$

$$f'(x) = x^2 \frac{d}{dx}(3 - \ln x) + (3 - \ln x)\frac{d}{dx}x^2$$

$$= x^2\left(-\frac{1}{x}\right) + (3 - \ln x)2x = -x + 6x - 2x \ln x = 5x - 2x \ln x$$

Critical values: $f'(x) = (5x - 2x \ln x) = 0$

$$x(5 - 2 \ln x) = 0$$

$$5 - 2 \ln x = 0$$

$$\ln x = \frac{5}{2} = 2.5$$

$$x = e^{2.5} \quad [\text{Note: } x \neq 0 \text{ on } (0, \infty)]$$

Now $f''(x) = 5 - 2x\left(\frac{1}{x}\right) - 2 \ln x$

$$= 3 - 2 \ln x$$

and $f''(e^{2.5}) = 3 - 2 \cdot \ln(e^{2.5}) = 3 - 2(2.5) = 3 - 5 = -2 < 0$

Therefore, f has a maximum value at $x = e^{2.5}$ and

$$f(e^{2.5}) = (e^{2.5})^2(3 - \ln e^{2.5}) = e^5(3 - 2.5) = \frac{e^5}{2} \approx 74.207$$

is the absolute maximum value of f.

53. $f(x) = \ln(xe^{-x}), \quad x > 0$

$$f'(x) = \frac{1}{xe^{-x}} \frac{d}{dx}(xe^{-x}) = \frac{1}{xe^{-x}}[e^{-x} - xe^{-x}] = \frac{1 - x}{x}$$

Critical values: $f'(x) = \frac{1 - x}{x} = 0; \quad x = 1$

Sign chart for $f'(x)$:

	x	$f(x)$
	$\frac{1}{2}$	$1 \, (+)$
	2	$-\frac{1}{2} \, (-)$

Test Numbers

$f'(x)$ $\quad + + + + 0 - - - -$

$f(x)$ $\qquad 0 \quad 1 \quad 2$

Increasing | Decreasing

Local maximum

By the first derivative test, f has a maximum value at $x = 1$;
$f(1) = \ln(e^{-1}) = -1$ is the absolute maximum value of f.

55. $\dfrac{d}{dx}\log_2(3x^2 - 1) = \dfrac{1}{\ln 2} \cdot \dfrac{1}{3x^2 - 1} \cdot 6x = \dfrac{1}{\ln 2} \cdot \dfrac{6x}{3x^2 - 1}$

57. $\dfrac{d}{dx}10^{x^2+x} = 10^{x^2+x}(\ln 10)(2x + 1) = (2x + 1)10^{x^2+x} \ln 10$

59. $\dfrac{d}{dx}\log_3(4x^3 + 5x + 7) = \dfrac{1}{\ln 3} \cdot \dfrac{1}{4x^3 + 5x + 7}(12x^2 + 5)$

$$= \dfrac{12x^2 + 5}{\ln 3(4x^3 + 5x + 7)}$$

61. $\dfrac{d}{dx}2^{x^3 - x^2 + 4x + 1} = 2^{x^3 - x^2 + 4x + 1}\ln 2(3x^2 - 2x + 4)$

$$= \ln 2(3x^2 - 2x + 4)2^{x^3 - x^2 + 4x + 1}$$

63. On a graphing utility, graph $y_1 = (\ln x)^2$ and $y_2(x) = x$. The curves intersect at $(0.49, 0.49)$ (two decimal places).

65. On a graphing utility, graph $y_1 = \ln x$ and $y_2 = x^{1/5}$. There is a point of intersection at $(3.65, 1.30)$ (two decimal places). Using the hint that $\ln x < x^{1/5}$ for large x, we find a second point of intersection at $(332,105.11, 12.71)$ (two decimal places).

67. $f'(x) = \dfrac{1}{5(x^2 + 3)^4}[20(x^2 + 3)^3](2x) = \dfrac{8x}{x^2 + 3}$

$g'(x) = 4 \cdot \dfrac{1}{x^2 + 3}(2x) = \dfrac{8x}{x^2 + 3}$

For another way to see this, recall the properties of logarithms discussed in Section 2-3:

$f(x) = \ln[5(x^2 + 3)^4] = \ln 5 + \ln(x^2 + 3)^4 = \ln 5 + 4\ln(x^2 + 3)$
$$= \ln 5 + g(x)$$

Now $\dfrac{d}{dx}f(x) = \dfrac{d}{dx}\ln 5 + \dfrac{d}{dx}g(x) = 0 + \dfrac{d}{dx}g(x) = \dfrac{d}{dx}g(x)$

Conclusion: $f'(x)$ and $g'(x)$ ARE the same function.

69. Demand: $p = 5 - \ln x$, $5 \leq x \leq 50$

Revenue: $R = xp = x(5 - \ln x) = 5x - x \ln x$

Cost: $C = x(1) = x$

Profit = Revenue - Cost: $P = 5x - x \ln x - x$

$$\text{or} \quad P(x) = 4x - x \ln x$$

$$P'(x) = 4 - x\left(\frac{1}{x}\right) - \ln x$$

$$= 3 - \ln x$$

Critical value(s): $P'(x) = 3 - \ln x = 0$

$$\ln x = 3$$

$$x = e^3$$

$P''(x) = -\dfrac{1}{x}$ and $P''(e^3) = -\dfrac{1}{e^3} < 0.$

Since $x = e^3$ is the only critical value and $P''(e^3) < 0$, the maximum weekly profit occurs when $x = e^3 \approx 20.09$ and the price $p = 5 - \ln(e^3) = 2$. Thus, the hot dogs should be sold at \$2.

71. Cost: $C(x) = 600 + 100x - 100 \ln x$, $x \geq 1$

Average cost: $\overline{C}(x) = \dfrac{600}{x} + 100 - \dfrac{100}{x}\ln x$

$$\overline{C}'(x) = \frac{-600}{x^2} - \frac{100}{x^2} + \frac{100 \ln x}{x^2} = \frac{-700 + 100 \ln x}{x^2}, \quad x \geq 1$$

Critical value(s): $\overline{C}'(x) = \dfrac{-700 + 100 \ln x}{x^2} = 0$

$$-700 + 100 \ln x = 0$$

$$\ln x = 7$$

$$x = e^7$$

$$\overline{C}''(x) = \frac{x^2 \frac{100}{x} - (-700 + 100 \ln x)(2x)}{x^4}$$

$$= \frac{100x + 1400x - 200x \ln x}{x^4} = \frac{1500 - 200 \ln x}{x^3}$$

$$\overline{C}''(e^7) = \frac{1500 - 200 \ln(e^7)}{e^{21}} = \frac{100}{e^{21}} > 0$$

Since $x = e^7$ is the only critical value and $\overline{C}''(e^7) > 0$, the minimum average cost is

$$\overline{C}(e^7) = \frac{600}{e^7} + 100 - \frac{100}{e^7}\ln(e^7) = \frac{600}{e^7} + 100 - \frac{700}{e^7} = 100 - \frac{100}{e^7} \approx 99.91$$

Thus, the minimal average cost is approximately \$99.91.

73. Let x = the number of jeans sold. Then

$$C(x) = 20x$$

The logarithmic regression equation for the price p is:

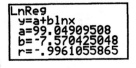

and revenue $R(x) = xp(x) = x(99.04909508 - 7.570425048 \ln x)$

$$= 99.04909508x - 7.570425048x \ln x.$$

Profit $P(x) = 99.04909508x - 7.570425048x \ln x - 20x$

$$= 79.04909508x - 7.570425048x \ln x$$

$$P'(x) = 79.04909508 - 7.570425048 - 7.570425048 \ln x$$

$$= 71.47867003 - 7.570425048 \ln x$$

Critical value: $71.47867003 - 7.570425048 \ln x = 0$

$$\ln x \approx \frac{71.47867003}{7.570425048} \approx 9.441830489$$

$$x = e^{9.441830489} \approx 12,605$$

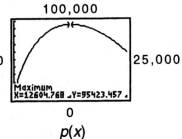

The maximum profit occurs when $x = 12,605$ jeans are sold at the price $p = \$27.57$.

75. Let x = the number of modems per week. The weekly cost is $C(x) = 100x$. The weekly revenue is $R(x) = xp(x)$, where $p(x) = ab^x$ is the exponential regression model for the given data.

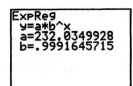

The weekly profit is $P(x) = R(x) - C(x)$. Using a graphing utility we find that the maximum profit is achieved at the demand level $x = 447$. The price that will maximize the profit is $p(447) = \$159.70$ (to the nearest cent).

77. $P(x) = 17.5(1 + \ln x)$, $10 \leq x \leq 100$

$$P'(x) = \frac{17.5}{x}$$

$$P'(40) = \frac{17.5}{40} \approx 0.44$$

$$P'(90) = \frac{17.5}{90} \approx 0.19$$

Thus, at the 40 pound weight level, blood pressure would increase at the rate of 0.44 mm of mercury per pound of weight gain; at the 90 pound weight level, blood pressure would increase at the rate of 0.19 mm of mercury per pound of weight gain.

79. $P(x) = 40 + 25 \ln(x + 1)$ $0 \le x \le 65$

$$P'(x) = 25\left(\frac{1}{x + 1}\right)(1) = \frac{25}{x + 1}$$

$$P'(10) = \frac{25}{11} \approx 2.27$$

$$P'(30) = \frac{25}{31} \approx 0.81$$

$$P'(60) = \frac{25}{61} \approx 0.41$$

Thus, the rate of change of pressure at the end of 10 years is 2.27 millimeters of mercury per year; at the end of 30 years the rate of change is 0.81 millimeters of mercury per year; at the end of 60 years the rate of change is 0.41 millimeters of mercury per year.

81. $A(t) = 5000 \cdot 2^{2t}$

$$A'(t) = 5000 \cdot 2^{2t}(2)(\ln 2) = 10,000 \cdot 2^{2t}(\ln 2)$$

$$A'(1) = 10,000 \cdot 2^2(\ln 2) = 40,000 \ln 2$$
$$\approx 27,726 \text{ rate of change of bacteria at the end of the first hour.}$$

$$A'(5) = 10,000 \cdot 2^{2 \cdot 5}(\ln 2) = 10,000 \cdot 2^{10}(\ln 2)$$
$$\approx 7,097,827 \text{ rate of change of bacteria at the end of the fifth hour}$$

83. $R = k \ln(S/S_0)$

$$= k[\ln S - \ln S_0]$$

$$\frac{dR}{dS} = \frac{k}{S}$$

EXERCISE 3-4

Things to remember:

<u>1</u>. THE CHAIN RULE: GENERAL FORM

If $y = f(u)$ and $u = g(x)$ define the composite function
$y = m(x) = f[g(x)]$,

then

$$\frac{dy}{dx} = \frac{dy}{du}\frac{du}{dx} \text{ provided that } \frac{dy}{du} \text{ and } \frac{du}{dx} \text{ exist.}$$

Or, equivalently,

$m'(x) = f'[g(x)]g'(x)$ provided that $f'[g(x)]$ and $g'(x)$ exist.

<u>2</u>. GENERAL DERIVATIVE RULES

(a) $\dfrac{d}{dx}[f(x)]^n = n[f(x)]^{n-1}f'(x)$

(b) $\dfrac{d}{dx}\ln[f(x)] = \dfrac{1}{f(x)}f'(x)$

(c) $\dfrac{d}{dx}e^{f(x)} = e^{f(x)}f'(x)$

3. RELATIVE AND PERCENTAGE RATES OF CHANGE

The RELATIVE RATE OF CHANGE of a function $f(x)$ is $\dfrac{f'(x)}{f(x)}$.

The PERCENTAGE RATE OF CHANGE is $100 \times \dfrac{f'(x)}{f(x)}$.

4. ELASTICITY OF DEMAND

If price and demand are related by $x = f(p)$, then the ELASTICITY OF DEMAND is given by

$$E(p) = -\frac{pf'(p)}{f(p)}$$

5. INTERPRETATION OF ELASTICITY OF DEMAND

$E(p)$	Demand	Interpretation
$0 < E(p) < 1$	Inelastic	Demand is not sensitive to changes in price. A change in price produces a smaller change in demand.
$E(p) > 1$	Elastic	Demand is sensitive to changes in price. A change in price produces a larger change in demand.
$E(p) = 1$	Unit	A change in price produces the same change in demand.

6. REVENUE AND ELASTICITY OF DEMAND

If $R(p) = pf(p)$ is the revenue function, then $R'(p)$ and $[1 - E(p)]$ always have the same sign.

Demand is inelastic $[E(p) < 1, R'(p) > 0]$:

    A price increase will increase revenue.

    A price decrease will decrease revenue.

Demand is elastic $[E(p) > 1, R'(p) < 0]$:

    A price increase will decrease revenue.

    A price decrease will increase revenue.

---

1. $y = u^2; \ u = 2 + e^x$

$$\frac{dy}{du} = 2u, \ \frac{du}{dx} = e^x; \ \frac{dy}{dx} = \frac{dy}{du} \cdot \frac{du}{dx} = 2ue^x$$
$$= 2(2 + e^x)e^x$$

3. $y = e^u; \ u = 2 - x^4$

$$\frac{dy}{du} = e^u, \ \frac{du}{dx} = -4x^3; \ \frac{dy}{dx} = \frac{dy}{du} \cdot \frac{du}{dx} = e^u(-4x^3)$$
$$= e^{(2-x^4)}(-4x^3)$$
$$= -4x^3 e^{(2-x^4)}$$

5. $y = \ln u;\ \ u = 4x^5 - 7$

$\dfrac{dy}{du} = \dfrac{1}{u},\ \dfrac{du}{dx} = 20x^4;\ \dfrac{dy}{dx} = \dfrac{dy}{du} \cdot \dfrac{du}{dx} = \dfrac{1}{u}(20x^4)$

$\qquad\qquad\qquad\qquad\qquad\qquad\quad = \dfrac{20x^4}{4x^5 - 7}$

7. $y = 1 + w^2;\ \ w = \ln u;\ \ u = 2 + e^x$

$\dfrac{dy}{dw} = 2w,\ \dfrac{dw}{du} = \dfrac{1}{u},\ \dfrac{du}{dx} = e^x;$

$\dfrac{dy}{dx} = \dfrac{dy}{dw} \cdot \dfrac{dw}{du} \cdot \dfrac{du}{dx} = 2w\left(\dfrac{1}{u}\right)e^x = 2 \ln u\left(\dfrac{1}{2 + e^x}\right)e^x$

$\qquad\qquad\qquad\qquad\qquad\quad = \dfrac{2e^x \ln(2 + e^x)}{2 + e^x}$

9. $y = \ln w;\ \ w = u^2 + 1;\ \ u = e^x$

$\dfrac{dy}{dw} = \dfrac{1}{w},\ \dfrac{dw}{du} = 2u,\ \dfrac{du}{dx} = e^x;$

$\dfrac{dy}{dx} = \dfrac{dy}{dw} \cdot \dfrac{dw}{du} \cdot \dfrac{du}{dx} = \dfrac{1}{w}(2u)\,e^x = \dfrac{1}{u^2 + 1}(2e^x)\,e^x$

$\qquad\qquad\qquad\qquad\qquad\quad = \dfrac{2e^{2x}}{e^{2x} + 1}$

11. $y = (w + 4)^2;\ \ w = \ln u;\ \ u = e^x$

$\dfrac{dy}{dw} = 2(w + 4),\ \dfrac{dw}{du} = \dfrac{1}{u},\ \dfrac{du}{dx} = e^x$

$\dfrac{dy}{dx} = \dfrac{dy}{dw} \cdot \dfrac{dw}{du} \cdot \dfrac{du}{dx} = 2(w + 4)\left(\dfrac{1}{u}\right)e^x = 2(\ln u + 4)\dfrac{1}{e^x}e^x$

$\qquad\qquad\qquad\qquad\qquad\quad = 2(\ln e^x + 4)$

$\qquad\qquad\qquad\qquad\qquad\quad = 2(x + 4)$

13. $f(x) = 10x + 500$

$f'(x) = 10$

Relative rate of change of f: $\dfrac{f'(x)}{f(x)} = \dfrac{10}{10x + 500} = \dfrac{1}{x + 50}$

15. $f(x) = 100x - 0.5x^2$

$f'(x) = 100 - x$

Relative rate of change of f: $\dfrac{f'(x)}{f(x)} = \dfrac{100 - x}{100x - 0.5x^2}$

17. $f(x) = 4 + 2e^{-2x}$

$f'(x) = -4e^{-2x}$

Relative rate of change of f: $\dfrac{f'(x)}{f(x)} = \dfrac{-4e^{-2x}}{4 + 2e^{-2x}}$

WHA?

$\qquad\qquad\qquad\qquad\qquad\quad = -\dfrac{2e^{-2x}}{2 + e^{-2x}} \cdot \dfrac{e^{2x}}{e^{2x}} = -\dfrac{2}{1 + 2e^{2x}}$

19. $f(x) = 25x + 3x \ln x$

$f'(x) = 25 + 3 \ln x + 3 = 28 + 3 \ln x$

Relative rate of change of f: $\dfrac{f'(x)}{f(x)} = \dfrac{28 + 3 \ln x}{25x + 3x \ln x}$

21. $x = f(p) = 12,000 - 10p^2$

$f'(p) = -20p$

Elasticity of demand: $E(p) = \dfrac{-pf'(p)}{f(p)} = \dfrac{20p^2}{12,000 - 10p^2}$

(A) At $p = 10$: $E(10) = \dfrac{2000}{12,000 - 1000} = \dfrac{2000}{11,000} = \dfrac{2}{11}$

Demand is inelastic.

(B) At $p = 20$: $E(20) = \dfrac{8000}{12,000 - 4000} = \dfrac{8000}{8000} = 1$; unit elasticity.

(C) At $p = 30$: $E(30) = \dfrac{18,000}{12,000 - 9,000} = \dfrac{18,000}{3,000} = 6$

Demand is elastic.

23. $x = f(p) = 950 - 2p - 0.1p^2$

$f'(p) = -2 - 0.2p$

Elasticity of demand: $E(p) = \dfrac{-pf'(p)}{f(p)} = \dfrac{2p + 0.2p^2}{950 - 2p - 0.1p^2}$

(A) At $p = 30$: $E(30) = \dfrac{60 + 180}{950 - 60 - 90} = \dfrac{240}{800} = \dfrac{3}{10}$

Demand is inelastic.

(B) At $p = 50$: $E(50) = \dfrac{100 + 500}{950 - 100 - 250} = \dfrac{600}{600} = 1$; unit elasticity.

(C) At $p = 70$: $E(70) = \dfrac{140 + 980}{950 - 140 - 490} = \dfrac{1120}{320} = 3.5$

Demand is elastic.

25. $p + 0.005x = 30$

(A) $x = \dfrac{30 - p}{0.005} = 6000 - 200p$, $0 \le p \le 30$

(B) $f(p) = 6000 - 200p$

$f'(p) = -200$

Elasticity of demand: $E(p) = \dfrac{-pf'(p)}{f(p)} = \dfrac{200p}{6000 - 200p}$

$= \dfrac{p}{30 - p}$

(C) At $p = 10$: $E(10) = \dfrac{10}{30 - 10} = \dfrac{1}{2} = 0.5$

If the price increases by 10%, the demand will decrease by approximately $0.5(10\%) = 5\%$.

(D) At $p = 25$: $E(25) = \dfrac{25}{30 - 25} = 5$

If the price increases by 10%, the demand will decrease by approximately $5(10\%) = 50\%$.

(E) At $p = 15$: $E(15) = \dfrac{15}{30 - 15} = 1$

If the price increases by 10%, the demand will decrease by approximately 10%.

27. $0.02x + p = 60$

(A) $x = \dfrac{60 - p}{0.02} = 3000 - 50p$, $0 \le p \le 60$

(B) $R(p) = p(3000 - 50p) = 3000p - 50p^2$

(C) $f(p) = 3000 - 50p$
$f'(p) = -50$

Elasticity of demand: $E(p) = \dfrac{-pf'(p)}{f(p)} = \dfrac{50p}{3000 - 50p}$

$= \dfrac{p}{60 - p}$

(D) Elastic: $E(p) = \dfrac{p}{60 - p} > 1$

$p > 60 - p$
$p > 30$, $\qquad 30 < p < 60$

Inelastic: $E(p) = \dfrac{p}{60 - p} < 1$

$p < 60 - p$
$p < 30$, $\qquad 0 < p < 30$

(E) $R'(p) = f(p)\,[1 - E(p)]$ (equation (9))
$R'(p) > 0$ if $E(p) < 1$; $R'(p) < 0$ if $E(p) > 1$
Therefore, revenue is increasing for $0 < p < 30$ and decreasing for $30 < p < 60$.

(F) If $p = \$10$ and the price is decreased, revenue will also decrease.

(G) If $p = \$40$ and the price is decreased, revenue will increase.

29. $x = f(p) = 10(p - 30)^2, \; 0 \le p \le 30$

$\qquad f'(p) = 20(p - 30)$

Elasticity of demand: $E(p) = \dfrac{-p[20(p - 30)]}{10(p - 30)^2} = \dfrac{-2p}{p - 30}$

Elastic: $E(p) = -\dfrac{2p}{p - 30} > 1$

$\qquad -2p < p - 30 \quad (p - 30 < 0 \text{ reverses inequality})$
$\qquad -3p < -30$
$\qquad p > 10; \qquad 10 < p < 30$

Inelastic: $E(p) = -\dfrac{2p}{p - 30} < 1$

$\qquad -2p > p - 30 \quad (p - 30 < 0 \text{ reverses inequality})$
$\qquad -3p > -30$
$\qquad p < 10; \qquad 0 < p < 10$

31. $x = f(p) = \sqrt{144 - 2p}, \; 0 \le p \le 72$

$\qquad f'(p) = \dfrac{1}{2}(144 - 2p)^{-1/2}(-2) = \dfrac{-1}{\sqrt{144 - 2p}}$

Elasticity of demand: $E(p) = \dfrac{p}{144 - 2p}$

Elastic: $E(p) = \dfrac{p}{144 - 2p} > 1$

$\qquad p > 144 - 2p$
$\qquad 3p > 144$
$\qquad p > 48, \qquad 48 < p < 72$

Inelastic: $E(p) = \dfrac{p}{144 - 2p} < 1$

$\qquad p < 144 - 2p$
$\qquad 3p < 144$
$\qquad p < 48, \qquad 0 < p < 48$

33. $x = f(p) = \sqrt{2,500 - 2p^2} \quad 0 \le p \le 25\sqrt{2}$

$\qquad f'(p) = \dfrac{1}{2}(2,500 - 2p^2)^{-1/2}(-4p) = \dfrac{-2p}{(2,500 - 2p^2)^{1/2}}$

Elasticity of demand: $E(p) = \dfrac{2p^2}{2,500 - 2p^2} = \dfrac{p^2}{1,250 - p^2}$

Elastic: $E(p) = \dfrac{p^2}{1,250 - p^2} > 1$

$\qquad p^2 > 1,250 - p^2$
$\qquad 2p^2 > 1,250$
$\qquad p^2 > 625$
$\qquad p > 25, \qquad 25 < p < 25\sqrt{2}$

Inelastic: $E(p) = \dfrac{p^2}{1,250 - p^2} < 1$

$$p^2 < 1,250 - p^2$$
$$2p^2 < 1,250$$
$$p^2 < 625$$
$$p < 25, \quad 0 < p < 25$$

35. $x = f(p) = 20(10 - p) \quad 0 \le p \le 10$

$R(p) = pf(p) = 20p(10 - p) = 200p - 20p^2$

$R'(p) = 200 - 40p$

Critical value: $R'(p) = 200 - 40p = 0$; $p = 5$

Sign chart for $R'(p)$:

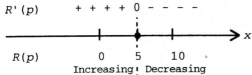

Test Numbers	
p	$R'(p)$
0	200 (+)
10	−200 (−)

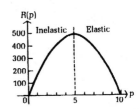

37. $x = f(p) = 40(p - 15)^2 \quad 0 \le p \le 15$

$R(p) = pf(p) = 40p(p - 15)^2$

$\begin{aligned} R'(p) &= 40(p - 15)^2 + 40p(2)(p - 15) \\ &= 40(p - 15)[p - 15 + 2p] \\ &= 40(p - 15)(3p - 15) \\ &= 120(p - 15)(p - 5) \end{aligned}$

Critical values [in (0, 15)]: $p = 5$

Sign chart for $R'(p)$:

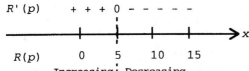

Test Numbers	
p	$R'(p)$
0	(+)
10	(−)

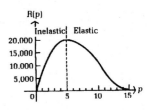

39. $x = f(p) = 30 - 10\sqrt{p} \quad 0 \le p \le 9$

$R(p) = pf(p) = 30p - 10p\sqrt{p}$

$R'(p) = 30 - 10\sqrt{p} - 10p \cdot \dfrac{1}{2}p^{-1/2}$

$\qquad = 30 - 10\sqrt{p} - \dfrac{5p}{\sqrt{p}} = 30 - 15\sqrt{p}$

Critical values: $R'(p) = 30 - 15\sqrt{p} = 0$

$\qquad\qquad\qquad\qquad \sqrt{p} = 2; \; p = 4$

Sign chart for $R'(p)$:

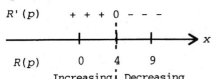

Test Numbers	
p	$R'(p)$
0	30 (+)
5	(−)

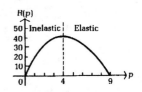

41. $p = g(x) = 50 - 0.1x$

$\quad\quad g'(x) = -0.1$

$\quad E(x) = -\dfrac{g(x)}{xg'(x)} = -\dfrac{50 - 0.1x}{-0.1x} = \dfrac{500}{x} - 1$

$\quad E(200) = \dfrac{500}{200} - 1 = \dfrac{3}{2}$

43. $p = g(x) = 50 - 2\sqrt{x}$

$\quad\quad g'(x) = -\dfrac{1}{\sqrt{x}}$

$\quad E(x) = -\dfrac{g(x)}{xg'(x)} = -\dfrac{50 - 2\sqrt{x}}{x\left(-\dfrac{1}{\sqrt{x}}\right)} = \dfrac{50}{\sqrt{x}} - 2$

$\quad E(400) = \dfrac{50}{20} - 2 = \dfrac{1}{2}$

45. $x = f(p) = Ap^{-k}$, A, k positive constants

$\quad\quad f'(p) = -Akp^{-k-1}$

$\quad E(p) = \dfrac{-pf'(p)}{f(p)} = \dfrac{Akp^{-k}}{Ap^{-k}} = k$

47. The company's daily cost is increasing by
$1.25(20) = \$25$ per day.

49. $x + 400p = 2{,}000$

$\quad x = f(p) = 2{,}000 - 400p$

$\quad\quad f'(p) = -400$

Elasticity of demand: $E(p) = \dfrac{400p}{2{,}000 - 400p} = \dfrac{p}{5 - p}$

$E(2) = \dfrac{2}{3} < 1$

The demand is inelastic; a price increase will increase revenue.

51. $x + 1{,}000p = 800$

$\quad x = f(p) = 800 - 1{,}000p$

$\quad\quad f'(p) = -1{,}000$

Elasticity of demand: $E(p) = \dfrac{1{,}000p}{800 - 1{,}000p} = \dfrac{5p}{4 - 5p}$

$E(0.30) = \dfrac{1.5}{4 - 1.5} = \dfrac{1.5}{2.5} = \dfrac{3}{5} < 1$

The demand is inelastic; a price decrease will decrease revenue.

53. From Problem 49, $R(p) = pf(p) = 2{,}000p - 400p^2$

$R'(p) = 2{,}000 - 800p$

Critical values: $R'(p) = 2{,}000 - 800p = 0$

$\quad\quad\quad\quad\quad\quad\quad\quad\quad 800p = 2000$

$\quad\quad\quad\quad\quad\quad\quad\quad\quad\quad p = 2.50$

$R''(p) = -800$

Since $p = 2.50$ is the only critical value and $R''(2.50) = -800 < 0$, the maximum revenue occurs when the price $p = \$2.50$.

55. $f(t) = 0.34t + 14.6$, $0 \le t \le 50$

$f'(t) = 0.34$

Percentage rate of change:

$$100 \frac{f'(t)}{f(t)} = \frac{34}{0.34t + 14.6}$$

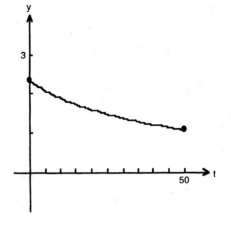

57. $r(t) = 11.3 - 3.6 \ln t$

$$r'(t) = -\frac{3.6}{t}$$

Relative rate of change of $f(t)$:

$$\frac{f'(t)}{f(t)} = \frac{\frac{-3.6}{t}}{11.3 - 3.6 \ln t}$$

$$= \frac{-3.6}{11.3t - 3.6 \, t \ln t} = C(t)$$

Relative rate of change in 2002: $C(12) = \dfrac{-3.6}{11.3(12) - 3.6(12) \ln(12)} \approx -0.13$

The relative rate of change for robberies annually per 1,000 population age 12 and over is approximately -0.13.

EXERCISE 3-5

Things to remember:

$\underline{1}$. Let $y = y(x)$. Then

    (a) $\dfrac{d}{dx} y^n = n y^{n-1} y'$ (General Power Rule)

    (b) $\dfrac{d}{dx} \ln y = \dfrac{1}{y} \cdot y' = \dfrac{y'}{y}$

    (c) $\dfrac{d}{dx} e^y = e^y \cdot y' = y' e^y$

---

1. $3x + 5y + 9 = 0$

  (A) Implicit differentiation:

$$\frac{d}{dx}(3x) + \frac{d}{dx}(5y) + \frac{d}{dx}(9) = \frac{d}{dx}(0)$$

$$3 + 5y' + 0 = 0$$

$$y' = -\frac{3}{5}$$

  (B) Solve for y:

$$5y = -9 - 3x$$

$$y = -\frac{9}{5} - \frac{3}{5}x$$

$$y' = -\frac{3}{5}$$

3. $3x^2 - 4y - 18 = 0$

  (A) Implicit differentiation:

$$\frac{d}{dx}(3x^2) - \frac{d}{dx}(4y) - \frac{d}{dx}(18) = \frac{d}{dx}(0)$$

$$6x - 4y' - 0 = 0$$

$$y' = \frac{6}{4}x = \frac{3}{2}x$$

  (B) Solve for y:

$$-4y = 18 - 3x^2$$

$$y = \frac{3}{4}x^2 - \frac{9}{2}$$

$$y' = \frac{6}{4}x = \frac{3}{2}x$$

5. $y - 5x^2 + 3 = 0$; (1, 2)

  Using implicit differentiation:

$$\frac{d}{dx}(y) - \frac{d}{dx}(5x^2) + \frac{d}{dx}(3) = \frac{d}{dx}(0)$$

$$y' - 10x = 0$$

$$y' = 10x$$

$$y'\Big|_{(1,2)} = 10(1) = 10$$

7. $x^2 - y^3 - 3 = 0$; (2, 1)

$$\frac{d}{dx}(x^2) - \frac{d}{dx}(y^3) - \frac{d}{dx}(3) = \frac{d}{dx}(0)$$

$$2x - 3y^2y' = 0$$

$$3y^2y' = 2x$$

$$y' = \frac{2x}{3y^2}$$

$$y'\Big|_{(2,1)} = \frac{4}{3}$$

9. $y^2 + 2y + 3x = 0$; (-1, 1)

$$\frac{d}{dx}(y^2) + \frac{d}{dx}(2y) + \frac{d}{dx}(3x) = \frac{d}{dx}(0)$$

$$2yy' + 2y' + 3 = 0$$

$$2y'(y + 1) = -3$$

$$y' = -\frac{3}{2(y + 1)}$$

$$y'\Big|_{(-1,1)} = \frac{-3}{2(2)} = -\frac{3}{4}$$

11. $xy - 6 = 0$

$$\frac{d}{dx}xy - \frac{d}{dx}6 = \frac{d}{dx}(0)$$

$$xy' + y - 0 = 0$$

$$xy' = -y$$

$$y' = -\frac{y}{x}$$

$$y' \text{ at } (2, 3) = -\frac{3}{2}$$

13. $2xy + y + 2 = 0$

$$2\frac{d}{dx}xy + \frac{d}{dx}y + \frac{d}{dx}2 = \frac{d}{dx}(0)$$

$$2xy' + 2y + y' + 0 = 0$$

$$y'(2x + 1) = -2y$$

$$y' = \frac{-2y}{2x + 1}$$

$$y' \text{ at } (-1, 2) = \frac{-2(2)}{2(-1) + 1} = 4$$

15. $x^2y - 3x^2 - 4 = 0$

$$\frac{d}{dx}x^2y - \frac{d}{dx}3x^2 - \frac{d}{dx}4 = \frac{d}{dx}(0)$$

$$x^2y' + y\frac{d}{dx}(x^2) - 6x - 0 = 0$$

$$x^2y' + y2x - 6x = 0$$

$$x^2y' = 6x - 2yx$$

$$y' = \frac{6x - 2yx}{x^2} \text{ or } \frac{6 - 2y}{x}$$

$$y'\Big|_{(2, 4)} = \frac{6 \cdot 2 - 2 \cdot 4 \cdot 2}{2^2} = \frac{12 - 16}{4} = -1$$

17. $e^y = x^2 + y^2$

$$\frac{d}{dx}e^y = \frac{d}{dx}x^2 + \frac{d}{dx}y^2$$

$$e^y y' = 2x + 2yy'$$

$$y'(e^y - 2y) = 2x$$

$$y' = \frac{2x}{e^y - 2y}$$

$$y'\Big|_{(1,\,0)} = \frac{2 \cdot 1}{e^0 - 2 \cdot 0} = \frac{2}{1} = 2$$

19. $x^3 - y = \ln y$

$$\frac{d}{dx}x^3 - \frac{d}{dx}y = \frac{d}{dx}\ln y$$

$$3x^2 - y' = \frac{y'}{y}$$

$$3x^2 = \left(1 + \frac{1}{y}\right)y'$$

$$3x^2 = \frac{y + 1}{y}y'$$

$$y' = \frac{3x^2 y}{y + 1}$$

$$y'\Big|_{(1,\,1)} = \frac{3 \cdot 1^2 \cdot 1}{1 + 1} = \frac{3}{2}$$

21. $x \ln y + 2y = 2x^3$

$$\frac{d}{dx}[x \ln y] + \frac{d}{dx}2y = \frac{d}{dx}2x^3$$

$$\ln y \cdot \frac{d}{dx}x + x\frac{d}{dx}\ln y + 2y' = 6x^2$$

$$\ln y \cdot 1 + x \cdot \frac{y'}{y} + 2y' = 6x^2$$

$$y'\left(\frac{x}{y} + 2\right) = 6x^2 - \ln y$$

$$y' = \frac{6x^2 y - y \ln y}{x + 2y}$$

$$y'\Big|_{(1,\,1)} = \frac{6 \cdot 1^2 \cdot 1 - 1 \cdot \ln 1}{1 + 2 \cdot 1} = \frac{6}{3} = 2$$

23. $x^2 - t^2 x + t^3 + 11 = 0$

$$\frac{d}{dt}x^2 - \frac{d}{dt}(t^2 x) + \frac{d}{dt}t^3 + \frac{d}{dt}11 = \frac{d}{dt}0$$

$$2xx' - [t^2 x' + x(2t)] + 3t^2 + 0 = 0$$

$$2xx' - t^2 x' - 2tx + 3t^2 = 0$$

$$x'(2x - t^2) = 2tx - 3t^2$$

$$x' = \frac{2tx - 3t^2}{2x - t^2}$$

$$x'\Big|_{(-2,\,1)} = \frac{2(-2)(1) - 3(-2)^2}{2(1) - (-2)^2}$$

$$= \frac{-4 - 12}{2 - 4} = \frac{-16}{-2} = 8$$

25. $(x - 1)^2 + (y - 1)^2 = 1$.

Differentiating implicitly, we have:

$$\frac{d}{dx}(x - 1)^2 + \frac{d}{dx}(y - 1)^2 = \frac{d}{dx}(1)$$

$$2(x - 1) + 2(y - 1)y' = 0$$

$$y' = -\frac{(x - 1)}{(y - 1)}$$

To find the points on the graph where $x = 1.6$, we solve the given equation for y:

$$(y - 1)^2 = 1 - (x - 1)^2$$

$$y - 1 = \pm\sqrt{1 - (x - 1)^2}$$

$$y = 1 \pm \sqrt{1 - (x - 1)^2}$$

Now, when $x = 1.6$, $y = 1 + \sqrt{1 - 0.36} = 1 + \sqrt{0.64} = 1.8$ and $y = 1 - \sqrt{0.64} = 0.2$. Thus, the points are $(1.6, 1.8)$ and $(1.6, 0.2)$. These values can be verified on the graph.

$$y'\Big|_{(1.6, 1.8)} = -\frac{(1.6 - 1)}{(1.8 - 1)} = -\frac{0.6}{0.8} = -\frac{3}{4}$$

$$y'\Big|_{(1.6, 0.2)} = -\frac{(1.6 - 1)}{(0.2 - 1)} = -\frac{0.6}{(-0.8)} = \frac{3}{4}$$

27. $xy - x - 4 = 0$

When $x = 2$, $2y - 2 - 4 = 0$, so $y = 3$. Thus, we want to find the equation of the tangent line at $(2, 3)$.

First, find y'.

$$\frac{d}{dx}xy - \frac{d}{dx}x - \frac{d}{dx}4 = \frac{d}{dx}0$$

$$xy' + y - 1 - 0 = 0$$

$$xy' = 1 - y$$

$$y' = \frac{1 - y}{x}$$

$$y'\Big|_{(2, 3)} = \frac{1 - 3}{2} = -1$$

Thus, the slope of the tangent line at $(2, 3)$ is $m = -1$. The equation of the line through $(2, 3)$ with slope $m = -1$ is:

$$(y - 3) = -1(x - 2)$$

$$y - 3 = -x + 2$$

$$y = -x + 5$$

29. $y^2 - xy - 6 = 0$
When $x = 1$,
$$y^2 - y - 6 = 0$$
$$(y - 3)(y + 2) = 0$$
$$y = 3 \quad \text{or} \quad -2.$$
Thus, we want to find the equations of the tangent lines at $(1, 3)$ and $(1, -2)$. First, find y'.

$$\frac{d}{dx}y^2 - \frac{d}{dx}xy - \frac{d}{dx}6 = \frac{d}{dx}0$$
$$2yy' - xy' - y - 0 = 0$$
$$y'(2y - x) = y$$
$$y' = \frac{y}{2y - x}$$
$$y'\Big|_{(1, 3)} = \frac{3}{2(3) - 1} = \frac{3}{5} \qquad [\text{Slope at } (1, 3)]$$

The equation of the tangent line at $(1, 3)$ with $m = \frac{3}{5}$ is:

$$(y - 3) = \frac{3}{5}(x - 1)$$
$$y - 3 = \frac{3}{5}x - \frac{3}{5}$$
$$\boxed{y = \frac{3}{5}x + \frac{12}{5}}$$
$$y'\Big|_{(1, -2)} = \frac{-2}{2(-2) - 1} = \frac{2}{5} \qquad [\text{Slope at } (1, -2)]$$

Thus, the equation of the tangent line at $(1, -2)$ with $m = \frac{2}{5}$ is:

$$(y + 2) = \frac{2}{5}(x - 1)$$
$$y + 2 = \frac{2}{5}x - \frac{2}{5}$$
$$\boxed{y = \frac{2}{5}x - \frac{12}{5}}$$

31. $xe^y = 1$

Implicit differentiation: $x \cdot \dfrac{d}{dx}e^y + e^y\dfrac{d}{dx}x = \dfrac{d}{dx}1$
$$xe^yy' + e^y = 0$$
$$y' = -\frac{e^y}{xe^y} = -\frac{1}{x}$$

Solve for y: $e^y = \dfrac{1}{x}$
$$y = \ln\left(\frac{1}{x}\right) = -\ln x \quad \text{(see Section 2-3)}$$
$$y' = -\frac{1}{x}$$

In this case, solving for y first and then differentiating is a little easier than differentiating implicitly.

33. $(1 + y)^3 + y = x + 7$

$$\frac{d}{dx}(1 + y)^3 + \frac{d}{dx}y = \frac{d}{dx}x + \frac{d}{dx}7$$

$$3(1 + y)^2 y' + y' = 1$$

$$y'[3(1 + y)^2 + 1] = 1$$

$$y' = \frac{1}{3(1 + y)^2 + 1}$$

$$y'\Big|_{(2,\,1)} = \frac{1}{3(1 + 1)^2 + 1} = \frac{1}{13}$$

35. $(x - 2y)^3 = 2y^2 - 3$

$$\frac{d}{dx}(x - 2y)^3 = \frac{d}{dx}(2y^2) - \frac{d}{dx}(3)$$

$$3(x - 2y)^2(1 - 2y') = 4yy' - 0 \quad \text{[Note: The chain rule is applied to the left-hand side.]}$$

$$3(x - 2y)^2 - 6(x - 2y)^2 y' = 4yy'$$

$$-6(x - 2y)^2 y' - 4yy' = -3(x - 2y)^2$$

$$-y'[6(x - 2y)^2 + 4y] = -3(x - 2y)^2$$

$$y' = \frac{3(x - 2y)^2}{6(x - 2y)^2 + 4y}$$

$$y'\Big|_{(1,\,1)} = \frac{3(1 - 2 \cdot 1)^2}{6(1 - 2)^2 + 4} = \frac{3}{10}$$

37. $\sqrt{7 + y^2} - x^3 + 4 = 0 \quad \text{or} \quad (7 + y^2)^{1/2} - x^3 + 4 = 0$

$$\frac{d}{dx}(7 + y^2)^{1/2} - \frac{d}{dx}x^3 + \frac{d}{dx}4 = \frac{d}{dx}0$$

$$\frac{1}{2}(7 + y^2)^{-1/2}\frac{d}{dx}(7 + y^2) - 3x^2 + 0 = 0$$

$$\frac{1}{2}(7 + y^2)^{-1/2}2yy' - 3x^2 = 0$$

$$\frac{yy'}{(7 + y^2)^{1/2}} = 3x^2$$

$$y' = \frac{3x^2(7 + y^2)^{1/2}}{y}$$

$$y'\Big|_{(2,\,3)} = \frac{3 \cdot 2^2(7 + 3^2)^{1/2}}{3} = \frac{12(16)^{1/2}}{3} = 16$$

39. $\ln(xy) = y^2 - 1$

$$\frac{d}{dx}[\ln(xy)] = \frac{d}{dx}y^2 - \frac{d}{dx}1$$

$$\frac{1}{xy} \cdot \frac{d}{dx}(xy) = 2yy'$$

$$\frac{1}{xy}(x \cdot y' + y) = 2yy'$$

$$\frac{1}{y} \cdot y' - 2yy' + \frac{1}{x} = 0$$

$$xy' - 2xy^2y' + y = 0$$

$$y'(x - 2xy^2) = -y$$

$$y' = \frac{-y}{x - 2xy^2} = \frac{y}{2xy^2 - x}$$

$$y'\Big|_{(1,1)} = \frac{1}{2 \cdot 1 \cdot 1^2 - 1} = 1$$

41. First find point(s) on the graph of the equation with abscissa $x = 1$:
Setting $x = 1$, we have
$$y^3 - y - 1 = 2 \quad \text{or} \quad y^3 - y - 3 = 0$$
Graphing this equation on a graphing utility, we get $y \approx 1.67$.

Now, differentiate implicitly to find the slope of the tangent line at
the point $(1, 1.67)$: $\frac{d}{dx}y^3 + x\frac{d}{dx}y + y\frac{d}{dx}x - \frac{d}{dx}x^3 = \frac{d}{dx}2$

$$3y^2y' - xy' - y - 3x^2 = 0$$

$$(3y^2 - x)y' = 3x^2 + y$$

$$y' = \frac{3x^2 + y}{3y^2 - x};$$

$$y'\Big|_{(1,1.67)} = \frac{3 + 1.67}{3(1.67)^2 - 1} = \frac{4.67}{7.37} \approx 0.63$$

Tangent line: $y - 1.67 = 0.63(x - 1)$ or $y = 0.63x + 1.04$

43. $x = p^2 - 2p + 1000$

$$\frac{d(x)}{dx} = \frac{d(p^2)}{dx} - \frac{d(2p)}{dx} + \frac{d(1000)}{dx}$$

$$1 = 2p\frac{dp}{dx} - 2\frac{dp}{dx} + 0$$

$$1 = (2p - 2)\frac{dp}{dx}$$

Thus, $\frac{dp}{dx} = p' = \frac{1}{2p - 2}.$

45. $x = \sqrt{10,000 - p^2} = (10,000 - p^2)^{1/2}$

$$\frac{d}{dx}x = \frac{d}{dx}(10,000 - p^2)^{1/2}$$

$$1 = \frac{1}{2}(10,000 - p^2)^{-1/2}\frac{d}{dx}[10,000 - p^2]$$

$$1 = \frac{1}{2(10,000 - p^2)^{1/2}} \cdot (-2pp')$$

$$1 = \frac{-pp'}{\sqrt{10,000 - p^2}}$$

$$p' = \frac{-\sqrt{10,000 - p^2}}{p}$$

EXERCISE 3-6

Things to remember:

1. SUGGESTIONS FOR SOLVING RELATED RATE PROBLEMS

Step 1. Sketch a figure.

Step 2. Identify all relevant variables, including those whose rates are given and those whose rates are to be found.

Step 3. Express all given rates and rates to be found as derivatives.

Step 4. Find an equation connecting the variables in step 2.

Step 5. Implicitly differentiate the equation found in step 4, using the chain rule where appropriate, and substitute in all given values.

Step 6. Solve for the derivative that will give the unknown rate.

---

1. $y = x^2 + 2$

Differentiating with respect to t:

$$\frac{dy}{dt} = 2x\frac{dx}{dt}; \quad \frac{dy}{dt} = 2(5)(3) = 30 \text{ when } x = 5, \quad \frac{dx}{dt} = 3$$

3. $x^2 + y^2 = 1$

Differentiating with respect to t:

$$2x\frac{dx}{dt} + 2y\frac{dy}{dt} = 0$$

$$2x\frac{dx}{dt} = -2y\frac{dy}{dt}$$

$$\frac{dx}{dt} = -\frac{y}{x}\frac{dy}{dt}; \quad \frac{dx}{dt} = -\frac{0.8}{(-0.6)}(-4) = -\frac{16}{3},$$

when $x = -0.6$, $y = 0.8$, $\dfrac{dy}{dt} = -4$

5. $x^2 + 3xy + y^2 = 11$

Differentiating with respect to t:

$$2x\frac{dx}{dt} + 2x\frac{dy}{dt} + 3y\frac{dx}{dt} + 2y\frac{dy}{dt} = 0$$

↑
ERROR

$$(3x + 2y)\frac{dy}{dt} = -(2x + 3y)\frac{dx}{dt}$$

$$\frac{dy}{dt} = -\frac{(2x + 3y)}{3x + 2y}\frac{dx}{dt}; \quad \frac{dy}{dt} = -\frac{(2 \cdot 1 + 3 \cdot 2)}{(3 \cdot 1 + 2 \cdot 2)}2 = -\frac{16}{7}$$

when $x = 1$, $y = 2$, $\frac{dx}{dt} = 2$

7. $xy = 36$

Differentiate with respect to t:

$$\frac{d(xy)}{dt} = \frac{d(36)}{dt}$$

$$x\frac{dy}{dt} + y\frac{dx}{dt} = 0$$

Given: $\frac{dx}{dt} = 4$ when $x = 4$ and $y = 9$. Therefore,

$$4\frac{dy}{dt} + 9(4) = 0$$

$$4\frac{dy}{dt} = -36$$

and $\frac{dy}{dt} = -9$.

The y coordinate is decreasing at 9 units per second.

9.

z = rope, $y = 4$, x

From the triangle,
$$x^2 + y^2 = z^2$$
or $x^2 + 16 = z^2$, since $y = 4$.

Differentiate with respect to t:

$$2x\frac{dx}{dt} = 2z\frac{dz}{dt}$$

or $x\frac{dx}{dt} = z\frac{dz}{dt}$

Given: $\frac{dz}{dt} = -3$. Also, when $x = 30$, $900 + 16 = z^2$ or $z = \sqrt{916}$.

Therefore,

$$30\frac{dx}{dt} = \sqrt{916}\,(-3) \quad \text{and} \quad \frac{dx}{dt} = \frac{-3\sqrt{916}}{30} = \frac{-\sqrt{916}}{10} \approx \frac{-30.27}{10}$$

$$\approx -3.03 \text{ feet per second.}$$

[<u>Note</u>: The negative sign indicates that the distance between the boat and the dock is decreasing.]

11. Area: $A = \pi R^2$

$$\frac{dA}{dt} = \frac{d\pi R^2}{dt} = \pi \cdot 2R\frac{dR}{dt}$$

Given: $\dfrac{dR}{dt} = 2$ ft/sec

$$\frac{dA}{dt} = 2\pi R \cdot 2 = 4\pi R$$

$$\left.\frac{dA}{dt}\right|_{R=10\text{ ft}} = 4\pi(10) = 40\pi \text{ ft}^2/\text{sec}$$
$$\approx 126 \text{ ft}^2/\text{sec}$$

13. $V = \dfrac{4}{3}\pi R^3$

$$\frac{dV}{dt} = \frac{4}{3}\pi 3R^2\frac{dR}{dt} = 4\pi R^2\frac{dR}{dt}$$

Given: $\dfrac{dR}{dt} = 3$ cm/min

$$\frac{dV}{dt} = 4\pi R^2 3 = 12\pi R^2$$

$$\left.\frac{dV}{dt}\right|_{R=10\text{ cm}} = 12\pi(10)^2 = 1200\pi$$
$$\approx 3768 \text{ cm}^3/\text{min}$$

15. $\dfrac{P}{T} = k \qquad\qquad (1)$

$P = kT$

Differentiate with respect to t:

$$\frac{dP}{dt} = k\frac{dT}{dt}$$

Given: $\dfrac{dT}{dt} = 3$ degrees per hour, $T = 250°$, $P = 500$ pounds per square inch.

From (1), for $T = 250$ and $P = 500$,

$k = \dfrac{500}{250} = 2$.

Thus, we have

$$\frac{dP}{dt} = 2\frac{dT}{dt}$$

$$\frac{dP}{dt} = 2(3) = 6$$

Pressure increases at 6 pounds per square inch per hour.

17. By the Pythagorean theorem,

$\qquad x^2 + y^2 = 10^2$

or $\quad x^2 + y^2 = 100 \qquad\qquad (1)$

Differentiate with respect to t:

$$2x\frac{dx}{dt} + 2y\frac{dy}{dt} = 0$$

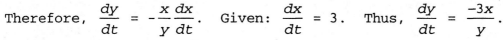

Therefore, $\dfrac{dy}{dt} = -\dfrac{x}{y}\dfrac{dx}{dt}$. Given: $\dfrac{dx}{dt} = 3$. Thus, $\dfrac{dy}{dt} = \dfrac{-3x}{y}$.

From (1), $y^2 = 100 - x^2$ and, when $x = 6$,

$y^2 = 100 - 6^2$

$\quad = 100 - 36 = 64$.

Thus, $y = 8$ when $x = 6$, and

$$\left.\frac{dy}{dt}\right|_{(6,\,8)} = \frac{-3(6)}{8} = \frac{-18}{8} = \frac{-9}{4}\text{ ft/sec}.$$

19. y = length of shadow
x = distance of man from light
z = distance of tip of shadow from light

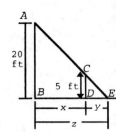

We want to compute $\dfrac{dz}{dt}$. Triangles ABE and CDE are similar

triangles; thus, the ratios of corresponding sides are equal.

Therefore, $\dfrac{z}{20} = \dfrac{y}{5} = \dfrac{z - x}{5}$ [<u>Note</u>: $y = z - x$.]

or $\qquad \dfrac{z}{20} = \dfrac{z - x}{5}$

$$z = 4(z - x)$$
$$z = 4z - 4x$$
$$4x = 3z$$

Differentiate with respect to t:

$$4\frac{dx}{dt} = 3\frac{dz}{dt}$$
$$\frac{dz}{dt} = \frac{4}{3}\frac{dx}{dt}$$

Given: $\dfrac{dx}{dt} = 5$.   Thus, $\dfrac{dz}{dt} = \dfrac{4}{3}(5) = \dfrac{20}{3}$ ft/sec.

21. $V = \dfrac{4}{3}\pi r^3$ (1)

Differentiate with respect to t:

$$\frac{dV}{dt} = 4\pi r^2 \frac{dr}{dt} \quad \text{and} \quad \frac{dr}{dt} = \frac{1}{4\pi r^2} \cdot \frac{dV}{dt}$$

Since $\dfrac{dV}{dt} = 4$ cu ft/sec,

$$\frac{dr}{dt} = \frac{1}{4\pi r^2}(4) = \frac{1}{\pi r^2} \text{ ft/sec} \quad (2)$$

At $t = 1$ minute = 60 seconds,

$V = 4(60) = 240$ cu ft and, from (1),

$$r^3 = \frac{3V}{4\pi} = \frac{3(240)}{4\pi} = \frac{180}{\pi}; \quad r = \left(\frac{180}{\pi}\right)^{1/3} \approx 3.855.$$

From (2)

$$\frac{dr}{dt} = \frac{1}{\pi(3.855)^2} \approx 0.0214 \text{ ft/sec}$$

At $t = 2$ minutes = 120 seconds,

$V = 4(120) = 480$ cu ft and

$$r^3 = \frac{3V}{4\pi} = \frac{3(480)}{4\pi} = \frac{360}{\pi}; \quad r = \left(\frac{360}{\pi}\right)^{1/3} \approx 4.857$$

From (2),

$$\frac{dr}{dt} = \frac{1}{\pi(4.857)^2} \approx 0.0135 \text{ ft/sec}$$

To find the time at which $\frac{dr}{dt} = 100$ ft/sec, solve

$$\frac{1}{\pi r^2} = 100$$

$$r^2 = \frac{1}{100\pi}$$

$$r = \frac{1}{\sqrt{100\pi}} = \frac{1}{10\sqrt{\pi}}$$

Now, when $r = \frac{1}{10\sqrt{\pi}}$,

$$V = \frac{4}{3}\pi\left(\frac{1}{10\sqrt{\pi}}\right)^3$$

$$= \frac{4}{3} \cdot \frac{1}{1000\sqrt{\pi}}$$

$$= \frac{1}{750\sqrt{\pi}}$$

Since the volume at time t is $4t$, we have

$$4t = \frac{1}{750\sqrt{\pi}} \text{ and}$$

$$t = \frac{1}{3000\sqrt{\pi}} \approx 0.00019 \text{ secs.}$$

23. $y = e^x + x + 1$; $\frac{dx}{dt} = 3$.

Differentiate with respect to t:

$$\frac{dy}{dt} = e^x\frac{dx}{dt} + \frac{dx}{dt} = e^x(3) + 3 = 3(e^x + 1)$$

To find where the point crosses the x axis, use a graphing utility to solve

$$e^x + x + 1 = 0$$

The result is $x \approx -1.278$.

Now, at $x = -1.278$,

$$\frac{dy}{dt} = 3(e^{-1.278} + 1) \approx 3.835 \text{ units/sec.}$$

25. $C = 90,000 + 30x$ (1)

$R = 300x - \dfrac{x^2}{30}$ (2)

$P = R - C$ (3)

(A) Differentiating (1) with respect to t:

$$\frac{dC}{dt} = \frac{d(90,000)}{dt} + \frac{d(30x)}{dt}$$

$$\frac{dC}{dt} = 30\frac{dx}{dt}$$

Thus, $\dfrac{dC}{dt} = 30(500)$ $\left(\dfrac{dx}{dt} = 500\right)$

$= \$15,000$ per week.

Costs are increasing at $15,000 per week at this production level.

(B) Differentiating (2) with respect to t:

$$\frac{dR}{dt} = \frac{d(300x)}{dt} - \frac{d\frac{x^2}{30}}{dt}$$

$$= 300\frac{dx}{dt} - \frac{2x}{30}\frac{dx}{dt}$$

$$= \left(300 - \frac{x}{15}\right)\frac{dx}{dt}$$

Thus, $\dfrac{dR}{dt} = \left(300 - \dfrac{6000}{15}\right)(500)$ $\left(x = 6000, \dfrac{dx}{dt} = 500\right)$

$= (-100)500$

$= -\$50,000$ per week.

Revenue is decreasing at $50,000 per week at this production level.

(C) Differentiating (3) with respect to t:

$$\frac{dP}{dt} = \frac{dR}{dt} - \frac{dC}{dt}$$

Thus, from parts (A) and (B), we have:

$\dfrac{dP}{dt} = -50,000 - 15,000 = -\$65,000$

Profits are decreasing at $65,000 per week at this production level.

27. $S = 60,000 - 40,000e^{-0.0005x}$

Differentiating implicitly with respect to t, we have

$\dfrac{ds}{dt} = -40,000(-0.0005)e^{-0.0005x}\dfrac{dx}{dt}$ and $\dfrac{ds}{dt} = 20e^{-0.0005x}\dfrac{dx}{dt}$

Now, for $x = 2000$ and $\dfrac{dx}{dt} = 300$, we have

$\dfrac{ds}{dt} = 20(300)e^{-0.0005(2000)}$

$= 6000e^{-1} = 2,207$

Thus, sales are increasing at the rate of $2,207 per week.

29. Price p and demand x are related by the equation

$$2x^2 + 5xp + 50p^2 = 80,000 \qquad (1)$$

Differentiating implicitly with respect to t, we have

$$4x\frac{dx}{dt} + 5x\frac{dp}{dt} + 5p\frac{dx}{dt} + 100p\frac{dp}{dt} = 0 \qquad (2)$$

(A) From (2), $\quad \dfrac{dx}{dt} = \dfrac{-(5x + 100p)\dfrac{dp}{dt}}{4x + 5p}$

Setting $p = 30$ in (1), we get

$$2x^2 + 150x + 45,000 = 80,000$$

or $\quad x^2 + 75x - 17,500 = 0$

Thus, $\quad x = \dfrac{-75 \pm \sqrt{(75)^2 + 70,000}}{2} = \dfrac{-75 \pm 275}{2} = 100, -175$

Since $x \geq 0$, $x = 100$

Now, for $x = 100$, $p = 30$ and $\dfrac{dp}{dt} = 2$, we have

$$\frac{dx}{dt} = \frac{-[5(100) + 100(30)] \cdot 2}{4(100) + 5(30)} = -\frac{7000}{550} \text{ and } \frac{dx}{dt} = -12.73$$

The demand is decreasing at the rate of -12.73 units/month.

(B) From (2), $\quad \dfrac{dp}{dt} = \dfrac{-(4x + 5p)\dfrac{dx}{dt}}{(5x + 100p)}$

Setting $x = 150$ in (1), we get

$$45,000 + 750p + 50p^2 = 80,000$$

or $\quad p^2 + 15p - 700 = 0$

and $p = \dfrac{-15 \pm \sqrt{225 + 2800}}{2} = \dfrac{-15 \pm 55}{2} = -35,\ 20$

Since $p \geq 0$, $p = 20$.

Now, for $x = 150$, $p = 20$ and $\dfrac{dx}{dt} = -6$, we have

$$\frac{dp}{dt} = -\frac{[4(150) + 5(20)](-6)}{5(150) + 100(20)} = \frac{4200}{2750} \approx 1.53$$

Thus, the price is increasing at the rate of $1.53 per month.

31. Volume $V = \pi R^2 h$, where h = thickness of the circular oil slick. Since $h = 0.1 = \dfrac{1}{10}$, we have:

$$V = \frac{\pi}{10}R^2$$

Differentiating with respect to t:

$$\frac{dV}{dt} = \frac{d\left(\dfrac{\pi}{10}R^2\right)}{dt} = \frac{\pi}{10}2R\frac{dR}{dt} = \frac{\pi}{5}R\frac{dR}{dt}$$

Given: $\dfrac{dR}{dt} = 0.32$ when $R = 500$. Therefore,

$$\frac{dV}{dt} = \frac{\pi}{5}(500)(0.32) = 100\pi(0.32) \approx 100.48 \text{ cubic feet per minute.}$$

1. $A(t) = 2000e^{0.09t}$

$A(5) = 2000e^{0.09(5)} = 2000e^{0.45} \approx 3136.62$ or $\$3136.62$

$A(10) = 2000e^{0.09(10)} = 2000e^{0.9} \approx 4919.21$ or $\$4919.21$

$A(20) = 2000e^{0.09(20)} = 2000e^{1.8} \approx 12,099.29$ or $\$12,099.29$ (5-1)

2. $\dfrac{d}{dx}(2 \ln x + 3e^x) = 2\dfrac{d}{dx}\ln x + 3\dfrac{d}{dx}e^x = \dfrac{2}{x} + 3e^x$ (5-2)

3. $\dfrac{d}{dx}e^{2x-3} = e^{2x-3}\dfrac{d}{dx}(2x - 3)$ (by the chain rule)

$\qquad = 2e^{2x-3}$ (5-2)

4. $y = \ln(2x + 7)$

$y' = \dfrac{1}{2x + 7}(2)$ (by the chain rule)

$\quad = \dfrac{2}{2x + 7}$ (5-2)

5. $y = \ln u$, where $u = 3 + e^x$.

(A) $y = \ln[3 + e^x]$

(B) $\dfrac{dy}{dx} = \dfrac{dy}{du} \cdot \dfrac{du}{dx} = \dfrac{1}{u}(e^x) = \dfrac{1}{3 + e^x}(e^x) = \dfrac{e^x}{3 + e^x}$ (5-3)

6. $\dfrac{d}{dx}2y^2 - \dfrac{d}{dx}3x^3 - \dfrac{d}{dx}5 = \dfrac{d}{dx}(0)$

$\qquad 4yy' - 9x^2 - 0 = 0$

$\qquad\qquad y' = \dfrac{9x^2}{4y}$

$\qquad \dfrac{dy}{dx}\Big|_{(1, 2)} = \dfrac{9 \cdot 1^2}{4 \cdot 2} = \dfrac{9}{8}$

$\qquad\qquad\qquad (5-4)$

7. $y = 3x^2 - 5$

$\dfrac{dy}{dt} = \dfrac{d(3x^2)}{dt} - \dfrac{d(5)}{dt}$

$\dfrac{dy}{dt} = 6x\dfrac{dx}{dt}$

$x = 12;\ \dfrac{dx}{dt} = 3$

$\dfrac{dy}{dt} = 6 \cdot 12 \cdot 3 = 216$ (5-4)

8. $25p + x = 1,000$

(A) $x = 1,000 - 25p$

(B) $x = f(p) = 1,000 - 25p$

$f'(p) = -25$

$E(p) = -\dfrac{pf'(p)}{f(p)} = \dfrac{25p}{1,000 - 25p} = \dfrac{p}{40 - p}$

(C) $E(15) = \dfrac{15}{40 - 15} = \dfrac{15}{25} = \dfrac{3}{5} = 0.6$

Demand is inelastic and insensitive to small changes in price.

(D) Revenue: $R(p) = pf(p) = 1,000p - 25p^2$

(E) From (B), $E(25) = \dfrac{25}{40 - 25} = \dfrac{25}{15} = \dfrac{5}{3} = 1.6$

Demand is elastic; a price cut will increase revenue. (5-4)

9. $y = 100e^{-0.1x}$

<u>Step 1. Analyze $f(x)$</u>:

(A) Domain: All real numbers, $(-\infty, \infty)$.

(B) Intercepts: y-intercept: $f(0) = 100e^{-0.1(0)} = 100$
                         x-intercept: Since $100e^{-0.1x} \neq 0$ for all x, there are
                                       no x-intercepts.

(C) Asymptotes:
$$\lim_{x \to \infty} 100e^{-0.1x} = \lim_{x \to \infty} \frac{100}{e^{0.1x}} = 0$$

$\lim\limits_{x \to -\infty} 100e^{-0.1x}$ does not exist.

Thus, $y = 0$ is a horizontal asymptote. There are no vertical asymptotes.

<u>Step 2. Analyze $f'(x)$</u>:
$$y' = 100e^{-0.1x}(-0.1)$$
$$= -10e^{-0.1x} < 0 \text{ on } (-\infty, \infty)$$
Thus, y is decreasing on $(-\infty, \infty)$; there are no local extrema.

<u>Step 3. Analyze $f''(x)$</u>:
$$y'' = -10e^{-0.1x}(-0.1)$$
$$= e^{-0.1x} > 0 \text{ on } (-\infty, \infty)$$
Thus, the graph of f is concave upward on $(-\infty, \infty)$; there are no inflection points.

<u>Step 4. Sketch the graph of f:</u>

x	y
0	100
-1	≈ 110
10	≈ 37

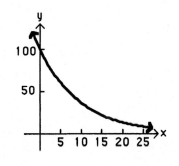

(5-2)

10.

n	1000	100,000	10,000,000	100,000,000
$\left(1 + \dfrac{2}{n}\right)^n$	7.374312	7.388908	7.389055	7.389056

$$\lim_{n \to \infty}\left(1 + \frac{2}{n}\right)^n \approx 7.38906 \text{ (5 decimal places)};$$

$$\lim_{n \to \infty}\left(1 + \frac{2}{n}\right)^n = e^2$$

(5-1)

11. $\dfrac{d}{dz}[(\ln\ z)^7 + \ln\ z^7] = \dfrac{d}{dz}[\ln\ z]^7 + \dfrac{d}{dz}7\ \ln\ z$

$$= 7[\ln\ z]^6 \dfrac{d}{dz}\ln\ z + 7\dfrac{d}{dz}\ln\ z$$

$$= 7[\ln\ z]^6 \dfrac{1}{z} + \dfrac{7}{z}$$

$$= \dfrac{7(\ln\ z)^6 + 7}{z} = \dfrac{7[(\ln\ z)^6 + 1]}{z} \qquad (5\text{-}3)$$

12. $\dfrac{d}{dx}x^6\ \ln\ x = x^6 \dfrac{d}{dx}\ln\ x + (\ln\ x)\dfrac{d}{dx}x^6$

$$= x^6\left(\dfrac{1}{x}\right) + (\ln\ x)6x^5 = x^5(1 + 6\ \ln\ x) \qquad (5\text{-}2)$$

13. $\dfrac{d}{dx}\left(\dfrac{e^x}{x^6}\right) = \dfrac{x^6 \dfrac{d}{dx}e^x - e^x \dfrac{d}{dx}x^6}{(x^6)^2} = \dfrac{x^6 e^x - 6x^5 e^x}{x^{12}} = \dfrac{xe^x - 6e^x}{x^7} = \dfrac{e^x(x - 6)}{x^7}$

$$(5\text{-}2)$$

14. $y = \ln(2x^3 - 3x)$

$$y' = \dfrac{1}{2x^3 - 3x}(6x^2 - 3) = \dfrac{6x^2 - 3}{2x^3 - 3x}$$

$$(5\text{-}3)$$

15. $f(x) = e^{x^3 - x^2}$

$$f'(x) = e^{x^3 - x^2}(3x^2 - 2x)$$

$$= (3x^2 - 2x)e^{x^3 - x^2} \qquad (5\text{-}3)$$

16. $y = e^{-2x}\ \ln\ 5x$

$$\dfrac{dy}{dx} = e^{-2x}\left(\dfrac{1}{5x}\right)(5) + (\ln\ 5x)(e^{-2x})(-2)$$

$$= e^{-2x}\left(\dfrac{1}{x} - 2\ \ln\ 5x\right) = \dfrac{1 - 2x\ \ln\ 5x}{xe^{2x}} \qquad (5\text{-}3)$$

17. $f(x) = 1 + e^{-x}$

$f'(x) = e^{-x}(-1) = -e^{-x}$

An equation for the tangent line to the graph of f at $x = 0$ is:

$y - y_1 = m(x - x_1)$,

where $x_1 = 0$, $y_1 = f(0) = 1 + e^0 = 2$, and $m = f'(0) = -e^0 = -1$.

Thus, $y - 2 = -1(x - 0)$ or $y = -x + 2$.

An equation for the tangent line to the graph of f at $x = -1$ is

$y - y_1 = m(x - x_1)$,

where $x_1 = -1$, $y_1 = f(-1) = 1 + e$, and $m = f'(-1) = -e$. Thus,

$y - (1 + e) = -e[x - (-1)]$ or $y - 1 - e = -ex - e$ and $y = -ex + 1$.

$$(5\text{-}2)$$

18. $x^2 - 3xy + 4y^2 = 23$

Differentiate implicitly:

$$2x - 3(xy' + y \cdot 1) + 8yy' = 0$$

$$2x - 3xy' - 3y + 8yy' = 0$$

$$8yy' - 3xy' = 3y - 2x$$

$$(8y - 3x)y' = 3y - 2x$$

$$y' = \frac{3y - 2x}{8y - 3x}$$

$$y'\Big|_{(-1,\,2)} = \frac{3 \cdot 2 - 2(-1)}{8 \cdot 2 - 3(-1)} = \frac{8}{19} \quad \text{[Slope at (-1, 2)]} \qquad (5\text{-}4)$$

19.

$$x^3 - 2t^2x + 8 = 0$$

$$3x^2x' - (2t^2x' + x \cdot 4t) + 0 = 0$$

$$3x^2x' - 2t^2x' - 4xt = 0$$

$$(3x^2 - 2t^2)x' = 4xt$$

$$x' = \frac{4xt}{3x^2 - 2t^2}$$

$$x'\Big|_{(-2,\,2)} = \frac{4 \cdot 2 \cdot (-2)}{3(2^2) - 2(-2)^2} = \frac{-16}{12 - 8} = \frac{-16}{4} = -4 \qquad (5\text{-}4)$$

20. $x - y^2 = e^y$

Differentiate implicitly:

$$1 - 2yy' = e^y y'$$

$$1 = e^y y' + 2yy'$$

$$1 = y'(e^y + 2y)$$

$$y' = \frac{1}{e^y + 2y}$$

$$y'\Big|_{(1,\,0)} = \frac{1}{e^0 + 2 \cdot 0} = 1$$

$$(5\text{-}4)$$

21. $\ln y = x^2 - y^2$

Differentiate implicitly:

$$\frac{y'}{y} = 2x - 2yy'$$

$$y'\left(\frac{1}{y} + 2y\right) = 2x$$

$$y'\left(\frac{1 + 2y^2}{y}\right) = 2x$$

$$y' = \frac{2xy}{1 + 2y^2}$$

$$y'\Big|_{(1,\,1)} = \frac{2 \cdot 1 \cdot 1}{1 + 2(1)^2} = \frac{2}{3} \qquad (5\text{-}4)$$

22. $y^2 - 4x^2 = 12$

Differentiate with respect to t:

$$2y\frac{dy}{dt} - 8x\frac{dx}{dt} = 0$$

Given: $\dfrac{dx}{dt} = -2$ when $x = 1$ and $y = 4$. Therefore,

$$2 \cdot 4\frac{dy}{dt} - 8 \cdot 1 \cdot (-2) = 0$$

$$8\frac{dy}{dt} + 16 = 0$$

$$\frac{dy}{dt} = -2.$$

The y coordinate is decreasing at 2 units per second. $\qquad (5\text{-}6)$

23. From the figure, $x^2 + y^2 = 17^2$.

Differentiate with respect to t:

$$2x\frac{dx}{dt} + 2y\frac{dy}{dt} = 0 \quad \text{or} \quad x\frac{dx}{dt} + y\frac{dy}{dt} = 0$$

We are given $\frac{dx}{dt} = -0.5$ feet per second. Therefore,

$$x(-0.5) + y\frac{dy}{dt} = 0 \quad \text{or} \quad \frac{dy}{dt} = \frac{0.5x}{y} = \frac{x}{2y}$$

Now, when $x = 8$, we have: $\quad 8^2 + y^2 = 17^2$

$$y^2 = 289 - 64 = 225$$
$$y = 15$$

Therefore, $\left.\dfrac{dy}{dt}\right|_{(8,\,15)} = \dfrac{8}{2(15)} = \dfrac{4}{15} \approx 0.27$ ft/sec.

(5-6)

24. $A = \pi R^2$. Given: $\dfrac{dA}{dt} = 24$ square inches per minute.

Differentiate with respect to t:

$$\frac{dA}{dt} = 2\pi R\frac{dR}{dt}$$
$$24 = 2\pi R\frac{dR}{dt}$$

Therefore, $\dfrac{dR}{dt} = \dfrac{24}{2\pi R} = \dfrac{12}{\pi R}$.

$$\left.\frac{dR}{dt}\right|_{R=12} = \frac{12}{\pi \cdot 12} = \frac{1}{\pi} \approx 0.318 \text{ inches per minute}$$

(5-6)

25. $x = f(p) = 20(p - 15)^2 \quad 0 \le p \le 15$

$f'(p) = 40(p - 15)$

$$E(p) = -\frac{pf'(p)}{f(p)} = \frac{-40p(p - 15)}{20(p - 15)^2} = \frac{-2p}{p - 15}$$

Elastic: $E(p) = \dfrac{-2p}{p - 15} > 1$

$$-2p < p - 15 \quad (p - 15 < 0 \text{ reverses inequality})$$
$$-3p < -15$$
$$p > 5; \qquad 5 < p < 15$$

Inelastic: $E(p) = \dfrac{-2p}{p - 15} < 1$

$$-2p > p - 15 \quad (p - 15 < 0 \text{ reverses inequality})$$
$$-3p > -15$$
$$p < 5; \qquad 0 < p < 5$$

(5-4)

26. $x = f(p) = 5(20 - p)$ $0 \le p \le 20$

$R(p) = pf(p) = 5p(20 - p) = 100p - 5p^2$

$R'(p) = 100 - 10p = 10(10 - p)$

Critical values: $p = 10$

Sign chart for $R'(p)$:

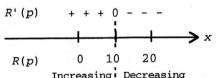

R'(p)   + + + 0 - - -

R(p)   0   10   20

Increasing Decreasing

Demand: Inelastic   Elastic

Test Numbers

p	$R'(p)$
5	50 (+)
15	−50 (−)

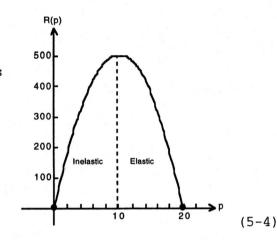

(5-4)

27. $f(x) = 11x - 2x \ln x, \ x > 0$

$f'(x) = 11 - 2x\left(\dfrac{1}{x}\right) - (\ln x)(2)$

$\qquad = 11 - 2 - 2 \ln x = 9 - 2 \ln x, \ x > 0$

Critical value(s): $f'(x) = 9 - 2 \ln x = 0$

$$2 \ln x = 9$$
$$\ln x = \frac{9}{2}$$
$$x = e^{9/2}$$

$f''(x) = -\dfrac{2}{x}$ and $f''(e^{9/2}) = -\dfrac{2}{e^{9/2}} < 0$

Since $x = e^{9/2}$ is the only critical value, and $f''(e^{9/2}) < 0$,
f has an absolute maximum at $x = e^{9/2}$. The absolute maximum is:

$f(e^{9/2}) = 11e^{9/2} - 2e^{9/2}\ln(e^{9/2})$

$\qquad = 11e^{9/2} - 9e^{9/2}$

$\qquad = 2e^{9/2} \approx 180.03$

(5-2)

28. $f(x) = 10xe^{-2x}, \ x > 0$

$f'(x) = 10xe^{-2x}(-2) + 10e^{-2x}(1) = 10e^{-2x}(1 - 2x), \ x > 0$

Critical value(s): $f'(x) = 10e^{-2x}(1 - 2x) = 0$

$$1 - 2x = 0$$
$$x = \frac{1}{2}$$

$f''(x) = 10e^{-2x}(-2) + 10(1 - 2x)e^{-2x}(-2)$

$\qquad = -20e^{-2x}(1 + 1 - 2x)$

$\qquad = -40e^{-2x}(1 - x)$

$f''\left(\dfrac{1}{2}\right) = -20e^{-1} < 0$

Since $x = \dfrac{1}{2}$ is the only critical value, and $f''\left(\dfrac{1}{2}\right) = -20e^{-1} < 0$,

f has an absolute maximum at $x = \dfrac{1}{2}$. The absolute maximum of f is:

$$f\left(\frac{1}{2}\right) = 10\left(\frac{1}{2}\right)e^{-2(1/2)}$$
$$= 5e^{-1} \approx 1.84 \tag{5-3}$$

29. $f(x) = 3x - x^2 + e^{-x}, \ x > 0$

$f'(x) = 3 - 2x - e^{-x}, \ x > 0$

Critical value(s): $f'(x) = 3 - 2x - e^{-x} = 0$
$$x \approx 1.373$$

$f''(x) = -2 + e^{-x}$ and $f''(1.373) = -2 + e^{-1.373} < 0$

Since $x \approx 1.373$ is the only critical value, and $f''(1.373) < 0$, f has an absolute maximum at $x = 1.373$. The absolute maximum of f is:

$$f(1.373) = 3(1.373) - (1.373)^2 + e^{-1.373}$$
$$\approx 2.487 \tag{5-2}$$

30. $f(x) = \dfrac{\ln x}{e^x}, \ x > 0$

$$f'(x) = \frac{e^x\left(\dfrac{1}{x}\right) - (\ln x)e^x}{(e^x)^2} = \frac{e^x\left(\dfrac{1}{x} - \ln x\right)}{e^{2x}}$$
$$= \frac{1 - x \ln x}{xe^x}, \ x > 0$$

Critical value(s): $f'(x) = \dfrac{1 - x \ln x}{xe^x} = 0$
$$1 - x \ln x = 0$$
$$x \ln x = 1$$
$$x \approx 1.763$$

$$f''(x) = \frac{xe^x[-1 - \ln x] - (1 - x \ln x)(xe^x + e^x)}{x^2 e^{2x}}$$
$$= \frac{-x(1 + \ln x) - (x + 1)(1 - x \ln x)}{x^2 e^x};$$
$$f''(1.763) \approx \frac{-1.763(1.567) - (2.763)(0.000349)}{(1.763)^2 e^{1.763}} < 0$$

Since $x = 1.763$ is the only critical value, and $f''(1.763) < 0$, f has an absolute maximum at $x = 1.763$. The absolute maximum of f is:

$$f(1.763) = \frac{\ln(1.763)}{e^{1.763}} \approx 0.097 \tag{5-2}$$

31. $f(x) = 5 - 5e^{-x}$

Step 1.   Analyze $f(x)$:

(A) Domain: All real numbers, $(-\infty, \infty)$.

(B) Intercepts: y intercept: $f(0) = 5 - 5e^{-0} = 0$

$\qquad\qquad\qquad$ x intercepts: $5 - 5e^{-x} = 0$
$\qquad\qquad\qquad\qquad\qquad\qquad$ $e^{-x} = 1$
$\qquad\qquad\qquad\qquad\qquad\qquad\quad$ $x = 0$

(C) Asymptotes:

$$\lim_{x\to\infty} (5 - 5e^{-x}) = \lim_{x\to\infty}\left(5 - \frac{5}{e^x}\right) = 5$$

$\lim\limits_{x\to-\infty} (5 - 5e^{-x})$ does not exist.

Thus, $y = 5$ is a horizontal asymptote.

Since $f(x) = 5 - \dfrac{5}{e^x} = \dfrac{5e^x - 5}{e^x}$ and $e^x \neq 0$ for all x, there are no

vertical asymptotes.

Step 2.   Analyze $f'(x)$:

$f'(x) = -5e^{-x}(-1) = 5e^{-x} > 0$ on $(-\infty, \infty)$

Thus, f is increasing on $(-\infty, \infty)$; there are no local extrema.

Step 3.   Analyze $f''(x)$:

$f''(x) = -5e^{-x} < 0$ on $(-\infty, \infty)$.

Thus, the graph of f is concave downward on $(-\infty, \infty)$; there are no inflection points.

Step 4.   Sketch the graph of f:

x	$f(x)$
0	0
-1	-8.59
2	4.32

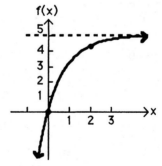

(5-2)

32. $f(x) = x^3 \ln x$

Step 1.   Analyze $f(x)$:

(A) Domain: all positive real numbers, $(0, \infty)$.

(B) Intercepts: y-intercept: Since $x = 0$ is not in the domain, there is
$\qquad\qquad\qquad\qquad\qquad\qquad$ no y-intercept.

$\qquad\qquad\qquad$ x-intercepts: $x^3 \ln x = 0$
$\qquad\qquad\qquad\qquad\qquad\qquad\qquad$ $\ln x = 0$
$\qquad\qquad\qquad\qquad\qquad\qquad\qquad\quad$ $x = 1$

(C) Asymptotes:

$\lim\limits_{x \to \infty} (x^3 \ln x)$ does not exist.

It can be shown that $\lim\limits_{x \to 0^+} (x^3 \ln x) = 0$. Thus, there are no horizontal or vertical asymptotes.

Step 2. Analyze $f'(x)$:

$$f'(x) = x^3 \left(\frac{1}{x}\right) + (\ln x) 3x^2$$

$$= x^2 [1 + 3 \ln x], \quad x > 0$$

Critical values: $x^2 [1 + 3 \ln x] = 0$

$$1 + 3 \ln x = 0 \quad (\text{since } x > 0)$$

$$\ln x = -\frac{1}{3}$$

$$x = e^{-1/3} \approx 0.72$$

Partition numbers: $x = e^{-1/3}$

Sign chart for f':

Test Numbers	
x	$f'(x)$
0.5	$-0.27 \, (-)$
1	$1 \, (+)$

Thus, f is decreasing on $(0, \; e^{-1/3})$ and increasing on $(e^{-1/3}, \; \infty)$; f has a local minimum at $x = e^{-1/3}$.

Step 3. Analyze $f''(x)$:

$$f''(x) = x^2 \left(\frac{3}{x}\right) + (1 + 3 \ln x) 2x$$

$$= x(5 + 6 \ln x), \quad x > 0$$

Partition numbers: $x(5 + 6 \ln x) = 0$

$$5 + 6 \ln x = 0$$

$$\ln x = -\frac{5}{6}$$

$$x = e^{-5/6} \approx 0.43$$

Sign chart for f'':

Test Numbers	
x	$f''(x)$
.2	$-0.93 \; (-)$
1	$5 \; (+)$

Thus, the graph of f is concave downward on $(0, \; e^{-5/6})$ and concave upward on $(e^{-5/6}, \; \infty)$; the graph has an inflection point at $x = e^{-5/6}$.

236

Step 4. Sketch the graph of f:

x	$f(x)$
$e^{-5/6}$	-0.07
$e^{-1/3}$	-0.12
1	0

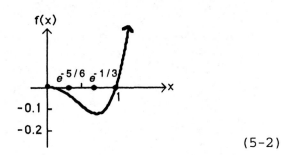

(5-2)

33. $y = w^3$, $w = \ln u$, $u = 4 - e^x$

(A) $y = [\ln(4 - e^x)]^3$

(B) $\dfrac{dy}{dx} = \dfrac{dy}{dw} \cdot \dfrac{dw}{du} \cdot \dfrac{du}{dx}$

$\quad = 3w^2 \cdot \dfrac{1}{u} \cdot (-e^x) = 3[\ln(4 - e^x)]^2 \left(\dfrac{1}{4 - e^x}\right)(-e^x)$

$\quad\quad = \dfrac{-3e^x[\ln(4 - e^x)]^2}{4 - e^x}$

(5-3)

34. $y = 5^{x^2 - 1}$

$y' = 5^{x^2 - 1}(\ln 5)(2x) = 2x5^{x^2 - 1}(\ln 5)$

(5-3)

35. $\dfrac{d}{dx}\log_5(x^2 - x) = \dfrac{1}{x^2 - x} \cdot \dfrac{1}{\ln 5} \cdot \dfrac{d}{dx}(x^2 - x) = \dfrac{1}{\ln 5} \cdot \dfrac{2x - 1}{x^2 - x}$

(5-3)

36. $\dfrac{d}{dx}\sqrt{\ln(x^2 + x)} = \dfrac{d}{dx}[\ln(x^2 + x)]^{1/2} = \dfrac{1}{2}[\ln(x^2 + x)]^{-1/2}\dfrac{d}{dx}\ln(x^2 + x)$

$\quad = \dfrac{1}{2}[\ln(x^2 + x)]^{-1/2}\dfrac{1}{x^2 + x}\dfrac{d}{dx}(x^2 + x)$

$\quad = \dfrac{1}{2}[\ln(x^2 + x)]^{-1/2} \cdot \dfrac{2x + 1}{x^2 + x} = \dfrac{2x + 1}{2(x^2 + x)[\ln(x^2 + x)]^{1/2}}$

(5-3)

37. $e^{xy} = x^2 + y + 1$

Differentiate implicitly:

$\dfrac{d}{dx}e^{xy} = \dfrac{d}{dx}x^2 + \dfrac{d}{dx}y + \dfrac{d}{dx}1$

$e^{xy}(xy' + y) = 2x + y'$

$xe^{xy}y' - y' = 2x - ye^{xy}$

$y' = \dfrac{2x - ye^{xy}}{xe^{xy} - 1}$

$y'\Big|_{(0,\,0)} = \dfrac{2 \cdot 0 - 0 \cdot e^0}{0 \cdot e^0 - 1} = 0$

(5-4)

38. $A = \pi r^2$, $r \geq 0$

Differentiate with respect to t:

$\dfrac{dA}{dt} = 2\pi r\dfrac{dr}{dt} = 6\pi r$ since $\dfrac{dr}{dt} = 3$

The area increases at the rate $6\pi r$. This is smallest when $r = 0$; there is no largest value.

(5-6)

39. $y = x^3$

Differentiate with respect to t:
$$\frac{dy}{dt} = 3x^2\frac{dx}{dt}$$

Solving for $\frac{dx}{dt}$, we get
$$\frac{dx}{dt} = \frac{1}{3x^2} \cdot \frac{dy}{dt} = \frac{5}{3x^2} \quad \text{since} \quad \frac{dy}{dt} = 5$$

To find where $\frac{dx}{dt} > \frac{dy}{dt}$, solve the inequality

$$\frac{5}{3x^2} > 5$$

$$\frac{1}{3x^2} > 1$$

$$3x^2 < 1$$

$$-\frac{1}{\sqrt{3}} < x < \frac{1}{\sqrt{3}} \quad \text{or} \quad \frac{-\sqrt{3}}{3} < x < \frac{\sqrt{3}}{3} \qquad (5\text{-}6)$$

40. (A) The compound interest formula is: $A = P(1 + r)^t$. Thus, the time for P to double when $r = 0.05$ and interest is compounded annually can be found by solving

$2P = P(1 + 0.05)^t$ or $2 = (1.05)^t$ for t.
$\ln(1.05)^t = \ln 2$
$t \ln(1.05) = \ln 2$
$$t = \frac{\ln 2}{\ln(1.05)} \approx 14.2 \text{ years}$$

(B) The continuous compound interest formula is: $A = Pe^{rt}$. Proceeding as above, we have

$2P = Pe^{0.05t}$ or $e^{0.05t} = 2$.
Therefore, $0.05t = \ln 2$ and
$$t = \frac{\ln 2}{.05} \approx 13.9 \text{ years} \qquad (5\text{-}1)$$

41. $A(t) = 100e^{0.1t}$
$A'(t) = 100(0.1)e^{0.1t} = 10e^{0.1t}$
$A'(1) = 11.05$ or $\$11.05$ per year
$A'(10) = 27.18$ or $\$27.18$ per year $\qquad (5\text{-}1)$

42. $R(x) = xp(x) = 1000xe^{-0.02x}$
$R'(x) = 1000[xD_x e^{-0.02x} + e^{-0.02x}D_x x]$
$\quad = 1000[x(-0.02)e^{-0.02x} + e^{-0.02x}]$
$\quad = (1000 - 20x)e^{-0.02x} \qquad (5\text{-}3)$

238

43. From Problem 42,

$R'(x) = (1000 - 20x)e^{-0.02x}$

Critical value(3s): $R'(x) = (1000 - 20x)e^{-0.02x} = 0$

$$1000 - 20x = 0$$
$$x = 50$$

$R''(x) = (1000 - 20x)e^{-0.02x}(-0.02) + e^{-0.02x}(-20)$

$\quad = e^{-0.02x}[0.4x - 20 - 20]$

$\quad = e^{-0.02x}(0.4x - 40)$

$R''(50) = e^{-0.02(50)}[0.4(50) - 40] = -20e^{-1} < 0$

Since $x = 50$ is the only critical value and $R''(50) < 0$, R has an absolute maximum at a production level of 50 units. The maximum revenue is $R(50) = 1000(50)e^{-0.02(50)} = 50,000e^{-1} \approx 18,394$ or \$18,394. The price per unit at the production level of 50 units is

$p(50) = 1000e^{-0.02(50)} = 1000e^{-1} \approx 367.88$ or \$367.88.　　　　　(5-3)

44. $R(x) = 1000xe^{-0.02x}$, $0 \le x \le 100$

Step 1.　Analyze $R(x)$:

(A) Domain: $0 \le x \le 100$ or [0, 100]

(B) Intercepts: y-intercept: $R(0) = 0$

$\qquad\qquad\qquad$ x-intercepts: $100xe^{-0.02x} = 0$

$\qquad\qquad\qquad\qquad\qquad x = 0$

(C) Asymptotes: There are no horizontal or vertical asymptotes.

Step 2.　Analyze $R'(x)$:

From Problems 47 and 48, $R'(x) = (1000 - 20x)e^{-0.02x}$ and $x = 50$ is a critical value.

Sign chart for R':

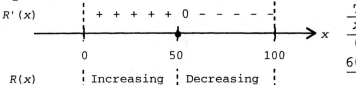

Test Numbers	
x	$R'(x)$
0	1000 (+)
60	≈ -60.24 (−)

Thus, R is increasing on (0, 50) and decreasing on (50, 100); R has a maximum at $x = 50$.

Step 3.　Analyze $R''(x)$:

$R''(x) = (0.4x - 40)e^{-0.02x} < 0$ on (0, 100)

Thus, the graph of R is concave downward on (0, 100).

Step 4.　Sketch the graph of R:

x	$R(x)$
0	0
50	18,394
100	13,533

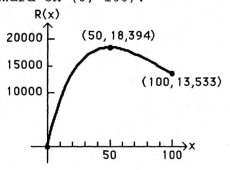

(5-3)

45. Cost: $C(x) = 220x$

Price-demand equation: $p(x) = 1,000e^{-0.02x}$

Revenue: $R(x) = xp(x) = 1,000xe^{-0.02x}$

Profit: $P(x) = R(x) - C(x) = 1,000xe^{-0.02x} - 220x$

On a graphing utility, graph $P(x)$ and calculate its maximum value. The maximum value is \$9,864 at a demand level of 29.969082 ($\approx$ 30). The price at this demand level is: $p = \$549.15$. (5-3)

46. Let x = the number of cream puffs.

Daily cost: $C(x) = x$ (dollars)

Daily revenue: $R(x) = xp(x)$, where

$p(x) = a + b \ln x$ is the logarithmic regression model for the given data.

```
LnReg
 y=a+blnx
 a=6.224213011
 b=-.5238332169
```

Profit: $P(x) = R(x) - C(x)$

Using a graphing utility, we find that the maximum profit is achieved at the demand level $x \approx 7887$. The price at this demand level is: $p(7887) = \$1.52$ (to the nearest cent). (5-2)

47. Cost: $C(x) = 200 + 50x - 50 \ln x,\ x \geq 1$

Average cost: $\overline{C} = \dfrac{C(x)}{x} = \dfrac{200}{x} + 50 - \dfrac{50}{x}\ln x,\ x \geq 1$

$\overline{C}'(x) = \dfrac{-200}{x^2} - \dfrac{50}{x}\left(\dfrac{1}{x}\right) + (\ln x)\dfrac{50}{x^2} = \dfrac{50(\ln x - 5)}{x^2},\ x \geq 1$

Critical value(s): $\overline{C}'(x) = \dfrac{50(\ln x - 5)}{x^2} = 0$

$$\ln x = 5$$
$$x = e^5$$

Sign chart for $\overline{C}'$:

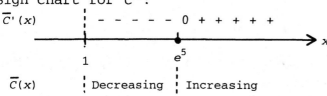

Test Numbers	
x	$\overline{C}'(x)$
1	-250 $(-)$
e^6	$\dfrac{50}{e^{12}}$ $(+)$

By the first derivative test, $\overline{C}$ has a local minimum at $x = e^5$. Since this is the only critical value of $\overline{C}$, $\overline{C}$ has as absolute minimum at $x = e^5$. Thus, the minimal average cost is:

$\overline{C}(e^5) = \dfrac{200}{e^5} + 50 - \dfrac{50}{e^5}\ln(e^5)$

$= 50 - \dfrac{50}{e^5} \approx 49.66$ or \$49.66 (5-2)

48. $x = \sqrt{5000 - 2p^3} = (5000 - 2p^3)^{1/2}$

Differentiate implicitly with respect to x:

$1 = \dfrac{1}{2}(5000 - 2p^3)^{-1/2}(-6p^2)\dfrac{dp}{dx}$

$1 = \dfrac{-3p^2}{(5000 - 2p^3)^{1/2}}\dfrac{dp}{dx}$

$\dfrac{dp}{dx} = \dfrac{-(5000 - 2p^3)^{1/2}}{3p^2}$ $\hfill$ (5-3)

49. Given: $R(x) = 36x - \dfrac{x^2}{20}$ and $\dfrac{dx}{dt} = 10$ when $x = 250$.

Differentiate with respect to t:

$\dfrac{dR}{dt} = 36\dfrac{dx}{dt} - \dfrac{1}{20}(2x)\dfrac{dx}{dt} = 36\dfrac{dx}{dt} - \dfrac{x}{10}\dfrac{dx}{dt}$

Thus, $\left.\dfrac{dR}{dt}\right|_{x=250 \text{ and } \frac{dx}{dt}=10} = 36(10) - \dfrac{250}{10}(10)$

$\qquad\qquad\qquad\qquad\qquad = \$110$ per day $\hfill$ (5-6)

50. $p = 16.8 - 0.002x$

$x = f(p) = \dfrac{16.8}{0.002} - \dfrac{1}{0.002}p = 8,400 - 500p$

$f'(p) = -500$

Elasticity of demand: $E(p) = \dfrac{-pf'(p)}{f(p)} = \dfrac{500p}{8,400 - 500p} = \dfrac{5p}{84 - 5p}$

$E(8) = \dfrac{40}{84 - 40} = \dfrac{40}{44} = \dfrac{10}{11} < 1$

Demand is inelastic, a (small) price increase will increase revenue. $\hfill$ (5-4)

51. $f(t) = 1,700t + 20,500$

$f'(t) = 1,700$

Relative rate of change: $\dfrac{f'(t)}{f(t)} = \dfrac{1,700}{1,700t + 20,500}$

Relative rate of change at $t = 30$: $\dfrac{1,700}{1,700(30) + 20,500} \approx 0.02378$ $\hfill$ (5-4)

52. $C(t) = 5e^{-0.3t}$

$C'(t) = 5e^{-0.3t}(-0.3) = -1.5e^{-0.3t}$

After one hour, the rate of change of concentration is

$C'(1) = -1.5e^{-0.3(1)} = -1.5e^{-0.3} \approx -1.111$ mg/ml per hour.

After five hours, the rate of change of concentration is

$C'(5) = -1.5e^{-0.3(5)} = -1.5e^{-1.5} \approx -0.335$ mg/ml per hour. $\hfill$ (5-3)

53. Given: $A = \pi R^2$ and $\dfrac{dA}{dt} = -45$ mm^2 per day (negative because the area is decreasing).

Differentiate with respect to t:

$$\frac{dA}{dt} = \pi 2R \frac{dR}{dt}$$

$$-45 = 2\pi R \frac{dR}{dt}$$

$$\frac{dR}{dt} = -\frac{45}{2\pi R}$$

$$\left.\frac{dR}{dt}\right|_{R=15} = \frac{-45}{2\pi \cdot 15} = \frac{-3}{2\pi} \approx -0.477 \text{ mm per day} \qquad (5\text{-}6)$$

54. $N(t) = 10(1 - e^{-0.4t})$

(A) $N'(t) = -10e^{-0.4t}(-0.4) = 4e^{-0.4t}$

$N'(1) = 4e^{-0.4(1)} = 4e^{-0.4} \approx 2.68$.

Thus, learning is increasing at the rate of 2.68 units per day after 1 day.

$N'(5) = 4e^{-0.4(5)} = 4e^{-2} \approx 0.54$

Thus, learning is increasing at the rate of 0.54 units per day after 5 days.

(B) From (A), $N'(t) = 4e^{-0.4t} > 0$ on $(0, 10)$. Thus, N is increasing on $(0, 10)$.

$N''(t) = 4e^{-0.4t}(-0.4) = -1.6e^{-0.4t} < 0$ on $(0, 10)$.

Thus, the graph of N is concave downward on $(0, 10)$. The graph of N is:

t	$N(t)$
0	0
5	8.65
10	9.82

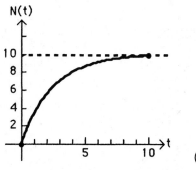

$(5\text{-}3)$

55. Given: $T = 2\left(1 + \dfrac{1}{x^{3/2}}\right) = 2 + 2x^{-3/2}$, and $\dfrac{dx}{dt} = 3$ when $x = 9$.

Differentiate with respect to t:

$$\frac{dT}{dt} = 0 + 2\left(-\frac{3}{2}x^{-5/2}\right)\frac{dx}{dt} = -3x^{-5/2}\frac{dx}{dt}$$

$$\left.\frac{dT}{dt}\right|_{x=9 \text{ and } \frac{dx}{dt}=3} = -3(9)^{-5/2}(3) = -3 \cdot 3^{-5} \cdot 3 = -3^{-3} = \frac{-1}{27}$$

$$\approx -0.037 \text{ minutes per operation per hour}$$

$(5\text{-}6$

4 Integration

Things to remember:

1.   A function $F(x)$ is an ANTIDERIVATIVE of $f(x)$ if $F'(x) = f(x)$.

2.   THEOREM ON ANTIDERIVATIVES

   If the derivatives of two functions are equal on an open interval (a, b), then the functions can differ by at most a constant. Symbolically: If F and G are differentiable functions on the interval (a, b) and $F'(x) = G'(x)$ for all x in (a, b), then $F(x) = G(x) + k$ for some constant k.

3.   The INDEFINITE INTEGRAL of $f(x)$, denoted

   $$\int f(x)dx,$$

   represents all antiderivatives of $f(x)$ and is given by

   $$\int f(x)dx = F(x) + C$$

   where $F(x)$ is any antiderivative of $f(x)$ and C is an arbitrary constant. The symbol $\int$ is called an INTEGRAL SIGN, the function $f(x)$ is called the INTEGRAND, and C is called the CONSTANT OF INTEGRATION.

4.   Indefinite integration and differentiation are reverse operations (except for the addition of the constant of integration). This is expressed symbolically by:

   (a) $\dfrac{d}{dx}\left(\int f(x)dx\right) = f(x)$

   (b) $\int F'(x)dx = F(x) + C$

5.   INDEFINITE INTEGRAL FORMULAS:

   (a) $\int x^n\, dx = \dfrac{x^{n+1}}{n+1} + C,\ n \neq -1$

   (b) $\int e^x\, dx = e^x + C$

   (c) $\int \dfrac{dx}{x} = \ln|x| + C,\ x \neq 0$

6.   INDEFINITE INTEGRATION PROPERTIES:

   (a) $\int kf(x)dx = k \int f(x)dx,\ k$ constant

   (b) $\int [f(x) \pm g(x)]dx = \int f(x)dx \pm \int g(x)dx$

1. $\int x^2 \, dx = \dfrac{1}{3}x^3 + C$ [Formula 5a]

Check: $\dfrac{d}{dx}\left(\dfrac{1}{3}x^3 + C\right) = x^2$

3. $\int x^7 \, dx = \dfrac{1}{8}x^8 + C$ [Formula 5a]

Check: $\dfrac{d}{dx}\left(\dfrac{1}{8}x^8 + C\right) = x^7$

5. $\int 2 \, dx = 2\int dx = 2[x + C] = 2x + C$

[Formula 5a, Property 6a,
$x^0 = 1$, replace $2C$ by C]

Check: $\dfrac{d}{dx}(2x + C) = 2$

7. $\int 5t^{-3} \, dt = 5\int t^{-3} \, dt = 5\dfrac{t^{-2}}{-2} + C = -\dfrac{5}{2}t^{-2} + C$ [Formula 5a,
Property 6a]

Check: $\dfrac{d}{dt}\left(-\dfrac{5}{2}t^{-2} + C\right) = 5t^{-3}$

9. $\int \pi^2 \, dx = \pi^2\int dx = \pi^2 x + C$

[Formula 5a,
Property 6a]

Check: $\dfrac{d}{dx}(\pi^2 x + C) = \pi^2$

11. $\int (6t + 3) \, dt = 6\int t \, dt + 3\int dt = 6\dfrac{t^2}{2} + 3t + C = 3t^2 + 3t + C$

Check: $\dfrac{d}{dt}(3t^2 + 3t + C) = 6t + 3$ [Formula 5a, Properties 6a, b]

13. $\int 3e^t \, dt = 3\int e^t \, dt = 3e^t + C$ [Formula 5b, Property 6a]

Check: $\dfrac{d}{dt}(3e^t + C) = 3e^t$

15. $\int \dfrac{6}{x} \, dx = 6\int \dfrac{1}{x} \, dx = 6\ln|x| + C$

Check: $\dfrac{d}{dx}(\ln|x| + C) = \dfrac{1}{x}$ [Formula 5c, Property 6a]

17. $\int 15x^{1/2} \, dx = 15\int x^{1/2} \, dx = 15\dfrac{x^{1/2+1}}{1/2 + 1} + C = 15\dfrac{x^{3/2}}{3/2} + C = 10x^{3/2} + C$

Check: $\dfrac{d}{dx}(10x^{3/2} + C) = 15x^{1/2}$ [Formula 5a, Property 6a]

19. $\int 7t^{-4/3} \, dt = 7\int t^{-4/3} \, dt = 7\dfrac{t^{-4/3+1}}{-4/3 + 1} + C = 7\dfrac{t^{-1/3}}{-1/3} + C = -21t^{-1/3} + C$

Check: $\dfrac{d}{dt}(-21t^{-1/3} + C) = 7t^{-4/3}$ [Formula 5a, Property 6a]

21. $\int (x - \sqrt{x}) \, dx = \int x \, dx - \int x^{1/2} \, dx = \dfrac{1}{2}x^2 - \dfrac{x^{3/2}}{3/2} + C = \dfrac{1}{2}x^2 - \dfrac{2}{3}x^{3/2} + C$

Check: $\dfrac{d}{dx}\left(\dfrac{1}{2}x^2 - \dfrac{2}{3}x^{3/2} + C\right) = x - x^{1/2}$ [Formula 5a, Property 6b]

$= x - \sqrt{x}$

23. $\dfrac{dy}{dx} = 200x^4$

$y = \int 200x^4\,dx = 200\int x^4 dx = 200\dfrac{x^5}{5} + C = 40x^5 + C$

25. $\dfrac{dP}{dx} = 24 - 6x$

$P = \int(24 - 6x)\,dx = \int 24\,dx - \int 6x\,dx = \int 24\,dx - 6\int x\,dx$

$\qquad = 24x - \dfrac{6x^2}{2} + C = 24x - 3x^2 + C$

27. $\dfrac{dy}{du} = 2u^5 - 3u^2 - 1$

$y = \int(2u^5 - 3u^2 - 1)\,du = \int 2u^5 du - \int 3u^2 du - \int 1\,du$

$\qquad\qquad = 2\int u^5 du - 3\int u^2 du - \int du$

$\qquad\qquad = \dfrac{2u^6}{6} - \dfrac{3u^3}{3} - u + C = \dfrac{u^6}{3} - u^3 - u + C$

29. $\dfrac{dy}{dx} = e^x + 3$

$y = \int(e^x + 3)\,dx = \int e^x dx + \int 3\,dx = e^x + 3x + C$

31. $\dfrac{dx}{dt} = 5t^{-1} + 1$

$x = \int(5t^{-1} + 1)\,dt = \int 5t^{-1}dt + \int 1\,dt = 5\int\dfrac{1}{t}dt + \int dt$

$\qquad\qquad = 5\ln|t| + t + C$

33. (A) False; x^{-1} does not have an antiderivative of the form $\dfrac{x^{n+1}}{n + 1}$.

   (B) True; $\dfrac{d}{dx}(\pi) = 0$ since π is a constant.

35. The graphs in this set ARE NOT graphs from a family of antiderivative functions since the graphs are not vertical translations of each other.

37. The graphs in this set could be graphs from a family of antiderivative functions since they appear to be vertical translations of each other.

39. $\int 5x(1 - x)\,dx = 5\int x(1 - x)\,dx = 5\int(x - x^2)\,dx$

$\qquad\qquad = 5\int x\,dx - 5\int x^2\,dx = \dfrac{5x^2}{2} - \dfrac{5x^3}{3} + C$

   Check: $\left(\dfrac{5x^2}{2} - \dfrac{5x^3}{3} + C\right)' = 5x - 5x^2 = 5x(1 - x)$

41. $\int (2 + x^2)(3 + x^2)\,dx = \int (6 + 5x^2 + x^4)\,dx = 6\int dx + 5\int x^2\,dx + \int x^4\,dx$

$$= 6x + \frac{5x^3}{3} + \frac{x^5}{5} + C = 6x + \frac{5x^3}{3} + \frac{x^5}{5} + C$$

Check: $\left(6x + \frac{5x^3}{3} + \frac{x^5}{5} + C\right)' = 6 + 5x^2 + x^4 = (2 + x^2)(3 + x^2)$

43. $\int \frac{du}{\sqrt{u}} = \int \frac{du}{u^{1/2}} = \int u^{-1/2}\,du = \frac{u^{(-1/2)+1}}{-1/2 + 1} + C = \frac{u^{1/2}}{1/2} + C$

$$= 2u^{1/2} + C \text{ or } 2\sqrt{u} + C$$

Check: $(2u^{1/2} + C)' = 2\left(\frac{1}{2}\right)u^{-1/2} = \frac{1}{u^{1/2}} = \frac{1}{\sqrt{u}}$

45. $\int \frac{dx}{4x^3} = \frac{1}{4}\int x^{-3}\,dx = \frac{1}{4} \cdot \frac{x^{-2}}{-2} + C = \frac{-x^{-2}}{8} + C$

Check: $\left(\frac{-x^{-2}}{8} + C\right)' = \frac{1}{8}(-2)(-x^{-3}) = \frac{1}{4}x^{-3} = \frac{1}{4x^3}$

47. $\int \frac{4 + u}{u}\,du = \int \left(\frac{4}{u} + 1\right)du = 4\int \frac{1}{u}\,du + \int 1\ du$

$$= 4\ \ln|u| + u + C$$

Check: $\frac{d}{du}(4\ \ln|u| + u + C) = \frac{4}{u} + 1 = \frac{4 + u}{u}$

49. $\int (5e^z + 4)\,dz = 5\int e^z\ dz + 4\int dz = 5e^z + 4z + C$

Check: $(5e^z + 4z + C)' = 5e^z + 4$

51. $\int \left(3x^2 - \frac{2}{x^2}\right)dx = \int 3x^2\,dx - \int \frac{2}{x^2}\,dx$

$$= 3\int x^2\,dx - 2\int x^{-2}\,dx = 3 \cdot \frac{x^3}{3} - \frac{2x^{-1}}{-1} + C = x^3 + 2x^{-1} + C$$

Check: $(x^3 + 2x^{-1} + C)' = 3x^2 - 2x^{-2} = 3x^2 - \frac{2}{x^2}$

53. $\int \left(10x^4 - \frac{8}{x^5} - 2\right)dx = \int 10x^4\,dx - \int 8x^{-5}\,dx - \int 2\ dx$

$$= 10\int x^4\,dx - 8\int x^{-5}\,dx - \int 2\ dx$$

$$= \frac{10x^5}{5} - \frac{8x^{-4}}{-4} - 2x + C = 2x^5 + 2x^{-4} - 2x + C$$

Check: $(2x^5 + 2x^{-4} - 2x + C)' = 10x^4 - 8x^{-5} - 2 = 10x^4 - \frac{8}{x^5} - 2$

55. $\displaystyle\int\left(3\sqrt{x} + \frac{2}{\sqrt{x}}\right)dx = 3\int x^{1/2}dx + 2\int x^{-1/2}dx$

$$= \frac{3x^{3/2}}{3/2} + \frac{2x^{1/2}}{1/2} + C = 2x^{3/2} + 4x^{1/2} + C$$

Check: $\displaystyle(2x^{3/2} + 4x^{1/2} + C)' = 2\left(\frac{3}{2}\right)x^{1/2} + 4\left(\frac{1}{2}\right)x^{-1/2}$

$$= 3x^{1/2} + 2x^{-1/2} = 3\sqrt{x} + \frac{2}{\sqrt{x}}$$

57. $\displaystyle\int\left(\sqrt[3]{x^2} - \frac{4}{x^3}\right)dx = \int x^{2/3}dx - 4\int x^{-3}dx = \frac{x^{5/3}}{5/3} - \frac{4x^{-2}}{-2} + C$

$$= \frac{3x^{5/3}}{5} + 2x^{-2} + C$$

Check: $\displaystyle\left(\frac{3}{5}x^{5/3} + 2x^{-2} + C\right)' = \frac{3}{5}\left(\frac{5}{3}\right)x^{2/3} + 2(-2)x^{-3}$

$$= x^{2/3} - 4x^{-3} = \sqrt[3]{x^2} - \frac{4}{x^3}$$

59. $\displaystyle\int\frac{e^x - 3x}{4}dx = \int\left(\frac{e^x}{4} - \frac{3x}{4}\right)dx = \frac{1}{4}\int e^x dx - \frac{3}{4}\int x\,dx$

$$= \frac{1}{4}e^x - \frac{3}{4}\cdot\frac{x^2}{2} + C = \frac{1}{4}e^x - \frac{3x^2}{8} + C$$

Check: $\displaystyle\left(\frac{1}{4}e^x - \frac{3x^2}{8} + C\right)' = \frac{1}{4}e^x - \frac{6x}{8} = \frac{1}{4}e^x - \frac{3}{4}x$

61. $\displaystyle\int\frac{12 + 5z - 3z^3}{z^4}dz = \int\left(\frac{12}{z^4} + \frac{5}{z^3} - \frac{3}{z}\right)dz$

$$= 12\int z^{-4}dz + 5\int z^{-3}dz - 3\int\frac{1}{z}dz$$

$$= 12\cdot\frac{z^{-3}}{-3} + 5\cdot\frac{z^{-2}}{-2} - 3\ln|z| + C$$

$$= -4z^{-3} - \frac{5}{2}z^{-2} - 3\ln|z| + C$$

Check: $\displaystyle\frac{d}{dz}\left(-4z^{-3} - \frac{5}{2}z^{-2} - 3\ln|z| + C\right) = 12z^{-4} + 5z^{-3} - \frac{3}{z} = \frac{12 + 5z - 3z^3}{z^4}$

63. $\displaystyle\int\left(\frac{6x^2}{5} - \frac{2}{3x}\right)dx = \frac{6}{5}\int x^2\,dx - \frac{2}{3}\int\frac{1}{x}dx$

$$= \frac{6}{5}\cdot\frac{x^3}{3} - \frac{2}{3}\ln|x| + C = \frac{2x^3}{5} - \frac{2}{3}\ln|x| + C$$

Check: $\displaystyle\left(\frac{2x^3}{5} - \frac{2}{3}\ln|x| + C\right) = \frac{6}{5}x^2 - \frac{2}{3}\cdot\frac{1}{x} = \frac{6x^2}{5} - \frac{2}{3x}$

65. $\dfrac{dy}{dx} = 2x - 3$

$$y = \int (2x - 3)\,dx = 2\int x\,dx - \int 3\,dx = \dfrac{2x^2}{2} - 3x + C = x^2 - 3x + C$$

Given $y(0) = 5$: $5 = 0^2 - 3(0) + C$. Hence, $C = 5$ and $y = x^2 - 3x + 5$.

67. $C'(x) = 6x^2 - 4x$

$$C(x) = \int (6x^2 - 4x)\,dx = 6\int x^2 dx - 4\int x\,dx = \dfrac{6x^3}{3} - \dfrac{4x^2}{2} + C = 2x^3 - 2x^2 + C$$

Given $C(0) = 3000$: $3000 = 2(0^3) - 2(0^2) + C$. Hence, $C = 3000$ and $C(x) = 2x^3 - 2x^2 + 3000$.

69. $\dfrac{dx}{dt} = \dfrac{20}{\sqrt{t}}$

$$x = \int \dfrac{20}{\sqrt{t}}\,dt = 20\int t^{-1/2} dt = 20\dfrac{t^{1/2}}{1/2} + C = 40\sqrt{t} + C$$

Given $x(1) = 40$: $40 = 40\sqrt{1} + C$ or $40 = 40 + C$. Hence, $C = 0$ and $x = 40\sqrt{t}$.

71. $\dfrac{dy}{dx} = 2x^{-2} + 3x^{-1} - 1$

$$y = \int (2x^{-2} + 3x^{-1} - 1)\,dx = 2\int x^{-2} dx + 3\int x^{-1} dx - dx$$

$$= \dfrac{2x^{-1}}{-1} + 3\ln|x| - x + C = \dfrac{-2}{x} + 3\ln|x| - x + C$$

Given $y(1) = 0$: $0 = -\dfrac{2}{1} + 3\ln|1| - 1 + C$. Hence, $C = 3$ and

$$y = -\dfrac{2}{x} + 3\ln|x| - x + 3.$$

73. $\dfrac{dx}{dt} = 4e^t - 2$

$$x = \int (4e^t - 2)\,dt = 4\int e^t dt - \int 2\,dt = 4e^t - 2t + C$$

Given $x(0) = 1$: $1 = 4e^0 - 2(0) + C = 4 + C$. Hence, $C = -3$ and $x = 4e^t - 2t - 3$.

75. $\dfrac{dy}{dx} = 4x - 3$

$$y = \int (4x - 3)\,dx = 4\int x\,dx - \int 3\,dx = \dfrac{4x^2}{2} - 3x + C = 2x^2 - 3x + C$$

Given $y(2) = 3$: $3 = 2 \cdot 2^2 - 3 \cdot 2 + C$. Hence, $C = 1$ and $y = 2x^2 - 3x + 1$.

77. $\int \dfrac{2x^4 - x}{x^3} dx = \int \left(\dfrac{2x^4}{x^3} - \dfrac{x}{x^3} \right) dx$

$$= 2\int x\, dx - \int x^{-2} dx = \dfrac{2x^2}{2} - \dfrac{x^{-1}}{-1} + C = x^2 + x^{-1} + C$$

79. $\int \dfrac{x^5 - 2x}{x^4} dx = \int \left(\dfrac{x^5}{x^4} - \dfrac{2x}{x^4} \right) dx$

$$= \int x\, dx - 2\int x^{-3} dx = \dfrac{x^2}{2} - \dfrac{2x^{-2}}{-2} + C = \dfrac{x^2}{2} + x^{-2} + C$$

81. $\int \dfrac{x^2 e^x - 2x}{x^2} dx = \int \left(\dfrac{x^2 e^x}{x^2} - \dfrac{2x}{x^2} \right) dx = e^x dx - 2\; x^{-1} dx = e^x - 2\ \ln|x| + C$

83. $\dfrac{dM}{dt} = \dfrac{t^2 - 1}{t^2}$

$$M = \int \dfrac{t^2 - 1}{t^2} dt = \int \left(\dfrac{t^2}{t^2} - \dfrac{1}{t^2} \right) dt = \int dt - \int t^{-2} dt = t - \dfrac{t^{-1}}{-1} + C = t + \dfrac{1}{t} + C$$

Given $M(4) = 5$: $5 = 4 + \dfrac{1}{4} + C$ or $C = 5 - \dfrac{17}{4} = \dfrac{3}{4}$.

Hence, $M = t + \dfrac{1}{t} + \dfrac{3}{4}$.

85. $\dfrac{dy}{dx} = \dfrac{5x + 2}{\sqrt[3]{x}}$

$$y = \int \dfrac{5x + 2}{\sqrt[3]{x}} dx = \int \left(\dfrac{5x}{x^{1/3}} - \dfrac{2}{x^{1/3}} \right) = 5\int x^{2/3} dx + 2\int x^{-1/3} dx$$

$$= \dfrac{5x^{5/3}}{5/3} + \dfrac{2x^{2/3}}{2/3} + C = 3x^{5/3} + 3x^{2/3} + C$$

Given $y(1) = 0$: $0 = 3 \cdot 1^{5/3} + 3 \cdot 1^{2/3} + C$.   Hence, $C = -6$ and
$y = 3x^{5/3} + 3x^{2/3} - 6$.

87. $p'(x) = -\dfrac{10}{x^2}$

$$p(x) = \int \dfrac{10}{x^2} dx = -10\int x^{-2} dx = \dfrac{-10x^{-1}}{-1} + C = \dfrac{10}{x} + C$$

Given $p(1) = 20$: $20 = \dfrac{10}{1} + C = 10 + C$.   Hence, $C = 10$ and

$$p(x) = \dfrac{10}{x} + 10.$$

89. $\dfrac{d}{dx} \left[\int x^3 dx \right] = x^3$ [by 4(a)]

91. $\int \dfrac{d}{dx}[x^4 + 3x^2 + 1]\,dx = x^4 + 3x^2 + 1 + C = x^4 + 3x^2 + C_1$ [by $\underline{4}$(b)]

($C_1 = 1 + C$ is an arbitrary constant since C is arbitrary)

93. $\dfrac{d}{dx}\left(\dfrac{x^{n+1}}{n+1} + C\right) = x^n$

95. Assume $x > 0$. Then $|x| = x$ and $\ln|x| = \ln x$.

Therefore, $\dfrac{d}{dx}(\ln|x| + C) = \dfrac{d}{dx}(\ln x + C) = \dfrac{1}{x}$.

97. Assume $\int f(x)\,dx = F(x) + C_1$ and $\int g(x)\,dx = G(x) + C_2$.

Then, $\dfrac{d}{dx}(F(x) + C_1) = f(x)$, $\dfrac{d}{dx}(G(x) + C_2) = g(x)$, and

$$\dfrac{d}{dx}(F(x) + C_1 + G(x) + C_2) = \dfrac{d}{dx}(F(x) + C_1) + \dfrac{d}{dx}(G(x) + C_2)$$
$$= f(x) + g(x).$$

99. $\overline{C}\,'(x) = -\dfrac{1,000}{x^2}$

$$\overline{C}(x) = \int \overline{C}\,'(x)\,dx = \int -\dfrac{1,000}{x^2}\,dx = -1,000\int x^{-2}\,dx$$

$$= -1,000\dfrac{x^{-1}}{-1} + C$$

$$= \dfrac{1,000}{x} + C$$

Given $\overline{C}(100) = 25$: $\quad \dfrac{1,000}{100} + C = 25$

$$C = 15$$

Thus, $\overline{C}(x) = \dfrac{1,000}{x} + 15$.

Cost function: $C(x) = x\overline{C}(x) = 15x + 1,000$
Fixed costs: $C(0) = \$1,000$

101. (A) The cost function increases from 0 to 8. The graph is concave downward from 0 to 4 and concave upward from 4 to 8. There is an inflection point at $x = 4$.

(B) $C(x) = \int C'(x)\,dx = \int (3x^2 - 24x + 53)\,dx$

$$= 3\int x^2\,dx - 24\int x\,dx + \int 53\,dx$$

$$= x^3 - 12x^2 + 53x + K$$

Since $C(0) = 30$, we have $K = 30$ and
$$C(x) = x^3 - 12x^2 + 53x + 30.$$

$C(4) = 4^3 - 12(4)^2 + 53(4) + 30 = \$114$ thousand
$C(8) = 8^3 - 12(8)^2 + 53(8) + 30 = \$198$ thousand

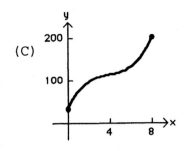

(C)

(D) Manufacturing plants are often inefficient at low and high levels of production.

103. $S'(t) = -25t^{2/3}$

$$S(t) = \int S'(t)\,dt = \int -25t^{2/3}\,dt = -25\int t^{2/3}\,dt = -25\frac{t^{5/3}}{5/3} + C = -15t^{5/3} + C$$

Given $S(0) = 2000$: $-15(0)^{5/3} + C = 2000$. Hence, $C = 2000$ and $S(t) = -15t^{5/3} + 2000$. Now, we want to find t such that $S(t) = 800$, that is: $-15t^{5/3} + 2000 = 800$

$$-15t^{5/3} = -1200$$
$$t^{5/3} = 80$$

and $t = 80^{3/5} \approx 14$

Thus, the company should manufacture the computer for 14 months.

105. $S'(t) = -25t^{2/3} - 70$

$$\begin{aligned}
S(t) = \int S'(t)\,dt &= \int (-25t^{2/3} - 70)\,dt \\
&= -25\int t^{2/3}\,dt - \int 70\,dt \\
&= -25\frac{t^{5/3}}{5/3} - 70t + C \\
&= -15t^{5/3} - 70t + C
\end{aligned}$$

Given $S(0) = 2{,}000$ implies $C = 2{,}000$ and
$$S(t) = 2{,}000 - 15t^{5/3} - 70t$$

Graphing $y_1 = 2{,}000 - 15t^{5/3} - 70t$, $y_2 = 800$ on $0 \le x \le 10$, $0 \le y \le 1000$, we see that the point of intersection is $x \approx 8.92066$, $y = 800$. So we get $t \approx 8.92$ months.

107. $L'(x) = g(x) = 2400x^{-1/2}$

$$L(x) = \int g(x)\,dx = \int 2400x^{-1/2}\,dx = 2400\int x^{-1/2}\,dx = 2400\,\frac{x^{1/2}}{1/2} + C$$

$$= 4800\,x^{1/2} + C$$

Given $L(16) = 19{,}200$: $19{,}200 = 4800(16)^{1/2} + C = 19{,}200 + C$. Hence, $C = 0$ and $L(x) = 4800x^{1/2}$.
$L(25) = 4800(25)^{1/2} = 4800(5) = 24{,}000$ labor hours.

109. $\dfrac{dW}{dh} = 0.0015h^2$

$$W = \int 0.0015h^2 \, dh = 0.0015 \int h^2 \, dh = 0.0015 \dfrac{h^3}{3} + C = 0.0005h^3 + C$$

Given $W(60) = 108$: $108 = 0.0005(60)^3 + C$ or $108 = 108 + C$.
Hence, $C = 0$ and $W(h) = 0.0005h^3$. Now $5'10" = 70"$ and
$W(70) = 0.0005(70)^3 = 171.5$ lb.

111. $\dfrac{dN}{dt} = 400 + 600\sqrt{t}, \ 0 \le t \le 9$

$$N = \int (400 + 600\sqrt{t}) \, dt = \int 400 \, dt + 600 \int t^{1/2} \, dt$$

$$= 400t + 600\dfrac{t^{3/2}}{3/2} + C = 400t + 400t^{3/2} + C$$

Given $N(0) = 5000$: $5000 = 400(0) + 400(0)^{3/2} + C$. Hence, $C = 5000$ and
$N(t) = 400t + 400t^{3/2} + 5000$.
$N(9) = 400(9) + 400(9)^{3/2} + 5000 = 3600 + 10,800 + 5000 = 19,400$

EXERCISE 4-2

Things to remember:

1. **REVERSING THE CHAIN RULE**

   The chain rule formula for differentiating a composite function:
   $$\dfrac{d}{dx} f[g(x)] = f'[g(x)]g'(x),$$
   yields the integral formula
   $$\int f'[g(x)]g'(x) \, dx = f[g(x)] + C$$

2. **GENERAL INDEFINITE INTEGRAL FORMULAS (Version 1)**

   (a) $\int [f(x)]^n f'(x) \, dx) = \dfrac{[f(x)]^{n+1}}{n+1} + C, \ n \ne -1$

   (b) $\int e^{f(x)} f'(x) \, dx = e^{f(x)} + C$

   (c) $\int \dfrac{1}{f(x)} f'(x) \, dx = \ln|f(x)| + C$

3. **DIFFERENTIALS**

   If $y = f(x)$ defines a differentiable function, then:

   (a) The DIFFERENTIAL dx of the independent variable x is an arbitrary real number.

   (b) The DIFFERENTIAL dy of the dependent variable y is defined as the product of $f'(x)$ and dx; that is: $dy = f'(x) \, dx$.

4. GENERAL INDEFINITE INTEGRAL FORMULAS (Version 2)

(a) $\int u^n du = \dfrac{u^{n+1}}{n+1} + C, \quad n \neq -1$

(b) $\int e^u du = e^u + C$

(c) $\int \dfrac{1}{u} du = \ln|u| + C$

5. INTEGRATION BY SUBSTITUTION

Step 1. Select a substitution that appears to simplify the integrand. In particular, try to select u so that du is a factor in the integrand.

Step 2. Express the integrand entirely in terms of u and du, completely eliminating the original variable and its differential.

Step 3. Evaluate the new integral, if possible.

Step 4. Express the antiderivative found in Step 3 in terms of the original variable.

---

1. $\int (3x + 5)^2 (3) \, dx = \int u^2 du = \dfrac{1}{3} u^3 + C = \dfrac{1}{3}(3x + 5)^3 + C$ [Formula 4a]

Let $u = 3x + 5$
Then $du = 3 \, dx$

Check: $\dfrac{d}{dx}\left[\dfrac{1}{3}(3x + 5)^3 + C \right] = \dfrac{1}{3} \cdot 3(3x + 5)^2 \dfrac{d}{dx}(3x + 5)$

$= (3x + 5)^2 (3)$

3. $\int (x^2 - 1)^5 (2x) \, dx = \int u^5 du = \dfrac{1}{6} u^6 + C = \dfrac{1}{6}(x^2 - 1)^6 + C$ [Formula 4a]

Let $u = x^2 - 1$
Then $du = 2x \, dx$

Check: $\dfrac{d}{dx}\left[\dfrac{1}{6}(x^2 - 1)^6 + C \right] = \dfrac{1}{6} \cdot 6(x^2 - 1)^5 \dfrac{d}{dx}(x^2 - 1)$

$= (x^2 - 1)^5 (2x)$

5. $\int (5x^3 + 1)^{-3} (15x^2) \, dx = \int u^{-3} du = \dfrac{u^{-2}}{-2} + C = -\dfrac{1}{2}(5x^3 + 1)^{-2} + C$

Let $u = 5x^3 + 1$ [Formula 4a]
Then $du = 15x^2 \, dx$

Check: $\dfrac{d}{dx}\left[-\dfrac{1}{2}(5x^3 + 1)^{-2} + C \right] = -\dfrac{1}{2}(-2)(5x^3 + 1)^{-3} \dfrac{d}{dx}(5x^3 + 1)$

$= (5x^3 + 1)^{-3}(15x^2)$

7. $\int e^{5x}(5) \, dx = \int e^u du = e^u + C = e^{5x} + C$ [Formula 4b]

Let $u = 5x$
Then $du = 5 \, dx$

Check: $\dfrac{d}{dx}(e^{5x} + C) = e^{5x} \dfrac{d}{dx}(5x) = e^{5x}(5)$

9. $\int \dfrac{1}{1 + x^2} (2x)\, dx = \int \dfrac{1}{u}\, du = \ln|u| + C = \ln|1 + x^2| + C$

    Let $\quad u = 1 + x^2 \qquad\qquad\qquad = \ln(1 + x^2) + C \quad (1 + x^2 > 0) \quad$ [Formula $\underline{4}$c]

    Then $du = 2x\, dx$

    <u>Check</u>: $\dfrac{d}{dx}(\ln(1 + x^2) + C) = \dfrac{1}{1 + x^2}\dfrac{d}{dx}(1 + x^2) = \dfrac{1}{1 + x^2}(2x)$

11. $\int \sqrt{1 + x^4}\, (4x^3)\, dx = \int \sqrt{u}\, du = u^{1/2}\, du = \dfrac{u^{3/2}}{3/2} + C$

    Let $u = 1 + x^4 \qquad\qquad\qquad\qquad = \dfrac{2}{3}u^{3/2} + C$

    Then $du = 4x^3 dx$

$$= \dfrac{2}{3}(1 + x^4)^{3/2} + C$$

    <u>Check</u>: $\dfrac{d}{dx}\left[\dfrac{2}{3}(1 + x^4)^{3/2} + C\right] = \dfrac{3}{2} \cdot \dfrac{2}{3}(1 + x^4)^{1/2}\dfrac{d}{dx}(1 + x^4)$

$$= (1 + x^4)^{1/2}(4x^3) = \sqrt{1 + x^4}\, (4x^3)$$

13. $\int (x + 3)^{10} dx = \int u^{10}\, du = \dfrac{1}{11}u^{11} + C = \dfrac{1}{11}(x + 3)^{11} + C$

    Let $\quad u = x + 3$

    Then $du = dx$

    <u>Check</u>: $\dfrac{d}{dx}\left[\dfrac{1}{11}(x + 3)^{11} + C\right] = \dfrac{1}{11} \cdot 11(x + 3)^{10}\dfrac{d}{dx}(x + 3) = (x + 3)^{10}$

15. $\int (6t - 7)^{-2} dt = \int (6t - 7)^{-2}\dfrac{6}{6}\, dt = \dfrac{1}{6}\int (6t - 7)^{-2}(6)\, dt$

    Let $\quad u = 6t - 7 \qquad\qquad\qquad = \dfrac{1}{6}\int u^{-2}\, du$

    Then $du = 6\, dt$

$$= \dfrac{1}{6} \cdot \dfrac{u^{-1}}{-1} + C$$

$$= -\dfrac{1}{6}(6t - 7)^{-1} + C$$

    <u>Check</u>: $\dfrac{d}{dt}\left[-\dfrac{1}{6}(6t - 7)^{-1} + C\right] = -\dfrac{1}{6}(-1)(6t - 7)^{-2}\dfrac{d}{dt}(6t - 7)$

$$= \dfrac{1}{6}(6t - 7)^{-2}(6) = (6t - 7)^{-2}$$

17. $\int (t^2 + 1)^5 t\, dt = \int (t^2 + 1)^5\dfrac{2}{2}t\, dt = \dfrac{1}{2}\int (t^2 + 1)^5 2t\, dt$

    Let $\quad u = t^2 + 1 \qquad\qquad\qquad = \dfrac{1}{2}\int u^5\, du$

    Then $du = 2t\, dt$

$$= \dfrac{1}{2} \cdot \dfrac{1}{6}u^6 + C$$

$$= \dfrac{1}{12}(t^2 + 1)^6 + C$$

    <u>Check</u>: $\dfrac{d}{dt}\left[\dfrac{1}{12}(t^2 + 1)^6 + C\right] = \dfrac{1}{12} \cdot 6(t^2 + 1)^5\dfrac{d}{dt}(t^2 + 1)$

$$= \dfrac{1}{2}(t^2 + 1)^5(2t) = (t^2 + 1)^5 t$$

19. $\int xe^{x^2}dx = \int e^{x^2}\dfrac{2}{2}x\,dx = \dfrac{1}{2}\int e^{x^2}(2x)\,dx$

Let $\quad u = x^2$ $\qquad\qquad = \dfrac{1}{2}\int e^u du = \dfrac{1}{2}e^u + C$

Then $du = 2x\,dx$

$\qquad\qquad\qquad\qquad\qquad\quad = \dfrac{1}{2}e^{x^2} + C$

Check: $\dfrac{d}{dx}\left(\dfrac{1}{2}e^{x^2} + C\right) = \dfrac{1}{2}e^{x^2}\dfrac{d}{dx}(x^2) = \dfrac{1}{2}e^{x^2}(2x) = xe^{x^2}$

21. $\int\dfrac{1}{5x+4}dx = \int\dfrac{1}{5x+4}\cdot\dfrac{5}{5}dx = \dfrac{1}{5}\int\dfrac{1}{5x+4}5\,dx$

Let $\quad u = 5x + 4$ $\qquad\qquad = \dfrac{1}{5}\int\dfrac{1}{u}\,du = \dfrac{1}{5}\ln|5x+4| + C$

Then $du = 5\,dx$

Check: $\dfrac{d}{dx}\left[\dfrac{1}{5}\ln|5x+4| + C\right] = \dfrac{1}{5}\cdot\dfrac{1}{5x+4}\dfrac{d}{dx}(5x+4)$

$\qquad\qquad\qquad\qquad\qquad = \dfrac{1}{5}\cdot\dfrac{1}{5x+4}\cdot 5 = \dfrac{1}{5x+4}$

23. $\int e^{1-t}dt = \int e^{1-t}\left(\dfrac{-1}{-1}\right)dt = \dfrac{1}{-1}\int e^{1-t}(-1)\,dt$

Let $\quad u = 1 - t$ $\qquad\quad = -\int e^u du = -e^u + C$

Then $du = -dt$ $\qquad\qquad = -e^{1-t} + C$

Check: $\dfrac{d}{dt}[-e^{1-t} + C] = -e^{1-t}\dfrac{d}{dt}(1-t) = -e^{1-t}(-1) = e^{1-t}$

25. Let $u = 3t^2 + 1$, then $du = 6t\,dt$.

$\int\dfrac{t}{(3t^2+1)^4}dt = \int(3t^2+1)^{-4}t\,dt = \int(3t^2+1)^{-4}\dfrac{6}{6}t\,dt$

$\qquad\qquad = \dfrac{1}{6}\int(3t^2+1)^{-4}6t\,dt = \dfrac{1}{6}\int u^{-4}du$

$\qquad\qquad = \dfrac{1}{6}\cdot\dfrac{u^{-3}}{-3} + C = \dfrac{-1}{18}(3t^2+1)^{-3} + C$

Check: $\dfrac{d}{dt}\left[\dfrac{-1}{18}(3t^2+1)^{-3} + C\right] = \left(\dfrac{-1}{18}\right)(-3)(3t^2+1)^{-4}(6t) = \dfrac{t}{(3t^2+1)^4}$

27. Let $u = 4 - x^3$, then $du = -3x^2 dx$.

$\int\dfrac{x^2}{(4-x^3)^2}dx = \int(4-x^3)^{-2}x^2dx = \int(4-x^3)^{-2}\left(\dfrac{-3}{-3}\right)x^2dx$

$\qquad\qquad = \dfrac{-1}{3}\int(4-x^3)^{-2}(-3x^2)\,dx = \dfrac{-1}{3}\int u^{-2}du = \dfrac{-1}{3}\cdot\dfrac{u^{-1}}{-1} + C$

$\qquad\qquad = \dfrac{1}{3}(4-x^3)^{-1} + C$

Check: $\dfrac{d}{dx}\left[\dfrac{1}{3}(4-x^3)^{-1} + C\right] = \dfrac{1}{3}(-1)(4-x^3)^{-2}(-3x^2) = \dfrac{x^2}{(4-x^3)^2}$

29. $\int x\sqrt{x+4}\,dx$

Let $u = x + 4$, then $du = dx$ and $x = u - 4$.

$\int x\sqrt{x+4}\,dx = \int (u-4)u^{1/2}du = \int (u^{3/2} - 4u^{1/2})\,du$

$$= \frac{u^{5/2}}{5/2} - \frac{4u^{3/2}}{3/2} + C = \frac{2}{5}u^{5/2} - \frac{8}{3}u^{3/2} + C$$

$$= \frac{2}{5}(x+4)^{5/2} - \frac{8}{3}(x+4)^{3/2} + C \quad \text{(since } u = x + 4\text{)}$$

Check: $\dfrac{d}{dx}\left[\dfrac{2}{5}(x+4)^{5/2} - \dfrac{8}{3}(x+4)^{3/2} + C\right]$

$$= \frac{2}{5}\left(\frac{5}{2}\right)(x+4)^{3/2}(1) - \frac{8}{3}\left(\frac{3}{2}\right)(x+4)^{1/2}(1)$$

$$= (x+4)^{3/2} - 4(x+4)^{1/2} = (x+4)^{1/2}[(x+4) - 4] = x\sqrt{x+4}$$

31. $\int \dfrac{x}{\sqrt{x-3}}\,dx$

Let $u = x - 3$, then $du = dx$ and $x = u + 3$.

$\int \dfrac{x}{\sqrt{x-3}}\,dx = \int \dfrac{u+3}{u^{1/2}}\,du = \int (u^{1/2} + 3u^{-1/2})\,du = \dfrac{u^{3/2}}{3/2} + \dfrac{3u^{1/2}}{1/2} + C$

$$= \frac{2}{3}u^{3/2} + 6u^{1/2} + C = \frac{2}{3}(x-3)^{3/2} + 6(x-3)^{1/2} + C$$

$$\text{(since } u = x - 3\text{)}$$

Check: $\dfrac{d}{dx}\left[\dfrac{2}{3}(x-3)^{3/2} + 6(x-3)^{1/2} + C\right]$

$$= \frac{2}{3}\left(\frac{3}{2}\right)(x-3)^{1/2}(1) + 6\left(\frac{1}{2}\right)(x-3)^{-1/2}(1)$$

$$= (x-3)^{1/2} + \frac{3}{(x-3)^{1/2}} = \frac{x-3+3}{(x-3)^{1/2}} = \frac{x}{\sqrt{x-3}}$$

33. $\int x(x-4)^9\,dx$

Let $u = x - 4$, then $du = dx$ and $x = u + 4$.

$\int x(x-4)^9\,dx = \int (u+4)u^9\,du = \int (u^{10} + 4u^9)\,du$

$$= \frac{u^{11}}{11} + \frac{4u^{10}}{10} + C = \frac{(x-4)^{11}}{11} + \frac{2}{5}(x-4)^{10} + C$$

Check: $\dfrac{d}{dx}\left[\dfrac{(x-4)^{11}}{11} + \dfrac{2}{5}(x-4)^{10} + C\right]$

$$= \frac{1}{11}(11)(x-4)^{10}(1) + \frac{2}{5}(10)(x-4)^9(1)$$

$$= (x-4)^9[(x-4) + 4] = x(x-4)^9$$

35. Let $u = 1 + e^{2x}$, then $du = 2e^{2x}dx$.

$$\int e^{2x}(1 + e^{2x})^3 dx = \int (1 + e^{2x})^3 \frac{2}{2} e^{2x}dx = \frac{1}{2}\int (1 + e^{2x})^3 2e^{2x}dx$$

$$= \frac{1}{2}\int u^3 du = \frac{1}{2} \cdot \frac{u^4}{4} + C = \frac{1}{2}(1 + e^{2x})^4 + C$$

Check: $\dfrac{d}{dx}\left[\dfrac{1}{8}(1 + e^{2x})^4 + C\right] = \left(\dfrac{1}{8}\right)(4)(1 + e^{2x})^3 e^{2x}(2) = e^{2x}(1 + e^{2x})^3$

37. Let $u = 4 + 2x + x^2$, then $du = (2 + 2x)dx = 2(1 + x)dx$.

$$\int \frac{1 + x}{4 + 2x + x^2}dx = \int \frac{1 + x}{4 + 2x + x^2} \cdot \frac{2(1 + x)}{2}dx = \frac{1}{2}\int \frac{1 + x}{4 + 2x + x^2}2(2 + x)dx$$

$$= \frac{1}{2}\int \frac{1}{u}du = \frac{1}{2}\ln|u| + C = \frac{1}{2}\ln|4 + 2x + x^2| + C$$

Check: $\dfrac{d}{dx}\left[\dfrac{1}{2}\ln|4 + 2x + x^2| + C\right] = \left(\dfrac{1}{2}\right)\dfrac{1}{4 + 2x + x^2}(2 + 2x) = \dfrac{1 + x}{4 + 2x + x^2}$

39. Let $u = x^4 + 2x^2 + 1$, then $du = (4x^3 + 4x)dx = 4(x^3 + x)dx$.

$$\int \frac{x^3 + x}{(x^4 + 2x^2 + 1)^4}dx = \int (x^4 + 2x^2 + 1)^{-4}\frac{4}{4}(x^3 + x)dx$$

$$= \frac{1}{4}\int (x^4 + 2x^2 + 1)^{-4}4(x^3 + x)dx$$

$$= \frac{1}{4}\int u^{-4}du = \frac{1}{4}\cdot\frac{u^{-3}}{-3} + C = \frac{-u^{-3}}{12} + C$$

$$= \frac{-(x^4 + 2x^2 + 1)^{-3}}{12} + C$$

Check: $\dfrac{d}{dx}\left[-\dfrac{1}{12}(x^4 + 2x^2 + 1)^{-3} + C\right] = \left(-\dfrac{1}{12}\right)(-3)(x^4 + 2x^2 + 1)^{-4}(4x^3 + 4x)$

$$= (x^4 + 2x^2 + 1)^{-4}(x^3 + x)$$

41. (A) Differentiate $F(x) = \ln|2x - 3| + C$ to see if you get the integrand
$$f(x) = \frac{1}{2x - 3}$$

(B) Wrong; $\dfrac{d}{dx}[\ln|2x - 3| + C] = \dfrac{1}{2x - 3}(2) = \dfrac{2}{2x - 3} \neq \dfrac{1}{2x - 3}$

(C) Let $u = 2x - 3$, then $du = 2\,dx$

$$\int \frac{1}{2x - 3}dx = \int \frac{1}{2x - 3} \cdot \frac{2}{2}dx = \frac{1}{2}\int \frac{1}{2x - 3}2\,dx$$

$$= \frac{1}{2}\int \frac{1}{u}du$$

$$= \frac{1}{2}\ln|u| + C$$

$$= \frac{1}{2}\ln|2x - 3| + C$$

Check: $\dfrac{d}{dx}\left[\dfrac{1}{2}\ln|2x - 3| + C\right] = \dfrac{1}{2} \cdot \dfrac{1}{2x - 3} \cdot 2 = \dfrac{1}{2x - 3}$

43. (A) Differentiate $F(x) = e^{x^4} + C$ to see if you get the integrand $f(x) = x^3 e^{x^4}$.

(B) Wrong; $\dfrac{d}{dx}[e^{x^4} + c] = e^{x^4}(4x^3) = 4x^3 e^{x^4} \neq x^3 e^{x^4}$

(C) Let $u = x^4$, then $du = 4x^3\, dx$

$$\int x^3 e^{x^4}\, dx = \int \frac{4}{4} x^3 e^{x^4}\, dx = \frac{1}{4}\int 4x^3 e^{x^4}\, dx$$
$$= \frac{1}{4}\int e^u\, du$$
$$= \frac{1}{4} e^u + C$$
$$= \frac{1}{4} e^{x^4} + C$$

Check: $\dfrac{d}{dx}\left[\dfrac{1}{4} e^{x^4} + C\right] = \dfrac{1}{4} e^{x^4}(4x^3) = x^3 e^{x^4}$

45. (A) Differentiate $F(x) = \dfrac{(x^2 - 2)^2}{3x} + C$ to see if you get the integrand
$$f(x) = 2(x^2 - 2)^2$$

(B) Wrong; $\dfrac{d}{dx}\left[\dfrac{(x^2 - 2)^2}{3x} + C\right] = \dfrac{3x \cdot 2(x^2 - 2)(2x) - (x^2 - 2)^2 \cdot 3}{9x^2}$

$$= \frac{(x^2 - 2)[9x^2 + 6]}{9x^2} = \frac{9x^4 - 12x^2 - 12}{9x^2}$$

$$= \frac{3x^4 - 4x^2 - 4}{3x^2}$$

$$\neq 2(x^2 - 2)^2$$

(C) $\int 2(x^2 - 2)^2\, dx = 2\int (x^4 - 4x^2 + 4)\, dx$

$$= 2 \cdot \left[\frac{1}{5} x^5 - \frac{4}{3} x^3 + 4x\right] + C$$

$$= \frac{2}{5} x^5 - \frac{8}{3} x^3 + 8x + C$$

Check: $\dfrac{d}{dx}\left[\dfrac{2}{5} x^5 - \dfrac{8}{3} x^3 + 8x + C\right] = 2x^4 - 8x^2 + 8 = 2[x^4 - 4x^2 + 4]$

$$= 2(x^2 - 2)^2$$

47. Let $u = 3x^2 + 7$, then $du = 6x\, dx$.
$$\int x\sqrt{3x^2 + 7}\, dx = \int (3x^2 + 7)^{1/2} x\, dx = \int (3x^2 + 7)^{1/2} \frac{6}{6} x\, dx$$

$$= \frac{1}{6}\int u^{1/2}\, du = \frac{1}{6} \cdot \frac{u^{3/2}}{3/2} + C = \frac{1}{9}(3x^2 + 7)^{3/2} + C$$

Check: $\dfrac{d}{dx}\left[\dfrac{1}{9}(3x^2 + 7)^{3/2} + C\right] = \dfrac{1}{9}\left(\dfrac{3}{2}\right)(3x^2 + 7)^{1/2}(6x) = x(3x^2 + 7)^{1/2}$

49. $\int x(x^3 + 2)^2 dx = \int x(x^6 + 4x^3 + 4)\,dx = \int (x^7 + 4x^4 + 4x)\,dx$

$$= \frac{x^8}{8} + \frac{4}{5}x^5 + 2x^2 + C$$

Check: $\dfrac{d}{dx}\left[\dfrac{x^8}{8} + \dfrac{4}{5}x^5 + 2x^2 + C\right] = x^7 + 4x^4 + 4x$

$$= x(x^6 + 4x^3 + 4) = x(x^3 + 2)^2$$

51. $\int x^2(x^3 + 2)^2 dx$

Let $u = x^3 + 2$, then $du = 3x^2\,dx$.

$\int x^2(x^3 + 2)^2 dx = \int x^2(x^3 + 2)^2 \dfrac{3x^2}{3}\,dx = \dfrac{1}{3}\int (x^3 + 2)^2 3x^2\,dx$

$$= \frac{1}{3}u^2\,du = \frac{1}{3} \cdot \frac{u^3}{3} + C = \frac{1}{9}u^3 + C = \frac{1}{9}(x^3 + 2)^3 + C$$

Check: $\dfrac{d}{dx}\left[\dfrac{1}{9}(x^3 + 2)^3 + C\right] = \dfrac{1}{9}(3)(x^3 + 2)^2(3x^2) = x^2(x^3 + 2)^2$

53. Let $u = 2x^4 + 3$, then $du = 8x^3\,dx$.

$\displaystyle\int \frac{x^3}{\sqrt{2x^4 + 3}}\,dx = \int (2x^4 + 3)^{-1/2} x^3\,dx = \int (2x^4 + 3)^{-1/2}\,\frac{8}{8}x^3\,dx$

$$= \frac{1}{8}\int u^{-1/2}\,du = \frac{1}{8} \cdot \frac{u^{1/2}}{1/2} + C = \frac{1}{4}(2x^4 + 3)^{1/2} + C$$

Check: $\dfrac{d}{dx}\left[\dfrac{1}{4}(2x^4 + 3)^{1/2} + C\right] = \dfrac{1}{4}\left(\dfrac{1}{2}\right)(2x^4 + 3)^{-1/2}(8x^3) = \dfrac{x^3}{(2x^4 + 3)^{1/2}}$

55. Let $u = \ln x$, then $du = \dfrac{1}{x}\,dx$.

$\displaystyle\int \frac{(\ln x)^3}{x}\,dx = \int u^3\,du = \frac{u^4}{4} + C = \frac{(\ln x)^4}{4} + C$

Check: $\dfrac{d}{dx}\left[\dfrac{(\ln x)^4}{4} + C\right] = \dfrac{1}{4}(4)(\ln x)^3 \cdot \dfrac{1}{x} = \dfrac{(\ln x)^3}{x}$

57. Let $u = \dfrac{-1}{x} = -x^{-1}$, then $du = \dfrac{1}{x^2}\,dx$.

$\displaystyle\int \frac{1}{x^2} e^{-1/x}\,dx = \int e^u\,du = e^u + C = e^{-1/x} + C$

Check: $\dfrac{d}{dx}[e^{-1/x} + C] = e^{-1/x}\left(\dfrac{1}{x^2}\right) = \dfrac{1}{x^2}e^{-1/x}$

59. $\dfrac{dx}{dt} = 7t^2(t^3 + 5)^6$

Let $u = t^3 + 5$, then $du = 3t^2\,dt$.

$x = \displaystyle\int 7t^2(t^3 + 5)^6\,dt = 7\int t^2(t^3 + 5)^6\,dt = 7\int (t^3 + 5)^6\,\frac{3}{3}t^2\,dt$

$$= \frac{7}{3}\int u^6\,du = \frac{7}{3} \cdot \frac{u^7}{7} + C = \frac{1}{3}(t^3 + 5)^7 + C$$

61. $\dfrac{dy}{dt} = \dfrac{3t}{\sqrt{t^2 - 4}}$

Let $u = t^2 - 4$, then $du = 2t\, dt$.

$$y = \int \frac{3t}{(t^2 - 4)^{1/2}}\, dt = 3\int (t^2 - 4)^{-1/2}t\, dt = 3\int (t^2 - 4)^{-1/2}\frac{2}{2}t\, dt$$

$$= \frac{3}{2}u^{-1/2}du = \frac{3}{2}\cdot\frac{u^{1/2}}{1/2} + C = 3(t^2 - 4)^{1/2} + C$$

63. $\dfrac{dp}{dx} = \dfrac{e^x + e^{-x}}{(e^x - e^{-x})^2}$

Let $u = e^x - e^{-x}$, then $du = (e^x + e^{-x})\, dx$.

$$p = \int \frac{e^x + e^{-x}}{(e^x - e^{-x})^2}\, dx = \int (e^x - e^{-x})^{-2}(e^x + e^{-x})\, dx = \int u^{-2}\, du$$

$$= \frac{u^{-1}}{-1} + C = -(e^x - e^{-x})^{-1} + C$$

65. Let $v = au$, then $dv = a\, du$.

$$\int e^{au}du = \int e^{au}\frac{a}{a}du = \frac{1}{a}\int e^{au}a\, du = \frac{1}{a}\int e^v dv = \frac{1}{a}e^v + C = \frac{1}{a}e^{au} + C$$

<u>Check</u>: $\dfrac{d}{du}\left[\dfrac{1}{a}e^{au} + C\right] + \dfrac{1}{a}e^{au}(a) = e^{au}$

67. $p'(x) = \dfrac{-6000}{(3x + 50)^2}$

Let $u = 3x + 50$, then $du = 3\, dx$.

$$p(x) = \int \frac{-6000}{(3x + 50)^2}\, dx = -6000\int (3x + 50)^{-2}\, dx = -6000\int (3x + 50)^{-2}\frac{3}{3}\, dx$$

$$= -2000\int u^{-2}\, du = -2000\cdot\frac{u^{-1}}{-1} + C = \frac{2000}{3x + 50} + C$$

Given $p(150) = 4$:

$$4 = \frac{2000}{(3\cdot 150 + 50)} + C$$

$$4 = \frac{2000}{500} + C$$

$$C = 0$$

Thus, $p(x) = \dfrac{2000}{3x + 50}$.

Now, $2.50 = \dfrac{2000}{3x + 50}$

$2.50(3x + 50) = 2000$

$7.5x + 125 = 2000$

$7.5x = 1875$

$x = 250$

Thus, the demand is 250 bottles when the price is \$2.50.

69. $C'(x) = 12 + \dfrac{500}{x + 1}, \quad x > 0$

$$C(x) = \int\left(12 + \frac{500}{x + 1}\right)dx = \int 12 \, dx + 500\int\frac{1}{x + 1}dx \quad (u = x = 1, \ du = dx)$$

$$= 12x + 500 \ln(x + 1) + C$$

Now, $C(0) = 2000$. Thus, $C(x) = 12x + 500 \ln(x + 1) + 2000$. The average cost is:

$$\bar{C}(x) = 12 + \frac{500}{x}\ln(x + 1) + \frac{2000}{x}$$

and

$$\bar{C}(1000) = 12 + \frac{500}{1000}\ln(1001) + \frac{2000}{1000} = 12 + \frac{1}{2}\ln(1001) + 2.$$
$$\approx 17.45 \text{ or } \$17.45 \text{ per pair of shoes}$$

71. $S'(t) = 10 - 10e^{-0.1t}, \quad 0 \le t \le 24$

(A) $S(t) = \int(10 - 10e^{-0.1t})dt = \int 10 \, dt - 10\int e^{-0.1t} \, dt$

$$= 10t - \frac{10}{-0.1}e^{-0.1t} + C = 10t + 100e^{-0.1t} + C$$

Given $S(0) = 0$: $\quad 0 + 100e^{0} + C = 0$
$$100 + C = 0$$
$$C = -100$$

Total sales at time t:
$$S(t) = 10t + 100e^{-0.1t} - 100$$

(B) $S(12) = 10(12) + 100e^{-0.1(12)} - 100$
$$= 20 + 100e^{-1.2} \approx 50$$

Total estimated sales for the first twelve months: $50 million.

(C) On a graphing utility, solve
$$10t + 100e^{-0.1t} - 100 = 100$$
or $\qquad 10t + 100e^{-0.1t} = 200$

The result is: $t \approx 18.41$ months.

73. $Q(t) = \int R(t) \, dt = \int\left(\dfrac{100}{t + 1} + 5\right)dt = 100\int\dfrac{1}{t + 1}dt + \int 5 dt$

$$= 100 \ln(t + 1) + 5t + C$$

Given $Q(0) = 0$:
$0 = 100 \ln(1) + 0 + C$
Thus, $C = 0$ and $Q(t) = 100 \ln(t + 1) + 5t, \quad 0 \le t \le 20$.
$Q(9) = 100 \ln(9 + 1) + 5(9) = 100 \ln 10 + 45 \approx 275$ thousand barrels.

75. $W(t) = \int W(t)\,dt = \int 0.2e^{0.1t}\,dt = \dfrac{0.2}{0.1}\int e^{0.1t}(0.1)\,dt = 2e^{0.1t} + C$

Given $W(0) = 2$:

$2 = 2e^0 + C$.

Thus, $C = 0$ and $W(t) = 2e^{0.1t}$.

The weight of the culture after 8 hours is given by:

$W(8) = 2e^{0.1(8)} = 2e^{0.8} \approx 4.45$ grams.

77. $\dfrac{dN}{dt} = -\dfrac{2000t}{1 + t^2}, \quad 0 \le t \le 10$

(A) To find the minimum value of $\dfrac{dN}{dt}$, calculate

$$\frac{d}{dt}\left(\frac{dN}{dt}\right) = \frac{d^2N}{dt^2} = -\frac{(1 + t^2)(2000) - 2000t\,(2t)}{(1 + t^2)^2}$$

$$= -\frac{2000[1 - t^2]}{(1 + t^2)^2} = \frac{-2000(1 - t)(1 + t)}{(1 + t^2)^2}$$

critical value: $t = 1$

Now $\dfrac{dN}{dt}\bigg|_{t=0} = 0$

$\dfrac{dN}{dt}\bigg|_{t=1} = -1,000$

$\dfrac{dN}{dt}\bigg|_{t=10} = \dfrac{-20,000}{101} \approx -198.02$

Thus, the minimum value of $\dfrac{dN}{dt}$ is $-1,000$ bacteria/ml per day.

(B) $N = \int \dfrac{-2,000t}{1 + t^2}\,dt$

Let $u = 1 + t^2$, then $du = 2t\,dt$

$N = \int \dfrac{-2,000t}{1 + t^2}\,dt = -1,000\int \dfrac{2t\,dt}{1 + t^2} = -1,000\int \dfrac{1}{u}\,du$

$\qquad\qquad\qquad = -1,000\,\ln|u| + C$

$\qquad\qquad\qquad = -1,000\,\ln(1 + t^2) + C$

Given $N(0) = 5,000$:

$5,000 = -1,000\,\ln(1) + C = C \quad (\ln 1 = 0)$

Thus, $C = 5,000$ and $N(t) = 5,000 - 1,000\,\ln(1 + t^2)$

Now, $N(10) = 5,000 - 1,000\,\ln(1 + 10^2)$

$\qquad\qquad = 5,000 - 1,000\,\ln(101)$

$\qquad\qquad \approx 385$ bacteria/ml

(C) Set $N(t) = 1,000$ and solve for t:

$1,000 = 5,000 - 1,000\,\ln(1 + t^2)$

$\ln(1 + t^2) = 4$

$1 + t^2 = e^4$

$t^2 = e^4 - 1$

$t = \sqrt{e^4 - 1} \approx 7.32$ days

79. $N'(t) = 6e^{-0.1t}$, $0 \leq t \leq 15$

$$N(t) = \int N(t)\,dt = \int 6e^{-0.1t}\,dt = 6\int e^{-0.1t}\,dt$$

$$= \frac{6}{-0.1}\int e^{-0.1t}(-0.1)\,dt = -60e^{-0.1t} + C$$

Given $N(0) = 40$:

$40 = -60e^0 + C$

Hence, $C = 100$ and $N(t) = 100 - 60e^{-0.1t}$, $0 \leq t \leq 15$.
The number of words per minute after completing the course is:

$N(15) = 100 - 60e^{-0.1(15)} = 100 - 60e^{-1.5} \approx 87$ words per minute.

81. $\dfrac{dE}{dt} = 5000(t + 1)^{-3/2}$, $t \geq 0$

Let $u = t + 1$, then $du = dt$

$$E = \int 5000(t + 1)^{-3/2}\,dt = 5000\int (t + 1)^{-3/2}\,dt = 5000\int u^{-3/2}\,du$$

$$= 5000\frac{u^{-1/2}}{-1/2} + C = -10,000(t + 1)^{-1/2} + C$$

$$= \frac{-10,000}{\sqrt{t + 1}} + C$$

Given $E(0) = 2000$:

$$2000 = \frac{-10,000}{\sqrt{1}} + C$$

Hence, $C = 12,000$ and $E(t) = 12,000 - \dfrac{10,000}{\sqrt{t + 1}}$.

The projected enrollment 15 years from now is:

$$E(15) = 12,000 - \frac{10,000}{\sqrt{15 + 1}} = 12,000 - \frac{10,000}{\sqrt{16}} = 12,000 - \frac{10,000}{4}$$

$$= 9500 \text{ students}$$

EXERCISE 4-3

Things to remember:

1. A DIFFERENTIAL EQUATION is an equation that involves an unknown function and one or more of its derivatives. The ORDER of a differential equation is the order of the highest derivative of the unknown function.

2. A SLOPE FIELD for a first-order differential equation is obtained by drawing tangent line segments determined by the equation at each point in a grid.

3. EXPONENTIAL GROWTH LAW

If $\dfrac{dQ}{dt} = rQ$ and $Q(0) = Q_0$, then $Q(t) = Q_0 e^{rt}$, where

Q_0 = Amount at $t = 0$

r = Continuous compound growth rate (expressed as a decimal)

t = Time

Q = Quantity at time t

4. COMPARISON OF EXPONENTIAL GROWTH PHENOMENA

DESCRIPTION	MODEL	SOLUTION	GRAPH	USES
Unlimited growth: Rate of growth is proportional to the amount present	$\dfrac{dy}{dt} = ky$ $k,\ t > 0$ $y(0) = c$	$y = ce^{kt}$		• Short-term population growth (people, bacteria, etc.) • Growth of money at continuous compound interest • Price-supply curves • Depletion of natural resources
Exponential decay: Rate of growth is proportional to the amount present	$\dfrac{dy}{dt} = -ky$ $k,\ t > 0$ $y(0) = c$	$y = ce^{-kt}$		• Radioactive decay • Light absorption in water • Price-demand curves • Atmospheric pressure (t is altitude)
Limited growth: Rate of growth is proportional to the difference between the amount present and a fixed limit	$\dfrac{dy}{dt} = k(M - y)$ $k,\ t > 0$ $y(0) = 0$	$y = M(1 - e^{-kt})$		• Sales fads (e.g., skateboards) • Depreciation of equipment • Company growth • Learning
Logistic growth: Rate of growth is proportional to the amount present and to the difference between the amount present and a fixed limit	$\dfrac{dy}{dt} = ky(M - y)$ $k,\ t > 0$ $y(0) = \dfrac{M}{1 + c}$	$y = \dfrac{M}{1 - ce^{-kMt}}$		• Long-term population growth • Epidemics • Sales of new products • Rumor spread • Company growth

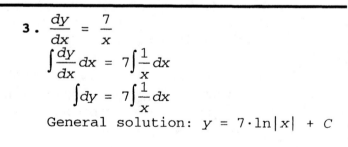

1. $\dfrac{dy}{dx} = 6x$

$\displaystyle\int \dfrac{dy}{dx}\, dx = \int 6x\, dx = 6\int x\, dx$

$\displaystyle\int dy = 6\int x\, dx$

$y = 6 \cdot \dfrac{x^2}{2} + C = 3x^2 + C$

General solution: $y = 3x^2 + C$

3. $\dfrac{dy}{dx} = \dfrac{7}{x}$

$\displaystyle\int \dfrac{dy}{dx}\, dx = 7\int \dfrac{1}{x}\, dx$

$\displaystyle\int dy = 7\int \dfrac{1}{x}\, dx$

General solution: $y = 7 \cdot \ln|x| + C$

264

5. $\dfrac{dy}{dx} = e^{0.02x}$

$\displaystyle\int \dfrac{dy}{dx}\,dx = \int e^{0.02x}\,dx$

$\displaystyle\int dy = \int e^{0.02x}\,dx \qquad (u = 0.02x,\ du = 0.02\,dx)$

$y = \displaystyle\int e^u\,\dfrac{1}{0.02}\,du = \dfrac{1}{0.02}\int e^u\,du = \dfrac{1}{0.02}e^u + C = 50e^{0.02x} + C$

General solution: $y = 50e^{0.02x} + C$

7. $\dfrac{dy}{dx} = x^2 - x;\ y(0) = 0$

$\displaystyle\int \dfrac{dy}{dx}\,dx = \dfrac{dy}{dx}\,(x^2 - x)\,dx$

$y = \dfrac{1}{3}x^3 - \dfrac{1}{2}x^2 + C$

Given $y(0) = 0$: $\dfrac{1}{3}(0)^3 - \dfrac{1}{2}(0)^2 + C = 0$

$C = 0$

Particular solution: $y = \dfrac{1}{3}x^3 - \dfrac{1}{2}x^2$

9. $\dfrac{dy}{dx} = -2xe^{-x^2};\ y(0) = 3$

$\displaystyle\int \dfrac{dy}{dx}\,dx = \int -2xe^{-x^2}\,dx$

$y = \displaystyle\int -2xe^{-x^2}\,dx$

Let $u = -x^2$, then $du = -2x\,dx$ and

$\displaystyle\int -2xe^{-x^2}\,dx = \int e^u\,du = e^u + c = e^{-x^2} + c$

Thus, $\qquad y = e^{-x^2} + c$

Given $y(0) = 3$: $3 = e^0 + c$

$3 = 1 + c$

$c = 2$

Particular solution: $y = e^{-x^2} + 2$

11. $\dfrac{dy}{dx} = \dfrac{2}{1 + x};\ y(0) = 5$

$\displaystyle\int \dfrac{dy}{dx}\,dx = \int \dfrac{2}{1 + x}\,dx = 2\int \dfrac{1}{1 + x}\,dx$

$\displaystyle\int dy = 2\int \dfrac{1}{1 + x}\,dx \qquad (u = 1 + x,\ du = dx)$

$y = 2\displaystyle\int \dfrac{1}{u}\,du = 2\,\ln|u| + C = 2\,\ln|1 + x| + C$

Given $y(0) = 5$: $5 = 2\,\ln 1 + C$

$5 = C$

Particular solution: $y = 2\,\ln|1 + x| + 5$

13. Figure (b). When $x = 1$, $\frac{dy}{dx} = 1 - 1 = 0$ for any y. When $x = 0$,

$\frac{dy}{dx} = 0 - 1 = -1$ for any y. When $x = 2$, $\frac{dy}{dx} = 2 - 1 = 1$ for any y; and

so on. These facts are consistent with the slope-field in Figure (b); they are not consistent with the slope-field in Figure (a).

15. $\frac{dy}{dx} = x - 1$

$\int \frac{dy}{dx} = \int (x - 1)\, dx$

General solution: $y = \frac{1}{2}x^2 - x + c$

Given $y(0) = -2$: $\frac{1}{2}(0)^2 - 0 + c = -2$

$c = -2$

Particular solution: $y = \frac{1}{2}x^2 - x - 2$

17.

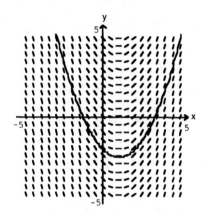

19. $\frac{dy}{dt} = 2y$

$\frac{1}{y}\frac{dy}{dt} = 2$

$\int \frac{1}{y}\frac{dy}{dt}\, dt = \int 2\, dt$

$\int \frac{1}{u}\, du = \int 2\, dt \quad [u = y, \; du = dy = \frac{dy}{dt} \cdot dt]$

$\ln |u| = 2t + K \quad [K \text{ an arbitrary constant}]$

$|u| = e^{2t+K} = e^K e^{2t}$

$|u| = Ce^{2t} \quad [C = e^K, \; C > 0]$

so $\quad |y| = Ce^{2t}$

Now, if we set $y(t) = Ce^{2t}$, C ANY constant, then

$y'(t) = 2Ce^{2t} = 2y(t)$,

So $\quad y = Ce^{2t}$ satisfies the differential equation where C is any constant. This is the general solution. Note, the differential equation is the model for exponential growth with growth rate 2.

21. $\dfrac{dy}{dx} = -0.5y$, $y(0) = 100$

$$\dfrac{1}{y}\dfrac{dy}{dx} = -0.5$$

$$\int \dfrac{1}{y}\dfrac{dy}{dx}\,dx = \int -0.5\,dx$$

$$\int \dfrac{1}{u}\,du = \int -0.5\,dx \quad [u = y,\ du = dy = \dfrac{dy}{dx}\,dx]$$

$$\ln|u| = -0.5x + K$$
$$|u| = e^{-0.5x+K} = e^K e^{-0.5x}$$
$$|y| = Ce^{-0.5x},\ C = e^K > 0.$$

So, general solution: $y = Ce^{-0.5x}$, C any constant.

Given $y(0) = 100$: $100 = Ce^0 = C$;
  particular solution: $y = 100e^{-0.5x}$

23. $\dfrac{dx}{dt} = -5x$

$$\dfrac{1}{x}\dfrac{dx}{dt} = -5$$

$$\int \dfrac{1}{x}\dfrac{dx}{dt}\,dt = \int -5\,dt$$

$$\int \dfrac{1}{x}\,dx = -5\int dt$$

$$\ln|x| = -5t + K$$
$$|x| = e^{-5t+K} = e^K e^{-5t} = Ce^{-5t},\ C = e^K > 0.$$

General solution: $x = Ce^{-5t}$, C any constant.

25. $\dfrac{dx}{dt} = -5t$

$$\int \dfrac{dx}{dt}\,dt = \int -5t\,dt = -5\int t\,dt$$

General solution: $x = -\dfrac{5t^2}{2} + C$

27. Figure (c). When $y = 1$, $\dfrac{dy}{dx} = 1 - 1 = 0$ for any x.

When $y = 2$, $\dfrac{dy}{dx} = 1 - 2 = -1$ for any x; and so on. This is consistent with the slope-field in Figure (c); it is not consistent with the slope-field in Figure (d).

29. $y = 1 - Ce^{-x}$

$$\frac{dy}{dx} = \frac{d}{dx}[1 - Ce^{-x}] = Ce^{-x}$$

From the original equation, $Ce^{-x} = 1 - y$
Thus, we have

$$\frac{dy}{dx} = 1 - y$$

and $y = 1 - Ce^{-x}$ is a solution of the differential equation for any number c.

Given $y(0) = 0$: $0 = 1 - Ce^0 = 1 - c$
$$c = 1$$

Particular solution: $y = 1 - e^{-x}$

31.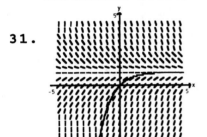

33.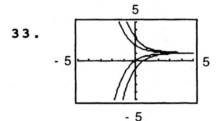

35. $y = 1,000e^{0.08t}$
$0 \le t \le 15,$
$0 \le y \le 3,500$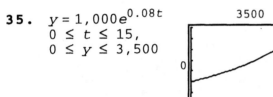

37. $p = 100e^{-0.05x}$
$0 \le x \le 30,$
$0 \le p \le 100$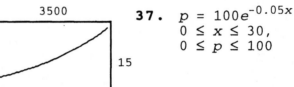

39. $N = 100(1 - e^{-0.05t})$
$0 \le t \le 100, \ 0 \le N \le 100$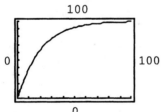

41. $N = \dfrac{1,000}{1 + 999e^{-0.4t}}$
$0 \le t \le 40, \ 0 \le N \le 1,000$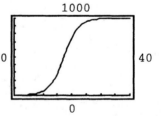

43. $\dfrac{dy}{dt} = ky(M - y)$, k, M positive constants. Set $f(y) = ky(M - y) = kMy - ky^2$.

This is a quadratic function which opens downward; it has a maximum value. Now

$$f'(y) = kM - 2ky$$

Critical value: $kM - 2ky = 0$

$$y = \frac{M}{2}$$

$$f''(y) = -2k < 0.$$

Thus, f has a maximum value at $y = \dfrac{M}{2}$.

45. In 1967: $\dfrac{dQ}{dt} = 3.5e^{0.02} \approx 3.571$

In 1999: $\dfrac{dQ}{dt} = 6e^{0.013} \approx 6.079$

The rate of growth in 1999 is almost twice the rate of growth in 1967.

47. $\dfrac{dA}{dt} = 0.08A$ and $A(0) = 1{,}000$ is an unlimited growth model. From **4**,

the amount in the account after t years is: $A(t) = 1000e^{0.08t}$.

49. $\dfrac{dA}{dt} = rA$, $A(0) = 8{,}000$

is an unlimited growth model. From **4**, $A(t) = 8{,}000e^{rt}$.

Since $A(2) = 9{,}020$, we solve $8{,}000e^{2r} = 9{,}020$ for r.

$$8000e^{2r} = 9{,}020$$
$$e^{2r} = \frac{902}{800}$$
$$2r = \ln(902/800)$$
$$r = \frac{\ln(902/800)}{2} \approx 0.06$$

Thus, $A(t) = 8{,}000e^{0.06t}$.

51. (A) $\dfrac{dp}{dx} = rp$, $p(0) = 100$

This is an UNLIMITED GROWTH MODEL. From **4**, $p(x) = 100e^{rx}$.

Since $p(5) = 77.88$, we have

$$77.88 = 100e^{5r}$$
$$e^{5r} = 0.7788$$
$$5r = \ln(0.7788)$$
$$r = \frac{\ln(0.7788)}{5} \approx -0.05$$

Thus, $p(x) = 100e^{-0.05x}$.

(B) $p(10) = 100e^{-0.05(10)} = 100e^{-0.5}$
$$\approx \$60.65 \text{ per unit}$$

(C)

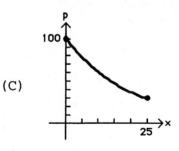

53. (A) $\dfrac{dN}{dt} = k(L - N)$; $N(0) = 0$

This is a LIMITED GROWTH MODEL. From **4**, $N(t) = L(1 - e^{-kt})$.

Since $N(10) = 0.4L$, we have

$$0.4L = L(1 - e^{-10k})$$
$$1 - e^{-10k} = 0.4$$
$$e^{-10k} = 0.6$$
$$-10k = \ln(0.6)$$
$$k = \frac{\ln(0.6)}{-10} \approx 0.051$$

Thus, $N(t) = L(1 - e^{-0.051t})$.

(B) $N(5) = L[1 - e^{-0.051(5)}] = L[1 - e^{-0.255}] \approx 0.225L$

Approximately 22.5% of the possible viewers will have been exposed after 5 days.

(C) Solve $L(1 - e^{-0.051t}) = 0.8L$ for t:

$$1 - e^{-0.051t} = 0.8$$
$$e^{-0.051t} = 0.2$$
$$-0.051t = \ln(0.2)$$
$$t = \frac{\ln(0.2)}{-0.051} \approx 31.56$$

It will take 32 days for 80% of the possible viewers to be exposed.

(D)

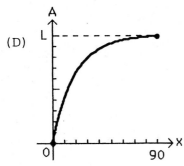

55. $\frac{dI}{dx} = -kI, \quad I(0) = I_0$

This is an exponential decay model. From **4**, $I(x) = I_0 e^{-kx}$ with $k = 0.00942$, we have

$$I(x) = I_0 e^{-0.00942x}$$

To find the depth at which the light is reduced to half of that at the surface, solve,

$$I_0 e^{-0.00942x} = \frac{1}{2} I_0$$

for x:

$$e^{-0.00942x} = 0.5$$
$$-0.00942x = \ln(0.5)$$
$$x = \frac{\ln(0.5)}{-0.00942} \approx 74 \text{ feet}$$

57. $\frac{dQ}{dt} = -0.04Q, \quad Q(0) = Q_0.$

(A) This is a model for exponential decay. From 4,

$$Q(t) = Q_0 e^{-0.04t}$$

With $Q_0 = 3$, we have

$$Q(t) = 3e^{-0.04t}$$

(B) $Q(10) = 3e^{-0.04(10)} = 3e^{-0.4} \approx 2.01.$

There are approximately 2.01 milliliters in the body after 10 hours.

(C) $3e^{-0.04t} = 1$

$e^{-0.04t} = \dfrac{1}{3}$

$-0.04t = \ln(1/3)$

$t = \dfrac{\ln(1/3)}{-0.04} \approx 27.47$

(D)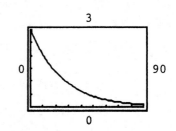

It will take approximately 27.47 hours for Q to decrease to 1 milliliter.

59. Using the exponential decay model, we have $\dfrac{dy}{dt} = -ky$, $y(0) = 100$, $k > 0$

where $y = y(t)$ is the amount of cesium-137 present at time t. From 4,
$$y(t) = 100e^{-kt}$$
Since $y(3) = 93.3$, we solve $93.3 = 100e^{-3k}$ for k to find the continuous compound decay rate:

$$93.3 = 100e^{-3k}$$

$$e^{-3k} = 0.933$$

$$-3k = \ln(0.933)$$

$$k = \dfrac{\ln(0.933)}{-3} \approx 0.023117$$

61. From Example 3: $Q = Q_0 e^{-0.0001238t}$

Now, the amount of radioactive carbon-14 present is 5% of the original amount. Thus, $0.05Q_0 = Q_0 e^{-0.0001238t}$ or $e^{-0.0001238t} = 0.05$.

Therefore, $-0.0001238t = \ln(0.05) \approx -2.9957$ and $t \approx 24,200$ years.

63. $N(k) = 180e^{-0.11(k-1)}$, $1 \le k \le 10$

Thus, $N(6) = 180e^{-0.11(6-1)} = 180e^{-0.55} \approx 104$ times

and $N(10) = 180e^{-0.11(10-1)} = 180e^{-0.99} \approx 67$ times.

65. (A) $x(t) = \dfrac{400}{1 + 399e^{-0.4t}}$

$x(5) = \dfrac{400}{1 + 399e^{(-0.4)5}} = \dfrac{400}{1 + 399e^{-2}} \approx \dfrac{400}{55} \approx 7$ people

$x(20) = \dfrac{400}{1 + 399e^{(-0.4)20}} = \dfrac{400}{1 + 399e^{-8}} \approx 353$ people

(B) $\lim\limits_{t \to \infty} x(t) = 400$.

(C)
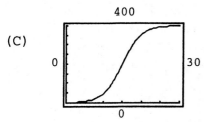

Things to remember:

1. APPROXIMATING AREAS BY LEFT AND RIGHT SUMS

   Let $f(x)$ be defined and positive on the interval $[a, b]$. Divide the interval into n subintervals of equal length $\Delta x = \dfrac{b - a}{n}$, with endpoints $a = x_0 < x_1 < x_2 < \ldots < x_{n-1} < x_n = b$.

   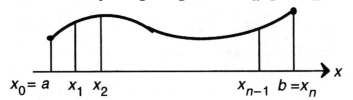

   Then

   $$L_n = f(x_0)\Delta x + f(x_1)\Delta x + f(x_2)\Delta x + \ldots + f(x_{n-1})\Delta x$$

   is called a LEFT SUM;

   $$R_n = f(x_1)\Delta x + f(x_2)\Delta x + \ldots + f(x_{n-1})\Delta x + f(x_n)\Delta x$$

   is called a RIGHT SUM.

   Left and right sums are approximations of the area between the graph of f and the x-axis from $x = a$ to $x = b$.

2. ERROR IN AN APPROXIMATION

   The ERROR IN AN APPROXIMATION is the absolute value of the difference between the approximation and the actual value.

3. ERROR BOUNDS FOR APPROXIMATIONS OF AREA BY LEFT AND RIGHT SUMS

   If $f(x) > 0$ and is either increasing on $[a, b]$ or decreasing on $[a, b]$, then

   $$\left| f(b) - f(a) \right| \cdot \frac{b - a}{n}$$

   is an error bound for the approximation of the area under the graph of f.

4. LIMITS OF LEFT AND RIGHT SUMS

   If $f(x) > 0$ and is either increasing on $[a, b]$ or decreasing on $[a, b]$, then its left and right sums approach the same real number I as $n \to \infty$. This number is the area between the graph of f and the x-axis from $x = a$ to $x = b$.

5. RIEMANN SUMS

Let f be defined on the interval $[a, b]$. Divide the interval into n subintervals of equal length $\Delta x = \dfrac{b - a}{n}$ with endpoints

$$a = x_0 < x_1 < x_2 < \ldots < x_{n-1} < x_n = b.$$

Choose a point $c_1 \in [x_0, x_1]$, a point $c_2 \in [x_1, x_2]$, ..., and a point $c_n \in [x_{n-1}, x_n]$. Then

$$S_n = f(c_1)\Delta x + f(c_2)\Delta x + \ldots + f(c_n)\Delta x$$

is called a RIEMANN SUM. Note that left sums and right sums are special cases of Riemann Sums.

6. LIMIT OF RIEMANN SUMS

If f is a continuous function on $[a, b]$ then the Riemann sums for f on $[a, b]$ approach a real number I as $n \to \infty$.

7. DEFINITE INTEGRAL

Let f be a continuous function on $[a, b]$. The limit I of Riemann sums for f on $[a, b]$ is called the DEFINITE INTEGRAL of f from a to b, denoted

$$\int_a^b f(x)dx$$

The INTEGRAND is $f(x)$, the LOWER LIMIT OF INTEGRATION is a, and the UPPER LIMIT OF INTEGRATION is b.

8. GEOMETRIC INTERPRETATION OF THE DEFINITE INTEGRAL

If $f(x)$ is positive for some value of x on $[a, b]$ and negative for others, then the DEFINITE INTEGRAL SYMBOL

$$\int_a^b f(x)dx$$

represents the cumulative sum of the signed areas between the curve $y = f(x)$ and the x-axis where the areas above the x-axis are counted positively and the areas below the x-axis are counted negatively (see the figure where A and B are actual areas of the indicated regions).

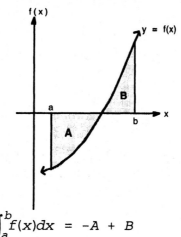

$$\int_a^b f(x)dx = -A + B$$

9. PROPERTIES OF DEFINITE INTEGRALS

   (a) $\int_a^a f(x)dx = 0$

   (b) $\int_a^b f(x)dx = -\int_b^a f(x)dx$

   (c) $\int_a^b Kf(x)dx = K\int_a^b f(x)dx \quad K$ is a constant

   (d) $\int_a^b [f(x) \pm g(x)]dx = \int_a^b f(x)dx \pm \int_a^b g(x)dx$

   (e) $\int_a^b f(x)dx = \int_a^c f(x)dx + \int_c^b f(x)dx$

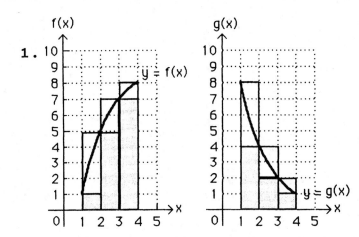

1.

3. For Figure (A):

$$L_3 = f(1)\cdot 1 + f(2)\cdot 1 + f(3)\cdot 1$$
$$= 1 + 5 + 7 = 13$$

$$R_3 = f(2)\cdot 1 + f(3)\cdot 1 + f(4)\cdot 1$$
$$= 5 + 7 + 8 = 20$$

For Figure (B):

$$L_3 = g(1)\cdot 1 + g(2)\cdot 1 + g(3)\cdot 1$$
$$= 8 + 4 + 2 = 14$$

$$R_3 = g(2)\cdot 1 + g(3)\cdot 1 + g(4)\cdot 1$$
$$= 4 + 2 + 1 = 7$$

5. $L_3 \leq \int_1^4 f(x)dx \leq R_3$, $R_3 \leq \int_1^4 g(x)dx \leq L_3$; since f is increasing on [1, 4], L_3 underestimates the area and R_3 overestimates the area; since g is decreasing on [1, 4], L_3 overestimates the area and R_3 underestimates th area.

7. For Figure (A).

Error bound for L_3 and R_3:

$$\text{Error} \leq |f(4) - f(1)|\left(\frac{4-1}{3}\right) = |8 - 1| = 7$$

For Figure (B).

Error bound for L_3 and R_3:

$$\text{Error} \leq |f(4) - f(1)|\left(\frac{4-1}{3}\right) = |1 - 8| = |-7| = 7$$

9. $f(x) = 25 - 3x^2$ on $[-2, 8]$

$\Delta x = \dfrac{8 - (-2)}{5} = \dfrac{10}{5} = 2$; $x_0 = -2$, $x_1 = 0$, $x_2 = 2$, ..., $x_5 = 8$

$c_i = \dfrac{x_{i-1} + x_i}{2}$; $c_1 = -1$, $c_2 = 1$, $c_3 = 3$, $c_4 = 5$, $c_5 = 7$

$S_5 = f(-1)2 + f(1)2 + f(3)2 + f(5)2 + f(7)2$

$\quad = [22 + 22 - 2 - 50 - 122]2 = (-130)2 = -260$

11. $f(x) = 25 - 3x^2$ on $[0, 12]$

$\Delta x = \dfrac{12 - 0}{4} = 3$; $x_0 = 0$, $x_1 = 3$, $x_2 = 6$, $x_3 = 9$, $x_4 = 12$

$c_i = \dfrac{2x_{i-1} + x_i}{3}$; $c_1 = 1$, $c_2 = 4$, $c_3 = 7$, $c_4 = 10$

$S_4 = f(1)3 + f(4)3 + f(7)3 + f(10)3$

$\quad = [22 - 23 - 122 - 275]3 = (-398)3 = -1194$

13. $f(x) = x^2 - 5x - 6$

$\Delta x = \dfrac{3 - 0}{3} = 1$; $x_0 = 0$, $x_1 = 1$, $x_2 = 2$, $x_3 = 3$

$S_3 = f(0.7)1 + f(1.8)1 + f(2.4)1$

$\quad = -9.01 - 11.76 - 12.24 = -33.01$

15. $f(x) = x^2 - 5x - 6$

$\Delta x = \dfrac{7 - 1}{6} = 1$; $x_0 = 1$, $x_1 = 2$, $x_3 = 3$, ..., $x_6 = 7$

$S_6 = f(1)1 + f(3)1 + f(3)1 + f(5)1 + f(5)1 + f(7)1$

$\quad = -10 - 12 - 12 - 6 - 6 + 8 = -38$

17. $\displaystyle\int_b^0 f(x)\,dx = -\text{area } B = -2.475$

19. $\displaystyle\int_a^c f(x)\,dx = \text{area } A - \text{area } B + \text{area } C = 1.408 - 2.475 + 5.333 = 4.266$

21. $\displaystyle\int_a^d f(x)\,dx = \text{area } A - \text{area } B + \text{area } C - \text{area } D$

$\quad = 1.408 - 2.475 + 5.333 - 1.792 = 2.474$

23. $\displaystyle\int_c^0 f(x)\,dx = -\int_0^c f(x)\,dx = -\text{area } C = -5.333$

25. $\int_0^a f(x)\,dx = -\int_a^0 f(x)\,dx = -[\text{area } A - \text{area } B] = -[1.408 - 2.475] = 1.067$

27. $\int_d^b f(x)\,dx = -\int_b^d f(x)\,dx = -[\text{area } B + \text{area } C - \text{area } D]$
$$= -[-2.475 + 5.333 - 1.792] = -1.066$$

29. $\int_1^4 2x\,dx = 2\int_1^4 x\,dx = 2(7.5) = 15$

31. $\int_1^4 (5x + x^2)\,dx = 5\int_1^4 x\,dx + \int_1^4 x^2\,dx = 5(7.5) + 21 = 58.5$

33. $\int_1^4 (x^2 - 10x)\,dx = \int_1^4 x^2\,dx - 10\int_1^4 x\,dx = 21 - 10(7.5) = -54$

35. $\int_1^5 6x^2\,dx = 6\int_1^5 x^2\,dx = 6\left[\int_1^4 x^2\,dx + \int_4^5 x^2\,dx\right] = 6\left[21 + \frac{61}{3}\right] = 126 + 122 = 248$

37. $\int_4^4 (7x - 2)^2\,dx = 0$

39. $\int_5^4 9x^2\,dx = -\int_4^5 9x^2\,dx = -9\int_4^5 x^2\,dx = -9\left(\frac{61}{3}\right) = -183$

41. (A) $f(x) = x^2 - 2x$ on $[0, 2]$.
$f'(x) = 2x - 2 = 2(x - 1)$; $f'(x) < 0$ on $[0, 1)$,
$f'(x) > 0$ on $(1, 2]$
False: f is not increasing on $[0, 2]$
(B) $f(x) = x^2 - 2x$ on $[1, 3]$
$f'(x) = 2x - 2 = 2(x - 1)$; $f'(x) > 0$ on $(1, 3]$
True: f is increasing on $[1, 3]$

43. $h(x)$ is an increasing function; $\Delta x = 100$
$L_{10} = h(0)100 + h(100)100 + h(200)100 + \ldots + h(900)(100)$
$$= [0 + 183 + 235 + 245 + 260 + 286 + 322 + 388 + 453 + 489]100$$
$$= (2,861)100 = 286,100 \text{ sq ft}$$
Error bound for L_{10}:
$$\text{Error} \leq |h(1,000) - h(0)|\left(\frac{1000 - 0}{10}\right) = 500(100) = 50,000 \text{ sq ft}$$
We want to find n such that $|I - L_n| \leq 2,500$:
$$|h(1000) - h(0)|\left(\frac{1000 - 0}{n}\right) \leq 2,500$$
$$500\left(\frac{1000}{n}\right) \leq 2,500$$
$$500,000 \leq 2,500n$$
$$n \geq 200$$

45. $f(x) = 0.25x^2 - 4$ on $[2, 5]$

$L_6 = f(2)\Delta x + f(2.5)\Delta x + f(3)\Delta x + f(3.5)\Delta x + f(4)\Delta x + f(4.5)\Delta x$

where $\Delta x = 0.5$

Thus,

$L_6 = [-3 - 2.44 - 1.75 - 0.94 + 0 + 1.06](0.5) = -3.53$

$R_6 = f(2.5)\Delta x + f(3)\Delta x + f(3.5)\Delta x + f(4)\Delta x + f(4.5)\Delta x + f(5)\Delta x$

where $\Delta x = 0.5$

Thus,

$R_6 = [-2.44 - 1.75 - 0.94 + 0 + 1.06 + 2.25](0.5) = -0.91$

Error bound for L_6 and R_6: Since f is increasing on $[2, 5]$,

$$\text{Error} \leq |f(5) - f(2)|\left(\frac{5-2}{6}\right) = |2.25 - (-3)|(0.5) = 2.63$$

Geometrically, the definite integral over the interval $[2, 5]$ is the area of the region which lies above the x-axis minus the area of the region which lies below the x-axis. From the figure, if R_1 represents the region bounded by the graph of f and the x-axis for $2 \leq x \leq 4$ and R_2 represents the region bounded by the graph of f and the x-axis for $4 \leq x \leq 5$, then

$$\int_2^5 f(x)dx = \text{area}(R_2) - \text{area}(R_1)$$

47. $f(x) = e^{-x^2}$

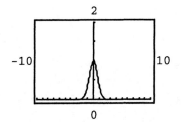

Thus, f is increasing on $(-\infty, 0]$ and decreasing on $[0, \infty)$.

49. $f(x) = x^4 - 2x^2 + 3$

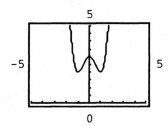

Thus, f is decreasing on $(-\infty, -1]$ and on $[0, 1]$, and increasing on $[-1, 0]$ and on $[1, \infty)$.

51. $\int_1^3 \ln x \, dx$

$$|I - R_n| \leq |\ln 3 - \ln 1|\frac{3-1}{n} \approx \frac{(1.0986)2}{n} = \frac{2.1972}{n}$$

Now $\dfrac{2.1972}{n} \leq 0.1$ implies $n \geq \dfrac{2.1972}{0.1} = 21.972$

so $n \geq 22$.

53. $\int_1^3 x^x dx$

$$|I - L_n| \leq |3^3 - 1^1|\frac{3-1}{n} = \frac{26 \cdot 2}{n} = \frac{52}{n}$$

Now $\dfrac{52}{n} \leq 0.5$ implies $n \geq \dfrac{52}{0.5} = 104$

55. From $t = 0$ to $t = 60$

$L_3 = N(0)20 + N(20)20 + N(40)20$

$= (10 + 51 + 68)20 = 2580$

$R_3 = N(20)20 + N(40)20 + N(60)20$

$= (51 + 68 + 76)20 = 3900$

Error bound for L_3 and R_3: Since $N(t)$ is increasing,

$$\text{Error} \leq |N(60) - N(0)|\left(\frac{60 - 0}{3}\right) = (76 - 10)20 = 1,320 \text{ units}$$

57. (A) $L_5 = A'(0)1 + A'(1)1 + A'(2)1 + A'(3)1 + A'(4)1$

$= 0.90 + 0.81 + 0.74 + 0.67 + 0.60$

$= 3.72$ sq cm

$R_5 = A'(1)1 + A'(2)1 + A'(3)1 + A'(4)1 + A'(5)1$

$= (0.81 + 0.74 + 0.67 + 0.60 + 0.55)$

$= 3.37$ sq cm

(B) Since $A'(t)$ is a decreasing function

$$R_5 = 3.37 \leq \int_0^5 A'(t)dt \leq 3.72 = L_5$$

59. $L_3 = N'(6)2 + N'(8)2 + N'(10)2$

$= (21 + 19 + 17)2 = 114$

$R_3 = N'(8)2 + N'(10)2 + N'(12)2$

$= (19 + 17 + 15)2 = 102$

Error bound for L_3 and R_3: Since $N'(x)$ is decreasing

$$\text{Error} \leq |N'(12) - N'(6)|\left(\frac{12 - 6}{3}\right) = |15 - 21|(2) = 12 \text{ code symbols}$$

EXERCISE 4-5

1. FUNDAMENTAL THEOREM OF CALCULUS

If f is a continuous function on the closed interval $[a, b]$ and F is any antiderivative of f, then

$$\int_a^b f(x)dx = F(x)\Big|_a^b = F(b) - F(a);$$

$$F'(x) = f(x)$$

2. AVERAGE VALUE OF A CONTINUOUS FUNCTION OVER $[a, b]$

Let f be continuous on $[a, b]$. Then the AVERAGE VALUE of f over $[a, b]$ is:

$$\frac{1}{b - a}\int_a^b f(x)dx$$

1. $F(x) = 3x^2 + 160$

(A) $F(15) - F(10) = 3(15)^2 + 160 - [3(10)^2 + 160]$
$$= 675 - 300 = 375$$

(B)

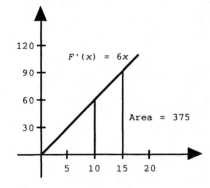

Area of trapezoid:

$$\frac{F'(15) + F'(10)}{2} \cdot 5 = \frac{90 + 60}{2} \cdot 5$$

$$= 75(5) = 375$$

(C) By the Fundamental Theorem of Calculus:
$$\int_{10}^{15} 6x\, dx = 3x^2 \Big|_{10}^{15} = 3(15)^2 - 3(10)^2 = 375$$

3. $F(x) = -x^2 + 42x + 240$

(A) $F(15) - F(10) = -(15)^2 + 42(15) + 240 - [-(10)^2 + 42(10) + 240]$
$$= -225 + 630 + 240 - (-100 + 420 + 240)$$
$$= -225 + 630 + 100 - 420 = 85$$

(B)

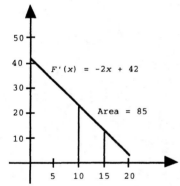

Area of trapezoid:

$$\frac{F'(15) + F'(10)}{2} \cdot 5 = \frac{(-30 + 42) + (-20 + 42)}{2} \cdot 5$$

$$= 17(5) = 85$$

(C) By the Fundamental Theorem of Calculus:
$$\int_{10}^{15} (-2x + 42)\, dx = \left[-x^2 + 42x\right]_{10}^{15} = -(15)^2 + 42(15) - [-(10)^2 + 42(10)]$$
$$= -225 + 630 + 100 - 420 = 85$$

5. $\int_{2}^{3} 2x\, dx = 2 \cdot \frac{x^2}{2} \Big|_{2}^{3} = 3^2 - 2^2 = 5$ **7.** $\int_{3}^{4} 5\, dx = 5x \Big|_{3}^{4} = 5 \cdot 4 - 5 \cdot 3 = 5$

9. $\int_{1}^{3} (2x - 3)\, dx = (x^2 - 3x) \Big|_{1}^{3} = (3^2 - 3 \cdot 3) - (1^2 - 3 \cdot 1) = 2$

11. $\int_{-3}^{4} (4 - x^2)\, dx = \left(4x - \frac{x^3}{3}\right)\Big|_{-3}^{4} = \left(4 \cdot 4 - \frac{4^3}{3}\right) - \left(4(-3) - \frac{(-3)^3}{3}\right)$

$$= 16 - \frac{64}{3} + 3 = -\frac{7}{3}$$

13. $\int_0^1 24x^{11}dx = 24\dfrac{x^{12}}{12}\Big|_0^1 = 2x^{12}\Big|_0^1 = 2\cdot 1^{12} - 2\cdot 0^{12} = 2$

15. $\int_0^1 e^{2x}dx = \dfrac{1}{2}e^{2x}\Big|_0^1 = \dfrac{1}{2}e^{2\cdot 1} - \dfrac{1}{2}e^{2\cdot 0} = \dfrac{1}{2}(e^2 - 1)$

17. $\int_1^{3.5} 2x^{-1}dx = 2\ln x\Big|_1^{3.5} = 2\ln 3.5 - 2\ln 1$

$$= 2\ln 3.5 \quad (\text{Recall: } \ln 1 = 0)$$

19. $\int_1^2 \dfrac{2}{x^3}dx = 2\int_1^2 x^{-3}dx = 2\dfrac{x^{-2}}{-2}\Big]_1^2 = -\dfrac{1}{x^2}\Big]_1^2$

$$= -\dfrac{1}{4} - (-1) = \dfrac{3}{4}$$

21. $\int_1^4 6x^{-1/2}dx = 6\int_1^4 x^{-1/2}dx = 12x^{1/2}\Big]_1^4 = 12(4)^{1/2} - 12(1)^{1/2} = 12$

23. $\int_1^2 (2x^{-2} - 3)dx = (-2x^{-1} - 3x)\Big|_1^2 = \left(-\dfrac{2}{x} - 3x\right)\Big|_1^2$

$$= -\dfrac{2}{2} - 3\cdot 2 - \left(-\dfrac{2}{1} - 3\cdot 1\right) = -7 - (-5) = -2$$

25. $\int_1^4 3\sqrt{x}\,dx = 3\int_1^4 x^{1/2}dx\,3 = 3\cdot\dfrac{2}{3}x^{3/2}\Big|_1^4 = 2x^{3/2}\Big|_1^4$

$$= 2\cdot 4^{3/2} - 2\cdot 1^{3/2} = 16 - 2 = 14$$

27. $\int_2^3 12(x^2 - 4)^5 x\,dx$. Consider the indefinite integral $\int 12(x^2 - 4)^5 x\,dx$.

Let $u = x^2 - 4$, then $du = 2x\,dx$.

$\int 12(x^2 - 4)^5 x\,dx = 6\int (x^2 - 4)^5 2x\,dx = 6\int u^5 du$

$$= 6\dfrac{u^6}{6} + C = u^6 + C = (x^2 - 4)^6 + C$$

Thus,

$$\int_2^3 12(x^2 - 4)^5 x\,dx = (x^2 - 4)^6\Big|_2^3 = (3^2 - 4)^6 - (2^2 - 4)^6 = 5^6 = 15{,}625.$$

29. $\int_3^9 \dfrac{1}{x - 1}dx$

Let $u = x - 1$. Then $du = dx$ and $u = 8$ when $x = 9$, $u = 2$ when $x = 3$.
Thus,

$$\int_3^9 \dfrac{1}{x - 1}dx = \int_2^8 \dfrac{1}{u}du = \ln u\Big|_2^8 = \ln 8 - \ln 2 = \ln 4 \approx 1.386.$$

31. $\int_{-5}^{10} e^{-0.05x} dx$

Let $u = -0.05x$. Then $du = -0.05\ dx$ and $u = -0.5$ when $x = 10$, $u = 0.25$ when $x = -5$. Thus,

$$\int_{-5}^{10} e^{-0.05x} dx = -\frac{1}{0.05} \int_{-5}^{10} e^{-0.05x}(-0.05) dx = -\frac{1}{0.05} \int_{0.25}^{-0.5} e^{u} du$$

$$= -\frac{1}{0.05} e^{u} \Big|_{0.25}^{-0.5} = -\frac{1}{0.05}\ [e^{-0.5} - e^{0.25}]$$

$$= 20(e^{0.25} - e^{-0.5}) \approx 13.550$$

33. $\int_{1}^{e} \frac{\ln t}{t} dt = \int_{0}^{1} u\,du = \frac{1}{2}u^2 \Big|_{0}^{1} = \frac{1}{2}$

Let $u = \ln t$

Then $du = \frac{1}{t} dt$

$t = 1$ implies $u = \ln 1 = 0$
$t = e$ implies $u = \ln e = 1$

35. $\int_{0}^{2} x\sqrt{4 - x^2}\,dx$

We evaluate the indefinite integral $\int x\sqrt{4 - x^2}\,dx$ first.

Let $u = 4 - x^2$. Then $du = -2x\,dx$ and

$$\int x\sqrt{4 - x^2}\,dx = \int \sqrt{4 - x^2}\left(\frac{-2}{-2}\right)x\,dx = -\frac{1}{2}\int u^{1/2}\,du$$

$$= -\frac{1}{2}\frac{u^{3/2}}{3/2} + C$$

$$= \frac{1}{3}u^{3/2} + C$$

$$= -\frac{1}{3}(4 - x^2)^{3/2} + C$$

Now $\int_{0}^{2} x\sqrt{4 - x^2}\,dx = -\frac{1}{3}(4 - x^2)^{3/2} \Big|_{0}^{2} = -\frac{1}{3}(4 - 4)^{3/2} + \frac{1}{3}(4)^{3/2}$

$$= \frac{8}{3} \approx 2.667.$$

37. $\int_{0}^{1} xe^{-x^2}\,dx = \int_{0}^{1} e^{-x^2}\left(\frac{-2}{-2}\right)x\,dx$

Let $u = -x^2$

Then $du = -2x\,dx$

$x = 0$ implies $u = 0$
$x = 1$ implies $u = -1$

$$= -\frac{1}{2}\int_{0}^{-1} e^{u}\,du$$

$$= -\frac{1}{2}e^{u} \Big|_{0}^{-1} = -\frac{1}{2}e^{-1} + \frac{1}{2}e^{0}$$

$$= \frac{1}{2}(1 - e^{-1})$$

$$\approx 0.316$$

39. $\int_{-2}^{-1} \dfrac{x^2 + 1}{x}\,dx = \int_{-2}^{-1}\left(x + \dfrac{1}{x}\right)dx = \left[\dfrac{1}{2}x^2 + \ln|x|\right]_{-2}^{-1}$

$$= \left(\dfrac{1}{2}(-1)^2 + \ln 1\right) - \left(\dfrac{1}{2}(-2)^2 + \ln 2\right)$$

$$= -\dfrac{3}{2} - \ln 2 \approx -2.193$$

41. $f(x) = 500 - 50x$ on $[0, 10]$

(A) Avg. $f(x) = \dfrac{1}{10 - 0}\int_0^{10}(500 - 50x)\,dx$ (B)

$$= \dfrac{1}{10}(500x - 25x^2)\Big|_0^{10}$$

$$= \dfrac{1}{10}[5,000 - 2,500] = 250$$

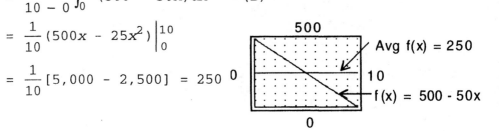

43. $f(t) = 3t^2 - 2t$ on $[-1, 2]$

(A) Avg. $f(t) = \dfrac{1}{2 - (-1)}\int_{-1}^{2}(3t^2 - 2t)\,dt$ (B)

$$= \dfrac{1}{3}(t^3 - t^2)\Big|_{-1}^{2}$$

$$= \dfrac{1}{3}[4 - (-2)] = 2$$

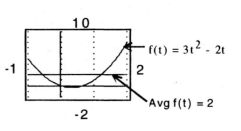

45. $f(x) = \sqrt[3]{x} = x^{1/3}$ on $[1, 8]$

(A) Avg. $f(x) = \dfrac{1}{8 - 1}\int_1^{8}x^{1/3}\,dx$ (B)

$$= \dfrac{1}{7}\left(\dfrac{3}{4}x^{4/3}\right)\Big|_1^{8}$$

$$= \dfrac{3}{28}(16 - 1) = \dfrac{45}{28} \approx 1.61$$

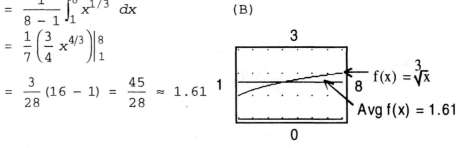

47. $f(x) = 4e^{-0.2x}$ on $[0, 10]$

(A) Avg. $f(x) = \dfrac{1}{10 - 0}\int_0^{10}4e^{-0.2x}\,dx$ (B)

$$= \dfrac{1}{10}(-20e^{-0.2x})\Big|_0^{10}$$

$$= \dfrac{1}{10}(20 - 20e^{-2}) \approx 1.73$$

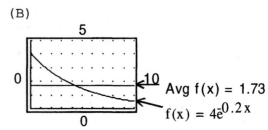

49. $\int_2^3 x\sqrt{2x^2 - 3}\,dx = \int_2^3 x(2x^2 - 3)^{1/2}dx$

$$= \frac{1}{4}\int_2^3 (2x^2 - 3)^{1/2}4x\,dx$$

[Note: The integrand has the form $u^{1/2}du$; the antiderivative is $\frac{2}{3}u^{3/2} = \frac{2}{3}(2x^2 - 3)^{3/2}$.]

$$= \frac{1}{4}\left(\frac{2}{3}\right)(2x^2 - 3)^{3/2}\Big|_2^3$$

$$= \frac{1}{6}[2(3)^2 - 3]^{3/2} - \frac{1}{6}[2(2)^2 - 3]^{3/2}$$

$$= \frac{1}{6}(15)^{3/2} - \frac{1}{6}(5)^{3/2} = \frac{1}{6}[15^{3/2} - 5^{3/2}] \approx 7.819$$

51. $\int_0^1 \dfrac{x - 1}{x^2 - 2x + 3}\,dx$

Consider the indefinite integral and let $u = x^2 - 2x + 3$.
Then $du = (2x - 2)\,dx = 2(x - 1)\,dx$.

$$\int \frac{x - 1}{x^2 - 2x + 3}\,dx = \frac{1}{2}\int \frac{2(x - 1)}{x^2 - 2x + 3}\,dx = \frac{1}{2}\int \frac{1}{u}\,du = \frac{1}{2}\ln|u| + C$$

Thus,

$$\int_0^1 \frac{x - 1}{x^2 - 2x + 3}\,dx = \frac{1}{2}\ln|x^2 - 2x + 3|\ \Big|_0^1$$

$$= \frac{1}{2}\ln 2 - \frac{1}{2}\ln 3 = \frac{1}{2}(\ln 2 - \ln 3) \approx -0.203$$

53. $\int_{-1}^1 \dfrac{e^{-x} - e^x}{(e^{-x} + e^x)^2}\,dx$

Consider the indefinite integral and let $u = e^{-x} + e^x$.
Then $du = (-e^{-x} + e^x)\,dx = -(e^{-x} - e^x)\,dx$.

$$\int \frac{e^{-x} - e^x}{(e^{-x} + e^x)^2}\,dx = -\int \frac{-(e^{-x} - e^x)}{(e^{-x} + e^x)^2}\,dx = -\int u^{-2}\,du = \frac{-u^{-1}}{-1} + C = \frac{1}{u} + C$$

Thus,

$$\int_{-1}^1 \frac{e^{-x} - e^x}{(e^{-x} + e^x)^2}\,dx = \frac{1}{e^{-x} + e^x}\Big|_{-1}^1 = \frac{1}{e^{-1} + e^1} - \frac{1}{e^{-(-1)} + e^{-1}}$$

$$= \frac{1}{e^{-1} + e} - \frac{1}{e^{-1} + e} = 0$$

55. $\int_{1.7}^{3.5} x \ln x\,dx \approx 4.566$

```
fnInt(X*ln X,X,1
.7,3.5)
      4.566415359
■
```

57. $\int_{-2}^2 \dfrac{1}{1 + x^2}\,dx \approx 2.214$

```
fnInt(1/(1+X²),X
,-2,2)
      2.214297436
■
```

59. If $F(t)$ denotes the position of the car at time t, then the average velocity over the time interval $t = a$ to $t = b$ is given by

$$\frac{F(b) - F(a)}{b - a}.$$

$F'(t)$ gives the instantaneous velocity of the car at time t. By the Mean Value Theorem, there exists at least one time $t = c$ at which

$$\frac{F(b) - F(a)}{b - a} = F'(c).$$

Thus, if $\dfrac{F(b) - F(a)}{b - a} = 60$, then the instantaneous velocity must equal 60 at least once during the 10 minute time interval.

61. $C'(x) = 500 - \dfrac{x}{3}$ on $[300, 900]$

The increase in cost from a production level of 300 bikes per month to a production level of 900 bikes per month is given by:

$$\int_{300}^{900} \left(500 - \frac{x}{3}\right) dx = \left(500x - \frac{1}{6}x^2\right)\Big|_{300}^{900}$$

$$= 315,000 - (135,000)$$
$$= \$180,000$$

63. Total loss in value in the first 5 years:

$$V(5) - V(0) = \int_0^5 V'(t)\,dt = \int_0^5 500(t - 12)\,dt = 500\left(\frac{t^2}{2} - 12t\right)\Big|_0^5$$

$$= 500\left(\frac{25}{2} - 60\right) = -\$23,750$$

Total loss in value in the second 5 years:

$$V(10) - V(5) = \int_5^{10} V'(t)\,dt = \int_5^{10} 500(t - 12)\,dt = 500\left(\frac{t^2}{2} - 12t\right)\Big|_5^{10}$$

$$= 500\left[(50 - 120) - \left(\frac{25}{2} - 60\right)\right] = -\$11,250$$

65. (A)

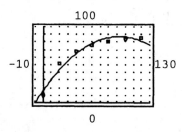

```
QuadReg
 y=ax²+bx+c
 a=-.0082142857
 b=1.528571429
 c=16
```

(B) Let $q(t)$ be the quadratic regression model found in part (A). The number of units produced by a new employee during the first 100 days is given (approximately) by

$$\int_0^{100} q(t)\,dt \approx 6505$$

```
fnInt(Y₁,X,0,100
)
          6504.761912
```

67. (A) To find the useful life, set $C'(t) = R'(t)$ and solve for t.

$$\frac{1}{11}t = 5te^{-t^2}$$
$$e^{t^2} = 55$$
$$t^2 = \ln 55$$
$$t = \sqrt{\ln 55} \approx 2 \text{ years}$$

(B) The total profit accumulated during the useful life is:

$$P(2) - P(0) = \int_0^2 [R'(t) - C'(t)]\,dt = \int_0^2 \left(5te^{-t^2} - \frac{1}{11}t\right)dt$$

$$= \int_0^2 5te^{-t^2}\,dt - \int_0^2 \frac{1}{11}t\,dt$$

$$= -\frac{5}{2}\int_0^2 e^{-t^2}(-2t)\,dt - \frac{1}{11}\int_0^2 t\,dt$$

[Note: In the first integral, the integrand has the form $e^u\,du$, where $u = -t^2$; an antiderivative is $e^u = e^{-t^2}$.]

$$= -\frac{5}{2}e^{-t^2}\Big|_0^2 - \frac{1}{22}t^2\Big|_0^2$$

$$= -\frac{5}{2}e^{-4} + \frac{5}{2} - \frac{4}{22} = \frac{51}{22} - \frac{5}{2}e^{-4} \approx 2.272$$

Thus, the total profit is approximately $2,272.

69. $C(x) = 60,000 + 300x$

(A) Average cost per unit:

$$\overline{C}(x) = \frac{C(x)}{x} = \frac{60,000}{x} + 300$$

$$\overline{C}(500) = \frac{60,000}{500} + 300 = \$420$$

(B) Avg. $C(x) = \dfrac{1}{500}\displaystyle\int_0^{500}(60,000 + 300x)\,dx$

$$= \frac{1}{500}(60,000x + 150x^2)\Big|_0^{500}$$

$$= \frac{1}{500}(30,000,000 + 37,500,000) = \$135,000$$

(C) $\overline{C}(500)$ is the average cost per unit at a production level of 500 units; Ave $C(x)$ is the average value of the total cost as production increases from 0 units to 500 units.

71. (A)

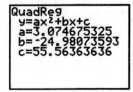
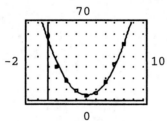

(B) Let $q(x)$ be the quadratic regression model found in part (A). The increase in cost in going from a production level of 2 thousand watches per month to 8 thousand watches per month is given (approximately) by

$$\int_2^8 q(x)\,dx \approx 100.505$$

Therefore, the increase in cost is approximately $100,505.

73. Average price:

$$\text{Avg. } S(x) = \frac{1}{30-20}\int_{20}^{30} 10(e^{0.02x} - 1)\,dx = \int_{20}^{30}(e^{0.02x} - 1)\,dx$$

$$= \int_{20}^{30} e^{0.02x}\,dx - \int_{20}^{30} dx$$

$$= \frac{1}{0.02}\int_{20}^{30} e^{0.02x}(0.02)\,dx - x\Big|_{20}^{30}$$

$$= 50e^{0.02x}\Big|_{20}^{30} - (30 - 20)$$

$$= 50e^{0.6} - 50e^{0.4} - 10$$

$$\approx 6.51 \text{ or } \$6.51$$

75. $g(x) = 2400x^{-1/2}$ and $L'(x) = g(x)$.

The number of labor hours to assemble the 17th through the 25th control units is:

$$L(25) - L(16) = \int_{16}^{25} g(x)\,dx = \int_{16}^{25} 2400x^{-1/2}\,dx = 2400(2)x^{1/2}\Big|_{16}^{25}$$

$$= 4800x^{1/2}\Big|_{16}^{25} = 4800[25^{1/2} - 16^{1/2}] = 4800 \text{ labor hours}$$

77. (A) The inventory function is obtained by finding the equation of the line joining $(0, 600)$ and $(3, 0)$.

Slope: $m = \dfrac{0-600}{3-0} = -200$, y intercept: $b = 600$

Thus, the equation of the line is: $I = -200t + 600$

(B) The average of I over $[0, 3]$ is given by:

$$\text{Avg. } I(t) = \frac{1}{3-0}\int_0^3 I(t)\,dt = \frac{1}{3}\int_0^3 (-200t + 600)\,dt$$

$$= \frac{1}{3}(-100t^2 + 600t)\Big|_0^3$$

$$= \frac{1}{3}[-100(3^2) + 600(3) - 0]$$

$$= \frac{900}{3} = 300 \text{ units}$$

79. Rate of production: $R(t) = \dfrac{100}{t+1} + 5$, $0 \le t \le 20$

Total production from year N to year M is given by:

$$P = \int_N^M R(t)\,dt = \int_N^M \left(\frac{100}{t+1} + 5\right)dt = 100\int_N^M \frac{1}{t+1} + 5\,dt$$

$$= 100\ \ln|t+1|\ \Big|_N^M + 5t\Big|_N^M$$

$$= 100\ \ln(M+1) - 100\ \ln(N+1) + 5(M - N)$$

Thus, for total production during the first 10 years, let $M = 10$ and $N = 0$.

$P = 100\ \ln 11 - 100\ \ln 1 + 5(10 - 0)$
  $= 100\ \ln 11 + 50 \approx 290$ thousand barrels

For the total production from the end of the 10th year to the end of the 20th year, let $M = 20$ and $N = 10$.

$P = 100\ \ln 21 - 100\ \ln 11 + 5(20 - 10)$
  $= 100\ \ln 21 - 100\ \ln 11 + 50 \approx 115$ thousand barrels

81. $W'(t) = 0.2e^{0.1t}$

The weight increase during the first eight hours is given by:

$$W(8) - W(0) = \int_0^8 W'(t)\,dt = \int_0^8 0.2e^{0.1t}\,dt = 0.2\int_0^8 e^{0.1t}\,dt$$

$$= \frac{0.2}{0.1}\int_0^8 e^{0.1t}(0.1)\,dt \qquad \text{(Let } u = 0.1t, \text{ then } du = 0.1dt.)$$

$$= 2e^{0.1t}\Big|_0^8 = 2e^{0.8} - 2 \approx 2.45 \text{ grams}$$

The weight increase during the second eight hours, i.e., from the 8th hour through the 16th hour, is given by:

$$W(16) - W(8) = \int_8^{16} W'(t)\,dt = \int_8^{16} 0.2e^{0.1t}\,dt = 2e^{0.1t}\Big|_8^{16}$$

$$= 2e^{1.6} - 2e^{0.8} \approx 5.45 \text{ grams}$$

83. Average temperature over time period [0, 2] is given by:

$$\frac{1}{2-0}\int_0^2 C(t)\,dt = \frac{1}{2}\int_0^2 (t^3 - 2t + 10)\,dt = \frac{1}{2}\left(\frac{t^4}{4} - \frac{2t^2}{2} + 10t\right)\Big|_0^2$$

$$= \frac{1}{2}(4 - 4 + 20) = 10° \text{ Celsius}$$

85. $P(t) = \dfrac{8.4t}{t^2 + 49} + 0.1, \quad 0 \le t \le 24$

(A) Average fraction of people during the first seven months:

$$\frac{1}{7-0}\int_0^7 \left[\frac{8.4t}{t^2 + 49} + 0.1\right]dt = \frac{4.2}{7}\int_0^7 \frac{2t}{t^2 + 49}\,dt + \frac{1}{7}\int_0^7 0.1\,dt$$

$$= 0.6\,\ln(t^2 + 49)\Big|_0^7 + \frac{0.1}{7}t\Big|_0^7$$

$$= 0.6[\ln 98 - \ln 49] + 0.1$$

$$= 0.6\,\ln 2 + 0.1 \approx 0.516$$

(B) Average fraction of people during the first two years:

$$\frac{1}{24-0}\int_0^{24} \left[\frac{8.4t}{t^2 + 49} + 0.1\right]dt = \frac{4.2}{24}\int_0^{24} \frac{2t}{t^2 + 49}\,dt + \frac{1}{24}\int_0^{24} 0.1\,dt$$

$$= 0.175\,\ln(t^2 + 49)\Big|_0^{24} + \frac{0.1}{24}t\Big|_0^{24}$$

$$= 0.175[\ln 625 - \ln 49] + 0.1 \approx 0.546$$

CHAPTER 4 REVIEW

1. $\displaystyle\int (6x + 3)\,dx = 6\int x\,dx + \int 3\,dx = 6 \cdot \frac{x^2}{2} + 3x + C$

$$= 3x^2 + 3x + C \hspace{4cm} (6\text{-}1)$$

2. $\displaystyle\int_{10}^{20} 5\,dx = 5x\Big|_{10}^{20} = 5(20) - 5(10) = 50 \hspace{3cm} (6\text{-}5)$

3. $\displaystyle\int_0^9 (4 - t^2)\,dt = \int_0^9 4\,dt - \int_0^9 t^2\,dt = 4t\Big|_0^9 - \frac{t^3}{3}\Big|_0^9$

$$= 36 - 243 = -207 \hspace{4cm} (6\text{-}5)$$

4. $\int (1 - t^2)^3 t\,dt = \int (1 - t^2)^3 \left(\dfrac{-2}{-2}\right) t\,dt = -\dfrac{1}{2}\int (1 - t^2)^3 (-2t)\,dt$

$$= -\dfrac{1}{2}\int u^3\,du = -\dfrac{1}{2}\cdot\dfrac{u^4}{4} + C$$

$$= -\dfrac{1}{8}(1 - t^2)^4 + C \qquad (6\text{-}2)$$

5. $\int \dfrac{1 + u^4}{u}\,du = \int\left(\dfrac{1}{u} + u^3\right)du = \int\dfrac{1}{u}\,du + \int u^3\,du$

$$= \ln|u| + \dfrac{1}{4}u^4 + C \qquad (6\text{-}1)$$

6. $\displaystyle\int_0^1 xe^{-2x^2}\,dx$

Let $u = -2x^2$ $\qquad \int xe^{-2x^2}\,dx = \int e^{-2x^2}\left(\dfrac{-4}{-4}\right)x\,dx = -\dfrac{1}{4}\int e^u\,du$

Then $du = -4x\,dx$ $\qquad\qquad\qquad\qquad\qquad = -\dfrac{1}{4}e^u + C$

$$= -\dfrac{1}{4}e^{-2x^2} + C$$

$\displaystyle\int_0^1 xe^{-2x^2}\,dx = -\dfrac{1}{4}e^{-2x^2}\,\Big|_0^1 = -\dfrac{1}{4}e^{-2} + \dfrac{1}{4} \approx 0.216 \qquad (6\text{-}5)$

7. $\dfrac{d}{dx}\left[\int e^{-2x^2}\,dx\right] = e^{-x^2}$ $\quad(6\text{-}1)$ $\qquad$ **8.** $\int \dfrac{d}{dx}(\sqrt{4 + 5x})\,dx = \sqrt{4 + 5x} + C \qquad (6\text{-}1)$

9. $\dfrac{dy}{dx} = 3x^2 - 2$

$\qquad y = f(x) = \int (3x^2 - 2)\,dx$

$\qquad\quad f(x) = x^3 - 2x + C$

$\qquad\quad f(0) = C = 4$

$\qquad\quad f(x) = x^3 - 2x + 4 \qquad\qquad (6\text{-}3)$

10. (A) $\int (8x^3 - 4x - 1)\,dx = 8\int x^3\,dx - 4\int x\,dx - \int dx$

$$= 8\cdot\dfrac{1}{4}x^4 - 4\,\dfrac{1}{2}x^2 - x + C$$

$$= 2x^4 - 2x^2 - x + C \qquad (6\text{-}1)$$

(B) $\int (e^t - 4^{t-1})\,dt = \int e^t - 4\int\dfrac{1}{t}\,dt$

$$= e^t - 4\ln|t| + C \qquad (6\text{-}1)$$

11. $f(x) = x^2 + 1$, $a = 1$, $b = 5$, $n = 2$, $\Delta x = \dfrac{5 - 1}{2} = 2$;

$\qquad R_2 = f(3)2 + f(5)2 = 10(2) + 26(2) = 72$

Error bound for R_2: f is increasing on $[1, 5]$, so

$|I - R_2| \le [f(5) - f(1)]\dfrac{5 - 1}{2} = (26 - 2)(2) = 48$

Thus, $I = 72 \pm 48$. $\qquad\qquad (6\text{-}5)$

12. $\int_1^5 (x^2 + 1)\,dx = \frac{1}{3}x^3 + x \Big]_1^5 = \frac{125}{3} + 5 - \left(\frac{1}{3} + 1\right) = \frac{136}{3} = 45\frac{1}{3}$

$|I - R_2| = \left|45\frac{1}{3} - 72\right| = 26\frac{2}{3} \approx 26.67$ (6-5)

13. Using the values of f in the table with $a = 1$, $b = 17$, $n = 4$

$\Delta x = \frac{17 - 1}{4} = 4$, we have

$L_4 = f(1)4 + f(5)4 + f(9)4 + f(13)4$

$\quad = [1.2 + 3.4 + 2.6 + 0.5]4 = 30.8$ (6-5)

14. $f(x) = 6x^2 + 2x$ on $[-1, 2]$;

Ave $f(x) = \dfrac{1}{2 - (-1)}\displaystyle\int_{-1}^2 (6x^2 + 2x)\,dx$

$\qquad = \frac{1}{3}(2x^3 + x^2)\Big|_{-1}^2 = \frac{1}{3}[20 - (-1)] = 7$ (6-5)

15. width $= 2 - (-1) = 3$, height $=$ Avg. $f(x) = 7$ (6-5)

16. $f(x) = 100 - x^2$

$\Delta x = \dfrac{11 - 3}{4} = \dfrac{8}{4} = 2$; $c_i = \dfrac{x_{i-1} + x_i}{2}$ (= midpoint of interval)

$S_4 = f(4)2 + f(6)2 + f(8)\cdot2 + f(10)\cdot2$

$\quad = [84 + 64 + 36 + 0]2 = (184)2 = 368$ (6-5)

17. $f(x) = 100 - x^2$

$\Delta x = \dfrac{5 - (-5)}{5} = \dfrac{10}{5} = 2$

$S_5 = f(-4)2 + f(-1)2 + f(1)2 + f(2)2 + f(5)2$

$\quad = [84 + 99 + 99 + 96 + 75]2 = (453)2 = 906$ (6-5)

18. $\displaystyle\int_a^b 5f(x)\,dx = 5\int_a^b f(x)\,dx = 5(-2) = -10$ (6-4, 6-5)

19. $\displaystyle\int_b^c \frac{f(x)}{5}\,dx = \frac{1}{5}\int_b^c f(x)\,dx = \frac{1}{5}(2) = \frac{2}{5} = 0.4$ (6-4, 6-5)

20. $\displaystyle\int_b^d f(x)\,dx = \int_b^c f(x)\,dx + \int_c^d f(x)\,dx = 2 - 0.6 = 1.4$ (6-4, 6-5)

21. $\displaystyle\int_a^c f(x)\,dx = \int_a^b f(x)\,dx + \int_b^c f(x)\,dx = -2 + 2 = 0$ (6-4, 6-5)

22. $\displaystyle\int_0^d f(x)\,dx = \int_0^a f(x)\,dx + \int_a^b f(x)\,dx + \int_b^c f(x)\,dx + \int_c^d f(x)\,dx$

$\qquad = 1 - 2 + 2 - 0.6 = 0.4$ (6-4, 6-5)

23. $\displaystyle\int_b^a f(x)\,dx = -\int_a^b f(x)\,dx = -(-2) = 2$ (6-4, 6-5)

24. $\displaystyle\int_c^b f(x)\,dx = -\int_b^c f(x)\,dx = -2$ (6-4, 6-5)

25. $\int_d^0 f(x)\,dx = -\int_0^d f(x)\,dx = -0.4$ (from Problem 22) (6-4, 6-5)

26. (A) $\dfrac{dy}{dx} = \dfrac{2y}{x}$; $\dfrac{dy}{dx}\bigg|_{(2,\ 1)} = \dfrac{2(1)}{2} = 1,\ \dfrac{dy}{dx}\bigg|_{(-2,\ -1)} = \dfrac{2(-1)}{-2} = 1$

   (B) $\dfrac{dy}{dx} = \dfrac{2x}{y}$; $\dfrac{dy}{dx}\bigg|_{(2,\ 1)} = \dfrac{2(2)}{1} = 4,\ \dfrac{dy}{dx}\bigg|_{(-2,\ -1)} = \dfrac{2(-2)}{-1} = 4$ (6-3)

27. $\dfrac{dy}{dx} = \dfrac{2y}{x}$; from the figure, the slopes at (2, 1) and (-2, -1) are
approximately equal to 1 as computed in Problem 26(A), not 4 as
computed in Problem 26(B). (6-3)

28. Let $y = Cx^2$. Then $\dfrac{dy}{dx} = 2Cx$. From the original equation, $C = \dfrac{y}{x^2}$ so

$$\frac{dy}{dx} = 2x\left(\frac{y}{x^2}\right) = \frac{2y}{x}$$ (6-3)

29. Letting $x = 2$ and $y = 1$ in $y = Cx^2$, we get
$$1 = 4C \quad \text{so} \quad C = \frac{1}{4} \quad \text{and} \quad y = \frac{1}{4}x^2$$
   Letting $x = -2$ and $y = -1$ in $y = Cx^2$, we get
$$-1 = 4C \quad \text{so} \quad C = -\frac{1}{4} \quad \text{and} \quad y = -\frac{1}{4}x^2$$ (6-3)

30.

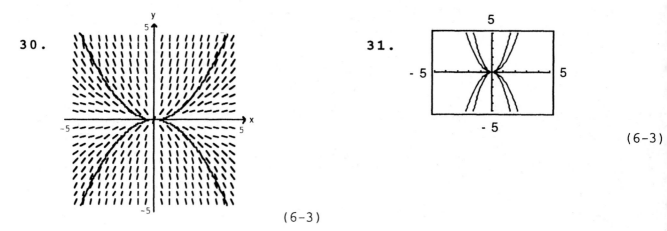

(6-3)

31.

(6-3)

32. $\displaystyle\int_{-1}^{1} \sqrt{1 + x}\,dx = \int_0^2 u^{1/2}\,du = \dfrac{u^{3/2}}{3/2}\bigg|_0^2 = \dfrac{2}{3}(2)^{3/2} \approx 1.886$

   Let $u = 1 + x$
   $du = dx$
   when $x = -1$, $u = 0$,
   when $x = 1$, $u = 2$ (6-5)

33. $\int_{-1}^{0} x^2(x^3+2)^{-2}dx = \int_{-1}^{0}(x^3+2)^{-2}\left(\frac{3}{3}\right)x^2dx = \frac{1}{3}\int_{-1}^{0}(x^3+2)^{-2}3x^2dx$

> Let $u = x^3 + 2$ $\qquad\qquad\qquad = \frac{1}{3}\int_{1}^{2}u^{-2}du$
> Then $du = 3x^2dx$
> When $x = -1$, $u = 1$ $\qquad\qquad = \frac{1}{3}\cdot\frac{u^{-1}}{-1}\Big]_{1}^{2} = -\frac{1}{3u}\Big]_{1}^{2}$
> when $x = 0$, $u = 2$
>
> $\qquad\qquad\qquad\qquad\qquad\qquad\quad = -\frac{1}{6} + \frac{1}{3} = \frac{1}{6}$

34. $\int 5e^{-t}dt = -\int 5e^{-t}(-dt) = -5\int e^{u}du = -5e^{u} + C$

> Let $u = -t$ $\qquad\qquad\qquad = -5e^{-t} + C$
> Then $du = -dt$

$\qquad\qquad\qquad\qquad\qquad\qquad\qquad\qquad\qquad\qquad\qquad\qquad\qquad\quad$ (6-2)

35. $\int_{1}^{e}\frac{1+t^2}{t}dt = \int_{1}^{e}\left(\frac{1}{t}+t\right)dt = \int_{1}^{e}\frac{1}{t}dt + \int_{1}^{e}tdt$

$\qquad\qquad\qquad\qquad = \ln t\Big]_{1}^{e} + \frac{1}{2}t^2\Big]_{1}^{e}$

$\qquad\qquad\qquad\qquad = \ln e - \ln 1 + \frac{1}{2}e^2 - \frac{1}{2}$

$\qquad\qquad\qquad\qquad = \frac{1}{2} + \frac{1}{2}e^2$

$\qquad\qquad\qquad\qquad\qquad\qquad\qquad\qquad\qquad\qquad\qquad\qquad\qquad\quad$ (6-5)

36. $\int xe^{3x^2}dx = \int e^{3x^2}\frac{6}{6}xdx = \frac{1}{6}\int e^{u}du = \frac{1}{6}e^{u} + C$

> Let $u = 3x^2$ $\qquad\qquad\qquad\qquad = \frac{1}{6}e^{3x^2} + C$
>
> Then $du = 6xdx$

$\qquad\qquad\qquad\qquad\qquad\qquad\qquad\qquad\qquad\qquad\qquad\qquad\qquad\quad$ (6-2)

37. $\int_{-3}^{1}\frac{1}{\sqrt{2-x}}dx = -\int_{-3}^{1}\frac{1}{\sqrt{2-x}}(-dx) = -\int_{5}^{1}u^{-1/2}du$

> Let $u = 2 - x$ $\qquad\qquad\qquad\qquad = \int_{1}^{5}u^{-1/2}du$
> Then $du = -dx$
> When $x = -3$, $u = 5$ $\qquad\qquad = 2u^{1/2}\Big]_{1}^{5}$
> when $x = 1$, $u = 1$
> $\qquad\qquad\qquad\qquad\qquad\qquad = 2\sqrt{5} - 2 \approx 2.472$

$\qquad\qquad\qquad\qquad\qquad\qquad\qquad\qquad\qquad\qquad\qquad\qquad\qquad\quad$ (6-5)

38. Let $u = 1 + x^2$, then $du = 2x\,dx$.

$\int_{0}^{3}\frac{x}{1+x^2}dx = \int_{0}^{3}\frac{1}{1+x^2}\frac{2}{2}x\,dx$

$\qquad\qquad\quad = \frac{1}{2}\int_{0}^{3}\frac{1}{1+x^2}\frac{2}{2}2x\,dx = \frac{1}{2}\ln(1 + x^2)\Big|_{0}^{3}$

$\qquad\qquad\quad = \frac{1}{2}\ln 10 - \frac{1}{2}\ln 1 = \frac{1}{2}\ln 10 \approx 1.151$

$\qquad\qquad\qquad\qquad\qquad\qquad\qquad\qquad\qquad\qquad\qquad\qquad\qquad\quad$ (6-5)

39. Let $u = 1 + x^2$, then $du = 2x\,dx$.

$$\int_0^3 \frac{x}{(1+x^2)^2}\,dx = \int_0^3 (1+x^2)^{-2}\frac{2}{2}x\,dx = \frac{1}{2}\int_0^3 (1+x^2)^{-2}\,2x\,dx$$

$$= \frac{1}{2}\cdot\frac{(1+x^2)^{-1}}{-1}\Big|_0^3 = \frac{-1}{2(1+x^2)}\Big|_0^3 = -\frac{1}{20} + \frac{1}{2} = \frac{9}{20} = 0.45$$

(6-5)

40. Let $u = 2x^4 + 5$, then $du = 8x^3\,dx$.

$$\int x^3 (2x^4 + 5)^5\,dx = \int (2x^4 + 5)^5 x^3\,dx = \frac{1}{8}\int u^5\,du$$

$$= \frac{1}{8}\cdot\frac{u^6}{6} + C = \frac{(2x^4 + 5)^6}{48} + C$$

(6-2)

41. Let $u = e^{-x} + 3$, then $du = -e^{-x}dx$.

$$\int \frac{e^{-x}}{e^{-x} + 3}\,dx = \int \frac{1}{e^{-x} + 3}\cdot\frac{(-1)}{(-1)}e^{-x}\,dx = -\int \frac{1}{u}\,du$$

$$= -\ln|u| + C = -\ln|e^{-x} + 3| + C = -\ln(e^{-x} + 3) + C$$

[<u>Note</u>: Absolute value not needed since $e^{-x} + 3 > 0$.]

(6-2)

42. Let $u = e^x + 2$, then $du = e^x dx$.

$$\int \frac{e^x}{(e^x + 2)^2}\,dx = \int (e^x + 2)^{-2}e^x\,dx = \int u^{-2}\,du$$

$$= \frac{u^{-1}}{-1} + C = -(e^x + 2)^{-1} + C = \frac{-1}{(e^x + 2)} + C$$

(6-2)

43. $\dfrac{dy}{dx} = 3x^{-1} - x^{-2}$

$$y = \int (3x^{-1} - x^{-2})\,dx = 3\int \frac{1}{x}\,dx - \int x^{-2}\,dx$$

$$= 3\ln|x| - \frac{x^{-1}}{-1} + C = 3\ln|x| + x^{-1} + C$$

Given $y(1) = 5$:

$5 = 3\ln 1 + 1 + C$ and $C = 4$

Thus, $y = 3\ln|x| + x^{-1} + 4$.

(6-2, 6-3)

44. $\dfrac{dy}{dx} = 6x + 1$

$$f(x) = y = \int (6x + 1)\,dx = \frac{6x^2}{2} + x + C = 3x^2 + x + C$$

We have $y = 10$ when $x = 2$: $3(2)^2 + 2 + C = 10$

$$C = 10 - 12 - 2 = -4$$

Thus, the equation of the curve is $y = 3x^2 + x - 4$.

(6-3)

45. (A) $f(x) = 3\sqrt{x} = 3x^{1/2}$ on $[1, 9]$

Avg. $f(x) = \dfrac{1}{9-1}\displaystyle\int_1^9 3x^{1/2}dx$

$= \dfrac{3}{8}\cdot\dfrac{x^{3/2}}{3/2}\Big|_1^9 = \dfrac{1}{4}x^{3/2}\Big|_1^9$

$= \dfrac{27}{4} - \dfrac{1}{4} = \dfrac{26}{4} = 6.5$

(B)

$(6-5)$

46. Let $u = \ln x$, then $du = \dfrac{1}{x}dx$.

$\displaystyle\int\dfrac{(\ln x)^2}{x}dx = \int(\ln x)^2\dfrac{1}{x}dx = \int u^2 du = \dfrac{u^3}{3} + C = \dfrac{(\ln x)^3}{3} + C$ $\qquad(6-2)$

47. $\displaystyle\int x(x^3 - 1)^2 dx = \int x(x^6 - 2x^3 + 1)dx$ $\quad$ (square $x^3 - 1$)

$= \displaystyle\int(x^7 - 2x^4 + x)dx = \dfrac{x^8}{8} - \dfrac{2x^5}{5} + \dfrac{x^2}{2} + C$ $\qquad(6-2)$

48. Let $u = 6 - x$, then $x = 6 - u$ and $dx = -du$.

$\displaystyle\int\dfrac{x}{\sqrt{6-x}}dx = -\int\dfrac{(6-u)du}{u^{1/2}} = \int(u^{1/2} - 6u^{-1/2})du$

$= \dfrac{u^{3/2}}{3/2} - \dfrac{6u^{1/2}}{1/2} + C = \dfrac{2}{3}u^{3/2} - 12u^{1/2} + C$

$= \dfrac{2}{3}(6-x)^{3/2} - 12(6-x)^{1/2} + C$ $\qquad(6-2)$

49. $\displaystyle\int_0^7 x\sqrt{16-x}\,dx$. First consider the indefinite integral:

Let $u = 16 - x$, then $x = 16 - u$ and $dx = -du$.

$\displaystyle\int x\sqrt{16-x}\,dx = -\int(16-u)u^{1/2}du = \int(u^{3/2} - 16u^{1/2})du = \dfrac{u^{5/2}}{5/2} - \dfrac{16u^{3/2}}{3/2} + C$

$= \dfrac{2}{5}u^{5/2} - \dfrac{32}{3}u^{3/2} + C = \dfrac{2(16-x)^{5/2}}{5} - \dfrac{32(16-x)^{3/2}}{3} + C$

$\displaystyle\int_0^7 x\sqrt{16-x}\,dx = \left[\dfrac{2(16-x)^{5/2}}{5} - \dfrac{32(16-x)^{3/2}}{3}\right]\Big|_0^7$

$= \dfrac{2\cdot 9^{5/2}}{5} - \dfrac{32\cdot 9^{3/2}}{3} - \left(\dfrac{2\cdot 16^{5/2}}{5} - \dfrac{32\cdot 16^{3/2}}{3}\right)$

$= \dfrac{2\cdot 3^5}{5} - \dfrac{32\cdot 3^3}{3} - \left(\dfrac{2\cdot 4^5}{5} - \dfrac{32\cdot 4^3}{3}\right)$

$= \dfrac{486}{5} - 288 - \left(\dfrac{2048}{5} - \dfrac{2048}{3}\right) = \dfrac{1234}{15} \approx 82.267$ $\qquad(6-5)$

50. Let $u = x + 1$, then $x = u - 1$, $dx = du$; and $u = 0$ when $x = -1$, $u = 2$ when $x = 1$.

$$\int_{-1}^{1} x(x + 1)^4 dx = \int_{0}^{2} (u - 1)u^4 du = \int_{0}^{2} (u^5 - u^4)du$$

$$= \left[\frac{u^6}{6} - \frac{u^5}{5}\right]\Bigg|_{0}^{2} = \frac{2^6}{6} - \frac{2^5}{5} = \frac{32}{3} - \frac{32}{5}$$

$$= \frac{160 - 96}{15} = \frac{64}{15} \approx 4.267 \qquad (6-5)$$

51. $\frac{dy}{dx} = 9x^2 e^{x^3}$, $f(0) = 2$

Let $u = x^3$, then $du = 3x^2 dx$.

$y = \int 9x^2 e^{x^3} dx = 3\int e^{x^3} \cdot 3x^2 dx = 3\int e^u du = 3e^u + C = 3e^{x^3} + C$

Given $f(0) = 2$:

$2 = 3e^0 + C = 3 + C$

Hence, $C = -1$ and $y = f(x) = 3e^{x^3} - 1$. $\qquad (6-3)$

52. $\frac{dN}{dt} = 0.06N$, $N(0) = 800$, $N > 0$

From the differential equation, $N(t) = Ce^{0.06t}$, where C is an arbitrary constant. Since $N(0) = 800$, we have

$\qquad 800 = Ce^0 = C$.

Hence, $C = 800$ and $N(t) = 800e^{0.06t}$. $\qquad (6-3)$

53. $N = 50(1 - e^{-0.07t})$,
$0 \le t \le 80$, $0 \le N \le 60$

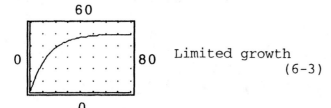

Limited growth

$(6-3)$

54. $p = 500e^{-0.03x}$,
$0 \le x \le 100$, $0 \le p \le 500$

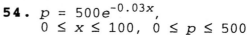
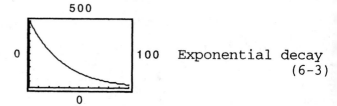

Exponential decay

$(6-3)$

55. $A = 200e^{0.08t}$,
$0 \le t \le 20$, $0 \le A \le 1{,}000$

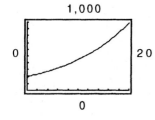

Unlimited growth

$(6-3)$

56. $N = \dfrac{100}{1 + 9e^{-0.3t}}$,
$0 \le t \le 25$, $0 \le N \le 100$

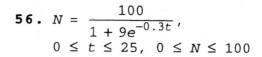
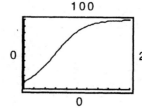

Logistic growth

$(6-3)$

57. $\int_{-0.5}^{0.6} \dfrac{1}{\sqrt{1-x^2}}\, dx \approx 1.167$

```
fnInt(Y₁,X, -0.5,
0.6)
        1.167099884
■
```

(6-5)

58. $\int_{-2}^{3} x^2 e^x dx \approx 99.074$

```
fnInt(Y₁,X, -2,3)
        99.07433178
```

(6-5)

59. $\int_{0.5}^{2.5} \dfrac{\ln x}{x^2}\, dx \approx -0.153$

```
fnInt(Y₁,X,0.5,2
.5)
        -.1528106539
■
```

(6-5)

60. $a = 200$, $b = 600$, $n = 2$, $\Delta x = \dfrac{600 - 200}{2} = 200$

$$L_2 = C'(200)\Delta x + C'(400)\Delta x$$
$$= [500 + 400]200 = \$180,000$$

$$R_2 = C'(400)\Delta x + C'(600)\Delta x$$
$$= [400 + 300]200 = \$140,000$$
$$140,000 \leq \int_{200}^{600} C'(x)dx \leq 180,000$$

(6-4)

61. The graph of $C'(x)$ is a straight line with y-intercept = 600 and

$$\text{slope} = \frac{300 - 600}{600 - 0} = -\frac{1}{2}$$

Thus, $C'(x) = -\dfrac{1}{2}x + 600$

Increase in costs:
$$\int_{200}^{600}\left(600 - \frac{1}{2}x\right)dx = \left(600x - \frac{1}{4}x^2\right)\Big|_{200}^{600}$$
$$= 270,000 - 110,000$$
$$= \$160,000$$

(6-5)

62. The total change in profit for a production change from 10 units per week to 40 units per week is given by:

$$\int_{10}^{40}\left(150 - \frac{x}{10}\right)dx = \left(150x - \frac{x^2}{20}\right)\Big|_{10}^{40}$$
$$= \left(150(40) - \frac{40^2}{20}\right) - \left(150(10) - \frac{10^2}{20}\right)$$
$$= 5920 - 1495 = \$4425$$

(6-5)

63. $P'(x) = 100 - 0.02x$

$P(x) = \int (100 - 0.02x)\,dx = 100x - 0.02\dfrac{x^2}{2} + C = 100x - 0.01x^2 + C$

$P(0) = 0 - 0 + C = 0$

$\qquad\qquad\quad C = 0$

Thus, $P(x) = 100x - 0.01x^2$.
The profit on 10 units of production is given by:

$P(10) = 100(10) - 0.01(10)^2 = \$999$ \hfill (6-3)

64. The required definite integral is:

$\displaystyle\int_0^{15} (60 - 4t)\,dt = (60t - 2t^2)\Big|_0^{15}$

$\qquad\qquad\qquad\qquad = 60(15) - 2(15)^2 = 450$ or $450{,}000$ barrels

The total production in 15 years is $450{,}000$ barrels. \hfill (6-5)

65. Average inventory from $t = 3$ to $t = 6$:

$\text{Avg. } I(t) = \dfrac{1}{6-3}\displaystyle\int_3^6 (10 + 36t - 3t^2)\,dt$

$\qquad\qquad = \dfrac{1}{3}[10t + 18t^2 - t^3]\Big|_3^6$

$\qquad\qquad = \dfrac{1}{3}[60 + 648 - 216 - (30 + 162 - 27)]$

$\qquad\qquad = 109$ items \hfill (6-5)

66. $S(x) = 8(e^{0.05x} - 1)$

Average price over the interval $[40, 50]$:

$\text{Avg. } S(x) = \dfrac{1}{50-40}\displaystyle\int_{40}^{50} 8(e^{0.05x} - 1)\,dx = \dfrac{8}{10}\displaystyle\int_{40}^{50} (e^{0.05x} - 1)\,dx$

$\qquad\qquad\qquad = \dfrac{4}{5}\left[\dfrac{e^{0.05x}}{0.05} - x\right]\Big|_{40}^{50}$

$\qquad\qquad\qquad = \dfrac{4}{5}[20e^{2.5} - 50 - (20e^2 - 40)]$

$\qquad\qquad\qquad = 16e^{2.5} - 16e^2 - 8 \approx \$68.70$ \hfill (6-5)

67. To find the useful life, set $R'(t) = C'(t)$:

$20e^{-0.1t} = 3$

$e^{-0.1t} = \dfrac{3}{20}$

$-0.1t = \ln\left(\dfrac{3}{20}\right) \approx -1.897$

$\qquad t = 18.97$ or 19 years

$\text{Total profit} = \displaystyle\int_0^{19} [R'(t) - C(t)]\,dt = \int_0^{19} (20e^{-0.1t} - 3)\,dt$

$\qquad\qquad = 20\displaystyle\int_0^{19} e^{-0.1t}(-0.1)\,dt - \int_0^{19} 3\,dt = \dfrac{20}{-0.1}\int_0^{19} e^{-0.1t}(-0.1)\,dt - \int_0^{19} 3\,dt$

$\qquad\qquad = -200e^{-0.1t}\Big|_0^{19} - 3t\Big|_0^{19}$

$\qquad\qquad = -200e^{-1.9} + 200 - 57 \approx 113.086$ or $\$113{,}086$ \hfill (6-5)

68. $S'(t) = 4e^{-0.08t}$, $0 \le t \le 24$. Therefore,

$$S(t) = \int 4e^{-0.08t}dt = \frac{4e^{-0.08t}}{-0.08} + C = -50e^{-0.08t} + C.$$

Now, $S(0) = 0$, so

$$0 = -50e^{-0.08(0)} + C = -50 + C.$$

Thus, $C = 50$, and $S(t) = 50(1 - e^{-0.08t})$ gives the total sales after t months.

Estimated sales after 12 months:

$$S(12) = 50(1 - e^{-0.08(12)}) = 50(1 - e^{-0.96}) \approx 31 \text{ or } \$31 \text{ million.}$$

To find the time to reach \$40 million in sales, solve

$$40 = 50(1 - e^{-0.08t})$$

for t.

$$0.8 = 1 - e^{-0.08t}$$
$$e^{-0.08t} = 0.2$$
$$-0.08t = \ln(0.2)$$
$$t = \frac{\ln(0.2)}{-0.08} \approx 20 \text{ months} \tag{6-3}$$

69. $\dfrac{dA}{dt} = -5t^{-2}$, $1 \le t \le 5$

$$A = \int -5t^{-2}dt = -5\int t^{-2}dt = -5 \cdot \frac{t^{-1}}{-1} + C = \frac{5}{t} + C$$

Now $A(1) = \dfrac{5}{1} + C = 5$. Therefore, $C = 0$ and

$$A(t) = \frac{5}{t}$$

$$A(5) = \frac{5}{5} = 1$$

The area of the wound after 5 days is 1 cm^2. $\tag{6-3}$

70. The total amount of seepage during the first four years is given by:

$$T = \int_0^4 R(t)dt = \int_0^4 \frac{1000}{1 + t^2}dt = 1000\int_0^4 (1 + t)^{-2}dt = 1000\left.\frac{(1 + t)^{-1}}{-1}\right|_0^4$$

$$[\text{Let } u = 1 + t, \text{ then } du = dt.] = \left.\frac{-1000}{1 + t}\right|_0^4 = \frac{-1000}{5} + 1000 = 800 \text{ gallons}$$

$\tag{6-5}$

71. (A) The exponential growth law applies and we have:

$$\frac{dP}{dt} = 0.015P, \quad P(0) = 100 \text{ (million)}$$

Thus $P(t) = 100e^{0.015t}$

and $P(25) = 100e^{0.015(25)} = 100e^{0.375} \approx 145$

Assuming that the population continues to grow at the rate 1.5% per year, the population in 2025 will be approximately 145 million.

(B) Time to double:
$$100e^{0.015t} = 200$$
$$e^{0.015t} = 2$$
$$0.015t = \ln 2$$
$$t = \frac{\ln 2}{0.015} \approx 46$$

At the current growth rate it will take approximately 46 years for the population to double. (6-3)

72. Let $Q = Q(t)$ be the amount of carbon-14 present in the bone at time t. Then,
$$\frac{dQ}{dt} = -0.0001238Q \quad \text{and} \quad Q(t) = Q_0 e^{-0.0001238t},$$
where Q_0 is the amount present originally (i.e., at the time the animal died). We want to find t such that $Q(t) = 0.04Q_0$.
$$0.04Q_0 = Q_0 e^{-0.0001238t}$$
$$e^{-0.0001238t} = 0.04$$
$$-0.0001238t = \ln 0.04$$
$$t = \frac{\ln 0.04}{-0.0001238} \approx 26,000 \text{ years}$$
(6-3)

73. $N'(t) = 7e^{-0.1t}$ and $N(0) = 25$.
$$N(t) = \int 7e^{-0.1t}dt = 7\int e^{-0.1t}dt = \frac{7}{-0.1}\int e^{-0.1t}(-0.1)\,dt$$
$$= -70e^{-0.1t} + C, \quad 0 \leq t \leq 15$$
Given $N(0) = 25$: $25 = -70e^0 + C = -70 + C$

Hence, $C = 95$ and $N(t) = 95 - 70e^{-0.1t}$. The student would be expected to type $N(15) = 95 - 70e^{-0.1(15)} = 95 - 70e^{-1.5} \approx 79$ words per minute after completing the course. (6-3)

5 Additional Integration Topics

Things to remember:

1. AREA BETWEEN TWO CURVES
    If f and g are continuous and $f(x) \geq g(x)$ over the interval $[a, b]$, then the area bounded by $y = f(x)$ and $y = g(x)$, for $a \leq x \leq b$, is given exactly by:

    $$A = \int_a^b [f(x) - g(x)] dx.$$

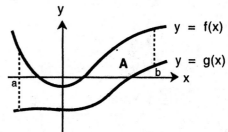

2. GINI INDEX OF INCOME CONCENTRATION
    If $y = f(x)$ is the equation of a Lorenz curve, then the
    $$\text{Gini Index} = 2\int_0^1 [x - f(x)] dx.$$

---

1. $A = \int_a^b g(x) dx$

3. $A = \int_a^b [-h(x)] dx)$

5. Since the shaded region in Figure (c) is below the x-axis, $h(x) \leq 0$. Thus, $\int_a^b h(x) dx$ represents the negative of the area of the region.

7. $A = \int_0^4 -[-2x - 1] dx$

$= \int_0^4 [2x + 1] dx = (x^2 + x)\Big|_0^4 = 20$

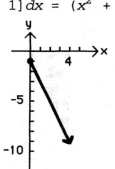

9. $A = \int_{-1}^0 (x^2 + 2) dx = \left(\dfrac{x^3}{3} + 2x\right)\Big|_{-1}^0$

$= 0 - \left(-\dfrac{1}{3} - 2\right) = \dfrac{7}{3} \approx 2.333$

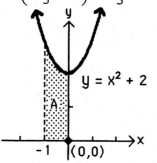

11. $A = \int_0^2 [x^3 + 1] dx = \left(\dfrac{1}{4}x^4 + x\right)\Big|_0^2 = 4 + 2 = 6$

13. $A = \int_{-1}^{2} e^x dx = e^x \Big|_{-1}^{2}$

$= e^2 - e^{-1} \approx 7.021$

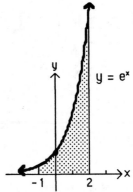

15. $A = \int_{0.5}^{1} -\left[-\frac{1}{t}\right] dt = \int_{0.5}^{1} \frac{1}{t} dt = \ln t \Big|_{0.5}^{1} = \ln 1 - \ln(0.5) \approx 0.693$

17. $A = \int_{a}^{b} [-f(x)] dx)$

19. $a = \int_{b}^{c} f(x) dx + \int_{c}^{d} [-f(x)] dx$

21. $A = \int_{c}^{d} [f(x) - g(x)] dx$

23. $A = \int_{a}^{b} [f(x) - g(x)] dx + \int_{b}^{c} [g(x) - f(x)] dx$

25. Find the x-coordinates of the points of intersection of the two curves on $[a, d]$ by solving the equation $f(x) = g(x)$, $a \le x \le d$, to find $x = b$ and $x = c$. Then note that $f(x) \ge g(x)$ on $[a, b]$, $g(x) \ge f(x)$ on $[b, c]$ and $f(x) \ge g(x)$ on $[c, d]$.

Thus,
$$\text{Area} = \int_{a}^{b} [f(x) - g(x)] dx + \int_{b}^{c} [g(x) - f(x)] dx + \int_{c}^{d} [f(x) - g(x)] dx$$

27. $A = A_1 + A_2 = \int_{-2}^{0} -x dx + \int_{0}^{1} -(-x) dx$

$= \int_{-2}^{0} x dx + \int_{0}^{1} x dx$

$= -\frac{x^2}{2}\Big|_{-2}^{0} + \frac{x^2}{2}\Big|_{0}^{1}$

$= -\left(0 - \frac{(-2)^2}{2}\right) + \left(\frac{1^2}{2} - 0\right)$

$= 2 + \frac{1}{2} = \frac{5}{2} = 2.5$

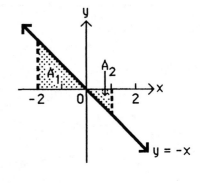

29. $A = A_1 + A_2 = \int_{0}^{2} -(x^2 - 4) dx + \int_{2}^{3} (x^2 - 4) dx$

$= \int_{0}^{2} (4 - x^2) dx + \int_{2}^{3} (x^2 - 4) dx$

$= \left(4x - \frac{x^3}{3}\right)\Big|_{0}^{2} + \left(\frac{x^3}{3} - 4x\right)\Big|_{2}^{3}$

$= \left(8 - \frac{8}{3}\right) + \left(\frac{27}{3} - 12\right) - \left(\frac{8}{3} - 8\right)$

$= 13 - \frac{16}{3} = \frac{39}{3} - \frac{16}{3} = \frac{23}{3} \approx 7.667$

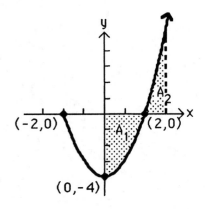

31. $A = A_1 + A_2 = \int_{-2}^{0} (x^2 - 3x)\,dx + \int_{0}^{2} -(x^2 - 3x)\,dx$

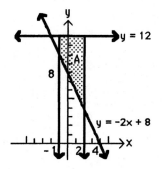

$$= \int_{-2}^{0} (x^2 - 3x)\,dx + \int_{0}^{2} (3x - x^2)\,dx$$

$$= \left(\frac{1}{3}x^3 - \frac{3}{2}x^2\right)\Big|_{-2}^{0} + \left(\frac{3}{2}x^2 - \frac{1}{3}x^3\right)\Big|_{0}^{2}$$

$$= 0 - \left(-\frac{8}{3} - 6\right) + \left(6 - \frac{8}{3}\right) - 0 = 12$$

33. $A = \int_{-1}^{2} [12 - (-2x + 8)]\,dx = \int_{-1}^{2} (2x + 4)\,dx$

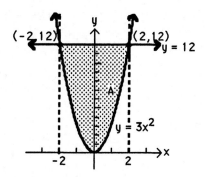

$$= \left(\frac{2x^2}{2} + 4x\right)\Big|_{-1}^{2} = (x^2 + 4x)\Big|_{-1}^{2}$$

$$= (4 + 8) - (1 - 4)$$

$$= 12 + 3 = 15$$

35. $A = \int_{-2}^{2} (12 - 3x^2)\,dx = \left(12x - \frac{3x^3}{3}\right)\Big|_{-2}^{2}$

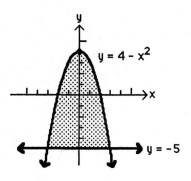

$$= (12x - x^3)\Big|_{-2}^{2}$$

$$= (12 \cdot 2 - 2^3) - [12 \cdot (-2) - (-2)^3]$$

$$= 16 - (-16) = 32$$

37. $(3, -5)$ and $(-3, -5)$ are the points of intersection.

$$A = \int_{-3}^{3} [4 - x^2 - (-5)]\,dx$$

$$= \int_{-3}^{3} (9 - x^2)\,dx = \left(9x - \frac{x^3}{3}\right)\Big|_{-3}^{3}$$

$$= \left(9 \cdot 3 - \frac{3^3}{3}\right) - \left(9(-3) - \frac{(-3)^3}{3}\right)$$

$$= 18 + 18 = 36$$

39. $A = \int_{-1}^{2} [(x^2 + 1) - (2x - 2)] \, dx$

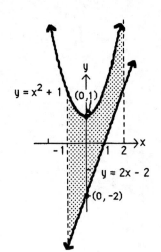

$= \int_{-1}^{2} (x^2 - 2x + 3) \, dx = \left(\dfrac{x^3}{3} - x^2 + 3x \right) \Bigg|_{-1}^{2}$

$= \left(\dfrac{8}{3} - 4 + 6 \right) - \left(-\dfrac{1}{3} - 1 - 3 \right)$

$= 3 - 4 + 6 + 1 + 3 = 9$

41. $A = \int_{1}^{2} \left[e^{0.5x} - \left(-\dfrac{1}{x} \right) \right] dx$

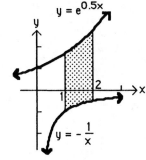

$= \int_{1}^{2} \left(e^{0.5x} + \dfrac{1}{x} \right) dx$

$= \left(\dfrac{e^{0.5x}}{0.5} + \ln|x| \right) \Bigg|_{1}^{2}$

$= 2e + \ln 2 - 2e^{0.5}$

≈ 2.832

43. The graphs of $y = 3 - 5x - 2x^2$ and $y = 2x^2 + 3x - 2$ are shown at the right. The x-coordinates of the points of intersection are: $x_1 = -2.5$, $x_2 = 0.5$.

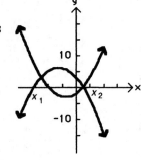

$A = \int_{-2.5}^{0.5} [(3 - 5x - 2x^2) - (2x^2 + 3x - 2)] \, dx$

$= \int_{-2.5}^{0.5} (5 - 8x - 4x^2) \, dx = \left(5x - 4x^2 - \dfrac{4}{3} x^3 \right) \Bigg|_{-2.5}^{0.5}$

$= 1.333 + 16.667 = 18$

45. The graphs of $y = -0.5x + 2.25$ and $y = \dfrac{1}{x}$ are shown below. The x-coordinates of the points of intersection are: $x_1 = 0.5$, $x_2 = 4$.

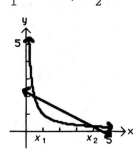

$A = \int_{0.5}^{4} \left[(-0.5x + 2.25) - \left(\dfrac{1}{x} \right) \right] dx$

$= \left(-\dfrac{1}{4} x^2 + \dfrac{9}{4} x - \ln x \right) \Bigg|_{0.5}^{4}$

$= [-4 + 9 - \ln 4] - [-0.0625 + 1.125 - \ln(0.5)]$

≈ 1.858

47. The graphs of $y = e^x$ and $y = e^{-x}$, $0 \le x \le 4$, are shown at the right.

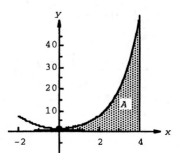

$$A = \int_0^4 (e^x - e^{-x})\, dx = (e^x + e^{-x})\Big|_0^4$$

$$= e^4 + e^{-4} - (1 + 1)$$

$$\approx 52.616$$

49. The graphs are given at the right. To find the points of intersection, solve:

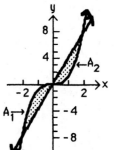

$$x^3 = 4x$$
$$x^3 - 4x = 0$$
$$x(x^2 - 4) = 0$$
$$x(x + 2)(x - 2) = 0$$

Thus, the points of intersection are $(-2, -8)$, $(0, 0)$, and $(2, 8)$.

$$A = A_1 + A_2 = \int_{-2}^0 (x^3 - 4x)\, dx + \int_0^2 (4x - x^3)\, dx$$

$$= \left(\frac{x^4}{4} - 2x^2\right)\Big|_{-2}^0 + \left(2x^2 - \frac{x^4}{4}\right)\Big|_0^2$$

$$= 0 - \left[\frac{(-2)^4}{4} - 2(-2)^2\right] + \left[2(2^2) - \frac{2^4}{4}\right] - 0$$

$$= -4 + 8 + 8 - 4 = 8$$

51. The graphs are given at the right. To find the points of intersection, solve:

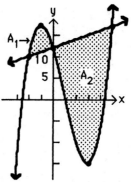

$$x^3 - 3x^2 - 9x + 12 = x + 12$$
$$x^3 - 3x^2 - 10x = 0$$
$$x(x^2 - 3x - 10) = 0$$
$$x(x - 5)(x + 2) = 0$$
$$x = -2, \; x = 0, \; x = 5$$

Thus, $(-2, 10)$, $(0, 12)$, and $(5, 17)$ are the points of intersection.

$$A = A_1 + A_2$$

$$= \int_{-2}^0 [x^3 - 3x^2 - 9x + 12 - (x + 12)]\, dx$$

$$\qquad\qquad + \int_0^5 [x + 12 - (x^3 - 3x^2 - 9x + 12)]\, dx$$

$$= \int_{-2}^0 (x^3 - 3x^2 - 10x)\, dx + \int_0^5 (-x^3 + 3x^2 + 10x)\, dx$$

$$= \left(\frac{x^4}{4} - x^3 - 5x^2\right)\Big|_{-2}^0 + \left(-\frac{x^4}{4} + x^3 + 5x^2\right)\Big|_0^5$$

$$= -\left[\frac{(-2)^4}{4} - (-2)^3 - 5(-2)^2\right] + \left(\frac{-5^4}{4} + 5^3 + 5 \cdot 5^2\right)$$

$$= 8 + \frac{375}{4} = \frac{407}{4} = 101.75$$

53. The graphs are given at the right. To find the points of intersection, solve:

$$x^4 - 4x^2 + 1 = x^2 - 3$$
$$x^4 - 5x^2 + 4 = 0$$
$$(x^2 - 4)(x^2 - 1) = 0$$
$$x = -2, -1, 1, 2$$

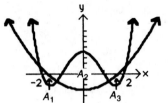

$A = A_1 + A_2 + A_3$

$= \int_{-2}^{-1} [(x^2 - 3) - (x^4 - 4x^2 + 1)] \, dx + \int_{-1}^{1} [(x^4 - 4x^2 + 1) - (x^2 - 3)] \, dx$

$\qquad + \int_{1}^{2} [(x^2 - 3) - (x^4 - 4x^2 + 1)] \, dx$

$= \int_{-2}^{-1} (-x^4 + 5x^2 - 4) \, dx + \int_{-1}^{1} (x^4 - 5x^2 + 4) \, dx + \int_{1}^{2} (-x^4 + 5x^2 - 4) \, dx$

$= \left(-\dfrac{x^5}{5} + \dfrac{5}{3} x^3 - 4x \right)\Big|_{-2}^{-1} + \left(\dfrac{x^5}{5} - \dfrac{5}{3} x^3 + 4x \right)\Big|_{-1}^{1} + \left(-\dfrac{x^5}{5} + \dfrac{5}{3} x^3 - 4x \right)\Big|_{1}^{2}$

$= \left(\dfrac{1}{5} - \dfrac{5}{3} + 4 \right) - \left(\dfrac{32}{5} - \dfrac{40}{3} + 8 \right) + \left(\dfrac{1}{5} - \dfrac{5}{3} + 4 \right) - \left(-\dfrac{1}{5} + \dfrac{5}{3} - 4 \right)$

$\qquad + \left(-\dfrac{32}{5} + \dfrac{40}{3} - 8 \right) - \left(-\dfrac{1}{5} + \dfrac{5}{3} - 4 \right) = 8$

55. The graphs are given below. The x-coordinates of the points of intersection are: $x_1 = -2$, $x_2 = 0.5$, $x_3 = 2$

$A = A_1 + A_2$

$= \int_{-2}^{0.5} [(x^3 - x^2 + 2) - (-x^3 + 8x - 2)] \, dx$

$\qquad + \int_{0.5}^{2} [(-x^3 + 8x - 2) - (x^3 - x^2 + 2)] \, dx$

$= \int_{-2}^{0.5} (2x^3 - x^2 - 8x + 4) \, dx + \int_{0.5}^{2} (-2x^3 + x^2 + 8x - 4) \, dx$

$= \left(\dfrac{1}{2} x^4 - \dfrac{1}{3} x^3 - 4x^2 + 4x \right)\Big|_{-2}^{0.5} + \left(-\dfrac{1}{2} x^4 + \dfrac{1}{3} x^3 + 4x^2 - 4x \right)\Big|_{0.5}^{2}$

$= \left(\dfrac{1}{32} - \dfrac{1}{24} - 1 + 2 \right) - \left(8 + \dfrac{8}{3} - 16 - 8 \right)$

$\qquad + \left(-8 + \dfrac{8}{3} + 16 - 8 \right) - \left(-\dfrac{1}{32} + \dfrac{1}{24} + 1 - 2 \right)$

$= 18 + \dfrac{1}{16} - \dfrac{1}{12} \approx 17.979$

57. The graphs are given at the right. The x-coordinates of the points of intersection are: $x_1 \approx -1.924$, $x_2 \approx 1.373$

$$A = \int_{-1.924}^{1.373} [(3 - 2x) - e^{-x}]\,dx$$

$$= (3x - x^2 + e^{-x})\Big|_{-1.924}^{1.373}$$

$$\approx 2.487 - (-2.626) = 5.113$$

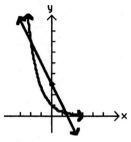

59. The graphs are given at the right. The x-coordinates of the points of intersection are: $x_1 \approx -2.247$, $x_2 \approx 0.264$, $x_3 \approx 1.439$

$$A = A_1 + A_2 = \int_{-2.247}^{0.264} [e^x - (5x - x^3)]\,dx$$

$$+ \int_{0.264}^{1.439} [5x - x^3 - e^x]\,dx$$

$$= \left(e^x - \frac{5}{2}x^2 + \frac{1}{4}x^4\right)\Big|_{-2.247}^{0.264} + \left(\frac{5}{2}x^2 - \frac{1}{4}x^4 - e^x\right)\Big|_{0.264}^{1.439}$$

$$\approx (1.129) - (-6.144) + (-0.112) - (-1.129) = 8.290$$

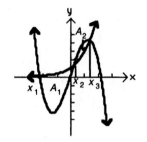

61. $y = e^{-x}$; $y = \sqrt{\ln x}$; $2 \leq x \leq 5$

The graphs of $y_1 = e^{-x}$ and $y_2 = \sqrt{\ln x}$ are

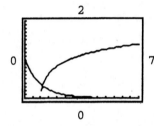

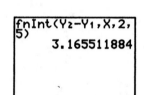

Thus, $A = \int_{2}^{5} (\sqrt{\ln x} - e^{-x})\,dx \approx 3.166$

63. $y = e^{x^2}$; $y = x + 2$

The graphs of $y_1 = e^{x^2}$ and $y_2 = x + 2$ are

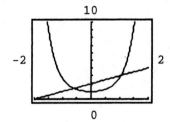

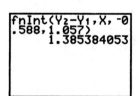

The curves intersect at

$x \approx -0.588 \qquad x \approx 1.057$

         and

$y \approx 1.412 \qquad y \approx 3.057$

$$\int_{-0.588}^{1.057} (x + 2 - e^{x^2})\,dx \approx 1.385$$

65. $\int_5^{10} R(t)\,dt = \int_5^{10}\left(\dfrac{100}{t+10}+10\right)dt = 100\int_5^{10}\dfrac{1}{t+10}\,dt + \int_5^{10}10\,dt$

$$= 100\,\ln(t+10)\Big|_5^{10} + 10t\Big|_5^{10}$$

$$= 100\,\ln 20 - 100\,\ln 15 + 10(10-5)$$

$$= 100\,\ln 20 - 100\,\ln 15 + 50 \approx 79$$

The total production from the end of the fifth year to the end of the tenth year is approximately 79 thousand barrels.

67. To find the useful life, set $R'(t) = C'(t)$ and solve for t:

$$9e^{-0.3t} = 2$$

$$e^{-0.3t} = \frac{2}{9}$$

$$-0.3t = \ln\frac{2}{9}$$

$$-0.3t \approx -1.5$$

$$t \approx 5 \text{ years}$$

$$\int_0^5 [R'(t) - C'(t)]\,dt] = \int_0^5 [9e^{-0.3t} - 2]\,dt$$

$$= 9\int_0^5 e^{-0.3t}\,dt - \int_0^5 2\,dt = \frac{9}{-0.3}\,e^{-0.3t}\Big|_0^5 - 2t\Big|_0^5$$

$$= -30e^{-1.5} + 30 - 10$$

$$= 20 - 30e^{-1.5} \approx 13.306$$

The total profit over the useful life of the game is approximately $13,306.

69. For 1935: $f(x) = x^{2.4}$

Gini Index $= 2\int_0^1 [x - f(x)] = 2\int_0^1 (x - x^{2.4})\,dx$

$$= 2\left(\frac{x^2}{2} - \frac{x^{3.4}}{3.4}\right)\Big|_0^1$$

$$= 2\left(\frac{1}{2} - \frac{1}{3.4}\right) \approx 0.412$$

For 1947: $g(x) = x^{1.6}$

Gini Index $= 2\int_0^1 [x - g(x)]\,dx = 2\int_0^1 (x - x^{1.6})\,dx$

$$= 2\left(\frac{x^2}{2} - \frac{x^{2.6}}{2.6}\right)\Big|_0^1$$

$$= 2\left(\frac{1}{2} - \frac{1}{2.6}\right) \approx 0.231$$

Interpretation: Income was more equally distributed in 1947.

71. For 1963: $f(x) = x^{10}$

$\text{Gini Index} = 2\int_0^1 [x - f(x)]\,dx = 2\int_0^1 (x - x^{10})\,dx$

$$= 2\left(\frac{x^2}{2} - \frac{x^{11}}{11}\right)\Big|_0^1$$

$$= 2\left(\frac{1}{2} - \frac{1}{11}\right) \approx 0.818$$

For 1983: $g(x) = x^{12}$

$\text{Gini Index} = 2\int_0^1 [x - g(x)]\,dx = 2\int_0^1 (x - x^{12})\,dx$

$$= 2\left(\frac{x^2}{2} - \frac{x^{13}}{13}\right)\Big|_0^1$$

$$= 2\left(\frac{1}{2} - \frac{1}{13}\right) \approx 0.846$$

Interpretation: Total assets were less equally distributed in 1983.

73. (A)

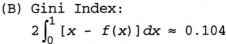

Lorenz curve:
$f(x) = 0.3125x^2 + 0.7175x - 0.015.$

(B) Gini Index:
$$2\int_0^1 [x - f(x)]\,dx \approx 0.104$$

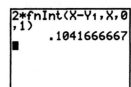

75. $W(t) = \int_0^{10} W'(t)\,dt = \int_0^{10} 0.3e^{0.1t}\,dt = 0.3\int_0^{10} e^{0.1t}\,dt$

$$= \frac{0.3}{0.1}\, e^{0.1t}\Big|_0^{10} = 3e^{0.1t}\Big|_0^{10} = 3e - 3 \approx 5.15$$

Total weight gain during the first 10 hours is approximately 5.15 grams.

77. $V = \int_2^4 \frac{15}{t}\,dt = 15\int_2^4 \frac{1}{t}\,dt = 15\,\ln t\Big|_2^4$

$$= 15\,\ln 4 - 15\,\ln 2 = 15\,\ln\left(\frac{4}{2}\right) = 15\,\ln 2 \approx 10$$

Average number of words learned during the second 2 hours is 10.

EXERCISE 5-2

Things to remember:

1. PROBABILITY DENSITY FUNCTION

   A function f which satisfies the following three conditions:
   a. $f(x) \geq 0$ for all real x.
   b. The area under the graph of f over the interval $(-\infty, \infty)$ is exactly 1.

<u>c</u>. If [c, d] is a subinterval of (-∞, ∞), then the probability that the outcome x of an experiment will be in the interval [c, d], denoted Probability (c ≤ x ≤ d), is given by

$$\text{Probability } (c \le x \le d) = \int_c^d f(x)\,dx$$

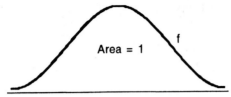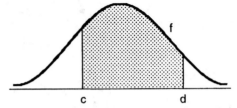

$$\int_c^d f(x)\,dx = \text{Probability } (c \le x \le d)$$

<u>2</u>. TOTAL INCOME FOR A CONTINUOUS INCOME STREAM

If $f(t)$ is the rate of flow of a continuous income stream, then the TOTAL INCOME produced during the time period from $t = a$ to $t = b$ is:

$$\text{Total income} = \int_a^b f(t)\,dt$$

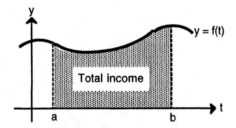

<u>3</u>. FUTURE VALUE OF A CONTINUOUS INCOME STREAM

If $f(t)$ is the rate of flow of a continuous income stream, $0 \le t \le T$, and if the income is continuously invested at a rate r, compounded continuously, then the FUTURE VALUE, FV, at the end of T years is given by:

$$FV = \int_0^T f(t)\,e^{r(T-t)}\,dt = e^{rT}\int_0^T f(t)\,e^{-rt}\,dt$$

The future value of a continuous income stream is the total value of all money produced by the continuous income stream (income and interest) at the end of T years.

<u>4</u>. CONSUMERS' SURPLUS

If $(\overline{x}, \overline{p})$ is a point on the graph of the price-demand equation $p = D(x)$ for a particular product, then the CONSUMERS' SURPLUS, CS, at a price level of $\overline{p}$ is

$$CS = \int_0^{\overline{x}} [D(x) - \overline{p}]\,dx$$

which is the area between $p = \overline{p}$ and $p = D(x)$ from $x = 0$ to $x = \overline{x}$.

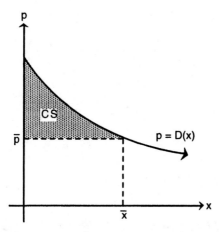

Consumers' surplus represents the total savings to consumers who are willing to pay more than $\overline{p}$ for the product but are still able to buy the product for $\overline{p}$.

5. PRODUCERS' SURPLUS

If $(\overline{x}, \overline{p})$ is a point on the graph of the price-supply equation $p = S(x)$, then the PRODUCERS' SURPLUS, PS, at a price level of $\overline{p}$ is

$$PS = \int_0^{\overline{x}} [\overline{p} - S(x)] \, dx$$

which is the area between $p = \overline{p}$ and $p = S(x)$ from $x = 0$ to $x = \overline{x}$.

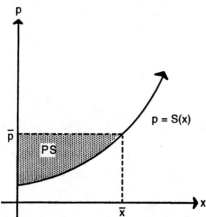

Producers' surplus represents the total gain to producers who are willing to supply units at a lower price than $\overline{p}$ but are still able to supply units at $\overline{p}$.

6. EQUILIBRIUM PRICE AND EQUILIBRIUM QUANTITY

If $p = D(x)$ and $p = S(x)$ are the price-demand and the price-supply equations, respectively, for a product and if $(\overline{x}, \overline{p})$ is the point of intersection of these equations, then $\overline{p}$ is called the EQUILIBRIUM PRICE and $\overline{x}$ is called the EQUILIBRIUM QUANTITY.

1. $\int_0^5 e^{-0.08t} dt = \dfrac{e^{-0.08t}}{-0.08} \Big|_0^5 = -12.5e^{-0.08t} \Big|_0^5$

$$= -12.5e^{-0.4} + 12.5$$
$$\approx -8.38 + 12.5 = 4.12$$

3. $\int_0^{30} e^{0.06t} \cdot e^{0.12(30-t)} dt = \int_0^{30} e^{0.06t} e^{3.6-0.12t} dt$

$$= \int_0^{30} e^{3.6-0.06t} dt = e^{3.6} \int_0^{30} e^{-0.06t} dt$$

$$= \dfrac{e^{3.6}}{-0.06} e^{-0.06t} \Big|_0^{30}$$

$$= -\dfrac{e^{3.6}}{0.06} [e^{-1.8} - 1] \approx 509.14$$

5. (A) $\int_0^8 e^{0.07(8-t)} dt = \int_0^8 e^{0.56 - 0.07} dt = \int_0^8 e^{0.56} \cdot e^{-0.07} dt$

$$= e^{0.56} \int_0^8 e^{-0.07} dt = \dfrac{e^{0.56}}{-0.07} e^{-0.07t} \Big|_0^8$$

$$= -\dfrac{e^{0.56}}{0.07} [e^{-0.56} - 1] \approx 10.72$$

(B) $\int_0^8 (e^{0.56} - e^{0.07}) dt = (e^{0.56})t \Big|_0^8 - \dfrac{e^{0.07t}}{0.07} \Big|_0^8$

$$= 8e^{0.56} - \dfrac{1}{0.07} [e^{0.56} - 1] \approx 3.28$$

(C) $e^{0.56} \int_0^8 e^{-0.07} dt \approx 10.72$ as in (A)

7. $f(x) = \begin{cases} \dfrac{2}{(x+2)^2}, & x \geq 0 \\ 0 & x < 0 \end{cases}$

(A) Probability $(0 \leq x \leq 6) = \int_0^6 f(x) dx = \int_0^6 \dfrac{2}{(x+2)^2} dx$

$$= 2\dfrac{(x+2)^{-1}}{-1} \Big|_0^6 = \dfrac{-2}{(x+2)} \Big|_0^6$$

$$= -\dfrac{1}{4} + 1 = \dfrac{3}{4} = 0.75$$

Thus, Probability $(0 \leq x \leq 6) = 0.75$

(B) Probability $(6 \leq x \leq 12) = \int_6^{12} f(x) dx = \int_6^{12} \dfrac{2}{(x+2)^2} dx$

$$= \dfrac{-2}{x+2} \Big|_6^{12} = -\dfrac{1}{7} + \dfrac{1}{4} = \dfrac{3}{28} \approx 0.11$$

(C)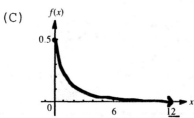

9. We want to find d such that

Probability $(0 \leq x \leq d) = \int_0^d f(x)\,dx = 0.8$:

$$\int_0^d f(x)\,dx = \int_0^d \frac{2}{(x+2)^2}\,dx = -\frac{2}{x+2}\Big|_0^d = \frac{-2}{d+2} + 1 = \frac{d}{d+2}$$

Now, $\dfrac{d}{d+2} = 0.8$

$$d = 0.8d + 1.6$$
$$0.2d = 1.6$$
$$d = 8 \text{ years}$$

11. $f(t) = \begin{cases} 0.01e^{-0.01t} & \text{if } t \geq 0 \\ 0 & \text{otherwise} \end{cases}$

(A) Since t is in months, the probability of failure during the warranty period of the first year is

Probability $(0 \leq t \leq 12) = \int_0^{12} f(t)\,dt = \int_0^{12} 0.01e^{-0.01t}\,dt$

$$= \frac{0.01}{-0.01}e^{-0.01t}\Big|_0^{12} = -1(e^{-0.12} - 1) \approx 0.11$$

(B) Probability $(12 \leq t \leq 24 = \int_{12}^{24} 0.01e^{-0.01t}\,dt = -1e^{-0.01t}\Big|_{12}^{24}$

$$= -1(e^{-0.24} - e^{-0.12}) \approx 0.10$$

13. Probability $(0 \leq t \leq \infty) = 1 = \int_0^{\infty} f(t)\,dt$

But, $\int_0^{\infty} f(t)\,dt = \int_0^{12} f(t)\,dt + \int_{12}^{\infty} f(t)\,dt$

Thus, Probability $(t \geq 12) = 1 - $ Probability $(0 \leq t \leq 12)$

$$\approx 1 - 0.11 = 0.89$$

15. $f(t) = 2500$

Total income $= \int_0^5 2500\,dt = 2500t\Big|_0^5 = \$12,500$

17.

If $f(t)$ is the rate of flow of a continuous income stream, then the total income produced from 0 to 5 years is the area under the curve $y = f(t)$ from $t = 0$ to $t = 5$.

19. $f(t) = 400e^{0.05t}$

Total income $= \int_0^3 400e^{0.05t}\,dt = \left.\frac{400}{0.05}e^{0.05t}\right|_0^3 = 8000(e^{0.15} - 1) \approx \$1295$

21.

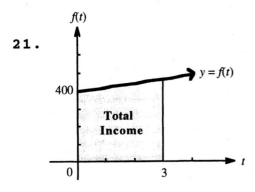

If $f(t)$ is the rate of flow of a continuous income stream, then the total income produced from 0 to 3 years is the area under the curve $y = f(t)$ from $t = 0$ to $t = 3$.

23. $f(t) = 2,000e^{0.05t}$

The amount in the account after 40 years is given by:

$$\int_0^{40} 2,000e^{0.05t}\,dt = \left.40,000e^{0.05t}\right|_0^{40} = 295,562.24 - 40,000 \approx \$255,562$$

Since $\$2,000 \times 40 = \$80,000$ was deposited into the account, the interest earned is:

$$\$255,562 - \$80,000 = \$175,562$$

25. $f(t) = 1,650e^{-0.02t}$, $r = 0.0625$, $T = 4$.

$FV = e^{0.0625(4)}\int_0^4 1,650e^{-0.02t}e^{-0.0625t}\,dt$

$= 1,650e^{0.25}\int_0^4 e^{-0.0825t}\,dt$

$= \left.1,650e^{0.25}\frac{e^{-0.0825t}}{-0.0825}\right|_0^4 = 20,000(e^{0.25} - e^{0.08}) \approx \$7,218.$

27. Total Income $= \int_0^4 1,650e^{-0.02t}\,dt = \left.\frac{1650}{-0.02}e^{-0.02t}\right|_0^4$

$= -82,500(e^{-0.08} - 1) \approx \$6,343.$

From Problem 25,

Interest earned $= \$7,218 - \$6,343 = \$875$

29. Clothing store: $f(t) = 12,000$, $r = 0.1$, $T = 5$.

$FV = e^{0.1(5)}\int_0^5 12,000e^{-0.1t}\,dt = 12,000e^{0.5}\int_0^5 e^{-0.1t}\,dt$

$= \left.\frac{12,000e^{0.5}}{-0.1}e^{-0.1t}\right|_0^5 = -120,000e^{0.5}(e^{-0.5} - 1)$

$= 120,000(e^{0.5} - 1) \approx \$77,847$

Computer store: $g(t) = 10,000e^{0.05t}$, $r = 0.1$, $T = 5$.

$$FV = e^{0.1(5)} \int_0^5 10,000e^{0.05t}e^{-0.1t}dt = 10,000e^{0.5}\int_0^5 e^{-0.05t}dt$$

$$= \frac{10,000e^{0.5}}{-0.05}e^{-0.05t}\Big|_0^5 = -200,000e^{0.5}(e^{-0.25} - 1)$$

$$= 200,000(e^{0.5} - e^{0.25}) \approx \$72,939$$

The clothing store is the better investment.

31. Bond: $P = \$10,000$, $r = 0.08$, $t = 5$.

$FV = 10,000e^{0.08(5)} = 10,000e^{0.4} \approx \$14,918$

Business: $f(t) = 2000$, $r = 0.08$, $T = 5$.

$$FV = e^{0.08(5)} \int_0^5 2000e^{-0.08t}dt = 2000e^{0.4}\int_0^5 e^{-0.08t}dt$$

$$= \frac{2000e^{0.4}}{-0.08}e^{-0.08t}\Big|_0^5 = -25,000e^{0.4}(e^{-0.4} - 1)$$

$$= 25,000(e^{0.4} - 1) \approx \$12,296$$

The bond is the better investment.

33. $f(t) = 9,000$, $r = 0.0695$, $T = 8$.

$$FV = e^{0.0695(8)} \int_0^8 9000e^{-0.0695t}dt$$

$$= 9000e^{0.556}\int_0^8 e^{-0.0695t} = \frac{9000e^{0.556}}{-0.0695}e^{-0.0695t}\Big]_0^8$$

$$\approx -225,800.78(e^{-0.556} - 1) \approx \$96,304.$$

The relationship between present value (PV) and future value (FV) at a continuously compounded interest rate r (expressed as a decimal) for t years is:

$$FV = PVe^{rt} \quad \text{or} \quad PV = FVe^{-rt}$$

Thus, we have:

$$PV = 96,304e^{-0.0695(8)} = 96,304e^{-0.556} \approx \$55,230$$

35. $f(t) = k$, rate r (expressed as a decimal), years T:

$$FV = e^{rT}\int_0^T ke^{-rt}dt = ke^{rT}\int_0^T e^{-rt}dt = \frac{ke^{rT}}{-r}e^{-rt}\Big|_0^T$$

$$= -\frac{k}{r}e^{rT}(e^{-rT} - 1) = \frac{k}{r}(e^{rT} - 1)$$

37. $D(x) = 400 - \frac{1}{20}x$, $\bar{p} = 150$

First, find $\bar{x}$: $150 = 400 - \frac{1}{20}\bar{x}$

$$\bar{x} = 5000$$

$$CS = \int_0^{5000}\left[400 - \frac{1}{20}x - 150\right]dx = \int_0^{5000}\left(250 - \frac{1}{20}x\right)dx$$

$$= \left(250x - \frac{1}{40}x^2\right)\Big|_0^{5000} = \$625,000$$

39.

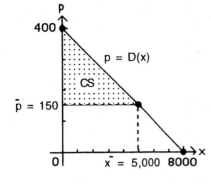

The shaded area is the consumers' surplus and represents the total savings to consumers who are willing to pay more than $150 for a product but are still able to buy the product for $150.

41. $p = S(x) = 10 + 0.1x + 0.0003x^2$, $\overline{p} = 67$.

First find $\overline{x}$: $67 = 10 + 0.1\overline{x} + 0.0003\overline{x}^2$

$$0.0003\overline{x}^2 + 0.1\overline{x} - 57 = 0$$

$$\overline{x} = \frac{-0.1 + \sqrt{0.01 + 0.0684}}{0.0006}$$

$$= \frac{-0.1 + 0.28}{0.0006} = 300$$

$$PS = \int_0^{300} [67 - (10 + 0.1x + 0.0003x^2)]\,dx$$

$$= \int_0^{300} (57 - 0.1x - 0.0003x^2)\,dx$$

$$= (57x - 0.05x^2 - 0.0001x^3)\Big|_0^{300} = \$9,900$$

43.

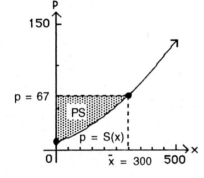

The area of the region PS is the producers' surplus and represents the total gain to producers who are willing to supply units at a lower price than $67 but are still able to supply the product at $67.

45. $p = D(x) = 50 - 0.1x$; $p = S(x) = 11 + 0.05x$

Equilibrium price: $D(x) = S(x)$

$$50 - 0.1x = 11 + 0.05x$$
$$39 = 0.15x$$
$$x = 260$$

Thus, $\overline{x} = 260$ and $\overline{p} = 50 - 0.1(260) = 24$.

$$CS = \int_0^{260} [(50 - 0.1x) - 24]\,dx = \int_0^{260} (26 - 0.1x)\,dx$$

$$= (26x - 0.05x^2) \Big|_0^{260}$$

$$= \$3,380$$

$$PS = \int_0^{260} [24 - (11 + 0.05x)]\,dx = \int_0^{260} [13 - 0.05x]\,dx$$

$$= (13x - 0.025x^2) \Big|_0^{260}$$

$$= \$1,690$$

47. $D(x) = 80e^{-0.001x}$ and $S(x) = 30e^{0.001x}$
Equilibrium price: $D(x) = S(x)$

$$80e^{-0.001x} = 30e^{0.001x}$$

$$e^{0.002x} = \frac{8}{3}$$

$$0.002x = \ln\left(\frac{8}{3}\right)$$

$$\overline{x} = \frac{\ln\left(\dfrac{8}{3}\right)}{0.002} \approx 490$$

Thus, $\overline{p} = 30e^{0.001(490)} \approx 49.$

$$CS = \int_0^{490} [80e^{-0.001x} - 49]\,dx = \left(\frac{80e^{-0.001x}}{-0.001} - 49x\right)\Big|_0^{490}$$

$$= -80,000e^{-0.49} + 80,000 - 24,010 \approx \$6,980$$

$$PS = \int_0^{490} [49 - 30e^{0.001x}]\,dx = \left(49x - \frac{30e^{0.001x}}{0.001}\right)\Big|_0^{490}$$

$$= 24,010 - 30,000(e^{0.49} - 1) \approx \$5,041$$

49. $D(x) = 80 - 0.04x;\ S(x) = 30e^{0.001x}$
Equilibrium price: $D(x) = S(x)$

$$80 - 0.04x = 30e^{0.001x}$$

Using a graphing utility, we find that
$$\overline{x} \approx 614$$
Thus, $\overline{p} = 80 - (0.04)614 \approx 55$

$$CS = \int_0^{614} [80 - 0.04x - 55]\,dx = \int_0^{614} (25 - 0.04x)\,dx$$

$$= (25x - 0.02x^2)\Big|_0^{614}$$

$$\approx \$7,810$$

$$PS = \int_0^{614} [55 - (30e^{0.001x})]\,dx = \int_0^{614} (55 - 30e^{0.001x})\,dx$$

$$= (55x - 30,000e^{0.001x})\Big|_0^{614}$$

$$\approx \$8,336$$

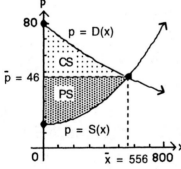

51. $D(x) = 80e^{-0.001x}$; $S(x) = 15 + 0.0001x^2$

Equilibrium price: $D(x) = S(x)$

Using a graphing utility, we find that
$$\overline{x} \approx 556$$

Thus, $\overline{p} = 15 + 0.0001(556)^2 \approx 46$

$$CS = \int_0^{556} [80e^{-0.001x} - 46]\,dx = (-80,000e^{-0.001x} - 46x)\Big|_0^{556}$$

$$\approx \$8,544$$

$$PS = \int_0^{556} [46 - (15 + 0.0001x^2)]\,dx = \int_0^{556} (31 - 0.0001x^2)\,dx$$

$$= \left(31x - \frac{0.0001}{3}x^3\right)\Big|_0^{556}$$

$$\approx \$11,507$$

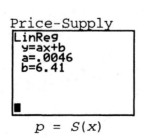

53. (A) Price–Demand

```
QuadReg
 y=ax²+bx+c
 a=1.4285714E-4
 b=-.0119142857
 c=6.698571429
```
$$p = D(x)$$

Price–Supply

```
LinReg
 y=ax+b
 a=.0046
 b=6.41

■
```
$$p = S(x)$$

Graph the price-demand and price-supply models and find their point of intersection.

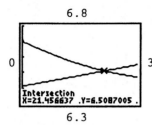

6.8

0   30

Intersection
X=21.456637 .Y=6.5087005 .

6.3

Equilibrium quantity $\bar{x}$ = 21.457
Equilibrium price $\bar{p}$ = 6.51

(B) Let $D(x)$ be the quadratic regression model in part (A).
Consumers' surplus:
$$CS = \int_0^{21.457} [D(x) - 6.51] \, dx \approx \$1,774.$$

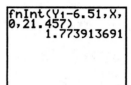

fnInt(Y₁-6.51,X,
0,21.457)
         1.773913691

Let $S(x)$ be the linear regression model in part (A).
Producers' surplus
$$PS = \int_0^{21.457} [6.51 - S(x)] \, dx \approx \$1,087$$

fnInt(6.51-Y₂,X,
0,21.457)
         1.086773447

EXERCISE 5-3

Things to remember:

1. INTEGRATION-BY-PARTS FORMULA
$$\int u \, dv = uv - \int v \, du$$

2. INTEGRATION-BY-PARTS: SELECTION OF u AND dv

(a) The product udv must equal the original integrand.

(b) It must be possible to integrate dv (preferably by using standard formulas or simple substitutions.)

(c) The new integral, $\int v \, du$, should not be more complicated than the original integral $\int u \, dv$.

(d) For integrals involving $x^p e^{ax}$, try
$$u = x^p; \quad dv = e^{ax} dx.$$

(e) For integrals involving $x^p (\ln x)^q$, try
$$u = (\ln x)^q; \quad dv = x^p dx.$$

1. $\int xe^{3x} dx$

Let $u = x$ and $dv = e^{3x} dx$. Then $du = dx$ and $v = \dfrac{e^{3x}}{3}$.

$$\int xe^{3x} dx = \frac{xe^{3x}}{3} - \int \frac{e^{3x}}{3} dx = \frac{1}{3} xe^{3x} - \frac{1}{3} \int e^{3x} dx = \frac{1}{3} xe^{3x} - \frac{1}{9} e^{3x} + C$$

3. $\int x^2 \ln x\, dx$

Let $u = \ln x$ and $dv = x^2 dx$. Then $du = \dfrac{dx}{x}$ and $v = \dfrac{x^3}{3}$.

$$\int x^2 \ln x\, dx = (\ln x)\left(\frac{x^3}{3}\right) - \int \frac{x^3}{3} \cdot \frac{dx}{x} = \frac{1}{3}x^3 \ln x - \frac{1}{3}\int x^2 dx$$

$$= \frac{x^3 \ln x}{3} - \frac{1}{3} \cdot \frac{x^3}{3} + C = \frac{x^3 \ln x}{3} - \frac{x^3}{9} + C$$

5. $\int (x + 1)^5 (x + 2)\, dx$

The better choice is $u = x + 2$, $dv = (x + 1)^5 dx$

The alternative is $u = (x + 1)^5$, $dv = (x + 2)\, dx$, which will lead to an integral of the form
$$\int (x + 1)^4 (x + 2)^2 dx.$$

Let $u = x + 2$ and $dv = (x + 1)^5 dx$. Then $du = dx$ and $v = \dfrac{1}{6}(x + 1)^6$.

Substitute into the integration by parts formula:

$$\int (x + 1)^5 (x + 2)\, dx = \frac{1}{6}(x + 1)^6 (x + 2) - \int \frac{1}{6}(x + 1)^6 dx$$

$$= \frac{1}{6}(x + 1)^6 (x + 2) - \frac{1}{42}(x + 1)^7 + C$$

7. $\int xe^{-x} dx$

Let $u = x$ and $dv = e^{-x} dx$. Then $du = dx$ and $v = -e^{-x}$.

$$\int xe^{-x} dx = x(-e^{-x}) - \int (-e^{-x})\, dx = -xe^{-x} + \int e^{-x} dx = -xe^{-x} - e^{-x} + C$$

9. $\int xe^{x^2} dx = \int e^{x^2} \dfrac{2}{2} x\, dx = \dfrac{1}{2}\int e^{x^2} 2x\, dx = \dfrac{1}{2}\int e^u du$

Let $u = x^2$,
then $du = 2x\, dx$. $\qquad = \dfrac{1}{2}e^u + C = \dfrac{1}{2}e^{x^2} + C$

11. $\int_0^1 (x - 3)e^x dx$

Let $u = (x - 3)$ and $dv = e^x dx$. Then $du = dx$ and $v = e^x$.

$$\int (x - 3)e^x dx = (x - 3)e^x - \int e^x dx = (x - 3)e^x - e^x + C$$

$$= xe^x - 4e^x + C.$$

Thus, $\int_0^1 (x - 3)e^x dx = (xe^x - 4e^x)\Big|_0^1 = (e - 4e) - (-4)$

$$= -3e + 4 \approx -4.1548.$$

13. $\int_1^3 \ln 2x\,dx$

Let $u = \ln 2x$ and $dv = dx$. Then $du = \dfrac{dx}{x}$ and $v = x$.

$\int \ln 2x\,dx = (\ln 2x)(x) - \int x \cdot \dfrac{dx}{x} = x \ln 2x - x + C$

Thus, $\int_1^3 \ln 2x\,dx = (x \ln 2x - x)\Big|_1^3$

$$= (3 \ln 6 - 3) - (\ln 2 - 1) \approx 2.6821.$$

15. $\int \dfrac{2x}{x^2 + 1}\,dx = \int \dfrac{1}{u}\,du = \ln|u| + C = \ln(x^2 + 1) + C$

Substitution: $u = x^2 + 1$
$du = 2x\,dx$

[<u>Note</u>: Absolute value not needed, since $x^2 + 1 \geq 0$.]

17. $\int \dfrac{\ln x}{x}\,dx = \int u\,du = \dfrac{u^2}{2} + C = \dfrac{(\ln x)^2}{2} + C$

Substitution: $u = \ln x$
$du = \dfrac{1}{x}\,dx$

19. $\int \sqrt{x} \ln x\,dx = \int x^{1/2} \ln x\,dx$

Let $u = \ln x$ and $dv = x^{1/2}\,dx$. Then $du = \dfrac{dx}{x}$ and $v = \dfrac{2}{3}x^{3/2}$.

$\int x^{1/2} \ln x\,dx = \dfrac{2}{3}x^{3/2} \ln x - \int \dfrac{2}{3}x^{3/2}\dfrac{dx}{x} = \dfrac{2}{3}x^{3/2} \ln x - \dfrac{2}{3}\int x^{1/2}\,dx$

$$= \dfrac{2}{3}x^{3/2} \ln x - \dfrac{4}{9}x^{3/2} + C$$

21.

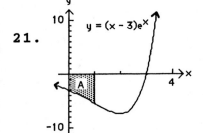

Since $f(x) = (x - 3)e^x < 0$ on $[0, 1]$, the integral represents the negative of the area between the graph of f and the x-axis from $x = 0$ to $x = 1$.

23.

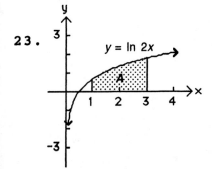

The integral represents the area between the curve $y = \ln 2x$ and the x-axis from $x = 1$ to $x = 3$.

25. $\int x^2 e^x dx$

Let $u = x^2$ and $dv = e^x dx$. Then $du = 2x\, dx$ and $v = e^x$.
$\int x^2 e^x dx = x^2 e^x - \int e^x (2x)\, dx = x^2 e^x - 2\int x e^x dx$

$\int x e^x dx$ can be computed by using integration-by-parts again.

Let $u = x$ and $dv = e^x dx$. Then $du = dx$ and $v = e^x$.
$\int x e^x dx = x e^x - \int e^x dx = x e^x - e^x + C$
and
$\int x^2 e^x dx = x^2 e^x - 2(x e^x - e^x) + C = x^2 e^x - 2x e^x + 2 e^x + C$
$$= (x^2 - 2x + 2) e^x + C$$

27. $\int x e^{ax} dx$

Let $u = x$ and $dv = e^{ax} dx$. Then $du = dx$ and $v = \dfrac{e^{ax}}{a}$.

$\int x e^{ax} dx = x \cdot \dfrac{e^{ax}}{a} - \int \dfrac{e^{ax}}{a}\, dx = \dfrac{x e^{ax}}{a} - \dfrac{e^{ax}}{a^2} + C$

29. $\int_1^e \dfrac{\ln x}{x^2}\, dx$

Let $u = \ln x$ and $dv = \dfrac{dx}{x^2}$. Then $du = \dfrac{dx}{x}$ and $v = \dfrac{-1}{x}$.

$\int \dfrac{\ln x}{x^2}\, dx = (\ln x)\left(-\dfrac{1}{x}\right) - \int -\dfrac{1}{x} \cdot \dfrac{dx}{x} = -\dfrac{\ln x}{x} + \int \dfrac{dx}{x^2} = -\dfrac{\ln x}{x} - \dfrac{1}{x} + C$

Thus, $\int_1^e \dfrac{\ln x}{x^2}\, dx = \left(-\dfrac{\ln x}{x} - \dfrac{1}{x}\right)\Big|_1^e = -\dfrac{\ln e}{e} - \dfrac{1}{e} - \left(-\dfrac{\ln 1}{1} - \dfrac{1}{1}\right)$

$$= -\dfrac{2}{e} + 1 \approx 0.2642.$$

[Note: $\ln e = 1$.]

31. $\int_0^2 \ln(x + 4)\, dx$

Let $t = x + 4$. Then $dt = dx$ and
$\int \ln(x + 4)\, dx = \int \ln t\, dt$.

Now, let $u = \ln t$ and $dv = dt$. Then $du = \dfrac{dt}{t}$ and $v = t$.

$\int \ln t\, dt = t \ln t - \int t\left(\dfrac{1}{t}\right) dt = t \ln t - \int dt = t \ln t - t + C$

Thus, $\int \ln(x + 4)\, dx = (x + 4)\,\ln(x + 4) - (x + 4) + C$
and

$\int_0^2 \ln(x + 4)\, dx = [(x + 4)\,\ln(x + 4) - (x + 4)]\Big|_0^2$
$$= 6 \ln 6 - 6 - (4 \ln 4 - 4) = 6 \ln 6 - 4 \ln 4 - 2 \approx 3.205.$$

33. $\int xe^{x-2}dx$

Let $u = x$ and $dv = e^{x-2}dx$. Then $du = dx$ and $v = e^{x-2}$.
$\int xe^{x-2}dx = xe^{x-2} - \int e^{x-2}\,dx = xe^{x-2} - e^{x-2} + C$

35. $\int x \ln(1 + x^2)\,dx$

Let $t = 1 + x^2$. Then $dt = 2x\,dx$ and
$\int x \ln(1 + x^2)\,dx = \int \ln(1 + x^2)x\,dx = \int \ln t \dfrac{dt}{2} = \dfrac{1}{2}\int \ln t\;dt.$

Now, for $\int \ln t\;dt$, let $u = \ln t$, $dv = dt$. Then $du = \dfrac{dt}{t}$ and $v = t$.

$\dfrac{1}{2}\int \ln t\;dt = t \ln t - \int t\left(\dfrac{1}{t}\right)dt = t \ln t - \int dt = t \ln t - t + C$

Therefore,
$\int x \ln(1 + x^2)\,dx = \dfrac{1}{2}(1 + x^2)\ln(1 + x^2) - \dfrac{1}{2}(1 + x^2) + C.$

37. $\int e^x \ln(1 + e^x)\,dx$

Let $t = 1 + e^x$. Then $dt = e^x dx$ and
$\int e^x \ln(1 + e^x)\,dx = \int \ln t\;dt.$

Now, as shown in Problems 31 and 35,
$\int \ln t\;dt = t \ln t - t + C.$

Thus, $\int e^x \ln(1 + e^x)\,dx = (1 + e^x)\ln(1 + e^x) - (1 + e^x) + C.$

39. $\int (\ln x)^2 dx$

Let $u = (\ln x)^2$ and $dv = dx$. Then $du = \dfrac{2 \ln x}{x}dx$ and $v = x$.

$\int (\ln x)^2 dx = x(\ln x)^2 - \int x \cdot \dfrac{2 \ln x}{x}dx = x(\ln x)^2 - 2\int \ln x\;dx$

$\int \ln x\;dx$ can be computed by using integration-by-parts again.

As shown in Problems 31 and 35,
$\int \ln x\;dx = x \ln x - x + C.$

Thus, $\int (\ln x)^2 dx = x(\ln x)^2 - 2(x \ln x - x) + C$
$$= x(\ln x)^2 - 2x \ln x + 2x + C.$$

41. $\int (\ln x^3)\,dx$

Let $u = (\ln x)^3$ and $dv = dx$. Then $du = 3(\ln x)^2 \cdot \dfrac{1}{x}dx$ and $v = x$.

$\int (\ln x^3)\,dx = x(\ln x)^3 - \int x \cdot 3(\ln x)^2 \cdot \dfrac{1}{x}dx = x(\ln x)^3 - 3\int (\ln x^3)\,dx$

Now, using Problem 39,

$$\int (\ln x^2)\, dx = x(\ln x)^2 - 2x \ln x + 2x + C.$$

Therefore, $\int (\ln x^3)\, dx = x(\ln x)^3 - 3[x(\ln x)^2 - 2x \ln x + 2x] + C$

$$= x(\ln x)^3 - 3x(\ln x)^2 + 6x \ln x - 6x + C.$$

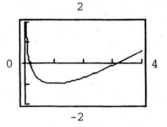

43. $y = x - 2 - \ln x,\ 1 \le x \le 4$

$y = 0$ at $x \approx 3.146$

$$A = \int_1^{3.146} [-(x - 2 - \ln x)]\, dx + \int_{3.146}^4 (x - 2 - \ln x)\, dx$$

$$= \int_1^{3.146} (\ln x + 2 - x)\, dx + \int_{3.146}^4 (x - 2 - \ln x)\, dx$$

Now, $\int \ln x\, dx$ is found using integration-by-parts. Let $u = \ln x$ and $dv = dx$. Then $du = \dfrac{1}{x} dx$ and $v = x$.

$$\int \ln x\, dx = x \ln x - \int x\left(\frac{1}{x}\right) dx = x \ln x - \int dx = x \ln x - x + C$$

Thus,

$$A = \left(x \ln x - x + 2x - \frac{1}{2}x^2\right)\Big|_1^{3.146} + \left(\frac{1}{2}x^2 - 2x - x \ln x + x\right)\Big|_{3.146}^4$$

$$= \left(x \ln x + x - \frac{1}{2}x^2\right)\Big|_1^{3.146} + \left(\frac{1}{2}x^2 - x - x \ln x\right)\Big|_{3.146}^4$$

$$\approx (1.803 - 0.5) + (-1.545 + 1.803) = 1.561$$

45. $y = 5 - xe^x,\ 0 \le x \le 3$

$y = 0$ at $x \approx 1.327$

$$A = \int_0^{1.327} (5 - xe^x)\, dx + \int_{1.327}^3 [-(5 - xe^x)]\, dx$$

$$= \int_0^{1.327} (5 - xe^x)\, dx + \int_{1.327}^3 (xe^x - 5)\, dx$$

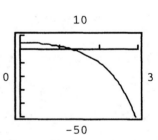

Now, $\int xe^x dx$ is found using integration-by-parts. Let $u = x$ and $dv = e^x\, dx$. Then, $du = dx$ and $v = e^x$.

$$\int xe^x dx = xe^x - \int e^x\, dx = xe^x - e^x + C$$

Thus,

$$A = (5x - [xe^x - e^x])\Big|_0^{1.327} + (xe^x - e^x - 5x)\Big|_{1.327}^3$$

$$\approx (5.402 - 1) + (25.171 - [-5.402]) \approx 34.98$$

47. Marginal profit: $P'(t) = 2t - te^{-t}$.

The total profit over the first 5 years is given by the definite integral:

$$\int_0^5 (2t - te^{-t})\,dt = \int_0^5 2t\,dt - \int_0^5 te^{-t}\,dt$$

We calculate the second integral using integration-by-parts. Let $u = t$ and $dv = e^{-t}\,dt$. Then $du = dt$ and $v = -e^{-t}$

$$\int te^{-t}\,dt = -te^{-t} - \int -e^{-t}\,dt = -te^{-t} - e^{-t} + C = -e^{-t}[t + 1] + C$$

Thus,

$$\text{Total profit} = t^2 \Big|_0^5 + (e^{-t}[t + 1]) \Big|_0^5$$

$$\approx 25 + (0.040 - 1) = 24.040$$

To the nearest million, the total profit is $24 million.

49.

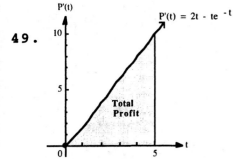

The total profit for the first five years (in millions of dollars) is the same as the area under the marginal profit function, $P'(t) = 2t - te^{-t}$, from $t = 0$ to $t = 5$.

51. From Exercise 7-2, Future Value $= e^{rT} \int_0^T f(t) e^{-rt}\,dt$. Now $r = 0.08$, $T = 5$, $f(t) = 1000 - 200t$. Thus,

$$FV = e^{(0.08)5} \int_0^5 (1000 - 200t) e^{-0.08t}\,dt$$

$$= 1000 e^{0.4} \int_0^5 e^{-0.08t}\,dt - 200 e^{0.4} \int_0^5 te^{-0.08t}\,dt.$$

We calculate the second integral using integration-by-parts.

Let $u = t$, $dv = e^{-0.08t}\,dt$. Then $du = dt$ and $v = \dfrac{e^{-0.08t}}{-0.08}$.

$$\int te^{-0.08t}\,dt = \frac{te^{-0.08t}}{-0.08} - \int \frac{e^{-0.08t}}{-0.08}\,dt = -12.5te^{-0.08t} - \frac{e^{-0.08t}}{0.0064} + C$$

$$= -12.5te^{-0.08t} - 156.25e^{-0.08t} + C$$

Thus, we have:

$$FV = 1000 e^{0.4}\frac{e^{-0.08t}}{-0.08}\Big|_0^5 - 200 e^{0.4}[-12.5te^{-0.08t} - 156.25e^{-0.08t}]\Big|_0^5$$

$$= -12,500 + 12,500 e^{0.4} - 200 e^{0.4}[-62.5e^{-0.4} - 156.25e^{-0.4} + 156.25]$$

$$= -12,500 + 12,500 e^{0.4} + 43,750 - 31,250 e^{0.4}$$

$$= 31,250 - 18,750 e^{0.4} \approx 3,278 \text{ or } \$3,278$$

53. Gini Index $= 2\int_0^1 (x - xe^{x-1})\,dx$

$$= 2\int_0^1 x\,dx - 2\int_0^1 xe^{x-1}\,dx$$

We calculate the second integral using integration-by-parts.
Let $u = x$, $dv = e^{x-1}\,dx$. Then $du = dx$, $v = e^{x-1}$.
$$\int xe^{x-1}\,dx = xe^{x-1} - \int e^{x-1}\,dx = xe^{x-1} - e^{x-1} + C$$

Therefore, $2\int_0^1 x\,dx - 2\int_0^1 xe^{x-1}\,dx = x^2 \Big|_0^1 - 2[xe^{x-1} - e^{x-1}]\Big|_0^1$

$$= 1 - 2[1 - 1 + (e^{-1})]$$
$$= 1 - 2e^{-1} \approx 0.264.$$

55.

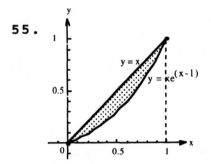

The area bounded by $y = x$ and the Lorenz curve $y = xe^{(x-1)}$ divided by the area under the curve $y = x$ from $x = 0$ to $x = 1$ is the index of income concentration, in this case 0.264. It is a measure of the concentration of income—the closer to zero, the closer to all the income being equally distributed; the closer to one, the closer to all the income being concentrated in a few hands.

57. $S'(t) = -4te^{0.1t}$, $S(0) = 2,000$

$$S(t) = \int -4te^{0.1t}\,dt = -4\int te^{0.1t}\,dt$$

Let $u = t$ and $dv = e^{0.1t}\,dt$. Then $du = dt$ and $v = \dfrac{e^{0.1t}}{0.1} = 10e^{0.1t}$

$$\int te^{0.1t}\,dt = 10te^{0.1t} - \int 10e^{0.1t}\,dt = 10te^{0.1t} - 100e^{0.1t} + C$$

Now, $S(t) = -40te^{0.1t} + 400e^{0.1t} + C$

Since $S(0) = 2,000$, we have
$$2,000 = 400 + C, \quad C = 1,600$$

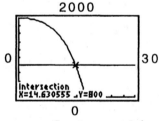

Thus,
$$S(t) = 1,600 + 400e^{0.1t} - 40te^{0.1t}$$

To find how long the company will continue to manufacture this computer, solve $S(t) = 800$ for t.

The company will manufacture the computer for 15 months.

59. $p = D(x) = 9 - \ln(x + 4)$; $\overline{p} = \$2.089$. To find $\overline{x}$, solve
$$9 - \ln(\overline{x} + 4) = 2.089$$
$$\ln(\overline{x} + 4) = 6.911$$
$$\overline{x} + 4 = e^{6.911} \quad \text{(take the exponential of both sides)}$$
$$\overline{x} \approx 1,000$$

Now,
$$CS = \int_0^{1,000} (D(x) - \overline{p})\,dx = \int_0^{1,000} [9 - \ln(x + 4) - 2.089]\,dx$$
$$= \int_0^{1,000} 6.911\,dx - \int_0^{1,000} \ln(x + 4)\,dx$$

To calculate the second integral, we first let $z = x + 4$ and $dz = dx$ to get

$$\int \ln(x + 4)\,dx = \int \ln z\,dz$$

Then we use integration-by-parts. Let $u = \ln z$ and $dv = dz$.
Then $du = \dfrac{1}{z}dz$ and $v = z$.

$$\int \ln z\,dz = z \ln z - \int z \cdot \frac{1}{z}dz = z \ln z - z + C$$

Therefore,

$$\int \ln(x + 4)\,dx = (x + 4)\ln(x + 4) - (x + 4) + C$$

and

$$CS = 6.911x\Big|_0^{1,000} - [(x + 4)\ln(x + 4) - (x + 4)]\Big|_0^{1,000}$$

$$\approx 6911 - (5935.39 - 1.55) \approx \$977$$

61.

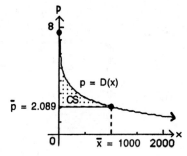

The area bounded by the price-demand equation, $p = 9 - \ln(x + 4)$, and the price equation, $y = \bar{p} = 2.089$, from $x = 0$ to $x = \bar{x} = 1,000$, represents the consumers' surplus. This is the amount saved by consumer's who are willing to pay more than \$2.089.

63. Average concentration: $= \dfrac{1}{5 - 0}\displaystyle\int_0^5 \dfrac{20 \ln(t + 1)}{(t + 1)^2}dt = 4\displaystyle\int_0^5 \dfrac{\ln(t + 1)}{(t + 1)^2}$

$\displaystyle\int \dfrac{\ln(t + 1)}{(t + 1)^2}dt$ is found using integration-by-parts.

Let $u = \ln(t + 1)$ and $dv = (t + 1)^{-2}dt$.
Then $du = \dfrac{1}{t + 1}dt = (t + 1)^{-1}dt$ and $v = -(t + 1)^{-1}$.

$$\int \dfrac{\ln(t + 1)}{(t + 1)^2}dt = -\dfrac{\ln(t + 1)}{t + 1} - \int -(t + 1)^{-1}(t + 1)^{-1}dt$$

$$= -\dfrac{\ln(t + 1)}{t + 1} + \int (t + 1)^{-2}dt = -\dfrac{\ln(t + 1)}{t + 1} - \dfrac{1}{t + 1} + C$$

Therefore, the average concentration is:

$$\dfrac{1}{5}\int_0^5 \dfrac{20 \ln(t + 1)}{(t + 1)^2}dt = 4\left[-\dfrac{\ln(t + 1)}{t + 1} - \dfrac{1}{t + 1}\right]\Big|_0^5$$

$$= 4\left(-\dfrac{\ln 6}{6} - \dfrac{1}{6}\right) - 4(-\ln 1 - 1)$$

$$= 4 - \dfrac{2}{3}\ln 6 - \dfrac{2}{3} = \dfrac{1}{3}(10 - 2 \ln 6) \approx 2.1388 \text{ ppm}$$

65. $N'(t) = (t + 6)e^{-0.25t}$, $0 \leq t \leq 15$; $N(0) = 40$

$N(t) - N(0) = \int_0^t N'(x)\,dx$;

$N(t) = 40 + \int_0^t (x + 6)e^{-0.25x}dx = 40 + 6\int_0^t e^{-0.25x}dx + \int_0^t xe^{-0.25x}dx$

$\qquad = 40 + 6(-4e^{-0.25x})\Big|_0^t + \int_0^t xe^{-0.25x}dx$

$\qquad = 64 - 24e^{-0.25t} + \int_0^t xe^{-0.25x}dx$

Let $u = x$ and $dv = e^{-0.25x}dx$. Then $du = dx$ and $v = -4e^{-0.25x}$;

$\int xe^{-0.25x}dx = -4xe^{-0.25x} - \int -4e^{-0.25x}dx = -4xe^{-0.25x} - 16e^{-0.25x} + C$

Now, $\int_0^t xe^{-0.25x}dx = (-4xe^{-0.25x} - 16e^{-0.25x})\Big|_0^t$

$\qquad\qquad\qquad = -4te^{-0.25t} - 16e^{-0.25t} + 16$

and

$N(t) = 80 - 40e^{-0.25t} - 4te^{-0.25t}$

To find how long it will take a student to achieve the 70 words per minute level, solve $N(t) = 70$:

It will take 8 weeks.

By the end of the course, a student should be able to type $N(15) = 80 - 40e^{-0.25(15)} - 60e^{-0.25(15)} \approx 78$ words per minute.

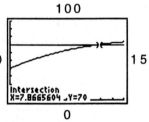

67. Average number of voters $= \dfrac{1}{5}\int_0^5 (20 + 4t - 5te^{-0.1t})\,dt$

$\qquad\qquad\qquad\qquad\qquad = \dfrac{1}{5}\int_0^5 (20 + 4t)\,dt - \int_0^5 te^{-0.1t}dt$

$\int te^{-0.1t}dt$ is found using integration-by-parts.

Let $u = t$ and $dv = e^{-0.1t}dt$. Then $du = dt$ and $v = \dfrac{e^{-0.1t}}{-0.1} = -10e^{-0.1t}$.

$\int te^{-0.1t}dt = -10te^{-0.1t} - \int -10e^{-0.1t}dt = -10te^{-0.1t} + 10\int e^{-0.1t}dt$

$\qquad\qquad = -10te^{-0.1t} + \dfrac{10e^{-0.1t}}{-0.1} + C = -10te^{-0.1t} - 100e^{-0.1t} + C$

Therefore, the average number of voters is:

$\dfrac{1}{5}\int_0^5 (20 + 4t)\,dt - \int_0^5 te^{-0.1t}dt$

$\qquad = \dfrac{1}{5}(20t + 2t^2)\Big|_0^5 - (-10te^{-0.1t} - 100e^{-0.1t})\Big|_0^5$

$\qquad = \dfrac{1}{5}(100 + 50) + (10te^{-0.1t} + 100e^{-0.1t})\Big|_0^5$

$\qquad = 30 + (50e^{-0.5} + 100e^{-0.5}) - 100$

$\qquad = 150e^{-0.5} - 70$

$\qquad \approx 20.98$ (thousands) or $20,980$

1. Use Formula 9 with $a = b = 1$.

$$\int \frac{1}{x(1 + x)} dx = \frac{1}{1} \ln\left|\frac{x}{1 + x}\right| + C = \ln\left|\frac{x}{x + 1}\right| + C$$

3. Use Formula 18 with $a = 3$, $b = 1$, $c = 5$, $d = 2$:

$$\int \frac{1}{(3 + x)^2(5 + 2x)} dx = \frac{1}{3 \cdot 2 - 5 \cdot 1} \cdot \frac{1}{3 + x} + \frac{2}{(3 \cdot 2 - 5 \cdot 1)^2} \ln\left|\frac{5 + 2x}{3 + x}\right| + C$$

$$= \frac{1}{3 + x} + 2 \ln\left|\frac{5 + 2x}{3 + x}\right| + C$$

5. Use Formula 25 with $a = 16$ and $b = 1$:

$$\int \frac{x}{\sqrt{16 + x}} dx = \frac{2(x - 2 \cdot 16)}{3 \cdot 1^2} \sqrt{16 + x} + C = \frac{2(x - 32)}{3} \sqrt{16 + x} + C$$

7. Use Formula 29 with $a = 1$:

$$\int \frac{1}{x\sqrt{1 - x^2}} dx = -\frac{1}{1} \ln\left|\frac{1 + \sqrt{1 - x^2}}{x}\right| + C$$

$$= -\ln\left|\frac{1 + \sqrt{1 - x^2}}{x}\right| + C$$

9. Use Formula 37 with $a = 2$ ($a^2 = 4$):

$$\int \frac{1}{x\sqrt{x^2 + 4}} dx = \frac{1}{2} \ln\left|\frac{x}{2 + \sqrt{x^2 + 4}}\right| + C$$

11. Use Formula 51 with $n = 2$:

$$\int x^2 \ln x \, dx = \frac{x^{2+1}}{2 + 1} \ln x - \frac{x^{2+1}}{(2 + 1)^2} + C = \frac{x^3}{3} \ln x - \frac{x^3}{9} + C$$

13. First let $u = e^x$. Then $du = e^x dx$ and $dx = \frac{1}{e^x} du = \frac{1}{u} du$.

Thus, $\int \frac{1}{1 + e^x} dx = \int \frac{1}{u(1 + u)} du$

Now use Formula 9 with $a = b = 1$:

$$\int \frac{1}{u(1 + u)} du = \frac{1}{1} \ln\left|\frac{u}{1 + u}\right| + C$$

$$= \ln\left|\frac{e^x}{1 + e^x}\right| + C$$

$$= \ln|e^x| - \ln|1 + e^x| + C$$

$$= x - \ln|1 + e^x| + C$$

15. First use Formula 5 with $a = 3$ and $b = 1$ to find the indefinite integral.

$$\int \frac{x^2}{3 + x}\,dx = \frac{(3 + x)^2}{2 \cdot 1^3} - \frac{2 \cdot 3(3 + x)}{1^3} + \frac{3^2}{1^3}\ln|3 + x| + C$$

$$= \frac{(3 + x)^2}{2} - 6(3 + x) + 9\ln|3 + x| + C$$

Thus, $\displaystyle\int_1^3 \frac{x^2}{3 + x}\,dx = \left[\frac{(3 + x)^2}{2} - 6(3 + x) + 9\ln|3 + x|\right]\Big|_1^3$

$$= \frac{(3 + 3)^2}{2} - 6(3 + 3) + 9\ln|3 + 3|$$

$$- \left[\frac{(3 + 1)^2}{2} - 6(3 + 1) + 9\ln|3 + 1|\right]$$

$$= 9\ln\frac{3}{2} - 2 \approx 1.6492.$$

17. First use Formula 15 with $a = 3$, $b = c = d = 1$ to find the indefinite integral.

$$\int \frac{1}{(3 + x)(1 + x)}\,dx = \frac{1}{3 \cdot 1 - 1 \cdot 1}\ln\left|\frac{1 + x}{3 + x}\right| + C = \frac{1}{2}\ln\left|\frac{1 + x}{3 + x}\right| + C$$

Thus, $\displaystyle\int_0^7 \frac{1}{(3 + x)(1 + x)}\,dx = \frac{1}{2}\ln\left|\frac{1 + x}{3 + x}\right|\Big|_0^7 = \frac{1}{2}\ln\left|\frac{1 + 7}{3 + 7}\right| - \frac{1}{2}\ln\left|\frac{1}{3}\right|$

$$= \frac{1}{2}\ln\left|\frac{4}{5}\right| - \frac{1}{2}\ln\left|\frac{1}{3}\right| = \frac{1}{2}\ln\frac{12}{5} \approx 0.4377.$$

19. First use Formula 36 with $a = 3$ $(a^2 = 9)$ to find the indefinite integral:

$$\int \frac{1}{\sqrt{x^2 + 9}}\,dx = \ln\left|x + \sqrt{x^2 + 9}\right| + C$$

Thus, $\displaystyle\int_0^4 \frac{1}{\sqrt{x^2 + 9}}\,dx = \ln\left|x + \sqrt{x^2 + 9}\right|\Big|_0^4 = \ln\left|4 + \sqrt{16 + 9}\right| - \ln\left|\sqrt{9}\right|$

$$= \ln 9 - \ln 3 = \ln 3 \approx 1.0986.$$

21. Consider Formula 35. Let $u = 2x$. Then $u^2 = 4x^2$, $x = \dfrac{u}{2}$, and $dx = \dfrac{du}{2}$.

$$\int \frac{\sqrt{4x^2 + 1}}{x^2}\,dx = \int \frac{\sqrt{u^2 + 1}}{\dfrac{u^2}{4}}\,\frac{du}{2} = 2\int \frac{\sqrt{u^2 + 1}}{u^2}\,du$$

$$= 2\left[-\frac{\sqrt{u^2 + 1}}{u} + \ln\left|u + \sqrt{u^2 + 1}\right|\right] + C$$

$$= 2\left[-\frac{\sqrt{4x^2 + 1}}{2x} + \ln\left|2x + \sqrt{4x^2 + 1}\right|\right] + C$$

$$= -\frac{\sqrt{4x^2 + 1}}{x} + 2\ln\left|2x + \sqrt{4x^2 + 1}\right| + C$$

23. Let $u = x^2$. Then $du = 2x\, dx$.

$$\int \frac{x}{\sqrt{x^4 - 16}}\, dx = \frac{1}{2}\int \frac{1}{\sqrt{u^2 - 16}}\, du$$

Now use Formula 43 with $a = 4$ $(a^2 = 16)$:

$$\frac{1}{2}\int \frac{1}{\sqrt{u^2 - 16}}\, du = \frac{1}{2}\ln\left|u + \sqrt{u^2 - 16}\right| + C = \frac{1}{2}\left|\ln x^2 + \sqrt{x^4 - 16}\right| + C$$

25. Let $u = x^3$. Then $du = 3x^2\, dx$.

$$\int x^2\sqrt{x^6 + 4}\, dx = \frac{1}{3}\int \sqrt{u^2 + 4}\, du$$

Now use Formula 32 with $a = 2$ $(a^2 = 4)$:

$$\frac{1}{3}\int \sqrt{u^2 + 4}\, du = \frac{1}{3}\cdot\frac{1}{2}\left[u\sqrt{u^2 + 4} + 4\ln\left|u + \sqrt{u^2 + 4}\right|\right] + C$$

$$= \frac{1}{6}\left[x^3\sqrt{x^6 + 4} + 4\ln\left|x^3 + \sqrt{x^6 + 4}\right|\right] + C$$

27. $$\int \frac{1}{x^3\sqrt{4 - x^4}}\, dx = \int \frac{x}{x^4\sqrt{4 - x^4}}\, dx$$

Let $u = x^2$. Then $du = 2x\, dx$.

$$\int \frac{x}{x^4\sqrt{4 - x^4}}\, dx = \frac{1}{2}\int \frac{1}{u^2\sqrt{4 - u^2}}\, du$$

Now use Formula 30 with $a = 2$ $(a^2 = 4)$:

$$\frac{1}{2}\int \frac{1}{u^2\sqrt{4 - u^2}}\, du = -\frac{1}{2}\cdot\frac{\sqrt{4 - u^2}}{4u} + C = \frac{-\sqrt{4 - x^4}}{8x^2} + C$$

29. $$\int \frac{e^x}{(2 + e^x)(3 + 4e^x)}\, dx = \int \frac{1}{(2 + u)(3 + 4u)}\, du$$

Substitution: $u = e^x$, $du = e^x dx$.
Now use Formula 15 with $a = 2$, $b = 1$, $c = 3$, $d = 4$:

$$\int \frac{1}{(2 + u)(3 + 4u)}\, du = \frac{1}{2\cdot 4 - 3\cdot 1}\ln\left|\frac{3 + 4u}{2 + u}\right| + C = \frac{1}{5}\ln\left|\frac{3 + 4e^x}{2 + e^x}\right| + C$$

31. $$\int \frac{\ln x}{x\sqrt{4 + \ln x}}\, dx = \int \frac{u}{\sqrt{4 + u}}\, du$$

Substitution: $u = \ln x$, $du = \frac{1}{x}dx$.

Use Formula 25 with $a = 4$, $b = 1$:

$$\int \frac{u}{\sqrt{4 + u}}\, du = \frac{2(u - 2\cdot 4)}{3\cdot 1^2}\sqrt{4 + u} + C = \frac{2(u - 8)}{3}\sqrt{4 + u} + C$$

$$= \frac{2(\ln x - 8)}{3}\sqrt{4 + \ln x} + C$$

33. Use Formula 47 with $n = 2$ and $a = 5$:

$$\int x^2 e^{5x} dx = \frac{x^2 e^{5x}}{5} - \frac{2}{5}\int x e^{5x} dx$$

To find $\int x e^{5x} dx$, use Formula 47 with $n = 1$, $a = 5$:

$$\int x e^{5x} dx = \frac{x e^{5x}}{5} - \frac{1}{5}\int e^{5x} dx = \frac{x e^{5x}}{5} - \frac{1}{5} \cdot \frac{e^{5x}}{5}$$

Thus, $\int x^2 e^{5x} dx = \frac{x^2 e^{5x}}{5} - \frac{2}{5}\left[\frac{x e^{5x}}{5} - \frac{1}{25} e^{5x}\right] + C$

$$= \frac{x^2 e^{5x}}{5} - \frac{2x e^{5x}}{25} + \frac{2 e^{5x}}{125} + C.$$

35. Use Formula 47 with $n = 3$ and $a = -1$.

$$\int x^3 e^{-x} dx = \frac{x^3 e^{-x}}{-1} - \frac{3}{-1}\int x^2 e^{-x} dx = -x^3 e^{-x} + 3\int x^2 e^{-x} dx$$

Now $\int x^2 e^{-x} dx = \frac{x^2 e^{-x}}{-1} - \frac{2}{-1}\int x e^{-x} dx = -x^2 e^{-x} + 2\int x e^{-x} dx$

and $\int x e^{-x} dx = \frac{x e^{-x}}{-1} - \frac{1}{-1}\int e^{-x} dx = -x e^{-x} - e^{-x}$, using Formula 47.

Thus, $\int x^3 e^{-x} dx = -x^3 e^{-x} + 3[-x^2 e^{-x} + 2(-x e^{-x} - e^{-x})] + C$

$$= -x^3 e^{-x} - 3x^2 e^{-x} - 6x e^{-x} - 6 e^{-x} + C.$$

37. Use Formula 52 with $n = 3$:

$$\int (\ln x)^3 dx = x(\ln x)^3 - 3\int (\ln x)^2 dx$$

Now $\int (\ln x)^2 dx = x(\ln x)^2 - 2\int \ln x \, dx$ using Formula 52 again, and

$\int \ln x \, dx = x \ln x - x$ by Formula 49.

Thus, $\int (\ln x)^3 dx = x(\ln x)^3 - 3[x(\ln x)^2 - 2(x \ln x - x)] + C$

$$= x(\ln x)^3 - 3x(\ln x)^2 + 6x \ln x - 6x + C.$$

39. $\int_3^5 x\sqrt{x^2 - 9}\, dx$. First consider the indefinite integral.

Let $u = x^2 - 9$. Then $du = 2x \, dx$ or $x \, dx = \frac{1}{2} du$. Thus,

$$\int x\sqrt{x^2 - 9}\, dx = \frac{1}{2}\int u^{1/2} du = \frac{1}{2} \cdot \frac{u^{3/2}}{3/2} + C = \frac{1}{3}(x^2 - 9)^{3/2} + C.$$

Now, $\int_3^5 x\sqrt{x^2 - 9}\, dx = \frac{1}{3}(x^2 - 9)^{3/2}\Big|_3^5 = \frac{1}{3} \cdot 16^{3/2} = \frac{64}{3}.$

41. $\int_2^4 \dfrac{1}{x^2 - 1}\,dx$. Consider the indefinite integral:

$$\int \frac{1}{x^2 - 1}\,dx = \frac{1}{2 \cdot 1}\,\ln\left|\frac{x - 1}{x + 1}\right| + C,\text{ using Formula 13 with } a = 1.$$

Thus,

$$\int_2^4 \frac{1}{x^2 - 1}\,dx = \frac{1}{2}\,\ln\left|\frac{x - 1}{x + 1}\right|\Bigg|_2^4 = \frac{1}{2}\,\ln\left|\frac{3}{5}\right| - \frac{1}{2}\,\ln\left|\frac{1}{3}\right| = \frac{1}{2}\,\ln\frac{9}{5} \approx 0.2939.$$

43. $\int \dfrac{\ln x}{x^2}\,dx = \int x^{-2}\ln x\,dx$

$$= \frac{x^{-1}}{-1}\ln x - \frac{x^{-1}}{(-1)^2} + C \quad [\text{Formula 51 with } n = -2]$$

$$= -\frac{1}{x}\ln x - \frac{1}{x} + C = \frac{-1 - \ln x}{x} + C$$

45. $\int \dfrac{x}{\sqrt{x^2 - 1}}\,dx = \int \dfrac{1}{\sqrt{x^2 - 1}}\left(\dfrac{2}{2}\right)x\,dx = \dfrac{1}{2}\int u^{-1/2}\,du$

Let $u = x^2 - 1$ $\qquad\qquad\qquad = u^{1/2} + C$

Then $du = 2x\,dx$ $\qquad\qquad\quad = \sqrt{x^2 - 1} + C$

47. $f(x) = \dfrac{10}{\sqrt{x^2 + 1}}$, $g(x) = x^2 + 3x$

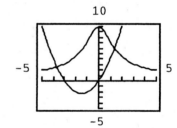

The graphs of f and g are shown at the right.
The x-coordinates of the points of intersection
are: $x_1 \approx -3.70$, $x_2 \approx 1.36$

$$A = \int_{-3.70}^{1.36}\left[\frac{1}{\sqrt{x^2 + 1}} - (x^2 + 3x)\right]dx$$

$$= 10\int_{-3.70}^{1.36}\frac{1}{\sqrt{x^2 + 1}}\,dx - \int_{-3.70}^{1.36}(x^2 + 3x)\,dx$$

For the first integral, use Formula 36 with $a = 1$:

$$A = (10\,\ln\,|x + \sqrt{x^2 + 1}\,|)\Bigg|_{-3.70}^{1.36} - \left(\frac{1}{3}x^3 + \frac{3}{2}x^2\right)\Bigg|_{-3.70}^{1.36}$$

$$\approx [11.15 - (-20.19)] - [3.61 - (3.65)] = 31.38$$

49. $f(x) = x\sqrt{x + 4}$, $g(x) = 1 + x$

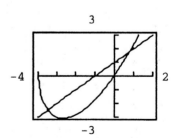

The graphs of f and g are shown at the right.
The x-coordinates of the points of intersection
are: $x_1 \approx -3.49$, $x_2 \approx 0.83$

$$A = \int_{-3.49}^{0.83}[1 + x - x\sqrt{x + 4}\,]\,dx = \int_{-3.49}^{0.83}(1 + x)\,dx - \int_{-3.49}^{0.83}x\sqrt{x + 4}\,dx$$

For the second integral, use Formula 22 with $a = 4$ and $b = 1$:

$$A = \left(x + \frac{1}{2}x^2\right)\Big|_{-3.49}^{0.83} - \left(\frac{2[3x - 8]}{15}\sqrt{(x + 4)^3}\right)\Big|_{-3.49}^{0.83}$$

$$\approx (1.17445 - 2.60005) - (-7.79850 + 0.89693) \approx 5.48$$

51. Find $\overline{x}$, the demand when the price $\overline{p} = 15$:

$$15 = \frac{7500 - 30\overline{x}}{300 - \overline{x}}$$

$$4500 - 15\overline{x} = 7500 - 30\overline{x}$$
$$15\overline{x} = 3000$$
$$\overline{x} = 200$$

Consumers' surplus:

$$CS = \int_0^{\overline{x}}[D(x) - \overline{p}]\,dx = \int_0^{200}\left[\frac{7500 - 30x}{300 - x} - 15\right]dx = \int_0^{200}\left[\frac{3000 - 15x}{300 - x}\right]dx$$

Use Formula 20 with $a = 3000$, $b = -15$, $c = 300$, $d = -1$:

$$CS = \left[\frac{-15x}{-1} + \frac{3000(-1) - (-15)(300)}{(-1)^2}\ln|300 - x|\right]\Big|_0^{200}$$

$$= [15x + 1500\ln|300 - x|]\Big|_0^{200}$$

$$= 3000 + 1500\ln(100) - 1500\ln(300)$$

$$= 3000 + 1500\ln\left(\frac{1}{3}\right) \approx 1352$$

Thus, the consumers' surplus is \$1352.

53.

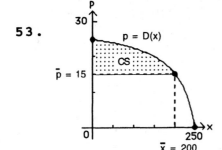

The shaded region represents the consumers' surplus.

55. $C'(x) = \dfrac{250 + 10x}{1 + 0.05x}$, $C(0) = 25,000$

$$C(x) = \int\frac{250 + 10x}{1 + 0.05x}\,dx = 250\int\frac{1}{1 + 0.05x}\,dx + 10\int\frac{x}{1 + 0.05x}\,dx$$

$$= 250\left(\frac{1}{0.05}\ln|1 + 0.05x|\right) + 10\left(\frac{x}{0.05} - \frac{1}{(0.05)^2}\ln|1 + 0.05x|\right) + K$$

(Formulas 3 and 4)

$$= 5,000\ln|1 + 0.05x| + 200x - 4,000\ln|1 + 0.05x| + K$$
$$= 1,000\ln|1 + 0.05x| + 200x + K$$

Since $C(0) = 25,000$, $K = 25,000$ and
$$C(x) = 1,000\ln(1 + 0.05x) + 200x + 25,000, \; x \geq 0$$

To find the production level that produces a
cost of $150,000, solve $C(x) = 150,000$ for x:

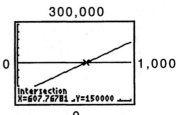

The production level is $x = 608$ pairs of skis.

At a production level of 850 pairs of skis,
$C(850) = 1,000 \ln(1 + 0.05[850]) + 200(850) + 25,000 \approx \$198,773$.

57. $FV = e^{rT} \int_0^T f(t) e^{-rt} dt$

Now, $r = 0.1$, $T = 10$, $f(t) = 50t^2$.

$FV = e^{(0.1)10} \int_0^{10} 50t^2 e^{-0.1t} dt = 50e \int_0^{10} t^2 e^{-0.1t} dt$

To evaluate the integral, use Formula 47 with $n = 2$ and $a = -0.1$:

$$\int t^2 e^{-0.1t} dt = \frac{t^2 e^{-0.1t}}{-0.1} - \frac{2}{-0.1} \int t e^{-0.1t} dt = -10t^2 e^{-0.1t} + 20 \int t e^{-0.1t} dt$$

Now, using Formula 47 again:

$$\int t e^{-0.1t} dt = \frac{t e^{-0.1t}}{-0.1} - \frac{1}{-0.1} \int e^{-0.1t} dt = -10t e^{-0.1t} + 10 \frac{e^{-0.1t}}{-0.1}$$

$$= -10t e^{-0.1t} - 100 e^{-0.1t}$$

Thus, $\int t^2 e^{-0.1t} dt = -10t^2 e^{-0.1t} - 200t e^{-0.1t} - 2000 e^{-0.1t} + C$.

$FV = 50e[-10t^2 e^{-0.1t} - 200t e^{-0.1t} - 2000 e^{-0.1t}] \Big|_0^{10}$

$= 50e[-1000e^{-1} - 2000e^{-1} - 2000e^{-1} + 2000] = 100,000e - 250,000$

$\approx 21,828$ or $\$21,828$

59. Gini Index:

$$2 \int_0^1 [x - f(x)] dx = 2 \int_0^1 \left[x - \frac{1}{2} x\sqrt{1 + 3x}\right] dx = \int_0^1 [2x - x\sqrt{1 + 3x}] dx$$

$$= \int_0^1 2x\, dx - \int_0^1 x\sqrt{1 + 3x}\, dx$$

For the second integral, use Formula 22 with $a = 1$ and $b = 3$:

$$= x^2 \Big|_0^1 - \frac{2(3 \cdot 3x - 2 \cdot 1)}{15(3)^2} \sqrt{(1 + 3x)^3} \Big|_0^1$$

$$= 1 - \frac{2(9x - 2)}{135} \sqrt{(1 + 3x)^3} \Big|_0^1$$

$$= 1 - \frac{14}{135} \sqrt{4^3} - \frac{4}{135} \sqrt{1^3}$$

$$= 1 - \frac{112}{135} - \frac{4}{135} = \frac{19}{135} \approx 0.1407$$

61.

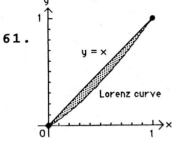

As the area bounded by the two curves gets smaller, the Lorenz curve approaches $y = x$ and the distribution of income approaches perfect equality — all individuals share equally in the income.

63. $S'(t) = \dfrac{t^2}{(1 + t)^2}$; $S(t) = \displaystyle\int \dfrac{t^2}{(1 + t)^2} dt$

Use Formula 7 with $a = 1$ and $b = 1$:

$$S(t) = \frac{1 + t}{1^3} - \frac{1^2}{1^3(1 + t)} - \frac{2(1)}{1^3}\ln|1 + t| + C$$

$$= 1 + t - \frac{1}{1 + t} - 2\ln|1 + t| + C$$

Since $S(0) = 0$, we have $0 = 1 - 1 - 2\ln 1 + C$ and $C = 0$. Thus,

$$S(t) = 1 + t - \frac{1}{1 + t} - 2\ln|1 + t|.$$

Now, the total sales during the first two years (= 24 months) is given by:

$$S(24) = 1 + 24 - \frac{1}{1 + 24} - 2\ln|1 + 24| = 24.96 - 2\ln 25 \approx 18.5$$

Thus, total sales during the first two years is approximately $18.5 million.

65.

The total sales, in millions of dollars, over the first two years (24 months) is the area under the curve $y = S'(t)$ from $t = 0$ to $t = 24$.

67. $P'(x) = x\sqrt{2 + 3x}$, $P(1) = -\$2,000$

$$P(x) = \int x\sqrt{2 + 3x}\, dx = \frac{2(9x - 4)}{135}(2 + 3x)^{3/2} + C$$
(Formula 22)

$$P(1) = \frac{2(5)}{135}5^{3/2} + C = -2,000$$

$$C = -2,000 - \frac{2}{27}5^{3/2} \approx -2,000.83$$

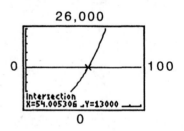

Thus, $P(x) = \dfrac{2(9x - 4)}{135}(2 + 3x)^{3/2} - 2,000.83.$

The number of cars that must be sold to have a profit of $13,000: 54

Profit if 10 cars are sold per week:

$$P(10) = \frac{2(86)}{135}(32)^{3/2} - 2,000.83 \approx -\$1,770$$

334

69. $\dfrac{dR}{dt} = \dfrac{100}{\sqrt{t^2 + 9}}$. Therefore,

$$R = \int \frac{100}{\sqrt{t^2 + 9}} dt = 100\int \frac{1}{\sqrt{t^2 + 9}} dt$$

Using Formula 36 with $a = 3$ $(a^2 = 9)$, we have:

$R = 100 \ln\left|t + \sqrt{t^2 + 9}\right| + C$

Now $R(0) = 0$, so $0 = 100 \ln|3| + C$ or $C = -100 \ln 3$. Thus,

$R(t) = 100 \ln\left|t + \sqrt{t^2 + 9}\right| - 100 \ln 3$

and

$\begin{aligned} R(4) &= 100 \ln(4 + \sqrt{4^2 + 9}) - 100 \ln 3 \\ &= 100 \ln 9 - 100 \ln 3 \\ &= 100 \ln 3 \approx 110 \text{ feet} \end{aligned}$

71. $N'(t) = \dfrac{60}{\sqrt{t^2 + 25}}$

The number of items learned in the first twelve hours of study is given by:

$$\begin{aligned} N &= \int_0^{12} \frac{60}{\sqrt{t^2 + 25}} dt = 60\int_0^{12} \frac{1}{\sqrt{t^2 + 25}} dt \\ &= 60\left(\ln\left|t + \sqrt{t^2 + 25}\right|\right)\Big|_0^{12}, \text{ using Formula 36} \\ &= 60\left[\ln\left|12 + \sqrt{12^2 + 25}\right| - \ln\sqrt{25}\right] \\ &= 60(\ln 25 - \ln 5) \\ &= 60 \ln 5 \approx 96.57 \text{ or } 97 \text{ items} \end{aligned}$$

73.

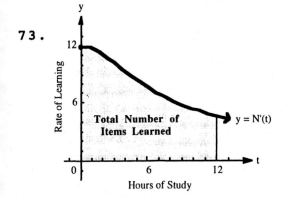

The area under the rate of learning curve, $y = N'(t)$, from $t = 0$ to $t = 12$ represents the total number of items learned in that time interval.

CHAPTER 5 REVIEW

1. $A = \displaystyle\int_a^b f(x)\, dx$ (7-1)   **2.** $A = \displaystyle\int_b^c [-f(x)]\, dx$ (7-1)

3. $A = \displaystyle\int_a^b f(x)\, dx + \int_b^c [-f(x)]\, dx$ (7-1)

4. $A = \int_{0.5}^{1} [-\ln x]\,dx + \int_{1}^{e} \ln x\,dx$

We evaluate the integral using integration-by-parts.
Let $u = \ln x$, $dv = dx$.

Then $du = \dfrac{1}{x}dx$, $v = x$, and $\int \ln x\,dx =$

$x \ln x - \int x\left(\dfrac{1}{x}\right)dx = x \ln x - x + C$

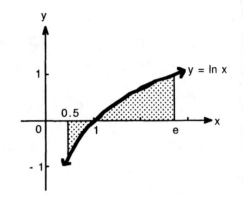

$y = \ln x$

Thus,

$A = -\int_{0.5}^{1} \ln x\,dx + \int_{1}^{e} \ln x\,dx$

$= (-x \ln x + x)\Big|_{0.5}^{1} + (x \ln x - x)\Big|_{1}^{e}$

$\approx (1 - 0.847) + (1) = 1.153$

5. $\int xe^{4x}\,dx$. Use integration-by-parts:

Let $u = x$ and $dv = e^{4x}dx$. Then $du = dx$ and $v = \dfrac{e^{4x}}{4}$.

$\int xe^{4x}\,dx = \dfrac{xe^{4x}}{4} - \int \dfrac{e^{4x}}{4}\,dx = \dfrac{xe^{4x}}{4} - \dfrac{e^{4x}}{16} + C$ $\qquad (7\text{-}3,\ 7\text{-}4)$

6. $\int x \ln x\,dx$. Use integration-by-parts:

Let $u = \ln x$ and $dv = x\,dx$. Then $du = \dfrac{1}{x}dx$ and $v = \dfrac{x^2}{2}$.

$\int x \ln x\,dx = \dfrac{x^2 \ln x}{2} - \int \dfrac{1}{x} \cdot \dfrac{x^2}{2}\,dx = \dfrac{x^2 \ln x}{2} - \dfrac{1}{2}\int x\,dx$

$= \dfrac{x^2 \ln x}{2} - \dfrac{x^2}{4} + C$ $\qquad (7\text{-}3,\ 7\text{-}4)$

7. $\int \dfrac{\ln x}{x}\,dx$

Let $u = \ln x$. Then $du = \dfrac{1}{x}dx$ and

$\int \dfrac{\ln x}{x}\,dx = \int u\,du = \dfrac{1}{2}u^2 + C = \dfrac{1}{2}[\ln x]^2 + C$ $\qquad (7\text{-}2)$

8. $\int \dfrac{x}{1 + x^2}\,dx$

Let $u = 1 + x^2$. Then $du = 2x\,dx$ and

$\int \dfrac{x}{1 + x^2}\,dx = \int \dfrac{1/2\ du}{u} = \dfrac{1}{2}\int \dfrac{1}{u}\,du = \dfrac{1}{2}\ln|u| + C = \dfrac{1}{2}\ln(1 + x^2) + C$ $\qquad (7\text{-}2)$

9. Use Formula 11 with $a = 1$ and $b = 1$.

$\int \dfrac{1}{x(1 + x)^2}\,dx = \dfrac{1}{1(1 + x)} + \dfrac{1}{1^2}\ln\left|\dfrac{x}{1 + x}\right| + C = \dfrac{1}{1 + x} + \ln\left|\dfrac{x}{1 + x}\right| + C$

$\qquad (7\text{-}4)$

10. Use Formula 28 with $a = 1$ and $b = 1$.

$$\int \frac{1}{x^2\sqrt{1+x}}\,dx = -\frac{\sqrt{1+x}}{1 \cdot x} - \frac{1}{2 \cdot 1\sqrt{1}}\ln\left|\frac{\sqrt{1+x}-\sqrt{1}}{\sqrt{1+x}+\sqrt{1}}\right| + C$$

$$= -\frac{\sqrt{1+x}}{x} - \frac{1}{2}\ln\left|\frac{\sqrt{1+x}-1}{\sqrt{1+x}+1}\right| + C \qquad (7\text{-}4)$$

11. $A = \int_a^b [f(x) - g(x)]\,dx$ $\qquad (7\text{-}1)$ **12.** $A = \int_b^c [g(x) - f(x)]\,dx$ $\qquad (7\text{-}1)$

13. $A = \int_b^c [g(x) - f(x)]\,dx + \int_c^d [f(x) - g(x)]\,dx$ $\qquad (7\text{-}1)$

14. $A = \int_a^b [f(x) - g(x)]\,dx + \int_b^c [g(x) - f(x)]\,dx + \int_c^d [f(x) - g(x)]\,dx$ $\qquad (7\text{-}1)$

15. $A = \int_0^5 [(9 - x) - (x^2 - 6x + 9)]\,dx$

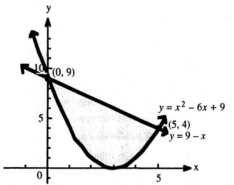

$$= \int_0^5 (5x - x^2)\,dx$$

$$= \left(\frac{5}{2}x^2 - \frac{1}{3}x^3\right)\Big|_0^5$$

$$= \frac{125}{2} - \frac{125}{3} = \frac{125}{6} \approx 20.833$$

16. $\int_0^1 xe^x\,dx.$ Use integration-by-parts.

Let $u = x$ and $dv = e^x\,dx$. Then $du = dx$ and $v = e^x$.

$\int xe^x\,dx = xe^x - \int e^x\,dx = xe^x - e^x + C$

Therefore, $\int_0^1 xe^x\,dx = (xe^x - e^x)\Big|_0^1 = 1 \cdot e - e - (0 \cdot 1 - 1)$

$$= 1 \qquad (7\text{-}3,\ 7\text{-}4)$$

17. Use Formula 38 with $a = 4$

$$\int_0^3 \frac{x^2}{\sqrt{x^2+16}}\,dx = \frac{1}{2}\left[x\sqrt{x^2+16} - 16\ln\left|x + \sqrt{x^2+16}\right|\right]\Big|_0^3$$

$$= \frac{1}{2}\left[3\sqrt{25} - 16\ln(3 + \sqrt{25})\right] - \frac{1}{2}(-16\ln\sqrt{16})$$

$$= \frac{1}{2}[15 - 16\ln 8] + 8\ln 4$$

$$= \frac{15}{2} - 8\ln 8 + 8\ln 4 \approx 1.955 \qquad (7\text{-}4)$$

18. Let $u = 3x$, then $du = 3\,dx$. Now, use Formula 40 with $a = 7$.

$$\int \sqrt{9x^2 - 49}\,dx = \frac{1}{3}\int \sqrt{u^2 - 49}\,du$$

$$= \frac{1}{3} \cdot \frac{1}{2}\left(u\sqrt{u^2 - 49} - 49\ln\left|u + \sqrt{u^2 - 49}\right|\right) + C$$

$$= \frac{1}{6}\left(3x\sqrt{9x^2 - 49} - 49\ln\left|3x + \sqrt{9x^2 - 49}\right|\right) + C \qquad (7\text{-}4)$$

19. $\int t e^{-0.5t} \, dt$. Use integration-by-parts.

Let $u = t$ and $dv = e^{-0.5t} dt$. Then $du = dt$ and $v = \dfrac{e^{-0.5t}}{-0.5}$.

$$\int t e^{-0.5t} \, dt = \frac{-t e^{-0.5t}}{0.5} + \int \frac{e^{-0.5t}}{0.5} \, dt = \frac{-t e^{-0.5t}}{0.5} + \frac{e^{-0.5t}}{-0.25} + C$$

$$= -2 t e^{-0.5t} - 4 e^{-0.5t} + C \qquad\qquad (7\text{-}3,\ 7\text{-}4)$$

20. $\int x^2 \ln x \, dx$. Use integration-by-parts.

Let $u = \ln x$ and $dv = x^2 dx$. Then $du = \dfrac{1}{x} dx$ and $v = \dfrac{x^3}{3}$.

$$\int x^2 \ln x \, dx = \frac{x^3 \ln x}{3} - \int \frac{1}{x} \cdot \frac{x^3}{3} \, dx = \frac{x^3 \ln x}{3} - \frac{1}{3} \int x^2 dx$$

$$= \frac{x^3 \ln x}{3} - \frac{x^3}{9} + C \qquad\qquad (7\text{-}3,\ 7\text{-}4)$$

21. Use Formula 48 with $a = 1$, $c = 1$, and $d = 2$.

$$\int \frac{1}{1 + 2e^x} \, dx = \frac{x}{1} - \frac{1}{1 \cdot 1} \ln|1 + 2e^x| + C = x - \ln|1 + 2e^x| + C \qquad (7\text{-}4)$$

22. (A)

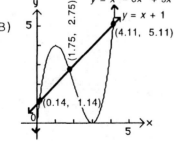

$y = x^3 - 6x^2 + 9x$
$y = x$
$(2, 2)$
$(4, 4)$

$$A = \int_0^2 [(x^3 - 6x^2 + 9x) - x] \, dx + \int_2^4 [x - (x^3 - 6x^2 + 9x)] \, dx$$

$$= \int_0^2 (x^3 - 6x^2 + 8x) \, dx + \int_2^4 (-x^3 + 6x^2 - 8x) \, dx$$

$$= \left(\frac{1}{4} x^4 - 2x^3 + 4x^2\right)\Big|_0^2 + \left(-\frac{1}{4} x^4 + 2x^3 - 4x^2\right)\Big|_2^4$$

$$= 4 + 4 = 8$$

(B)

$y = x^3 - 6x^2 + 9x$
$y = x + 1$
$(1.75,\ 2.75)$
$(4.11,\ 5.11)$
$(0.14,\ 1.14)$

The x-coordinates of the points of intersection are: $x_1 \approx 0.14$, $x_2 \approx 1.75$, $x_3 \approx 4.11$.

$$A = \int_{0.14}^{1.75} [(x^3 - 6x^2 + 9x) - (x + 1)]\,dx$$

$$+ \int_{1.75}^{4.11} [(x + 1) - (x^3 - 6x^2 + 9x)]\,dx$$

$$= \int_{0.14}^{1.75} (x^3 - 6x^2 + 8x - 1)\,dx + \int_{1.75}^{4.11} (1 - x^3 + 6x^2 - 8x)\,dx$$

$$= \left(\frac{1}{4}x^4 - 2x^3 + 4x^2 - x\right)\Big|_{0.14}^{1.75} + \left(x - \frac{1}{4}x^4 + 2x^3 - 4x^2\right)\Big|_{1.75}^{4.11}$$

$$= [2.126 - (-0.066)] + [4.059 - (-2.126)] \approx 8.38 \qquad (7\text{-}1)$$

23. $\displaystyle\int \frac{(\ln x)^2}{x}\,dx = \int u^2 du = \frac{u^3}{3} + C = \frac{(\ln x)^3}{3} + C$ Substitution: $u = \ln x$

$$du = \frac{1}{x}\,dx \qquad (7\text{-}2)$$

24. $\displaystyle\int x(\ln x)^2 dx.$ Use integration-by-parts.

Let $u = (\ln x)^2$ and $dv = x\,dx$. Then $du = 2(\ln x)\dfrac{1}{x}\,dx$ and $v = \dfrac{x^2}{2}$.

$$\int x(\ln x)^2 dx = \frac{x^2(\ln x)^2}{2} - \int 2(\ln x)\frac{1}{x}\cdot\frac{x^2}{2}\,dx = \frac{x^2(\ln x)^2}{2} - \int x \ln x\,dx$$

Let $u = \ln x$ and $dv = x\,dx$. Then $du = \dfrac{1}{x}\,dx$ and $v = \dfrac{x^2}{2}$.

$$\int x \ln x\,dx$$

Thus, $\displaystyle\int x(\ln x)^2 dx = \frac{x^2(\ln x)^2}{2} - \left[\frac{x^2 \ln x}{2} - \frac{x^2}{4}\right] + C$

$$= \frac{x^2(\ln x)^2}{2} - \frac{x^2 \ln x}{2} + \frac{x^2}{4} + C. \qquad (7\text{-}3,\ 7\text{-}4)$$

25. Let $u = x^2 - 36$. Then $du = 2x\,dx$.

$$\int \frac{x}{\sqrt{x^2 - 36}}\,dx = \int \frac{x}{(x^2 - 36)^{1/2}}\,dx = \frac{1}{2}\int \frac{1}{u^{1/2}}\,du = \frac{1}{2}\int u^{-1/2}\,du$$

$$= \frac{1}{2}\cdot\frac{u^{1/2}}{1/2} + C = u^{1/2} + C = \sqrt{x^2 - 36} + C \qquad (6\text{-}2)$$

26. Let $u = x^2$, $du = 2x\,dx$.

Then use Formula 43 with $a = 6$.

$$\int \frac{x}{\sqrt{x^4 - 36}}\,dx = \frac{1}{2}\int \frac{du}{\sqrt{u^2 - 36}} = \frac{1}{2}\ln\left|u + \sqrt{u^2 - 36}\right| + C$$

$$= \frac{1}{2}\ln\left|x^2 + \sqrt{x^4 - 36}\right| + C \qquad (7\text{-}4)$$

27. $\int_0^4 x \ln(10 - x)\,dx$

Substitution: $t = 10 - x$
$dt = -dx$
$x = 10 - t$

Consider

$$\int x \ln(10 - x)\,dx = \int (10 - t)\ln t\,(-dt)$$

$$= \int t \ln t\,dt - 10\int \ln t\,dt.$$

Now use integration-by-parts on the two integrals.

Let $u = \ln t$, $dv = t\,dt$. Then $du = \dfrac{1}{t}\,dt$, $v = \dfrac{t^2}{2}$.

$$\int t \ln t\,dt = \frac{t^2}{2}\ln t - \int \frac{t^2}{2}\cdot\frac{1}{t}\,dt = \frac{t^2 \ln t}{2} - \frac{t^2}{4} + C$$

Let $u = \ln t$, $dv = dt$. Then $du = \dfrac{1}{t}\,dt$, $v = t$.

$$\int t \ln t\,dt = t \ln t - \int t\cdot\frac{1}{t}\,dt = t \ln t - t + C$$

Thus, $\displaystyle\int_0^4 x \ln(10 - x)\,dx = \left[\frac{(10 - x)^2 \ln(10 - x)}{2} - \frac{(10 - x)^2}{4}\right.$

$$\left. -10(10 - x)\ln(10 - x) + 10(10 - x)\right]\Bigg|_0^4$$

$$= \frac{36 \ln 6}{2} - \frac{36}{4} - 10(6)\ln 6 + 10(6)$$

$$- \left[\frac{100 \ln 10}{2} - \frac{100}{4} - 10(10)\ln 10 + 10(10)\right]$$

$$= 18 \ln 6 - 9 - 60 \ln 6 + 60 - 50 \ln 10 + 25$$
$$+ 100 \ln 10 - 100$$

$$= 50 \ln 10 - 42 \ln 6 - 24 \approx 15.875. \qquad (7\text{-}3,\ 7\text{-}4)$$

28. Use Formula 52 with $n = 2$.

$$\int (\ln x)^2\,dx = x(\ln x)^2 - 2\int \ln x\,dx$$

Now use integration-by-parts to calculate $\int \ln x\,dx$.

Let $u = \ln x$, $dv = dx$. Then $du = \dfrac{1}{x}\,dx$, $v = x$.

$$\int \ln x\,dx = x \ln x - \int x\cdot\frac{1}{x}\,dx = x \ln x - x + C$$

Therefore, $\displaystyle\int (\ln x)^2\,dx = x(\ln x)^2 - 2[x \ln x - x] + C$

$$= x(\ln x)^2 - 2x \ln x + 2x + C. \qquad (7\text{-}3,\ 7\text{-}4)$$

29. $\int xe^{-2x^2}\,dx$

Let $u = -2x^2$. Then $du = -4x\,dx$.
$$\int xe^{-2x^2}\,dx = -\frac{1}{4}\int e^u\,du = -\frac{1}{4}e^u + C$$

$$= -\frac{1}{4}e^{-2x^2} + C \qquad (6\text{-}2)$$

30. $\int x^2 e^{-2x}\, dx$. Use integration-by-parts. Let $u = x^2$ and $dv = e^{-2x}dx$.

Then $du = 2x\, dx$ and $v = -\dfrac{1}{2}e^{-2x}$.

$$\int x^2 e^{-2x}\, dx = -\frac{1}{2}x^2 e^{-2x} + \int xe^{-2x}\, dx$$

Now use integration-by-parts again. Let $u = x$ and $dv = e^{-2x}dx$.
Then $du = dx$ and $v = -\dfrac{1}{2}e^{-2x}$.

$$\int xe^{-2x}\, dx = -\frac{1}{2}xe^{-2x} + \frac{1}{2}\int e^{-2x}\, dx$$

$$= -\frac{1}{2}xe^{-2x} - \frac{1}{4}e^{-2x} + C$$

Thus,

$$\int x^2 e^{-2x}\, dx = -\frac{1}{2}x^2 e^{-2x} + \left[-\frac{1}{2}xe^{-2x} - \frac{1}{4}e^{-2x} \right] + C$$

$$= -\frac{1}{2}x^2 e^{-2x} - \frac{1}{2}xe^{-2x} - \frac{1}{4}e^{-2x} + C \qquad\qquad (7\text{-}3,\ 7\text{-}4)$$

31. First graph the two functions to find the points of intersection.

The curves intersect at the points where $x = 1.448$ and $x = 6.915$.

Area $A = \displaystyle\int_{1.448}^{6.915}\left(\frac{6}{2 + 5e^{-x}} - [0.2x + 1.6] \right)dx$

≈ 1.703

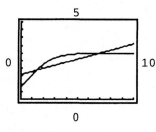

$(7\text{-}1)$

32. (A) Probability $(0 \le t \le 1) = \displaystyle\int_0^1 0.21e^{-0.21t}\, dt$

$$= -e^{-0.21t}\Big|_0^1$$

$$= -e^{-0.21} + 1 \approx 0.189$$

(B) Probability $(1 \le t \le 2) = \displaystyle\int_1^2 0.21e^{-0.21t}\, dt$

$$= -e^{-0.21t}\Big|_1^2$$

$$= e^{-0.21} - e^{-0.42} \approx 0.154 \qquad\qquad (7\text{-}2)$$

33.

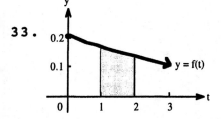

The probability that the product will fail during the second year of warranty is the area under the probability density function $y = f(t)$ from $t = 1$ to $t = 2$.

34. $R'(x) = 65 - 6 \ln(x + 1)$, $R(0) = 0$

$R(x) = \int [65 - 6 \ln(x + 1)] dx = 65x - 6\int \ln(x + 1) dx$

Let $z = x + 1$. Then $dz = dx$ and $\int \ln(x + 1) dx = \int \ln z \, dz$.

Now, let $u = \ln z$ and $dv = dz$. Then $du = \dfrac{1}{z} dz$ and $v = z$:

$$\int \ln z \, dz = z \ln z - \int z\left(\frac{1}{z}\right) dz = z \ln z - \int dz = z \ln z - z + C$$

Therefore, $\int \ln(x + 1) dx = (x + 1) \ln(x + 1) - (x + 1) + C$ and

$R(x) = 65x - 6[(x + 1)\ln(x + 1) - (x + 1)] + C$

Since $R(0) = 0$, $C = -6$. Thus,

$R(x) = 65x - 6[(x + 1)\ln(x + 1) - x]$

To find the production level for a revenue of $20,000 per week, solve $R(x) = 20,000$ for x.

The production level should be 618 hair dryers per week.

At a production level of 1,000 hair dryers per week, revenue

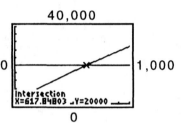

$R(1,000) = 65,000 - 6[(1,001)\ln(1,001) - 1,000] \approx \$29,506$ (7-3)

35. (A)

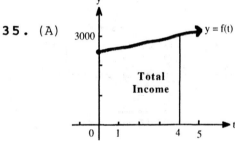

(B) Total income $= \displaystyle\int_1^4 2,500e^{0.05t} \, dt$

$= 50,000e^{0.05t} \Big|_1^4$

$= 50,000[e^{0.2} - e^{0.05}] \approx \$8,507$ (7-2)

36. $f(t) = 2,500e^{0.05t}$, $r = 0.15$, $T = 5$

(A) $FV = e^{(0.15)5} \displaystyle\int_0^5 2,500e^{0.05t} e^{-0.15t} \, dt = 2,500e^{0.75} \int_0^5 e^{-0.1t} \, dt$

$= -25,000e^{0.75} \; e^{-0.1t} \Big|_0^5$

$= 25,000[e^{0.75} - e^{0.25}] \approx \$20,824$

(B) Total income $= \displaystyle\int_0^5 2,500e^{0.05t} \, dt = 50,000e^{0.05t} \Big|_0^5$

$= 50,000[e^{0.25} - 1]$

$\approx \$14,201$

Interest $= FV - $ Total income $= \$20,824 - \$14,201 = \$6,623$ (7-2)

37. (A)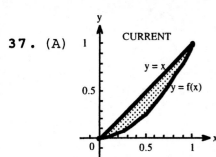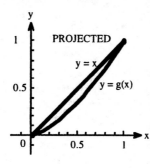

(B) The income will be more equally distributed 10 years from now since the area between $y = x$ and the projected Lorenz curve is less than the area between $y = x$ and the current Lorenz curve.

(C) Current:

$$\text{Gini Index} = 2\int_0^1 [x - (0.1x + 0.9x^2)]\,dx$$

$$= 2\int_0^1 (0.9x - 0.9x^2)\,dx = 2(0.45x^2 - 0.3x^3)\Big|_0^1 = 0.30$$

Projected:

$$\text{Gini Index} = 2\int_0^1 (x - x^{1.5})\,dx$$

$$= 2\int_0^1 (x - x^{3/2})\,dx = 2\left(\frac{1}{2}x^2 - \frac{2}{5}x^{5/2}\right)\Big|_0^1 = 2\left(\frac{1}{10}\right) = 0.2$$

Thus, income will be more equally distributed 10 years from now, as indicated in part (B). (7-1)

38. (A) $p = D(x) = 70 - 0.2x$, $p = S(x) = 13 + 0.0012x^2$
Equilibrium price: $D(x) = S(x)$

$$70 - 0.2x = 13 + 0.0012x^2$$

$$0.0012x^2 + 0.2x - 57 = 0$$

$$x = \frac{-0.2 \pm \sqrt{0.04 + 0.2736}}{0.0024} = \frac{-0.2 \pm 0.56}{0.0024}$$

Therefore, $\bar{x} = \dfrac{-0.2 + 0.56}{0.0024} = 150$, and $\bar{p} = 70 - 0.2(150) = 40$.

$$CS = \int_0^{150} (70 - 0.2x - 40)\,dx = \int_0^{150} (30 - 0.2x)\,dx$$

$$= (30x - 0.1x^2)\Big|_0^{150}$$

$$= \$2,250$$

$$PS = \int_0^{150} [40 - (13 + 0.012x^2)]\,dx = \int_0^{150} (27 - 0.012x^2)\,dx$$

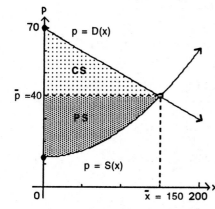

$$= (27x - 0.0004x^3)\Big|_0^{150}$$

$$= \$2,700$$

(B) $p = D(x) = 70 - 0.2x$, $p = S(x) = 13e^{0.006x}$

Equilibrium price: $D(x) = S(x)$
$$70 - 0.2x = 13e^{0.006x}$$

Using a graphing utility to solve for x, we get $\bar{x} \approx 170$ and $\bar{p} = 70 - 0.2(170) \approx 36$.

$$CS = \int_0^{170} (70 - 0.2x - 36)\,dx = \int_0^{170} (34 - 0.2x)\,dx$$
$$= (34x - 0.1x^2)\Big|_0^{170}$$
$$= \$2,890$$

$$PS = \int_0^{170} (36 - 13e^{0.006x})\,dx = (36x - 2,166.67e^{0.006x})\Big|_0^{170}$$
$$\approx \$2,278$$

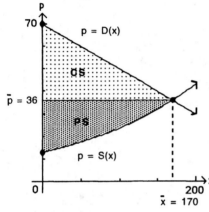

(7-2)

39. (A)

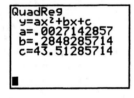

Graph the quadratic regression model and the line $p = 52.50$ to find the point of intersection.

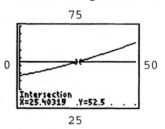

The demand at a price of 52.50 cents per pound is 25,403 lbs.

(B) Let $S(x)$ be the quadratic regression model found in part (A). Then the producers' surplus at the price level of 52.5 cents per pound is given by
$$PS = \int_0^{25.403} [52.5 - S(x)]\,dx \approx \$1,216$$

(7-2)

40. $R(t) = \dfrac{60t}{(t + 1)^2(t + 2)}$

The amount of the drug eliminated during the first hour is given by
$$A = \int_0^1 \frac{60t}{(t + 1)^2(t + 2)} \, dt$$

We will use the Table of Integration Formulas to calculate this integral. First, let $u = t + 2$. Then $t = u - 2$, $t + 1 = u - 1$, $du = dt$ and

$$\int \frac{60t}{(t + 1)^2(t + 2)} \, dt = 60 \int \frac{u - 2}{(u - 1)^2 \cdot u} \, du$$
$$= 60 \int \frac{1}{(u - 1)^2} \, du - 120 \int \frac{1}{u(u - 1)^2} \, du$$

In the first integral, let $v = u - 1$, $dv = du$. Then
$$60 \int \frac{1}{(u - 1)^2} \, du = 60 \int v^{-2} \, dv = -60v^{-1} = \frac{-60}{u - 1}$$

For the second integral, use Formula 11 with $a = -1$, $b = 1$:
$$-120 \int \frac{1}{u(u - 1)^2} \, du = -120 \left[\frac{-1}{u - 1} + \ln \left| \frac{u}{u - 1} \right| \right]$$

Combining these results and replacing u by $t + 2$, we have:
$$\int \frac{60t}{(t + 1)^2(t + 2)} \, dt = \frac{-60}{t + 1} + \frac{120}{t + 1} - 120 \ln \left| \frac{t + 2}{t + 1} \right| + C$$
$$= \frac{60}{t + 1} - 120 \ln \left| \frac{t + 2}{t + 1} \right| + C$$

Now,
$$A = \int_0^1 \frac{60t}{(t + 1)^2(t + 2)} \, dt = \left[\frac{60}{t + 1} - 120 \ln \left(\frac{t + 2}{t + 1} \right) \right] \Big|_0^1$$
$$= 30 - 120 \ln \left(\frac{3}{2} \right) - 60 + 120 \ln 2$$
$$\approx 4.522 \text{ milliliters}$$

The amount of drug eliminated during the 4th hour is given by:
$$A = \int_3^4 \frac{60t}{(t + 1)^2(t + 2)} \, dt = \left[\frac{60}{t + 1} - 120 \ln \left(\frac{t + 2}{t + 1} \right) \right] \Big|_3^4$$
$$= 12 - 120 \ln \left(\frac{6}{5} \right) - 15 + 120 \ln \left(\frac{5}{4} \right)$$
$$\approx 1.899 \text{ milliliters}$$

(6-5, 7-4)

41.

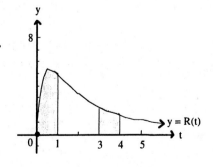

(7-2)

345

42. $f(t) = \begin{cases} \dfrac{4/3}{(t+1)^2} & 0 \leq t \leq 3 \\ 0 & \text{otherwise} \end{cases}$

(A) Probability $(0 \leq t \leq 1) = \int_0^1 \dfrac{4/3}{(t+1)^2}\,dt$

To calculate the integral, let $u = t + 1$, $du = dt$. Then,

$$\int \dfrac{4/3}{(t+1)^2}\,dt = \dfrac{4}{3}\int u^{-2}\,du = \dfrac{4}{3}\dfrac{u^{-1}}{-1} = -\dfrac{4}{3u} + C = \dfrac{-4}{3(t+1)} + C$$

Thus,

$$\int_0^1 \dfrac{4/3}{(t+1)^2}\,dt = \dfrac{-4}{3(t+1)}\bigg|_0^1 = -\dfrac{2}{3} + \dfrac{4}{3} = \dfrac{2}{3} \approx 0.667$$

(B) Probability $(t \geq 1) = \int_1^3 \dfrac{4/3}{(t+1)^2}\,dt$

$$= \dfrac{-4}{3(t+1)}\bigg|_1^3$$

$$= -\dfrac{1}{3} + \dfrac{2}{3} = \dfrac{1}{3} \approx 0.333 \tag{7-2}$$

43.

The probability that the doctor will spend more than an hour with a randomly selected patient is the area under the probability density function $y = f(t)$ from $t = 1$ to $t = 3$.

44. $N'(t) = \dfrac{100t}{(1 + t^2)^2}$. To find $N(t)$, we calculate

$$\int \dfrac{100t}{(1 + t^2)^2}\,dt$$

Let $u = 1 + t^2$. Then $du = 2t\,dt$, and

$$N(t) = \int \dfrac{100t}{(1 + t^2)^2}\,dt = 50\int \dfrac{1}{u^2}\,du = 50\int u^{-2}\,du$$

$$= -50\dfrac{1}{u} + C$$

$$= \dfrac{-50}{1 + t^2} + C$$

At $t = 0$, we have
$$N(0) = -50 + C$$
Therefore, $C = N(0) + 50$ and
$$N(t) = \dfrac{-50}{1 + t^2} + 50 + N(0)$$

Now,
$$N(3) = \dfrac{-5}{1 + 3^2} + 50 + N(0) = 45 + N(0)$$

Thus, the population will increase by 45 thousand during the next 3 years. $\qquad (6-5, 7-1)$

45. We want to find Probability $(t \geq 2) = \int_2^\infty f(t)\,dt$

Since

$$\int_{-\infty}^\infty f(t)\,dt = \int_{-\infty}^2 f(t)\,dt + \int_2^\infty f(t)\,dt = 1,$$

$$\int_2^\infty f(t)\,dt = 1 - \int_{-\infty}^2 f(t)\,dt = 1 - \int_0^2 f(t)\,dt \text{ (since } f(t) = 0 \text{ for } t \leq 0)$$

$$= 1 - \text{Probability } (0 \leq t \leq 2)$$

Now, Probability $(0 \leq t \leq 2) = \int_0^2 0.5 e^{-0.5t}\,dt$

$$= -e^{-0.5t}\,\Big|_0^2$$

$$= -e^{-1} + 1 \approx 0.632$$

Therefore, Probability $(t \geq 2) = 1 - 0.632 = 0.368$ (7-2)

6 Multivariate Calculus

Things to remember:

1. An equation of the form $z = f(x, y)$ describes a FUNCTION OF TWO INDEPENDENT VARIABLES if for each permissible ordered pair (x, y) there is one and only one value of z determined by $f(x, y)$. The variables x and y are INDEPENDENT VARIABLES, and the variable z is a DEPENDENT VARIABLE. The set of all ordered pairs of permissible values of x and y is the DOMAIN of the function, and the set of all corresponding values $f(x, y)$ is the RANGE of the function.

2. CONVENTION ON DOMAINS

   Unless otherwise stated, the domain of a function specified by an equation of the form $z = f(x, y)$ is the set of all ordered pairs of real numbers (x, y) such that $f(x, y)$ is also a real number.

3. Functions of three independent variables $w = f(x, y, z)$, four independent variables $u = f(x, y, z, w)$, and so on, are defined similarly.

In Problems 1 - 9, $f(x, y) = 2x + 7y - 5$ and $g(x, y) = \dfrac{88}{x^2 + 3y}$.

1. $f(4, -1) = 2(4) + 7(-1) - 5 = -4$ | **3.** $f(8, 0) = 2(8) + 7(0) - 5 = 11$

5. $g(1, 7) = \dfrac{88}{1^2 + 3(7)} = \dfrac{88}{22} = 4$ **7.** $g(3, -3)$ not defined; $3^2 + 3(-3) = 0$

9. $3f(-2, 2) + 5g(-2, 2) = 3[2(-2) + 7(2) - 5] + 5 \cdot \dfrac{88}{(-2)^2 + 3(2)}$

$$= 3(5) + 5 \cdot \dfrac{88}{10} = 59$$

In Problems 11 - 13, $f(x, y, z) = 2x - 3y^2 + 5z^3 - 1$.

11. $f(0, 0, 0) = 2(0) - 3(0) + 5(0) - 1 = -1$

13. $f(6, -5, 0) = 2(6) - 3(-5)^2 + 5(0) - 1 = 12 - 75 - 1 = -64$

15. $V(r, h) = \pi r^2 h$
$V(2, 4) = \pi \cdot 2^2 \cdot 4 = 16\pi$
($r = 2$ and $h = 4$)

17. $R(x, y) = -5x^2 + 6xy - 4y^2 + 200x + 300y$
$R(1, 2) = -5(1)^2 + 6 \cdot 1 \cdot 2 - 4 \cdot 2^2 + 200 \cdot 1 + 300 \cdot 2$
$= -5 + 12 - 16 + 200 + 600$
$= 791$
($x = 1$ and $y = 2$)

19. $R(L, r) = .002 \dfrac{L}{r^4}$
$R(6, 0.5) = 0.002 \dfrac{6}{(0.5)^4} = \dfrac{0.012}{0.0625} = 0.192$
($L = 6$ and $r = 0.5$)

21. $A(P, r, t) = P + Prt$
$A(100, 0.06, 3) = 100 + 100(0.06)3 = 118$
($P = 100$, $r = 0.06$, and $t = 3$)

23. $P(r, t) = \displaystyle\int_0^T 4000e^{-rt}dt,$

$P(0.05, 12) = \displaystyle\int_0^{12} 4000e^{-0.05t}dt = \dfrac{4000}{-0.05} e^{-0.05t} \Big|_0^{12}$

$= -80,000[e^{-0.6} - 1]$
$\approx 36,095.07$

25. $F(x, y) = x^2 + e^x y - y^2$; $F(x, 2) = x^2 + 2e^x - 4$.

We use a graphing utility to solve $F(x, 2) = 0$.
The graph of $u = F(x, 2)$ is shown at the right.
The solutions of $F(x, 2) = 0$ are: $x_1 \approx -1.926$,
$x_2 \approx 0.599$

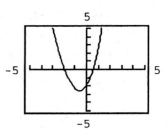

27. $f(x, y) = x^2 + 2y^2$
$\dfrac{f(x + h, y) - f(x, y)}{h} = \dfrac{(x + h)^2 + 2y^2 - (x^2 + 2y^2)}{h}$

$= \dfrac{x^2 + 2xh + h^2 + 2y^2 - x^2 - 2y^2}{h}$

$= \dfrac{2xh + h^2}{h} = \dfrac{h(2x + h)}{h} = 2x + h, \quad h \neq 0$

29. $f(x, y) = 2xy^2$
$\dfrac{f(x + h, y) - f(x, y)}{h} = \dfrac{2(x + h)y^2 - 2xy^2}{h}$

$= \dfrac{2xy^2 + 2hy^2 - 2xy^2}{h} = \dfrac{2hy^2}{h} = 2y^2, \quad h \neq 0$

31. Coordinates of point $E = E(0, 0, 3)$.
Coordinates of point $F = F(2, 0, 3)$.

33. $f(x, y) = x^2$

(A) In the plane $y = c$, c any constant, the graph of $z = x^2$ is a parabola.

(B) Cross-section corresponding to $x = 0$: the y-axis

Cross-section corresponding to $x = 1$: the line passing through $(1, 0, 1)$ parallel to the y-axis.

Cross-section corresponding to $x = 2$: the line passing through $(2, 0, 4)$ parallel to the y-axis.

(C) The surface $z = x^2$ is a parabolic trough lying on the y-axis.

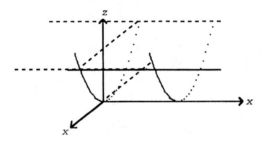

35. $f(x, y) = \sqrt{36 - x^2 - y^2}$

(A) Cross-sections corresponding to $y = 1$, $y = 2$, $y = 3$, $y = 4$, $y = 5$: Upper semicircles with centers at $(0, 1, 0)$, $(0, 2, 0)$, $(0, 3, 0)$, $(0, 4, 0)$, and $(0, 5, 0)$, respectively.

(B) Cross-sections corresponding to $x = 0$, $x = 1$, $x = 2$, $x = 3$, $x = 4$, $x = 5$: Upper semicircles with centers at $(0, 0, 0)$, $(1, 0, 0)$, $(2, 0, 0)$, $(3, 0, 0)$, $(4, 0, 0)$ and $(5, 0, 0)$, respectively.

(C) The upper hemisphere of radius 6 with center at the origin.

37. (A) If the points (a, b) and (c, d) both lie on the same circle centered at the origin, then $a^2 + b^2 = r^2 = c^2 + d^2$, where r is the radius of the circle.

(B) The cross-sections are:

(i) $x = 0$, $f(0, y) = e^{-y^2}$

(ii) $y = 0$, $f(x, 0) = e^{-x^2}$

(iii) $x = y$, $f(x, x) = e^{-2x^2}$

These are bell-shaped curves with maximum value 1 at $y = 0$ in (i) and $x = 0$ in (ii) and (iii).

(C) A "bell" with maximum value 1 at the origin, extending infinitely far in all directions, and approaching the x-y plane as x, $y \to \pm\infty$.

39. Monthly cost function = $C(x, y) = 2000 + 70x + 100y$

$$C(20, 10) = 2000 + 70 \cdot 20 + 100 \cdot 10 = \$4400$$
$$C(50, 5) = 2000 + 70 \cdot 50 + 100 \cdot 5 = \$6000$$
$$C(30, 30) = 2000 + 70 \cdot 30 + 100 \cdot 30 = \$7100$$

41. $R(p, q) = p \cdot x + q \cdot y = 200p - 5p^2 + 4pq + 300q - 4q^2 + 2pq$ or

$R(p, q) = -5p^2 + 6pq - 4q^2 + 200p + 300q$

$R(2, 3) = -5 \cdot 2^2 + 6 \cdot 2 \cdot 3 - 4 \cdot 3^2 + 200 \cdot 2 + 300 \cdot 3 = 1280$ or \$1280

$R(3, 2) = -5 \cdot 3^2 + 6 \cdot 3 \cdot 2 - 4 \cdot 2^2 + 200 \cdot 3 + 300 \cdot 2 = 1175$ or \$1175

43. $f(x, y) = 20x^{0.4}y^{0.6}$

$f(1250, 1700) = 20(1250)^{0.4}(1700)^{0.6}$

$\approx 20(17.3286)(86.7500) \approx 30,065$ units

45. $F(p, i, n) = p\dfrac{(1 + i)^n - 1}{i}$

(A) $p = 2,000$, $i = 0.09$, $n = 30$

$$F(2000, 0.09, 30) = 2000\dfrac{(1.09)^{30} - 1}{0.09} = \$272,615.08$$

(B) Set $y_1 = 2000\dfrac{(1 + i)^{30} - 1}{i}$, $y_2 = 500,000$

and find the intersection of the two curves.

Rate of interest: $i = 12.18\%$

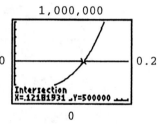

47. $T(V, x) = \dfrac{33V}{x + 33}$

$T(70, 47) = \dfrac{33 \cdot 70}{47 + 33} = \dfrac{33 \cdot 70}{80} = 28.8 \approx 29$ minutes

$T(60, 27) = \dfrac{33 \cdot 60}{27 + 33} = 33$ minutes

49. $C(W, L) = 100\dfrac{W}{L}$

$C(6, 8) = 100\dfrac{6}{8} = 75$

$C(8.1, 9) = 100\dfrac{8.1}{9} = 90$

51. $Q(M, C) = \dfrac{M}{C}100$

$Q(12, 10) = \dfrac{12}{10}100 = 120$

$Q(10, 12) = \dfrac{10}{12}100 = 83.33 \approx 83$

EXERCISE 6-2

Things to remember:

<u>1</u>. Let $z = f(x, y)$ be a function of two independent variables. The PARTIAL DERIVATIVE OF z WITH RESPECT TO x, denoted by $\dfrac{\partial z}{\partial x}$, f_x, or $f_x(x, y)$, is given by

$$\frac{\partial z}{\partial x} = \lim_{h \to 0} \frac{f(x + h, y) - f(x, y)}{h}$$

provided this limit exists. Similarly, the PARTIAL DERIVATIVE OF z WITH RESPECT TO y, denoted by $\dfrac{\partial z}{\partial y}$, f_y, or $f_y(x, y)$, is given by

$$\frac{\partial z}{\partial y} = \lim_{k \to 0} \frac{f(x, y + k) - f(x, y)}{k}$$

provided this limit exists.

2. SECOND-ORDER PARTIAL DERIVATIVES

If $z = f(x, y)$, then:

$$\frac{\partial^2 z}{\partial x^2} = \frac{\partial\left(\frac{\partial z}{\partial x}\right)}{\partial x} = f_{xx}(x, y) = f_{xx}$$

$$\frac{\partial^2 z}{\partial x \partial y} = \frac{\partial\left(\frac{\partial z}{\partial y}\right)}{\partial x} = f_{yx}(x, y) = f_{yx}$$

$$\frac{\partial^2 z}{\partial y \partial x} = \frac{\partial\left(\frac{\partial z}{\partial x}\right)}{\partial y} = f_{xy}(x, y) = f_{xy}$$

$$\frac{\partial^2 z}{\partial y^2} = \frac{\partial\left(\frac{\partial z}{\partial y}\right)}{\partial y} = f_{yy}(x, y) = f_{yy}$$

[Note: For the functions being considered in this text, the mixed partial derivatives f_{xy} and f_{yx} are equal, i.e., $\dfrac{\partial^2 z}{\partial x \partial y} = \dfrac{\partial^2 z}{\partial y \partial x}$.]

1. $z = 3 + 4x - 5y^2$
$\dfrac{\partial z}{\partial x} = 0 + 4 - 0 = 4$

3. $z = 3 + 4x - 5y^2$
$f_y = 0 + 0 - 10y$; $f_y(1, 2) = -20$

In Problems 5 - 9, $z = f(x, y) = 8x + 6y^3 - 3xy^2$.

5. $\dfrac{\partial z}{\partial y} = 18y^2 - 6xy$

7. From Problem 5, $\dfrac{\partial^2 z}{\partial y^2} = 36y - 6x$.

9. $f_x = 8 - 3y^2$; $f_x(2, 3) = 8 - 27 = -19$

In Problems 11 - 17, $C(x, y) = -7x^2 + 10xy + 4y^2 - 9x + 8y + 12$.

11. $C_x(x, y) = -14x + 10y - 9$

13. From Problem 11, $C_x(2, 2) = -28 + 20 - 9 = -17$

15. From Problem 11, $C_{xy} = 10$.

17. From Problem 11, $C_{xx} = -14$.

In Problems 19-23, $S(x, y) = 2y^3 e^x + 5x^4 \ln y$.

19. $S_x(x, y) = 2y^3 e^x + 20x^3 \ln y$

21. $S_y(x, y) = 6y^2 e^x + \dfrac{5x^4}{y}$; $\quad S_y(2, 1) = 6e^2 + 80$

23. From Problem 19, $S_{xy}(x, y) = 6y^2 e^x + \dfrac{20x^3}{y}$.

In Problems 25 - 32, $z = f(x, y) = e^{4x^2+5y}$.

25. $\dfrac{\partial z}{\partial x} = e^{4x^2+5y} \cdot \dfrac{\partial}{\partial x}(4x^2 + 5y) = e^{4x^2+5y}(8x) = 8xe^{4x^2+5y}$

27. From Problem 25, $\dfrac{\partial z}{\partial x} = 8xe^{4x^2+5y}$. Therefore,

$$\dfrac{\partial^2 z}{\partial x \partial y} = \dfrac{\partial}{\partial y}(8xe^{4x^2+5y}) = 8xe^{4x^2+5y}\dfrac{\partial}{\partial y}(4x^2 + 5y)$$
$$= 8xe^{4x^2+5y}(5)$$
$$= 40xe^{4x^2+5y}$$

29. From Problem 27, $f_{xy} = 40xe^{4x^2+5y}$. Therefore,

$f_{xy}(1, 0) = 40e^4$

31. From Problem 25, $f_x = 8xe^{4x^2+5y}$. Therefore,

$$f_{xx} = 8xe^{4x^2+5y}\dfrac{\partial}{\partial x}(4x^2 + 5y) + e^{4x^2+5y}(8)$$
$$= 8xe^{4x^2+5y}(8x) + 8e^{4x^2+5y}$$
$$= 64x^2 e^{4x^2+5y} + 8e^{4x^2+5y}$$
$f_{xx}(0, 1) = 8e^5$

33. $f(x, y) = (x^2 - y^3)^3$

$f_x(x, y) = 3(x^2 - y^3)^2 \dfrac{\partial(x^2 - y^3)}{\partial x} = 3(x^2 - y^3)^2 2x = 6x(x^2 - y^3)^2$

$f_y(x, y) = 3(x^2 - y^3)^2 \dfrac{\partial(x^2 - y^3)}{\partial y} = 3(x^2 - y^3)^2(-3y^2) = -9y^2(x^2 - y^3)^2$

35. $f(x, y) = (3x^2y - 1)^4$

$f_x(x, y) = 4(3x^2y - 1)^3 \dfrac{\partial(3x^2y - 1)}{\partial x} = 4(3x^2y - 1)^3 6xy = 24xy(3x^2y - 1)^3$

$f_y(x, y) = 4(3x^2y - 1)^3 \dfrac{\partial(3x^2y - 1)}{\partial y} = 4(3x^2y - 1)^3 3x^2 = 12x^2(3x^2y - 1)^3$

37. $f(x, y) = \ln(x^2 + y^2)$

$f_x(x, y) = \dfrac{1}{x^2 + y^2} \cdot \dfrac{\partial(x^2 + y^2)}{\partial x} = \dfrac{2x}{x^2 + y^2}$

$f_y(x, y) = \dfrac{1}{x^2 + y^2} \cdot \dfrac{\partial(x^2 + y^2)}{\partial y} = \dfrac{2y}{x^2 + y^2}$

39. $f(x, y) = y^2 e^{xy^2}$

$f_x(x, y) = y^2 e^{xy^2} \dfrac{\partial(xy^2)}{\partial x} = y^2 e^{xy^2} y^2 = y^4 e^{xy^2}$

$f_y(x, y) = y^2 \dfrac{\partial(e^{xy^2})}{\partial y} + e^{xy^2} \dfrac{\partial(y^2)}{\partial y}$ (Product rule)

$= y^2 e^{xy^2} 2yx + y^2 e^{xy^2} 2y = 2xy^3 e^{xy^2} + 2y e^{xy^2}$

41. $f(x, y) = \dfrac{x^2 - y^2}{x^2 + y^2}$

Applying the quotient rule:

$f_x(x, y) = \dfrac{(x^2 + y^2) \dfrac{\partial(x^2 - y^2)}{\partial x} - (x^2 - y^2) \dfrac{\partial(x^2 + y^2)}{\partial x}}{(x^2 + y^2)^2}$

$= \dfrac{(x^2 + y^2)(2x) - (x^2 - y^2)(2x)}{(x^2 + y^2)^2}$

$= \dfrac{2x^3 + 2y^2x - 2x^3 + 2y^2x}{(x^2 + y^2)^2} = \dfrac{4xy^2}{(x^2 + y^2)^2}$

Again, applying the quotient rule:

$f_y(x, y) = \dfrac{(x^2 + y^2)(-2y) - (x^2 - y^2)(2y)}{(x^2 + y^2)^2} = \dfrac{-4x^2y}{(x^2 + y^2)^2}$

43. (A) $f(x, y) = y^3 + 4y^2 - 5y + 3$

Since f is independent of x, $\dfrac{\partial f}{\partial x} = 0$

(B) If $g(x, y)$ depends on y only, that is, if $g(x, y) = G(y)$ is independent of x, then

$$\frac{\partial g}{\partial x} = 0$$

Clearly there are an infinite number of such functions.

45. $f(x, y) = x^2y^2 + x^3 + y$

$f_x(x, y) = 2xy^2 + 3x^2$ $\qquad\qquad$ $f_y(x, y) = 2x^2y + 1$

$f_{xx}(x, y) = 2y^2 + 6x$ $\qquad\qquad$ $f_{yx}(x, y) = 4xy$

$f_{xy}(x, y) = 4xy$ $\qquad\qquad$ $f_{yy}(x, y) = 2x^2$

47. $f(x, y) = \dfrac{x}{y} - \dfrac{y}{x}$

$f_x(x, y) = \dfrac{1}{y} + \dfrac{y}{x^2}$ $\qquad\qquad$ $f_y(x, y) = -\dfrac{x}{y^2} - \dfrac{1}{x}$

$f_{xx}(x, y) = -\dfrac{2y}{x^3}$ $\qquad\qquad$ $f_{yx}(x, y) = -\dfrac{1}{y^2} + \dfrac{1}{x^2}$

$f_{xy}(x, y) = -\dfrac{1}{y^2} + \dfrac{1}{x^2}$ $\qquad\qquad$ $f_{yy}(x, y) = \dfrac{2x}{y^3}$

49. $f(x, y) = xe^{xy}$

$f_x(x, y) = xye^{xy} + e^{xy}$ $\qquad\qquad$ $f_y(x, y) = x^2e^{xy}$

$f_{xx}(x, y) = xy^2e^{xy} + 2ye^{xy}$ $\qquad\qquad$ $f_{yx}(x, y) = x^2ye^{xy} + 2xe^{xy}$

$f_{xy}(x, y) = x^2ye^{xy} + 2xe^{xy}$ $\qquad\qquad$ $f_{yy}(x, y) = x^3e^{xy}$

51. $P(x, y) = -x^2 + 2xy - 2y^2 - 4x + 12y - 5$

$P_x(x, y) = -2x + 2y - 0 - 4 + 0 - 0 = -2x + 2y - 4$

$P_y(x, y) = 0 + 2x - 4y - 0 + 12 - 0 = 2x - 4y + 12$

$P_x(x, y) = 0$ and $P_y(x, y) = 0$ when

$\qquad -2x + 2y - 4 = 0 \qquad$ (1)

$\qquad 2x - 4y + 12 = 0 \qquad$ (2)

Add equations (1) and (2): $-2y + 8 = 0$

$\qquad\qquad\qquad\qquad\qquad\qquad y = 4$

Substitute $y = 4$ into (1): $-2x + 2 \cdot 4 - 4 = 0$

$\qquad\qquad\qquad\qquad\qquad\qquad -2x + 4 = 0$

$\qquad\qquad\qquad\qquad\qquad\qquad\qquad x = 2$

Thus, $P_x(x, y) = 0$ and $P_y(x, y) = 0$ when $x = 2$ and $y = 4$.

53. $F(x, y) = x^3 - 2x^2y^2 - 2x - 4y + 10$;

$F_x(x, y) = 3x^2 - 4xy^2 - 2$; $F_y(x, y) = -4x^2y - 4$.

Set $F_x(x, y) = 0$ and $F_y(x, y) = 0$ and solve simultaneously:

$$3x^2 - 4xy^2 - 2 = 0 \qquad (1)$$
$$-4x^2y - 4 = 0 \qquad (2)$$

From (2), $y = -\dfrac{1}{x^2}$. Substituting this into (1),

$$3x^2 - 4x\left(-\frac{1}{x^2}\right)^2 - 2 = 0$$

$$3x^2 - 4x\left(\frac{1}{x^4}\right) - 2 = 0$$

$$3x^5 - 2x^3 - 4 = 0$$

Using a graphing utility, we find that

$$x \approx 1.200$$

Then, $y \approx -0.694$.

55. $f(x, y) = 3x^2 + y^2 - 4x - 6y + 2$

(A) $f(x, 1) = 3x^2 + 1 - 4x - 6 + 2$

$\qquad = 3x^2 - 4x - 3$

$\dfrac{d}{dx}[f(x, 1)] = 6x - 4$; critical values: $6x - 4 = 0$

$$x = \frac{2}{3}$$

$\dfrac{d^2}{dx^2}[f(x, 1)] = 6 > 0$

Therefore, $f\left(\dfrac{2}{3}, 1\right) = 3\left(\dfrac{2}{3}\right)^2 - 4\left(\dfrac{2}{3}\right) - 3 = -\dfrac{13}{3}$ is the minimum value of $f(x, 1)$.

(B) $-\dfrac{13}{3}$ is the minimum value of $f(x, y)$ on the curve $f(x, 1)$; $f(x, y)$ may have smaller values on other curves $f(x, k)$, k constant, or $f(h, y)$, h constant. For example, the minimum value of $f(x, 2) = 3x^2 - 4x - 6$ is $f\left(\dfrac{2}{3}, 2\right) = -\dfrac{22}{3}$; the minimum value of $f(0, y) = y^2 - 6y + 2$ is $f(0, 3) = -7$.

57. $f(x, y) = 4 - x^4y + 3xy^2 + y^5$

(A) Let $y = 2$ and find the maximum value of $f(x, 2) = 4 - 2x^4 + 12x + 32$ $= -2x^4 + 12x + 36$. Using a graphing utility we find that the maximum value of $f(x, 2)$ is 46.302 at $x = 1.1447152 \approx 1.145$.

(B) $f_x(x, y) = -4x^3y + 3y^2$

$f_x(1.145, 2) = -0.008989 \approx 0$

$f_y(x, y) = -x^4 + 6xy + 5y^4$

$f_y(1.145, 2) = 92.021$

59. $f(x, y) = \ln(x^2 + y^2)$ (see Problem 37)

$$f_x(x, y) = \frac{2x}{x^2 + y^2} \qquad\qquad f_y(x, y) = \frac{2y}{x^2 + y^2}$$

$$f_{xx}(x, y) = \frac{(x^2 + y^2)2 - 2x(2x)}{(x^2 + y^2)^2} \qquad f_{yy}(x, y) = \frac{(x^2 + y^2)2 - 2y(2y)}{(x^2 + y^2)^2}$$

$$= \frac{2(y^2 - x^2)}{(x^2 + y^2)^2} \qquad\qquad = \frac{2(x^2 - y^2)}{(x^2 + y^2)^2} = \frac{-2(y^2 - x^2)}{(x^2 + y^2)^2}$$

$$f_{xx}(x, y) + f_{yy}(x, y) = \frac{2(y^2 - x^2)}{(x^2 + y^2)^2} + \frac{-2(y^2 - x^2)}{(x^2 + y^2)^2} = 0$$

61. $f(x, y) = x^2 + 2y^2$

(A) $\displaystyle\lim_{h \to 0} \frac{f(x + h, y) - f(x, y)}{h} = \lim_{h \to 0} \frac{(x + h)^2 + 2y^2 - (x^2 + 2y^2)}{h}$

$$= \lim_{h \to 0} \frac{x^2 + 2xh + h^2 + 2y^2 - x^2 - 2y^2}{h}$$

$$= \lim_{h \to 0} \frac{h(2x + h)}{h} = \lim_{h \to 0} (2x + h)$$

$$= 2x$$

(B) $\displaystyle\lim_{k \to 0} \frac{f(x, y + k) - f(x, y)}{k} = \lim_{k \to 0} \frac{x^2 + 2(y + k)^2 - (x^2 + 2y^2)}{k}$

$$= \lim_{k \to 0} \frac{x^2 + 2(y^2 + 2yk + k^2) - x^2 - 2y^2}{k}$$

$$= \lim_{k \to 0} \frac{4yk + 2k^2}{k} = \lim_{k \to 0} (4y + 2k)$$

$$= 4y$$

63. $R(x, y) = 80x + 90y + 0.04xy - 0.05x^2 - 0.05y^2$
$C(x, y) = 8x + 6y + 20,000$
The profit $P(x, y)$ is given by:
$P(x, y) = R(x, y) - C(x, y)$

$$= 80x + 90y + 0.04xy - 0.05x^2 - 0.05y^2 - (8x + 6y + 20,000)$$

$$= 72x + 84y + 0.04xy - 0.05x^2 - 0.05y^2 - 20,000$$

Now
$P_x(x, y) = 72 + 0.04y - 0.1x$
and
$P_x(1200, 1800) = 72 + 0.04(1800) - 0.1(1200)$

$$= 72 + 72 - 120 = 24;$$

$P_y(x, y) = 84 + 0.04x - 0.1y$
and
$P_y(1200, 1800) = 84 + 0.04(1200) - 0.1(1800)$

$$= 84 + 48 - 180 = -48.$$

Thus, at the (1200, 1800) output level, profit will increase approximately \$24 per unit increase in production of type A calculators; and profit will decrease \$48 per unit increase in production of type B calculators.

65. $x = 200 - 5p + 4q$

$y = 300 - 4q + 2p$

$\dfrac{\partial x}{\partial p} = -5, \quad \dfrac{\partial y}{\partial p} = 2$

A \$1 increase in the price of brand A will decrease the demand for brand A by 5 pounds at any price level (p, q).

A \$1 increase in the price of brand A will increase the demand for brand B by 2 pounds at any price level (p, q).

67. $f(x, y) = 10x^{0.75}y^{0.25}$

(A) $f_x(x, y) = 10(0.75)x^{-0.25}y^{0.25} = 7.5x^{-0.25}y^{0.25}$

$f_y(x, y) = 10(0.25)x^{0.75}y^{-0.75} = 2.5x^{0.75}y^{-0.75}$

(B) Marginal productivity of labor = $f_x(600, 100)$

$$= 7.5(600)^{-0.25}(100)^{0.25} \approx 4.79$$

Marginal productivity of capital = $f_y(600, 100)$

$$= 2.5(600)^{0.75}(100)^{-0.75} \approx 9.58$$

(C) The government should encourage the increased use of capital.

69. $x = f(p, q) = 8000 - 0.09p^2 + 0.08q^2$ (Butter)

$y = g(p, q) = 15,000 + 0.04p^2 - 0.3q^2$ (Margarine)

$f_q(p, q) = 0.08(2)q = 0.16q > 0$

$g_p(p, q) = 0.04(2)p = 0.08p > 0$

Thus, the products are competitive.

71. $x = f(p, q) = 800 - 0.004p^2 - 0.003q^2$ (Skis)

$y = g(p, q) = 600 - 0.003p^2 - 0.002q^2$ (Ski boots)

$f_q(p, q) = -0.003(2)q = -0.006q < 0$

$g_p(p, q) = -0.003(2)p = -0.006p < 0$

Thus, the products are complementary.

73. $A = f(w, h) = 15.64w^{0.425}h^{0.725}$

(A) $f_w(w, h) = 15.64(0.425)w^{-0.575}h^{0.725} \approx 6.65w^{-0.575}h^{0.725}$

$f_h(w, h) = 15.64(0.725)w^{0.425}h^{-0.275} \approx 11.34w^{0.425}h^{-0.275}$

(B) $f_w(65, 57) = 6.65(65)^{-0.575}(57)^{0.725} \approx 11.31$

For a 65 pound child 57 inches tall, the rate of change of surface area is approximately 11.31 square inches for a one-pound gain in weight, height held fixed.

$f_h(65, 57) = 11.34(65)^{0.425}(57)^{-0.275} \approx 21.99$

For a 65 pound child 57 inches tall, the rate of change of surface area is approximately 21.99 square inches for a one-inch gain in height, weight held fixed.

75. $C(W, L) = 100\dfrac{W}{L}$

$C_W(W, L) = \dfrac{100}{L}$

$C_W(6, 8) = \dfrac{100}{8} = 12.5$

The index increases 12.5 units per 1-inch increase in the width of the head (length held fixed) when $W = 6$ and $L = 8$.

$C_L(W, L) = -\dfrac{100W}{L^2}$

$C_L(6, 8) = -\dfrac{100 \times 6}{8^2}$

$\qquad\quad = -\dfrac{600}{64} = -9.38$

The index decreases 9.38 units per 1-inch increase in length (width held fixed) when $W = 6$ and $L = 8$.

EXERCISE 6-3

Things to remember:

1. $f(a, b)$ is a LOCAL MAXIMUM if there exists a circular region in the domain of $f(x, y)$ with (a, b) as the center, such that $f(a, b) \geq f(x, y)$ for all (x, y) in the region. Similarly, $f(a, b)$ is a LOCAL MINIMUM if $f(a, b) \leq f(x, y)$ for all (x, y) in the region.

2. LOCAL EXTREMA AND PARTIAL DERIVATIVES

   Let $f(a, b)$ be a local extremum (a local maximum or a local minimum) for the function f. If both f_x and f_y exist at (a, b) then

   $\qquad f_x(a, b) = 0 \qquad$ and $\qquad f_y(a, b) = 0$

3. SECOND-DERIVATIVE TEST FOR LOCAL EXTREMA FOR $z = f(x, y)$
   Given:

   (a) $f_x(a, b) = 0$ and $f_y(a, b) = 0$ [(a, b) is a critical point].

   (b) All second-order partial derivatives of f exist in some circular region containing (a, b) as center.

   (c) $A = f_{xx}(a, b)$, $B = f_{xy}(a, b)$, $C = f_{yy}(a, b)$.

   Then:

       i) If $AC - B^2 > 0$ and $A < 0$, then $f(a, b)$ is a local maximum.

       ii) If $AC - B^2 > 0$ and $A > 0$, then $f(a, b)$ is a local minimum.

       iii) If $AC - B^2 < 0$, then f has a saddle point at (a, b).

       iv) If $AC - B^2 = 0$, then the test fails.

---

1. $f(x, y) = 4x + 5y - 6$
   $f_x(x, y) = 4 \neq 0$; $f_y(x, y) = 5 \neq 0$; the functions $f_x(x, y)$ and $f_y(x, y)$ are nonzero for all (x, y).

3. $f(x, y) = 3.7 - 1.2x + 6.8y + 0.2y^3 + x^4$
   $f_x(x, y) = -1.2 + 4x^3$; $f_y = 6.8 + 0.6y^2$; the function $f_y(x, y)$ is nonzero for all (x, y).

5. $f(x, y) = 6 - x^2 - 4x - y^2$
$f_x(x, y) = -2x - 4 = 0$
$$x = -2$$
$f_y(x, y) = -2y = 0$
$$y = 0$$
Thus, $(-2, 0)$ is a critical point.

$f_{xx} = -2$, $f_{xy} = 0$, $f_{yy} = -2$,

$f_{xx}(-2, 0) \cdot f_{yy}(-2, 0) - [f_{xy}(-2, 0)]^2 = (-2)(-2) - 0^2 = 4 > 0$

and $f_{xx}(-2, 0) = -2 < 0.$

Thus, $f(-2, 0) = 6 - (-2)^2 - 4(-2) - 0^2 = 10$ is a local maximum (using $\underline{3}$).

7. $f(x, y) = x^2 + y^2 + 2x - 6y + 14$
$f_x(x, y) = 2x + 2 = 0$
$$x = -1$$
$f_y(x, y) = 2y - 6 = 0$
$$y = 3$$
Thus, $(-1, 3)$ is a critical point.

$f_{xx} = 2$	$f_{xy} = 0$	$f_{yy} = 2$
$f_{xx}(-1, 3) = 2 > 0$	$f_{xy}(-1, 3) = 0$	$f_{yy}(-1, 3) = 2$

$f_{xx}(-1, 3) \cdot f_{yy}(-1, 3) - [f_{xy}(-1, 3)]^2 = 2 \cdot 2 - 0^2 = 4 > 0$
Thus, using $\underline{3}$, $f(-1, 3) = 4$ is a local minimum.

9. $f(x, y) = xy + 2x - 3y - 2$
$f_x = y + 2 = 0$
$$y = -2$$
$f_y = x - 3 = 0$
$$x = 3$$
Thus, $(3, -2)$ is a critical point.

$f_{xx} = 0$	$f_{xy} = 1$	$f_{yy} = 0$
$f_{xx}(3, -2) = 0$	$f_{xy}(3, -2) = 1$	$f_{yy}(3, -2) = 0$

$f_{xx}(3, -2) \cdot f_{yy}(3, -2) - [f_{xy}(3, -2)]^2 = 0 \cdot 0 - [1]^2 = -1 < 0$

Thus, using $\underline{3}$, f has a saddle point at $(3, -2)$.

11. $f(x, y) = -3x^2 + 2xy - 2y^2 + 14x + 2y + 10$
$f_x = -6x + 2y + 14 = 0 \quad (1)$
$f_y = 2x - 4y + 2 = 0 \quad (2)$
Solving (1) and (2) for x and y, we obtain $x = 3$ and $y = 2$.
Thus, $(3, 2)$ is a critical point.

$f_{xx} = -6$	$f_{xy} = 2$	$f_{yy} = -4$
$f_{xx}(3, 2) = -6 < 0$	$f_{xy}(3, 2) = 2$	$f_{yy}(3, 2) = -4$

$f_{xx}(3, 2) \cdot f_{yy}(3, 2) - [f_{xy}(3, 2)]^2 = (-6)(-4) - 2^2 = 20 > 0$

Thus, using $\underline{3}$, $f(3, 2)$ is a local maximum and
$f(3, 2) = -3 \cdot 3^2 + 2 \cdot 3 \cdot 2 - 2 \cdot 2^2 + 14 \cdot 3 + 2 \cdot 2 + 10 = 33.$

13. $f(x, y) = 2x^2 - 2xy + 3y^2 - 4x - 8y + 20$

$f_x = 4x - 2y - 4 = 0$ (1)

$f_y = -2x + 6y - 8 = 0$ (2)

Solving (1) and (2) for x and y, we obtain $x = 2$ and $y = 2$.
Thus, (2, 2) is a critical point.

$f_{xx} = 4$ $f_{xy} = -2$ $f_{yy} = 6$

$f_{xx}(2, 2) = 4 > 0$ $f_{xy}(2, 2) = -2$ $f_{yy}(2, 2) = 6$

$f_{xx}(2, 2) \cdot f_{yy}(2, 2) - [f_{xy}(2, 2)]^2 = 4 \cdot 6 - [-2]^2 = 20 > 0$

Thus, using $\underline{3}$, $f(2, 2)$ is a local minimum and

$f(2, 2) = 2 \cdot 2^2 - 2 \cdot 2 \cdot 2 + 3 \cdot 2^2 - 4 \cdot 2 - 8 \cdot 2 + 20 = 8$.

15. $f(x, y) = e^{xy}$

$f_x = e^{xy}\dfrac{\partial(xy)}{\partial x}$ $f_y = e^{xy}\dfrac{\partial(xy)}{\partial y}$

$\quad = e^{xy}y = 0$ $\quad = e^{xy}x = 0$

$\qquad y = 0 \; (e^{xy} \neq 0)$ $\qquad x = 0 \; (e^{xy} \neq 0)$

Thus, (0, 0) is a critical point.

$f_{xx} = ye^{xy}\dfrac{\partial(xy)}{\partial x}$ $f_{xy} = e^{xy}\cdot 1 + ye^{xy}x$ $f_{yy} = xe^{xy}\dfrac{\partial(xy)}{\partial y}$

$\quad = ye^{xy}y$ $\quad = e^{xy} + xye^{xy}$ $\quad = x^2 e^{xy}$

$\quad = y^2 e^{xy}$

$f_{xx}(0, 0) = 0$ $f_{xy}(0, 0) = 1 + 0 = 1$ $f_{yy}(0, 0) = 0$

$f_{xx}(0, 0) \cdot f_{yy}(0, 0) - [f_{xy}(0, 0)]^2 = 0 - [1]^2 = -1 < 0$

Thus, using $\underline{3}$, $f(x, y)$ has a saddle point at (0, 0).

17. $f(x, y) = x^3 + y^3 - 3xy$

$f_x = 3x^2 - 3y = 3(x^2 - y) = 0$

Thus, $y = x^2$.   (1)

$f_y = 3y^2 - 3x = 3(y^2 - x) = 0$

Thus, $y^2 = x$.   (2)

Combining (1) and (2), we obtain $x = x^4$ or $x(x^3 - 1) = 0$. Therefore, $x = 0$ or $x = 1$, and the critical points are (0, 0) and (1, 1).

$f_{xx} = 6x$ $f_{xy} = -3$ $f_{yy} = 6y$

For the critical point (0, 0):

$f_{xx}(0, 0) = 0$ $f_{xy}(0, 0) = -3$ $f_{yy}(0, 0) = 0$

$f_{xx}(0, 0) \cdot f_{yy}(0, 0) - [f_{xy}(0, 0)]^2 = 0 - (-3)^2 = -9 < 0$

Thus, using $\underline{3}$, $f(x, y)$ has a saddle point at (0, 0).

For the critical point (1, 1):

$f_{xx}(1, 1) = 6$ $f_{xy}(1, 1) = -3$ $f_{yy}(1, 1) = 6$

$f_{xx}(1, 1) \cdot f_{yy}(1, 1) - [f_{xy}(1, 1)]^2 = 6 \cdot 6 - (-3)^2 = 27 > 0$

$f_{xx}(1, 1) > 0$

Thus, using $\underline{3}$, $f(1, 1)$ is a local minimum and

$f(1, 1) = 1^3 + 1^3 - 3 \cdot 1 \cdot 1 = 2 - 3 = -1$.

19. $f(x, y) = 2x^4 + y^2 - 12xy$

$f_x = 8x^3 - 12y = 0$

Thus, $y = \dfrac{2}{3}x^3$.

$f_y = 2y - 12x = 0$

Thus, $y = 6x$

Therefore, $6x = \dfrac{2}{3}x^3$

$x^3 - 9x = 0$

$x(x^2 - 9) = 0$

$x = 0, \; x = 3, \; x = -3$

Thus, the critical points are $(0, 0)$, $(3, 18)$, $(-3, -18)$. Now,

$f_{xx} = 24x^2 \qquad\qquad f_{xy} = -12 \qquad\qquad f_{yy} = 2$

For the critical point $(0, 0)$:

$f_{xx}(0, 0) = 0 \qquad\qquad f_{xy}(0, 0) = -12 \qquad\qquad f_{yy}(0, 0) = 2$

and

$f_{xx}(0, 0) \cdot f_{yy}(0, 0) - [f_{xy}(0, 0)]^2 = 0 \cdot 2 - (-12)^2 = -144$.

Thus, $f(x, y)$ has a saddle point at $(0, 0)$.

For the critical point $(3, 18)$:

$f_{xx}(3, 18) = 24 \cdot 3^2 = 216 > 0 \qquad f_{xy}(3, 18) = -12 \qquad f_{yy}(3, 18) = 2$

and

$f_{xx}(3, 18) \cdot f_{yy}(3, 18) - [f_{xy}(3, 18)]^2 = 216 \cdot 2 - (-12)^2 = 288 > 0$

Thus, $f(3, 18) = -162$ is a local minimum.

For the critical point $(-3, -18)$:

$f_{xx}(-3, -18) = 216 > 0 \qquad f_{xy}(-3, -18) = -12 \qquad f_{yy}(-3, -18) = 2$

and

$f_{xx}(-3, -18) \cdot f_{yy}(-3, -18) - [f_{xy}(-3, -18)]^2 = 288 > 0$

Thus, $f(-3, -18) = -162$ is a local minimum.

21. $f(x, y) = x^3 - 3xy^2 + 6y^2$

$f_x = 3x^2 - 3y^2 = 0$

Thus, $y^2 = x^2$ or $y = \pm x$.

$f_y = -6xy + 12y = 0$ or $-6y(x - 2) = 0$

Thus, $y = 0$ or $x = 2$.

Therefore, the critical points are $(0, 0)$, $(2, 2)$, and $(2, -2)$.

Now,

$f_{xx} = 6x \qquad\qquad f_{xy} = -6y \qquad\qquad f_{yy} = -6x + 12$

For the critical point $(0, 0)$:

$f_{xx}(0, 0) \cdot f_{yy}(0, 0) - [f_{xy}(0, 0]^2 = 0 \cdot 12 - 0^2 = 0$

Thus, the second-derivative test fails.

362

For the critical point $(2, 2)$:

$f_{xx}(2, 2) \cdot f_{yy}(2, 2) - [f_{xy}(2, 2)]^2 = 12 \cdot 0 - (-12)^2 = -144 < 0$

Thus, $f(x, y)$ has a saddle point at $(2, 2)$.

For the critical point $(2, -2)$:

$f_{xx}(2, -2) \cdot f_{yy}(2, -2) - [f_{xy}(2, -2)]^2 = 12 \cdot 0 - (12)^2 = -144 < 0$

Thus, $f(x, y)$ has a saddle point at $(2, -2)$.

23. $f(x, y) = y^3 + 2x^2 y^2 - 3x - 2y + 8$;

$f_x = 4xy^2 - 3$; $f_y = 3y^2 + 4x^2 y - 2$

Set $f_x = 0$ and $f_y = 0$ to find the critical points:

$$4xy^2 - 3 = 0 \qquad (1)$$
$$3y^2 + 4x^2 y - 2 = 0 \qquad (2)$$

From (1) $x = \dfrac{3}{4y^2}$. Substituting this into (2), we have

$$3y^2 + 4\left(\frac{3}{4y^2}\right)^2 y - 2 = 0$$

$$3y^2 + 4\left(\frac{9}{16y^4}\right)y - 2 = 0$$

$$12y^5 - 8y^3 + 9 = 0$$

Using a graphing utility, we find that $y \approx -1.105$ and $x \approx 0.614$.

Now, $f_{xx} = 4y^2$ and $f_{xx}(0.614, -1.105) \approx 4.884$

$f_{xy} = 8xy$ and $f_{xy}(0.614, -1.105) \approx -5.428$

$f_{yy} = 6y + 4x^2$ and $f_{yy}(0.614, -1.105) \approx -5.122$

$f_{xx}(0.614, -1.105) \cdot f_{yy}(0.614, -1.105) - [f_{xy}(0.614, -1.105)]^2$

$\approx -54.479 < 0$

Thus, $f(x, y)$ has a saddle point at $(0.614, -1.105)$.

25. $f(x, y) = x^2 \geq 0$ for all (x, y) and $f(x, y) = 0$ when $x = 0$. Thus, f has a local minimum at each point $(0, y, 0)$ on the y-axis.

27. $f(x, y) = x^4 e^y + x^2 y^4 + 1$

(A) $f_x = 4x^3 e^y + 2xy^4 = 0$ (1)

$f_y = x^4 e^y + 4x^2 y^3 = 0$ (2)

The values $x = 0$, $y = 0$ satisfy (1) and (2) so $(0, 0)$ is a critical point.

$A = f_{xx} = 12x^2 e^y + 2y^4 = 0$ at $(0, 0)$,

$B = f_{xy} = 4x^3 e^y + 8xy^3 = 0$ at $(0, 0)$,

$C = f_{yy} = x^4 e^y + 12x^2 y^2 = 0$ at $(0, 0)$.

$AC - B^2 = 0$; the second derivative test fails.

(B) Cross-sections of f by the planes $y = 0$,
$x = 0$, $y = x$ and $y = -x$ are shown at the
right.

The cross-sections indicate that f has a
local minimum at $(0, 0)$.

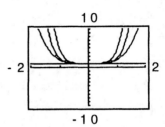

29. $P(x, y) = R(x, y) - C(x, y)$
$= 2x + 3y - (x^2 - 2xy + 2y^2 + 6x - 9y + 5)$
$= -x^2 + 2xy - 2y^2 - 4x + 12y - 5$

$P_x = -2x + 2y - 4 = 0$ (1)

$P_y = 2x - 4y + 12 = 0$ (2)

Solving (1) and (2) for x and y, we obtain $x = 2$ and $y = 4$. Thus,
$(2, 4)$ is a critical point.

$P_{xx} = -2$ and $P_{xx}(2, 4) = -2 < 0$

$P_{xy} = 2$ and $P_{xy}(2, 4) = 2$

$P_{yy} = -4$ and $P_{yy}(2, 4) = -4$

$P_{xx}(2, 4) \cdot P_{yy}(2, 4) - [P_{xy}(2, 4)]^2 = (-2)(-4) - [2]^2 = 4 > 0$

The maximum occurs when 2000 type A and 4000 type B calculators are
produced. The maximum profit is given by $P(2, 4)$. Hence,

max $P = P(2, 4) = -(2)^2 + 2 \cdot 2 \cdot 4 - 2 \cdot 4^2 - 4 \cdot 2 + 12 \cdot 4 - 5$
$= -4 + 16 - 32 - 8 + 48 - 5 = \$15$ million.

31. $x = 116 - 30p + 20q$ (Brand A)
$y = 144 + 16p - 24q$ (Brand B)

(A)

p	q	x	y
10	12	56	16
11	11	6	56

(B) In terms of p and q, the cost function C is given by:
$C = 6x + 8y = 6(116 - 30p + 20q) + 8(144 + 16p - 24q)$
$= 1848 - 52p - 72q$

The revenue function R is given by:
$R = px + qy = p(116 - 30p + 20q) + q(144 + 16p - 24q)$
$= 116p - 30p^2 + 20pq + 144q + 16pq - 24q^2$
$= -30p^2 + 36pq - 24q^2 + 116p + 144q$

Thus, the profit $P = R - C$ is given by:
$P = -30p^2 + 36pq - 24q^2 + 116p + 144q - (1848 - 52p - 72q)$

$= -30p^2 + 36pq - 24q^2 + 168p + 216q - 1848$

Now, calculating P_p and P_q and setting these equal to 0, we have:

$P_p = -60p + 36q + 168 = 0$ (1)

$P_q = 36p - 48q + 216 = 0$ (2)

Solving (1) and (2) for p and q, we get $p = 10$ and $q = 12$. Thus,
$(10, 12)$ is a critical point of the profit function P.

$$P_{pp} = -60 \quad \text{and} \quad P_{pp}(10, 12) = -60$$
$$P_{pq} = 36 \quad \text{and} \quad P_{pq}(10, 12) = 36$$
$$P_{qq} = -48 \quad \text{and} \quad P_{qq}(10, 12) = -48$$
$$P_{pp} \cdot P_{qq} - [P_{pq}]^2 = (-60)(-48) - (36)^2 = 1584 > 0$$

Since $P_{pp}(10, 12) = -60 < 0$, we conclude that the maximum profit occurs when $p = \$10$ and $q = \$12$. The maximum profit is:

$$P(10, 12) = -30(10)^2 + 36(10)(12) - 24(12)^2 + 168(10) + 216(12) - 1848$$
$$= \$288$$

33. The square of the distance from P to A is: $x^2 + y^2$
    The square of the distance from P to B is:
    $(x - 2)^2 + (y - 6)^2 = x^2 - 4x + y^2 - 12y + 40$
    The square of the distance from P to C is:
    $(x - 10)^2 + y^2 = x^2 - 20x + y^2 + 100$
    Thus, we have:
    $P(x, y) = 3x^2 - 24x + 3y^2 - 12y + 140$

    $$P_x = 6x - 24 = 0 \qquad\qquad P_y = 6y - 12 = 0$$
    $$x = 4 \qquad\qquad\qquad\qquad y = 2$$
    Therefore, $(4, 2)$ is a critical point.

    $$P_{xx} = 6 \quad \text{and} \quad P_{xx}(4, 2) = 6 > 0$$
    $$P_{xy} = 0 \quad \text{and} \quad P_{xy}(4, 2) = 0$$
    $$P_{yy} = 6 \quad \text{and} \quad P_{yy}(4, 2) = 6$$
    $$P_{xx} \cdot P_{yy} - [P_{xy}]^2 = 6 \cdot 6 - 0 = 36 > 0$$
    Therefore, P has a minimum at the point $(4, 2)$.

35. Let x = length, y = width, and z = height. Then $V = xyz = 64$ or $z = \dfrac{64}{xy}$. The surface area of the box is:

    $$S = xy + 2xz + 4yz \quad \text{or} \quad S(x, y) = xy + \frac{128}{y} + \frac{256}{x}, \quad x > 0, \; y > 0$$

    $$S_x = y - \frac{256}{x^2} = 0 \quad \text{or} \quad y = \frac{256}{x^2} \quad (1)$$

    $$S_y = x - \frac{128}{y^2} = 0 \quad \text{or} \quad x = \frac{128}{y^2}$$

    Thus, $y = \dfrac{256}{\dfrac{(128)^2}{y^4}}$ or $y^4 - 64y = 0$
    and $y(y^3 - 64) = 0$ (Since $y > 0$, $y = 0$ does not
    $y = 4$ yield a critical point.)

    Setting $y = 4$ in (1), we find $x = 8$. Therefore, the critical point is $(8, 4)$.

Now we have:

$$S_{xx} = \frac{512}{x^3} \quad \text{and} \quad S_{xx}(8, 4) = 1 > 0$$

$$S_{xy} = 1$$

$$S_{yy} = \frac{256}{y^3} \quad \text{and} \quad S_{yy}(8, 4) = 4$$

$$S_{xx}(8, 4) \cdot S_{yy}(8, 4) - [S_{xy}(8, 4)]^2 = 1 \cdot 4 - 1^2 = 3 > 0$$

Thus, the dimensions that will require the least amount of material are:

Length $x = 8$ inches; Width $y = 4$ inches; Height $z = \dfrac{64}{8(4)} = 2$ inches.

37. Let x = length of the package, y = width, and z = height. Then
$$x + 2y + 2z = 120 \qquad (1)$$
Volume = $V = xyz$.

From (1), $z = \dfrac{120 - x - 2y}{2}$. Thus, we have:

$$V(x, y) = xy\left(\frac{120 - x - 2y}{2}\right) = 60xy - \frac{x^2 y}{2} - xy^2, \quad x > 0, \ y > 0$$

$$V_x = 60y - xy - y^2 = 0$$

$$y(60 - x - y) = 0$$

$$60 - x - y = 0 \qquad (2) \qquad \text{(Since } y > 0, \ y = 0 \text{ does not yield a critical point.)}$$

$$V_y = 60x - \frac{x^2}{2} - 2xy = 0$$

$$x\left(60 - \frac{x}{2} - 2y\right) = 0$$

$$120 - x - 4y = 0 \qquad (3) \qquad \text{(Since } x > 0, \ x = 0 \text{ does not yield a critical point.)}$$

Solving (2) and (3) for x and y, we obtain $x = 40$ and $y = 20$. Thus, $(40, 20)$ is the critical point.

$$V_{xx} = -y \qquad \text{and} \quad V_{xx}(40, 20) = -20 < 0$$
$$V_{xy} = 60 - x - 2y \quad \text{and} \quad V_{xy}(40, 20) = 60 - 40 - 40 = -20$$
$$V_{yy} = -2x \qquad \text{and} \quad V_{yy}(40, 20) = -80$$

$$
\begin{aligned}
V_{xx}(40, 20) \cdot V_{yy}(40, 20) - [V_{xy}(40, 20)]^2 &= (-20)(-80) - [-20]^2 \\
&= 1600 - 400 \\
&= 1200 > 0
\end{aligned}
$$

Thus, the maximum volume of the package is obtained when $x = 40$, $y = 20$, and $z = \dfrac{120 - 40 - 2 \cdot 20}{2} = 20$ inches. The package has dimensions:

Length $x = 40$ inches; Width $y = 20$ inches; Height $z = 20$ inches.

Things to remember:

1. Any local maxima or minima of the function $z = f(x, y)$ subject to the constraint $g(x, y) = 0$ will be among those points (x_0, y_0) for which (x_0, y_0, λ_0) is a solution to the system:

$$F_x(x, y, \lambda) = 0$$
$$F_y(x, y, \lambda) = 0$$
$$F_\lambda(x, y, \lambda) = 0$$

where $F(x, y, \lambda) = f(x, y) + \lambda g(x, y)$, provided all the partial derivatives exist.

2. METHOD OF LAGRANGE MULTIPLIERS FOR FUNCTIONS OF TWO INDEPENDENT VARIABLES

(a) Formulate the problem in the form:
Maximize (or Minimize) $z = f(x, y)$
Subject to: $g(x, y) = 0$

(b) Form the function F:
$$F(x, y, \lambda) = f(x, y) + \lambda g(x, y)$$

(c) Find the critical points (x_0, y_0, λ_0) for F, that is, solve the system:

$$F_x(x, y, \lambda) = 0$$
$$F_y(x, y, \lambda) = 0$$
$$F_\lambda(x, y, \lambda) = 0$$

(d) If (x_0, y_0, λ_0) is the only critical point of F, then assume that (x_0, y_0) is the solution to the problem. If F has more than one critical point, then evaluate $z = f(x, y)$ at (x_0, y_0) for each critical point (x_0, y_0, λ_0) of F.

Assume that the largest of these values is the maximum value of $f(x, y)$ subject to the constraint $g(x, y) = 0$, and the smallest is the minimum value of $f(x, y)$ subject to the constraint $g(x, y) = 0$.

3. METHOD OF LAGRANGE MULTIPLIERS FOR FUNCTIONS OF THREE VARIABLES

Any local maxima or minima of the function $w = f(x, y, z)$ subject to the constraint $g(x, y, z) = 0$ will be among the set of points (x_0, y_0, z_0) for which $(x_0, y_0, z_0, \lambda_0)$ is a solution to the system

$$F_x(x, y, z, \lambda) = 0$$
$$F_y(x, y, z, \lambda) = 0$$
$$F_z(x, y, z, \lambda) = 0$$
$$F_\lambda(x, y, z, \lambda) = 0$$

where $F(x, y, z, \lambda) = f(x, y, z) + \lambda g(x, y, z)$, provided that all the partial derivatives exist.

1. Step 1. Maximize $f(x, y) = 2xy$
Subject to: $g(x, y) = x + y - 6 = 0$

Step 2. $F(x, y, \lambda) = f(x, y) + \lambda g(x, y)$
$$= 2xy + \lambda(x + y - 6)$$

Step 3. $F_x = 2y + \lambda = 0$ (1)

$F_y = 2x + \lambda = 0$ (2)

$F_\lambda = x + y - 6 = 0$ (3)

From (1) and (2), we obtain:
$$x = -\frac{\lambda}{2}, \quad y = -\frac{\lambda}{2}$$
Substituting these into (3), we have:
$$-\frac{\lambda}{2} - \frac{\lambda}{2} - 6 = 0$$
$$\lambda = -6.$$
Thus, the critical point is $(3, 3, -6)$.

Step 4. Since $(3, 3, -6)$ is the only critical point for F, we conclude that max $f(x, y) = f(3, 3) = 2 \cdot 3 \cdot 3 = 18$.

3. Step 1. Minimize $f(x, y) = x^2 + y^2$
Subject to: $g(x, y) = 3x + 4y - 25 = 0$

Step 2. $F(x, y, \lambda) = f(x, y) + \lambda g(x, y)$
$$= x^2 + y^2 + \lambda(3x + 4y - 25)$$

Step 3. $F_x = 2x + 3\lambda = 0$ (1)

$F_y = 2y + 4\lambda = 0$ (2)

$F_\lambda = 3x + 4y - 25 = 0$ (3)

From (1) and (2), we obtain:

$$x = -\frac{3\lambda}{2}, \quad y = -2\lambda$$

Substituting these into (3), we have:

$$3\left(-\frac{3\lambda}{2}\right) + 4(-2\lambda) - 25 = 0$$

$$\frac{25}{2}\lambda = -25$$

$$\lambda = -2$$

The critical point is $(3, 4, -2)$.

Step 4. Since $(3, 4, -2)$ is the only critical point for F, we conclude that min $f(x, y) = f(3, 4) = 3^2 + 4^2 = 25$.

5. Step 1.   Maximize $f(x, y) = 4y - 3x$ subject to $2x + 5y - 3 = 0$

Step 2. $F(x, y, \lambda) = f(x, y) + \lambda g(x, y) = 4y - 3x + \lambda(2x + 5y - 3)$

Step 3. $F_x = -3 + 2\lambda = 0$ (1)

         $F_y = 4 + 5\lambda = 0$ (2)

         $F_\lambda = 2x + 5y - 3 = 0$ (3)

         From (1), $\lambda = \dfrac{3}{2}$, from (2), $\lambda = -\dfrac{4}{5}$. Thus, the system (1),

         (2), (3) does not have a solution.

7. Step 1.   Maximize and minimize $f(x, y) = 2xy$

         Subject to: $g(x, y) = x^2 + y^2 - 18 = 0$

Step 2. $F(x, y, \lambda) = f(x, y) + \lambda g(x, y)$

               $= 2xy + \lambda(x^2 + y^2 - 18)$

Step 3. $F_x = 2y + 2\lambda x = 0$ (1)

         $F_y = 2x + 2\lambda y = 0$ (2)

         $F_\lambda = x^2 + y^2 - 18 = 0$ (3)

         From (1), (2), and (3), we obtain the critical points
         $(3, 3, -1)$, $(3, -3, 1)$, $(-3, 3, 1)$ and $(-3, -3, -1)$.

Step 4. $f(3, 3) = 2 \cdot 3 \cdot 3 = 18$

         $f(3, -3) = 2 \cdot 3(-3) = -18$

         $f(-3, 3) = 2(-3) \cdot 3 = -18$

         $f(-3, -3) = 2(-3)(-3) = 18$

         Thus, max $f(x, y) = f(3, 3) = f(-3, -3) = 18$;
             min $f(x, y) = f(3, -3) = f(-3, 3) = -18$.

9. Let x and y be the required numbers.

Step 1.   Maximize $f(x, y) = xy$

         Subject to: $x + y = 10$ or $g(x, y) = x + y - 10 = 0$

Step 2. $F(x, y, \lambda) = xy + \lambda(x + y - 10)$

Step 3. $F_x = y + \lambda = 0$ (1)

         $F_y = x + \lambda = 0$ (2)

         $F_\lambda = x + y - 10 = 0$ (3)

         From (1) and (2), we obtain:
         $x = -\lambda$, $y = -\lambda$
         Substituting these into (3), we have:
         $\lambda = -5$
         The critical point is $(5, 5, -5)$.

Step 4.   Since $(5, 5, -5)$ is the only critical point for F, we conclude
         that max $f(x, y) = f(5, 5) = 5 \cdot 5 = 25$. Thus, the maximum
         product is 25 when $x = 5$ and $y = 5$.

11. Step 1. Minimize $f(x, y, z) = x^2 + y^2 + z^2$

Subject to: $g(x, y) = 2x - y + 3z + 28 = 0$

Step 2. $F(x, y, z, \lambda) = x^2 + y^2 + z^2 + \lambda(2x - y + 3z + 28)$

Step 3. $F_x = 2x + 2\lambda = 0 \qquad (1)$

$F_y = 2y - \lambda = 0 \qquad (2)$

$F_z = 2z + 3\lambda = 0 \qquad (3)$

$F_\lambda = 2x - y + 3z + 28 = 0 \qquad (4)$

From (1), (2), and (3), we obtain:

$x = -\lambda, \; y = \dfrac{\lambda}{2}, \; z = -\dfrac{3}{2}\lambda$

Substituting these into (4), we have:

$2(-\lambda) - \dfrac{\lambda}{2} + 3\left(-\dfrac{3}{2}\lambda\right) + 28 = 0$

$-\dfrac{14}{2}\lambda + 28 = 0$

$\lambda = 4$

The critical point is $(-4, 2, -6, 4)$.

Step 4. Since $(-4, 2, -6, 4)$ is the only critical point for F, we conclude that min $f(x, y, z) = f(-4, 2, -6) = 56$.

13. Step 1. Maximize and minimize $f(x, y, z) = x + y + z$

Subject to: $g(x, y, z) = x^2 + y^2 + z^2 - 12 = 0$

Step 2. $F(x, y, z, \lambda) = f(x, y, z) + \lambda g(x, y, z)$

$= x + y + z + \lambda(x^2 + y^2 + z^2 - 12)$

Step 3. $F_x = 1 + 2x\lambda = 0 \qquad (1)$

$F_y = 1 + 2y\lambda = 0 \qquad (2)$

$F_z = 1 + 2z\lambda = 0 \qquad (3)$

$F_\lambda = x^2 + y^2 + z^2 - 12 = 0 \qquad (4)$

From (1), (2), and (3), we obtain:

$x = -\dfrac{1}{2\lambda}, \; y = -\dfrac{1}{2\lambda}, \; z = -\dfrac{1}{2\lambda}$

Substituting these into (4), we have:

$\left(-\dfrac{1}{2\lambda}\right)^2 + \left(-\dfrac{1}{2\lambda}\right)^2 + \left(-\dfrac{1}{2\lambda}\right)^2 - 12 = 0$

$\dfrac{3}{4\lambda^2} - 12 = 0$

$1 - 16\lambda^2 = 0$

$\lambda = \pm\dfrac{1}{4}$

Thus, the critical points are $\left(2, 2, 2, -\dfrac{1}{4}\right)$ and $\left(-2, -2, -2, \dfrac{1}{4}\right)$.

Step 4. $f(2, 2, 2) = 2 + 2 + 2 = 6$

$f(-2, -2, -2) = -2 - 2 - 2 = -6$

Thus, max $f(x, y, z) = f(2, 2, 2) = 6$;

min $f(x, y, z) = f(-2, -2, -2) = -6$.

15. Step 1. Maximize $f(x, y) = y + xy^2$

Subject to: $x + y^2 = 1$ or $g(x, y) = x + y^2 - 1 = 0$

Step 2. $F(x, y, \lambda) = y + xy^2 + \lambda(x + y^2 - 1)$

Step 3. $F_x = y^2 + \lambda = 0$ (1)

$F_y = 1 + 2xy + 2y\lambda = 0$ (2)

$F_\lambda = x + y^2 - 1 = 0$ (3)

From (1), $\lambda = -y^2$ and from (3), $x = 1 - y^2$. Substituting these values into (2), we have

$$1 + 2(1 - y^2)y - 2y^3 = 0$$

or $\qquad\qquad 4y^3 - 2y - 1 = 0$

Using a graphing utility to solve this equation, we get $y \approx 0.885$. Then $x \approx 0.217$ and max $f(x, y) = f(0.217, 0.885) \approx 1.055$.

17. Step 1. Maximize $f(x, y) = e^x + 3e^y$ subject to $g(x, y) = x - 2y - 6 = 0$

Step 2. $F(x, y, \lambda) = f(x, y) + \lambda g(x, y) = e^x + 3e^y + \lambda(x - 2y - 6)$

Step 3. $F_x = e^x + \lambda = 0$ (1)

$F_y = 3e^y - 2\lambda = 0$ (2)

$F_\lambda = x - 2y - 6 = 0$ (3)

From (1), $\lambda = -e^x$, which implies λ is negative.

From (2), $\lambda = \dfrac{3}{2}e^y$ which implies λ is positive.

Thus, (1) and (2) have no simultaneous solution.

19. The constraint $g(x, y) = y - 5 = 0$ implies $y = 5$. Replacing y by 5 in the function f, the problem reduces to maximizing the function $h(x) = f(x, 5)$, a function of one independent variable.

21. Maximize $f(x, y) = e^{-(x^2 + y^2)}$

Subject to: $g(x, y) = x^2 + y - 1 = 0$

(A) $x^2 + y - 1 = 0$; $y = 1 - x^2$

Substituting $y = 1 - x^2$ into $f(x, y)$, we get
$$h(x) = f(x, 1 - x^2) = e^{-(x^2 + [1 - x^2]^2)}$$
$$= e^{-(x^4 - x^2 + 1)}$$

Now, $h'(x) = e^{-(x^4 - x^2 + 1)}(-4x^3 + 2x)$.

Critical numbers: $(2x - 4x^3)e^{-(x^4 - x^2 + 1)} = 0$
$$2x(1 - 2x^2) = 0$$
$$x = 0, \frac{\sqrt{2}}{2}, -\frac{\sqrt{2}}{2}$$

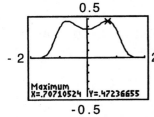

0.5

-2 | | 2

Maximum
X=.70710524 Y=.47236655

-0.5

From the constraint equation, $y = \frac{1}{2}$ when $x = \pm\frac{\sqrt{2}}{2}$.

Max $f(x, y) = f\left(-\frac{\sqrt{2}}{2}, \frac{1}{2}\right) = f\left(\frac{\sqrt{2}}{2}, \frac{1}{2}\right) \approx 0.47$.

(B) $F(x, y, \lambda) = e^{-(x^2 + y^2)} + \lambda(x^2 + y - 1)$

$F_x = -2xe^{-(x^2 + y^2)} + 2x\lambda = 0$ (1)
$F_y = -2ye^{-(x^2 + y^2)} + \lambda = 0$ (2)
$F_\lambda = x^2 + y - 1 = 0$ (3)

From (3), $y = 1 - x^2$ and from (2)
$$\lambda = 2ye^{-(x^2 + y^2)} = 2(1 - x^2)e^{-(x^4 - x^2 + 1)}$$

Substituting these values into (1), we have
$$-2xe^{-(x^4 - x^2 + 1)} + 2x[2(1 - x^2)e^{-(x^4 - x^2 + 1)}] = 0$$
$$2x[2 - 2x^2 - 1] = 0$$
$$2x(1 - 2x^2) = 0$$
$$x = 0, \frac{\sqrt{2}}{2}, -\frac{\sqrt{2}}{2}$$

Now, $y = 1$ when $x = 0$, and $y = \frac{1}{2}$ when $x = \pm\frac{\sqrt{2}}{2}$.

$f(0, 1) = e^{-1} \approx 0.37$

$f\left(\frac{\sqrt{2}}{2}, \frac{1}{2}\right) = f\left(-\frac{\sqrt{2}}{2}, \frac{1}{2}\right) \approx 0.47$

Thus, Max $f(x, y) \approx 0.47$.

23. <u>Step 1.</u> Minimize cost function $C(x, y) = 6x^2 + 12y^2$
Subject to: $x + y = 90$ or $g(x, y) = x + y - 90 = 0$

<u>Step 2.</u> $F(x, y, \lambda) = 6x^2 + 12y^2 + \lambda(x + y - 90)$

<u>Step 3.</u> $F_x = 12x + \lambda = 0$ (1)

$F_y = 24y + \lambda = 0$ (2)

$F_\lambda = x + y - 90 = 0$ (3)

From (1) and (2), we obtain

$$x = -\frac{\lambda}{12}, \quad y = -\frac{\lambda}{24}$$

Substituting these into (3), we have:

$$-\frac{\lambda}{12} - \frac{\lambda}{24} - 90 = 0$$

$$\frac{3\lambda}{24} = -90$$

$$\lambda = -720$$

The critical point is (60, 30, -720).

<u>Step 4.</u> Since (60, 30, -720) is the only critical point for F, we conclude that:

$$\min C(x, y) = C(60, 30) = 6 \cdot 60^2 + 12 \cdot 30^2$$
$$= 21,600 + 10,800$$
$$= \$32,400$$

Thus, 60 of model A and 30 of model B will yield a minimum cost of $32,400 per week.

25. **(A)** <u>Step 1.</u> Maximize the production function $N(x, y) = 50x^{0.8}y^{0.2}$

Subject to the constraint: $C(x, y) = 40x + 80y = 400,000$

i.e., $g(x, y) = 40x + 80y - 400,000 = 0$

<u>Step 2.</u> $F(x, y, \lambda) = 50x^{0.8}y^{0.2} + \lambda(40x + 80y - 400,000)$

<u>Step 3.</u> $F_x = 40x^{-0.2}y^{0.2} + 40\lambda = 0$ (1)

$F_y = 10x^{0.8}y^{-0.8} + 80\lambda = 0$ (2)

$F_\lambda = 40x + 80y - 400,000 = 0$ (3)

From (1), $\lambda = -\dfrac{y^{0.2}}{x^{0.2}}$. From (2), $\lambda = -\dfrac{x^{0.8}}{8y^{0.8}}$.

Thus, we obtain

$$-\frac{y^{0.2}}{x^{0.2}} = -\frac{x^{0.8}}{8y^{0.8}} \quad \text{or} \quad x = 8y$$

Substituting into (3), we have:
$320y + 80y - 400,000 = 0$
$$y = 1000$$

Therefore, $x = 8000$, $\lambda \approx -0.6598$, and the critical point is (8000, 1000, -0.6598). Thus, we conclude that:

$$\max N(x, y) = N(8000, 1000) = 50(8000)^{0.8}(1000)^{0.2}$$
$$\approx 263,902 \text{ units}$$

and production is maximized when 8000 labor units and 1000 capital units are used.

(B) The marginal productivity of money is $-\lambda \approx 0.6598$. The increase in production if an additional \$50,000 is budgeted for production is: $0.6598(50,000) = 32,990$ units

27. Let x = length, y = width, and $\overset{\bullet}{z}$ = height.

Step 1. Maximize volume $V = xyz$
Subject to: $S(x, y, z) = xy + 3xz + 3yz - 192 = 0$

Step 2. $F(x, y, z, \lambda) = xyz + \lambda(xy + 3xz + 3yz - 192)$

Step 3. $F_x = yz + \lambda(y + 3z) = 0$ (1)

$F_y = xz + \lambda(x + 3z) = 0$ (2)

$F_z = xy + \lambda(3x + 3y) = 0$ (3)

$F_\lambda = xy + 3xz + 3yz - 192 = 0$ (4)

Solving this system of equations, (1)-(4), simultaneously, yields:

$x = 8, \quad y = 8, \quad z = \dfrac{8}{3}, \quad \lambda = -\dfrac{4}{3}$

Thus, the critical point is $\left(8, 8, \dfrac{8}{3}, -\dfrac{4}{3}\right)$.

Step 4. Since $\left(8, 8, \dfrac{8}{3}, -\dfrac{4}{3}\right)$ is the only critical point for F:

$\max V(x, y, z) = V\left(8, 8, \dfrac{8}{3}\right) = \dfrac{512}{3} \approx 170.67$

Thus, the dimensions that will maximize the volume of the box are: Length $x = 8$ inches; Width $y = 8$ inches; Height $z = \dfrac{8}{3}$ inches.

29. Step 1. Maximize $A = xy$
Subject to: $P(x, y) = y + 4x - 400 = 0$

Step 2. $F(x, y, \lambda) = xy + \lambda(y + 4x - 400)$

Step 3. $F_x = y + 4\lambda = 0$ (1)

$F_y = x + \lambda = 0$ (2)

$F_\lambda = y + 4x - 400 = 0$ (3)

From (1) and (2), we have:
$y = -4\lambda$ and $x = -\lambda$
Substituting these into (3), we obtain:
$-4\lambda - 4\lambda - 400 = 0$
Thus, $\lambda = -50$ and the critical point is $(50, 200, -50)$.

Step 4. Since $(50, 200, -50)$ is the only critical point for F,
$\max A(x, y) = A(50, 200) = 10,000$.
Therefore, $x = 50$ feet, $y = 200$ feet will produce the maximum area $A(50, 200) = 10,000$ square feet.

Things to remember:

1. LEAST SQUARES APPROXIMATION FORMULAS

    For a set of n points (x_1, y_1), (x_2, y_2), ... , (x_n, y_n), the coefficients of the least squares line $y = ax + b$ are the solutions of the system of the NORMAL EQUATIONS

    $$\left(\sum_{k=1}^{n} x_k^2 \right) a + \left(\sum_{k=1}^{n} x_k \right) b = \sum_{k=1}^{n} x_k y_k \tag{1}$$

    $$\left(\sum_{k=1}^{n} x_k \right) a + nb = \sum_{k=1}^{n} y_k$$

    and are given by the formulas

    $$a = \frac{n \left(\sum_{k=1}^{n} x_k y_k \right) - \left(\sum_{k=1}^{n} x_k \right) \left(\sum_{k=1}^{n} y_k \right)}{n \left(\sum_{k=1}^{n} x_k^2 \right) - \left(\sum_{k=1}^{n} x_k \right)^2} \tag{2}$$

    $$b = \frac{\sum_{k=1}^{n} y_k - a \left(\sum_{k=1}^{n} x_k \right)}{n} \tag{3}$$

    [Note: To find a and b, either solve system (1) directly, or use formulas (2) and (3). If the formulas are used, the value of a must be calculated first since it is used in the formula for b.

1.

	x_k	y_k	$x_k y_k$	x_k^2
	1	1	1	1
	2	3	6	4
	3	4	12	9
	4	3	12	16
Totals	10	11	31	30

Thus, $\sum_{k=1}^{4} x_k = 10$, $\sum_{k=1}^{4} y_k = 11$, $\sum_{k=1}^{4} x_k y_k = 31$, $\sum_{k=1}^{4} x_k^2 = 30$.

Substituting these values into formulas (2) and (3) for m and d, respectively, we have:

$$m = \frac{n \left(\sum_{k=1}^{n} x_k y_k \right) - \left(\sum_{k=1}^{n} x_k \right) \left(\sum_{k=1}^{n} y_k \right)}{n \left(\sum_{k=1}^{n} x_k^2 \right) - \left(\sum_{k=1}^{n} x_k \right)^2} = \frac{4(31) - (10)(11)}{4(30) - (10)^2} = \frac{14}{20} = 0.7$$

$$d = \frac{\sum\limits_{k=1}^{n} y_k - m\left(\sum\limits_{k=1}^{n} x_k\right)}{n} = \frac{11 - 0.7(10)}{4} = 1$$

Thus, the least squares line is $y = mx + d = 0.7x + 1$. Refer to the graph at the right.

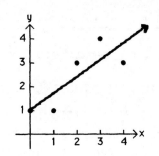

3.

	x_k	y_k	$x_k y_k$	x_k^2
	1	8	8	1
	2	5	10	4
	3	4	12	9
	4	0	0	16
Totals	10	17	30	30

Thus, $\sum\limits_{k=1}^{4} x_k = 10$, $\sum\limits_{k=1}^{4} y_k = 17$, $\sum\limits_{k=1}^{4} x_k y_k = 30$,

$\sum\limits_{k=1}^{4} x_k^2 = 30$.

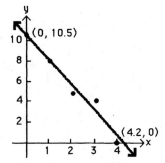

Substituting these values into system (1), we have:

$$10m + 4d = 17$$
$$30m + 10d = 30$$

The solution of this system is $m = -2.5$, $d = 10.5$. Thus, the least squares line is $y = mx + d = -2.5x + 10.5$. Refer to the graph above.

5.

	x_k	y_k	$x_k y_k$	x_k^2
	1	3	3	1
	2	4	8	4
	3	5	15	9
	4	6	24	16
Totals	10	18	50	30

Thus, $\sum\limits_{k=1}^{4} x_k = 10$, $\sum\limits_{k=1}^{4} y_k = 18$, $\sum\limits_{k=1}^{4} x_k y_k = 50$,

$\sum\limits_{k=1}^{4} x_k^2 = 30$.

Substituting these values into the formulas for m and d [formulas (2) and (3)], we have:

$$m = \frac{4(50) - (10)(18)}{4(30) - (10)^2} = \frac{20}{20} = 1$$

$$d = \frac{18 - 1(10)}{4} = \frac{8}{4} = 2$$

Thus, the least squares line is $y = mx + d = x + 2$. Refer to the graph at the right.

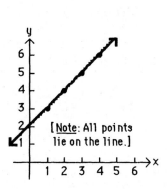

[Note: All points lie on the line.]

7.

	x_k	y_k	$x_k y_k$	x_k^2
	1	3	3	1
	2	1	2	4
	2	2	4	4
	3	0	0	9
Totals	8	6	9	18

Thus, $\sum_{k=1}^{4} x_k = 8$, $\sum_{k=1}^{4} y_k = 6$, $\sum_{k=1}^{4} x_k y_k = 9$, $\sum_{k=1}^{4} x_k^2 = 18$.

Substituting these values into formulas (2) and (3) for m and d, respectively, we have:

$$m = \frac{4(9) - 8(6)}{4(18) - 8^2} = \frac{36 - 48}{72 - 64} = \frac{-12}{8} = -\frac{3}{2} = -1.5$$

$$d = \frac{6 - (-3/2)(8)}{4} = \frac{6 + 12}{4} = \frac{9}{2} = 4.5$$

Thus, the least squares line is $y = -1.5x + 4.5$.
When $x = 2.5$, $y = -1.5(2.5) + 4.5 = 0.75$.

9.

	x_k	y_k	$x_k y_k$	x_k^2
	0	10	0	0
	5	22	110	25
	10	31	310	100
	15	46	690	225
	20	51	1020	400
Totals	50	160	2130	750

Thus, $\sum_{k=1}^{5} x_k = 50$, $\sum_{k=1}^{5} y_k = 160$, $\sum_{k=1}^{5} x_k y_k = 2130$, $\sum_{k=1}^{5} x_k^2 = 750$.

Substituting these values into formulas (2) and (3) for m and d, respectively, we have:

$$m = \frac{5(2130) - (50)(160)}{5(750) - (50)^2} = \frac{2650}{1250} = 2.12$$

$$d = \frac{160 - 2.12(50)}{5} = \frac{54}{5} = 10.8$$

Thus, the least squares line is $y = 2.12x + 10.8$.
When $x = 25$, $y = 2.12(25) + 10.8 = 63.8$.

11.

	x_k	y_k	$x_k y_k$	x_k^2
	-1	14	-14	1
	1	12	12	1
	3	8	24	9
	5	6	30	25
	7	5	35	49
Totals	15	45	87	85

Thus, $\displaystyle\sum_{k=1}^{5} x_k = 15$, $\displaystyle\sum_{k=1}^{5} y_k = 45$, $\displaystyle\sum_{k=1}^{5} x_k y_k = 87$, $\displaystyle\sum_{k=1}^{5} x_k^2 = 85$.

Substituting these values into formulas (2) and (3) for m and d, respectively, we have:

$$m = \frac{5(87) - (15)(45)}{5(85) - (15)^2} = \frac{-240}{200} = -1.2$$

$$d = \frac{45 - (-1.2)(15)}{5} = 12.6$$

Thus, the least squares line is
$y = -1.2x + 12.6$.
When $x = 2$, $y = -1.2(2) + 12.6 = 10.2$.

13.

x_k	y_k	$x_k y_k$	x_k^2
0.5	25	12.5	0.25
2.0	22	44.0	4.00
3.5	21	73.5	12.25
5.0	21	105.0	25.00
6.5	18	117.0	42.25
9.5	12	114.0	90.25
11.0	11	121.0	121.00
12.5	8	100.0	156.25
14.0	5	70.0	196.00
15.5	1	15.5	240.25
Totals 80.0	144	772.5	887.50

Thus, $\displaystyle\sum_{k=1}^{10} x_k = 80$, $\displaystyle\sum_{k=1}^{10} y_k = 144$, $\displaystyle\sum_{k=1}^{10} x_k y_k = 772.5$, $\displaystyle\sum_{k=1}^{10} x_k^2 = 887.5$.

Substituting these values into formulas (2) and (3) for m and d, respectively, we have:

$$m = \frac{10(772.5) - (80)(144)}{10(887.5) - (80)^2} = \frac{-3795}{2475} \approx -1.53$$

$$d = \frac{144 - (-1.53)(80)}{10} = \frac{266.4}{10} = 26.64$$

Thus, the least squares line is
$y = -1.53x + 26.64$.
When $x = 8$, $y = -1.53(8) + 26.64 = 14.4$.

15. Minimize
$$F(a, b, c) = (a + b + c - 2)^2 + (4a + 2b + c - 1)^2$$
$$+ (9a + 3b + c - 1)^2 + (16a + 4b + c - 3)^2$$

$$F_a(a, b, c) = 2(a + b + c - 2) + 8(4a + 2b + c - 1)$$
$$+ 18(9a + 3b + c - 1) + 32(16a + 4b + c - 3)$$
$$= 708a + 200b + 60c - 126$$

$$F_b(a, b, c) = 2(a + b + c - 2) + 4(4a + 2b + c - 1)$$
$$+ 6(9a + 3b + c - 1) + 8(16a + 4b + c - 3)$$
$$= 200a + 60b + 20c - 38$$

$$F_c(a, b, c) = 2(a + b + c - 2) + 2(4a + 2b + c - 1)$$
$$+ 2(9a + 3b + c - 1) + 2(16a + 4b + c - 3)$$
$$= 60a + 20b + 8c - 14$$

The system is: $F_a(a, b, c) = 0$

$\qquad\qquad\qquad F_b(a, b, c) = 0$

$\qquad\qquad\qquad F_c(a, b, c) = 0$

or:

$$708a + 200b + 60c = 126$$
$$200a + 60b + 20c = 38$$
$$60a + 20b + 8c = 14$$

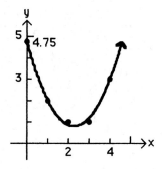

The solution is $(a, b, c) = (0.75, -3.45, 4.75)$, which gives us the equation for the parabola shown at the right:

$y = ax^2 + bx + c$

or

$y = 0.75x^2 - 3.45x + 4.75$

The given points: $(1, 2)$, $(2, 1)$, $(3, 1)$, $(4, 3)$ also appear on the graph.

17. System (1) is:

$$\left(\sum_{k=1}^{n} x_k \right) m + nd = \sum_{k=1}^{n} y_k \qquad \text{(a)}$$

$$\left(\sum_{k=1}^{n} x_k^2 \right) m + \left(\sum_{k=1}^{n} x_k \right) d = \sum_{k=1}^{n} x_k y_k \qquad \text{(b)}$$

Multiply equation (a) by $-\left(\sum_{k=1}^{n} x_k \right)$, equation (b) by n, and add the resulting equations. This will eliminate d from the system.

$$\left[-\left(\sum_{k=1}^{n} x_k \right)^2 + n \sum_{k=1}^{n} x_k^2 \right] m = -\left(\sum_{k=1}^{n} x_k \right)\left(\sum_{k=1}^{n} y_k \right) + n \sum_{k=1}^{n} x_k y_k$$

Thus,

$$m = \frac{n\left(\sum_{k=1}^{n} x_k y_k \right) - \left(\sum_{k=1}^{n} x_k \right)\left(\sum_{k=1}^{n} y_k \right)}{n\left(\sum_{k=1}^{n} x_k^2 \right) - \left(\sum_{k=1}^{n} x_k \right)^2}$$

which is equation (2). Solving equation (a) for d, we have

$$d = \frac{\sum_{k=1}^{n} y_k - m\left(\sum_{k=1}^{n} x_k \right)}{n}$$

which is equation (3).

19. (A) Suppose that $n = 5$ and $x_1 = -2$, $x_2 = -1$, $x_3 = 0$, $x_4 = 1$, $x_5 = 2$.

Then $\sum_{k=1}^{5} x_k = -2 - 1 + 0 + 1 + 2 = 0$. Therefore, from formula (2),

$$m = \frac{5 \sum_{k=1}^{5} x_k y_k}{5 \sum_{k=1}^{5} x_k^2} = \frac{\sum x_k y_k}{\sum x_k^2} \qquad \text{From formula (3),} \quad d = \frac{\sum_{k=1}^{5} y_k}{5},$$

which is the average of y_1, y_2, y_3, y_4, and y_5.

(B) If the average of the x-coordinates is 0, then

$$\frac{\sum_{k=1}^{n} x_k}{n} = 0$$

Then all calculations will be the same as in part (A) with "n" instead of 5.

21. (A)
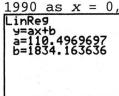
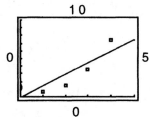

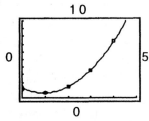

(B) The quadratic regression function best fits the data.

23. The cubic regression function has the form $y = ax^3 + bx^2 + cx + d$. The normal equations form a system of 4 linear equations in the 4 variables a, b, c and d. The system can be solved using Gauss-Jordan elimination.

25. (A) We use the linear regression feature on a graphing utility with 1990 as $x = 0$, 1991 as $x = 1$, etc.

```
LinReg
y=ax+b
a=110.4969697
b=1834.163636
```

Thus, the least squares line is: $y = 110.5x + 1834$.

(B) The year 2010 corresponds to $x = 20$; $y(20) \approx 4{,}044$ thousand or $4{,}044{,}000$

27. (A)

x_k	y_k	$x_k y_k$	x_k^2
5.0	2.0	10.0	25.00
5.5	1.8	9.9	30.25
6.0	1.4	8.4	36.00
6.5	1.2	7.8	42.25
7.0	1.1	7.7	49.00
Totals 30.0	7.5	43.8	182.50

Thus, $\sum_{k=1}^{5} x_k = 30$, $\sum_{k=1}^{5} y_k = 7.5$, $\sum_{k=1}^{5} x_k y_k = 43.8$, $\sum_{k=1}^{5} x_k^2 = 182.5$.

Substituting these values into the formulas for m and d, we have:

$$m = \frac{5(43.8) - (30)(7.5)}{5(182.5) - (30)^2} = \frac{-6}{12.5} = -0.48$$

$$d = \frac{7.5 - (-0.48)(30)}{5} = 4.38$$

Thus, a demand equation is $y = -0.48x + 4.38$.

(B) Cost: $C = 4y$

Revenue: $R = xy = -0.48x^2 + 4.38x$

Profit: $P = R - C = -0.48x^2 + 4.38x - 4(-0.48x + 4.38)$

or $P(x) = -0.48x^2 + 6.3x - 17.52$

Now, $P'(x) = -0.96x + 6.3$.

Critical value: $P'(x) = -0.96x + 6.3 = 0$

$$x = \frac{6.3}{0.96} \approx 6.56$$

$P''(x) = -0.96$ and $P''(6.56) = -0.96 < 0$

Thus, $P(x)$ has a maximum at $x = 6.56$; the price per bottle should be $6.56 to maximize the monthly profit.

29.

x_k	y_k	$x_k y_k$	x_k^2
50	15	750	2500
55	13	715	3025
60	10	600	3600
65	6	390	4225
70	2	140	4900
Totals 300	46	2595	18,250

Thus, $\displaystyle\sum_{k=1}^{5} x_k = 300$, $\displaystyle\sum_{k=1}^{5} y_k = 46$, $\displaystyle\sum_{k=1}^{5} x_k y_k = 2595$, $\displaystyle\sum_{k=1}^{5} x_k^2 = 18,250$.

Substituting these values into the formulas for m and d, we have:

$$m = \frac{5(2595) - (300)(46)}{5(18,250) - (300)^2} = \frac{-825}{1250} = -0.66$$

$$d = \frac{46 - (-0.66)300}{5} = 48.8$$

(A) The least squares line for the data is $P = -0.66T + 48.8$.

(B) $P(57) = -0.66(57) + 48.8 = 11.18$ beats per minute.

31. (A) We use the linear regression feature on a graphing utility with 1885 as $x = 0$, 1895 as $x = 10$, ..., 1995 as $x = 110$.

```
LinReg
y=ax+b
a=.0085664336
b=56.47884615
```

Thus, the least squares line is:
$y = 0.0086x + 56.48$

(B) The year 2085 corresponds to $x = 200$; $y(200) \approx 58.19\,°F$.

33. (A) Enter the data in a calculator or computer. (We used a TI-85.)
The totals are:
$n = 23$, $\sum x = 1098$, $\sum y = 343.61$,
$\sum x^2 = 73,860$, $\sum xy = 18,259.08$

Now, the least squares line can be calculated either by using formulas (2) and (3), or by using the linear regression feature. We used the latter to get

$$m = 0.08653 \quad \text{and} \quad b = 10.81$$

Therefore, the least squares line is:

$$y = 0.08653x + 10.81$$

(B) Using the result in (A), an estimate for the winning height in the pole vault in the Olympic games of 2008 is:

$$y = 0.08653(112) + 10.81 \approx 20.50 \text{ feet}$$

35. (A) We use the linear regression feature on a graphing utility with 1896 as $x = 0$, 1900 as $x = 4$, ..., 2000 as $x = 104$.

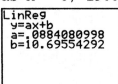

```
LinReg
 y=ax+b
 a=.0884080998
 b=10.69554292
```

Thus, the least squares line is: $y = 0.0884x + 10.70$.

(B) The year 2016 corresponds to $x = 120$; $y(120) \approx 21.30$ ft.

EXERCISE 8-6

Things to remember:

GIVEN A FUNCTION $z = f(x, y)$:

1. $\int f(x, y)\,dx$ means antidifferentiate $f(x, y)$ with respect to x, holding y fixed.

   $\int f(x, y)\,dy$ means antidifferentiate $f(x, y)$ with respect to y, holding x fixed.

2. The DOUBLE INTEGRAL of $f(x, y)$ over the rectangle $R = \{(x, y) \mid a \le x \le b, c \le y \le d\}$ is:

   $$\iint\limits_{R} f(x, y)\,dA = \int_a^b \left[\int_c^d f(x, y)\,dy\right]dx$$

   $$= \int_c^d \left[\int_a^b f(x, y)\,dx\right]dy$$

   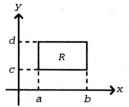

3. The AVERAGE VALUE of $f(x, y)$ over the rectangle $R = \{(x, y) \mid a \le x \le b, c \le y \le d\}$ is:

   $$\frac{1}{(b - a)(d - c)}\iint\limits_{R} f(x, y)\,dA$$

VOLUME UNDER A SURFACE

If $f(x, y) \geq 0$ over a rectangle $R = \{(x, y) \mid a \leq x \leq b, c \leq y \leq d\}$, then the volume of the solid formed by graphing f over the rectangle R is given by:

$$V = \iint\limits_{R} f(x, y)\, dA$$

---

1. (A) $\int 12x^2 y^3\, dy = 12x^2 \int y^3\, dy$ (x is treated as a constant.)

$$= 12x^2 \frac{y^4}{4} + C(x) \quad \begin{array}{l}\text{(The "constant" of integration} \\ \text{is a function of } x.)\end{array}$$

$$= 3x^2 y^4 + C(x)$$

(B) $\int_0^1 12x^2 y^3\, dy = 3x^2 y^4 \Big|_0^1 = 3x^2$

3. (A) $\int (4x + 6y + 5)\, dx$

$$= \int 4x\, dx + \int (6y + 5)\, dx \quad (y \text{ is treated as a constant.})$$

$$= 2x^2 + (6y + 5)x + E(y) \quad \begin{array}{l}\text{(The "constant" of integration} \\ \text{is a function of } y.)\end{array}$$

$$= 2x^2 + 6xy + 5x + E(y)$$

(B) $\int_{-2}^{3} (4x + 6y + 5)\, dx = (2x^2 + 6xy + 5x)\Big|_{-2}^{3}$

$$= 2 \cdot 3^2 + 6 \cdot 3y + 5 \cdot 3 - [2(-2)^2 + 6(-2)y + 5(-2)]$$
$$= 30y + 35$$

5. (A) $\int \dfrac{x}{\sqrt{y + x^2}}\, dx = \int (y + x^2)^{-1/2} x\, dx = \dfrac{1}{2} \int (y + x^2)^{-1/2} 2x\, dx$

Let $u = y + x^2$, then $du = 2x\, dx$.

$$= \frac{1}{2} \int u^{-1/2}\, du$$

$$= u^{1/2} + E(y) = \sqrt{y + x^2} + E(y)$$

(B) $\int_0^2 \dfrac{x}{\sqrt{y + x^2}}\, dx = \sqrt{y + x^2}\,\Big|_0^2 = \sqrt{y + 4} - \sqrt{y}$

7. (A) $\int \dfrac{\ln x}{xy}\, dy = \dfrac{\ln x}{x} \int \dfrac{1}{y}\, dy = \dfrac{\ln x}{x} \cdot \ln y + C(x)$

(B) $\int_1^{e^2} \dfrac{\ln x}{xy}\, dy = \dfrac{\ln x \ln y}{x}\,\Big|_1^{e^2} = \dfrac{\ln x \ln e^2}{x} - \dfrac{\ln x \ln 1}{x} = \dfrac{2 \ln x}{x}$

9. $\int_{-1}^{2} \int_0^1 12x^2 y^3\, dy\, dx = \int_{-1}^{2} \left[\int_0^1 12x^2 y^3\, dy\right] dx = \int_{-1}^{2} 3x^2\, dx$ (see Problem 1)

$$= x^3 \Big|_{-1}^{2} = 8 + 1 = 9$$

11. $\displaystyle\int_1^4 \int_{-2}^3 (4x + 6y + 5)\,dx\,dy = \int_1^4 \left[\int_{-2}^3 (4x + 6y + 5)dx \right] dy$

$$= \int_1^4 (30y + 35)\,dy \quad \text{(see Problem 3)}$$

$$= (15y^2 + 35y) \Big|_1^4$$

$$= 15 \cdot 4^2 + 35 \cdot 4 - (15 + 35) = 330$$

13. $\displaystyle\int_1^5 \int_0^2 \frac{x}{\sqrt{y + x^2}}\,dx\,dy = \int_1^5 \left[\int_0^2 \frac{x}{\sqrt{y + x^2}}\,dx \right] dy$

$$= \int_1^5 (\sqrt{4 + y} - \sqrt{y})\,dy \quad \text{(see Problem 5)}$$

$$= \left[\frac{2}{3}(4 + y)^{3/2} - \frac{2}{3}y^{3/2} \right]\Big|_1^5$$

$$= \frac{2}{3}(9)^{3/2} - \frac{2}{3}(5)^{3/2} - \left(\frac{2}{3} \cdot 5^{3/2} - \frac{2}{3} \cdot 1^{3/2} \right)$$

$$= 18 - \frac{4}{3}(5)^{3/2} + \frac{2}{3} = \frac{56 - 20\sqrt{5}}{3}$$

15. $\displaystyle\int_1^e \int_1^{e^2} \frac{\ln x}{xy}\,dy\,dx = \int_1^e \left[\int_1^{e^2} \frac{\ln x}{xy}\,dy \right] dx$

$$= \int_1^e \frac{2\ln x}{x}\,dx \quad \text{(see Problem 7)}$$

$$= 2\int_1^e \frac{\ln x}{x}\,dx$$

$$= [\ln x]^2 \Big|_1^e \qquad\qquad \text{Substitution: } u = \ln x$$

$$= 1 \qquad\qquad\qquad\qquad\qquad du = \frac{1}{x}\,dx$$

17. $\displaystyle\iint_R xy\,dA = \int_0^2 \int_0^4 xy\,dy\,dx = \int_0^2 \left[\int_0^4 xy\,dy \right] dx = \int_0^2 \left[\frac{xy^2}{2} \Big|_0^4 \right] dx$

$$= \int_0^2 8x\,dx = 4x^2 \Big|_0^2 = 16$$

$\displaystyle\iint_R xy\,dA = \int_0^4 \int_0^2 xy\,dy\,dx = \int_0^4 \left[\int_0^2 xy\,dx \right] dy = \int_0^4 \left[\frac{x^2 y}{2} \Big|_0^2 \right] dy$

$$= \int_0^4 2y\,dy = y^2 \Big|_0^4 = 16$$

19. $\displaystyle\iint_R (x + y)^5\,dA = \int_{-1}^1 \int_1^2 (x + y)^5\,dy\,dx = \int_{-1}^1 \left[\int_1^2 (x + y)^5\,dy \right] dx$

$$= \int_{-1}^1 \left[\frac{(x + y)^6}{6} \Big|_1^2 \right] dx = \int_{-1}^1 \left[\frac{(x + 2)^6}{6} - \frac{(x + 1)^6}{6} \right] dx$

$$= \left[\frac{(x + 2)^7}{42} - \frac{(x + 1)^7}{42} \right]\Big|_{-1}^1 = \frac{3^7}{42} - \frac{2^7}{42} - \frac{1}{42} = 49$$

$$\iint\limits_{R} (x + y)^5 dA = \int_1^2 \int_{-1}^1 (x + y)^5 dx\, dy = \int_1^2 \left[\int_{-1}^1 (x + y)^5 dx \right] dy$$

$$= \int_1^2 \left[\frac{(x + y)^6}{6} \Big|_{-1}^1 \right] dy = \int_1^2 \left[\frac{(y + 1)^6}{6} - \frac{(y - 1)^6}{6} \right] dy$$

$$= \left[\frac{(y + 1)^7}{42} - \frac{(y - 1)^7}{42} \right] \Big|_1^2 = \frac{3^7}{42} - \frac{1}{42} - \frac{2^7}{42} = 49$$

21. Average value $= \dfrac{1}{(5 - 1)[1 - (-1)]} \iint\limits_{R} (x + y)^2 dA$

$$= \frac{1}{8} \int_{-1}^1 \int_1^5 (x + y)^2 dx\, dy = \frac{1}{8} \int_{-1}^1 \left[\frac{(x + y)^3}{3} \Big|_1^5 \right] dy$$

$$= \frac{1}{8} \int_{-1}^1 \left[\frac{(5 + y)^3}{3} - \frac{(1 + y)^3}{3} \right] dy = \frac{1}{8} \left[\frac{(5 + y)^4}{12} - \frac{(1 + y)^4}{12} \right] \Big|_{-1}^1$$

$$= \frac{1}{96} [6^4 - 2^4 - 4^4] = \frac{32}{3}$$

23. Average value $= \dfrac{1}{(4 - 1)(7 - 2)} \iint\limits_{R} \dfrac{x}{y} dA = \dfrac{1}{15} \int_1^4 \int_2^7 \dfrac{x}{y} dy\, dx$

$$= \frac{1}{15} \int_1^4 \left[x \ln y \right]_2^7 dx = \frac{1}{15} \int_1^4 [x \ln 7 - x \ln 2]\, dx$$

$$= \frac{\ln 7 - \ln 2}{15} \int_1^4 x\, dx = \frac{\ln 7 - \ln 2}{15} \cdot \frac{x^2}{2} \Big|_1^4$$

$$= \frac{\ln 7 - \ln 2}{15} \left(\frac{4^2}{2} - \frac{1^2}{2} \right) = \frac{1}{2} (\ln 7 - \ln 2)$$

$$= \frac{1}{2} \ln\left(\frac{7}{2} \right) \approx 0.626$$

25. $V = \iint\limits_{R} (2 - x^2 - y^2)\, dA = \int_0^1 \int_0^1 \iint\limits_{R} (2 - x^2 - y^2)\, dy\, dx$

$$= \int_0^1 \left[\int_0^1 (2 - x^2 - y^2) dy \right] dx = \int_0^1 \left[\left(2y - x^2 y - \frac{y^3}{3} \right) \Big|_0^1 \right] dx$$

$$= \int_0^1 \left(2 - x^2 - \frac{1}{3} \right) dx = \int_0^1 \left(\frac{5}{3} - x^2 \right) dx = \left(\frac{5}{3} x - \frac{x^3}{3} \right) \Big|_0^1 = \frac{5}{3} - \frac{1}{3} = \frac{4}{3}$$

27. $V = \iint\limits_{R} (4 - y^2)\, dA = \int_0^2 \int_0^2 (4 - y^2)\, dx\, dy = \int_0^2 \left[\int_0^2 (4 - y^2) dx \right] dy$

$$= \int_0^2 \left[(4x - xy^2) \Big|_0^2 \right] dy = \int_0^2 (8 - 2y^2)\, dy = \left(8y - \frac{2}{3} y^3 \right) \Big|_0^2$$

$$= 16 - \frac{16}{3} = \frac{32}{3}$$

29. $\displaystyle\iint\limits_{R} xe^{xy}\,dA = \int_0^1 \int_1^2 xe^{xy}\,dy\,dx = \int_0^1 \left[\int_1^2 xe^{xy}\,dy\right]dx$

$\displaystyle = \int_0^1 \left[x\int_1^2 e^{xy}\,dy\right]dx = \int_0^1 \left[x \cdot \frac{e^{xy}}{x}\Big|_1^2\right]dx = \int_0^1 \left[\frac{e^{xy}}{x}\Big|_1^2\right]dx$

$\displaystyle = \int_0^1 (e^{2x} - e^x)\,dx = \left(\frac{e^{2x}}{2} - e^x\right)\Big|_0^1 = \frac{e^2}{2} - e - \left(\frac{1}{2} - 1\right)$

$\displaystyle = \frac{e^2}{2} - e + \frac{1}{2}$

31. $\displaystyle\iint\limits_{R} \frac{2y + 3xy^2}{1 + x^2}\,dA = \int_0^1 \int_{-1}^1 \frac{2y + 3xy^2}{1 + x^2}\,dy\,dx = \int_0^1 \left[\int_{-1}^1 \frac{2y + 3xy^2}{1 + x^2}\,dy\right]dx$

$\displaystyle = \int_0^1 \left[\frac{1}{1 + x^2}(y^2 + xy^3)\Big|_{-1}^1\right]dx$

$\displaystyle = \int_0^1 \left[\frac{1}{1 + x^2}(1 + x - [1 - x])\right]dx$

$\displaystyle = \int_0^1 \frac{2x}{1 + x^2}\,dx = \ln(1 + x^2)\Big|_0^1 \qquad$ Substitution: $u = 1 + x^2$

$\qquad\qquad\qquad\qquad\qquad\qquad\qquad\qquad\qquad du = 2x\,dx$

$= \ln 2$

33. $\displaystyle\int_0^2 \int_0^2 (1 - y)\,dx\,dy = \int_0^2 \left[\int_0^2 (1 - y)\,dx\right]dy$

$\displaystyle = \int_0^2 \left[(x - xy)\Big|_0^2\right]dy$

$\displaystyle = \int_0^2 (2 - 2y)\,dy$

$\displaystyle = (2y - y^2)\Big|_0^2 = 0$

Since $f(x, y) = 1 - y$ is NOT nonnegative over the rectangle
$R = \{(x, y) \mid 0 \le x \le 2,\ 0 \le y \le 2\}$ the double integral does not
represent the volume of solid.

35. $f(x, y) = x^3 + y^2 - e^{-x} - 1$ on $R = \{(x, y) \mid -2 \le x \le 2,\ -2 \le y \le 2\}$.
 (A) Average value of f:

$\displaystyle \frac{1}{b - a} \cdot \frac{1}{d - c}\iint\limits_{R} f(x, y)\,dA$

$\displaystyle = \frac{1}{2 - (-2)} \cdot \frac{1}{2 - (-2)}\int_{-2}^2 \int_{-2}^2 (x^3 + y^2 - e^{-x} - 1)\,dx\,dy$

$\displaystyle = \frac{1}{16}\int_{-2}^2 \left[\left(\frac{1}{4}x^4 + xy^2 + e^{-x} - x\right)\Big|_{-2}^2\right]dy$

$\displaystyle = \frac{1}{16}\int_{-2}^2 [4y^2 + e^{-2} - e^2 - 4]\,dy$

$\displaystyle = \frac{1}{16}\left[\frac{4}{3}y^3 + e^{-2}y - e^2 y - 4y\right]\Big|_{-2}^2$

$\displaystyle = \frac{1}{16}\left[\frac{64}{3} + 4e^{-2} - 4e^2 - 16\right] = \frac{1}{3} + \frac{1}{4}e^{-2} - \frac{1}{4}e^2$

(B)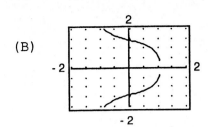

(C) $f(x, y) > 0$ at the points which lie to the right of the curve in part (B); $f(x, y) < 0$ at the points which lie to the left of the curve in part (B).

37. $S(x, y) = \dfrac{y}{1 - x}$, $0.6 \leq x \leq 0.8$, $5 \leq y \leq 7$.

The *average* total amount of spending is given by:

$$T = \dfrac{1}{(0.8 - 0.6)(7 - 5)} \iint_R \dfrac{y}{1 - x}\, dA = \dfrac{1}{0.4} \int_{0.6}^{0.8} \int_5^7 \dfrac{y}{1 - x}\, dy\, dx$$

$$= \dfrac{1}{0.4} \int_{0.6}^{0.8} \left[\dfrac{1}{1 - x} \cdot \dfrac{y^2}{2} \Big|_5^7 \right] dx = \dfrac{1}{0.4} \int_{0.6}^{0.8} \dfrac{1}{1 - x}\left(\dfrac{49}{2} - \dfrac{25}{2} \right) dx$$

$$= \dfrac{12}{0.4} \int_{0.6}^{0.8} \dfrac{1}{1 - x}\, dx = 30\left[-\ln(1 - x) \right]\Big|_{0.6}^{0.8}$$

$$= 30[-\ln(0.2) + \ln(0.4)] = 30 \ln 2 \approx \$20.8 \text{ billion}$$

39. $N(x, y) = x^{0.75} y^{0.25}$, $10 \leq x \leq 20$, $1 \leq y \leq 2$

Average value $= \dfrac{1}{(20 - 10)(2 - 1)} \int_{10}^{20} \int_1^2 x^{0.75} y^{0.25}\, dy\, dx$

$$= \dfrac{1}{10} \int_{10}^{20} \left[x^{0.75} \dfrac{y^{1.25}}{1.25} \Big|_1^2 \right] dx = \dfrac{1}{10} \int_{10}^{20} \left[x^{0.75} \dfrac{2^{1.25} - 1}{1.25} \right] dx$$

$$= \dfrac{1}{12.5} (2^{1.25} - 1) \int_{10}^{20} x^{0.75}\, dx = \dfrac{1}{12.5} (2^{1.25} - 1) \dfrac{x^{1.75}}{1.75} \Big|_{10}^{20}$$

$$= \dfrac{1}{21.875} (2^{1.25} - 1)(20^{1.75} - 10^{1.75}) \approx 8.375 \text{ or } 8375 \text{ items}$$

41. $C = 10 - \dfrac{1}{10} d^2 = 10 - \dfrac{1}{10}(x^2 + y^2) = C(x, y)$, $-8 \leq x \leq 8$, $-6 \leq y \leq 6$

Average concentration

$$= \dfrac{1}{16(12)} \int_{-8}^8 \int_{-6}^6 \left[10 - \dfrac{1}{10}(x^2 + y^2) \right] dy\, dx$$

$$= \dfrac{1}{192} \int_{-8}^8 \left[10y - \dfrac{1}{10}\left(x^2 y + \dfrac{y^3}{3} \right) \right]\Big|_{-6}^6 dx$$

$$= \dfrac{1}{192} \int_{-8}^8 \left\{ 60 - \dfrac{1}{10}\left(6x^2 + \dfrac{216}{3} \right) - \left[-60 - \dfrac{1}{10}\left(-6x^2 - \dfrac{216}{3} \right) \right] \right\} dx$$

$$= \dfrac{1}{192} \int_{-8}^8 \left[120 - \dfrac{1}{10}(12x^2 + 144) \right] dx$$

$$= \dfrac{1}{192} \left[120x - \dfrac{1}{10}(4x^3 + 144x) \right]\Big|_{-8}^8$$

$$= \dfrac{1}{192}(1280) = \dfrac{20}{3} \approx 6.67 \text{ insects per square foot}$$

43. $C = 100 - 15d^2 = 100 - 15(x^2 + y^2) = C(x, y)$, $-2 \leq x \leq 2$, $-1 \leq y \leq 1$

Average concentration $= \dfrac{1}{4(2)} \displaystyle\int_{-2}^{2} \int_{-1}^{1} [100 - 15(x^2 + y^2)]\, dy\, dx$

$$= \frac{1}{8} \int_{-2}^{2} (100y - 15x^2 y - 5y^3) \Big|_{-1}^{1}\, dx$$

$$= \frac{1}{8} \int_{-2}^{2} (190 - 30x^2)\, dx = \frac{1}{8}(190x - 10x^3) \Big|_{-2}^{2}$$

$$= \frac{1}{8}(600) = 75 \text{ parts per million}$$

45. $L = 0.0000133xy^2$, $2000 \leq x \leq 3000$, $50 \leq y \leq 60$

Average length $= \dfrac{1}{10,000} \displaystyle\int_{2000}^{3000} \int_{50}^{60} 0.0000133xy^2\, dy\, dx$

$$= \frac{0.0000133}{10,000} \int_{2000}^{3000} \left[\frac{xy^3}{3} \Big|_{50}^{60} \right]\, dx$$

$$= \frac{0.0000133}{10,000} \int_{2000}^{3000} \frac{91,000}{3} x\, dx = \frac{1.2103}{30,000} \cdot \frac{x^2}{2} \Big|_{2000}^{3000}$$

$$= \frac{1.2103}{30,000}(5,000,000) \approx 100.86 \text{ feet}$$

47. $Q(x, y) = 100\left(\dfrac{x}{y}\right)$, $8 \leq x \leq 16$, $10 \leq y \leq 12$

Average intelligence $= \dfrac{1}{16} \displaystyle\int_{8}^{16} \int_{10}^{12} 100\left(\frac{x}{y}\right) dy\, dx = \frac{100}{16} \int_{8}^{16} \left[x \ln y \Big|_{10}^{12} \right] dx$

$$= \frac{100}{16} \int_{8}^{16} x(\ln 12 - \ln 10)\, dx$$

$$= \frac{100(\ln 12 - \ln 10)}{16} \cdot \frac{x^2}{2} \Big|_{8}^{16}$$

$$= \frac{100(\ln 12 - \ln 10)}{32}(192)$$

$$= 600 \ln(1.2) \approx 109.4$$

CHAPTER 6 REVIEW

1. $f(x, y) = 2000 + 40x + 70y$

$f(5, 10) = 2000 + 40 \cdot 5 + 70 \cdot 10 = 2900$

$f_x(x, y) = 40$

$f_y(x, y) = 70$ (8-1, 8-2)

2. $z = x^3 y^2$

$$\frac{\partial z}{\partial x} = 3x^2 y^2$$

$$\frac{\partial^2 z}{\partial x^2} = \frac{\partial \left(\frac{\partial z}{\partial x} \right)}{\partial x} = \frac{\partial (3x^2 y^2)}{\partial x} = 6xy^2$$

$$\frac{\partial z}{\partial y} = 2x^3 y$$

$$\frac{\partial^2 z}{\partial x \partial y} = \frac{\partial \left(\frac{\partial z}{\partial y} \right)}{\partial x} = \frac{\partial (2x^3 y)}{\partial x} = 6x^2 y \qquad (8\text{-}2)$$

3. $\int (6xy^2 + 4y)\, dy = 6x \int y^2\, dy + 4 \int y\, dy = 6x \cdot \dfrac{y^3}{3} + 4 \cdot \dfrac{y^2}{2} + C(x)$

$$= 2xy^3 + 2y^2 + C(x) \qquad (8\text{-}6)$$

4. $\int (6xy^2 + 4y)\, dx = 6y^2 \int x\, dx + 4y \int dx = 6y^2 \cdot \dfrac{x^2}{2} + 4yx + E(y)$

$$= 3x^2 y^2 + 4xy + E(y) \qquad (8\text{-}6)$$

5. $\int_0^1 \int_0^1 4xy\, dy\, dx = \int_0^1 \left[\int_0^1 4xy\, dy \right] dx = \int_0^1 \left[2xy^2 \Big|_0^1 \right] dx$

$$= \int_0^1 2x\, dx = x^2 \Big|_0^1 = 1 \qquad (8\text{-}6)$$

6. $f(x,\ y) = 6 + 5x - 2y + 3x^2 + x^3$

$f_x(x,\ y) = 5 + 6x + 3x^2$

$f_y(x,\ y) = -2 \neq 0$

The function $f_y(x,\ y)$ is nonzero for all $(x,\ y)$. $\qquad (8\text{-}3)$

7. $f(x,\ y) = 3x^2 - 2xy + y^2 - 2x + 3y - 7$

$f(2,\ 3) = 3 \cdot 2^2 - 2 \cdot 2 \cdot 3 + 3^2 - 2 \cdot 2 + 3 \cdot 3 - 7 = 7$

$f_y(x,\ y) = -2x + 2y + 3$

$f_y(2,\ 3) = -2 \cdot 2 + 2 \cdot 3 + 3 = 5 \qquad (8\text{-}1,\ 8\text{-}2)$

8. $f(x,\ y) = -4x^2 + 4xy - 3y^2 + 4x + 10y + 81$

$f_x(x,\ y) = -8x + 4y + 4 \qquad\qquad f_y(x,\ y) = 4x - 6y + 10$

$f_{xx}(x,\ y) = -8 \qquad\qquad\qquad\quad f_{yy}(x,\ y) = -6$

$f_{xy}(x,\ y) = 4$

Now, $f_{xx}(2,\ 3) \cdot f_{yy}(2,\ 3) - [f_{xy}(2,\ 3)]^2 = (-8)(-6) - 4^2 = 32.$ $\qquad (8\text{-}2)$

9. $f(x, y) = x + 3y$ and $g(x, y) = x^2 + y^2 - 10$.

Let $F(x, y, \lambda) = f(x, y) + \lambda g(x, y) = x + 3y + \lambda(x^2 + y^2 - 10)$.

Then, we have:

$F_x = 1 + 2x\lambda$

$F_y = 3 + 2y\lambda$

$F_\lambda = x^2 + y^2 - 10$

Setting $F_x = F_y = F_\lambda = 0$, we obtain:

$1 + 2x\lambda = 0$ (1)

$3 + 2y\lambda = 0$ (2)

$x^2 + y^2 - 10 = 0$ (3)

From the first equation, $x = -\dfrac{1}{2\lambda}$; from the second equation, $y = -\dfrac{3}{2\lambda}$.

Substituting these into the third equation gives:

$\dfrac{1}{4\lambda^2} + \dfrac{9}{4\lambda^2} - 10 = 0$

$$40\lambda^2 = 10$$

$$\lambda^2 = \frac{1}{4}$$

$$\lambda = \pm\frac{1}{2}$$

Thus, the critical points are $\left(-1, -3, \dfrac{1}{2}\right)$ and $\left(1, 3, -\dfrac{1}{2}\right)$.   (8-4)

10.

	x_k	y_k	$x_k y_k$	x_k^2
	2	12	24	4
	4	10	40	16
	6	7	42	36
	8	3	24	64
Totals	20	32	130	120

Thus, $\displaystyle\sum_{k=1}^{4} x_k = 20$, $\displaystyle\sum_{k=1}^{4} y_k = 32$, $\displaystyle\sum_{k=1}^{4} x_k y_k = 130$, $\displaystyle\sum_{k=1}^{4} x_k^2 = 120$.

Substituting these values into the formulas for m and d, we have:

$$m = \frac{4\left(\displaystyle\sum_{k=1}^{4} x_k y_k\right) - \left(\displaystyle\sum_{k=1}^{4} x_k\right)\left(\displaystyle\sum_{k=1}^{4} y_k\right)}{4\left(\displaystyle\sum_{k=1}^{4} x_k^2\right) - \left(\displaystyle\sum_{k=1}^{4} x_k\right)^2} = \frac{4(130) - (20)(32)}{4(120) - (20)^2} = \frac{-120}{80} = -1.5$$

$$d = \frac{\displaystyle\sum_{k=1}^{4} y_k - (-1.5)\displaystyle\sum_{k=1}^{4} x_k}{4} = \frac{32 + (1.5)(20)}{4} = \frac{62}{4} = 15.5$$

Thus, the least squares line is:

$y = mx + d = -1.5x + 15.5$

When $x = 10$, $y = -1.5(10) + 15.5 = 0.5$.   (8-5)

11. $\displaystyle\iint\limits_{R} (4x + 6y)\,dA = \int_{-1}^{1} \int_{1}^{2} (4x + 6y)\,dy\,dx = \int_{-1}^{1} \left[\int_{1}^{2} (4x + 6y)\,dy \right] dx$

$$= \int_{-1}^{1} \left[(4xy + 3y^2) \Big|_{1}^{2} \right] dx = \int_{-1}^{1} (8x + 12 - 4x - 3)\,dx$$

$$= \int_{-1}^{1} (4x + 9)\,dx = (2x^2 + 9x) \Big|_{-1}^{1} = 2 + 9 - (2 - 9) = 18$$

$\displaystyle\iint\limits_{R} (4x + 6y)\,dA = \int_{1}^{2} \int_{-1}^{1} (4x + 6y)\,dx\,dy = \int_{1}^{2} \left[\int_{-1}^{1} (4x + 6y)\,dx \right] dy$

$$= \int_{1}^{2} \left[(2x^2 + 6xy) \Big|_{-1}^{1} \right] dy = \int_{1}^{2} [2 + 6y - (2 - 6y)]\,dy$$

$$= \int_{1}^{2} 12y\,dy = 6y^2 \Big|_{1}^{2} = 24 - 6 = 18 \qquad\qquad (8\text{-}6)$$

12. $f(x, y) = e^{x^2+2y}$

$f_x(x, y) = e^{x^2+2y} \cdot 2x = 2xe^{x^2+2y}$

$f_y(x, y) = e^{x^2+2y} \cdot 2 = 2e^{x^2+2y}$

$f_{xy}(x, y) = 2xe^{x^2+2y} \cdot 2 = 4xe^{x^2+2y} \qquad\qquad (8\text{-}2)$

13. $f(x, y) = (x^2 + y^2)^5$

$f_x(x, y) = 5(x^2 + y^2)^4 \cdot 2x = 10x(x^2 + y^2)^4$

$f_{xy}(x, y) = 10x(4)(x^2 + y^2)^3 \cdot 2y = 80xy(x^2 + y^2)^3 \qquad\qquad (8\text{-}2)$

14. $f(x, y) = x^3 - 12x + y^2 - 6y$

$f_x(x, y) = 3x^2 - 12 \qquad\qquad f_y(x, y) = 2y - 6$

$3x^2 - 12 = 0 \qquad\qquad\qquad 2y - 6 = 0$

$\qquad x^2 = 4 \qquad\qquad\qquad\qquad y = 3$

$\qquad\quad x = \pm 2$

Thus, the critical points are (2, 3) an (-2, 3).

$f_{xx}(x, y) = 6x \qquad f_{xy}(x, y) = 0 \qquad f_{yy}(x, y) = 2$

For the critical point (2, 3):

$f_{xx}(2, 3) = 12 > 0$

$f_{xy}(2, 3) = 0$

$f_{yy}(2, 3) = 2$

$f_{xx}(2, 3) \cdot f_{yy}(2, 3) - [f_{xy}(2, 3)]^2 = 12 \cdot 2 = 24 > 0$

Therefore, $f(2, 3) = 2^3 - 12 \cdot 2 + 3^2 - 6 \cdot 3 = -25$ is a local minimum.

For the critical point (-2, 3):

$f_{xx}(-2, 3) = -12 < 0$

$f_{xy}(-2, 3) = 0$

$f_{yy}(-2, 3) = 2$

$f_{xx}(-2, 3) \cdot f_{yy}(-2, 3) - [f_{xy}(-2, 3)]^2 = -12 \cdot 2 - 0 = -24 < 0$

Thus, f has a saddle point at (-2, 3). $\qquad\qquad (8\text{-}3)$

15. <u>Step 1.</u> Maximize $f(x, y) = xy$
Subject to: $g(x, y) = 2x + 3y - 24 = 0$

<u>Step 2.</u> $F(x, y, \lambda) = f(x, y) + \lambda g(x, y) = xy + \lambda(2x + 3y - 24)$

<u>Step 3.</u> $F_x = y + 2\lambda = 0$ $\qquad\qquad$ (1)

$F_y = x + 3\lambda = 0$ $\qquad\qquad$ (2)

$F_\lambda = 2x + 3y - 24 = 0$ $\qquad$ (3)

From (1) and (2), we obtain:
$y = -2\lambda$ $\qquad$ and $\qquad$ $x = -3\lambda$

Substituting these into (3), we have:
$-6\lambda - 6\lambda - 24 = 0$

$\qquad\qquad \lambda = -2$

Thus, the critical point is $(6, 4, -2)$.

<u>Step 4.</u> Since $(6, 4, -2)$ is the only critical point for F, we conclude
that max $f(x, y) = f(6, 4) = 6 \cdot 4 = 24$. $\qquad\qquad\qquad$ (8-4)

16. <u>Step 1.</u> Minimize $f(x, y, z) = x^2 + y^2 + z^2$
Subject to: $2x + y + 2z = 9$ or $g(x, y, z) = 2x + y + 2z - 9 = 0$

<u>Step 2.</u> $F(x, y, z, \lambda) = x^2 + y^2 + z^2 + \lambda(2x + y + 2z - 9)$

<u>Step 3.</u> $F_x = 2x + 2\lambda = 0$ $\qquad\qquad$ (1)

$F_y = 2y + \lambda = 0$ $\qquad\qquad$ (2)

$F_z = 2z + 2\lambda = 0$ $\qquad\qquad$ (3)

$F_\lambda = 2x + y + 2z - 9 = 0$ $\qquad$ (4)

From equations (1), (2), and (3), we have:

$x = -\lambda, \quad y = -\dfrac{\lambda}{2}, \quad$ and $z = -\lambda$

Substituting these into (4), we obtain:

$-2\lambda - \dfrac{\lambda}{2} - 2\lambda - 9 = 0$

$\qquad\qquad \dfrac{9}{2}\lambda = -9$

$\qquad\qquad \lambda = -2$

The critical point is: $(2, 1, 2, -2)$

<u>Step 4.</u> Since $(2, 1, 2, -2)$ is the only critical point for F, we
conclude that min $f(x, y, z) = f(2, 1, 2) = 2^2 + 1^2 + 2^2 = 9$.

$\qquad\qquad\qquad$ (8-4)

17.

	x_k	y_k	$x_k y_k$	x_k^2
	10	50	500	100
	20	45	900	400
	30	50	1,500	900
	40	55	2,200	1,600
	50	65	3,250	2,500
	60	80	4,800	3,600
	70	85	5,950	4,900
	80	90	7,200	6,400
	90	90	8,100	8,100
	100	110	11,000	10,000
Totals	550	720	45,400	38,500

Thus, $\displaystyle\sum_{k=1}^{10} x_k = 550$, $\displaystyle\sum_{k=1}^{10} y_k = 720$, $\displaystyle\sum_{k=1}^{10} x_k y_k = 45,400$, $\displaystyle\sum_{k=1}^{10} x_k^2 = 38,500$.

Substituting these values into the formulas for m and d, we have:

$$m = \frac{10(45,400) - (550)(720)}{10(38,500) - (550)^2} = \frac{58,000}{82,500} = \frac{116}{165}$$

$$d = \frac{720 - \left(\dfrac{116}{165}\right)550}{10} = \frac{100}{3}$$

Therefore, the least squares line is:

$$y = \frac{116}{165}x + \frac{100}{3} \approx 0.703x + 33.33 \tag{8-5}$$

18. $\displaystyle\frac{1}{(b-a)(d-c)} \iint\limits_{R} f(x,\ y)\, dA = \frac{1}{[8 - (-8)](27 - 0)} \int_{-8}^{8} \int_{0}^{27} x^{2/3} y^{1/3}\, dy\, dx$

$$= \frac{1}{16 \cdot 27} \int_{-8}^{8} \left(\frac{3}{4} x^{2/3} y^{4/3} \bigg|_{y=0}^{y=27}\right) dx$$

$$= \frac{1}{16 \cdot 27} \int_{-8}^{8} \frac{3^5}{4} x^{2/3}\, dx = \frac{9}{64} \int_{-8}^{8} x^{2/3}\, dx$$

$$= \frac{9}{64} \cdot \frac{3}{5} x^{5/3} \bigg|_{-8}^{8} = \frac{9}{64} \cdot \frac{3}{5} [2^5 - (-2)^5]$$

$$= \frac{9}{64} \cdot \frac{3}{5} \cdot 2^6 = \frac{27}{5} \tag{8-6}$$

19. $V = \displaystyle\iint\limits_{R} (3x^2 + 3y^2)\, dA = \int_{0}^{1} \int_{-1}^{1} (3x^2 + 3y^2)\, dy\, dx = \int_{0}^{1}\left[\int_{-1}^{1} (3x^2 + 3y^2)\, dy\right] dx$

$$= \int_{0}^{1} \left[(3x^2 y + y^3)\bigg|_{-1}^{1}\right] dx = \int_{0}^{1} [3x^2 + 1 - (-3x^2 - 1)]\, dx$$

$$= \int_{0}^{1} (6x^2 + 2)\, dx = (2x^3 + 2x)\bigg|_{0}^{1} = 4 \text{ cubic units} \tag{8-6}$$

20. $f(x, y) = x + y;\ -10 \le x \le 10,\ -10 \le y \le 10$

Prediction: average value = $f(0, 0) = 0$.

Verification:

$$\text{average value} = \frac{1}{[10 - (-10)\,]\,[10 - (-10)\,]} \int_{-10}^{10} \int_{-10}^{10} (x + y)dy\,dx$$

$$= \frac{1}{400} \int_{-10}^{10} \left[\left(xy + \frac{1}{2}\,y^2\right)\bigg|_{-10}^{10}\right] dy$$

$$= \frac{1}{400} \int_{-10}^{10} 20x\,dx$$

$$= \frac{1}{400}(10x^2)\bigg|_{-10}^{10} = 0 \qquad\qquad (8\text{-}6)$$

21. $f(x, y) = \dfrac{e^x}{y + 10}$

(A) $S = \{x, y) \mid -a \le x \le a,\ -a \le y \le a\}$

The average value of f over S is given by:

$$\frac{1}{[a - (-a)\,]\,[a - (-a)\,]} \int_{-a}^{a} \int_{-a}^{a} \frac{e^x}{y + 10}\,dx\,dy$$

$$= \frac{1}{4a^2} \int_{-a}^{a} \left[\frac{e^x}{y + 10}\bigg|_{-a}^{a}\right] dy$$

$$= \frac{1}{4a^2} \int_{-a}^{a} \left(\frac{e^a}{y + 10} - \frac{e^{-a}}{y + 10}\right) dy$$

$$= \frac{e^a - e^{-a}}{4a^2} \int_{-a}^{a} \frac{1}{y + 10}\,dy$$

$$= \frac{e^a - e^{-a}}{4a^2} (\ln|y + 10|)\bigg|_{-a}^{a}$$

$$= \frac{e^a - e^{-a}}{4a^2} [\ln(10 + a) - \ln(10 - a)]$$

$$= \frac{e^a - e^{-a}}{4a^2} \ln\left(\frac{10 + a}{10 - a}\right)$$

Now, $\dfrac{e^a - e^{-a}}{4a^2} \ln\left(\dfrac{10 + a}{10 - a}\right) = 5$ is equivalent to

$$(e^a - e^{-a})\ln\left(\frac{10 + a}{10 - a}\right) - 20a^2 = 0.$$

Using a graphing utility, the graph of

$$f(x) = (e^x - e^{-x})\ln\left(\frac{10 + x}{10 - x}\right) - 20x^2$$

is shown at the right and $f(x) = 0$ at $x \approx \pm 6.28$.

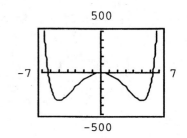

The dimensions of the square are: 12.56×12.56.

(B) To determine whether there is a square centered at (0, 0) such that
$$\frac{e^a - e^{-a}}{4a^2} \ln\left(\frac{10 + a}{10 - a}\right) = 0.05,$$

graph,
$$f(x) = (e^x - e^{-x}) \ln\left(\frac{10 + x}{10 - x}\right) - 0.20x^2$$

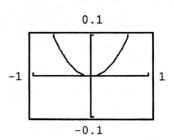

The result is shown at the right
and $f(x) = 0$ only at $x = 0$.
Thus, there does not exist a square
centered at (0, 0) such that the average
value of $f = 0.05$.

(8-6)

22. Step 1. Extremize $f(x, y) = 4x^3 - 5y^3$
    subject to $g(x, y) = 3x + 2y - 7 = 0$.

    Step 2. $F(x, y, \lambda) = 4x^3 - 5y^3 + \lambda(3x + 2y - 7)$

    Step 3. $F_x = 12x^2 + 3\lambda = 0$ (1)

    $F_y = -15y^2 + 2\lambda = 0$ (2)
    $F_\lambda = 3x + 2y - 7 = 0$ (3)

    From (1), $\lambda = -4x^2 \le 0$; from (2), $\lambda = \frac{15}{2}y^2 \ge 0$. This implies

    $x = y = \lambda = 0$ and $x = y = 0$ does not satisfy (3). The system
    (1), (2), (3) does not have a simultaneous solution.

(8-4)

23. $P(x, y) = -4x^2 + 4xy - 3y^2 + 4x + 10y + 81$

    (A) $P_x(x, y) = -8x + 4y + 4$
    $P_x(1, 3) = -8 \cdot 1 + 4 \cdot 3 + 4 = 8$

    At the output level (1, 3), profit will increase by $8000 for 100
    units increase in product A if the production of product B is held
    fixed.

    (B) $P_x = -8x + 4y + 4 = 0$ (1)
    $P_y = 4x - 6y + 10 = 0$ (2)
    Solving (1) and (2) for x and y, we obtain $x = 2$, $y = 3$.
    Thus, (2, 3) is a critical point.
    $P_{xx} = -8$ $P_{yy} = -6$ $P_{xy} = 4$
    $P_{xx}(2, 3) = -8 < 0$ $P_{yy}(2, 3) = -6$ $P_{xy}(2, 3) = 4$

    $P_{xx}(2, 3) \cdot P_{yy}(2, 3) - [P_{xy}(2, 3)]^2 = (-8)(-6) - 4^2 = 32 > 0$

    Thus, $P(2, 3)$ is a maximum and
    max $P(x, y) = P(2, 3) = -4 \cdot 2^2 + 4 \cdot 2 \cdot 3 - 3 \cdot 3^2 + 4 \cdot 2 + 10 \cdot 3 + 81$
    $= -16 + 24 - 27 + 8 + 30 + 81$
    $= 100$.
    Thus, the maximum profit is $100,000. This is obtained when
    200 units of A and 300 units of B are produced per month.

(8-2, 8-3)

24. Minimize $S(x, y, z) = xy + 4yz + 3xz$

Subject to: $V(x, y, z) = xyz - 96 = 0$

Put $F(x, y, z, \lambda) = S(x, y, z) + \lambda V(x, y, z) = xy + 4yz + 3xz + \lambda(xyz - 96)$. Then, we have:

$$F_x = y + 3z + \lambda yz = 0 \qquad (1)$$

$$F_y = x + 4z + \lambda xz = 0 \qquad (2)$$

$$F_z = 4y + 3x + \lambda xy = 0 \qquad (3)$$

$$F_\lambda = xyz - 96 = 0 \qquad (4)$$

Solving the system of equations, (1)–(4), simultaneously, yields $x = 8$, $y = 6$, $z = 2$, and $\lambda = -1$. Thus, the critical point is $(8, 6, 2, -1)$ and
$S(8, 6, 2) = 8 \cdot 6 + 4 \cdot 6 \cdot 2 + 3 \cdot 8 \cdot 2 = 144$
is the minimum value of S subject to the constraint $V = xyz - 96 = 0$.

The dimensions of the box that will require the minimum amount of material are:
Length $x = 8$ inches; Width $y = 6$ inches; Height $z = 2$ inches $\qquad$ (8-3)

25.

	x_k	y_k	$x_k y_k$	x_k^2
	1	2.0	2.0	1
	2	2.5	5.0	4
	3	3.1	9.3	9
	4	4.2	16.8	16
	5	4.3	21.5	25
Totals	15	16.1	54.6	55

Thus, $\sum_{k=1}^{5} x_k = 15$, $\sum_{k=1}^{5} y_k = 16.1$, $\sum_{k=1}^{5} x_k y_k = 54.6$, $\sum_{k=1}^{5} x_k^2 = 55$.

Substituting these values into the formulas for m and d, we have:

$$m = \frac{5(54.6) - (15)(16.1)}{5(55) - (15)^2} = \frac{31.5}{50} \approx 0.63$$

$$d = \frac{16.1 - (0.63)(15)}{5} = 1.33$$

Therefore, the least squares line is:
$y = 0.63x + 1.33$
When $x = 6$, $y = 0.63(6) + 1.33 = 5.11$, and the profit for the sixth year is estimated to be \$5.11 million. $\qquad$ (8-4)

26. $N(x, y) = 10x^{0.8}y^{0.2}$

(A) $N_x(x, y) = 8x^{-0.2}y^{0.2}$

$\qquad N_x(40, 50) = 8(40)^{-0.2}(50)^{0.2} \approx 8.36$

$\qquad N_y(x, y) = 2x^{0.8}y^{-0.8}$

$\qquad N_y(40, 50) = 2(40)^{0.8}(50)^{-0.8} \approx 1.67$

Thus, at the level of 40 units of labor and 50 units of capital, the marginal productivity of labor is approximately 8.36 and the marginal productivity of capital is approximately 1.67. Management should encourage increased use of labor.

(B) <u>Step 1</u>. Maximize the production function $N(x, y) = 10x^{0.8}y^{0.2}$
Subject to the constraint: $C(x, y) = 100x + 50y = 10,000$
i.e., $g(x, y) = 100x + 50y - 10,000 = 0$

<u>Step 2</u>. $F(x, y, \lambda) = 10x^{0.8}y^{0.2} + \lambda(100x + 50y - 10,000)$

<u>Step 3</u>. $F_x = 8x^{-0.2}y^{0.2} + 100\lambda = 0$ (1)

$F_y = 2x^{0.8}y^{-0.8} + 50\lambda = 0$ (2)

$F_\lambda = 100x + 50y - 10,000 = 0$ (3)

From equation (1), $\lambda = \dfrac{-0.08y^{0.2}}{x^{0.2}}$, and from (2),

$\lambda = \dfrac{-0.04x^{0.8}}{y^{0.8}}$. Thus, $\dfrac{0.08y^{0.2}}{x^{0.2}} = \dfrac{0.04x^{0.8}}{y^{0.8}}$ and $x = 2y$.

Substituting into (3) yields:
$200y + 50y = 10,000$
$250y = 10,000$
$y = 40$

Therefore, $x = 80$ and $\lambda \approx -0.0696$. The critical point is $(80, 40, -0.0696)$. Thus, we conclude that max $N(x, y) = N(80, 40) = 10(80)^{0.8}(40)^{0.2} \approx 696$ units.

Production is maximized when 80 units of labor and 40 units of capital are used.

The marginal productivity of money is $-\lambda \approx 0.0696$. The increase in production resulting from an increase of \$2000 in the budget is: $0.0696(2000) \approx 139$ units

(C) Average number of units

$= \dfrac{1}{(100 - 50)(40 - 20)} \int_{50}^{100} \int_{20}^{40} 10x^{0.8}y^{0.2}\,dy\,dx$

$= \dfrac{1}{(50)(20)} \int_{50}^{100} \left[\dfrac{10x^{0.8}y^{1.2}}{1.2} \Big|_{20}^{40} \right] dx = \dfrac{1}{1000} \int_{50}^{100} \dfrac{10}{1.2} x^{0.8}(40^{1.2} - 20^{1.2})\,dx$

$= \dfrac{40^{1.2} - 20^{1.2}}{120} \int_{50}^{100} x^{0.8}\,dx = \dfrac{40^{1.2} - 20^{1.2}}{120} \cdot \dfrac{x^{1.8}}{1.8}\Big|_{50}^{100}$

$= \dfrac{(40^{1.2} - 20^{1.2})(100^{1.8} - 50^{1.8})}{216} \approx \dfrac{(47.24)(2837.81)}{216} \approx 621$

Thus, the average number of units produced is approximately 621.

(8-4)

27. $T(V, x) = \dfrac{33V}{x + 33} = 33V(x + 33)^{-1}$

$T_x(V, x) = -33V(x + 33)^{-2} = \dfrac{-33V}{(x + 33)^2}$

$T_x(70, 17) = \dfrac{-33(70)}{(17 + 33)^2} = \dfrac{-33(70)}{2500}$

$= -0.924$ minutes per unit increase in depth when $V = 70$ cubic feet and $x = 17$ ft.   (8-2)

28. $C = 100 - 24d^2 = 100 - 24(x^2 + y^2)$

$C(x, y) = 100 - 24(x^2 + y^2)$, $-2 \leq x \leq 2$, $-2 \leq y \leq 2$

Average concentration

$$= \frac{1}{4(4)} \int_{-2}^{2} \int_{-2}^{2} [100 - 24(x^2 + y^2)] \, dy \, dx$$

$$= \frac{1}{16} \int_{-2}^{2} [100y - 24x^2y - 8y^3] \Big|_{-2}^{2} \, dx$$

$$= \frac{1}{16} \int_{-2}^{2} [400 - 96x^2 - 128] \, dx = \frac{1}{16} \int_{-2}^{2} (272 - 96x^2) \, dx$$

$$= \frac{1}{16} [272x - 32x^3] \Big|_{-2}^{2} = \frac{1}{16}(544 - 256) - \frac{1}{16}(-544 + 256)$$

$$= 18 + 18 = 36 \text{ parts per million} \tag{8-6}$$

29. $n(P_1, P_2, d) = 0.001 \dfrac{P_1 P_2}{d}$

$$n(100,000, 50,000, 100) = 0.001 \frac{100,000 \times 50,000}{100} = 50,000 \tag{8-1}$$

30.

x_k	y_k	$x_k y_k$	x_k^2
30	60	1,800	900
50	75	3,750	2,500
60	80	4,800	3,600
70	85	5,950	4,900
90	90	8,100	8,100
Totals 300	390	24,400	20,000

Thus, $\displaystyle\sum_{k=1}^{5} x_k = 300$, $\displaystyle\sum_{k=1}^{5} y_k = 390$, $\displaystyle\sum_{k=1}^{5} x_k y_k = 24,400$, $\displaystyle\sum_{k=1}^{5} x_k^2 = 20,000$.

Substituting these values into the formulas for m and d, we have:

$$m = \frac{5(24,400) - (300)(390)}{5(20,000) - (300)^2} = \frac{5000}{10,000} = 0.5$$

$$d = \frac{390 - 0.5(300)}{5} = \frac{240}{5} = 48$$

Therefore, the least squares line is:

$y = 0.5x + 48$

When $x = 40$, $y = 0.5(40) + 48 = 68$. $\tag{8-5}$

31. (A) We use the linear regression feature on a graphing utility with 1900 as $x = 0$, 1910 as $x = 10$, ..., 2000 as $x = 100$.

```
LinReg
y=ax+b
a=.4932727273
b=25.2
```

Thus, the least squares line is:

$y = 0.4933x + 25.20$.

(B) The year 2020 corresponds to $x = 120$; $y(120) \approx 84.40$ people/sq. mi.

(C)
```
QuadReg
y=ax²+bx+c
a=.0012587413
b=.3673986014
c=27.08811189
```
```
ExpReg
y=a*b^x
a=28.18046065
b=1.010414421
```

Quadratic regression: Exponential regression:
$y(120) \approx 89.30$ people/sq. mi. $y(120) \approx 97.70$ people/sq. mi.   (8-5)

32.
```
LinReg
y=ax+b
a=1.069267604
b=.5223226384
r=.9793163189
```

(A) The least squares line is $y \approx 1.069x + 0.522$.

(B) Evaluate the result in (A) at $x = 60$: $y \approx 64.68$ yr

(C)
```
QuadReg
y=ax²+bx+c
a=-.0083659329
b=2.13769365
c=-33.36800618
```
```
LnReg
y=a+blnx
a=-213.2879278
b=67.91982728
r=.9800944981
```

Evaluate at $x = 60$: $y \approx 64.78$ yr   Evaluate at $x = 60$: $y \approx 64.80$ yr   (8-5)

33. (A) A scatter plot of the data points is shown at the right.

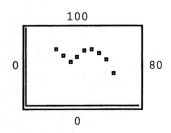

A continuous curve that passes through these points would intersect certain horizontal lines in three places. Thus we would expect cubic regression to give a better fit than either linear or quadratic regression.

(B) The cubic regression curve clearly gives the best fit.

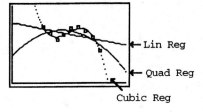
← Lin Reg
← Quad Reg
← Cubic Reg

```
LinReg
y=ax+b
a=-.3633333333
b=78.48222222
```

```
QuadReg
y=ax²+bx+c
a=-.0267965368
b=1.887575758
c=35.67922078
```

```
CubicReg
y=ax³+bx²+cx+d
a=-.0042356902
b=.5069004329
c=-19.27816835
d=297.0128369
```

(8-5)

7 Differential Equations

Things to remember:

1. A DIFFERENTIAL EQUATION is an equation involving an unknown function and one or more of its derivatives.

2. The ORDER of a differential equation is the order of the highest derivative of the unknown function present in the equation.

3. Remember the terms (a) general solution, (b) particular solution, and (c) initial condition.

---

1. Substituting $y = Cx^2$ and $y' = 2Cx$ in the given differential equation, we have

$$x(2Cx) = 2Cx^2$$
$$\text{or} \quad 2Cx^2 = 2Cx^2.$$

Thus, $y = Cx^2$ is the general solution. The particular solutions corresponding to $C = -2, -1, 0, 1,$ and 2 are graphed in the figure at the right.

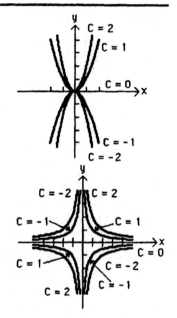

3. Substituting $y = \dfrac{C}{x}$, $y' = -\dfrac{C}{x^2}$ in the given differential equation, we have

$$x\left(-\frac{C}{x^2}\right) = -\left(\frac{C}{x}\right) \quad \text{or} \quad -\frac{C}{x} = -\frac{C}{x}.$$

Thus, $y = \dfrac{C}{x}$ is the general solution.

The particular solutions corresponding to $C = -2, -1, 0, 1,$ and 2 are graphed in the figure shown at the right.

5. Substituting $y = Ce^x - 5x - 5$, $y' = Ce^x - 5$ in the differential equation, we have
$$Ce^x - 5 = (Ce^x - 5x - 5) + 5x \quad \text{or} \quad Ce^x - 5 = Ce^x - 5.$$
Thus, $y = Ce^x - 5x - 5$ is the general solution. Letting $x = 0$ and $y = 2$ in the general solution yields

$$2 = Ce^0 - 5(0) - 5 \quad \text{or} \quad 2 = C - 5 \quad \text{and} \quad C = 7.$$

Therefore, the particular solution satisfying the initial condition $y(0) = 2$ is
$$y = 7e^x - 5x - 5.$$

7. Substituting $y = e^x + Ce^{2x}$, $y' = e^x + 2Ce^{2x}$ in the differential equation, we have
$$e^x + 2Ce^{2x} = 2(e^x + Ce^{2x}) - e^x$$
$$e^x + 2Ce^{2x} = 2e^x + 2Ce^{2x} - e^x$$
$$e^x + 2Ce^{2x} = e^x + 2Ce^{2x}.$$
Thus, $y = e^x + Ce^{2x}$ is the general solution. Letting $x = 0$ and $y = -1$ in the general solution yields
$$-1 = e^0 + Ce^{2\cdot 0} \quad \text{or} \quad -1 = 1 + C \quad \text{and} \quad C = -2.$$
Therefore, the particular solution satisfying the initial condition $y(0) = -1$ is
$$y = e^x - 2e^{2x}.$$

9. Substituting $y = x + \dfrac{C}{x}$, $y' = 1 - \dfrac{C}{x^2}$ in the differential equation, we have
$$x\left(1 - \frac{C}{x^2}\right) = 2x - \left(x + \frac{C}{x}\right)$$
$$x - \frac{C}{x} = 2x - x - \frac{C}{x}$$
$$x - \frac{C}{x} = x - \frac{C}{x}.$$
Thus, $y = x + \dfrac{C}{x}$ is the general solution. Letting $x = 2$ and $y = 3$ in the general solution yields
$$3 = 2 + \frac{C}{2} \quad \text{or} \quad 1 = \frac{C}{2} \quad \text{and} \quad C = 2.$$
Therefore, the particular solution satisfying the initial condition $y(2) = 3$ is
$$y = x + \frac{2}{x}.$$

11. Differentiating $y^3 + xy - x^3 = C$ implicitly, we have
$$D_x(y^3 + xy - x^3) = D_x C$$
$$D_x y^3 + D_x(xy) - D_x x^3 = 0$$
$$3y^2 y' + xy' + y - 3x^2 = 0$$
$$(3y^2 + x)y' = 3x^2 - y.$$
Thus, y is a solution of the given differential equation.

13. Differentiating $xy + e^{y^2} - x^2 = C$ implicitly, we have
$$D_x(xy + e^{y^2} - x^2) = D_x C$$
$$D_x(xy) + D_x e^{y^2} - D_x x^2 = 0$$
$$xy' + y + e^{y^2} D_x y^2 - 2x = 0$$
$$xy' + y + 2yy' e^{y^2} - 2x = 0$$
$$(x + 2ye^{y^2})y' = 2x - y.$$
Thus, y is a solution of the given differential equation.

15. Differentiating $y^2 + x^2 = C$ implicitly, we have

$$D_x(y^2 + x^2) = D_x C$$
$$D_x y^2 + D_x x^2 = 0$$
$$2yy' + 2x = 0$$
$$yy' = -x$$

Thus, y is a solution of the given differential equation. Substituting $x = 0$ and $y = 3$ in $y^2 + x^2 = C$ yields

$$3^2 + 0^2 = C \quad \text{or} \quad C = 9.$$

Therefore, the particular solution satisfying $y(0) = 3$ is a solution of the equation

$$y^2 + x^2 = 9 \quad \text{or} \quad y^2 = 9 - x^2.$$

This equation has two continuous solutions

$$y_1(x) = \sqrt{9 - x^2} \quad \text{and} \quad y_2(x) = -\sqrt{9 - x^2}.$$

Clearly, $y_1(x) = \sqrt{9 - x^2}$ is the solution that satisfies the initial condition $y(0) = 3$.

17. Differentiating $\ln(2 - y) = x + C$ implicitly, we have

$$D_x[\ln(2 - y)] = D_x(x + C)$$
$$\frac{1}{2 - y}(-y') = 1$$
$$-y' = 2 - y$$
$$y' = y - 2.$$

Thus, y is a solution of the given differential equation. Substituting $x = 0$ and $y = 1$ in $\ln(2 - y) = x + C$ yields

$$\ln(2 - 1) = 0 + C \quad \text{or} \quad \ln 1 = C \quad \text{and} \quad C = 0.$$

Therefore, the particular solution satisfying $y(0) = 1$ is a solution of the equation

$$\ln(2 - y) = x.$$

We can solve this equation for y by taking the exponential of both sides. We have

$$e^{\ln(2-y)} = e^x \quad \text{or} \quad 2 - y = e^x \quad \text{and} \quad y = 2 - e^x.$$

19. Given the general solution $y = 2 + Ce^{-x}$.

(A) Substituting $x = 0$ and $y = 1$ in the general solution yields

$$1 = 2 + Ce^0$$
$$C = -1.$$

Thus, the particular solution satisfying $y(0) = 1$ is $y_a = 2 - e^{-x}$.

(B) Substituting $x = 0$ and $y = 2$ in the general solution yields

$$2 = 2 + Ce^0$$
$$C = 0.$$

Thus, the particular solution satisfying $y(0) = 2$ is $y_b = 2$.

(C) Substituting $x = 0$ and $y = 3$ in the general solution yields

$$3 = 2 + Ce^0$$
$$C = 1.$$

Thus, the particular solution satisfying $y(0) = 3$ is $y_c = 2 + e^{-x}$.

The graphs of the particular solutions for $x \geq 0$ are shown at the right.

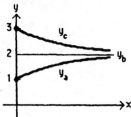

21. Given the general solution $y = 2 + Ce^x$.

(A) Substituting $x = 0$ and $y = 1$ in the general solution yields
$$1 = 2 + Ce^0$$
$$C = -1$$
Thus, the particular solution satisfying $y(0) = 1$ is $y_a = 2 - e^x$.

(B) Substituting $x = 0$ and $y = 2$ in the general solution yields
$$2 = 2 + Ce^0$$
$$C = 0.$$
Thus, the particular solution satisfying $y(0) = 2$ is $y_b = 2$.

(C) Substituting $x = 0$ and $y = 3$ in the general solution yields
$$3 = 2 + Ce^0$$
$$C = 1.$$
Thus, the particular solution satisfying $y(0) = 3$ is $y_c = 2 + e^x$.

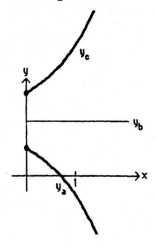

The graphs of these solutions for $x \geq 0$ are shown at the right.

23. Given the general solution $y = \dfrac{10}{1 + Ce^{-x}}$.

(A) Substituting $x = 0$ and $y = 1$ in the general solution yields
$$1 = \frac{10}{1 + Ce^0} = \frac{10}{1 + C}.$$
Therefore, $1 + C = 10$ or $C = 9$.
Thus, the particular solution satisfying $y(0) = 1$ is $y_a = \dfrac{10}{1 + 9e^{-x}}$.

(B) Substituting $x = 0$ and $y = 10$ in the general solution yields
$$10 = \frac{10}{1 + Ce^0} = \frac{10}{1 + C}.$$
Therefore, $10 + 10C = 10$ and $C = 0$.
Thus, the particular solution satisfying $y(0) = 10$ is $y_b = 10$.

(C) Substituting $x = 0$ and $y = 20$ in the general solution yields
$$20 = \frac{10}{1 + Ce^0} = \frac{10}{1 + C}.$$
Therefore, $20 + 20C = 10$ and $C = -0.5$.
Thus, the particular solution satisfying $y(0) = 20$ is
$$y_c = \frac{10}{1 - 0.5e^{-x}}.$$

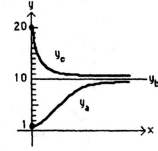

The graphs of these solutions for $x \geq 0$ are shown at the right.

25. Given the general solution $y = Cx^3 + 2$.
   (A) Substituting $x = 0$, $y = 2$ in the general solution yields
      $$2 = C \cdot 0 + 2$$
      This equation is satisfied for all values of C. Thus, $y = Cx^3 + 2$
      satisfies the initial condition $y(0) = 2$ for any C.
   (B) Substituting $x = 0$, $y = 0$ in the general solution yields
      $$0 = C \cdot 0 + 2 \quad \text{or} \quad 0 = 2.$$
      This equation is <u>not</u> satisfied for any value of C. There is <u>no</u>
      particular solution of the differential equation which satisfies the
      initial condition $y(0) = 0$.
   (C) Substituting $x = 1$, $y = 1$ in the general solution yields
      $$1 = C \cdot 1 + 2 \quad \text{and} \quad C = -1$$
      Thus, $y = 2 - x^3$ is the particular solution of the differential
      equation which satisfies the initial condition $y(1) = 1$.

27. (A) The graphs of $y = x + e^{-x}$, $y = x + 2e^{-x}$, $y = x + 3e^{-x}$ and the graph
      of $y = x$ are shown below

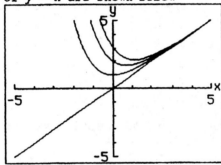

   (B) Each of the graphs $y = x + Ce^{-x}$, $C = 1, 2, 3$, lies above the line
      $y = x$, each decreases to a local minimum and then increases,
      approaching $y = x$ as x approaches ∞.
   (C) The graphs of $y = x - e^{-x}$, $y = x - 2e^{-x}$, $y = x - 3e^{-x}$ and the graph
      of $y = x$ are shown below

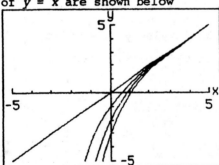

   (D) Each of the graphs $y = x - Ce^{-x}$, $C = 1, 2, 3$, is increasing and
      approaches $y = x$ as x approaches ∞.

29. Substituting $p = 5 - Ce^{-0.1t}$, $\frac{dp}{dt} = 0.1Ce^{-0.1t}$ in the differential equation, we have

$$0.1Ce^{-0.1t} = 0.5 - 0.1(5 - Ce^{-0.1t})$$
$$= 0.5 - 0.5 + Ce^{-0.1t}$$
$$= Ce^{-0.1t}$$

Thus, $p = 5 - Ce^{-0.1t}$ is the general solution of the differential equation. The equilibrium price $\bar{p}$ is given by:

$$\bar{p} = \lim_{t \to \infty} p(t) = \lim_{t \to \infty} (5 - Ce^{-0.1t}) = \lim_{t \to \infty} 5 - C\lim_{t \to \infty} e^{-0.1t} = 5$$

since $\lim_{t \to \infty} e^{-0.1t} = 0$.

Letting $t = 0$ and $p = 1$ in the general solution yields

$$1 = 5 - Ce^0 = 5 - C$$

and $C = 4$

Thus, the particular solution satisfying the initial condition $p(0) = 1$ is

$$p(t) = 5 - 4e^{-0.1t}$$

Letting $t = 0$ and $p = 10$ in the general solution yields

$$10 = 5 - Ce^0 = 5 - C$$

and $C = -5$

Thus, the particular solution satisfying the initial condition $p(0) = 10$ is

$$p(t) = 5 + 5e^{-0.1t}$$

The graphs of these solutions are shown at the right.

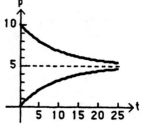

31. Substituting $A(t) = Ce^{0.08t} - 2,500$ and $\frac{dA}{dt} = 0.08Ce^{0.08t}$ into the differential equation, we have

$$0.08Ce^{0.08t} = 0.08[Ce^{0.08t} - 2500] + 200$$
$$= 0.08Ce^{0.08t} - 200 + 200$$
$$= 0.08Ce^{0.08t}$$

Thus, $A(t) = Ce^{0.08t} - 2500$ is the general solution. Letting $t = 0$ and $A = 0$ in the general solution yields

$$0 = Ce^0 - 2500 \quad \text{or} \quad C = 2500$$

Thus, the particular solution satisfying the initial condition $A(0) = 0$ is

$$A(t) = 2500e^{0.08t} - 2500$$

Letting $t = 0$ and $A = 1000$ in the general solution yields

$$1000 = Ce^0 - 2500 \quad \text{or} \quad C = 3500$$

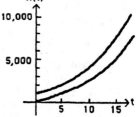

Thus, the particular solution satisfying the initial condition $A(0) = 1000$ is

$$A(t) = 3500e^{0.08t} - 2500$$

The graphs of these solutions appear at the right.

33. Substituting $N(t) = 200 - Ce^{-0.5t}$, $\frac{dN}{dt} = 0.5Ce^{-0.5t}$ in the differential

equation, we have
$$0.5Ce^{-0.5t} = 100 - 0.5(200 - Ce^{-0.5t})$$
$$= 100 - 100 + 0.5Ce^{-0.5t} = 0.5Ce^{-0.5t}.$$

Thus, $N(t) = 200 - Ce^{-0.5t}$ is the general solution. Calculating the
equilibrium size of the population, we have
$$\overline{N} = \lim_{t \to \infty} (200 - Ce^{-0.5t}) = 200 - C \lim_{t \to \infty} e^{-0.5t} = 200.$$

Letting $t = 0$ and $N = 50$ in the general solution
yields
$$50 = 200 - Ce^0 \quad \text{or} \quad C = 150.$$
Therefore, the particular solution satisfying
the initial condition $N(0) = 50$ is
$$N(t) = 200 - 150e^{-0.5t}.$$
Letting $t = 0$ and $N = 300$ in the general
solution yields
$$300 = 200 - Ce^0 \quad \text{or} \quad C = -100.$$
Therefore, the particular solution satisfying the initial condition
$N(0) = 300$ is
$$N(t) = 200 + 100Ce^{-0.5t}.$$

The graphs of these solutions are shown at the right.

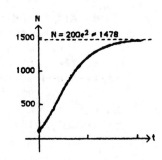

35. Substituting $N(t) = Ce^{-2e^{-0.5t}}$, $\frac{dN}{dt} = Ce^{-2e^{-0.5t}}(-2e^{-0.5t})(-0.5) = Ce^{-0.5t}e^{-2e^{-0.5t}}$

in the differential equation, we have
$$Ce^{-0.5t}e^{-2e^{-0.5t}} = [Ce^{-2e^{-0.5t}}]e^{-0.5t} = Ce^{-0.5t}e^{-2e^{-0.5t}}.$$

Thus, $N(t) = Ce^{-2e^{-0.5t}}$ is the general solution.
Letting $t = 0$ and $N = 200$ in the general solution yields
$$200 = Ce^{-2e^0} \quad \text{or} \quad C = 200e^2.$$
Therefore, the particular solution satisfying
the initial condition $N(0) = 200$ is
$$N(t) = 200e^2 \cdot e^{-2e^{-0.5t}} = 200e^{2-2e^{-0.5t}}.$$
Now, $\overline{N} = \lim_{t \to \infty} N(t) = \lim_{t \to \infty} 200e^{2-2e^{-0.5t}} = 200e^2.$
The graph of $N(t)$ is shown at the right.

Things to remember:

1. The method of SEPARATION OF VARIABLES is applied to first-order differential equations of the form

(A) $f(y)y' = g(x)$

The GENERAL SOLUTION of equation (A) is given implicitly by the equation

$$\int f(y)\,dy = \int g(x)\,dx$$

2. EXPONENTIAL GROWTH LAW

If the rate of change with respect to time of a quantity y at time t is proportional to the amount present at time t, then $y = y(t)$ satisfies the differential equation

$$\frac{dy}{dt} = ky$$

where k is a constant.

3. LIMITED GROWTH LAW

If the rate of change with respect to time of a quantity y is proportional to the difference between y and a limiting value M, then $y = y(t)$ satisfies the differential equation

$$\frac{dy}{dt} = k(M - y)$$

where k and M are constants.

4. LOGISTIC GROWTH LAW

If the rate of change with respect to time of a quantity y is proportional to the product of y and the difference between y and a limiting value M, then $y = y(t)$ satisfies the differential equation

$$\frac{dy}{dt} = ky(M - y)$$

where k and M are constants.

1. $y' = 1$; $y(0) = 2$

$\int dy = \int dx$

$y = x + C.$ *General solution*

Applying the initial condition $y(0) = 2$, we have

$2 = 0 + C$ or $C = 2$

Thus,

$y = x + 2.$ *Particular solution*

3. $y' = \dfrac{1}{\sqrt{x}} = \dfrac{1}{x^{1/2}}$; $y(1) = -2$

$\int dy = \int \dfrac{dx}{x^{1/2}}$

$y = 2x^{1/2} + C$ *General solution*

Applying the initial condition $y(1) = -2$, we have

$-2 = 2(1)^{1/2} + C$ or $C = -4$

Thus,

$y = 2x^{1/2} - 4$ *Particular solution*

5. $y' = y$; $y(0) = 10$.

$\dfrac{y'}{y} = 1.$ Separate the variables

$\int \dfrac{dy}{y} = \int dx$

$\ln|y| = x + C$

$y = e^{x+C}$

$\quad = e^C e^x$ (put $K = e^C$)

$\quad = Ke^x.$ *General solution*

Applying the initial condition $y(0) = 10$, we have

$10 = Ke^0$ or $K = 10$.

Thus,

$y = 10e^x.$ *Particular solution*

7. $y' = 25 - y$; $y(0) = 5$.

$\dfrac{y'}{25 - y} = 1.$ Separate the variables

$\int \dfrac{dy}{25 - y} = \int dx$

$-\ln|25 - y| = x + C$

$\ln|25 - y| = -(x + C)$

$25 - y = e^{-x-C}$

$25 - y = e^{-C}e^{-x}$

$25 - y = Ke^{-x}$ (put $K = e^{-C}$)

$y = 25 - Ke^{-x}.$ *General solution*

Applying the initial condition $y(0) = 5$, we have

$5 = 25 - Ke^0$ or $K = 20$.

Thus,

$y = 25 - 20e^{-x}.$ *Particular solution*

9. $y' = \dfrac{y}{x}$; $y(1) = 5$, $x > 0$.

$\dfrac{y'}{y} = \dfrac{1}{x}.$ Separate the variables

$\int \dfrac{dy}{y} = \int \dfrac{dx}{x}$

$\ln|y| = \ln x + C$ (<u>Note</u>: $x > 0$, so $|x| = x$.)

$y = e^{\ln x + C}$

$\quad = e^C e^{\ln x}$

$\quad = Kx.$ (<u>Note</u>: $e^{\ln x} = x$, put $K = e^C$.)

Thus,

$y = Kx.$ *General solution*

Applying the initial condition $y(1) = 5$, we have

$5 = K(1)$ or $K = 5$.

Therefore,

$y = 5x.$ *Particular solution*

11. $y' = \dfrac{1}{y^2}$; $y(1) = 3$.

$y^2 y' = 1$

$\int y^2 dy = \int dx$

$\dfrac{y^3}{3} = x + C$

$y^3 = 3x + 3C$

$\quad = 3x + A.$ (put $A = 3C$)

Thus,

$y = (3x + A)^{1/3}.$ *General solution*

Applying the initial condition $y(1) = 3$, we have

$3 = (3 + A)^{1/3}$

$27 = 3 + A$ and $A = 24$.

Therefore,

$y = (3x + 24)^{1/3}.$ *Particular solution*

13. $y' = ye^x$; $y(0) = 3e$

$$\frac{y'}{y} = e^x$$

$$\int \frac{dy}{y} = \int e^x dx$$

$$\ln|y| = e^x + C$$

$$y = e^{e^x + C}$$

$$= e^C e^{e^x}$$

$$= Ke^{e^x}. \quad \textit{General solution}$$

Applying the initial condition
$y(0) = 3e$, we have

$$3e = Ke^{e^0}$$

$$= Ke \quad \text{and} \quad K = 3.$$

Thus,

$$y = 3e^{e^x}. \quad \textit{Particular solution}$$

15. $y' = \frac{e^x}{e^y}$; $y(0) = \ln 2$.

$$e^y y' = e^x$$

$$\int e^y dy = \int e^x dx$$

$$e^y = e^x + C$$

$$y = \ln(e^x + C) \quad \textit{General solution}$$

Applying the initial condition
$y(0) = \ln 2$, we have

$$\ln 2 = \ln(e^0 + C)$$

$$= \ln(1 + C).$$

Therefore,

$$1 + C = 2 \quad \text{and} \quad C = 1.$$

Thus,

$$y = \ln(e^x + 1). \quad \textit{Particular solution}$$

17. $y' = xy + x$; $y(0) = 2$

$$y' = x(y + 1)$$

$$\frac{y'}{y + 1} = x$$

$$\int \frac{dy}{y + 1} = \int x \, dx$$

$$\ln|y + 1| = \frac{x^2}{2} + C$$

$$y + 1 = e^{x^2/2 + C}$$

$$y + 1 = e^C e^{x^2/2}$$

$$y + 1 = Ke^{x^2/2}$$

$$y = Ke^{x^2/2} - 1. \quad \textit{General solution}$$

Applying the initial condition
$y(0) = 2$, we have

$$2 = Ke^0 - 1 = K - 1 \quad \text{and} \quad K = 3.$$

Thus,

$$y = 3e^{x^2/2} - 1 \quad \textit{Particular solution}$$

19. $y' = (2 - y)^2 e^x$; $y(0) = 1$.

$$\frac{y'}{(2 - y)^2} = e^x$$

$$\int \frac{dy}{(2 - y)^2} = \int e^x dx$$

$$\frac{1}{2 - y} = e^x + C$$

$$2 - y = \frac{1}{e^x + C}$$

$$y = 2 - \frac{1}{e^x + C}. \quad \textit{General solution}$$

Applying the initial condition
$y(0) = 1$, we have

$$1 = 2 - \frac{1}{e^0 + C}$$

$$\frac{1}{1 + C} = 1$$

$$1 + C = 1 \quad \text{and} \quad C = 0.$$

Thus,

$$y = 2 - \frac{1}{e^x} \quad \text{or} \quad y = 2 - e^{-x}.$$

$$\textit{Particular solution}$$

21. $y' = \frac{1 + x^2}{1 + y^2}$

$$(1 + y^2)y' = 1 + x^2 \quad \text{Separate the variables}$$

$$\int (1 + y^2) \, dy = \int (1 + x^2) \, dx$$

$$y + \frac{y^3}{3} = x + \frac{x^3}{3} + C. \quad \textit{General solution}$$

23. $xyy' = (1 + x^2)(1 + y^2)$

$\dfrac{yy'}{1 + y^2} = \dfrac{1 + x^2}{x}$ Separate the variables

$\displaystyle\int \dfrac{y\ dy}{1 + y^2} = \int\left(\dfrac{1}{x} + x\right)dx$

$\dfrac{1}{2}\displaystyle\int \dfrac{2y\ dy}{1 + y^2} = \ln|x| + \dfrac{x^2}{2} + C$

$\dfrac{1}{2}\ln(1 + y^2) = \ln|x| + \dfrac{x^2}{2} + C,$ *General solution*

or $\ln(1 + y^2) = \ln(x^2) + x^2 + C.$

25. $x^2 e^y y' = x^3 + x^3 e^y$

$x^2 e^y y' = x^3(1 + e^y)$

$\dfrac{e^y y'}{1 + e^y} = x$ Separate the variables

$\displaystyle\int \dfrac{e^y dy}{1 + e^y} = \int x\ dx$ (**Note:** Put $u = 1 + e^y$, $du = e^y dy$.)

$\ln(1 + e^y) = \dfrac{x^2}{2} + C.$ *General solution*

27. $xyy' = \ln x;\ y(1) = 1$

$yy' = \dfrac{\ln x}{x}$

$\displaystyle\int y\ dy = \int \dfrac{\ln x}{x}dx$ (**Note:** Put $u = \ln x$, $du = \dfrac{1}{x}dx$.)

$\dfrac{y^2}{2} = \dfrac{[\ln x]^2}{2} + C$

$y^2 = [\ln x]^2 + 2C$ or

$y^2 = [\ln x]^2 + A.$ *General solution.*

Solving this equation for y, we have

$y = \pm\sqrt{[\ln x]^2 + A}$

Applying the initial condition $y(1) = 1$, we choose the function

$y = \sqrt{[\ln x]^2 + A}$

and get

$1 = \sqrt{[\ln 1]^2 + A}$

$1 = \sqrt{0 + A}$ and $A = 1.$

Thus,

$y = \sqrt{[\ln x]^2 + 1}.$ *Particular solution*

29. $xy' = x\sqrt{y} + 2\sqrt{y};\ y(1) = 4$

$xy' = \sqrt{y}(x + 2)$

$\dfrac{y'}{\sqrt{y}} = \dfrac{x + 2}{x}$ Separate the variables

$\displaystyle\int \dfrac{dy}{\sqrt{y}} = \int\left(1 + \dfrac{2}{x}\right)dx$

$2y^{1/2} = x + 2\ln|x| + C$

$y^{1/2} = \dfrac{1}{2}(x + 2\ln|x| + C)$

$y = \dfrac{1}{4}(x + 2\ln|x| + C)^2$ or

$y = \dfrac{1}{4}[x + \ln(x^2) + C]^2.$

General solution

Applying the initial condition $y(1) = 4$, we have

$4 = \dfrac{1}{4}[1 + \ln(1^2) + C]^2$

$16 = (1 + C)^2$

$1 + C = 4$

$C = 3.$

Thus,

$y = \dfrac{1}{4}[x + \ln(x^2) + 3]^3.$

Particular solution

31. $yy' = xe^{-y^2}$; $y(0) = 1$

$ye^{y^2}y' = x$

$\int ye^{y^2}dy = \int x\,dx$ (Note: Put $u = y^2$, $dy = 2y\,dy$.)

$\frac{1}{2}e^{y^2} = \frac{x^2}{2} + C$

$e^{y^2} = x^2 + 2C$

$e^{y^2} = x^2 + A$

$y^2 = \ln(x^2 + A)$. *General solution*

Solving this equation for y, we have

$y = \pm\sqrt{\ln(x^2 + A)}$

We choose the function

$y = \sqrt{\ln(x^2 + A)}$ and apply the initial condition $y(0) = 1$ to obtain

$1 = \sqrt{\ln(0 + A)}$

$\ln A = 1$

$A = e$

Thus, $y = \sqrt{\ln(x^2 + e)}$. *Particular solution*

33. The model for this problem is
$\frac{dA}{dt} = 0.12A$; $A(0) = 5000$.

$\frac{dA}{A} = 0.12dt$

$\int\frac{dA}{A} = \int 0.12dt$

$\ln|A| = 0.12t + C$

$A = e^{0.12t+c}$

$A = e^c e^{0.12t}$

$A = ke^{0.12t}$. *General solution*

Applying the initial condition $A(0) = 5000$, we have

$5000 = ke^0$, $k = 5000$.

Thus, $A = 5000e^{0.12t}$ is the particular solution.

When $t = 10$ years,

$A = 5000e^{(0.12)10} = 5000e^{1.2}$

$\approx \$16,600$.

35. Let $s(t)$ denote the number of people who have heard about the new product. Then the model for this problem is

$\frac{ds}{dt} = k(100,000 - s)$; $s(0) = 0$, $s(7) = 20,000$, $k > 0$.

$\frac{ds}{(100,000 - s)} = k\,dt$

$\int\frac{ds}{100,000 - s} = \int k\,dt$

$-\ln|100,000 - s| = kt + C$ $(0 < s < 100,000)$

$\ln|100,000 - s| = -kt - C$

$100,000 - s = e^{-kt-C}$

$100,000 - s = e^{-C}e^{-kt}$

Thus, $= Ae^{-kt}$.

$s = 100,000 - Ae^{-kt}$. *General solution*

We use the conditions $s(0) = 0$, $s(7) = 20,000$ to determine the constants A and k.

$s(0) = 0 = 100,000 - Ae^0$, $A = 100,000$.

Thus, $s = 100,000 - 100,000e^{-kt}$.

$s(7) = 20,000 = 100,000 - 100,000e^{-7k}$

$100,000e^{-7k} = 80,000$

$e^{-7k} = 0.8$

$-7k = \ln(0.8)$

$k = \frac{-\ln(0.8)}{7}$.

Therefore, the particular solution is $s(t) = 100,000 - 100,000e^{[\ln(0.8)/7]t}$.

Finally, we want to find time t such that $s(t) = 50,000$:

$$50,000 = 100,000 - 100,000e^{[\ln(0.8)/7]t}$$
$$e^{[\ln(0.8)/7]t} = 0.5$$
$$\frac{\ln 0.8}{7}t = \ln(0.5).$$

Thus, $t = \dfrac{7 \ln(0.5)}{\ln(0.8)} \sim 22$ days.

37. Let $s(t)$ denote the percentage of the deodorizer that is present at time t. Then the model for this problem is

$$\frac{ds}{dt} = ks; \quad s(0) = 1, \quad s(30) = 0.5, \quad k < 0.$$

Separating the variables, we have

$$\frac{ds}{s} = k \, dt$$

$$\int \frac{ds}{s} = \int k \, dt$$

$$\ln|s| = kt + C$$
$$s = e^{kt+c}$$
$$s = Ae^{kt}. \quad \textit{General solution}$$

We use the conditions $s(0) = 1$, $s(30) = 0.5$, to evaluate the constants A and k.

$$s(0) = 1 = Ae^0, \quad A = 1.$$

Thus, $s(t) = e^{kt}$

$$s(30) = 0.5 = e^{30k}$$
$$30k = \ln(0.5)$$
$$k = \frac{\ln(0.5)}{30}.$$

Therefore, $s(t) = e^{[\ln(0.5)/30]t}$ *Particular solution*

Now, we want to find time t such that $s(t) = 0.1$:

$$0.1 = e^{[\ln(0.5)/30]t}$$
$$\frac{\ln(0.5)}{30}t = \ln(0.1)$$
$$t = \frac{30 \ln(0.1)}{\ln(0.5)} \sim 100 \text{ days.}$$

39. If $s(t)$ is the annual sales at time t, then the model for this problem is:

$$\frac{ds}{dt} = k(5 - s); \quad s(0) = 0, \quad s(4) = 1, \quad k > 0.$$

$$\frac{ds}{5 - s} = k \, dt$$

$$\int \frac{ds}{5 - s} = \int k \, dt$$

$$-\ln|5 - s| = kt + C$$
$$\ln|5 - s| = -kt - C$$
$$5 - s = e^{-kt-c}$$
$$5 - s = Ae^{-kt}$$
$$s = 5 - Ae^{-kt}.$$

We use the conditions $s(0) = 0$ and $s(4) = 1$ to evaluate the constants A and k.

$$s(0) = 0 = 5 - Ae^0, \quad A = 5.$$

Thus, $s(t) = 5 - 5e^{-kt}$

$$s(4) = 1 = 5 - 5e^{-4k}$$
$$-5e^{-4k} = -4$$
$$e^{-4k} = \frac{4}{5} = 0.8$$
$$-4k = \ln(0.8)$$
$$k = \frac{-\ln(0.8)}{4}.$$

Therefore, $s(t) = 5 - 5e^{[\ln(0.8)/4]t}$.

Now we want to find time t such that $s(t) = 4$:

$$4 = 5 - 5e^{[\ln(0.8)/4]t}$$
$$-5e^{[\ln(0.8)/4]t} = -1$$
$$e^{[\ln(0.8)/4]t} = \frac{1}{5} = 0.2$$
$$\frac{\ln(0.8)}{4} t = \ln(0.2).$$

Thus, $t = \dfrac{4 \ln(0.2)}{\ln(0.8)} \approx 29$ years.

41. Let $T(t)$ denote the temperature of the bar at time t. Then the model for this problem is

$$\frac{dT}{dt} = k(T - 800), \quad k < 0; \quad T(0) = 80, \quad T(2) = 200.$$

Separating the variables, we have

$$\frac{dT}{T - 800} = k\,dt$$
$$\int \frac{dT}{T - 800} = \int k\,dt$$
$$\ln|T - 800| = kt + C$$
$$T - 800 = e^{kt+C}$$
$$T = 800 + Ae^{kt} \quad \textit{General solution}$$

Using the conditions $T(0) = 80$ and $T(2) = 200$ to evaluate the constants A and k, we have

$$T(0) = 80 = 800 + Ae^0, \quad A = -720.$$

Thus, $T(t) = 800 - 720e^{kt}$.

$$T(2) = 200 = 800 - 720e^{2k}$$
$$720e^{2k} = 600$$
$$e^{2k} = \frac{5}{6}$$
$$2k = \ln\left(\frac{5}{6}\right)$$
$$k = \frac{1}{2} \ln\left(\frac{5}{6}\right)$$

Therefore, $T(t) = 800 - 720e^{1/2 \ln(5/6)t}$.

Finally, we want to find t such that $T(t) = 500$. Thus,

$$500 = 800 - 720e^{1/2 \ln(5/6)t}$$
$$720e^{1/2 \ln(5/6)t} = 300$$
$$e^{1/2 \ln(5/6)t} = \frac{5}{12}$$
$$\frac{1}{2} \ln\left(\frac{5}{6}\right) t = \ln\left(\frac{5}{12}\right)$$
$$t = \frac{2 \ln\left(\frac{5}{12}\right)}{\ln\left(\frac{5}{6}\right)} \approx 9.6 \text{ minutes.}$$

43. Let $T(t)$ denote the temperature of the pie at time t. Then the model for this problem is:

$$\frac{dT}{dt} = k(T - 25), \quad k < 0; \quad T(0) = 325, \quad T(1) = 225.$$

Separating the variables, we have $\dfrac{dT}{T - 25} = k\,dt$

$$\int \frac{dT}{T - 25} = \int k\,dt$$
$$\ln|T - 25| = kt + C$$
$$T - 25 = e^{kt+c}$$
$$T = 25 + Ae^{kt}$$

Using the initial conditions $T(0) = 325$ and $T(1) = 225$ to evaluate the constants A and k, we have:

$$T(0) = 325 = 25 + Ae^0, \quad A = 300$$

Thus, $T(t) = 25 + 300e^{kt}$.

$$T(1) = 225 = 25 + 300e^k$$
$$300e^k = 200$$
$$e^k = \frac{2}{3}$$
$$k = \ln\left(\frac{2}{3}\right)$$

Therefore, $T(t) = 25 + 300e^{t \ln(2/3)}$.

Finally, we want to determine $T(4)$:

$$T(4) = 25 + 300e^{4 \ln(2/3)}$$
$$= 25 + 300e^{\ln(2/3)^4}$$
$$= 25 + 300\left(\frac{2}{3}\right)^4 \approx 84.26°$$

45. If $P(t)$ is the number of bacteria present at time t, then the model for this problem is:

$$\frac{dP}{dt} = kP; \quad P(0) = 100, \quad P(1) = 140, \quad k > 0.$$

$$\frac{dP}{P} = k\,dt$$
$$\int \frac{dP}{P} = \int k\,dt$$
$$\ln|P| = kt + C$$
$$P = e^{kt+c}$$
$$P = Ae^{kt}. \quad \textit{General solution}$$

We use the conditions $P(0) = 100$ and $P(1) = 140$ to evaluate the constants A and k.

$$P(0) = 100 = Ae^0, \quad A = 100.$$

Thus,

$$P(t) = 100e^{kt}$$
$$P(1) = 140 = 100e^k$$
$$e^k = 1.4$$
$$k = \ln(1.4).$$

Therefore,

$$P(t) = 100e^{(\ln 1.4)t}. \quad \textit{Particular solution}$$

(A) When $t = 5$,
$$P(5) = 100e^{\ln(1.4)5}$$
$$\approx 538 \text{ bacteria.}$$

(B) When $P = 1000$,
$$1000 = 100e^{\ln(1.4)t}$$
$$e^{\ln(1.4)t} = 10$$
$$\ln(1.4)t = \ln 10$$
$$t = \frac{\ln 10}{\ln(1.4)} \approx 6.8 \text{ hours.}$$

47. If $P(t)$ is the number of people infected at time t, then the model for this problem is:

$$\frac{dP}{dt} = kP(50{,}000 - P); \quad P(0) = 100, \quad P(10) = 500.$$

$$\frac{dP}{P(50{,}000 - P)} = k \, dt$$

$$\int \frac{dP}{P(50{,}000 - P)} = \int k \, dt$$

$$\frac{1}{50{,}000} \int \left[\frac{1}{P} + \frac{1}{50{,}000 - P} \right] dP = kt + C$$

$$\frac{1}{50{,}000} [\ln P - \ln(50{,}000 - P)] = kt + C$$

$$\ln \left[\frac{P}{50{,}000 - P} \right] = 50{,}000(kt + C)$$

$$\frac{P}{50{,}000 - P} = e^{50{,}000kt + 50{,}000C}$$

$$= e^{50{,}000C} e^{50{,}000kt}$$

$$= Ae^{50{,}000kt}$$

Solving this equation for P, we obtain

$$P = (50{,}000 - P)Ae^{50{,}000kt}$$

$$P = \frac{50{,}000Ae^{50{,}000kt}}{1 + Ae^{50{,}000kt}},$$

which can be written

$$P(t) = \frac{50{,}000}{1 + Be^{-50{,}000kt}}, \quad B = \frac{1}{A}.$$

Using the conditions $P(0) = 100$ and $P(10) = 500$ to evaluate the constants B and k, we obtain

$$P(0) = 100 = \frac{50,000}{1 + Be^0}$$

$$100(1 + B) = 50,000$$

$$1 + B = 500$$

$$B = 499.$$

$$P(t) = \frac{50,000}{1 + 499e^{-50,000kt}}.$$

$$P(10) = 500 = \frac{50,000}{1 + 499e^{-500,000k}}$$

$$1 + 499e^{-500,000k} = 100$$

$$499e^{-500,000k} = 99$$

$$-500,000k = \ln\left(\frac{99}{499}\right)$$

$$k = -\frac{1}{500,000} \ln\left(\frac{99}{499}\right).$$

Therefore,

$$P(t) = \frac{50,000}{1 + 499e^{0.1\ln(99/499)t}}. \qquad \textit{Particular solution}$$

(A) When $t = 20$,

$$P(20) = \frac{50,000}{1 + 499e^{2\ln(99/499)}} \approx 2422 \text{ people.}$$

(B) When $P = 25,000$,

$$25,000 = \frac{50,000}{1 + 499e^{0.1\ln(99/499)t}}$$

$$1 + 499e^{0.1\ln(99/499)t} = 2$$

$$e^{0.1\ln(99/499)t} = \frac{1}{499}$$

$$0.1 \ln\left(\frac{99}{499}\right)t = \ln\left(\frac{1}{499}\right)$$

$$t = \frac{10 \ln\left(\frac{1}{499}\right)}{\ln\left(\frac{99}{499}\right)} \approx 38.4 \text{ days.}$$

49. $\frac{dI}{ds} = k\frac{I}{s}$, $I > 0$, $s > 0$.

$$\frac{dI}{I} = \frac{k}{s}ds$$

$$\int \frac{dI}{I} = \int \frac{k}{s}ds$$

$$\ln I = k \ln s + C$$
$$= \ln s^k + C \qquad (k \ln s = \ln s^k)$$
$$I = e^{\ln s^k + C}$$
$$= e^C e^{\ln s^k}.$$

Therefore,

$$I = As^k. \qquad (\underline{\text{Note}}: e^{\ln s^k} = s^k.)$$

51. If $P(t)$ is the number of people who have heard the rumor at time t, then the model for this problem is:

$$\frac{dP}{dt} = kP(1000 - P); \quad P(0) = 5, \ P(1) = 10.$$

$$\frac{dP}{P(1000 - P)} = k \ dt$$

$$\int \frac{dP}{P(1000 - P)} = \int k \ dt$$

$$\frac{1}{1000} \int \left[\frac{1}{P} + \frac{1}{1000 - P} \right] dP = kt + C$$

$$\frac{1}{1000}[\ln P - \ln(1000 - P)] = kt + C$$

$$\ln\left(\frac{P}{1000 - P}\right) = 1000(kt + C)$$

$$\frac{P}{1000 - P} = e^{1000kt + 1000C}$$

$$= e^{1000C}e^{1000kt}$$

$$= Ae^{1000kt}$$

Solving this equation for P, we obtain

$$P = \frac{1000Ae^{1000kt}}{1 + Ae^{1000kt}} \quad \text{or} \quad P = \frac{1000}{1 + Be^{-1000kt}} \quad \left(B = \frac{1}{A}\right). \quad \textit{General solution}$$

Using the conditions $P(0) = 5$ and $P(1) = 10$ to evaluate the constants B and k, we have

$$P(0) = 5 = \frac{1000}{1 + Be^0}$$

$$5(1 + B) = 1000$$

$$1 + B = 200$$

$$B = 199.$$

Thus,

$$P(t) = \frac{1000}{1 + 199e^{-1000kt}}$$

$$P(1) = 10 = \frac{1000}{1 + 199e^{-1000k}}$$

$$1 + 199e^{-1000k} = 100$$

$$199e^{-1000k} = 99$$

$$e^{-1000k} = \frac{99}{199}$$

$$-1000k = \ln\left(\frac{99}{199}\right)$$

$$k = -\frac{1}{1000}\ln\left(\frac{99}{199}\right).$$

Therefore,

$$P(t) = \frac{1000}{1 + 199e^{\ln(99/199)t}}. \quad \textit{Particular solution}$$

(A) When $t = 7$,

$$P(7) = \frac{1000}{1 + 199e^{\ln(99/199)7}} \approx 400 \text{ people.}$$

(B) When $P = 850$,

$$850 = \frac{1000}{1 + 199e^{\ln(99/199)t}}$$

$$1 + 199e^{\ln(99/199)t} = \frac{1000}{850} = \frac{20}{17}$$

$$e^{\ln(99/199)t} = \frac{3}{3383}$$

$$\ln\left(\frac{99}{199}\right)t = \ln\left(\frac{3}{3383}\right)$$

$$t = \frac{\ln\left(\frac{3}{3383}\right)}{\ln\left(\frac{99}{199}\right)} \approx 10 \text{ days.}$$

53. From Problem 35, $s(t) = 100,000 - 100,000e^{\ln[0.8/7]t}$
The graphs of s and $s = 70,000$ are given below

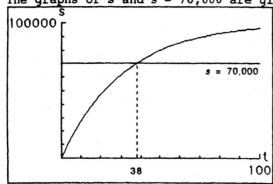

It will take approximately 38 days for 70,000 people to become aware of the product.

55. $S(t) = M(1 - e^{kt})$ where k is a negative constant
We have $S(1) = M(1 - e^{k}) = 2$ (million)
and $S(3) = M(1 - e^{3k}) = 5$

From the first equation, $M = \frac{2}{1 - e^{k}}$. Substituting this in the second equation yields

$$\frac{2}{1 - e^{k}}(1 - e^{3k}) = 5$$

$$2 - 2e^{3k} = 5 - 5e^{k}$$

(1) $2e^{3k} - 5e^{k} + 3 = 0$

Now let $t = e^{k}$ ($k = \ln t$). Then equation (1) becomes

$$2t^{3} - 5t + 3 = 0$$

418

The graph of $y = 2t^3 - 5t + 3$ is shown below

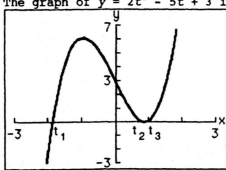

Since $k = \ln t$ we can disregard the solutions t_1 (since $t_1 < 0$) $t_3 = 1$. The solution $t_2 \approx 0.82$. Thus, $k = \ln 0.82 \approx -0.2$. Finally,

$$M = \frac{2}{1 - e^{-0.2}} \approx 11 \text{ million.}$$

57. From Problem 47, $P(t) = \dfrac{50,000}{1 + 499e^{0.11\ln(99/499)t}}$

The graphs of P and $P = 40,000$ are shown at the right.

It will take approximately 47 days for 40,000 people to be infected.

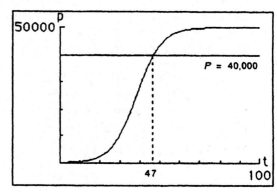

EXERCISE 7-3

Things to remember:

1. A differential equation that can be expressed in the form

   (A) $y' + f(x)y = g(x)$

   is a FIRST-ORDER LINEAR DIFFERENTIAL EQUATION.

2. The procedure for solving a first-order linear differential equation is as follows:

   Step 1: Write the equation in the STANDARD FORM (A).

   Step 2: Compute the INTEGRATING FACTOR

   $$I(x) = e^{\int f(x)\,dx}$$

   (Note: when evaluating $\int f(x)\,dx$, choose $C = 0$ for the constant of integration.)

Step 3: Multiply both sides of (A) by the integrating factor. The left side will be in the form $[I(x)y]'$:

$$[I(x)y]' = I(x)g(x)$$

Step 4: Integrate both sides:

$$I(x)y = \int I(x)g(x)\,dx$$

(**Note**: when evaluating $\int I(x)g(x)\,dx$, include the arbitrary constant of integration.)

Step 5: Solve for y to obtain the GENERAL SOLUTION:

$$y = \frac{1}{I(x)}\int I(x)g(x)\,dx$$

---

1. $y' + 2y = 4$; $y(0) = 1$

   Step 1: The equation is in standard form.

   Step 2: Find the integrating factor.
   $$f(x) = 2 \quad \text{and} \quad I(x) = e^{\int f(x)\,dx} = e^{\int 2\,dx} = e^{2x}$$

   Step 3: Multiply both sides of the standard form by the integrating factor.
   $$e^{2x}(y' + 2y) = e^{2x}(4)$$
   $$e^{2x}y' + 2e^{2x}y = 4e^{2x}$$
   $$[e^{2x}y]' = 4e^{2x}$$

   Step 4: Integrate both sides.
   $$\int [e^{2x}y]'\,dx = \int 4e^{2x}\,dx$$
   $$e^{2x}y = 2e^{2x} + C$$

   Step 5: Solve for y.
   $$y = \frac{1}{e^{2x}}(2e^{2x} + C) = 2 + Ce^{-2x} \quad \textit{General solution}$$

   To find the particular solution satisfying the initial condition $y(0) = 1$, substitute $x = 0$, $y = 1$ in the general solution:
   $$1 = 2 + Ce^0 = 2 + C.$$
   Thus, $C = -1$ and the particular solution is
   $$y = 2 - e^{-2x}$$

3. $y' + y = e^{-2x}$; $y(0) = 3$

   Step 1: The equation is in standard form.

   Step 2: Find the integrating factor.
   $$f(x) = 1 \quad \text{and} \quad I(x) = e^{\int f(x)\,dx} = e^{\int 1\,dx} = e^x$$

Step 3: Multiply both sides of the standard form by the integrating factor.

$$e^x[y' + y] = e^x \cdot e^{-2x}$$
$$e^x y' + e^x y = e^{-x}$$
$$[e^x y]' = e^{-x}$$

Step 4: Integrate both sides.

$$\int [e^x y]' \, dx = \int e^{-x} \, dx$$

$$e^x y = \frac{e^{-x}}{-1} + C = -e^{-x} + C$$

Step 5: Solve for y.

$$y = \frac{1}{e^x}[-e^{-x} + C] = -e^{-2x} + Ce^{-x} \quad \textit{General solution}$$

To find the particular solution satisfying the initial condition $y(0) = 3$, substitute $x = 0$, $y = 3$ in the general solution:

$$3 = -e^0 + Ce^0 = -1 + C$$

Thus, $C = 4$ and the particular solution is

$$y = -e^{-2x} + 4e^{-x}$$

5. $y' - y = 2e^x$; $y(0) = -4$

Step 1: The equation is in standard form.

Step 2: Find the integrating factor.

$$f(x) = -1 \quad \text{and} \quad I(x) = e^{\int f(x)\,dx} = e^{\int (-1)\,dx} = e^{-x}$$

Step 3: Multiply both sides of the standard form by the integrating factor.

$$e^{-x}[y' - y] = e^{-x}(2e^x)$$
$$e^{-x} y' - e^{-x} y = 2$$
$$[e^{-x} y]' = 2$$

Step 4: Integrate both sides.

$$\int [e^{-x} y]' \, dx = \int 2 \, dx$$

$$e^{-x} y = 2x + C$$

Step 5: Solve for y.

$$y = \frac{1}{e^{-x}}[2x + C] = 2xe^x + Ce^x \quad \textit{General solution}$$

To find the particular solution satisfying the initial condition $y(0) = -4$, substitute $x = 0$, $y = -4$ in the general solution:

$$-4 = 2(0)e^0 + Ce^0 = C$$

Thus, $C = -4$ and the particular solution is

$$y = 2xe^x - 4e^x$$

7. $y' + y = 9x^2e^{-x}$; $y(0) = 2$

   Step 1: The equation is in standard form.

   Step 2: Find the integrating factor.
   $$f(x) = 1 \quad \text{and} \quad I(x) = e^{\int f(x)\,dx} = e^{\int 1\,dx} = e^x$$

   Step 3: Multiply both sides of the standard form by the integrating factor.
   $$e^x[y' + y] = e^x(9x^2e^{-x})$$
   $$e^xy' + e^xy = 9x^2$$
   $$[e^xy]' = 9x^2$$

   Step 4: Integrate both sides.
   $$\int [e^xy]'\,dx = \int 9x^2\,dx$$
   $$e^xy = 3x^3 + C$$

   Step 5: Solve for y.
   $$y = \frac{1}{e^x}(3x^3 + C) = 3x^3e^{-x} + Ce^{-x} \quad \textit{General solution}$$

   To find the particular solution satisfying the initial condition $y(0) = 2$, substitute $x = 0$, $y = 2$ in the general solution:
   $$2 = 3(0)^3e^0 + Ce^0 = C$$
   Thus, $C = 2$ and the particular solution is
   $$y = 3x^3e^{-x} + 2e^{-x}$$

9. $y' + \frac{1}{x}y = 2$; $y(1) = 1$

   Step 1: The equation is in standard form.

   Step 2: Find the integrating factor.
   $$f(x) = \frac{1}{x} \quad \text{and} \quad I(x) = e^{\int f(x)\,dx} = e^{\int (1/x)\,dx} = e^{\ln x} = x$$

   Step 3: Multiply both sides of the standard form by the integrating factor.
   $$x\left(y' + \frac{1}{x}y\right) = x(2)$$
   $$xy' + y = 2x$$
   $$[xy]' = 2x$$

   Step 4: Integrate both sides.
   $$\int [xy]'\,dx = \int 2x\,dx$$
   $$xy = x^2 + C$$

   Step 5: Solve for y.
   $$y = \frac{1}{x}(x^2 + C) = x + \frac{C}{x} \quad \textit{General solution}$$

To find the particular solution satisfying the initial condition $y(1) = 1$, substitute $x = 1$, $y = 1$ in the general solution:

$$1 = 1 + \frac{C}{1} = 1 + C$$

Thus, $C = 0$ and the particular solution is

$$y = x$$

11. $y' + \frac{2}{x}y = 10x^2$; $y(2) = 8$

Step 1: The equation is in standard form.

Step 2: Find the integrating factor.

$$f(x) = \frac{2}{x} \quad \text{and} \quad I(x) = e^{\int f(x)\,dx} = e^{\int (2/x)\,dx} = e^{2\ln x} = e^{\ln x^2} = x^2$$

Step 3: Multiply both sides of the standard form by the integrating factor.

$$x^2\left(y' + \frac{2}{x}y\right) = x^2(10x^2)$$
$$x^2 y' + 2xy = 10x^4$$
$$[x^2 y]' = 10x^4$$

Step 4: Integrate both sides.

$$\int [x^2 y]'\,dx = \int 10x^4\,dx$$
$$x^2 y = 2x^5 + C$$

Step 5: Solve for y.

$$y = \frac{1}{x^2}(2x^5 + C) = 2x^3 + \frac{C}{x^2} \quad \textit{General solution}$$

To find the particular solution satisfying the initial condition $y(2) = 8$, substitute $x = 2$, $y = 8$ in the general solution:

$$8 = 2(2)^3 + \frac{C}{2^2} = 16 + \frac{C}{4}$$

and $\quad -8 = \frac{C}{4}$.

Thus, $C = -32$ and the particular solution is

$$y = 2x^3 - \frac{32}{x^2}$$

13. $y' + xy = 5x$

$$I(x) = e^{\int f(x)\,dx} = e^{\int x\,dx} = e^{x^2/2} \quad \textit{Integrating factor}$$

$$y = \frac{1}{I(x)} \int I(x)g(x)\,dx$$

$$= \frac{1}{e^{x^2/2}} \int e^{x^2/2} 5x\,dx$$

$$= 5e^{-x^2/2} \int xe^{x^2/2}\,dx \qquad \left(u = \frac{x^2}{2},\ du = x\,dx\right)$$

$$= 5e^{-x^2/2}[e^{x^2/2} + C] = 5 + 5Ce^{-x^2/2}$$

$$y = 5 + Ae^{-x^2/2}. \quad \textit{General solution}$$

15. $y' - 2y = 4x$

$\quad I(x) = e^{\int (-2)\,dx} = e^{-2x}$ $\qquad$ *Integrating factor*

$\quad y = \dfrac{1}{I(x)} \int I(x)g(x)\,dx = \dfrac{1}{e^{-2x}} \int e^{-2x}4x\,dx$

$\qquad = 4e^{2x} \int xe^{-2x}\,dx$ $\qquad$ (Integrate by parts)

$\qquad = 4e^{2x}\left[-\dfrac{1}{2}xe^{-2x} - \dfrac{1}{4}e^{-2x} + C\right]$

$\qquad = -2x - 1 + 4Ce^{2x}$ $\qquad (A = 4C)$

$\quad y = -2x - 1 + Ae^{2x}.$ $\quad$ *General solution*

17. $y' + \dfrac{1}{x}y = e^x$

$\quad I(x) = e^{\int f(x)\,dx} = e^{\int (1/x)\,dx} = e^{\ln x} = x$ $\qquad$ *Integrating factor*

$\quad y = \dfrac{1}{I(x)} \int I(x)g(x)\,dx$

$\qquad = \dfrac{1}{x} \int xe^x\,dx$ $\qquad$ (Integrate by parts)

$\qquad = \dfrac{1}{x}[xe^x - e^x + C]$

$\quad y = e^x - \dfrac{e^x}{x} + \dfrac{C}{x}.$ $\quad$ *General solution*

19. $y' + \dfrac{1}{x}y = \ln x$

$\quad I(x) = e^{\int f(x)\,dx} = e^{\int (1/x)\,dx} = e^{\ln x} = x$ $\qquad$ *Integrating factor*

$\quad y = \dfrac{1}{I(x)} \int I(x)g(x)\,dx$

$\qquad = \dfrac{1}{x} \int x \ln x\,dx$ $\qquad$ (Integrate by parts)

$\qquad = \dfrac{1}{x}\left[\dfrac{x^2}{2} \ln x - \dfrac{1}{4}x^2 + C\right]$

$\qquad = \dfrac{1}{2}x \ln x - \dfrac{1}{4}x + \dfrac{C}{x}.$ $\quad$ *General solution*

21. $y' = \dfrac{1 - y}{x}$

This equation can be rewritten as a first-order linear differential
equation in the standard form.

(A) $y' + \dfrac{1}{x}y = \dfrac{1}{x}.$

$\qquad$ Then $f(x) = \dfrac{1}{x}$ and the integrating factor is

$\qquad I(x) = e^{\int (1/x)\,dx} = e^{\ln x} = x.$

$\qquad$ Thus, $y = \dfrac{1}{x} \int x \cdot \dfrac{1}{x}\,dx = \dfrac{1}{x} \int dx = \dfrac{1}{x}(x + C) = 1 + \dfrac{C}{x}.$

Using separation of variables on the original equation, we have:

$$\frac{y'}{1 - y} = \frac{1}{x}$$

$$\int \frac{dy}{1 - y} = \int \frac{1}{x}\, dx$$

$$-\ln(1 - y) = \ln(x) + C \qquad \text{(assuming } 1 - y > 0 \text{ and } x > 0\text{)}$$

$$\ln(1 - y) = -\ln(x) - C$$

$$1 - y = e^{-\ln x - C}$$

$$1 - y = e^{-C} e^{\ln x^{-1}}$$

$$1 - y = \frac{K}{x} \qquad \left(e^{\ln x^{-1}} = \frac{1}{x} \right)$$

$$y = 1 + \frac{K}{x}$$

23. $y' = \dfrac{2x + 2xy}{1 + x^2}$

This equation can be rewritten as a first-order linear differential equation in the standard form.

(A) $y' - \dfrac{2x}{1 + x^2} y = \dfrac{2x}{1 + x^2}.$

Then, $f(x) = \dfrac{-2x}{1 + x^2}$ and the integrating factor is:

$$I(x) = e^{\int (-2x/1+x^2)\, dx} = e^{-\ln(1+x^2)} = \frac{1}{1 + x^2}$$

Thus, $y = \dfrac{1}{\dfrac{1}{1 + x^2}} \displaystyle\int \dfrac{1}{1 + x^2} \cdot \dfrac{2x}{1 + x^2}\, dx$

$$= (1 + x^2) \int \frac{2x}{(1 + x^2)^2}\, dx = (1 + x^2) \left[\frac{-1}{1 + x^2} + C \right]$$

and $y = -1 + C(1 + x^2).$

Using separation of variables on the original equation, we have:

$$\frac{y'}{1 + y} = \frac{2x}{1 + x^2}$$

$$\int \frac{dy}{1 + y} = \int \frac{2x}{1 + x^2}\, dx$$

$$\ln|1 + y| = \ln(1 + x^2) + C$$

$$1 + y = e^{\ln(1+x^2) + C}$$

$$1 + y = e^C e^{\ln(1+x^2)}$$

$$1 + y = K(1 + x^2) \qquad (e^{\ln(1+x^2)} = 1 + x^2)$$

$$y = -1 + K(1 + x^2)$$

25. $y' = 2x(y + 1)$

This equation can be rewritten as a first-order linear differential equation in the standard form.

(A) $y' - 2xy = 2x$

Then, $f(x) = -2x$ and the integrating factor is:

$$I(x) = e^{\int -2x\, dx} = e^{-x^2}$$

Thus, $y = \dfrac{1}{e^{-x^2}} \displaystyle\int e^{-x^2} 2x\ dx = e^{x^2} \displaystyle\int 2xe^{-x^2}\ dx = e^{x^2}[-e^{-x^2} + C]$

and $\quad y = -1 + Ce^{x^2}$.

Using separation of variables on the original equation, we have:

$$\dfrac{y'}{y + 1} = 2x$$

$$\int \dfrac{dy}{y + 1} = \int 2x\ dx$$

$$\ln|y + 1| = x^2 + C$$

$$y + 1 = e^{x^2+c}$$

$$y + 1 = e^{c}e^{x^2}$$

$$= Ke^{x^2}$$

Thus, $y = -1 + Ke^{x^2}$.

27. $\dfrac{dy}{dt} = ky$.

This equation can be rewritten as

(A) $\dfrac{dy}{dt} - ky = 0$

Here $f(t) = -k$ and the integrating factor is:
$I(t) = e^{\int -k\,dt} = e^{-kt}$

Thus, $y = \dfrac{1}{e^{-kt}} \displaystyle\int e^{-kt} \cdot 0\ dt = e^{kt} \displaystyle\int 0\ dt = e^{kt}C$

and $\quad y = Ce^{kt}$.

29. The amount A in the account at any time t must satisfy
$$\dfrac{dA}{dt} - 0.04A = -4000.$$

Now $f(t) = -0.04$ and the integrating factor is:

$$I(t) = e^{\int(-0.04)dt} = e^{-0.04t}$$

Thus, $A = \dfrac{1}{e^{-0.04t}} \displaystyle\int -4000e^{-0.04t}\ dt$

$$\approx e^{0.04t}\left[\dfrac{-4000e^{-0.04t}}{-0.04} + C\right]$$

$A = 100,000 + Ce^{0.04t}$ *General solution*

Applying the initial condition $A(0) = 20,000$ yields:
$A(0) = 100,000 + Ce^{0} = 20,000$ and $C = -80,000$
Thus, the amount in the account at any time t is:
$A(t) = 100,000 - 80,000e^{0.04t}$

To determine when the amount in the account is 0, we must solve $A(t) = 0$
for t:

$$100,000 - 80,000e^{0.04t} = 0$$
$$80,000e^{0.04t} = 100,000$$
$$e^{0.04t} = \dfrac{5}{4}$$

$$t = \frac{\ln\left(\frac{5}{4}\right)}{0.04} \approx 5.579$$

Thus, the account is depleted after 5.579 years. The total amount withdrawn from the account is:

$$4000(5.579) = \$22,316.$$

31. The amount in the account at any time t must satisfy

$$\frac{dA}{dt} - 0.05A = -1500.$$

Now $f(t) = -0.05$ and the integrating factor is:

$$I(t) = e^{\int (-0.05)dt} = e^{-0.05t}$$

Thus,

$$A = \frac{1}{e^{-0.05t}} \int -1500e^{-0.05t}dt = e^{0.05t}\left[\frac{-1500e^{-0.05t}}{-0.05} + C\right]$$

$$= 30,000 + Ce^{0.05t} \qquad \textit{General solution}$$

Applying the initial condition $A(0) = P$ yields:

$$30,000 + C = P$$
$$C = P - 30,000$$

Thus, the amount in the account at any time t is:

$$A(t) = 30,000 + (P - 30,000)e^{0.05t}$$

Since $A(10) = 0$, we have:

$$0 = 30,000 + (P - 30,000)e^{0.05(10)}$$
$$(P - 30,000)e^{0.5} = -30,000$$

Solving for the initial deposit P yields:

$$P = \frac{-30,000}{e^{0.5}} + 30,000 = 30,000(1 - e^{-0.5}) \approx 11,804$$

Thus, the initial deposit was $11,804.

33. The amount in the account at any time t must satisfy

$$\frac{dA}{dt} - 0.08A = 2000.$$

Now $f(t) = -0.08$ and the integrating factor is

$$I(t) = e^{\int (-0.08)dt} = e^{-0.08t}$$

Thus,

$$A = \frac{1}{e^{-0.08t}} \int 2000e^{-0.08t}dt = e^{0.08t}\left[\frac{2000e^{-0.08t}}{-0.08} + C\right]$$

$$= -25,000 + Ce^{0.08t}$$

Applying the initial condition $A(0) = 7000$ yields:

$$7000 = -25,000 + C$$
$$\text{and} \quad C = 32,000$$

Thus, the amount in the account at any time t is:

$$A(t) = 32,000e^{0.08t} - 25,000$$

After 5 years, the amount in the account is
$$A(5) = 32,000e^{0.08(5)} - 25,000 = 32,000e^{0.4} - 25,000$$
$$\approx \$22,738.39$$

35. The equilibrium price at time t is the solution of the equation
$$95 - 5p(t) + 2p'(t) = 35 - 2p(t) + 3p'(t)$$
which satisfies the initial condition $p(0) = 30$.

The equation simplifies to
$$p'(t) + 3p(t) = 60,$$
a first-order linear equation. The integrating factor is:
$$I(t) = e^{\int 3\,dt} = e^{3t}$$
Thus,
$$p(t) = \frac{1}{e^{3t}} \int 60e^{3t}\,dt = e^{-3t}\left[\frac{60e^{3t}}{3} + c\right]$$
$$= 20 + Ce^{-3t} \qquad General\ solution$$

Applying the initial condition yields
$$p(0) = 20 + C = 30$$
$$C = 10$$
Thus, the equilibrium price at time t is:
$$p(t) = 20 + 10e^{-3t}$$

The long-range equilibrium price is:
$$\bar{p} = \lim_{t \to \infty} (20 + 10e^{-3t}) = 20$$

37. Let $p(t)$ be the amount of pollutants in the tank at time t. The initial amount of pollutants in the tank is $p(0) = 2 \cdot 200 = 400$ pounds.

Pollutants are entering the tank at the constant rate of $3 \cdot 75 = 225$ pounds per hour.

The amount of water in the tank at time t is $200 + 25t$.

The amount of pollutants in each gallon of water at time t is $\frac{p(t)}{200 + 25t}$.

The rate at which pollutants are leaving the tank is
$$\frac{50p(t)}{200 + 25t} = \frac{2p(t)}{8 + t}.$$
Thus, the model for this problem is
$$p'(t) = 225 - \frac{2p(t)}{8 + t}; \quad p(0) = 400 \quad \text{or} \quad p'(t) + \frac{2p(t)}{8 + t} = 225; \quad p(0) = 400.$$

Now $f(t) = \frac{2}{8 + t}$ and the integrating factor is:
$$I(t) = e^{\int (2/(8+t))\,dt} = e^{2\ln(8+t)} = e^{\ln(8+t)^2} = (8 + t)^2$$
Thus,
$$p(t) = \frac{1}{(8 + t)^2} \int 225(8 + t)^2\,dt = \frac{1}{(8 + t)^2}\left[225\frac{(8 + t)^3}{3} + c\right]$$
$$p(t) = 75(8 + t) + \frac{C}{(8 + t)^2}. \quad General\ solution$$

We use the initial condition $p(0) = 400$ to evaluate the constant C.

$$p(0) = 400 = 75(8) + \frac{C}{8^2}$$

$$\frac{C}{64} = -200$$

$$C = -12,800$$

$$p(t) = 75(8 + t) - \frac{12,800}{(8 + t)^2}. \qquad \textit{Particular solution}$$

To find the total amount of pollutants in the tank after two hours, we evaluate $p(2)$:

$$p(2) = 75(10) - \frac{12,800}{(10)^2} = 750 - 128 = 622$$

After two hours, the tank contains 250 gallons of water. Thus, the rate at which pollutants are being released is

$$\frac{622}{250} \approx 2.5 \text{ pounds per gallon.}$$

39. Let $p(t)$ be the amount of pollutants in the tank at time t. The initial amount of pollutants in the tank is $p(0) = 2 \cdot 200 = 400$ pounds.

Pollutants are entering the tank at the constant rate of $3(50) = 150$ pounds per hour.

Since water is entering and leaving the tank at the same rate, the amount of water in the tank at all times t is 200 gallons.

The amount of pollutants in each gallon of water at time t is $\frac{p(t)}{200}$.

The rate at which pollutants are leaving the tank is $\frac{50p(t)}{200} = \frac{p(t)}{4}$.

Thus, the model for this problem is:

$$p'(t) = 150 - \frac{p(t)}{4}; \quad p(0) = 400 \quad \text{or} \quad p'(t) + \frac{1}{4}p(t) = 150; \quad p(0) = 400$$

Now $f(t) = \frac{1}{4}$ and the integrating factor is:

$$I(t) = e^{\int (1/4)dt} = e^{t/4}$$

Thus,

$$p(t) = \frac{1}{e^{t/4}} \int e^{t/4} (150)dt$$

$$= 150e^{-t/4} \int e^{t/4}dt = 150e^{-t/4} [4e^{t/4} + C]$$

$$= 600 + 150Ce^{-t/4} \qquad (A = 150C)$$

$$p(t) = 600 + Ae^{-t/4}. \qquad \textit{General solution}$$

We use the initial condition $p(0) = 400$ to evaluate the constant A.

$$p(0) = 400 = 600 + Ae^0, \quad A = -200$$

Therefore,

$$p(t) = 600 - 200e^{-t/4}. \qquad \textit{Particular solution}$$

To find the amount of pollutants in the tank after two hours, we evaluate $p(2)$:

$p(2) = 600 - 200e^{-1/2} \approx 479$ pounds

The rate at which pollutants are being released after two hours is

$$\frac{600 - 200e^{-1/2}}{200} = 3 - e^{-1/2} \approx 2.4 \text{ pounds per gallon.}$$

41. The model for this problem is:

$$\frac{dw}{dt} + 0.005w = \frac{2100}{3500} \quad \text{or} \quad \frac{dw}{dt} + 0.005w = \frac{3}{5}$$

Now $f(t) = 0.005$, and the integrating factor is:

$$I(t) = e^{\int 0.005 dt} = e^{0.005t}$$

Thus,

$$w(t) = \frac{1}{e^{0.005t}} \int \frac{3}{5} e^{0.005t} dt$$

$$= \frac{3}{5} e^{-0.005t} \left[\frac{e^{0.005t}}{0.005} + k \right]$$

$$= 120 + \frac{3}{5} k e^{-0.005t}$$

$$= 120 + A e^{-0.005t} \qquad \textit{General solution}$$

Applying the initial condition $w(0) = 160$, we have:

$160 = 120 + Ae^{0}$

$A = 40$

Thus,

$w(t) = 120 + 40e^{-0.005t}$.

Now, we want to find t such that $w(t) = 150$.

$150 = 120 + 40e^{-0.005t}$

$40e^{-0.005t} = 30$

$e^{-0.005t} = \frac{3}{4}$

$-0.005t = \ln\left(\frac{3}{4}\right)$

$$t = \frac{-\ln\left(\frac{3}{4}\right)}{0.005} \approx 58$$

Thus, it will take 58 days to lose 10 pounds.

Finally, $\lim_{t \to \infty} w(t) = \lim_{t \to \infty} (120 + 40e^{-0.005t}) = 120$, since $\lim_{t \to \infty} e^{-0.005t} = 0$.

Therefore, the person's weight will approach 120 pounds if this diet is maintained for a long period.

43. The model for this problem is

$$\frac{dw}{dt} + 0.005w = \frac{1}{3500} C,$$

where C is to be determined.

Now, $f(t) = 0.005$, and the integrating factor is:

$$I(t) = e^{\int 0.005 dt} = e^{0.005t}$$

Thus,

$$w(t) = \frac{1}{e^{0.005t}} \int \frac{C}{3500} e^{0.005t} \, dt$$

$$= \frac{C}{3500} e^{-0.005t} \left[\frac{e^{0.005t}}{0.005} + k \right]$$

$$= \frac{C}{17.5} + \frac{Ck}{3500} e^{-0.005t}$$

$$= \frac{C}{17.5} + Ae^{-0.005t} \qquad \textit{General solution}$$

Applying the initial condition $w(0) = 130$, we have

$$130 = \frac{C}{17.5} + Ae^0$$

$$A = 130 - \frac{C}{17.5}$$

and

$$w(t) = \frac{C}{17.5} + \left(130 - \frac{C}{17.5} \right) e^{-0.005t}$$

Now, we want to determine C such that $w(30) = 125$.

$$125 = \frac{C}{17.5} + \left(130 - \frac{C}{17.5} \right) e^{-0.005(30)}$$

$$125 = \frac{C}{17.5} + \left(130 - \frac{C}{17.5} \right) e^{-0.15}$$

$$\frac{C}{17.5} (1 - e^{-0.15}) = 125 - 130e^{-0.15}$$

$$C = \frac{17.5(125 - 130e^{-0.15})}{1 - e^{-0.15}} \approx 1647$$

Thus, the person should consume 1647 calories per day.

45. The model for this problem is

$$\frac{dk}{dt} + \ell k = \lambda \ell,$$

where ℓ and λ are constants.

Now, $f(t) = \ell$, and the integrating factor is:

$$I(t) = e^{\int \ell \, dt} = e^{\ell t}$$

Thus,

$$k(t) = \frac{1}{e^{\ell t}} \int \ell \lambda e^{\ell t} \, dt = e^{-\ell t} \left[\ell \lambda \frac{e^{\ell t}}{\ell} + C \right] = \lambda + \frac{C}{\ell} e^{-\ell t}$$

$$= \lambda + Me^{-\ell t} \qquad \textit{General solution}$$

For Student A, $\ell = 0.8$ and $\lambda = 0.9$. Thus,

$$k(t) = 0.9 + Me^{-0.8t}.$$

Applying the initial condtion $k(0) = 0.1$ yields:

$$0.1 = 0.9 + Me^0 \quad \text{or} \quad M = -0.8$$

and $k(t) = 0.9 - 0.8e^{-0.8t}$.

When $t = 6$, we have:

$$k(6) = 0.9 - 0.8e^{-0.8(6)} = 0.9 - 0.8e^{-4.8} \approx 0.8934 \text{ or } 89.34\%$$

For Student B, $\ell = 0.8$ and $\lambda = 0.7$. Thus,
$$k(t) = 0.7 + Me^{-0.8t}.$$

Applying the initial condition $k(0) = 0.4$ yields:
$$0.4 = 0.7 + Me^0 \quad \text{or} \quad M = -0.3$$
and $k(t) = 0.7 - 0.3e^{-0.8t}$

When $t = 6$, we have:
$$k(6) = 0.7 - 0.3e^{-0.8(6)} = 0.7 - 0.3e^{-4.8} \approx 0.6975 \text{ or } 69.75\%$$

47. From Problem 33, $A(t) = 32,000e^{0.08t} - 25,000$
The graphs of this function and $A(t) = 50,000$ are shown below

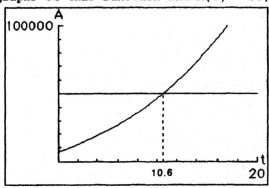

It will take approximately 10.6 years for the account to contain $50,000.

49. From Problem 37, $p(t) = 75(8 + t) - \dfrac{12,800}{(8 + t)^2}$
The graphs of this function and $p = 1000$ are shown below

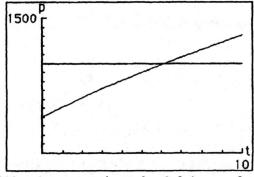

It will take approximately 6.2 hours for the tank to contain 1000 pounds of pollutants.

Things to remember:

<u>1</u>. The differential equation

(A) $ay'' + by' + cy = 0$

where a, b, and c are constants, is called a SECOND-ORDER LINEAR HOMOGENEOUS DIFFERENTIAL EQUATION WITH CONSTANT COEFFICIENTS.

<u>2</u>. The quadratic equation

$am^2 + bm + c = 0$

is called the CHARACTERISTIC EQUATION for the differential equation (A). If m is a real root of the characteristic equation, then $y = e^{mx}$ is a solution of the differential equation.

<u>3</u>. If the characteristic equation $am^2 + bm + c = 0$ for the differential equation (A) has:
(a) two distinct real roots, m_1 and m_2, then

$$y = C_1 e^{m_1 x} + C_2 e^{m_2 x}$$

is the general solution of (A);

(b) a single, repeated real root m, then

$$y = C_1 e^{mx} + C_2 x e^{mx}$$

is the general solution of (A);

(c) imaginary roots $m_1 = p + qi$, $m_2 = p - qi$, then

$$y = e^{px}(C_1 \cos qx + C_2 \sin qx)$$

is the general solution of (A).

<u>4</u>. The differential equation

(C) $ay'' + by' + cy = d$

where a, b, c, and d are constants is a SECOND-ORDER NONHOMOGENEOUS DIFFERENTIAL EQUATION WITH CONSTANT COEFFICIENTS. Equation (C) can be solved using the following steps.

<u>Step 1</u>: If $c \neq 0$, determine a constant function $y = k$ which satisfies the nonhomogeneous equation. If $c = 0$, determine a function of the form $y = kx$, k a constant, which satisfies the nonhomogeneous equation.

Step 2: Determine the general solution of the associated homogeneous differential equation

$$ay'' + by' + cy = 0.$$

Step 3: Add the solutions found in Steps 1 and 2. This is the general solution of (C).

---

1. $y'' + 3y' + 2y = 0$
   The characteristic equation is:
   $m^2 + 3m + 2 = 0$
   $(m + 1)(m + 2) = 0$
   $m_1 = -1$, $m_2 = -2$ are the roots.

   By 3(a), the general solution is:
   $y = C_1 e^{-x} + C_2 e^{-2x}$

3. $y'' + 2y' - 15y = 0$
   $m^2 + 2m - 15 = 0$ Characteristic equation
   $(m + 5)(m - 3) = 0$
   $m_1 = -5$, $m_2 = 3$ Roots of characteristic equation
   By 3(a), the general solution is:
   $y = C_1 e^{-5x} + C_2 e^{3x}$

5. $y'' + 6y' = 0$
   $m^2 + 6m = 0$ Characteristic equation
   $m(m + 6) = 0$
   $m_1 = 0$, $m_2 = -6$ Roots of characteristic equation
   By 3(a), the general solution is:
   $y = C_1 e^0 + C_2 e^{-6x} = C_1 + C_2 e^{-6x}$

7. $y'' - 4y' + 4y = 0$
   $m^2 - 4m + 4 = 0$ Characteristic equation
   $(m - 2)^2 = 0$
   $m = 2$ Repeated root of the characteristic equation
   By 3(b), the general solution is:
   $y = C_1 e^{2x} + C_2 x e^{2x}$

9. $y'' - y = 0$; $y(0) = 3$, $y'(0) = 1$
   $m^2 - 1 = 0$ Characteristic equation
   $(m - 1)(m + 1) = 0$
   $m_1 = 1$, $m_2 = -1$ Roots of characteristic equation
   The general solution is:
   $y = C_1 e^x + C_2 e^{-x}$

   Applying the initial conditions, $y(0) = 3$ and $y'(0) = 1$, we obtain the system of equations:
   $y(0) = C_1 e^0 + C_2 e^0 = 3$
   $$C_1 + C_2 = 3 \qquad (A)$$

$$y' = C_1 e^x - C_2 e^{-x}$$
$$y'(0) = C_1 e^0 - C_2 e^0 = 1$$
$$C_1 - C_2 = 1 \qquad \text{(B)}$$

Solve (A) and (B) for C_1 and C_2:
$$C_1 = 2, \ C_2 = 1$$
Thus, the particular solution is $y = 2e^x + e^{-x}$.

11. $3y'' - 10y' + 3y = 0$; $y(0) = 1$, $y'(0) = -1$
$$3m^2 - 10m + 3 = 0 \quad \text{Characteristic equation}$$
$$(3m - 1)(m - 3) = 0$$
$$m_1 = \frac{1}{3}, \ m_2 = 3 \qquad \text{Roots of characteristic equation}$$

The general solution is:
$$y = C_1 e^{(1/3)x} + C_2 e^{3x}$$

Applying the initial conditions, $y(0) = 1$ and $y'(0) = -1$, we obtain the system of equations:
$$y(0) = C_1 + C_2 = 1 \qquad \text{(A)}$$
$$y' = \frac{C_1}{3} e^{(1/3)x} + 3C_2 e^{3x}$$
$$y'(0) = \frac{1}{3} C_1 + 3C_2 = -1$$
$$\text{or} \qquad C_1 + 9C_2 = -3 \qquad \text{(B)}$$

Solve for (A) and (B) for C_1, C_2:
$$C_2 = -\frac{1}{2}, \ C_1 = \frac{3}{2}$$
Thus, the particular solution is $y = \frac{3}{2} e^{(1/3)x} - \frac{1}{2} e^{3x}$.

13. $y'' + 2y' + y = 0$; $y(0) = 2$, $y'(0) = 4$
$$m^2 + 2m + 1 = 0 \quad \text{Characteristic equation}$$
$$(m + 1)^2 = 0$$
$m = -1$ Repeated root of the characteristic equation
The general solution is:
$$y = C_1 e^{-x} + C_2 x e^{-x}$$

Applying the initial conditions, $y(0) = 2$ and $y'(0) = 4$, we obtain the system of equations:
$$y(0) = C_1 + 0 = 2, \ C_1 = 2$$
$$y' = -C_1 e^{-x} + C_2(-xe^{-x} + e^{-x})$$
$$y'(0) = -C_1 + C_2(0 + 1) = 4$$
$$-C_1 + C_2 = 4$$
$$C_2 = 4 + C_1 = 6$$
Thus, the particular solution is $y = 2e^{-x} + 6xe^{-x}$.

15. $y'' - 3y' - 4y = 12$.

    <u>Step 1</u>: Find a constant function satisfying the nonhomogeneous equation.
        Let $y = k$, constant. Then $y' = y'' = 0$ and

$$y'' - 3y' - 4y = 12$$
$$0 - 3 \cdot 0 - 4k = 12$$
$$k = -3$$

        Thus, $y = -3$ is a solution of the nonhomogeneous equation.

    <u>Step 2</u>: Solve the associated homogeneous equation $y'' - 3y' - 4y = 0$.
        The characteristic equation is:

$$m^2 - 3m - 4 = 0$$
$$(m - 4)(m + 1) = 0$$
$$m_1 = 4 \text{ and } m_2 = -1 \text{ are the roots.}$$

        $y = C_1 e^{4x} + C_2 e^{-x}$ is the general solution of the homogeneous equation.

    <u>Step 3</u>: Add the solutions from Steps 1 and 2.

$$y = -3 + C_1 e^{4x} + C_2 e^{-x}$$

        This is the general solution of the given equation.

17. $y'' + y' - 2y = 6$; $y(0) = 0$, $y'(0) = 0$.
    First find the general solution of the differential equation.

    <u>Step 1</u>: Let $y = k$, constant. Then $y' = y'' = 0$ and

$$y'' + y' - 2y = 6$$
$$0 + 0 - 2k = 6$$
$$k = -3$$

        Thus, $y = -3$ is a solution of the nonhomogeneous equation.

    <u>Step 2</u>: $y'' + y' - 2y = 0$
        The characteristic equation is:

$$m^2 + m - 2 = 0$$
$$(m + 2)(m - 1) = 0$$
$$m_1 = -2 \text{ and } m_2 = 1 \text{ are the roots.}$$

        $y = C_1 e^{-2x} + C_2 e^{x}$ is the general solution of the associated homogeneous equation.

    <u>Step 3</u>: $y = -3 + C_1 e^{-2x} + C_2 e^{x}$ is the general solution of the given nonhomogeneous differential equation.

Now, applying the initial conditions $y(0) = 0$ and $y'(0) = 0$, we obtain the system of equations:

$$y(0) = -3 + C_1 + C_2 = 0$$
$$\text{or } C_1 + C_2 = 3 \quad (A)$$

$$y' = -2C_1 e^{-2x} + C_2 e^x$$
$$y'(0) = -2C_1 + C_2 = 0$$
$$\text{or } -2C_1 + C_2 = 0 \qquad \text{(B)}$$

Solve (A) and (B) for C_1 and C_2:

$$C_1 = 1, \ C_2 = 2$$

Thus, the particular solution is $y = -3 + e^{-2x} + 2e^x$.

19. $2y'' + y' = 1$

Step 1: Let $y = kx$, k constant. Then $y' = k$ and $y'' = 0$. Substituting into the differential equation, we have:
$$2y'' + y' = 1$$
$$2 \cdot 0 + k = 1$$
$$k = 1$$
Thus, $y = x$ is a solution of the nonhomogeneous equation.

Step 2: $2y'' + y' = 0$
The characteristic equation is:
$$2m^2 + m = 0$$
$$m(2m + 1) = 0$$
$m_1 = 0$ and $m_2 = -\frac{1}{2}$ are the roots.

$y = C_1 e^0 + C_2 e^{(-1/2)x} = C_1 + C_2 e^{(-1/2)x}$ is the general solution of the associated homogeneous equation.

Step 3: $y = x + C_1 + C_2 e^{(-1/2)x}$ is the general solution of the given nonhomogeneous differential equation.

21. $y'' - 2y' = 3$

Step 1: Let $y = kx$, k a constant. Then $y' = k$, $y'' = 0$. Substituting into the differential equation, we have:
$$y'' - 2y' = 3$$
$$0 - 2 \cdot k = 3$$
$$k = -\frac{3}{2}$$
Thus, $y = -\frac{3}{2}x$ is a solution of the nonhomogeneous equation.

Step 2: $y'' - 2y' = 0$
The characteristic equation is:
$$m^2 - 2m = 0$$
$$m(m - 2) = 0$$
$m_1 = 0$ and $m_2 = 2$ are the roots.

$y = C_1 e^{0x} + C_2 e^{2x} = C_1 + C_2 e^{2x}$ is the general solution of the associated homogeneous equation.

Step 3: $y = -\frac{3}{2}x + C_1 + C_2 e^{2x}$ is the general solution of the given nonhomogeneous differential equation.

23. $y'' - 8y' + 16y = 0$; $y(0) = 1$, $y(1) = e^4$

$m^2 - 8m + 16 = 0$ Characteristic equation

$(m - 4)^2 = 0$

$m = 4$ Repeated root of the characteristic equation

The general solution is:

$y = C_1 e^{4x} + C_2 x e^{4x}$

Applying the boundary conditions, we obtain the system of equations:

$y(0) = 1 = C_1 e^0 + C_2 0 e^0$

$C_1 = 1$

$y(1) = e^4 = C_1 e^4 + C_2 e^4$

$e^4 = e^4 + C_2 e^4$

$C_2 = 0$

Thus, the particular solution is: $y = e^{4x}$

25. $2y'' - 5y' + 2y = 0$; $y(0) = 0$, $y(2) = e^4 - e$

$2m^2 - 5m + 2 = 0$ Characteristic equation

$(2m - 1)(m - 2) = 0$

$m_1 = \frac{1}{2}$, $m_2 = 2$ Roots of characteristic equation

The general solution is:

$y = C_1 e^{x/2} + C_2 e^{2x}$

Applying the boundary conditions, we obtain the system of equations:

$y(0) = 0 = C_1 e^0 + C_2 e^0$

$C_1 + C_2 = 0$ (1)

$y(2) = e^4 - e = C_1 e + C_2 e^4$

$C_1 e + C_2 e^4 = e^4 - e$ (2)

Solving (1) and (2) for C_1 and C_2, we get $C_1 = -1$ and $C_2 = 1$.

Therefore, the particular solution is:

$y = e^{2x} - e^{x/2}$.

27. $y'' + y = 0$

$m^2 + 1 = 0$ Characteristic equation

$m_1 = i$, $m_2 = -i$ Imaginary roots of the characteristic equation

Therefore, by <u>3</u>(c), the general solution is:

$y = e^{0x}(C_1 \cos x + C_2 \sin x)$ or $y = C_1 \cos x + C_2 \sin x$

29. $y'' - 4y' + 13y = 0$

$\qquad m^2 - 4m + 13 = 0$ Characteristic equation

$\qquad m = \dfrac{4 \pm \sqrt{16 - 4(13)}}{2}$ $\left(\text{using the quadratic equation formula: } \dfrac{-b \pm \sqrt{b^2 - 4ac}}{2a}\right)$

$\qquad = \dfrac{4 \pm \sqrt{-36}}{2} = \dfrac{4 \pm 6i}{2}$

$\qquad m = 2 \pm 3i$

$\qquad m_1 = 2 + 3i, \; m_2 = 2 - 3i$ Imaginary roots of the characteristic equation

By 3(c), the general solution is:

$y = e^{2x}(C_1 \cos 3x + C_2 \sin 3x)$

31. Set $S = D$.

$\qquad 3 + 0.2p' - 0.05p - p'' = 2 + 0.8p' - 0.01p + p''$

$\qquad 2p'' + 0.6p' + 0.04p = 1$

This is a nonhomogeneous equation.

Step 1: Let $p = k$, constant. Then $p' = p'' = 0$ and

$\qquad\qquad 2p'' + 0.6p' + 0.04p = 1$

$\qquad\qquad 2(0) + 0.6(0) + 0.04k = 1$

$\qquad\qquad\qquad\qquad\qquad k = 25$

$\qquad$ Thus, $p = 25$ is a solution of the nonhomogeneous equation.

Step 2: $2p'' + 0.6p' + 0.04p = 0$

$\qquad$ The characteristic equation is:

$\qquad\qquad 2m^2 + 0.6m + 0.04 = 0$

$\qquad\qquad m^2 + 0.3m + 0.02 = 0$

$\qquad\qquad (m + 0.2)(m + 0.1) = 0$

$\qquad\qquad m_1 = -0.2$ and $m_2 = -0.1$ are the roots.

$\qquad$ Thus, the general solution of the associated homogeneous equation is:

$\qquad\qquad p = C_1 e^{-0.2t} + C_2 e^{-0.1t}$

Step 3: $p = 25 + C_1 e^{-0.2t} + C_2 e^{-0.1t}$ is the general solution of the given nonhomogeneous differential equation.

Applying the initial conditions, $p(0) = 75$ and $p'(0) = -15$, we obtain the system of equations:

$p(0) = C_1 + C_2 + 25 = 75$

$\qquad\qquad C_1 + C_2 = 50 \qquad\qquad (1)$

$\qquad p' = -0.1C_2 e^{-0.1t} - 0.2C_1 e^{-0.2t}$

$p'(0) = -0.1C_2 - 0.2C_1 = -15.$ Multiply by -10.

$\qquad\qquad C_2 + 2C_1 = 150 \qquad (2)$

Solving (1) and (2) for C_1 and C_2, we get $C_2 = -50$ and $C_1 = 100$. Thus, the particular solution is:

Equilibrium price: $p_e(t) = -50e^{-0.1t} + 100e^{-0.2t} + 25$

$$\bar{p} = \lim_{t \to \infty} p_e(t) = -\lim_{t \to \infty} 50e^{-0.1t} + \lim_{t \to \infty} 100e^{-0.2t} + \lim_{t \to \infty} 25$$
$$= \quad 0 \quad + \quad 0 \quad + \quad 25 = 25$$

and $\bar{p} = 25$ is the long-range equilibrium price.

33. $y'' + 5y' + 4y = 8$

Step 1: Let $y = k$, constant. Then $y' = y'' = 0$ and
$$y'' + 5y' + 4y = 8$$
$$0 + 5 \cdot 0 + 4k = 8$$
$$k = 2$$
Thus, $y = 2$ is a solution of the nonhomogeneous equation.

Step 2: $y'' + 5y' + 4y = 0$

The characteristic equation is:
$$m^2 + 5m + 4 = 0$$
$$(m + 4)(m + 1) = 0$$
$m_1 = -4$ and $m_2 = -1$ are the roots.

Thus, the general solution of the associated homogeneous equation is:
$$y = C_1 e^{-4t} + C_2 e^{-t}$$

Step 3: $y = 2 + C_1 e^{-4t} + C_2 e^{-t}$ is the general solution of the given nonhomogeneous differential equation.

Applying the initial conditions, $y(0) = 1$ and $y'(0) = 1$, we obtain the system of equations:
$$y(0) = C_1 + C_2 + 2 = 1 \quad \text{or} \quad C_1 + C_2 = -1 \qquad (1)$$
$$y' = -4C_1 e^{-4t} - C_2 e^{-t}$$
$$y'(0) = -4C_1 - C_2 = 1 \quad \text{or} \quad 4C_1 + C_2 = -1 \qquad (2)$$

Solving (1) and (2), we get $C_1 = 0$ and $C_2 = -1$. Thus, the particular solution is:
$$y = 0 - e^{-t} + 2 \quad \text{or} \quad y(t) = 2 - e^{-t}$$
$$\lim_{t \to \infty} y(t) = \lim_{t \to \infty} (2 - e^{-t}) = 2$$

EXERCISE 7-5

Things to remember:

1. A pair of differential equations of the form

$$\frac{dx}{dt} = ax + by \qquad \frac{dy}{dt} = cx + dy$$

where $x(t)$ and $y(t)$ are unknown functions and a, b, c, and d are constants, is called a FIRST-ORDER LINEAR SYSTEM OF DIFFERENTIAL EQUATIONS.

2. The system in 1 can be solved by eliminating one of the unknown functions (variables) in the same way that systems of linear algebraic equations are solved.

---

1. $\dfrac{dx}{dt} = -x + y$ (1)

$\dfrac{dy}{dt} = 2x$ (2)

Differentiating (1) with respect to t, we obtain:

$\dfrac{d^2x}{dt^2} = -\dfrac{dx}{dt} + \dfrac{dy}{dt}$ and $\dfrac{dy}{dt} = \dfrac{d^2x}{dt^2} + \dfrac{dx}{dt}$. Substititute into (2).

$\dfrac{d^2x}{dt^2} + \dfrac{dx}{dt} = 2x$

$\dfrac{d^2x}{dt^2} + \dfrac{dx}{dt} - 2x = 0$ This is a second-order linear homogeneous equation (in x and t)

$m^2 + m - 2 = 0$ Characteristic equation

$(m - 1)(m + 2) = 0$

$m_1 = 1, \; m_2 = -2$ Roots of characteristic equation

Thus,

$x = C_1 e^t + C_2 e^{-2t}$.

To determine y, we find $\dfrac{dx}{dt}$: $\dfrac{dx}{dt} = C_1 e^t - 2C_2 e^{-2t}$, and substitute $\dfrac{dx}{dt}$ and x into (1):

$C_1 e^t - 2C_2 e^{-2t} = -(C_1 e^t + C_2 e^{-2t}) + y$

$\qquad\qquad y = 2C_1 e^t - C_2 e^{-2t}$

Thus, the general solution of the system is: $x = C_1 e^t + C_2 e^{-2t}$

$\qquad\qquad\qquad\qquad\qquad\qquad\qquad\qquad\qquad\quad y = 2C_1 e^t - C_2 e^{-2t}$

3. $\dfrac{dx}{dt} = 2x - y$ (1)

$\dfrac{dy}{dt} = 3x - 2y$ (2) $x(0) = 1, \; y(0) = -1$

Differentiating (1) with respect to t, we obtain:

$\dfrac{d^2x}{dt^2} = 2\dfrac{dx}{dt} - \dfrac{dy}{dt}$ (3)

Substituting $\dfrac{dy}{dt}$ and y from (2) and (1), respectively, into (3), we have:

$\dfrac{d^2x}{dt^2} = 2\dfrac{dx}{dt} - (3x - 2y)$

$\dfrac{d^2x}{dt^2} = 2\dfrac{dx}{dt} - 3x + 2\left(2x - \dfrac{dx}{dt}\right)$

$\dfrac{d^2x}{dt^2} = x$

$\dfrac{d^2x}{dt^2} - x = 0$ Second-order linear homogeneous equation

$$m^2 - 1 = 0 \quad \text{Characteristic equation}$$
$$(m - 1)(m + 1) = 0$$
$$m_1 = 1, \ m_2 = -1 \qquad \text{Roots of characteristic equation}$$

Thus,

$$x = C_1 e^t + C_2 e^{-t} \quad \text{and} \quad \frac{dx}{dt} = C_1 e^t - C_2 e^{-t}.$$

Substituting x and $\frac{dx}{dt}$ into (1), we get:

$$C_1 e^t - C_2 e^{-t} = 2(C_1 e^t + C_2 e^{-t}) - y$$
$$y = C_1 e^t + 3C_2 e^{-t}$$

Thus, the general solution of the system is: $x = C_1 e^t + C_2 e^{-t}$
$$y = C_1 e^t + 3C_2 e^{-t}$$

We now apply the initial conditions, $x(0) = 1$ and $y(0) = -1$, and solve for C_1 and C_2:

$$x(0) = C_1 + C_2 = 1$$
$$y(0) = C_1 + 3C_2 = -1 \quad C_1 = 2 \quad \text{and} \quad C_2 = -1$$

Thus, the particular solution is: $x = 2e^t - e^{-t}$
$$y = 2e^t - 3e^{-t}$$

5. $\frac{dx}{dt} = 2x + y \qquad (1) \qquad x(0) = 2, \ y(0) = -1$

$\frac{dy}{dt} = 2x + y \qquad (2)$

Differentiating (1) with respect to t, we obtain:

$$\frac{d^2 x}{dt^2} = 2\frac{dx}{dt} + \frac{dy}{dt} \qquad (3)$$

Substituting $\frac{dy}{dt}$ and y from (2) and (1), respectively, into (3), we have:

$$\frac{d^2 x}{dt^2} = 2\frac{dx}{dt} + \left[2x + \left(\frac{dx}{dt} - 2x \right) \right]$$

$$\frac{d^2 x}{dt^2} = 3\frac{dx}{dt} \quad \text{and} \quad \frac{d^2 x}{dt^2} - 3\frac{dx}{dt} = 0$$

$$m^2 - 3m = 0 \qquad \text{Characteristic equation}$$
$$m(m - 3) = 0$$
$$m_1 = 0, \ m_2 = 3 \quad \text{Roots of characteristic equation}$$

Thus,

$$x = C_1 e^0 + C_2 e^{3t} = C_1 + C_2 e^{3t}.$$

Also, $\frac{dx}{dt} = 3C_2 e^{3t}.$

Substituting x and $\frac{dx}{dt}$ into (1), we have

$$3C_2 e^{3t} = 2(C_1 + C_2 e^{3t}) + y,$$

so that $y = -2C_1 + C_2 e^{3t}$. Thus, the general solution of the system is:

$$x = C_1 + C_2 e^{3t}$$
$$y = -2C_1 + C_2 e^{3t}$$

Applying the initial conditions $x(0) = 2$ and $y(0) = -1$, we obtain the system of equations:

$x(0) = 2 = C_1 + C_2$

$y(0) = -1 = -2C_1 + C_2$

The solution of this system is $C_1 = 1$, $C_2 = 1$. Therefore, the particular solution of the system of differential equations is:

$x = e^{3t} + 1$

$y = e^{3t} - 2$

7. $\dfrac{dx}{dt} = -2x + y$ (1)

$\dfrac{dy}{dt} = -3x + 2y$ (2)

Differentiating (1) with respect to t yields:

$\dfrac{d^2 x}{dt^2} = -2\dfrac{dx}{dt} + \dfrac{dy}{dt}$ (3)

Substitute $\dfrac{dy}{dt}$ and y from (2) and (1), respectively, into (3):

$\dfrac{d^2 x}{dt^2} = -2\dfrac{dx}{dt} + \left[-3x + 2\left(\dfrac{dx}{dt} + 2x\right)\right]$

$\dfrac{d^2 x}{dt^2} = x$

$\dfrac{d^2 x}{dt^2} - x = 0$

$m^2 - 1 = 0$ Characteristic equation

$(m - 1)(m + 1) = 0$

$m_1 = 1, \ m_2 = -1$ Roots of characteristic equation

Thus,

$x = C_1 e^t + C_2 e^{-t}$.

Also, $\dfrac{dx}{dt} = C_1 e^t - C_2 e^{-t}$. Substituting x and $\dfrac{dx}{dt}$ into (1), we have

$C_1 e^t - C_2 e^{-t} = -2(C_1 e^t + C_2 e^{-t}) + y$,

so that

$y = 3C_1 e^t + C_2 e^{-t}$.

Therefore, the general solution of the system is: $x = C_1 e^t + C_2 e^{-t}$

$y = 3C_1 e^t + C_2 e^{-t}$

9. $x' = 5x - 3y + 2$ (1)

$y' = 6x - 4y + 4$ (2)

Differentiating (1) with respect to t yields:

$x'' = 5x' - 3y'$ (3)

Substitute y' and y from (2) and (1), respectively, into (3):

$x'' = 5x' - 3\left[6x - 4\left(-\dfrac{x'}{3} + \dfrac{5x}{3} + \dfrac{2}{3}\right) + 4\right]$

$x'' = 5x' - 18x - 4x' + 20x + 8 - 12$

or

$x'' - x' - 2x = -4$ (4)   A second-order linear nonhomogeneous equation.

Step 1: Let $x = k$, constant. Then $x' = x'' = 0$. Thus,

$$x'' - x' - 2x = -4$$
$$0 - 0 - 2k = -4$$
$$k = 2$$

Therefore, $x = 2$ is a solution of the nonhomogeneous equation.

Step 2: Consider the associated homogeneous equation $x'' - x' - 2x = 0$:

$$m^2 - m - 2 = 0 \qquad \text{Characteristic equation}$$
$$(m - 2)(m + 1) = 0$$
$$m_1 = 2, \ m_2 = -1 \qquad \text{Roots of the characteristic equation}$$

Thus, $x = C_1 e^{2t} + C_2 e^{-t}$.

Step 3: $x = 2 + C_1 e^{2t} + C_2 e^{-t}$ is the general solution of the nonhomogeneous equation (4).

Now, $x = C_1 e^{2t} + C_2 e^{-t} + 2$ and $x' = 2C_1 e^{2t} - C_2 e^{-t}$. Substituting x and x' into (1), we have:

$$2C_1 e^{2t} - C_2 e^{-t} = 5(C_1 e^{2t} + C_2 e^{-t} + 2) - 3y + 2$$
$$3y = 3C_1 e^{2t} + 6C_2 e^{-t} + 12$$
$$y = C_1 e^{2t} + 2C_2 e^{-t} + 4$$

Therefore, the general solution of the system is: $x = C_1 e^{2t} + C_2 e^{-t} + 2$

$$y = C_1 e^{2t} + 2C_2 e^{-t} + 4$$

11. $\dfrac{dp}{dt} = -4p + q + 260$ (1)

$\dfrac{dq}{dt} = -2p - q + 250$ (2)

Differentiate (1) with respect to t:

$$\frac{d^2 p}{dt^2} = -4\frac{dp}{dt} + \frac{dq}{dt}$$

Substitute $\dfrac{dq}{dt}$ from (2):

$$\frac{d^2 p}{dt^2} = -4\frac{dp}{dt} - 2p - q + 250$$

Substitute q from (1):

$$\frac{d^2 p}{dt^2} = -4\frac{dp}{dt} - 2p - \left[\frac{dp}{dt} + 4p - 260\right] + 250$$

$$\frac{d^2 p}{dt^2} + 5\frac{dp}{dt} + 6p = 510 \qquad (3)$$

This is a second-order linear nonhomogeneous equation.

Step 1: Let $p = k$, constant. Then $\frac{dp}{dt} = \frac{d^2p}{dt^2} = 0$ and

$$\frac{d^2p}{dt^2} + 5\frac{dp}{dt} + 6p = 510$$
$$0 + 5\cdot 0 + 6k = 510$$
$$k = 85$$

Thus, $p = 85$ is a solution of the nonhomogeneous equation (3).

Step 2: Consider the associated homogeneous equation:

$$\frac{d^2p}{dt^2} + 5\frac{dp}{dt} + 6p = 0$$

$$m^2 + 5m + 6 = 0 \qquad \text{Characteristic equation}$$
$$(m + 3)(m + 2) = 0$$
$$m_1 = -3, \ m_2 = -2 \qquad \text{Roots of the characteristic equation}$$

Thus, $p = C_1 e^{-3t} + C_2 e^{-2t}$.

Step 3: $p = C_1 e^{-3t} + C_2 e^{-2t} + 85$ is the general solution of the nonhomogeneous equation (3).

Now $p = C_1 e^{-3t} + C_2 e^{-2t} + 85$ and $\frac{dp}{dt} = -3C_1 e^{-3t} - 2C_2 e^{-2t}$.

Substituting p and $\frac{dp}{dt}$ into (1) we get:

$$-3C_1 e^{-3t} - 2C_2 e^{-2t} = -4(C_1 e^{-3t} + C_2 e^{-2t} + 85) + q + 260$$
$$q = C_1 e^{-3t} + 2C_2 e^{-2t} + 80$$

Therefore, the general solution of the system is:

$$p = C_1 e^{-3t} + C_2 e^{-2t} + 85$$
$$q = C_1 e^{-3t} + 2C_2 e^{-2t} + 80$$

Applying the initial conditions, $p(0) = 100$ and $q(0) = 100$, we obtain the system of equations:

$$p(0) = C_1 + C_2 + 85 = 100 \quad \text{or} \quad C_1 + C_2 = 15$$
$$q(0) = C_1 + 2C_2 + 80 = 100 \quad \text{or} \quad C_1 + 2C_2 = 20$$

The solution of this system is $C_1 = 10$, $C_2 = 5$. The particular solution of the system of differential equations is:

$$p = 10e^{-3t} + 5e^{-2t} + 85$$
$$q = 10e^{-3t} + 10e^{-2t} + 80$$

To determine the behavior of p and q for large values of t, first note that

$$p' = -30e^{-3t} - 10e^{-2t} < 0 \quad \text{for all } t,$$
$$q' = -30e^{-3t} - 20e^{-2t} < 0 \quad \text{for all } t.$$

Thus, p and q are both decreasing functions. Furthermore,

$$\lim_{t\to\infty} p = \lim_{t\to\infty} (10e^{-3t} + 5e^{-2t} + 85) = 85,$$

and

$$\lim_{t\to\infty} q = \lim_{t\to\infty} (10e^{-3t} + 10e^{-2t} + 80) = 80.$$

Thus, p decreases to the limiting value of 85 and q decreases to the limiting value of 80.

13. $\dfrac{dx}{dt} = y - 5x$ (1) $x(0) = 50, \; y(0) = 0$

$\dfrac{dy}{dt} = x - 5y$ (2)

Differentiating (1) with respect to t yields

$$\dfrac{d^2 x}{dt^2} = \dfrac{dy}{dt} - 5\dfrac{dx}{dt} \qquad (3)$$

Substitute $\dfrac{dy}{dt}$ and y from (2) and (1), respectively, into (3):

$$\dfrac{d^2 x}{dt^2} = x - 5\left(\dfrac{dx}{dt} + 5x\right) - 5\dfrac{dx}{dt}$$

$$\dfrac{d^2 x}{dt^2} + 10\dfrac{dx}{dt} + 24x = 0$$

$m^2 + 10m + 24 = 0$ Characteristic equation

$(m + 4)(m + 6) = 0$

$m_1 = -4, \; m_2 = -6$ Roots of characteristic equation

Thus, $x = C_1 e^{-4t} + C_2 e^{-6t}$.   Also, $\dfrac{dx}{dt} = -4C_1 e^{-4t} - 6C_2 e^{-6t}$.

Substituting $\dfrac{dx}{dt}$ and x into (1), we have:

$$-4C_1 e^{-4t} - 6C_2 e^{-6t} = y - 5(C_1 e^{-4t} + C_2 e^{-6t})$$

$$y = C_1 e^{-4t} - C_2 e^{-6t}$$

Therefore, the general solution of the system of differential equations is:

$x = C_1 e^{-4t} + C_2 e^{-6t}$

$y = C_1 e^{-4t} - C_2 e^{-6t}$

Applying the initial conditions, $x(0) = 50$ and $y(0) = 0$, we obtain:

$x(0) = C_1 + C_2 = 50$

$y(0) = C_1 - C_2 = 0$ $C_1 = 25$ and $C_2 = 25$

Thus, the particular solution is: $x = 25e^{-4t} + 25e^{-6t}$

$$y = 25e^{-4t} - 25e^{-6t}$$

Finally,

$x(0.1) = 25e^{-0.4} + 25e^{-0.6} = 30.5$ units   [<u>Note</u>: 6 minutes = 0.1 hour.]

$y(0.1) = 25e^{-0.4} - 25e^{-0.6} = 3.0$ units

$x(0.5) = 25e^{-2} + 25e^{-3} = 4.6$ units

$y(0.5) = 25e^{-2} - 25e^{-3} = 2.1$ units

$x(1.0) = 25e^{-4} + 25e^{-6} = 0.5$ units

$y(1.0) = 25e^{-4} - 25e^{-6} = 0.4$ units

15. From Problem 11, the particular solution is:
$$p = 10e^{-3t} + 5e^{-2t} + 85$$
$$q = 10e^{-3t} + 10e^{-2t} + 80$$
The graphs of these functions for $0 \leq t \leq 2$ and $80 \leq p$, $q \leq 100$ are:

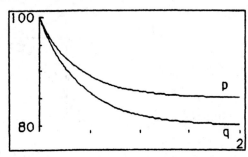

17. From Problem 13, the particular solution is:
$$x = 25e^{-4t} + 25e^{-6t}$$
$$y = 25e^{-4t} - 25e^{-6t}$$
The graphs of these functions for $0 \leq t \leq 1$, $0 \leq x$, $y \leq 50$ are:

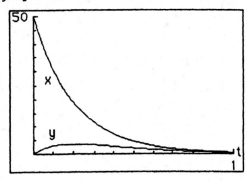

EXERCISE 7-6   CHAPTER REVIEW

1. $y = C\sqrt{x}$; $2xy' = y$

Substituting $y = C\sqrt{x} = Cx^{1/2}$ and $y' = \frac{1}{2}Cx^{-1/2}$

into the differential equation yields

$$2x\left(\frac{1}{2}Cx^{-1/2}\right) = Cx^{1/2}$$
$$Cx^{1/2} = Cx^{1/2}.$$

Thus, $y = C\sqrt{x}$ is the general solution of the differential equation.

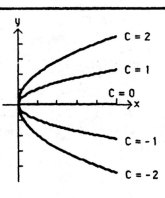

2. $y = 1 + Ce^{-x}$; $y' + y = 1$

Substituting $y = 1 + Ce^{-x}$, $y' = -Ce^{-x}$
into the differential equation yields:

$-Ce^{-x} + 1 + Ce^{-x} = 1$
$$1 = 1$$

Thus, $y = 1 + Ce^{-x}$ is the general
solution of the differential equation.

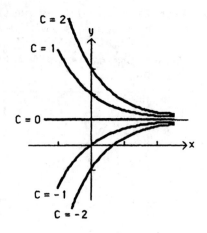

3. $y' = -\dfrac{4y}{x}$

$\dfrac{y'}{y} = \dfrac{-4}{x}$ Separate the variables

$\displaystyle\int \dfrac{dy}{y} = \int \dfrac{-4}{x}\,dx$

$\ln|y| = -4\ln|x| + C = \ln x^{-4} + C$

$\quad y = e^{\ln x^{-4}+C}$

$\quad\quad = e^C e^{\ln x^{-4}}$

$\quad y = Ax^{-4} = \dfrac{A}{x^4}$ *General solution*

4. $y' = \dfrac{-4y}{x} + x$

$y' + \dfrac{4}{x}y = x$ First-order linear equation

Integrating factor: $I(x) = e^{\int f(x)\,dx} = e^{\int (4/x)\,dx} = e^{4\ln x} = e^{\ln x^4} = x^4$

Therefore,

$y = \dfrac{1}{I(x)} \displaystyle\int I(x)g(x)\,dx, \ g(x) = x$

$\quad = \dfrac{1}{x^4}\displaystyle\int x^4 x\,dx = \dfrac{1}{x^4}\int x^5\,dx = \dfrac{1}{x^4}\left[\dfrac{x^6}{6} + C\right]$

$y = \dfrac{x^2}{6} + \dfrac{C}{x^4}$ *General solution*

5. $y' = 3x^2 y^2$

$\dfrac{y'}{y^2} = 3x^2$ Separate the variables

$\displaystyle\int \dfrac{dy}{y^2} = \int 3x^2\,dx$

$-\dfrac{1}{y} = x^3 + C$

$\quad y = \dfrac{-1}{x^3 + C}$ *General solution*

6. $y' = 2y - e^x$

$y' - 2y = -e^x$ First-order linear equation

Integrating factor: $I(x) = e^{\int (-2)\,dx} = e^{-2x}$

$$y = \frac{1}{I(x)} \int I(x)g(x)\,dx, \qquad g(x) = -e^x$$

$$= \frac{1}{e^{-2x}} \int e^{-2x}(-e^x)\,dx = e^{2x} \int -e^{-x}\,dx = e^{2x}[e^{-x} + C]$$

$$y = e^x + Ce^{2x} \qquad \textit{General solution}$$

7. $y' = \frac{5}{x}y + x^6$

$y' - \frac{5}{x}y = x^6 \qquad$ First-order linear equation

Integrating factor: $I(x) = e^{\int(-5/x)\,dx} = e^{-5\ln x} = e^{\ln x^{-5}} = x^{-5}$

$$y = \frac{1}{I(x)} \int I(x)g(x)\,dx, \quad g(x) = x^6$$

$$= \frac{1}{x^{-5}} \int x^{-5}x^6\,dx = x^5 \int x\,dx = x^5\left[\frac{x^2}{2} + C\right]$$

$$y = \frac{x^7}{2} + Cx^5 \qquad \textit{General solution}$$

8. $y' = \frac{3 + y}{2 + x}$

$\dfrac{y'}{3 + y} = \dfrac{1}{2 + x} \qquad$ Separate the variables

$$\int \frac{dy}{3 + y} = \int \frac{dx}{2 + x}$$

$\ln|3 + y| = \ln(2 + x) + C \qquad$ (<u>Note</u>: $2 + x > 0$.)

$3 + y = e^{\ln(2+x)+C} = e^C(2 + x) = A(2 + x)$

$y = A(2 + x) - 3 \qquad \textit{General solution}$

9. $y'' - 4y' - 21y = 0 \qquad$ Second-order linear homogeneous equation

$m^2 - 4m - 21 = 0 \qquad$ Characteristic equation

$(m - 7)(m + 3) = 0$

$m_1 = 7, \ m_2 = -3 \qquad$ Roots of characteristic equation

Therefore, $y = C_1 e^{7x} + C_2 e^{-3x}$. $\quad$ *General solution*

10. $y'' + 12y' + 36y = 0$

$m^2 + 12m + 36 = 0 \qquad$ Characteristic equation

$(m + 6)^2 = 0$

$m = -6 \qquad$ Repeated root of the characteristic equation

Therefore, $y = C_1 e^{-6x} + C_2 x e^{-6x} \qquad$ *General solution*

11. $y' = 10 - y; \ y(0) = 0$

$\dfrac{y'}{10 - y} = 1 \qquad$ Separate the variables

$$\int \frac{dy}{10 - y} = \int dx$$

$-\ln|10 - y| = x + C$

$\ln|10 - y| = -x - C$

$10 - y = e^{-x-C}$

$$= e^{-C}e^{-x} = Ae^{-x}$$

$y = 10 - Ae^{-x}$. *General solution*

Applying the initial condition $y(0) = 0$, we have:

$0 = 10 - Ae^0$, $A = 10$

Thus, $y = 10 - 10e^{-x}$. *Particular solution*

12. $y' + y = x$; $y(0) = 0$

Integrating factor: $I(x) = e^{\int 1\,dx} = e^x$

Thus, $y = \dfrac{1}{I(x)} \int I(x)g(x)\,dx$, $g(x) = x$

$$= \frac{1}{e^x} \int e^x x\,dx = e^{-x} \int x e^x dx = e^{-x}[xe^x - e^x + C]$$

$y = x - 1 + Ce^{-x}$. *General solution*

Applying the initial condition $y(0) = 0$, we have:

$0 = 0 - 1 + Ce^0$, $C = 1$

Therefore, $y = x - 1 + e^{-x}$. *Particular solution*

13. $y' = 2ye^{-x}$; $y(0) = 1$

$\dfrac{y'}{y} = 2e^{-x}$ Separate the variables

$$\int \frac{dy}{y} = \int 2e^{-x}dx$$

$\ln|y| = -2e^{-x} + C$

$y = e^{-2e^{-x}+C} = e^0 e^{-2e^{-x}}$

$y = Ae^{-2e^{-x}}$ *General solution*

Applying the initial condition $y(0) = 1$, we have:

$1 = Ae^{-2e^0} = Ae^{-2}$, $A = e^2$

Thus, $y = e^2 e^{-2e^{-x}}$. *Particular solution*

14. $y' = \dfrac{2x - y}{x + 4}$; $y(0) = 1$

$y' + \dfrac{1}{x + 4}y = \dfrac{2x}{x + 4}$ First-order linear equation

Integrating factor: $I(x) = e^{\int (1/(x+4))dx} = e^{\ln(x+4)} = x + 4$

Thus, $y = \dfrac{1}{I(x)} \int I(x)g(x)\,dx$, $g(x) = \dfrac{2x}{x + 4}$

$$= \frac{1}{x + 4} \int (x + 4)\frac{2x}{x + 4}\,dx = \frac{1}{x + 4} \int 2x\,dx = \frac{1}{x + 4}[x^2 + C]$$

$y = \dfrac{x^2}{x + 4} + \dfrac{C}{x + 4}$.   *General solution*

Applying the initial condition $y(0) = 1$, we have:

$1 = 0 + \dfrac{C}{4}$, $C = 4$

Therefore, $y = \dfrac{x^2}{x + 4} + \dfrac{4}{x + 4} = \dfrac{x^2 + 4}{x + 4}$. *Particular solution*

15. $y' = \dfrac{x}{y+4}$; $y(0) = 0$

$(y+4)y' = x$ Separate the variables

$\displaystyle\int (y+4)\,dy = \int x\,dx$

$$\dfrac{(y+4)^2}{2} = \dfrac{x^2}{2} + C$$

$(y+4)^2 = x^2 + 2C$

or $(y+4)^2 = x^2 + A.$ *General solution, implicit form*

Solving for y and applying the initial condition $y(0) = 0$, we have:

$y + 4 = \sqrt{x^2 + A}$

$0 + 4 = \sqrt{0 + A}$

$A = 16$

Therefore, $y = \sqrt{x^2 + 16} - 4.$ *Particular solution*

16. $y' + \dfrac{2}{x}y = \ln x$; $y(1) = 2$

Integrating factor: $I(x) = e^{\int (2/x)\,dx} = e^{2\ln x} = e^{\ln x^2} = x^2$

Thus, $y = \dfrac{1}{I(x)} \displaystyle\int I(x)g(x)\,dx, \quad g(x) = \ln x$

$\qquad = \dfrac{1}{x^2} \displaystyle\int x^2 \ln x\,dx$ (Integrate by parts)

$\qquad = \dfrac{1}{x^2}\left[\dfrac{1}{3}x^3 \ln x - \dfrac{x^3}{9} + C \right]$

$y = \dfrac{1}{3}x \ln x - \dfrac{x}{9} + \dfrac{C}{x^2}.$ *General solution*

Applying the initial condition $y(1) = 2$, we have:

$2 = \dfrac{1}{3}(1)\ln 1 - \dfrac{1}{9} + C, \quad C = \dfrac{19}{9}$

Therefore, $y = \dfrac{1}{3}x \ln x - \dfrac{x}{9} + \dfrac{19}{9x^2}.$ *Particular solution*

17. $yy' = \dfrac{x(1+y^2)}{1+x^2}$; $y(0) = 1$

$\dfrac{yy'}{1+y^2} = \dfrac{x}{1+x^2}$ Separate the variables

$\displaystyle\int \dfrac{y\,dy}{1+y^2} = \int \dfrac{x\,dx}{1+x^2}$

$\dfrac{1}{2}\ln(1+y^2) = \dfrac{1}{2}\ln(1+x^2) + C$

$\ln(1+y^2) = \ln(1+x^2) + 2C$

$1 + y^2 = e^{\ln(1+x^2)+2C}$

$\qquad = e^{2C}e^{\ln(1+x^2)}$

$\qquad = A(1+x^2)$

$y^2 = A(1+x^2) - 1.$ *General solution, implicit form*

Solving this equation for y and applying the initial condition $y(0) = 1$, we have:

$$y = \sqrt{A(1 + x^2) - 1}$$
$$1 = \sqrt{A - 1}$$
$$A - 1 = 1$$
$$A = 2$$

Thus, $y = \sqrt{2(1 + x^2) - 1} = \sqrt{1 + 2x^2}$.   *Particular solution*

18. $y' + 2xy = 2e^{-x^2}$; $y(0) = 1$

Integrating factor: $I(x) = e^{\int 2x\,dx} = e^{x^2}$

Thus, $y = \frac{1}{I(x)} \int I(x)g(x)\,dx$, $g(x) = 2e^{-x^2}$

$$= \frac{1}{e^{x^2}} \int e^{x^2} 2e^{-x^2}\,dx = e^{-x^2} \int 2\,dx = e^{-x^2}[2x + C]$$

$$y = 2xe^{-x^2} + Ce^{-x^2}.$$ *General solution*

Applying the initial condition $y(0) = 1$, we have:

$$1 = 2 \cdot 0 \cdot e^0 + Ce^0, \quad C = 1$$

Therefore, $y = 2xe^{-x^2} + e^{-x^2} = (2x + 1)e^{-x^2}$.   *Particular solution.*

19. $y'' + 4y' = 0$; $y(0) = 1$, $y'(0) = -2$

$m^2 + 4m = 0$ Characteristic equation

$m(m + 4) = 0$

$m_1 = 0$, $m_2 = -4$ Roots of characteristic equation

Thus, $y = C_1 e^{0x} + C_2 e^{-4x} = C_1 + C_2 e^{-4x}$.   *General solution*

Applying the initial conditions, $y(0) = 1$ and $y'(0) = -2$, we obtain the system of equations:

$$y(0) = 1 = C_1 + C_2 \quad (1)$$
$$y' = -4C_2 e^{-4x}$$
$$y'(0) = -2 = -4C_2 \quad (2)$$

Solving (1) and (2) for C_1 and C_2, we get $C_1 = \frac{1}{2}$ and $C_2 = \frac{1}{2}$.

Thus, $y = \frac{1}{2} + \frac{1}{2}e^{-4x}$.   *Particular solution*

20. $y'' - 16y = 16$; $y(0) = 1$, $y'(0) = 0$

$y'' - 16y = 16$ Second-order linear nonhomogeneous equation

Step 1: Let $y = k$, constant. Then $y' = y'' = 0$ and

$$y'' - 16y = 16$$
$$0 - 16k = 16$$
$$k = -1$$

Thus, $y = -1$ is a solution of the nonhomogeneous equation.

Step 2: Consider the associated homogeneous equation $y'' - 16y = 0$.

$$m^2 - 16 = 0$$ Characteristic equation

$$(m - 4)(m + 4) = 0$$

$$m_1 = 4, \quad m_2 = -4 \qquad \text{Roots of the characteristic equation}$$

Thus, $y = C_1 e^{4x} + C_2 e^{-4x}$.

Step 3: $y = C_1 e^{4x} + C_2 e^{-4x} - 1$ is the general solution of the nonhomogeneous equation.

Applying the initial conditions, $y(0) = 1$ and $y'(0) = 0$, we obtain the system of equations:

$$y(0) = 1 = C_1 e^0 + C_2 e^0 - 1$$
$$C_1 + C_2 = 2 \qquad (1)$$

$$y'(x) = 4C_1 e^{4x} - 4C_2 e^{-4x}$$
$$y'(0) = 0 = 4C_1 e^0 - 4C_2 e^0$$
$$C_1 - C_2 = 0 \qquad (2)$$

Solving (1) and (2) for C_1 and C_2 yields $C_1 = C_2 = 1$. Therefore,

$$y = e^{4x} + e^{-4x} - 1. \qquad \textit{Particular solution}$$

21. $\dfrac{dx}{dt} = -2x + y \qquad (1)$

$\dfrac{dy}{dt} = -4x + 2y \qquad (2)$ $\qquad x(0) = 1, \ y(0) = 1$

Differentiating (1) with respect to t yields:

$$\frac{d^2 x}{dt^2} = -2\frac{dx}{dt} + \frac{dy}{dt} \qquad (3)$$

Substituting $\dfrac{dy}{dt}$ and y from (2) and (1), respectively, into (3), we have:

$$\frac{d^2 x}{dt^2} = -2\frac{dx}{dt} + \left[-4x + 2\left(\frac{dx}{dt} + 2x\right)\right]$$

$$\frac{d^2 x}{dt^2} = 0$$

Therefore, $\dfrac{dx}{dt} = C_1$ and $x = C_1 t + C_2$.

Substituting x and $\dfrac{dx}{dt}$ into (1), we have:

$$C_1 = -2(C_1 t + C_2) + y$$
$$y = 2C_1 t + 2C_2 + C_1$$

Thus, the general solution of the system is:
$$x = C_1 t + C_2$$
$$y = 2C_1 t + 2C_2 + C_1$$

Applying the initial conditions, $x(0) = 1$ and $y(0) = 1$, we obtain the system of equations:
$$x(0) = 1 = C_2$$
$$y(0) = 1 = 2C_2 + C_1$$
The solution of this system is $C_1 = -1$ and $C_2 = 1$.

Therefore, the particular solution of the system of differential equations is:

$x = 1 - t$

$y = 1 - 2t$

22. $\dfrac{dx}{dt} = -2x + 2y + 6$ (1)

$\dfrac{dy}{dt} = 4x - 8$ (2) $x(0) = 2,\ y(0) = 2$

Differentiating (2) with respect to t yields:

$\dfrac{d^2y}{dt^2} = 4\dfrac{dx}{dt}$ (3)

Substitute $\dfrac{dx}{dt}$ and x from (1) and (2), respectively, into (3):

$\dfrac{d^2y}{dt^2} = 4\left[-2\left(\dfrac{1}{4}\dfrac{dy}{dt} + 2\right) + 2y + 6\right]$

$\dfrac{d^2y}{dt^2} = -2\dfrac{dy}{dt} + 8y + 8$

$\dfrac{d^2y}{dt^2} + 2\dfrac{dy}{dt} - 8y = 8$ (4)   Second-order linear nonhomogeneous equation

<u>Step 1</u>: Let $y = k$, constant. Then $y' = y'' = 0$ and

$\dfrac{d^2y}{dt^2} + 2\dfrac{dy}{dt} - 8y = 8$

$0 + 2\cdot 0 - 8k = 8$

$k = -1$

Thus, $y = -1$ is a solution of the nonhomogeneous equation.

<u>Step 2</u>: Consider the associated homogeneous equation $\dfrac{d^2y}{dt^2} + 2\dfrac{dy}{dt} - 8y = 0$:

$m^2 + 2m - 8 = 0$ Characteristic equation

$(m - 2)(m + 4) = 0$

$m_1 = 2,\ m_2 = -4$ Roots of the characteristic equation

Thus, $y = C_1 e^{2t} + C_2 e^{-4t}$.

<u>Step 3</u>: $y = C_1 e^{2t} + C_2 e^{-4t} - 1$ is the general solution of the nonhomogeneous equation.

Now $y = C_1 e^{2t} + C_2 e^{-4t} - 1$ and $\dfrac{dy}{dt} = 2C_1 e^{2t} - 4C_2 e^{-4t}$.

Substituting $\dfrac{dy}{dt}$ into (2), we have

$2C_1 e^{2t} - 4C_2 e^{-4t} = 4x - 8$

$x = \dfrac{1}{2}C_1 e^{2t} - C_2 e^{-4t} + 2$

Therefore, the general solution of the system is:

$$x = \frac{1}{2}C_1 e^{2t} - C_2 e^{-4t} + 2$$
$$y = C_1 e^{2t} + C_2 e^{-4t} - 1$$

Applying the initial conditions, $x(0) = 2$ and $y(0) = 2$, we obtain the system of equations:

$$x(0) = 2 = \frac{1}{2}C_1 e^0 - C_2 e^0 + 2$$
$$C_1 - 2C_2 = 0 \qquad\qquad (4)$$

$$y(0) = 2 = C_1 e^0 + C_2 e^0 - 1$$
$$C_1 + C_2 = 3 \qquad\qquad (5)$$

The solution of the system (4), (5) is: $C_1 = 2$, $C_2 = 1$. Therefore, the particular solution of the system of differential equations is:

$$x = e^{2t} - e^{-4t} + 2$$
$$y = 2e^{2t} + e^{-4t} - 1$$

23. Let $V(t)$ denote the value of the refrigerator at time t. Then the model for this problem is:

$$\frac{dV}{dt} = kV; \quad V(0) = 500, \ V(20) = 25$$

$$\frac{dV}{dt} - kV = 0$$

Integrating factor: $I(t) = e^{\int(-k)\,dt} = e^{-kt}$

Thus, $V = \dfrac{1}{I(t)} \displaystyle\int I(t)g(t)\,dt, \qquad g(t) = 0$

$$= \frac{1}{e^{-kt}}\int e^{-kt} \cdot 0 \ dt = e^{kt}\int 0 \ dt$$

$V = Ce^{kt}$.   *General solution*

Applying the conditions $V(0) = 500$ and $V(20) = 25$, we have:

$V(0) = 500 = Ce^0$, $C = 500$

Therefore, $V(t) = 500e^{kt}$.

$$V(20) = 25 = 500e^{k(20)}$$
$$e^{20k} = \frac{25}{500} = \frac{1}{20}$$
$$20k = \ln\left(\frac{1}{20}\right)$$
$$k = \frac{1}{20}\ln\left(\frac{1}{20}\right)$$

Therefore, $V(t) = 500e^{(1/20)\ln(1/20)t}$.

Finally, we want to calculate V when $t = 5$:

$$V(5) = 500e^{(1/20)\ln(1/20)5} = 500e^{(1/4)\ln(1/20)} = 500e^{-0.25\ln 20} \approx \$236.44$$

24. The model for this problem is:

$$\frac{ds}{dt} = k(200{,}000 - s); \quad s(0) = 0, \; s(1) = 50{,}000$$

$$\frac{ds}{200{,}000 - s} = k \, dt \qquad \text{Separate the variables}$$

$$\int \frac{ds}{200{,}000 - s} = \int k \, dt$$

$$\ln(200{,}000 - s) = kt + C$$

$$200{,}000 - s = e^{kt+C}$$
$$= e^C e^{kt}$$
$$= A e^{kt}$$

$$s = 200{,}000 - A e^{kt}. \qquad \textit{General solution}$$

We use the conditions $s(0) = 0$ and $s(1) = 50{,}000$ to evaluate the constants A and k.

$$s(0) = 0 = 200{,}000 - A e^0$$
$$A = 200{,}000$$

Thus, $s = 200{,}000 - 200{,}000 e^{kt}$.

$$s(1) = 50{,}000 = 200{,}000 - 200{,}000 e^k$$
$$200{,}000 e^k = 150{,}000$$
$$e^k = \frac{150{,}000}{200{,}000} = \frac{3}{4}$$
$$k = \ln\left(\frac{3}{4}\right)$$

Therefore, $s = 200{,}000 - 200{,}000 e^{\ln(3/4)t}$.
Finally, we determine t such that $s(t) = 150{,}000$.

$$150{,}000 = 200{,}000 - 200{,}000 e^{\ln(3/4)t}$$
$$200{,}000 e^{\ln(3/4)t} = 50{,}000$$
$$e^{\ln(3/4)t} = \frac{50{,}000}{200{,}000} = \frac{1}{4}$$
$$\ln\left(\frac{3}{4}\right)t = \ln\left(\frac{1}{4}\right)$$
$$t = \frac{\ln\left(\frac{1}{4}\right)}{\ln\left(\frac{3}{4}\right)} \approx 5 \text{ years}$$

25. The equilibrium price $p(t)$ at time t satisfies
$S = D$; $p(0) = 75$. Thus, $100 + p + p' = 200 - p' - p$

$$2p' + 2p = 100$$
$$p' + p = 50$$

Integrating factor: $I(t) = e^{\int f(t) dt} = e^{\int 1 dt} = e^t$

Thus, $p = \dfrac{1}{I(t)} \displaystyle\int I(t) g(t) dt, \quad g(t) = 50$

$$= \frac{1}{e^t} \int e^t \cdot 50 \, dt = 50 e^{-t}[e^t + C]$$
$$= 50 + 50 C e^{-t} \qquad (A = 50C)$$
$$p = 50 + A e^{-t}. \qquad \textit{General solution}$$

Applying the initial condition $p(0) = 75$, we have:

$75 = 50 + Ae^0$, $A = 25$

Therefore, $p = 50 + 25e^{-t}$.   *Particular solution*

The long-range equilibrium price $\bar{p}$ is given by

$\bar{p} = \lim\limits_{t \to \infty} (50 + 25e^{-t}) = 50 + 25 \lim\limits_{t \to \infty} e^{-t} = 50.$

26. The amount in the account at any time t must satisfy

$\dfrac{dA}{dt} - 0.05A = -5000.$

Now, $f(t) = -0.05$, and the integrating factor is:

$I(t) = e^{\int (-0.05)dt} = e^{-0.05t}$

Thus, $A = \dfrac{1}{e^{-0.05t}} \int -5000e^{-0.05t}dt = e^{0.05t}\left[-5000\dfrac{e^{-0.05t}}{-0.05} + C\right]$

$A = 100{,}000 + Ce^{0.05t}$ *General solution*

Applying the initial condition $A(0) = 60{,}000$ yields:

$A(0) = 100{,}000 + Ce^0 = 60{,}000$

$C = -40{,}000$

Thus, the amount in the account at any time t is:

$A(t) = 100{,}000 - 40{,}000e^{0.05t}$

To determine when the amount in the account is 0, we must solve $A(t) = 0$ for t:

$100{,}000 - 40{,}000e^{0.05t} = 0$

$e^{0.05t} = \dfrac{100{,}000}{40{,}000} = \dfrac{5}{2}$

$t = \dfrac{\ln\left(\frac{5}{2}\right)}{0.05} \approx 18.326$

Thus, the account will be depleted after 18.326 years. The total amount withdrawn from the account is:

$5000(18.326) = \$91{,}630$

27. $p' = -2p + q + 125$ (1)

$q' = -2p - 5q + 575$ (2)

Differentiate (1) with respect to t.

$p'' = -2p' + q' = -2p' - 2p - 5q + 575$

$p'' = -2p' - 2p - 5(p' + 2p - 125) + 575$ Substitute q from (1)

$p'' + 7p' + 12p = 1200$ (3)   Second-order linear nonhomogeneous equation

Step 1: Let $p = k$, constant. Then $p' = p'' = 0$ and

$p'' + 7p' + 12p = 1200$

$0 + 7 \cdot 0 + 12k = 1200$

$k = 100$

Thus, $p = 100$ is a solution of the nonhomogeneous equation.

Step 2: Consider the associated homogeneous equation $p'' + 7p' + 12p = 0$.

$m^2 + 7m + 12 = 0$ Characteristic equation

$(m + 3)(m + 4) = 0$

$m_1 = -3$, $m_2 = -4$ Roots of the characteristic equation

Thus, $p = C_1 e^{-3t} + C_2 e^{-4t}$.

<u>Step 3</u>: $p = C_1 e^{-3t} + C_2 e^{-4t} + 100$ is the general solution of the nonhomogeneous equation (3).

Now, $p = C_1 e^{-3t} + C_2 e^{-4t} + 100$ and $p' = -3C_1 e^{-3t} - 4C_2 e^{-4t}$. Substituting p and p' into (1), we obtain:

$$-3C_1 e^{-3t} - 4C_2 e^{-4t} = -2(C_1 e^{-3t} + C_2 e^{-4t} + 100) + q + 125$$
$$q = -C_1 e^{-3t} - 2C_2 e^{-4t} + 75$$

Therefore, the general solution of the system of differential equations is:

$$p = C_1 e^{-3t} + C_2 e^{-4t} + 100$$
$$q = -C_1 e^{-3t} - 2C_2 e^{-4t} + 75$$

Applying the initial conditions, $p(0) = 50$ and $q(0) = 150$, we obtain the system of equations:

$$p(0) = C_1 + C_2 + 100 = 50$$
$$C_1 + C_2 = -50 \qquad (4)$$
$$q(0) = -C_1 - 2C_2 + 75 = 150$$
$$C_1 + 2C_2 = -75 \qquad (5)$$

Solving (4) and (5) for C_1 and C_2, we get:
$C_1 = -25$, $C_2 = -25$.

Thus, the particular solution is:

$$p = -25e^{-3t} - 25e^{-4t} + 100$$
$$q = 25e^{-3t} + 50e^{-4t} + 75$$
$$p' = 75e^{-3t} + 100e^{-4t} > 0 \qquad (p \text{ is increasing})$$
$$q' = -75e^{-3t} - 200e^{-4t} < 0 \qquad (q \text{ is decreasing})$$

$\lim\limits_{t \to \infty} p = 100$ and $\lim\limits_{t \to \infty} q = 75$ [<u>Note</u>: $\lim\limits_{t \to \infty} e^{-3t} = 0$ and $\lim\limits_{t \to \infty} e^{-4t} = 0$.]

Thus, p increases to a limiting value of 100 and q decreases to a limiting value of 75.

28. $\dfrac{dy}{dt} = 100 + e^{-t} - y$; $y(0) = 0$

$\dfrac{dy}{dt} + y = 100 + e^{-t}$

Integrating factor: $I(t) = e^{\int 1 \, dt} = e^t$

Thus, $y = \dfrac{1}{I(t)} \int I(t) g(t) \, dt$, $\quad g(t) = 100 + e^{-t}$

$$= \dfrac{1}{e^t} \int e^t (100 + e^{-t}) \, dt = e^{-t} \int (100e^t + 1) \, dt = e^{-t} [100e^t + t + C]$$

$y = 100 + te^{-t} + Ce^{-t}$.   *General solution*

Applying the initial condition, we have:
$0 = 100 + 0e^0 + Ce^0$, $C = -100$
Therefore, $y = 100 + te^{-t} - 100e^{-t}$. *Particular solution*

29. Let $p(t)$ be the amount of pollutants in the tank at time t. The initial amount of pollutants in the tank is $p(0) = 0$.

Pollutants are entering the tank at the constant rate of $2(100) = 200$ pounds per hour.

The amount of water in the tank at time t is $100 + 50t$.

The amount of pollutants in each gallon of water at time t is $\dfrac{p(t)}{100 + 50t}$.

The rate at which pollutants are leaving the tank at time t is $\dfrac{50p(t)}{100 + 50t} = \dfrac{p(t)}{2 + t}$.

The model for this problem is:

$$\frac{dp}{dt} = 200 - \frac{p}{2 + t}; \quad p(0) = 0$$

$$\frac{dp}{dt} + \left(\frac{1}{2 + t}\right)p = 200$$

Integrating factor: $I(t) = e^{\int(1/(2+t))\,dt} = e^{\ln(2+t)} = 2 + t$

Thus, $p = \dfrac{1}{I(t)} \displaystyle\int I(t)g(t)\,dt, \quad g(t) = 200$

$$= \frac{1}{2 + t} \int (2 + t)200\,dt = \frac{200}{2 + t}\left[\frac{(2 + t)^2}{2} + C\right].$$

$$= 100(2 + t) + \frac{200C}{2 + t} \qquad (A = 200C)$$

$$p = 100(2 + t) + \frac{A}{2 + t}. \qquad \textit{General solution}$$

Use the initial condition $p(0) = 0$ to evaluate the constant A:

$$p(0) = 0 = 100(2) + \frac{A}{2}, \quad A = -400$$

Therefore, $p = 100(2 + t) - \dfrac{400}{2 + t}$. *Particular solution*

To find the total amount of pollutants in the tank after two hours, we evaluate $p(2)$:

$$p(2) = 100(2 + 2) - \frac{400}{2 + 2} = 400 - 100 = 300 \text{ pounds}$$

30. $\dfrac{dx}{dt} = 0.03x - 0.01y \qquad (1)$

$\dfrac{dy}{dt} = -0.02x + 0.02y \qquad (2)$

Differentiate (1) with respect to t.

$$\frac{d^2x}{dt^2} = 0.03\frac{dx}{dt} - 0.01\frac{dy}{dt}$$

$$\frac{d^2x}{dt^2} = 0.03\frac{dx}{dt} - 0.01(-0.02x + 0.02y) \qquad \text{Substitute } \frac{dy}{dt} \text{ from (2)}$$

$$\frac{d^2x}{dt^2} = 0.03\frac{dx}{dt} + 0.0002x - 0.0002\left(3x - 100\frac{dx}{dt}\right) \qquad \text{Substitute } y \text{ from (1)}$$

$$\frac{d^2x}{dt^2} - 0.05\frac{dx}{dt} + 0.0004x = 0$$

$$m^2 - 0.05m + 0.0004 = 0 \qquad \text{Characteristic equation}$$

$(m - 0.01)(m - 0.04) = 0$

$m_1 = 0.01$, $m_2 = 0.04$ Roots of characteristic equation

Thus, $x = C_1 e^{0.01t} + C_2 e^{0.04t}$. Also,

$\frac{dx}{dt} = 0.01 C_1 e^{0.01t} + 0.04 C_2 e^{0.04t}$.

Substituting x and $\frac{dx}{dt}$ into (1), we obtain:

$0.01 C_1 e^{0.01t} + 0.04 C_2 e^{0.04t} = 0.03(C_1 e^{0.01t} + C_2 e^{0.04t}) - 0.01y$

$$0.01y = 0.02 C_1 e^{0.01t} - 0.01 C_2 e^{0.04t}$$

$$y = 2C_1 e^{0.01t} - C_2 e^{0.04t}$$

Therefore, the general solution of the system of differential equations is:

$x = C_1 e^{0.01t} + C_2 e^{0.04t}$

$y = 2C_1 e^{0.01t} - C_2 e^{0.04t}$

Now, we apply the initial condition $x(0) = 75$ and $y(0) = 75$:

$x(0) = C_1 + C_2 = 75$ (3)

$y(0) = 2C_1 - C_2 = 75$ (4)

Solving (3) and (4) for C_1 and C_2, we get $C_1 = 50$ and $C_2 = 25$. Thus, the particular solution is:

$x = 50 e^{0.01t} + 25 e^{0.04t}$

$y = 100 e^{0.01t} - 25 e^{0.04t}$

$x' = 0.5 e^{0.01t} + e^{0.04t} > 0$ (increasing)

$y' = e^{0.01t} - e^{0.04t}$

$\lim\limits_{t \to \infty} x = \lim\limits_{t \to \infty} [50 e^{0.01t} + 25 e^{0.04t}] = \infty$ and $y = [100 e^{0.01t} - 25 e^{0.04t}] = 0$

when $t = 46.2$ years.

Thus, the first species increases without bound, whereas the second species dies out after approximately 46.2 years.

31. Let $p(t)$ denote the number of people who have heard the rumor at time t. Then the model for this problem is:

$\frac{dp}{dt} = k(200 - p)$; $p(0) = 1$, $p(2) = 10$

$\frac{dp}{200 - p} = k\, dt$ Separating the variables

$\int \frac{dp}{200 - p} = \int k\, dt$

$-\ln(200 - p) = kt + C$

$\ln(200 - p) = -kt - C$

$200 - p = e^{-kt-C}$

$= e^{-C} e^{-kt}$

$= A e^{-kt}$

$p = 200 - A e^{-kt}$ *General solution*

Apply the conditions $p(0) = 1$ and $p(2) = 10$ to evaluate the constants A and k:

$p(0) = 1 = 200 - Ae^0$, $A = 199$

Thus, $p = 200 - 199e^{-kt}$.

$p(2) = 10 = 200 - 199e^{-2k}$

$$199e^{-2k} = 190$$

$$e^{-2k} = \frac{190}{199}$$

$$-2k = \ln\left(\frac{190}{199}\right)$$

$$k = \frac{-1}{2} \ln\left(\frac{190}{199}\right)$$

Therefore, $p = 200 - 199e^{(1/2)\ln(190/199)t}$.   *Particular solution*

(A) When $t = 5$,

$$p(5) = 200 - 199e^{(1/2)\ln(190/199)5}$$
$$= 200 - 199e^{(5/2)\ln(190/199)} \approx 23 \text{ people}$$

(B) Find t such that $p(t) = 100$.

$$100 = 200 - 199e^{(1/2)\ln(190/199)t}$$
$$199e^{(1/2)\ln(190/199)t} = 100$$
$$e^{(1/2)\ln(190/199)t} = \frac{100}{199}$$
$$\frac{1}{2} \ln\left(\frac{190}{199}\right) t = \ln\left(\frac{100}{199}\right)$$
$$t = \frac{2 \ln\left(\frac{100}{199}\right)}{\ln\left(\frac{190}{199}\right)} \approx 30 \text{ days}$$

8 No material available for this chapter

9 Numerical Techniques

Things to remember:

1. **NEWTON'S METHOD FOR APPROXIMATING ROOTS**

   Given a differentiable function f and an initial approximation x_1. Define the sequence $\{x_n\}$ by

   $$x_n = x_{n-1} - \frac{f(x_{n-1})}{f'(x_{n-1})}, \quad n > 1, \quad f'(x_{n-1}) \neq 0.$$

   If $\lim_{n \to \infty} x_n$ exists, then $r = \lim_{n \to \infty} x_n$ is a zero of f.

---

1. $f(x) = x^2 - 4$, $x_1 = 1$, $n = 5$

   $f'(x) = 2x$

   $$x_n = x_{n-1} - \frac{f(x_{n-1})}{f'(x_{n-1})} = x_{n-1} - \frac{(x_{n-1})^2 - 4}{2(x_{n-1})} = \frac{2x_{n-1}^2 - x_{n-1}^2 + 4}{2x_{n-1}}$$

   or $\quad x_n = \frac{x_{n-1}^2 + 4}{2x_{n-1}}$

   Let $n = 2$:

   $$x_2 = \frac{x_1^2 + 4}{2x_1} = \frac{(1)^2 + 4}{2(1)} = \frac{5}{2} = 2.5$$

   $n = 3$:

   $$x_3 = \frac{x_2^2 + 4}{2x_2} = \frac{(2.5)^2 + 4}{2(2.5)} = \frac{6.25 + 4}{5} = \frac{10.25}{5} = 2.05$$

   $n = 4$:

   $$x_4 = \frac{x_3^2 + 4}{2x_3} = \frac{(2.05)^2 + 4}{2(2.05)} = \frac{4.2025 + 4}{4.10} = \frac{8.2025}{4.10} = 2.0006098$$

   $n = 5$:

   $$x_5 = \frac{x_4^2 + 4}{2x_4} = \frac{(2.0006098)^2 + 4}{2(2.0006098)} = \frac{4.0024394 + 4}{4.0012196} = 2.0000001$$

3. $f(x) = x^3 - 8$, $x_1 = 3$, $n = 5$

   $f'(x) = 3x^2$

   $$x_n = x_{n-1} - \frac{f(x_{n-1})}{f'(x_{n-1})} = x_{n-1} - \frac{x_{n-1}^3 - 8}{3x_{n-1}^2} = \frac{3x_{n-1}^3 - x_{n-1}^3 + 8}{3x_{n-1}^2} \quad \text{or} \quad x_n = \frac{2x_{n-1}^3 + 8}{3x_{n-1}^2}$$

Let $n = 2$:

$$x_2 = \frac{2x_1^3 + 8}{3x_1^2} = \frac{2(3)^3 + 8}{3(3)^2} = \frac{54 + 8}{27} = \frac{62}{27} = 2.2962963$$

$n = 3$:

$$x_3 = \frac{2x_2^3 + 8}{3x_2^2} = \frac{2(2.2962963)^3 + 8}{3(2.2962963)^2} = \frac{32.216634}{15.81893} = 2.0365874$$

$n = 4$:

$$x_4 = \frac{2x_3^3 + 8}{3x_3^2} = \frac{2(2.0365874)^3 + 8}{3(2.0365874)^2} = \frac{24.894259}{12.443065} = 2.0006533$$

$n = 5$:

$$x_5 = \frac{2x_4^3 + 8}{3x_4^2} = \frac{2(2.0006533)^3 + 8}{3(2.0006533)^2} = \frac{24.015684}{12.007841} = 2.0000002$$

5. $f(x) = e^x + x$, $x_1 = 0$, $n = 5$

$f'(x) = e^x + 1$

We have:

$$x_n = x_{n-1} - \frac{f(x_{n-1})}{f'(x_{n-1})}$$

$$= x_{n-1} - \frac{e^{x_{n-1}} + x_{n-1}}{e^{x_{n-1}} + 1} = \frac{x_{n-1}(e^{x_{n-1}} + 1) - (e^{x_{n-1}} + x_{n-1})}{e^{x_{n-1}} + 1}$$

$$= \frac{e^{x_{n-1}}(x_{n-1} - 1)}{e^{x_{n-1}} + 1}$$

Let $n = 2$:

$$x_2 = \frac{e^{x_1}(x_1 - 1)}{e^{x_1} + 1} = \frac{e^0(0 - 1)}{e^0 + 1} = \frac{1(-1)}{1 + 1} = \frac{-1}{2} = -.5$$

$n = 3$:

$$x_3 = \frac{e^{x_2}(x_2 - 1)}{e^{x_2} + 1} = \frac{e^{-.5}(-.5 - 1)}{e^{-.5} + 1} = \frac{.6065307(-1.5)}{.6065307 + 1} = -.56631100$$

$n = 4$:

$$x_4 = \frac{e^{x_3}(x_3 - 1)}{e^{x_3} + 1} = \frac{e^{-.566311}(-.566311 - 1)}{e^{-.566311} + 1} = \frac{-.88990624}{1.5676155} = -.56714316$$

$n = 5$:

$$x_5 = \frac{e^{x_4}(x_4 - 1)}{e^{x_4} + 1} = \frac{e^{-.56714316}(-.56414316)}{e^{-.56714316} + 1} = -.56714329$$

464

7. $f(x) = \ln x + x$, $x_1 = 1$, $n = 5$

$$f'(x) = \frac{1}{x} + 1$$

$$x_n = x_{n-1} - \frac{f(x_{n-1})}{f'(x_{n-1})} = x_{n-1} - \frac{\ln x_{n-1} + x_{n-1}}{\frac{1}{x_{n-1}} + 1} = x_{n-1} - \frac{x_{n-1}(\ln x_{n-1} + x_{n-1})}{1 + x_{n-1}}$$

$$= \frac{x_{n-1} + x_{n-1}^2 - x_{n-1}\ln x_{n-1} - x_{n-1}^2}{1 + x_{n-1}} = \frac{x_{n-1}(1 - \ln x_{n-1})}{1 + x_{n-1}}$$

Let $n = 2$:

$$x_2 = \frac{x_1(1 - \ln x_1)}{1 + x_1} \qquad (x_1 = 1, \ \ln 1 = 0)$$

$$= \frac{1(1 - 0)}{1 + 1} = \frac{1}{2} = .5$$

$n = 3$:

$$x_3 = \frac{x_2(1 - \ln x_2)}{1 + x_2} = \frac{.5(1 - \ln .5)}{1 + .5} = \frac{.5(1 + .6931472)}{1.5}$$

$$= \frac{1.6931472}{3} = .5643824$$

$n = 4$:

$$x_4 = \frac{x_3(1 - \ln x_3)}{1 + x_3} = \frac{.5643824(1 - \ln .5643824)}{1 + .5643824} = .5671390$$

$n = 5$:

$$x_5 = \frac{x_4(1 - \ln x_4)}{1 + x_4} = \frac{.567139(1 - \ln .567139)}{1 + .567139} = .56714329$$

9. $f(x) = \ln x + x^2$, $x_1 = 2$, $n = 5$

$$f'(x) = \frac{1}{x} + 2x$$

$$x_n = x_{n-1} - \frac{f(x_{n-1})}{f'(x_{n-1})} = x_{n-1} - \frac{\ln x_{n-1} + x_{n-1}^2}{\frac{1}{x_{n-1}} + 2x_{n-1}} = x_{n-1} - \frac{x_{n-1}(\ln x_{n-1} + x_{n-1}^2)}{1 + 2x_{n-1}^2}$$

$$= \frac{x_{n-1}(1 + x_{n-1}^2 - \ln x_{n-1})}{1 + 2x_{n-1}^2}$$

Let $n = 2$, $x_1 = 2$, $\ln 2 = .6931472$:

$$x_2 = \frac{x_1(1 + x_1^2 - \ln x_1)}{1 + 2x_1^2} = \frac{2(1 + 4 - .6931472)}{1 + 8} = .9570784$$

$n = 3$:

$$x_3 = \frac{x_2(1 + x_2^2 - \ln x_2)}{1 + 2x_2^2} = \frac{.9570784[1 + (.9570784)^2 - \ln .9570784]}{1 + 2(.9570784)^2}$$

$$= \frac{1.8757483}{2.8319981} = .66234094$$

$n = 4$:

$$x_4 = \frac{x_3(1 + x_3^2 - \ln x_3)}{1 + 2x_3^2} = \frac{.66234094[1 + (.66234094)^2 - \ln .66234094]}{1 + 2(.66234094)^2}$$

$$= \frac{1.2257747}{1.877391} = .65291392$$

$n = 5$:

$$x_5 = \frac{x_4(1 + x_4^2 - \ln x_4)}{1 + 2x_4^2} = \frac{1.2095926}{1.8525932} = .65291864$$

11. $f(x) = x^2 - 7x + 2$

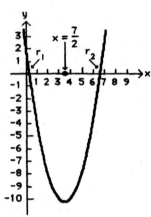

Step 1: Sketch the graph of f.

$f'(x) = 2x - 7$

Critical values:
$f'(x) = 2x - 7 = 0$

$$x = \frac{7}{2}$$

The graph of f falls for x on the interval $\left(-\infty, \frac{7}{2}\right)$ and rises for x on the interval $\left(\frac{7}{2}, \infty\right)$.

$f''(x) = 2 > 0$

The graph of f is concave up on the interval $(-\infty, +\infty)$.

Step 2: Approximate r_1. The graph in the above figure indicates that f has two zeros: r_1 in $(0, 1)$, r_2 in $(6, 7)$. We will use $x_1 = 0$ for the initial approximation and place the calculations in the following table.

n	x_{n-1}	$f(x_{n-1})$	$f'(x_{n-1})$	$x_n = x_{n-1} - \dfrac{f(x_{n-1})}{f'(x_{n-1})}$
2	0	2	-7	$0 - \dfrac{2}{-7} = .2857143$
3	.2857143	.0816327	-6.4285714	$.2857143 - \dfrac{.0816327}{-6.4285714} = .2984127$
4	.2984127	.0001612	-6.4031746	$.2984127 - \dfrac{.0001612}{-6.4031746} = .2984379$
5	.2984379	6×10^{-10}	-6.4031242	$.2984379 - \dfrac{6 \times 10^{-10}}{-6.4031242} = .29843788$

Since x_4 and x_5 are very close to each other, we conclude that $r_1 \approx .29843788$.

The initial approximation $x_1 = 6$.

n	x_{n-1}	$f(x_{n-1})$	$f'(x_{n-1})$	$x_n = x_{n-1} - \dfrac{f(x_{n-1})}{f'(x_{n-1})}$
2	6	-4	5	$6 - \dfrac{-4}{5} = 6.8$
3	6.8	.64	6.6	$6.8 - \dfrac{.64}{6.6} = 6.7030303$
4	6.7030303	.0094031	6.406061	$6.7030303 - \dfrac{.0094031}{6.406061} = 6.7015625$
5	6.7015625	.0000021	6.403125	$6.7015625 - \dfrac{.0000021}{6.403125} = 6.7015621$

$r_2 \approx 6.7015621$

13. $f(x) = x^3 + 4x + 10$

Step 1: Sketch the graph of f.

$f'(x) = 3x^2 + 4$

There are no critical values, since
$f'(x) = 3x^2 + 4 > 0$ for all x.
$f''(x) = 6x$
Point of inflection:
$f''(x) = 6x = 0$
Thus, $(0, f(0)) = (0, 10)$ is a point
of inflection.

Now, $f(-2) = (-2)^3 + 4(-2) + 10 = -6$
and $f(-1) = (-1)^3 + 4(-1) + 10 = 5$.

Therefore, it is easy to conclude that we have one real root r_1
in $(-2, -1)$. A good first approximation is $x_1 = -1$. We give
the calculations in the following table.

Initial approximation $x_1 = -1$

n	x_{n-1}	$f(x_{n-1})$	$f'(x_{n-1})$	$x_n = x_{n-1} - \dfrac{f(x_{n-1})}{f'(x_{n-1})}$
2	-1	5	7	$-1 - \dfrac{5}{7} = -1.7142857$
3	-1.7142857	-1.895044	12.816327	$-1.7142857 - \dfrac{-1.895044}{12.816327} = -1.566424$
4	-1.566424	-.109206	11.361053	$-1.566424 - \dfrac{-.109206}{11.361053} = -1.556812$
5	-1.556812	-.000433	11.270988	$-1.556812 - \dfrac{-.000433}{11.270988} = -1.5567733$

$r_1 \approx -1.5567733$

15. $f(x) = x^3 - 12x^2 + 22$

Step 1: Sketch the graph of f.

$$f'(x) = 3x^2 - 24x = 3x(x - 8)$$

Critical values: $x = 0$, $x = 8$

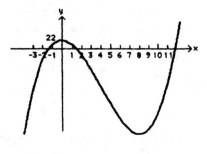

The graph of f rises for x in the intervals $(-\infty, 0)$ and $(8, \infty)$, and falls for x in the interval $(0, 8)$.

$$f''(x) = 6x - 24 = 6(x - 4)$$

The graph of f is concave downward in the interval $(-\infty, 4)$ and concave upward in the interval $(4, \infty)$.

Using this information and point-by-point plotting, we obtain the graph of f shown at the right.

We conclude that f has three zeros: r_1 in $(-2, -1)$, r_2 in $(1, 2)$, and r_3 in $(11, 12)$.

Step 2: Approximate r_1.

We will use $x_1 = -2$ for an initial approximation and give the calculations in the following table.

n	x_{n-1}	$f(x_{n-1})$	$f'(x_{n-1})$	$x_n = x_{n-1} - \dfrac{f(x_{n-1})}{f'(x_{n-1})}$
2	-2	-34	60	$-2 - \dfrac{-34}{60} = -1.4333333$
3	-1.4333333	-5.598037	40.563333	$-1.4333333 - \dfrac{-5.598037}{40.563333} = -1.295326$
4	-1.295326	-.3078216	36.121433	$-1.295326 - \dfrac{-.3078216}{36.121433} = -1.2868042$
5	-1.2868042	-.001153	35.850895	$-1.2868042 - \dfrac{-.001153}{35.850895} = -1.286772$

$r_1 \approx -1.286772$

Step 3: Approximate r_2.

Initial approximation $x_1 = 1$

n	x_{n-1}	$f(x_{n-1})$	$f'(x_{n-1})$	$x_n = x_{n-1} - \dfrac{f(x_{n-1})}{f'(x_{n-1})}$
2	1	11	-21	$1 - \dfrac{11}{-21} = 1.5238095$
3	1.5238095	-2.3256668	-29.605442	$1.5238095 - \dfrac{-2.3256668}{-29.605442} = 1.4452541$
4	1.4452541	-.0463261	-28.41982	$1.4452541 - \dfrac{-.0463261}{-28.41982} = 1.4436241$
5	1.4436241	-.0000204	-28.394827	$1.4436241 - \dfrac{-.0000204}{-28.394827} = 1.4436234$

$r_2 \approx 1.4436234$

: Approximate r_3.
<u>Step 4</u>: Approximate r_3.
   Initial approximation $x_1 = 10$ (chosen to simplify the first calculation)

n	x_{n-1}	$f(x_{n-1})$	$f'(x_{n-1})$	$x_n = x_{n-1} - \dfrac{f(x_{n-1})}{f'(x_{n-1})}$
2	10	−178	60	$10 - \dfrac{-178}{60} = 12.9666667$
3	12.9666667	184.52996	193.20333	$12.9666667 - \dfrac{184.52996}{193.20333} = 12.011559$
4	12.011559	23.667720	144.55524	$12.011559 - \dfrac{23.667720}{144.55524} = 11.847831$
5	11.847831	.6399050	136.76536	$11.847831 - \dfrac{.6399050}{136.76536} = 11.843152$
6	11.843152	.0005149	136.5451	$11.843152 - \dfrac{.0005149}{136.5451} = 11.843149$

$r_3 \approx 11.843149$

17. $f(x) = x^4 - 4x^3 - 8x^2 + 4$

<u>Step 1</u>: Sketch the graph of f.
$$f'(x) = 4x^3 - 12x^2 - 16x$$
$$= 4x(x^2 - 3x - 4)$$
$$= 4x(x - 4)(x + 1)$$

Critical values: $x = 0$, $x = -1$,
$\qquad\qquad\qquad x = 4$
$$f''(x) = 12x^2 - 24x - 16$$
$$= 4(3x^2 - 6x - 4)$$

Now, $f''(0) = -16$, so $(0, 4)$ is a
relative maximum; $f''(-1) = 20$, so
$(-1, 1)$ is a relative minimum;
$f''(4) = 80$, so $(4, -124)$ is a
relative minimum.
The graph of f is shown at the right. This graph indicates that
f has two roots: r_1 in $(0, 1)$ and r_2 in $(5, 6)$.

<u>Step 2</u>: Approximate r_1.
   Use $x_1 = 1$ for the initial approximation.

n	x_{n-1}	$f(x_{n-1})$	$f'(x_{n-1})$	$x_n = x_{n-1} - \dfrac{f(x_{n-1})}{f'(x_{n-1})}$
2	1	−7	−24	$1 - \dfrac{-7}{-24} = .7083333$
3	.7083333	−1.1837341	−15.93258	$.7083333 - \dfrac{-1.1837341}{-15.93258} = .6340368$
4	.6340368	−0.073953	−13.949083	$.6340368 - \dfrac{-0.073953}{-13.949083} = .6287352$
5	.6287352	−0.0003707	−13.809281	$.6287352 - \dfrac{-0.0003707}{-13.809281} = .6287083$

$r_1 \approx .6287083$

Use $x_1 = 5$ for the initial approximation.

n	x_{n-1}	$f(x_{n-1})$	$f'(x_{n-1})$	$x_n = x_{n-1} - \dfrac{f(x_{n-1})}{f'(x_{n-1})}$
2	5	-71	120	$5 - \dfrac{-71}{120} = 5.5916667$
3	5.5916667	32.142245	234.66517	$5.5916667 - \dfrac{32.142245}{234.66517} = 5.454696$
4	5.454696	2.0637619	204.8701	$5.454696 - \dfrac{2.0637619}{204.8701} = 5.4446225$
5	5.4446225	.0106476	202.75876	$5.4446225 - \dfrac{.0106476}{202.75876} = 5.44457$
6	5.44457	.0000029	202.74778	$5.44457 - \dfrac{.0000029}{202.74778} = 5.444569$

$r_2 = 5.444569$

19. The figure indicates that the graphs of
$f(x)$ and $g(x)$ have one point of
intersection. Furthermore, $x_1 = 2$
appears to be a good initial
approximation to the x-coordinate of the
point of intersection. Since Newton's
method can only be used to find the root
of a single function, we define
$$F(x) = f(x) - g(x) = x^3 - x - 4$$
Then, the root of F will be the
x-coordinate of point of intersection
of the graphs of f and g.

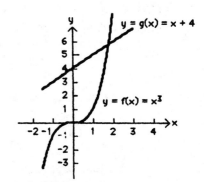

Step 1: Find a formula for x_n.

$$x_n = x_{n-1} - \frac{F(x_{n-1})}{F'(x_{n-1})} = x_{n-1} - \frac{x_{n-1}^3 - x_{n-1} - 4}{3x_{n-1}^2 - 1}$$

$$= \frac{3x_{n-1}^3 - x_{n-1} - x_{n-1}^3 + x_{n-1} + 4}{3x_{n-1}^2 - 1} = \frac{2x_{n-1}^3 + 4}{3x_{n-1}^2 - 1}$$

By using $x_n = \dfrac{2x_{n-1}^3 + 4}{3x_{n-1}^2 - 1}$ and initial approximation $x_1 = 2$, we find
$x_2, x_3, x_4, x_5, \dots$

$$x_2 = \frac{2x_1^3 + 4}{3x_1^2 - 1} = \frac{2(2)^3 + 4}{3(2)^2 - 1} = \frac{20}{11} = 1.8181818$$

$$x_3 = \frac{2(x_2)^3 + 4}{3(x_2)^2 - 1} = \frac{16.021036}{8.9173554} = 1.796613$$

$$x_4 = \frac{2x_3^3 + 4}{3x_3^2 - 1} = \frac{15.598281}{8.6834551} = 1.796322$$

$$x_5 = \frac{2x_4^3 + 4}{3x_4^2 - 1} = \frac{15.592645}{8.6803177} = 1.7963219$$

Since (approximately) $f(1.7963219) = 5.7963219 = g(1.7963219)$, the point of intersection is approximately $(1.7963219, 5.7963219)$.

21. $f(x) = x^{1/3}$, $g(x) = 12 - x$
$F(x) = f(x) - g(x)$
$\quad\ \ = x^{1/3} - 12 + x$

First we graph $f(x)$ and $g(x)$. The graphs indicate that the point of intersection is in $(9, 10)$. Therefore, let the first approximation be $x_1 = 10$.

$F(x) = x^{1/3} - 12 + x$

$F'(x) = \frac{1}{3}x^{-2/3} + 1$

$x_n = x_{n-1} - \dfrac{F(x_{n-1})}{F'(x_{n-1})}$

$\quad = x_{n-1} - \dfrac{x_{n-1}^{1/3} + x_{n-1} - 12}{\frac{1}{3}x_{n-1}^{-2/3} + 1}$

$\quad = \dfrac{-2x_{n-1} + 36x_{n-1}^{2/3}}{1 + 3x_{n-1}^{2/3}} = \dfrac{36x_{n-1}^{2/3} - 2x_{n-1}}{3x_{n-1}^{2/3} + 1}$

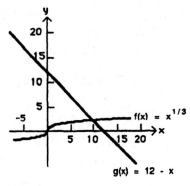

Let $n = 2$ and $x_1 = 10$; then,

$x_2 = \dfrac{36x_1^{2/3} - 2x_1}{3x_1^{2/3} + 1} = \dfrac{36(10)^{2/3} - 20}{3(10)^{2/3} + 1} = \dfrac{147.0972}{14.924766} = 9.8559129$

$x_3 \approx 9.855959$
$x_4 \approx 9.855959$

Since $f(9.855959) = 2.1440404 \approx g(9.855959)$, the point of intersection is approximately $(9.855959, 2.1440404)$.

23. $f(x) = e^x$, $g(x) = x + 2$

First we graph both $f(x)$ and $g(x)$, and then we use $F(x) = f(x) - g(x)$ and Newton's formula.

It is clear that we have two points of intersection: one is in the interval $(-2, -1)$ and the other is in the interval $(1, 2)$.

$F(x) = f(x) - g(x) = e^x - (x + 2) = e^x - x - 2$

$F'(x) = e^x - 1$

$x_n = x_{n-1} - \dfrac{F(x_{n-1})}{F'(x_{n-1})} = x_{n-1} - \dfrac{e^{x_{n-1}} - x_{n-1} - 2}{e^{x_{n-1}} - 1}$

$= \dfrac{x_{n-1}e^{x_{n-1}} - e^{x_{n-1}} + 2}{e^{x_{n-1}} - 1}$

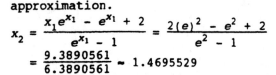

In order to find the first point of intersection, let $x_1 = 2$ be an initial approximation.

$x_2 = \dfrac{x_1 e^{x_1} - e^{x_1} + 2}{e^{x_1} - 1} = \dfrac{2(e)^2 - e^2 + 2}{e^2 - 1}$

$= \dfrac{9.3890561}{6.3890561} \approx 1.4695529$

$x_3 = 1.207329$, $x_4 = 1.1488056$,

$x_5 = 1.1461932$

In order to find the second point of intersection, let $x_1 = -2$ be an initial approximation.

$x_2 = \dfrac{-2(e)^{-2} - e^{-2} + 2}{e^{-2} - 1} = \dfrac{-3 + 2e^2}{1 - e^2} = \dfrac{11.778112}{-6.3890561} = -1.8434824$

$x_3 = \dfrac{1.5499754}{-.8417347} = -1.84140607$, $x_4 = \dfrac{1.5493692}{-.8414057} = -1.84140566$,

$x_5 = -1.8414057$

Since $f(1.1461932) = 3.1461932 = g(1.1461932)$ and $f(-1.8414057) = .1585943 = g(-1.8414057)$, the points of intersection are $(1.1461932, 3.1461932)$ and $(-1.8414057, .1585943)$.

25. If $f(x) = x^2 - A$, then $f(x_{n-1}) = x_{n-1}^2 - A$ and $f'(x_{n-1}) = 2x_{n-1}$.

Substituting into Newton's formula, we find

$x_n = x_{n-1} - \dfrac{f(x_{n-1})}{f'(x_{n-1})} = x_{n-1} - \dfrac{x_{n-1}^2 - A}{2x_{n-1}}$

$= \dfrac{2x_{n-1}}{2} - \dfrac{x_{n-1}}{2} + \dfrac{A}{2x_{n-1}} = \dfrac{x_{n-1}}{2} + \dfrac{A}{2x_{n-1}}$.

27. $x_n = x_{n-1} - \dfrac{f(x_{n-1})}{f'(x_{n-1})}$

If $f(x) = x^P - A$, then $f(x_{n-1}) = x_{n-1}^P - A$ and $f'(x_{n-1}) = px_{n-1}^{P-1}$ or

$x_n = x_{n-1} - \dfrac{x_{n-1}^P - A}{px_{n-1}^{(P-1)}} = \dfrac{px_{n-1}}{p} - \dfrac{x_{n-1}}{p} + \dfrac{A}{px_{n-1}^{(P-1)}} = \dfrac{p-1}{p}x_{n-1} + \dfrac{A}{px_{n-1}^{P-1}}$

29. $f(x) = \dfrac{x}{\sqrt{1 + x^2}}$ or $f(x) = x(1 + x^2)^{-1/2}$

$f'(x) = (1 + x^2)^{-1/2} + x\left[-\dfrac{1}{2}(1 + x^2)^{-3/2}(2x)\right] = (1 + x^2)^{-1/2} - x^2(1 + x^2)^{-3/2}$

$f(1) = 1(1 + 1)^{-1/2} = \dfrac{1}{\sqrt{2}}$

$f'(1) = (1 + 1)^{-1/2} - 1(1 + 1)^{-3/2} = \dfrac{1}{\sqrt{2}} - \dfrac{1}{2\sqrt{2}} = \dfrac{1}{2\sqrt{2}}$

$x_n = x_{n-1} - \dfrac{f(x_{n-1})}{f'(x_{n-1})}$

If $x_1 = 1$, then $f(x_1) = f(1)$ and $f'(x_1) = f'(1)$ or

$x_2 = 1 - \dfrac{\dfrac{1}{\sqrt{2}}}{\dfrac{1}{2\sqrt{2}}} = 1 - \dfrac{2\sqrt{2}}{\sqrt{2}} = -1$

$f(-1) = -1(1 + 1)^{-1/2} = -\dfrac{1}{\sqrt{2}}$

$f'(-1) = (1 + 1)^{-1/2} - 1(1 + 1)^{-3/2} = \dfrac{1}{\sqrt{2}} - \dfrac{1}{2\sqrt{2}} = \dfrac{1}{2\sqrt{2}}$

$x_3 = x_2 - \dfrac{f(x_2)}{f'(x_2)} = -1 - \dfrac{f(-1)}{f'(-1)} = -1 - \dfrac{-\dfrac{1}{\sqrt{2}}}{\dfrac{1}{2\sqrt{2}}} = -1 + \dfrac{2\sqrt{2}}{\sqrt{2}} = -1 + 2 = 1$

Therefore, $x_4 = -1$, $x_5 = 1$, $x_6 = -1$, ... We cannot find the roots, since the values for x_n oscillate between -1 and $+1$.

31. Let $f(x) = \dfrac{x}{\sqrt{1 + x^2}} = \dfrac{x}{(1 + x^2)^{1/2}}$. The equations for the tangent lines to the graph of f at $x = 1$ and $x = -1$ are given by

$x = 1$: $y - f(1) = f'(1)(x - 1)$; $x = -1$: $y - f(-1) = f'(-1)(x + 1)$

Now, $f(1) = \dfrac{1}{2^{1/2}}$ and $f(-1) = \dfrac{-1}{2^{1/2}}$. Also,

$f'(x) = \dfrac{(1 + x^2)^{1/2} - x\left(\dfrac{1}{2}\right)(1 + x^2)^{-1/2}2x}{1 + x^2} = \dfrac{1}{(1 + x^2)^{3/2}}$

and $f'(1) = \dfrac{1}{2^{3/2}}$, $f'(-1) = \dfrac{1}{2^{3/2}}$

Thus, the equations of the tangent lines are:

$x = 1$: $y - \dfrac{1}{\sqrt{2}}$, $= \dfrac{1}{2^{3/2}}(x - 1)$ $x = -1$: $y + \dfrac{1}{2^{1/2}} = \dfrac{1}{2^{3/2}}(x + 1)$

or $y = \dfrac{1}{2^{3/2}}x + \dfrac{1}{2^{3/2}} = \dfrac{\sqrt{2}}{4}(x + 1)$ or $y = \dfrac{1}{2^{3/2}}x - \dfrac{1}{2^{3/2}} = \dfrac{\sqrt{2}}{4}(x - 1)$

The graphs of f and the two tangent lines are shown below.

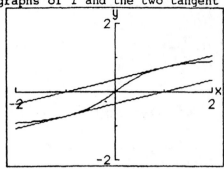

33. To find the number of units that must be sold to generate a revenue of $600,000, we must solve the equation:

$$100xe^{-0.05x} = 600 \quad \text{or} \quad xe^{-0.05x} - 6 = 0$$

Let $f(x) = xe^{-0.05x} - 6$, $x \geq 0$. Using the methods of Chapter 4, the graph of f is:

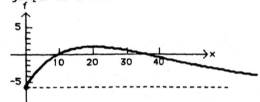

Thus, f has a zero between 0 and 10 (close to 10) and a zero between 30 and 40. We apply Newton's method to $f(x)$, first with an initial approximation of 10 and then with an initial approximation of 35.

$$f(x) = xe^{-0.05x} - 6$$
$$f'(x) = e^{-0.05x} - 0.05xe^{-0.05x}$$
$$x_n = x_{n-1} - \frac{f(x_{n-1})}{f'(x_{n-1})}$$

(A) Near $x = 10$:

n	x_n	$f(x_n)$	$f'(x_n)$
1	10	0.065307	0.303265
2	9.784655	-0.001061	0.313150
3	9.788044	0	0.312993

(B) Near $x = 35$:

n	x_n	$f(x_n)$	$f'(x_n)$
1	35	0.082088	-0.130330
2	35.629845	-0.000409	-0.131593
3	35.626740	0	-0.131587

Thus, $R(x) \approx 600$ when $x = 9.788$ and when $x = 35.627$. The revenue is approximately $600,000 when either 9788 or 35,627 units are sold.

35. To find the equilibrium price, we set $S(x) = D(x)$, that is

$$e^{0.02x} = 20 - e^{0.08x}$$

and solve for x.

Let $f(x) = e^{0.02x} + e^{0.08x} - 20$. Note that $f(0) = -18$,
$f'(x) = 0.02e^{0.02x} + 0.08e^{0.08x} > 0$ and $\lim_{x \to \infty} f(x) = \infty$.

Thus, f has one zero on $(0, \infty)$.

It can be verified that $f(30) < 0$ and $f(40) > 0$. We will use Newton's method with an initial approximation $x_1 = 40$ to find the zero of f.

n	x_n	$f(x_n)$	$f'(x_n)$
1	40	6.758071	2.007113
2	36.632940	0.820135	1.540774
3	36.100652	0.016869	1.477835
4	36.089238	0.000007	1.476514

Thus, $f(x) \approx 0$ when $x = 36.1$. To find the equilibrium price, set $x = 36.1$ in either S or D. Using S,

$$\bar{p} = e^{0.02(36.1)} \approx 2.06.$$

Therefore, the equilibrium price $\bar{p} \approx \$2.06$.

37. The internal rate of return r is the solution of the equation

$$6 = \frac{5}{1 + r} + \frac{3}{(1 + r)^2}$$

or $\quad 6 - \frac{5}{1 + r} - \frac{3}{(1 + r)^2} = 0$

Let $x = 1 + r$ and $f(x) = 6 - 5x^{-1} - 3x^{-2}$. Since r is an interest rate, $0 < r < 1$, implying that $1 < x < 2$.

Now, $f(1) = -2$ and $f(2) = 6 - \frac{5}{2} - \frac{3}{4} = \frac{11}{4} > 0$. Thus, f does have a zero between $x = 1$ and $x = 2$. Moreover, since

$$f'(x) = 5x^{-2} + 6x^{-3} > 0$$

for $x > 0$, f is increasing on $(0, \infty)$ and consequently has exactly one positive zero.

By Newton's method,

$$x_n = x_{n-1} - \frac{f(x_{n-1})}{f'(x_{n-1})}$$

$$= x_{n-1} - \frac{[6 - 5x_{n-1}^{-1} - 3x_{n-1}^{-2}]}{5x_{n-1}^{-2} + 6x_{n-1}^{-3}}$$

$$= x_{n-1} - \frac{6x_{n-1}^3 - 5x_{n-1}^2 - 3x_{n-1}}{5x_{n-1} + 6}$$

Letting $x_1 = 1$, we have

n	x_n	$f(x_n)$	$f'(x_n)$
1	1	-2	11
2	1.181818	0.3786979	7.214837
3	1.234307	-0.0199881	6.472554
4	1.237395	-0.0000620	6.432366
5	1.237405	0.0000002	6.432241

Thus, $f(x) \approx 0$ when $x \approx 1.2374$ (to four decimal places). Now $r = x - 1$ = 0.2374 and the internal rate of return is 23.74% compounded annually.

39. The internal rate of return r is the solution of the equation

$$160,000 = \frac{10,000}{1 + r} + \frac{10,000}{(1 + r)^2} + \frac{10,000}{(1 + r)^3} + \frac{10,000}{(1 + r)^4} + \frac{200,000}{(1 + r)^4}$$

or $16 - \dfrac{1}{1 + r} - \dfrac{1}{(1 + r)^2} - \dfrac{1}{(1 + r)^3} - \dfrac{21}{(1 + r)^4} = 0$

Let $x = 1 + r$ and $f(x) = 16 - x^{-1} - x^{-2} - x^{-3} - 21x^{-4}$.

Since r is an interest rate, $0 < r < 1$, implying that $1 < x < 2$.
Now, $f(1) = 16 - 24 = -8$ and $f(2) = 16 - \frac{1}{2} - \frac{1}{4} - \frac{1}{8} - \frac{21}{16} = 13.8125$.
Thus, f has a zero between $x = 1$ and $x = 2$. Moreover, since

$$f'(x) = x^{-2} + 2x^{-3} + 3x^{-4} + 84x^{-5} > 0$$

for $x > 0$, f is increasing on $(0, \infty)$ and consequently has exactly one positive zero.

By Newton's method

$$x_n = x_{n-1} - \frac{f(x_{n-1})}{f'(x_{n-1})}$$

$$= x_{n-1} - \frac{16x_{n-1}^5 - x_{n-1}^4 - x_{n-1}^3 - x_{n-1}^2 - 21x_{n-1}}{x_{n-1}^3 + 2x_{n-1}^2 + 3x_{n-1} + 84}$$

Letting $x_1 = 1$, we have

n	x_n	$f(x_n)$	$f'(x_n)$
1	1	-8	90
2	1.088889	-1.474062	59.39982
3	1.113705	-0.782528	53.23037
4	1.115175	-0.000251	52.88997
5	1.11518	-0.000003	52.88887

Thus, $f(x) \approx 0$ when $x \approx 1.1152$ (to four decimal places). Now, $r = x - 1$ = 0.1152 and the internal rate of return is 11.52% compounded annually.

41. The graph of $N(t)$ is:

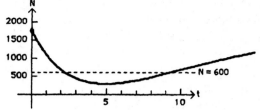

To determine the time interval where $N(t) < 600$, we must solve the equation:
$$N(t) = 600$$
$$1750 - 800te^{-0.2t} = 600$$
which reduces to $23 - 16te^{-0.2t} = 0$.

Let $f(t) = 23 - 16te^{-0.2t}$ and apply Newton's method, first with an initial approximation of $t_1 = 3$ and then with an initial approximation of $t_1 = 10$.

$$f(t) = 23 - 16te^{-0.2t}$$
$$f'(t) = e^{-0.2t}(3.2t - 16)$$
$$t_n = t_{n-1} - \frac{f(t_{n-1})}{f'(t_{n-1})}$$

(A) Near $t = 3$:

n	t_n	$f(t_n)$	$f'(t_n)$
1	3	-3.342959	-3.512394
2	2.048239	1.243307	-6.270805
3	2.246509	0.064997	-5.622176
4	2.258069	0.000211	-5.585641
5	2.258107	0	-5.58522

(B) Near $t = 10$:

n	t_n	$f(t_n)$	$f'(t_n)$
1	10	1.346350	2.165365
2	9.378232	0.003694	2.147167
3	9.376511	0	2.147062

Thus, $f(t) \approx 0$ when $t \approx 2.3$ and when $t \approx 9.4$ and the bacteria level, $N(t)$, will be less than 600 when $2.3 < t < 9.4$.

43. The graph of $C(t) = 10e^{-0.1t} + 15e^{-0.2t}$ is (approximately):

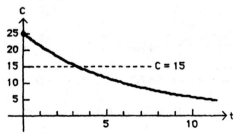

To find when the concentration reaches 15 milligrams per milliliter, we must solve the equation:

$$C(t) = 15 \quad \text{or} \quad 10e^{-0.1t} + 15e^{-0.2t} = 15$$

which reduces to $2e^{-0.1t} + 3e^{-0.2t} - 3 = 0$.

Let $f(t) = 2e^{-0.1t} + 3e^{-0.2t} - 3$ and apply Newton's method with an initial approximation of $t_1 = 5$.

$$f(t) = 2e^{-0.1t} + 3e^{-0.2t} - 3$$
$$f'(t) = -0.2e^{-0.1t} - 0.6e^{-0.2t}$$

$$t_n = t_{n-1} - \frac{f(t_{n-1})}{f'(t_{n-1})}$$

n	t_n	$f(t_n)$	$f'(t_n)$
1	5	−0.683300	−0.342034
2	3.002243	0.127001	−0.477270
3	3.268341	0.002809	−0.546321
4	3.274498	0	−0.455848

Thus, $f(t) \approx 0$ when $t \approx 3.3$. The second injection should be administered 3.3 hours after the first injection.

45. $N(t) = t^3 - 6t^2 + 25t$

We want to find t such that $N(t) = 500$; that is, we want to find the first positive zero of

$$g(t) = t^3 - 6t^2 + 25t - 500$$

Now, $g'(t) = 3t^2 - 12t + 25$. By Newton's formula,

$$t_n = t_{n-1} - \frac{g(t_{n-1})}{g'(t_{n-1})} = t_{n-1} - \frac{t_{n-1}^3 - 6t_{n-1}^2 + 25t_{n-1} - 500}{3t_{n-1}^2 - 12t_{n-1} + 25}$$

$$= \frac{2t_{n-1}^3 - 6t_{n-1}^2 + 500}{3t_{n-1}^2 - 12t_{n-1} + 25}$$

Since $g(9) = -32 < 0$ and $g(10) = 150 > 0$, we choose $t_1 = 9$ as our initial approximation.

$$t_2 = \frac{2(9)^3 - 6(9)^2 + 500}{3(9)^2 - 12(9) + 25} = 9.2$$

$$t_3 = \frac{2(9.2)^3 - 6(9.2)^2 + 500}{3(9.2)^2 - 12(9.2) + 25} = 9.194968$$

$$t_4 = \frac{2(9.194968)^3 - 6(9.194968)^2 + 500}{3(9.194968)^2 - 12(9.194968) + 25} = 9.194965$$

$$t_5 = \frac{2(9.194965)^3 - 6(9.194965)^2 + 500}{3(9.194965)^2 - 12(9.194965) + 25} = 9.194965$$

Thus, $t = 9.195$ or 9.2 hours correct to one decimal place.

Things to remember:

1. THE INTERPOLATING POLYNOMIAL

   If $f(x)$ is the function defined by the following table of $n + 1$ points:

x	x_0	x_1 $\cdots$ x_n
$f(x)$	y_0	y_1 $\cdots$ y_n

   then the INTERPOLATING POLYNOMIAL for $f(x)$ is the polynomial $p(x)$ of degree less than or equal to n which satisfies

   $$p(x_0) = y_0 = f(x_0)$$
   $$p(x_1) = y_1 = f(x_1)$$
   $$\vdots \qquad \vdots$$
   $$p(x_n) = y_n = f(x_n)$$

   The GENERAL FORM of the interpolating polynomial is

   $$p(x) = a_0 + a_1(x - x_0) + a_2(x - x_0)(x - x_1) + \cdots$$
   $$+ a_n(x - x_0)(x - x_1) \cdot \ldots \cdot (x - x_{n-1})$$

2. STEPS FOR FINDING THE INTERPOLATING POLYNOMIAL

   Write the general form of $p(x)$ and proceed as follows:

   Step 1: Use the condition $p(x_0) = y_0$ to find a_0.

   Step 2: Use the condition $p(x_1) = y_1$ and the value of a_0 determined in the preceding step to find a_1.

   Step 3: Use the condition $p(x_2) = y_2$ and the values of a_0 and a_1 determined in the preceding steps to find a_2.

   $\vdots$

   Step $n + 1$: Use the condition $p(x_n) = y_n$ and the values of a_0, a_1, ..., a_{n-1} determined in the preceding steps to find a_n.

3. DIVIDED DIFFERENCE TABLES AND INTERPOLATING POLYNOMIALS

   Given the defining table for function $f(x)$ with $n + 1$ points

x	x_0	x_1 $\cdots$ x_n
$f(x)$	y_0	y_1 $\cdots$ y_n

   where $x_0 < x_1 < \ldots < x_n$. Then the DIVIDED DIFFERENCE TABLE is computed as follows:

   Column 1: x values from the defining table.

Column 2: y values from the defining table.

Column 3: First divided differences computed using columns 1 and 2.

Column 4: Second divided differences computed using columns 1 and 3.

⋮

Column $n + 2$: nth divided differences computed using columns 1 and $n + 1$.

The coefficients in the general form of the interpolating polynomial

$$p(x) = a_0 + a_1(x - x_0) + a_2(x - x_0)(x - x_1) + \cdots$$
$$+ a_n(x - x_0)(x - x_1) \cdot \ldots \cdot (x - x_{n-1})$$

are the first numbers in each column of the divided difference table, beginning with column 2.

1.

x	1	3	4
$f(x)$	2	6	11

The general form of $p(x)$ for this table is:
$$p(x) = a_0 + a_1(x - 1) + a_2(x - 1)(x - 3)$$

Step 1: $f(1) = 2 = p(1)$
$$2 = a_0$$

Step 2: $f(3) = 6 = p(3)$
$$6 = a_0 + a_1(2)$$
$$6 = 2 + 2a_1$$
$$2 = a_1$$

Step 3: $f(4) = 11 = p(4)$
$$11 = a_0 + a_1(3) + a_2(3)(1)$$
$$11 = 2 + 6 + 3a_2$$
$$3 = 3a_2$$
$$1 = a_2$$

Therefore, $p(x) = 2 + 2(x - 1) + (x - 1)(x - 3) = x^2 - 2x + 3$ is the interpolating polynomial for this table.

3.

x	-1	0	2	4
$f(x)$	6	5	15	-39

The general form of $p(x)$ for this table is:
$$p(x) = a_0 + a_1(x + 1) + a_2(x + 1)x + a_3(x + 1)x(x - 2)$$
or $p(x) = a_0 + a_1(x + 1) + a_2x(x + 1) + a_3x(x + 1)(x - 2)$

Step 1: $f(-1) = 6 = p(-1)$
$$6 = a_0$$

Step 2: $f(0) = 5 = p(0)$

$$5 = a_0 + a_1(1)$$
$$5 = 6 + a_1$$
$$-1 = a_1$$

Step 3: $f(2) = 15 = p(2)$

$$15 = a_0 + a_1(3) + a_2(2)(3)$$
$$15 = 6 + (-1)(3) + 6a_2$$
$$12 = 6a_2$$
$$2 = a_2$$

Step 4: $f(4) = -39 = p(4)$

$$-39 = a_0 + a_1(5) + a_2(4)(5) + a_3(4)(5)(2)$$
$$-39 = 6 + (-1)(5) + 2(4)(5) + 40a_3$$
$$-39 = 41 + 40a_3$$
$$-80 = 40a_3$$
$$-2 = a_3$$

Therefore, $p(x) = 6 - (x + 1) + 2x(x + 1) - 2x(x + 1)(x - 2)$ is the interpolating polynomial for this table.

5.

x	1	2	3
$f(x)$	4	8	14

The divided difference table is:

x_k	y_k	1st D.D.	2nd D.D.
1	4		
		$\dfrac{8 - 4}{2 - 1} = 4$	
2	8		$\dfrac{6 - 4}{3 - 1} = 1$
		$\dfrac{14 - 8}{3 - 2} = 6$	
3	14		

The general form of the interpolating polynomial is:
   $p(x) = a_0 + a_1(x - 1) + a_2(x - 1)(x - 2)$.
From the divided difference table,
   $p(x) = 4 + 4(x - 1) + (x - 1)(x - 2)$

7.

x	-1	0	1	2
$f(x)$	-3	1	3	9

The divided difference table is:

x_k	y_k	1st D.D.	2nd D.D.	3rd D.D.
-1	-3			
		$\frac{1 - (-3)}{0 - (-1)} = 4$		
0	1		$\frac{2 - 4}{1 - (-1)} = -1$	
		$\frac{3 - 1}{1 - 0} = 2$		$\frac{2 - (-1)}{2 - (-1)} = 1$
1	3		$\frac{6 - 2}{2 - 0} = 2$	
		$\frac{9 - 3}{2 - 1} = 6$		
2	9			

The general form of the interpolating polynomial is:
$$p(x) = a_0 + a_1(x + 1) + a_2(x + 1)x + a_3(x + 1)x(x - 1)$$
or $p(x) = a_0 + a_1(x + 1) + a_2 x(x + 1) + a_3 x(x + 1)(x - 1)$
From the divided difference table,
$$p(x) = -3 + 4(x + 1) + (-1)x(x + 1) + x(x + 1)(x - 1)$$
$$= -3 + 4(x + 1) - x(x + 1) + x(x + 1)(x - 1)$$

9.

x	-2	1	2	4
$f(x)$	25	10	17	13

The divided difference table is:

x_k	y_k	1st D.D.	2nd D.D.	3rd D.D.
-2	25			
		$\frac{10 - 25}{1 - (-2)} = -5$		
1	10		$\frac{7 - (-5)}{2 - (-2)} = 3$	
		$\frac{17 - 10}{2 - 1} = 7$		$\frac{-3 - 3}{4 - (-2)} = -1$
2	17		$\frac{-2 - 7}{4 - 1} = -3$	
		$\frac{13 - 17}{4 - 2} = -2$		
4	13			

The general form of the interpolating polynomial is:
$$p(x) = a_0 + a_1(x + 2) + a_2(x + 2)(x - 1) + a_3(x + 2)(x - 1)(x - 2)$$
From the divided difference table,
$$p(x) = 25 - 5(x + 2) + 3(x + 2)(x - 1) - (x + 2)(x - 1)(x - 2)$$

11.

x	-4	0	4	8
$f(x)$	-64	32	0	224

The divided difference table is shown on the following page.

x_k	y_k	1st D.D.	2nd D.D.	3rd D.D.
-4	-64			
		$\dfrac{32 - (-64)}{0 - (-4)} = 24$		
0	32		$\dfrac{-8 - 24}{4 - (-4)} = -4$	
		$\dfrac{0 - 32}{4 - 0} = -8$		$\dfrac{8 - (-4)}{8 - (-4)} = 1$
4	0		$\dfrac{56 - (-8)}{8 - 0} = 8$	
		$\dfrac{224 - 0}{8 - 4} = 56$		
8	224			

The general form of the interpolating polynomial is:
$$p(x) = a_0 + a_1(x + 4) + a_2(x + 4)x + a_3(x + 4)x(x - 4)$$
Thus,
$$p(x) = -64 + 24(x + 4) - 4(x + 4)x + (x + 4)x(x - 4)$$

(A) $f(2) \approx p(2) = -64 + 24(6) - 4(6)(2) + (6)(2)(-2)$
$$= -64 + 144 - 48 - 24 = 8$$

(B) $f(6) \approx p(6) = -64 + 24(10) - 4(10)(6) + (10)(6)(2)$
$$= -64 + 240 - 240 + 120 = 56$$

13.

x	-1	0	1	4
$f(x)$	0	0	0	15

The divided difference table is:

x_k	y_k	1st D.D.	2nd D.D.	3rd D.D.
-1	0			
		$\dfrac{0 - 0}{0 - (-1)} = 0$		
0	0		$\dfrac{0 - 0}{1 - (-1)} = 0$	
		$\dfrac{0 - 0}{1 - 0} = 0$		$\dfrac{\frac{5}{4} - 0}{4 - (-1)} = \dfrac{1}{4}$
1	0		$\dfrac{5 - 0}{4 - 0} = \dfrac{5}{4}$	
		$\dfrac{15 - 0}{4 - 1} = 5$		
4	15			

The general form of the interpolating polynomial is:
$$p(x) = a_0 + a_1(x + 1) + a_2(x + 1)x + a_3(x + 1)x(x - 1)$$
Thus,
$$p(x) = 0 + 0(x + 1) + 0(x + 1)x + \frac{1}{4}(x + 1)x(x - 1)$$
or $p(x) = \dfrac{1}{4}(x + 1)x(x - 1)$

(A) $f(2) \approx p(2) = \dfrac{1}{4}(3)(2)(1) = \dfrac{6}{4} = \dfrac{3}{2} = 1.5$

(B) $f(3) \approx p(3) = \dfrac{1}{4}(4)(3)(2) = 6$

15.

x	-4	-2	0	2	4
f(x)	24	2	0	-6	8

The divided difference table is:

x_k	y_k	1st D.D.	2nd D.D.	3rd D.D.	4th D.D.

$x_k = -4$, $y_k = 24$

$$\frac{2 - 24}{-2 - (-4)} = -11$$

$x_k = -2$, $y_k = 2$

$$\frac{-1 - (-11)}{0 - (-4)} = \frac{5}{2}$$

$$\frac{0 - 2}{0 - (-2)} = -1$$

$$\frac{-\frac{1}{2} - \frac{5}{2}}{2 - (-4)} = -\frac{1}{2}$$

$x_k = 0$, $y_k = 0$

$$\frac{-3 - (-1)}{2 - (-2)} = -\frac{1}{2}$$

$$\frac{\frac{5}{2} - \left(-\frac{1}{2}\right)}{4 - (-2)} = \frac{1}{2}$$

$$\frac{\frac{1}{2} - \left(-\frac{1}{2}\right)}{4 - (-4)} = \frac{1}{8}$$

$$\frac{-6 - 0}{2 - 0} = -3$$

$x_k = 2$, $y_k = -6$

$$\frac{7 - (-3)}{4 - 0} = \frac{5}{2}$$

$x_k = 4$, $y_k = 8$

$$\frac{8 - (-6)}{4 - 2} = 7$$

The general form of the interpolating polynomial is:

$$p(x) = a_0 + a_1(x + 4) + a_2(x + 4)(x + 2) + a_3(x + 4)(x + 2)x$$
$$+ a_4(x + 4)(x + 2)x(x - 2)$$

Thus, $p(x) = 24 - 11(x + 4) + \frac{5}{2}(x + 4)(x + 2) - \frac{1}{2}(x + 4)(x + 2)x$
$$+ \frac{1}{8}(x + 4)(x + 2)x(x - 2)$$

(A) $f(-3) \sim p(-3) = 24 - 11(1) + \frac{5}{2}(1)(-1) - \frac{1}{2}(1)(-1)(-3)$
$$+ \frac{1}{8}(1)(-1)(-3)(-5)$$
$$= 24 - 11 - \frac{5}{2} - \frac{3}{2} - \frac{15}{8} = \frac{104}{8} - \frac{20}{8} - \frac{12}{8} - \frac{15}{8} = \frac{57}{8} = 7.125$$

(B) $f(1) \sim p(1) = 24 - 11(5) + \frac{5}{2}(5)(3) - \frac{1}{2}(5)(3)(1) + \frac{1}{8}(5)(3)(1)(-1)$
$$= 24 - 55 + \frac{75}{2} - \frac{15}{2} - \frac{15}{8} = -\frac{23}{8} = -2.875$$

17.

x	-3	-2	-1	1	2	3
f(x)	-24	-6	0	0	6	24

The divided difference table is:

x_k	y_k	1st D.D.	2nd D.D.	3rd D.D.	4th D.D.	5th D.D.
-3	-24					
		18				
-2	-6		-6			
		6		1		
-1	0		-2		0	
		0		1		0
1	0		2		0	
		6		1		
2	6		6			
		18				
3	24					

The general form of the interpolating polynomial is:
$$p(x) = a_0 + a_1(x + 3) + a_2(x + 3)(x + 2) + a_3(x + 3)(x + 2)(x + 1)$$
$$+ a_4(x + 3)(x + 2)(x + 1)(x - 1)$$
$$+ a_5(x + 3)(x + 2)(x + 1)(x - 1)(x - 2)$$

From the divided difference table,
$$p(x) = -24 + 18(x + 3) - 6(x + 3)(x + 2) + (x + 3)(x + 2)(x + 1)$$

(A) $f(-0.5) \approx p(-0.5) = p\left(-\frac{1}{2}\right) = -24 + 18\left(\frac{5}{2}\right) - 6\left(\frac{5}{2}\right)\left(\frac{3}{2}\right) + \left(\frac{5}{2}\right)\left(\frac{3}{2}\right)\left(\frac{1}{2}\right)$

$$= -24 + 45 - \frac{45}{2} + \frac{15}{8}$$

$$= \frac{3}{8} = 0.375$$

(B) $f(2.5) \approx p(2.5) = -24 + 18(5.5) - 6(5.5)(4.5) + (5.5)(4.5)(3.5)$
$$= -24 + 99 - 148.5 + 86.625$$
$$= 13.125$$

19.

x	-2	0	2
$f(x)$	2	0	2

The divided difference table is:

x_k	y_k	1st D.D.	2nd D.D.
-2	2		
		-1	
0	0		$\frac{1}{2}$
		1	
2	2		

The general form of the interpolating polynomial is
$$p(x) = a_0 + a_1(x + 2) + a_2(x + 2)x$$
From the divided difference table,
$$p(x) = 2 - (x + 2) + \frac{1}{2}(x + 2)x = \frac{1}{2}x^2$$

The graph of $p(x)$ is shown at the right.

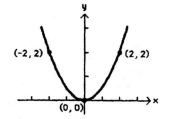

21.

x	0	1	2
$f(x)$	-4	-2	0

The divided difference table is:

x_k	y_k	1st D.D.	2nd D.D.
0	-4		
		2	
1	-2		0
		2	
2	0		

The form of the interpolating polynomial is
$$p(x) = a_0 + a_1 x + a_2 x(x - 1)$$
From the divided difference table,
$$p(x) = -4 + 2x$$
The graph of $p(x)$ is shown at the right.

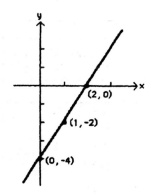

23.

x	-1	0	2	3
$f(x)$	0	2	0	-4

The divided difference table is:

x_k	y_k	1st D.D.	2nd D.D.	3rd D.D.
-1	0			
		2		
0	2		-1	
		-1		0
2	0		-1	
		-4		
3	-4			

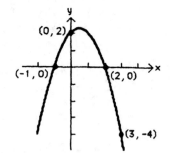

The form of the interpolating polynomial is
$$p(x) = a_0 + a_1(x + 1) + a_2(x + 1)x$$
$$+ a_3(x + 1)x(x - 2)$$

From the divided difference table,
$$p(x) = 2(x + 1) - (x + 1)x = 2 + x - x^2$$

The graph of $p(x)$ is shown at the right.

25.

x	-2	-1	0	1	2
$f(x)$	1	5	3	1	5

The divided difference table is:

x_k	y_k	1st D.D.	2nd D.D.	3rd D.D.	4th D.D.
-2	1				
		4			
-1	5		-3		
		-2		1	
0	3		0		0
		-2		1	
1	1		3		
		4			
2	5				

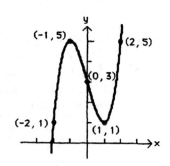

The form of the interpolating polynomial is
$$p(x) = a_0 + a_1(x + 2) + a_2(x + 2)(x + 1)$$
$$+ a_3(x + 2)(x + 1)x$$
$$+ a_4(x + 2)(x + 1)x(x - 1)$$

From the divided difference table,
$$p(x) = 1 + 4(x + 2) - 3(x + 2)(x + 1)$$
$$+ (x + 2)(x + 1)x$$
$$= 1 + 4x + 8 - 3x^2 - 9x - 6 + x^3$$
$$+ 3x^2 + 2x$$
$$= x^3 - 3x + 3$$

The graph of $p(x)$ is shown at the right.

27.

x	-2	-1	0	1	2
$f(x)$	-3	0	5	0	-3

The divided difference table is:

x_k	y_k	1st D.D.	2nd D.D.	3rd D.D.	4th D.D.
-2	-3				
		3			
-1	0		1		
		5		-2	
0	5		-5		1
		-5		2	
1	0		1		
		-3			
2	-3				

The form of the interpolating polynomial is
$$p(x) = a_0 + a_1(x + 2) + a_2(x + 2)(x + 1)$$
$$+ a_3(x + 2)(x + 1)x$$
$$+ a_4(x + 2)(x + 1)x(x - 1)$$

From the divided difference table,
$$\begin{aligned}
p(x) &= -3 + 3(x + 2) + (x + 2)(x + 1) \\
&\quad - 2(x + 2)(x + 1)x \\
&\quad + (x + 2)(x + 1)x(x - 1) \\
&= -3 + 3x + 6 + x^2 + 3x + 2 - 2x^3 \\
&\quad - 6x^2 - 4x + x^4 + 2x^3 - x^2 - 2x \\
&= x^4 - 6x^2 + 5
\end{aligned}$$

The graph of $p(x)$ is shown at the right.

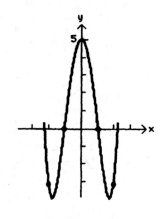

29. $f(x) = \sqrt{x}$

x	1	4	9
$f(x)$	1	2	3

The form of the interpolating polynomial is:
$$p(x) = a_0 + a_1(x - 1) + a_2(x - 1)(x - 4)$$

<u>Step 1</u>: $f(1) = 1 = p(1)$
$$1 = a_0$$

<u>Step 2</u>: $f(4) = 2 = p(4)$
$$2 = a_0 + a_1(3)$$
$$2 = 1 + 3a_1$$
$$\frac{1}{3} = a_1$$

<u>Step 3</u>: $f(9) = 3 = p(9)$
$$3 = a_0 + a_1(8) + a_2(8)(5)$$
$$3 = 1 + \frac{8}{3} + 40a_2$$
$$-\frac{2}{3} = 40a_2$$
$$-\frac{1}{60} = a_2$$

Thus, $p(x) = 1 + \frac{1}{3}(x - 1) - \frac{1}{60}(x - 1)(x - 4)$.

x	1	2	3	4	5	6	7	8	9
$p(x)$	1	1.3	1.7	2	2.3	2.5	2.7	2.9	3
$f(x)$	1	1.4	1.7	2	2.2	2.4	2.6	2.8	3

31. $f(x) = \dfrac{10x}{1 + x^2}$

x	-2	-1	0	1	2
$f(x)$	-4	-5	0	5	4

The divided difference table is:

x_k	y_k	1st D.D.	2nd D.D.	3rd D.D.	4th D.D.
-2	-4				
		-1			
-1	-5		3		
		5		-1	
0	0		0		0
		5		-1	
1	5		-3		
		-1			
2	4				

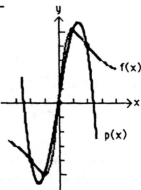

The form of the interpolating polynomial is

$p(x) = a_0 + a_1(x + 2) + a_2(x + 2)(x + 1)$
$\qquad + a_3(x + 2)(x + 1)x$
$\qquad + a_4(x + 2)(x + 1)x(x - 1)$

and from the divided difference table, we have

$p(x) = -4 - (x + 2) + 3(x + 2)(x + 1)$
$\qquad - (x + 2)(x + 1)x$
$\quad = -4 - x - 2 + 3x^2 + 9x + 6 - x^3 - 3x^2 - 2x$
$\quad = 6x - x^3$

The graphs of $f(x)$ and $p(x)$ are shown at the right.

33. We are looking for the interpolating polynomial through the points

x	$-x_1$	0	x_1
y	y_1	y_2	y_1

The divided difference table is:

x_k	y_k	1st D.D.	2nd D.D.
$-x_1$	y_1		
		$\dfrac{y_2 - y_1}{x_1}$	
0	y_2		$\dfrac{y_1 - y_2}{x_1^2}$
		$\dfrac{y_1 - y_2}{x_1}$	
x_1	y_1		

The interpolating polynomial is

$$p(x) = y_1 + \frac{y_2 - y_1}{x_1}(x + x_1) + \frac{(y_1 - y_2)}{x_1^2}(x + x_1)x$$

$$= y_1 + \frac{(y_2 - y_1)x}{x_1} + (y_2 - y_1) + \frac{(y_1 - y_2)x^2}{x_1^2} + \frac{(y_1 - y_2)x}{x_1}$$

$$= y_2 + \frac{(y_1 - y_2)}{x_1^2}x^2$$

35. Given

t	0	4	8	12
C(t)	2	32	38	20

The divided difference table is:

t_k	y_k	1st D.D.	2nd D.D.	3rd D.D.
0	2			
		7.5		
4	32		-0.75	
		1.5		0
8	38		-0.75	
		-4.5		
12	20			

The interpolating polynomial is

$$p(t) = 2 + 7.5t - 0.75t(t - 4)$$
$$= 2 + 10.5t - 0.75t^2$$

The approximate cash reserves after six months are:

$$C(6) \sim p(6) = 2 + 10.5(6) - 0.75(36) = 38 \text{ or } \$38,000$$

The average cash reserves for the first quarter is given by the definite integral $\frac{1}{3}\int_0^3 C(t)dt$ which is approximately equal to

$$\frac{1}{3}\int_0^3 p(t)dt = \frac{1}{3}\int_0^3 (2 + 10.5t - 0.75t^2)dt$$

$$= \frac{1}{3}\left[2t + \frac{10.5}{2}t^2 - \frac{0.75}{3}t^3\right]\Big|_0^3$$

$$= \frac{1}{3}[6 + 47.25 - 6.75]$$

$$= 15.5 \quad \text{or} \quad \$15,500$$

37. Given

x	0	0.2	0.8	1
f(x)	0	0.1	0.4	1

The divided difference table is shown on the following page.

x_k	y_k	1st D.D.	2nd D.D.	3rd D.D.
0	0			
		0.5		
0.2	0.1		0	
		0.5		3.125
0.8	0.4		3.125	
		3		
1	1			

The interpolating polynomial is

$$p(x) = 0 + 0.5x + 3.125x(x - 0.2)(x - 0.8)$$
$$= x - 3.125x^2 + 3.125x^3$$

Coefficient of inequality $= 2\int_0^1 [x - f(x)]dx \approx 2\int_0^1 [x - p(x)]dx$

$$= 2\int_0^1 [x - (x - 3.125x^2 + 3.125x^3)]dx$$

$$= 2\int_0^1 (3.125x^2 - 3.125x^3)dx$$

$$= 2(3.125)\left(\frac{x^3}{3} - \frac{x^4}{4}\right)\Big|_0^1$$

$$= 6.25\left(\frac{1}{3} - \frac{1}{4}\right) = 6.25\left(\frac{1}{12}\right)$$

$$\approx 0.5208$$

39. Given

x	2	4	6
$R(x)$	24.4	36	34.8

The divided difference table is:

x_k	y_k	1st D.D.	2nd D.D.
2	24.4		
		5.8	
4	36		-1.6
		-0.6	
6	34.8		

The interpolating polynomial is

$$p(x) = 24.4 + 5.8(x - 2) - 1.6(x - 2)(x - 4)$$
$$= 15.4x - 1.6x^2$$

The approximate revenue if 5000 units are produced is:

$$R(5) \approx p(5) = 15.4(5) - 1.6(5)^2$$
$$= 77 - 40 = 37 \quad \text{or} \quad \$37,000$$

To approximate the maximum value of R, we maximize p. Note that p is a quadratic whose graph opens down. Now,

$$p'(x) = 15.4 - 3.2x$$

The critical value corresponds to the maximum value of p:

$$15.4 - 3.2x = 0$$
$$x = \frac{15.4}{3.2} = 4.8125 \approx 4.813$$

Therefore, the approximate production level that will maximize the revenue is 4813 units.

41. Given

t	0	1	2	3	4
$C(t)$	14	13	16	17	10

The divided difference table is:

t_k	y_k	1st D.D.	2nd D.D.	3rd D.D.	4th D.D.
0	14				
		−1			
1	13		2		
		3		−1	
2	16		−1		0
		1		−1	
3	17		−4		
		−7			
4	10				

Thus, the interpolating polynomial is:
$$p(t) = 14 - t + 2t(t - 1) - t(t - 1)(t - 2)$$
$$= 14 - 5t + 5t^2 - t^3$$

The average temperature over the four-hour period is given by the definite integral

$$\frac{1}{4}\int_0^4 C(t) \approx \frac{1}{4}\int_0^4 p(t)\,dt = \frac{1}{4}\int_0^4 (14 - 5t + 5t^2 - t^3)\,dt$$

$$= \frac{1}{4}\left(14t - \frac{5}{2}t^2 + \frac{5}{3}t^3 - \frac{t^4}{4}\right)\Big|_0^4$$

$$= \frac{1}{4}\left(56 - 40 + \frac{320}{3} - 64\right)$$

$$= \frac{44}{3} \approx 14.667 \quad \text{or} \quad 14.7\,°C$$

43. Given

t	0	2	4	6
$C(t)$	450	190	90	150

The divided difference table is:

t_k	y_k	1st D.D.	2nd D.D.	3rd D.D.
0	450			
		−130		
2	190		20	
		−50		0
4	90		20	
		30		
6	150			

The interpolating polynomial is
$$p(t) = 450 - 130t + 20t(t - 2)$$
$$= 450 - 170t + 20t^2$$

To approximate the minimum value of $C(t)$, we find the minimum of $p(t)$. Note that p is a quadratic whose graph opens up. Now
$$p'(t) = -170 + 40t \quad \text{and} \quad -170 + 40t = 0$$
$$t = \frac{170}{40} = 4.25$$

Thus, the bacteria concentration will reach its maximum level in approximately 4.25 days.

45. Given

t	0	10	20	30
$N(t)$	10,000	13,500	20,000	23,500

The divided difference table is:

t_k	y_k	1st D.D.	2nd D.D.	3rd D.D.
0	10,000			
		350		
10	13,500		15	
		650		-1
20	20,000		-15	
		350		
30	23,500			

The interpolating polynomial is:

$$p(t) = 10,000 + 350t + 15t(t - 10) - t(t - 10)(t - 20)$$
$$= 10,000 + 45t^2 - t^3$$

The average number of voters over the first 20 years is given by the definite integral

$$\frac{1}{20}\int_0^{20} N(t)\,dt \approx \frac{1}{20}\int_0^{20} p(t)\,dt$$

$$= \frac{1}{20}\int_0^{20} (10,000 + 45t^2 - t^3)\,dt$$

$$= \frac{1}{20}\left(10,000t + 15t^3 - \frac{t^4}{4}\right)\Big|_0^{20}$$

$$= \frac{1}{20}(200,000 + 120,000 - 40,000)$$

$$= 14,000$$

Therefore, the average number of voters over the first 20 years is approximately 14,000.

EXERCISE 9-3

Things to remember:

1. TRAPEZOID RULE

   Divide the interval $a \le x \le b$ into n equal subintervals of length $\Delta x = \dfrac{b - a}{n}$. Let $a = x_0 < x_1 < x_2 < \cdots < x_n = b$ be the endpoints of these subintervals. Then

   $$\int_a^b f(x)\,dx \approx T_n = \frac{\Delta x}{2}[f(x_0) + 2f(x_1) + \cdots + 2f(x_{n-1}) + f(x_n)].$$

2. SIMPSON'S RULE

   Given an even integer n. Divide the interval $a \le x \le b$ into n equal subintervals of length $\Delta x = \dfrac{b - a}{n}$. Let $a = x_0 < x_1 < \cdots < x_n = b$ be the endpoints of these subintervals. Then

   $$\int_a^b f(x)\,dx \approx S_n = \frac{\Delta x}{3}[f(x_0) + 4f(x_1) + 2f(x_2) + 4f(x_3) + \cdots$$
   $$+ 2f(x_{n-2}) + 4f(x_{n-1}) + f(x_n)].$$

3. ERROR ESTIMATES

Given the definite integral

$$\int_a^b f(x)\,dx.$$

Let $\text{Err}(T_n) = \int_a^b f(x)\,dx - T_n$, and

$$\text{Err}(S_n) = \int_a^b f(x)\,dx - S_n$$

be the errors in using the trapezoid rule and Simpson's rule, respectively. If

$$\left| f''(x) \right| \le M_1 \text{ for } a \le x \le b,$$

then

$$\left| \text{Err}(T_n) \right| \le \frac{(b-a)^3}{12n^2} M_1.$$

If $\left| f^{(4)}(x) \right| \le M_2$ for $a \le x \le b$, then

$$\left| \text{Err}(S_n) \right| \le \frac{(b-a)^5}{180n^4} M_2.$$

---

1. Using 1,
$$T_5 = \frac{\Delta x}{2}[f(x_0) + 2f(x_1) + 2f(x_2) + 2f(x_3) + 2f(x_4) + f(x_5)].$$

3. Using 2,
$$S_6 = \frac{\Delta x}{3}[f(x_0) + 4f(x_1) + 2f(x_2) + 4f(x_3) + 2f(x_4) + 4f(x_5) + f(x_6)].$$

5. Using 1 with $a = 0$, $b = 2$, $n = 5$, we have:

$\Delta x = 0.4$ and
$$T_5 = \frac{0.4}{2}[f(0) + 2f(0.4) + 2f(0.8) + 2f(1.2) + 2f(1.6) + f(2)]$$
$$= 0.2[f(0) + 2f(0.4) + 2f(0.8) + 2f(1.2) + 2f(1.6) + f(2)].$$

7. Using 2 with $a = 0$, $b = 3$, $n = 4$, we have
$$\Delta x = \frac{3-0}{4} = 0.75, \text{ and}$$
$$S_4 = \frac{0.75}{3}[f(0) + 4f(0.75) + 2f(1.5) + 4f(2.25) + f(3)]$$
$$= 0.25[f(0) + 4f(0.75) + 2f(1.5) + 4f(2.25) + f(3)].$$

9. $\int_0^1 \sqrt{1 + x^3}\,dx$; $a = 0$, $b = 1$, $n = 5$, $f(x) = \sqrt{1 + x^3}$

Thus, $\Delta x = \frac{1-0}{5} = \frac{1}{5} = 0.2$. The endpoints of the subintervals are:

$$T_5 = \frac{\Delta x}{2}[f(x_0) + 2f(x_1) + 2f(x_2) + 2f(x_3) + 2f(x_4) + f(x_5)]$$

$$= \frac{0.2}{2}[f(0) + 2f(0.2) + 2f(0.4) + 2f(0.6) + 2f(0.8) + f(1)]$$

$$= 0.1[1 + 2.007984 + 2.063008 + 2.205448 + 2.459268 + 1.414214]$$

$$= 0.1(11.149922)$$

$$= 1.114992 \quad \text{or} \quad 1.1150 \text{ rounded to four decimal places}$$

Thus, $\int_0^1 \sqrt{1 + x^3}\, dx \approx T_5 = 1.115$

11. $\int_2^4 \ln(1 + x^2)dx;\quad a = 2,\ b = 4,\ n = 5,\ f(x) = \ln(1 + x^2).$

Thus, $\Delta x = \frac{4 - 2}{5} = \frac{2}{5} = 0.4$. The endpoints of the subintervals are:

$$T_5 = \frac{\Delta x}{2}[f(x_0) + 2f(x_1) + 2f(x_2) + 2f(x_3) + 2f(x_4) + f(x_5)]$$

$$= \frac{0.4}{2}[f(2) + 2f(2.4) + 2f(2.8) + 2f(3.2) + 2f(3.6) + f(4)]$$

$$= 0.2[1.609379 + 3.822046 + 4.358574 + 4.838958 + 5.272392 + 2.833213]$$

$$= 0.2(22.734562)$$

$$= 4.5469124 \quad \text{or} \quad 4.5469 \text{ rounded to four decimal places}$$

Thus, $\int_2^4 \ln(1 + x^2)dx \approx T_5 = 4.5469.$

13. $\int_0^1 e^{x^2}dx;\quad a = 0,\ b = 1,\ n = 4,\ f(x) = e^{x^2}$

$\Delta x = \frac{1 - 0}{4} = 0.25$. The endpoints of the subintervals are:

$$S_4 = \frac{\Delta x}{3}[f(x_0) + 4f(x_1) + 2f(x_2) + 4f(x_3) + f(x_4)]$$

$$= \frac{0.25}{3}[f(0) + 4f(0.25) + 2f(0.5) + 4f(0.75) + f(1)]$$

$$= 0.083333[1 + 4.25797784 + 2.56805083 + 7.02021863 + 2.71828183]$$

$$= 0.08333(17.5645291) = 1.463704903$$

$$= 1.4637 \text{ rounded to four decimal places}$$

Thus, $\int_0^1 e^{x^2}dx \approx S_4 = 1.4637.$

15. $\int_{-1}^1 \frac{1}{\sqrt{4 + x^3}}dx;\quad a = -1,\ b = 1,\ n = 4,\ f(x) = \frac{1}{\sqrt{4 + x^3}}$

$\Delta x = \frac{1 - (-1)}{4} = 0.5$. The endpoints of the subintervals are:

$$S_4 = \frac{\Delta x}{3}[f(x_0) + 4f(x_1) + 2f(x_2) + 4f(x_3) + f(x_4)]$$

$$= \frac{0.5}{3}[f(-1) + 4f(-0.5) + 2f(0) + 4f(0.5) + f(1)]$$

$$= 0.166667[0.577350269 + 2.03200203 + 1 + 1.96946386 + 0.4472135]$$

$$= 0.166667(6.02602975) = 1.0043403$$

$$= 1.0043 \text{ rounded to four decimal places}$$

Thus, $\displaystyle\int_{-1}^{1} \frac{1}{\sqrt{4 + x^3}} dx \approx S_4 = 1.0043$.

17.

x	0	0.5	1	1.5	2
$f(x)$	5	7	6	4	2

$a = 0$, $b = 2$, $n = 4$, $\Delta x = \dfrac{2 - 0}{4} = 0.5$

$$\int_0^2 f(x)\,dx \approx T_4 = \frac{\Delta x}{2}[f(x_0) + 2f(x_1) + 2f(x_2) + 2f(x_3) + f(x_4)]$$

$$= \frac{0.5}{2}[5 + 2\cdot7 + 2\cdot6 + 2\cdot4 + 2]$$

$$= 0.25(41) = 10.25$$

19.

x	-3	-2	-1	0	1	2	3
$f(x)$	10	12	14	15	13	11	9

$a = -3$, $b = 3$, $n = 6$, $\Delta x = \dfrac{3 - (-3)}{6} = 1$

$$\int_{-3}^{3} f(x)\,dx \approx T_6 = \frac{\Delta x}{2}[f(x_0) + 2f(x_1) + 2f(x_2) + 2f(x_3) + 2f(x_4)$$
$$+ 2f(x_5) + f(x_6)]$$

$$= \frac{1}{2}[10 + 2(12) + 2(14) + 2(15) + 2(13) + 2(11) + 9]$$

$$= \frac{1}{2}(149) = 74.5$$

21. The area bounded by the graphs $y = \dfrac{10}{4 + x^2}$, $y = 0$, on the interval $0 \le x \le 4$ is given by

$$\int_0^4 \frac{10}{4 + x^2} dx.$$

Using Simpson's rule with $a = 0$, $b = 4$, $n = 8$, $f(x) = \dfrac{10}{4 + x^2}$, we have

$$\Delta x = \frac{4 - 0}{8} = \frac{4}{8} = 0.5.$$

The endpoints of the subintervals are:

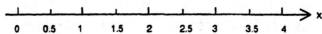

Thus,

$$\int_0^4 \frac{10}{4 + x^2}\, dx \sim S_8 = \frac{\Delta x}{3}[f(0) + 4f(0.5) + 2f(1) + 4f(1.5) + 2f(2)$$

$$+ 4f(2.5) + 2f(3) + 4f(3.5) + f(4)]$$

$$= \frac{0.5}{3}[2.5 + 9.411765 + 4 + 6.4 + 2.5 + 3.902439$$

$$+ 1.538462 + 2.461539 + 0.5]$$

$$= 0.166667(33.214205)$$

$$= 5.53570.$$

23. The area bounded by the graphs $y = \sqrt{x - x^2}$, $y = 0$, on the interval $0 \le x \le 1$ is given by

$$\int_0^1 \sqrt{x - x^2}\, dx$$

Using Simpson's rule with $a = 0$, $b = 1$, $n = 10$, $f(x) = \sqrt{x - x^2}$, we have $\Delta x = \frac{1 - 0}{10} = 0.1$.

The endpoints of the subintervals are:

Thus,

$$\int_0^1 \sqrt{x - x^2}\, dx \sim S_{10} = \frac{\Delta x}{3}[f(0) + 4f(0.1) + 2f(0.2) + \cdots + 4f(0.9)$$

$$+ f(1)]$$

$$= \frac{0.1}{3}[0 + 1.2 + 0.8 + 1.8330303 + 0.9797959 + 2$$

$$+ 0.9797959 + 1.8330303 + 0.8 + 1.2 + 0]$$

$$= 0.033333(11.6255786) \sim 0.38752.$$

25. The exact value of the integral $\int_0^1 e^x dx$ is

$$\int_0^1 e^x dx = e^x \Big|_0^1 = e - 1 \ (\sim 1.718282).$$

We now calculate T_n, Err(T_n), S_n, and Err(S_n) for (A) $n = 4$ and (B) $n = 10$.

(A) $a = 0$, $b = 1$, $n = 4$, $f(x) = e^x$, and $\Delta x = \frac{1 - 0}{4} = 0.25$

The endpoints of the subintervals are:

$$T_4 = \frac{\Delta x}{2}[f(0) + 2f(0.25) + 2f(0.5) + 2f(0.75) + f(1)]$$

$$= \frac{0.25}{2}[e^0 + 2e^{0.25} + 2e^{0.5} + 2e^{0.75} + e]$$

$$= 0.125[1 + 2.5680508 + 3.2974425 + 4.234 + 2.7182818]$$

$$= 0.125(13.8177751)$$

$$= 1.7272218 \sim 1.727222$$

$$S_4 = \frac{\Delta x}{3}[f(0) + 4f(0.25) + 2f(0.5) + 4f(0.75) + f(1)]$$

$$= \frac{0.25}{3}[1 + 5.1361017 + 3.2974425 + 8.468 + 2.7182818]$$

$$= 0.08333333(20.619826)$$

$$= 1.7183187 \approx 1.718319$$

Now $\text{Err}(T_4) = \displaystyle\int_0^1 e^x dx - T_4$

$$= 1.718282 - 1.727222 = -0.008940$$

and $\text{Err}(S_4) = \displaystyle\int_0^1 e^x dx - S_4$

$$= 1.718282 - 1.718319 = -0.000037.$$

(B) $a = 0$, $b = 1$, $n = 10$, $f(x) = e^x$, and $\Delta x = \dfrac{1 - 0}{10} = 0.1$.

The endpoints of the subintervals are:

$$T_{10} = \frac{\Delta x}{2}[f(0) + 2f(0.1) + 2f(0.2) + \ldots + 2f(0.9) + f(1)]$$

$$= \frac{0.1}{2}[e^0 + 2e^{0.1} + 2e^{0.2} + 2e^{0.3} + 2e^{0.4} + 2e^{0.5} + 2e^{0.6} + 2e^{0.7}$$
$$+ 2e^{0.8} + 2e^{0.9} + e]$$

$$= 0.05(34.3942698)$$

$$= 1.719713$$

$$S_{10} = \frac{\Delta x}{3}[f(0) + 4f(0.1) + 2f(0.2) + 4f(0.3) + \ldots + 4f(0.9) + f(1)]$$

$$= \frac{0.1}{3}[e^0 + 4e^{0.1} + 2e^{0.2} + 4e^{0.3} + 2e^{0.4} + 4e^{0.5} + 2e^{0.6} + 4e^{0.7}$$
$$+ 2e^{0.8} + 4e^{0.9} + e]$$

$$= 0.0333333(51.548542)$$

$$= 1.718283$$

Now $\text{Err}(T_{10}) = \displaystyle\int_0^1 e^x dx - T_{10}$

$$= 1.718282 - 1.719713 = -0.001431$$

and $\text{Err}(S_{10}) = \displaystyle\int_0^1 e^x dx - S_{10}$

$$= 1.718282 - 1.718283 = -0.000001.$$

n	T_n	$\text{Err}(T_n)$	S_n	$\text{Err}(S_n)$
4	1.727222	-0.008940	1.718319	-0.000037
10	1.719713	-0.001431	1.718283	-0.000001

27. Given the definite integral

$$\int_1^3 x \ln x \, dx.$$

To obtain the error estimates $\mathrm{Err}(T_n)$ and $\mathrm{Err}(S_n)$ for the trapezoid rule and Simpson's rule, respectively, we must maximize the absolute value of the second and fourth derivatives of $f(x) = x \ln x$ for $1 \le x \le 3$. Now,

$$f'(x) = x \cdot \frac{1}{x} + \ln x = 1 + \ln x$$

$$f''(x) = \frac{1}{x}$$

$$f^{(3)}(x) = \frac{-1}{x^2}$$

$$f^{(4)}(x) = \frac{2}{x^3}$$

Examining the graphs of $f''(x)$ and $f^{(4)}(x)$ for $1 \le x \le 3$,

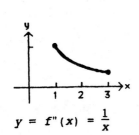

$$y = f''(x) = \frac{1}{x} \qquad\qquad y = f(4)(x) = \frac{2}{x^3}$$

we see that $M_1 = \mathrm{Max}\left|f''(x)\right| = \left|f''(1)\right| = 1,\ 1 \le x \le 3$,

and $\qquad M_2 = \mathrm{Max}\left|f^{(4)}(x)\right| = \left|f^{(4)}(1)\right| = 2,\ 1 \le x \le 3$.

Thus, $\left|\mathrm{Err}(T_n)\right| \le \dfrac{(b-a)^3 \cdot M_1}{12n^2} = \dfrac{(3-1)^3 \cdot 1}{12n^2} = \dfrac{2}{3n^2}$

and $\left|\mathrm{Err}(S_n)\right| \le \dfrac{(b-a)^5 \cdot M_2}{180n^4} = \dfrac{(3-1)^5 \cdot 2}{180n^4} = \dfrac{16}{45n^4}$

Error estimates for $n = 10, 20, 30, 40,$ and 50 are given in the following table.

n	ESTIMATE FOR $\mathrm{Err}(T_n)$ $\frac{2}{3n^2}$	ESTIMATE FOR $\mathrm{Err}(S_n)$ $\frac{16}{45n^4}$
10	0.007	0.00004
20	0.002	0.000002
30	0.0007	0.0000004
40	0.0004	0.0000001
50	0.0003	0.00000006

29. By <u>3</u>, the error in using the trapezoid rule to approximate $\int_a^b f(x)\,dx$ is given by

$$\left|\text{Err}(T_n)\right| \le \frac{(b - a)^3 \cdot M_1}{12n^2}$$

where $\left|f''(x)\right| \le M_1$ for $a \le x \le b$. Now, if $f(x) = Ax + B$, A and B constants, then $f''(x) = 0$. Therefore, we can use $M_1 = 0$ in the error estimate and we have

$$0 \le \left|\text{Err}(T_n)\right| \le \frac{(b - a)^3 \cdot 0}{12n^2} \quad \text{or} \quad \text{Err}(T_n) = 0.$$

Thus, the error is 0 and the trapezoid rule gives the exact value of $\int_a^b (Ax + B)\,dx$.

Simpson's rule on a TI-81 calculator was used in Problems 31-37. The X and Y ranges and the number of subdivisions used to insure 4 decimal place accuracy are indicated in each case.

31. X range $[-1, 2]$, Y range $[-10, 10]$
Number of subdivisions $N = 6$.

$$\int_0^1 \sqrt{1 + x^3}\,dx \approx 1.1114$$

33. X range $[1, 5]$, Y range $[-10, 10]$
Number of subdivisions $N = 6$

$$\int_2^4 \ln(1 + x^2)\,dx \approx 4.5513$$

35. X range $[-1, 2]$, Y range $[-10, 10]$
Number of subdivisions $N = 8$

$$\int_0^1 e^{x^2}\,dx \approx 1.4627$$

37. X range $[-2, 2]$, Y range $[-10, 10]$
Number of subdivisions $N = 8$

$$\int_{-1}^1 \frac{1}{\sqrt{4 + x^3}}\,dx \approx 1.0034$$

39. Given the demand and supply functions

$$D(x) = \sqrt{400 - 4x^3} \quad \text{and} \quad S(x) = \sqrt{16 + 2x^3}.$$

To find the equilibrium price, set $D(x) = S(x)$ and solve for x:

$$\sqrt{400 - 4x^3} = \sqrt{16 + 2x^3}$$
$$400 - 4x^3 = 16 + 2x^3$$
$$6x^3 = 384$$
$$x^3 = 64$$
$$x = 4$$

Thus, the equilibrium price is
$$\bar{p} = D(4) = S(4) = 12.$$
Now,
Consumers' surplus $= \int_0^4 [D(x) - \bar{p}]dx = \int_0^4 [\sqrt{400 - 4x^3} - 12]dx.$

Using Simpson's rule with $a = 0$, $b = 4$, and $n = 4$, we have
$$\Delta x = \frac{4 - 0}{4} = 1$$
and

$$\int_0^4 [\sqrt{400 - 4x^3} - 12]dx \approx S_4 = \frac{\Delta x}{3}[f(0) + 4f(1) + 2f(2) + 4f(3) + f(4)]$$

$$= \frac{1}{3}[8 + 31.598995 + 14.366652$$
$$+ 20.35203 + 0]$$
$$= \frac{1}{3}(74.3176772)$$
$$= 24.7725591.$$

Thus, the consumers' surplus is (approximately) 24.77.
The producers' surplus is

$$\int_0^4 [12 - \sqrt{16 + 2x^3}]dx \approx S_4 = \frac{\Delta x}{3}[f(0) + 4f(1) + 2f(2) + 4f(3) + f(4)]$$

$$= \frac{1}{3}[8 + 31.029437 + 12.686292$$
$$+ 14.533599 + 0]$$
$$= \frac{1}{3}(66.249328)$$
$$= 22.083109.$$

Thus, the producers' surplus is (approximately) 22.08.

41. The total loss during the first eight months of operation is given by the definite integral
$$\int_0^8 [C'(t) - R'(t)]dt$$

Using Simpson's rule with $a = 0$, $b = 8$, $n = 4$, and $\Delta x = 2$, we have

$$\int_0^8 [C'(t) - R'(t)]dt \approx S_4 = \frac{\Delta x}{3}[f(0) + 4f(2) + 2f(4) + 4f(6) + f(8)]$$

$$= \frac{2}{3}[1 + 4(1.5) + 2(1.5) + 4(1) + 0]$$
$$= \frac{2}{3}[1 + 6 + 3 + 4]$$
$$= \frac{28}{3}$$
$$= 9.333$$

Thus, the total loss during the first eight months of operation is approximately $9333.

43. Area Lot $A \approx S_4 = \frac{\Delta x}{3}[f(x_0) + 4f(x_1) + 2f(x_2) + 4f(x_3) + f(x_4)]$

$$= \frac{100}{3}[300 + 4(350) + 2(370) + 4(360) + 340]$$

$$= \frac{100}{3}(300 + 1400 + 740 + 1440 + 340)$$

$$= \frac{100}{3}(4220)$$

$$\approx 140{,}667 \text{ square feet.}$$

45. Introduce a coordinate system such that the x-axis bisects the pond lengthwise and the y-axis is tangent to the left side of the pond.

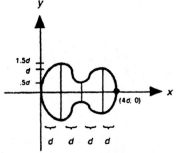

Let f be the function whose graph is the top shore of the pond. Then the surface area of the pond is given by

$$A = 2 \int_0^{4d} f(x)\,dx.$$

Using Simpson's rule with $a = 0$, $b = 4d$, and $n = 4$, we have

$$\Delta x = \frac{4d - 0}{4} = d$$

and

$$A = 2 \int_0^{4d} f(x)\,dx \approx 2S_4 = 2 \cdot \frac{\Delta x}{3}[f(0) + 4f(d) + 2f(2d) + 4f(3d) + f(4d)]$$

$$= \frac{2d}{3}[0 + 4(1.5d) + 2(0.5d) + 4(d) + 0]$$

$$= \frac{2d}{3}(6d + d + 4d) = \frac{22d^2}{3}.$$

Now, the surface area of the pond is 1650 square meters. Thus,

$$\frac{22d^2}{3} = 1650 \quad \text{or} \quad d^2 = 225 \quad \text{and} \quad d = 15 \text{ meters.}$$

47. The total amount of the drug assimilated in the first three hours is given by

$$\int_0^3 [7 - 3\ln(t^2 - 6t + 10)]\,dt.$$

Using Simpson's rule with $a = 0$, $b = 3$, and $n = 4$, we have

$$\Delta x = \frac{3 - 0}{4} = 0.75$$

and

$$\int_0^3 [7 - 3\ln(t^2 - 6t + 10)]\,dt \approx S_4 = \frac{\Delta x}{3}[f(0) + 4f(0.75) + 2f(1.5)$$

$$+ 4f(2.25) + f(3)]$$

$$= \frac{0.75}{3}[0.0922447 + 6.3745329$$

$$+ 6.92807 + 22.6445548 + 7]$$

$$= 0.25(43.0394024)$$

$$= 10.7598506$$

Thus, the total amount of drug assimilated in the first three hours is (approximately) 10.76.

49. Let f be the function graphed by the recording device. Then, the average temperature over the two-hour period $[0, 2]$ is given by

$$T = \frac{1}{2}\int_0^2 f(t)\,dt.$$

Using Simpson rule with $a = 0$, $b = 2$, and $n = 4$, we have

$$\Delta x = \frac{2 - 0}{4} = \frac{1}{2}$$

and

$$T = \frac{1}{2}\int_0^2 f(t)\,dt \approx \frac{1}{2}S_4 = \frac{1}{2}\frac{\Delta x}{3}[f(0) + 4f(0.5) + 2f(1) + 4f(1.5) + f(2)]$$

$$= \frac{1}{12}[10 + 4(25) + 2(40) + 4(15) + 5]$$

$$= \frac{1}{12}(255) = 21.25.$$

Thus, the average temperature over the two-hour period is (approximately) $21.25°C$.

51. A person learns N items at the rate

$$N'(t) = \sqrt{24 + \frac{1}{t^2}}$$

The total number of items learned during the period from $t = 1$ to $t = 6$ hours of study is given by

$$\int_1^6 N'(t)\,dt = \int_1^6 \sqrt{24 + \frac{1}{t^2}}\,dt.$$

Using Simpson's rule with $a = 1$, $b = 6$, and $n = 4$, we have

$$\Delta x = \frac{6 - 1}{4} = \frac{5}{4} = 1.25$$

and

$$\int_1^6 \sqrt{24 + \frac{1}{t^2}}\,dt \approx S_4 = \frac{\Delta x}{3}[f(1) + 4f(2.25) + 2f(3.50) + 4f(4.75)$$

$$+ f(6)]$$

$$= \frac{5}{12}[5 + 19.6763943 + 9.8146080 + 19.614007$$

$$+ 4.90181373]$$

$$= \frac{5}{12}(59.0068198) = 24.5861749.$$

Thus, the total number of items learned during the five hours of study is (approximately) 25.

Things to remember:

1. **EULER'S METHOD**

    If $y(x)$ is the exact solution to the initial value problem
    $$y' = f(x, y); \quad y(x_0) = y_0,$$
    $x_0, x_1, x_2, \ldots, x_n$ is a sequence of values defined by
    $$x_k = x_{k-1} + \Delta x, \quad k = 1, 2, \ldots, n$$
    and $y_1, y_2, \ldots, y_n,$ is the sequence of values defined by
    $$y_k = y_{k-1} + f(x_{k-1}, y_{k-1})\Delta x, \quad k = 1, 2, \ldots, n,$$
    then $y(x_k) \sim y_k,$ $k = 1, 2, \ldots, n.$

2. **EULER'S METHOD FOR A SYSTEM OF DIFFERENTIAL EQUATIONS**

    If $x = x(t)$ and $y = y(t)$ is the solution to the initial value problem
    $$\frac{dx}{dt} = f(x, y); \quad x(t_0) = x_0,$$
    $$\frac{dy}{dt} = g(x, y); \quad y(t_0) = y_0,$$
    $t_0, t_1, \ldots, t_n$ is the sequence of values defined by
    $$t_k = t_{k-1} + \Delta t, \quad k = 1, 2, \ldots, n$$
    and $x_1, x_2, \ldots, x_n, y_1, y_2, \ldots, y_n$ are defined by
    $$x_k = x_{k-1} + f(x_{k-1}, y_{k-1})\Delta t$$
    $$y_k = y_{k-1} + g(x_{k-1}, y_{k-1})\Delta t, \quad k = 1, 2, \ldots, n,$$
    then $x(t_k) \sim x_k$ and $y(t_k) \sim y_k,$ $k = 1, 2, \ldots, n.$

---

1. $y' = x + y;$ $y(0) = 2,$ $0 \le x \le 1.$

    Let $x_0 = 0,$ $y_0 = 2,$ $\Delta x = 0.2$ and $f(x, y) = x + y.$ Euler's formula for y_k is:
    $$\begin{aligned} y_k &= y_{k-1} + f(x_{k-1}, y_{k-1})\Delta x \\ &= y_{k-1} + (x_{k-1} + y_{k-1})(0.2) \end{aligned}$$

    Now, the approximate values for $y' = x + y;$ $y(0) = 2,$ are:

k	x_k	$y_k = y_{k-1} + (x_{k-1} + y_{k-1})(0.2)$
0	0	2
1	0.2	$2 + (0 + 2)(.2) = 2.4$
2	0.4	$2.4 + (0.2 + 2.4)(.2) = 2.92$
3	0.6	$2.92 + (0.4 + 2.92)(.2) = 3.584 \sim 3.58$
4	0.8	$3.58 + (0.6 + 3.58)(.2) = 4.416 \sim 4.42$
5	1	$4.42 + (0.8 + 4.42)(.2) = 5.464 \sim 5.46$

The graph of the approximate solution is:

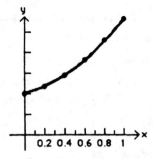

3. $y' = y$; $y(0) = 1$, $0 \le x \le 1$.

Let $x_0 = 0$, $y_0 = 1$, $\Delta x = 0.2$ and $f(x, y) = y$. Euler's formula for y_k is:

$$y_k = y_{k-1} + f(x_{k-1}, y_{k-1})\Delta x$$
$$= y_{k-1} + y_{k-1}(0.2)$$
$$= (1.2)y_{k-1}$$

Now, the approximate values for $y' = y$; $y(0) = 1$, are:

k	x_k	$y_k = (1.2)y_{k-1}$
0	0	1
1	0.2	$(1.2)(1) = 1.2$
2	0.4	$(1.2)(1.2) = 1.44$
3	0.6	$(1.2)(1.44) = 1.728 \approx 1.73$
4	0.8	$(1.2)(1.728) = 2.0736 \approx 2.07$
5	1	$(1.2)(2.074) = 2.4888 \approx 2.49$

The graph of the approximate solution is shown at the right.

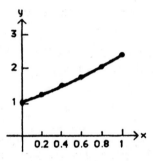

5. $y' = 2\sqrt{y} - 8x$; $y(0) = 1$, $0 \le x \le 1$.

Let $x_0 = 0$, $y_0 = 1$, $\Delta x = 0.2$ and $f(x, y) = 2\sqrt{y} - 8x$. Euler's formula for y_k is:

$$y_k = y_{k-1} + f(x_{k-1}, y_{k-1})\Delta x$$
$$= y_{k-1} + (2\sqrt{y_{k-1}} - 8x_{k-1})(0.2)$$

The approximate values are:

k	x_k	$y_k = y_{k-1} + (2\sqrt{y_{k-1}} - 8x_{k-1})(0.2)$
0	0	1
1	0.2	$1 + (2\sqrt{1} - 8 \cdot 0)(0.2) = 1.4$
2	0.4	$1.4 + [2\sqrt{1.4} - 8(0.2)](0.2) \approx 1.55$
3	0.6	$1.55 + [2\sqrt{1.55} - 8(0.4)](0.2) \approx 1.41$
4	0.8	$1.41 + [2\sqrt{1.41} - 8(0.6)](0.2) \approx 0.93$
5	1	$0.93 + [2\sqrt{0.93} - 8(0.8)](0.2) \approx 0.03$

The graph of the approximate solution is shown at the right.

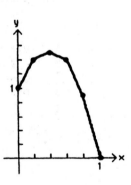

504

7. $y' = -y$; $y(0) = 1$, $0 \le x \le 1$.

Let $x_0 = 0$, $y_0 = 1$, $\Delta x = 0.2$ and $f(x, y) = -y$. Euler's formula for y_k is:

$$y_k = y_{k-1} + f(x_{k-1}, y_{k-1})\Delta x$$
$$= y_{k-1} + (-y_{k-1})(0.2)$$
$$= 0.8y_{k-1}$$

The approximate values are:

k	x_k	$y_k = 0.8y_{k-1}$
0	0	1
1	0.2	$(0.8)1 = 0.8$
2	0.4	$(0.8)(0.8) = 0.64$
3	0.6	$(0.8)(0.64) = 0.512 \approx 0.51$
4	0.8	$(0.8)(0.512) = 0.4096 \approx 0.41$
5	1	$(0.8)(0.4096) = 0.32768 \approx 0.33$

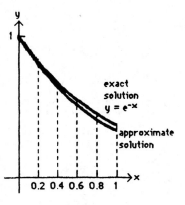

The exact solution of the initial value problem is $y(x) = e^{-x}$. The graphs of the approximate solution and exact solution are shown at the right.

9. $y' = 1 + y$; $y(0) = 0$, $0 \le x \le 1$.

Let $x_0 = 0$, $y_0 = 0$, $\Delta x = 0.2$ and $f(x, y) = 1 + y$. Euler's formula for y_k is:

$$y_k = y_{k-1} + f(x_{k-1}, y_{k-1})\Delta x$$
$$= y_{k-1} + (1 + y_{k-1})(0.2)$$
$$= 0.2 + (1.2)y_{k-1}$$

The approximate values are:

k	x_k	$y_k = 0.2 + (1.2)y_{k-1}$
0	0	0
1	0.2	$0.2 + (1.2)0 = 0.2$
2	0.4	$0.2 + (1.2)(0.2) = 0.44$
3	0.6	$0.2 + (1.2)(0.44) = 0.728 \approx 0.73$
4	0.8	$0.2 + (1.2)(0.73) \approx 1.07$
5	1	$0.2 + (1.2)(1.07) = 1.488 \approx 1.49$

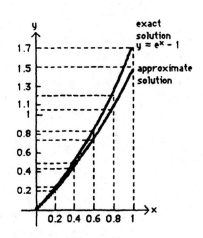

The exact solution of the initial value problem is $y(x) = e^x - 1$. The graphs of the approximate solution and exact solution are shown at the right.

11. $y' = y - 6x$; $y(0) = 1$.

Let $x_0 = 0$, $y_0 = 1$, $\Delta x = 0.2$. Euler's formula for y_k is:

$$y_k = y_{k-1} + f(x_{k-1}, y_{k-1})\Delta x$$
$$= y_{k-1} + (y_{k-1} - 6x_{k-1})(0.2)$$

$$= (1.2)y_{k-1} - (1.2)x_{k-1}$$
$$= (1.2)(y_{k-1} - x_{k-1})$$

The approximate values are:

k	x_k	$y_k = (1.2)(y_{k-1} - x_{k-1})$
0	0	1
1	0.2	$(1.2)(1) = 1.2$
2	0.4	$(1.2)(1.2 - 0.2) = 1.2$
3	0.6	$(1.2)(1.2 - 0.4) = 0.96$
4	0.8	$(1.2)(0.96 - 0.6) = 0.432 \approx 0.43$
5	1	$(1.2)(0.432 - 0.8) = -0.4416 \approx -0.44$

For $\Delta x = 0.1$, $0 \le x \le 1$, Euler's formula is:
$$y_k = y_{k-1} + (y_{k-1} - 6x_{k-1})(0.1)$$
$$= (1.1)y_{k-1} - (0.6)x_{k-1}$$

The approximate values are:

k	x_k	$y_k = (1.1)y_{k-1} - (0.6)x_{k-1}$
0	0	1
1	0.1	$(1.1)(1) - (0.6)(0) = 1.1$
2	0.2	$(1.1)(1.1) - (0.6)(0.1) = 1.15$
3	0.3	$(1.1)(1.15) - (0.6)(0.2) = 1.145 \approx 1.15$
4	0.4	$(1.1)(1.145) - (0.6)(0.3) = 1.0795 \approx 1.08$
5	0.5	$(1.1)(1.0795) - (0.6)(0.4) = 0.94745 \approx 0.95$
6	0.6	$(1.1)(0.94745) - (0.6)(0.5) = 0.742195 \approx 0.74$
7	0.7	$(1.1)(0.742195) - (0.6)(0.6) = 0.456415 \approx 0.46$
8	0.8	$(1.1)(0.456415) - (0.6)(0.7) = 0.082057 \approx 0.08$
9	0.9	$(1.1)(0.082057) - (0.6)(0.8) = -0.3897 \approx -0.39$
10	1	$(1.1)(-0.3897) - (0.6)(0.9) = -0.9687 \approx -0.97$

The exact solution of the initial value problem is $y(x) = -5e^x + 6x + 6$. The graphs of the approximate solutions and the exact solution are shown at the right.

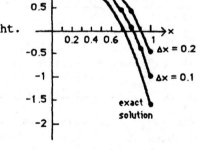

13. $y' = 1 + y^2$; $y(0) = 0$, $\Delta x = 0.2$.

Euler's formula for y_k is:
$$y_k = y_{k-1} + f(x_{k-1}, y_{k-1})\Delta x$$
$$= y_{k-1} + (1 + y_{k-1}^2)(0.2)$$
$$= 0.2y_{k-1}^2 + y_{k-1} + 0.2$$

The approximate values are:

k	x_k	$y_k = 0.2y_{k-1}^2 + y_{k-1} + 0.2$
0	0	0
1	0.2	$0.2(0)^2 + 0 + 0.2 = 0.2$
2	0.4	$0.2(0.2)^2 + 0.2 + 0.2 = 0.408 \approx 0.41$
3	0.6	$0.2(0.408)^2 + 0.408 + 0.2 = 0.641293 \approx 0.64$
4	0.8	$0.2(0.641293)^2 + 0.641293 + 0.2 = 0.923544 \approx 0.92$
5	1	$0.2(0.923544)^2 + 0.923544 + 0.2 = 1.294131 \approx 1.29$

Thus, $y(1) \approx 1.29$.

15. $y' = y^2 - x^2$; $y(1) = -1$, $\Delta x = 0.4$.

Euler's formula for y_k is:

$$y_k = y_{k-1} + f(x_{k-1}, y_{k-1})\Delta x$$
$$= y_{k-1} + (y_{k-1}^2 - x_{k-1}^2)(0.4)$$

The approximate values are:

k	x_k	$y_k = y_{k-1} + (y_{k-1}^2 - x_{k-1}^2)(0.4)$
0	1	-1
1	1.4	$-1 + [(-1)^2 - 1^2](0.4) = -1$
2	1.8	$-1 + [(-1)^2 - (1.4)^2](0.4) = -1.384$
3	2.2	$-1.384 + [(-1.384)^2 - (1.8)^2](0.4) = -1.9138$
4	2.6	$-1.9138 + [(-1.9138)^2 - (2.2)^2](0.4) = -2.3847$
5	3	$-2.3847 + [(-2.3847)^2 - (2.6)^2](0.4) = -2.8139$

Thus, $y(3) \approx -2.81$.

17. $y' = x + e^{-y}$; $y(0) = 0$, $\Delta x = 0.1$.

Euler's formula for y_k is:

$$y_k = y_{k-1} + f(x_{k-1}, y_{k-1})\Delta x$$
$$= y_{k-1} + (x_{k-1} + e^{-y_{k-1}})(0.1)$$

The approximate values are:

k	x_k	$y_k = y_{k-1} + (x_{k-1} + e^{-y_{k-1}})(0.1)$
0	0	0
1	0.1	$0 + (0 + e^0)(0.1) = 0.1$
2	0.2	$0.1 + (0.1 + e^{-0.1})(0.1) = 0.2004$
3	0.3	$0.2004 + (0.2 + e^{-0.2004})(0.1) = 0.3023$
4	0.4	$0.3023 + (0.3 + e^{-0.3023})(0.1) = 0.4062$
5	0.5	$0.4062 + (0.4 + e^{-0.4062})(0.1) = 0.5128$
6	0.6	$0.5128 + (0.5 + e^{-0.5128})(0.1) = 0.6227$
7	0.7	$0.6227 + (0.6 + e^{-0.6227})(0.1) = 0.7364$

8	0.8	$0.7364 + (0.7 + e^{-0.7364})(0.1) = 0.8543$
9	0.9	$0.8543 + (0.8 + e^{-0.8543})(0.1) = 0.9768$
10	1	$0.9768 + (0.9 + e^{-0.9768})(0.1) = 1.1045$

Thus, $y(1) \approx 1.10$.

19. $y' = \ln(x + y)$; $y(1) = 0$, $\Delta x = 0.2$.

Euler's formula for y_k is:

$$y_k = y_{k-1} + f(x_{k-1}, y_{k-1})\Delta x$$
$$= y_{k-1} + \ln(x_{k-1} + y_{k-1})(0.2)$$

The approximate values are:

k	x_k	$y_k = y_{k-1} + \ln(x_{k-1} + y_{k-1})(0.2)$
0	1	0
1	1.2	$0 + \ln(1)(0.2) = 0$
2	1.4	$0 + \ln(1.2)(0.2) = 0.0365$
3	1.6	$0.0365 + \ln(1.4365)(0.2) = 0.1089$
4	1.8	$0.1089 + \ln(1.7089)(0.2) = 0.2161$
5	2	$0.2161 + \ln(2.0161)(0.2) = 0.3563$
6	2.2	$0.3563 + \ln(2.5363)(0.2) = 0.5277$
7	2.4	$0.5277 + \ln(2.7277)(0.2) = 0.7284$
8	2.6	$0.7284 + \ln(3.1284)(0.2) = 0.9565$
9	2.8	$0.9565 + \ln(3.5565)(0.2) = 1.2103$
10	3	$1.2103 + \ln(4.0103)(0.2) = 1.4880$

Thus, $y(3) \approx 1.49$.

21. $\dfrac{dx}{dt} = 2x - y$, $\dfrac{dy}{dt} = 3x - 2y$; $x(0) = 1$, $y(0) = -1$, $\Delta t = 0.2$.

Euler's formula for x_k and y_k are:

$$x_k = x_{k-1} + f(x_{k-1}, y_{k-1})\Delta t$$
$$= x_{k-1} + (2x_{k-1} - y_{k-1})(0.2)$$
$$= (1.4)x_{k-1} - (0.2)y_{k-1}$$

and

$$y_k = y_{k-1} + g(x_{k-1}, y_{k-1})\Delta t$$
$$= y_{k-1} + (3x_{k-1} - 2y_{k-1})(0.2)$$
$$= (0.6)(y_{k-1} + x_{k-1})$$

The approximate values are:

k	t_k	$x_k = (1.4)x_{k-1} - (0.2)y_{k-1}$	$y_k = (0.6)(y_{k-1} + x_{k-1})$
0	0	1	-1
1	0.2	$(1.4)(1) - (0.2)(-1) = 1.6$	$(0.6)(-1 + 1) = 0$
2	0.4	$(1.4)(1.6) - (0.2)(0) = 2.24$	$(0.6)(1.6) = 0.96$
3	0.6	$(1.4)(2.24) - (0.2)(0.96) = 2.94$	$(0.6)(0.96 + 2.24) = 1.92$
4	0.8	$(1.4)(2.94) - (0.2)(1.92) = 3.73$	$(0.6)(1.92 + 2.94) = 2.92$
5	1	$(1.4)(3.73) - (0.2)(2.92) = 4.64$	$(0.6)(2.92 + 3.73) = 3.99$

23. $\dfrac{dx}{dt} = 2x + y$, $\dfrac{dy}{dt} = 2x + y$; $x(0) = 2$, $y(0) = -1$, $\Delta t = 0.2$.

Euler's formula for x_k and y_k are:
$$x_k = x_{k-1} + f(x_{k-1}, y_{k-1})\Delta t$$
$$= x_{k-1} + (2x_{k-1} + y_{k-1})(0.2)$$
$$= (1.4)x_{k-1} + (0.2)y_{k-1}$$

and
$$y_k = y_{k-1} + g(x_{k-1}, y_{k-1})\Delta t$$
$$= y_{k-1} + (2x_{k-1} + y_{k-1})(0.2)$$
$$= (0.4)x_{k-1} + (1.2)y_{k-1}$$

The approximate values are:

k	t_k	$x_k = (1.4)x_{k-1} + (0.2)y_{k-1}$	$y_k = (0.4)x_{k-1} + (1.2)y_{k-1}$
0	0	2	-1
1	0.2	$(1.4)(2) + (0.2)(-1) = 2.6$	$(0.4)(2) + (1.2)(-1) = -0.4$
2	0.4	$(1.4)(2.6) + (0.2)(-0.4) = 3.56$	$(0.4)(2.6) + (1.2)(-0.4) = 0.56$
3	0.6	$(1.4)(3.56) + (0.2)(0.56) \approx 5.10$	$(0.4)(3.56) + (1.2)(0.56) \approx 2.10$
4	0.8	$(1.4)(5.10) + (0.2)(2.10) = 7.56$	$(0.4)(5.10) + (1.2)(2.10) = 4.56$
5	1	$(1.4)(7.56) + (0.2)(4.56) \approx 11.50$	$(0.4)(7.56) + (1.2)(4.56) \approx 8.50$

25. $y' = 5x - 2\sqrt{y}$ for $0 \le x \le 1$.

Euler's formula for y_k is:
$$y_k = y_{k-1} + f(x_{k-1}, y_{k-1})\Delta x$$
$$= y_{k-1} + (5x_{k-1} - 2\sqrt{y_{k-1}})(0.2)$$

(A) $y' = 5x - 2\sqrt{y}$; $y(0) = 1$.

The approximate values are:

k	x_k	$y_k = y_{k-1} + (5x_{k-1} - 2\sqrt{y_{k-1}})(0.2)$
0	0	1
1	0.2	$1 + [5(0) - 2\sqrt{1}](0.2) = 0.6$
2	0.4	$0.6 + [5(0.2) - 2\sqrt{0.6}](0.2) = 0.490161 \approx 0.49$
3	0.6	$0.490161 + [5(0.4) - 2\sqrt{0.490161}](0.2) = 0.610115 \approx 0.61$
4	0.8	$0.610115 + [5(0.6) - 2\sqrt{0.610115}](0.2) = 0.897676 \approx 0.90$
5	1	$0.897676 + [5(0.8) - 2\sqrt{0.897676}](0.2) = 1.318693 \approx 1.32$

(B) $y' = 5x - 2\sqrt{y}$; (C) $y' = 5x - 2\sqrt{y}$;
$y(0) = 2$. $y(0) = 3$.

k	x_k	y_k
0	0	2
1	0.2	1.43
2	0.4	1.16
3	0.6	1.13
4	0.8	1.30
5	1	1.64

k	x_k	y_k
0	0	3
1	0.2	2.31
2	0.4	1.90
3	0.6	1.75
4	0.8	1.82
5	1	2.08

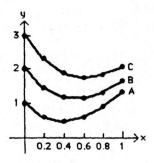

27. $y' = \sqrt{y}(2 - \sqrt{y})$; $y(1) = 2$.

Euler's formula for y_k is:

$$y_k = y_{k-1} + f(x_{k-1}, y_{k-1})\Delta x$$

$$= y_{k-1} + \sqrt{y_{k-1}}(2 - \sqrt{y_{k-1}})\Delta x$$

(A) Let $\Delta x = 1$. The approximate values are:

k	x_k	$y_k = y_{k-1} + \sqrt{y_{k-1}}(2 - \sqrt{y_{k-1}})$
0	1	2
1	2	$2 + \sqrt{2}(2 - \sqrt{2}) = 2.828427$
2	3	$2.828427 + \sqrt{2.828427}(2 - \sqrt{2.828427}) = 3.363586$

Thus, $y(3) \approx 3.4$.

(B) Let $\Delta x = 0.5$. The approximate values are:

k	x_k	$y_k = y_{k-1} + \sqrt{y_{k-1}}(2 - \sqrt{y_{k-1}})(0.5)$
0	1	2
1	1.5	$2 + \sqrt{2}(2 - \sqrt{2})(0.5) = 2.414214$
2	2	$2.414214 + \sqrt{2.414214}(2 - \sqrt{2.414214})(0.5) = 2.760881$
3	2.5	$2.760881 + \sqrt{2.760881}(2 - \sqrt{2.760881})(0.5) = 3.042030$
4	3	$3.042030 + \sqrt{3.042030}(2 - \sqrt{3.042030})(0.5) = 3.265157$

Thus, $y(3) \approx 3.3$.

(C) Let $\Delta x = 0.25$. The approximate values are:

k	x_k	$y_k = y_{k-1} + \sqrt{y_{k-1}}(2 - \sqrt{y_{k-1}})(0.25)$
0	1	2
1	1.25	$2 + \sqrt{2}(2 - \sqrt{2})(0.25) = 2.207107$
2	1.5	$2.207107 + \sqrt{2.207107}(2 - \sqrt{2.207107})(0.25) = 2.398147$
3	1.75	$2.398147 + \sqrt{2.398147}(2 - \sqrt{2.398147})(0.25) = 2.572908$
4	2	$2.572908 + \sqrt{2.572908}(2 - \sqrt{2.572908})(0.25) = 2.731695$
5	2.25	$2.731695 + \sqrt{2.731695}(2 - \sqrt{2.731695})(0.25) = 2.875163$
6	2.5	$2.875163 + \sqrt{2.875163}(2 - \sqrt{2.875163})(0.25) = 3.004188$
7	2.75	$3.004188 + \sqrt{3.004188}(2 - \sqrt{3.004188})(0.25) = 3.119770$
8	3	$3.119770 + \sqrt{3.119770}(2 - \sqrt{3.119770})(0.25) = 3.222971$

Thus, $y(3) \approx 3.2$.

29. $\dfrac{dN}{dt} = 0.1N(10 - \sqrt{N})$; $N(0) = 1$.

Euler's formula for N_k is:
$$N_k = N_{k-1} + f(t_{k-1}, N_{k-1})\Delta t$$
$$= N_{k-1} + 0.1N_{k-1}(10 - \sqrt{N_{k-1}})\Delta t$$
Now, with $\Delta t = 1$, we have
$$N_k = N_{k-1} + 0.1N_{k-1}(10 - \sqrt{N_{k-1}})$$
$$= 2N_{k-1} - 0.1N_{k-1}^{3/2}$$

The approximate values are:

k	t_k	$N_k = 2N_{k-1} - 0.1N_{k-1}^{3/2}$
0	0	1
1	1	$2(1) - (0.1)(1)^{3/2} = 1.9$
2	2	$2(1.9) - (0.1)(1.9)^{3/2} = 3.538103$
3	3	$2(3.538103) - (0.1)(3.538103)^{3/2} = 6.410694$
4	4	$2(6.410694) - (0.1)(6.410694)^{3/2} = 11.198243$
5	5	$2(11.198243) - (0.1)(11.198243)^{3/2} = 18.649131$

Thus, $N(5) \approx 18.649$ or 18,649 people.

31. $\dfrac{dp}{dt} = 2p - q$; $p(0) = 100$, $\Delta t = 0.5$

$\dfrac{dq}{dt} = -p + q$; $q(0) = 160$

Euler's formulas for p_k and q_k are:
$$p_k = p_{k-1} + f(p_{k-1}, q_{k-1})\Delta t$$
$$= p_{k-1} + (2p_{k-1} - q_{k-1})(0.5)$$
$$= 2p_{k-1} - 0.5q_{k-1}$$
and

$$q_k = q_{k-1} + g(p_{k-1},\ q_{k-1})\Delta t$$
$$= q_{k-1} + (-p_{k-1} + q_{k-1})(0.5)$$
$$= 1.5q_{k-1} - 0.5p_{k-1}$$

The approximate values are:

k	t_k	$p_k = 2p_{k-1} - 0.5q_{k-1}$	$q_k = 1.5q_{k-1} - 0.5p_{k-1}$
0	0	100	160
1	0.5	$2(100) - 0.5(160) = 120$	$1.5(160) - 0.5(100) = 190$
2	1	$2(120) - 0.5(190) = 145$	$1.5(190) - 0.5(120) = 225$
3	1.5	$2(145) - 0.5(225) = 177.5$	$1.5(225) - 0.5(145) = 265$
4	2	$2(177.5) - 0.5(265) = 222.5$	$1.5(265) - 0.5(177.5) = 308.75$

Thus, $p(2) \approx 222.5$ and $q(2) \approx 308.8$.

33. $\dfrac{dN}{dt} = 0.1\sqrt{N}\,(10 - \sqrt{N});\ N(0) = 1,\ \Delta t = 1.$

Euler's formula for N_k is:
$$N_k = N_{k-1} + f(t_{k-1},\ N_{k-1})\Delta t$$
$$= N_{k-1} + 0.1\sqrt{N_{k-1}}\,(10 - \sqrt{N_{k-1}})$$
$$= 0.9N_{k-1} + \sqrt{N_{k-1}}$$

The approximate values are:

k	t_k	$N_k = 0.9N_{k-1} + \sqrt{N_{k-1}}$
0	0	1
1	1	$0.9(1) + \sqrt{1} = 1.9$
2	2	$0.9(1.9) + \sqrt{1.9} = 3.088405$
3	3	$0.9(3.088405) + \sqrt{3.088405} = 4.536951$
4	4	$0.9(4.536951) + \sqrt{4.536951} = 6.213268$

Thus, $N(4) \approx 6.213268$ or 6213 infected individuals.

35. $\dfrac{dy}{dt} = y(0.8 - 0.04x);\ y(0) = 55,\ \Delta t = 1$

$\dfrac{dx}{dt} = x(0.006y - 0.3);\ x(0) = 15$

Euler's formulas for y_k and x_k are:
$$y_k = y_{k-1} + f(x_{k-1},\ y_{k-1})\Delta t$$
$$= y_{k-1} + y_{k-1}(0.8 - 0.04x_{k-1})$$
$$= 1.8y_{k-1} - 0.04y_{k-1}x_{k-1}$$
and
$$x_k = x_{k-1} + g(x_{k-1},\ y_{k-1})\Delta t$$
$$= x_{k-1} + x_{k-1}(0.006y_{k-1} - 0.3)$$
$$= 0.7x_{k-1} + 0.006y_{k-1}x_{k-1}$$

The approximate values are:

k	t_k	$y_k = 1.8y_{k-1} - 0.04y_{k-1}x_{k-1}$	$x_k = 0.7x_{k-1} + 0.006y_{k-1}x_{k-1}$
0	0	55	15
1	1	$1.8(55) - 0.04(55)(15) = 66$	$0.7(15) + 0.006(55)(15) \approx 15.5$
2	2	$1.8(66) - 0.04(66)(15.5) \approx 77.9$	$0.7(15.5) + 0.006(66)(15.5) \approx 17$
3	3	$1.8(77.9) - 0.04(77.9)(17) \approx 87.2$	$0.7(17) + 0.006(77.9)(17) \approx 19.8$
4	4	$1.8(87.2) - 0.04(87.2)(19.8) \approx 87.9$	$0.7(19.8) + 0.006(87.2)(19.8) \approx 24.2$

Thus, $y(4) \approx 87.9$ and $x(4) \approx 24.2$ or 87,900 rabbits and 24,200 foxes.

37. $\frac{dN}{dt} = 0.1N^{2/3}(100 - N^{1/3}); \ N(0) = 1000, \ \Delta t = 1.$

Euler's formula for N_k is:
$$N_k = N_{k-1} + f(t_{k-1}, N_{k-1})\Delta t$$
$$= N_{k-1} + 0.1N_{k-1}^{2/3}(100 - N_{k-1}^{1/3})$$
$$= 0.9N_{k-1} + 10N_{k-1}^{2/3}$$

The approximate values are:

k	t_k	$N_k = 0.9N_{k-1} + 10N_{k-1}^{2/3}$
0	0	1000
1	1	$0.9(1000) + 10(1000)^{2/3} = 1900$
2	2	$0.9(1900) + 10(1900)^{2/3} = 3244.03665$
3	3	$0.9(3244.03665) + 10(3244.03665)^{2/3} = 5111.0440$
4	4	$0.9(5111.0440) + 10(5111.0440)^{2/3} = 7567.09124$

Thus, $N(4) \approx 7567$.

EXERCISE 9-5   CHAPTER REVIEW

1. $f(x) = x^2 - 10, \ x_1 = 3, \ n = 4.$

   $f'(x) = 2x$

   Newton's formula:
   $$x_n = x_{n-1} - \frac{f(x_{n-1})}{f'(x_{n-1})} = x_{n-1} - \frac{x_{n-1}^2 - 10}{2x_{n-1}} = \frac{x_{n-1}^2 + 10}{2x_{n-1}}$$

   $$x_2 = \frac{x_1^2 + 10}{2x_1} = \frac{19}{6} \approx 3.1666667$$

   $$x_3 = \frac{x_2^2 + 10}{2x_2} = 3.1622807 \qquad x_4 = \frac{x_3^2 + 10}{2x_3} = 3.1622777$$

2. $f(x) = \ln x + x + 1$, $x_1 = 0.5$, $n = 5$.

$$f'(x) = \frac{1}{x} + 1$$

Newton's formula:

$$x_n = x_{n-1} - \frac{f(x_{n-1})}{f'(x_{n-1})} = x_{n-1} - \frac{(\ln x_{n-1} + x_{n-1} + 1)}{\frac{1}{x_{n-1}} + 1}$$

$$= x_{n-1} - \frac{(\ln x_{n-1} + x_{n-1} + 1)x_{n-1}}{x_{n-1} + 1} = \frac{-x_{n-1} \ln x_{n-1}}{x_{n-1} + 1}$$

$$x_2 = \frac{-x_1 \ln x_1}{x_1 + 1} = \frac{-(0.5)\ln(0.5)}{1.5} = 0.2310491$$

$$x_3 = \frac{-x_2 \ln x_2}{x_2 + 1} = 0.2749816$$

$$x_4 = \frac{-x_3 \ln x_3}{x_3 + 1} = 0.2784474 \qquad x_5 = \frac{-x_4 \ln x_4}{x_4 + 1} = 0.27846454$$

3.

x	1	2	5
$f(x)$	11	12	3

The general form of the interpolating polynomial is:

$$p(x) = a_0 + a_1(x - 1) + a_2(x - 1)(x - 2)$$

<u>Step 1</u>: $f(1) = 11 = p(1)$

$$11 = a_0$$

<u>Step 2</u>: $f(2) = 12 = p(2)$

$$12 = a_0 + a_1(1)$$
$$12 = 11 + a_1$$
$$1 = a_1$$

<u>Step 3</u>: $f(5) = 3 = p(5)$

$$3 = a_0 + a_1(4) + a_2(4)(3)$$
$$3 = 11 + 4 + 12a_2$$
$$-12 = 12a_2$$
$$-1 = a_2$$

Thus, $p(x) = 11 + (x - 1) - (x - 1)(x - 2)$.

4.

x	−1	0	1	2
$f(x)$	1	6	5	10

The divided difference table is:

x_k	y_k	1st D.D.	2nd D.D.	3rd D.D.
-1	1			
		$\dfrac{6 - 1}{0 - (-1)} = 5$		
0	6		$\dfrac{-1 - 5}{1 - (-1)} = -3$	
		$\dfrac{5 - 6}{1 - 0} = -1$		$\dfrac{3 - (-3)}{2 - (-1)} = 2$
1	5		$\dfrac{5 - (-1)}{2 - 0} = 3$	
		$\dfrac{10 - 5}{2 - 1} = 5$		
2	10			

The form of the interpolating polynomial is:
$$p(x) = a_0 + a_1(x + 1) + a_2(x + 1)x + a_3(x + 1)x(x - 1)$$
and, from the divided difference table,
$$p(x) = 1 + 5(x + 1) - 3(x + 1)x + 2(x + 1)x(x - 1)$$

5. $\displaystyle\int_0^2 e^{-x^2}dx$; $a = 0$, $b = 2$, $n = 5$, $f(x) = e^{-x^2}$.

Thus, $\Delta x = \dfrac{2 - 0}{5} = \dfrac{2}{5} = 0.4$.

The endpoints of the subintervals are:

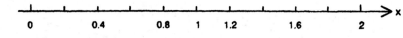

$$
\begin{aligned}
T_5 &= \frac{\Delta x}{2}[f(0) + 2f(0.4) + 2f(0.8) + 2f(1.2) + 2f(1.6) + f(2)] \\
&= \frac{0.4}{2}[e^0 + 2e^{-0.16} + 2e^{-0.64} + 2e^{-1.44} + 2e^{-2.56} + e^{-4}] \\
&= 0.2(4.40565306) = 0.881131
\end{aligned}
$$

Thus, $\displaystyle\int_0^2 e^{-x^2}dx \approx T_5 = 0.881$ (rounded to three decimal places).

6. $\displaystyle\int_0^3 \sqrt{4 + x^3}\,dx$; $a = 0$, $b = 3$, $n = 4$, $f(x) = \sqrt{4 + x^3}$.

Thus, $\Delta x = \dfrac{3 - 0}{4} = 0.75$.

The endpoints of the subintervals are:

$$
\begin{aligned}
S_4 &= \frac{\Delta x}{3}[f(0) + 4f(0.75) + 2f(1.5) + 4f(2.25) + f(3)] \\
&= \frac{0.75}{3}[2 + 4\sqrt{4.421875} + 2\sqrt{7.375} + 4\sqrt{15.390625} + \sqrt{31}] \\
&= 0.25(37.1028114) = 9.27570284
\end{aligned}
$$

Thus, $\displaystyle\int_0^3 \sqrt{4 + x^3}\,dx \approx S_4 = 9.276$ (rounded to three decimal places).

7. $y' = -2y$; $y(0) = 3$, $0 \le x \le 1$.

Let $x_0 = 0$, $y_0 = 3$, $\Delta x = 0.2$ and $f(x, y) = -2y$.
Euler's formula for y_k is:

$$y_k = y_{k-1} + f(x_{k-1}, y_{k-1})\Delta x$$
$$= y_{k-1} + (-2y_{k-1})(0.2)$$
$$= 0.6y_{k-1}$$

The approximate values are:

k	x_k	$y_k = 0.6y_{k-1}$
0	0	3
1	0.2	$0.6(3) = 1.8$
2	0.4	$0.6(1.8) = 1.08$
3	0.6	$0.6(1.08) = 0.648 \approx 0.65$
4	0.8	$0.6(0.648) = 0.3888 \approx 0.39$
5	1	$0.6(0.3888) = 0.23328 \approx 0.23$

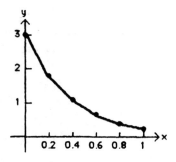

The graph of the approximate solution is shown
at the right.

8. $y' = y - 5x$; $y(0) = 1$.

Let $x_0 = 0$, $y_0 = 1$, $\Delta x = 0.2$ and $f(x, y) = y - 5x$.
Euler's formula for y_k is:

$$y_k = y_{k-1} + f(x_{k-1}, y_{k-1})\Delta x$$
$$= y_{k-1} + (y_{k-1} - 5x_{k-1})(0.2)$$
$$= 1.2y_{k-1} - x_{k-1}$$

The approximate values are:

k	x_k	$y_k = 1.2y_{k-1} - x_{k-1}$
0	0	1
1	0.2	$(1.2)(1) - 0 = 1.2$
2	0.4	$(1.2)(1.2) - 0.2 = 1.24$
3	0.6	$(1.2)(1.24) - 0.4 = 1.088 \approx 1.09$
4	0.8	$(1.2)(1.088) - 0.6 = 0.7056 \approx 0.71$
5	1	$(1.2)(0.7056) - 0.8 = 0.04672 \approx 0.05$

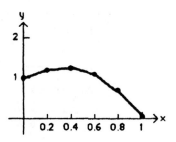

The graph of the approximate solution is shown
at the right.

9. The graph of $f(x) = x^3 - 12x + 3$ is shown at the right.

We conclude that r has three roots: r_1 in $(-4, -3)$, r_2 in $(0, 1)$, and r_3 in $(3, 4)$.

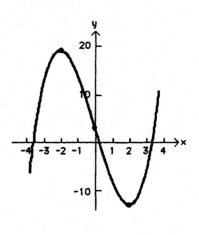

Now, $f'(x) = 3x^2 - 12$, and Newton's formula is

$$x_n = x_{n-1} - \frac{f(x_{n-1})}{f'(x_{n-1})}$$

$$= x_{n-1} - \frac{x_{n-1}^3 - 12x_{n-1} + 3}{3x_{n-1}^2 - 12}$$

$$= \frac{2x_{n-1}^3 - 3}{3x_{n-1}^2 - 12}.$$

Approximate r_1: Initial approximation, $x_1 = -3$.

n	x_{n-1}	$f(x_{n-1})$	$f'(x_{n-1})$	$x_{n-1} - \dfrac{f(x_{n-1})}{f'(x_{n-1})}$
2	-3	12	15	$-3 - \frac{12}{15} = -3.8$
3	-3.8	-6.272	31.32	$-3.8 - \frac{-6.272}{31.32} = -3.599745$
4	-3.599745	-0.449135	26.874483	$-3.599745 - \frac{-0.449135}{26.874483} = 3.583032$
5	-3.583032	-0.0030116	26.514361	$-3.583032 - \frac{-0.0030116}{26.514361} = -3.582919$
6	-3.582919	0	26.511919	

Thus, $r_1 \approx -3.582919$

Approximate r_2: Initial approximation, $x_1 = 1$.

n	x_{n-1}	$f(x_{n-1})$	$f'(x_{n-1})$	$x_{n-1} - \dfrac{f(x_{n-1})}{f'(x_{n-1})}$
2	1	-8	-9	$1 - \frac{-8}{-9} = 0.111111$
3	0.111111	1.668038	-11.962963	$0.111111 - \frac{1.668038}{-11.962963} = 0.250545$
4	0.250545	0.0091874	-11.811682	$0.250545 - \frac{0.0091874}{-11.811682} = 0.251323$
5	0.251323	-.0000016	-11.810511	$0.251323 - \frac{-.0000016}{-11.810511} = 0.251322$
6	0.251322	0	-11.810511	

Thus, $r_2 \approx 0.251322$.

Approximate r_3: Initial approximation, $x_1 = 4$.

n	x_{n-1}	$f(x_{n-1})$	$f'(x_{n-1})$	$x_{n-1} - \dfrac{f(x_{n-1})}{f'(x_{n-1})}$
2	4	19	36	$4 - \dfrac{19}{36} = 3.472222$
3	3.472222	3.195580	24.168982	$3.472222 - \dfrac{3.195580}{24.168982} = 3.340004$
4	3.340004	0.179790	21.466876	$3.340004 - \dfrac{0.179790}{21.466876} = 3.331629$
5	3.331629	0.0007023	21.299251	$3.331629 - \dfrac{0.0007023}{21.299251} = 3.331596$
6	3.331596	0	21.298592	

Thus, $r_3 \approx 3.331596$

10. Given $f(x) = x^3 - 9x^2 + 15x + 30$. Then
$f'(x) = 3x^2 - 18x + 15 = 3(x^2 - 6x + 5)$
and the critical values of f are:
$x = 1$ and $x = 5$.

The critical points are:
$(1, f(1)) = (1, 37)$ and $(5, f(5)) = (5, 5)$
Also, $f(-1) = 5 > 0$ and $f(-2) = -44 < 0$.
Thus, the graph of f is shown at the
right.

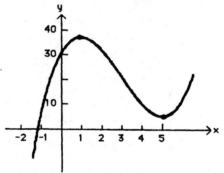

Now, f has a root, r_1, in the interval $(-2, -1)$. Newton's formula is:

$$x_n = x_{n-1} - \frac{f(x_{n-1})}{f'(x_{n-1})} = x_{n-1} - \frac{x_{n-1}^3 - 9x_{n-1}^2 + 15x_{n-1} + 30}{3x_{n-1}^2 - 18x_{n-1} + 15}$$

$$= \frac{2x_{n-1}^3 - 9x_{n-1}^2 - 30}{3x_{n-1}^2 - 18x_{n-1} + 15}.$$

Using $x_1 = -1$ as our initial approximation, we have:

n	x_{n-1}	$f(x_{n-1})$	$f'(x_{n-1})$	$x_{n-1} - \dfrac{f(x_{n-1})}{f'(x_{n-1})}$
2	-1	5	36	-1.13888889
3	-1.1388889	-0.234161	39.391204	-1.132944
4	-1.132944	0.0004386	39.243688	-1.132933
5	-1.132933	0	39.243411	

Thus, $r_1 \approx -1.132933$.

11. The graphs of $f(x) = e^{-x}$ and $g(x) = x^3$ are as shown in the diagram at the right. Thus, $h(x) = f(x) - g(x) = e^{-x} - x^3$ has a root, r_1, in the interval $(0, 1)$.

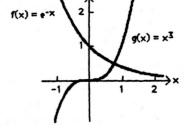

Newton's formula, for $h = h(x)$, is:

$$x_n = x_{n-1} - \frac{h(x_{n-1})}{h'(x_{n-1})} = x_{n-1} - \frac{e^{-x_{n-1}} - x_{n-1}^3}{-e^{-x_{n-1}} - 3x_{n-1}^2}$$

$$= \frac{-2x_{n-1}^3 - x_{n-1}e^{-x_{n-1}} - e^{-x_{n-1}}}{-e^{-x_{n-1}} - 3x_{n-1}^2} = \frac{2x_{n-1}^3 + x_{n-1}e^{-x_{n-1}} + e^{-x_{n-1}}}{e^{-x_{n-1}} + 3x_{n-1}^2}$$

Using $x_1 = 0$ as our initial approximation, we have:

n	x_{n-1}	$h(x_{n-1})$	$h'(x_{n-1})$	$x_{n-1} - \dfrac{h(x_{n-1})}{h'(x_{n-1})}$
2	0	1	−1	1
3	1	−0.632121	−3.367879	0.812309
4	0.812309	−0.921668	−2.423370	0.774277
5	0.774277	−0.0031448	−2.259550	0.772885
6	0.772885	−0.00000498	−2.2537319	0.772883
7	0.772883	0		

Thus, the point of intersection of the two graphs is (approximately) $(0.772883, f(0.772883)) = (0.772883, 0.461680)$.

12. The graphs of $f(x) = \dfrac{1}{x^3}$ and $f(x) = x + 1$ are shown at the right.

Thus, $h(x) = f(x) - g(x) = \dfrac{1}{x^3} - (x + 1)$ has a root, r_1, in $(-2, -1)$ and a root, r_2, in $(0, 1)$.

Newton's formula, for $h = h(x)$, is:

$$x_n = x_{n-1} - \frac{h(x_{n-1})}{h'(x_{n-1})} = x_{n-1} - \frac{\dfrac{1}{x_{n-1}^3} - (x_{n-1} + 1)}{\dfrac{-3}{x_{n-1}^4} - 1} = x_{n-1} - \frac{\dfrac{1 - x_{n-1}^4 - x_{n-1}^3}{x_{n-1}^3}}{\dfrac{-3 - x_{n-1}^4}{x_{n-1}^4}}$$

$$= x_{n-1} - \frac{x_{n-1} - x_{n-1}^5 - x_{n-1}^4}{-3 - x_{n-1}^4} = \frac{-4x_{n-1} + x_{n-1}^4}{-3 - x_{n-1}^4} = \frac{4x_{n-1} - x_{n-1}^4}{3 + x_{n-1}^4}$$

Approximation of r_1:

Using $x_1 = -1$ as our initial approximation, we have the following table of values.

n	x_{n-1}	$h(x_{n-1})$	$h'(x_{n-1})$	$x_{n-1} - \dfrac{h(x_{n-1})}{h'(x_{n-1})}$
2	-1	-1	-4	-1.25
3	-1.25	-0.2610	-2.2288001	-1.3675520
4	-1.3675520	-0.0234404	-1.8577206	-1.3801699
5	-1.3801699	-0.0001967	-1.8267288	-1.3802776
6	-1.3802776	0		

Thus, $r_1 \approx -1.3802776$.

Approximation of r_2:

Using $x_1 = 1$ as our initial guess, we have:

n	x_{n-1}	$h(x_{n-1})$	$h'(x_{n-1})$	$x_{n-1} - \dfrac{h(x_{n-1})}{h'(x_{n-1})}$
2	1	-1	-4	0.75
3	0.75	0.6203706	-10.4814816	0.8091873
4	0.8091873	0.0781641	-7.9972119	0.8189612
5	0.8189612	0.0061986	-7.6691113	0.8191724
6	0.8191724	0.00000776	-7.6622343	0.8191725
7	0.8191725	0.0000004		

Thus, $r_2 \approx 0.8191725$.

13.

x	1	2	3	5
$f(x)$	16	10	8	40

The divided difference table is:

x_k	y_k	1st D.D.	2nd D.D.	3rd D.D.
1	16			
		-6		
2	10		2	
		-2		1
3	8		6	
		16		
5	40			

The interpolating polynomial is:
$$p(x) = 16 - 6(x - 1) + 2(x - 1)(x - 2) + (x - 1)(x - 2)(x - 3)$$
Now,
$$f(4) \approx p(4) = 16 - 6(3) + 2(3)(2) + (3)(2)(1)$$
$$= 16 - 18 + 12 + 6 = 16$$
Thus, $f(4) \approx 16$.

14.

x	-4	-2	0	2	4
$f(x)$	20	40	124	80	100

The divided difference table is:

x_k	y_k	1st D.D.	2nd D.D.	3rd D.D.	4th D.D.
-4	20				
		10			
-2	40		8		
		42		-4	
0	124		-16		1
		-22		4	
2	80		8		
		10			
4	100				

The interpolating polynomial is:
$$p(x) = 20 + 10(x + 4) + 8(x + 4)(x + 2) - 4(x + 4)(x + 2)x$$
$$+ (x + 4)(x + 2)x(x - 2)$$

Now,
$$f(1) \approx p(1) = 20 + 10(5) + 8(5)(3) - 4(5)(3)(1) + (5)(3)(1)(-1)$$
$$= 20 + 50 + 120 - 60 - 15$$
$$= 115$$

Thus, $f(1) \approx 115$.

15.

x	0	2	5
$f(x)$	10	2	5

The form of the interpolating polynomial is:
$$p(x) = a_0 + a_1 x + a_2 x(x - 2)$$

Now,

Step 1: $f(0) = 10 = p(0)$
$$10 = a_0$$

Step 2: $f(2) = 2 = p(2)$
$$2 = a_0 + a_1(2)$$
$$2 = 10 + 2a_1$$
$$-8 = 2a_1$$
$$-4 = a_1$$

Step 3: $f(5) = 5 = p(5)$
$$5 = a_0 + a_1(5) + a_2(5)(3)$$
$$5 = 10 - 4(5) + 15a_2$$
$$5 = 10 - 20 + 15a_2$$
$$15 = 15a_2$$
$$1 = a_2$$

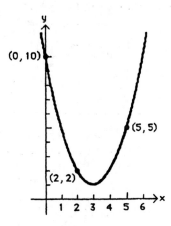

Thus, $p(x) = 10 - 4x + x(x - 2)$
or $p(x) = 10 - 6x + x^2$
The graph of $p(x)$ is shown at the right.

16.

x	-3	-1	1	3
$f(x)$	16	12	32	-20

The divided difference table is:

x_k	y_k	1st D.D.	2nd D.D.	3rd D.D.
-3	16			
		-2		
-1	12		3	
		10		-2
1	32		-9	
		-26		
3	-20			

Thus, the interpolating polynomial is:

$$p(x) = 16 - 2(x + 3) + 3(x + 3)(x + 1)$$
$$- 2(x + 3)(x + 1)(x - 1)$$

and

$$p(x) = 25 + 12x - 3x^2 - 2x^3$$

The graph of $p(x)$ is shown at the right.

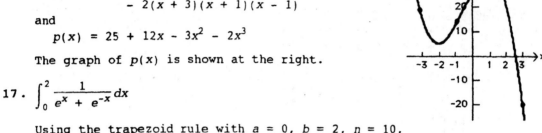

17. $\int_0^2 \frac{1}{e^x + e^{-x}} dx$

Using the trapezoid rule with $a = 0$, $b = 2$, $n = 10$,

$\Delta x = \frac{2 - 0}{10} = \frac{1}{5} = 0.2$ and $f(x) = \frac{1}{e^x + e^{-x}}$,

we have:

$$T_{10} = \frac{\Delta x}{2}[f(0) + 2f(0.2) + 2f(0.4) + \cdots + 2f(1.8) + f(2)]$$

$= 0.1[0.5 + 0.9803249 + 0.9250095 + 0.8435473 + 0.7477027$
$\qquad + 0.6480545 + 0.5522848 + 0.4649217 + 0.3879789$
$\qquad + 0.3218052 + 0.1329011]$

$= 0.1(6.5045306) = 0.650453$

Thus, $\int_0^2 \frac{1}{e^x + e^{-x}} dx \approx 0.650453$.

18. $\int_1^3 [\ln(1 + x^2)]^2 dx.$

Using Simpson's rule with $a = 1$, $b = 3$, $n = 8$, $f(x) = [\ln(1 + x^2)]^2$
and $\Delta x = \frac{3 - 1}{8} = \frac{1}{4} = 0.25$, we have:

$$S_8 = \frac{\Delta x}{3}[f(1) + 4f(1.25) + 2f(1.5) + \cdots + 4f(2.75) + f(3)]$$

$= \frac{\frac{1}{4}}{3}[.4804530 + 3.5417986 + 2.7784552 + 7.8601567 + 5.1805808$
$\qquad + 12.9905785 + 7.8487336 + 18.4451731 + 5.3018981]$

$= \frac{1}{12}(64.4278276) = 5.36898563$

Thus, $\int_1^3 [\ln(1 + x^2)]^2 dx \approx 5.36899$.

19.

x	-3	-2	-1	0	1	2	3
$f(x)$	5	7	8	12	11	6	4

$a = -3$, $b = 3$, $n = 6$, $\Delta x = \dfrac{3 - (-3)}{6} = 1$

$\displaystyle\int_{-3}^{3} f(x)\,dx \approx T_6 = \dfrac{\Delta x}{2}[f(-3) + 2f(-2) + 2f(-1) + \cdots + 2f(2) + f(3)]$

$\qquad\qquad\qquad = \dfrac{1}{2}[5 + 14 + 16 + 24 + 22 + 12 + 4]$

$\qquad\qquad\qquad = \dfrac{1}{2}(97) = 48.5$

20. The area of the region bounded by the graphs of $y = \dfrac{1}{\ln x}$ and $y = 0$, $2 \le x \le 3$, is given by

$\displaystyle\int_{2}^{3} \dfrac{1}{\ln x}\,dx.$

Using Simpson's rule with $n = 10$, $a = 2$, $b = 3$,

$\qquad \Delta x = \dfrac{3 - 2}{10} = \dfrac{1}{10} = 0.1$, and $f(x) = \dfrac{1}{\ln x}$,

we have:

$S_{10} = \dfrac{\Delta x}{3}[f(2) + 4f(2.1) + 2f(2.2) + \cdots + 2f(2.8) + 4f(2.9) + f(3)]$

$\qquad = \dfrac{\frac{1}{10}}{3}[1.4426950 + 5.3912908 + 2.5365988 + 4.8024447 + 2.2844905$

$\qquad\qquad\qquad + 4.3654267 + 2.0931199 + 4.0271763 + 1.9424653$

$\qquad\qquad\qquad + 3.7568889 + 0.9102391]$

$\qquad = \dfrac{1}{30}(33.5528361) = 1.11842787$

Thus, the area of the region is (approximately) 1.11843.

21. $y' = -\dfrac{x}{y}$; $y(0) = 1$, $0 \le x \le 1$.

Let $x_0 = 0$, $y_0 = 1$, $\Delta x = 0.2$, and $f(x, y) = -\dfrac{x}{y}$.
Euler's formula for y_k is:

$\qquad y_k = y_{k-1} + f(x_{k-1}, y_{k-1})\Delta x$

$\qquad\quad = y_{k-1} - (0.2)\left(\dfrac{x_{k-1}}{y_{k-1}}\right).$

The approximate values appear on the following page.

k	x_k	$y_k = y_{k-1} - (0.2)\left(\dfrac{x_{k-1}}{y_{k-1}}\right)$
0	0	1
1	0.2	1
2	0.4	$1 - 0.2\left(\dfrac{0.2}{1}\right) = 0.96$
3	0.6	$0.96 - 0.2\left(\dfrac{0.4}{0.96}\right) = 0.876667 \approx 0.88$
4	0.8	$0.876667 - 0.2\left(\dfrac{0.6}{0.876667}\right) = 0.739785 \approx 0.74$
5	1	$0.739785 - 0.2\left(\dfrac{0.8}{0.739785}\right) = 0.523505 \approx 0.52$

The exact solution is $y(x) = \sqrt{1 - x^2}$.

The graphs of the approximate and exact solutions are shown at the right.

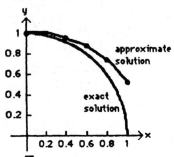

22. $y' = x + \sqrt{y};\ y(0) = 0$.
Let $x_0 = 0$, $y_0 = 0$, $\Delta x = 0.2$, and $f(x, y) = x + \sqrt{y}$.
Euler's formula for y_k is:
$$y_k = y_{k-1} + f(x_{k-1},\ y_{k-1})\Delta x$$
$$= y_{k-1} + (x_{k-1} + \sqrt{y_{k-1}})(0.2)$$

The approximate values are:

k	x_k	$y_k = y_{k-1} + (0.2)\ (x_{k-1} + \sqrt{y_{k-1}})$
0	0	0
1	0.2	0
2	0.4	$0 + (0.2)(0.2) = 0.04$
3	0.6	$0.04 + (0.2)(0.4 + \sqrt{0.4}) = 0.16$
4	0.8	$0.16 + (0.2)(0.6 + \sqrt{0.16}) = 0.36$
5	1	$0.36 + (0.2)(0.8 + \sqrt{0.36}) = 0.64$

Thus, $y(1) \approx 0.64$.

23. $y' = \dfrac{1}{y} + \dfrac{1}{x};\ y(1) = 1$.

Let $x_0 = 1$, $y_0 = 1$, $\Delta x = 0.4$, and $f(x, y) = \dfrac{1}{y} + \dfrac{1}{x}$.
Euler's formula for y_k is:
$$y_k = y_{k-1} + f(x_{k-1},\ y_{k-1})\Delta x$$
$$= y_{k-1} + \left(\dfrac{1}{y_{k-1}} + \dfrac{1}{x_{k-1}}\right)(0.4)$$

The approximate values are:

k	x_k	$y_k = y_{k-1} + (0.4)\left(\dfrac{1}{y_{k-1}} + \dfrac{1}{x_{k-1}}\right)$
0	1	1
1	1.4	$1 + (0.4)(2) = 1.8$
2	1.8	$1.8 + (0.4)\left(\dfrac{1}{1.8} + \dfrac{1}{1.4}\right) = 2.307937$
3	2.2	$2.307937 + (0.4)\left(\dfrac{1}{2.307937} + \dfrac{1}{1.8}\right) = 2.703474$
4	2.6	$2.703474 + (0.4)\left(\dfrac{1}{2.703474} + \dfrac{1}{2.2}\right) = 3.033250$
5	3	$3.033250 + (0.4)\left(\dfrac{1}{3.033250} + \dfrac{1}{2.6}\right) = 3.318968$

Thus, $y(3) \approx 3.318968$.

24. $\dfrac{dx}{dt} = x + 2y$, $\dfrac{dy}{dt} = y + 4x$; $x(0) = 1$, $y(0) = 0$, $\Delta t = 0.2$.

Euler's formula for x_k and y_k are:
$$x_k = x_{k-1} + f(x_{k-1}, y_{k-1})\Delta t$$
$$= x_{k-1} + (x_{k-1} + 2y_{k-1})(0.2)$$
$$= 1.2x_{k-1} + 0.4y_{k-1}$$
and
$$y_k = y_{k-1} + g(x_{k-1}, y_{k-1})\Delta t$$
$$= y_{k-1} + (y_{k-1} + 4x_{k-1})(0.2)$$
$$= 1.2y_{k-1} + 0.8x_{k-1}$$

The approximate values are:

k	t_k	$x_k = 1.2x_{k-1} + 0.4y_{k-1}$	$y_k = 1.2y_{k-1} + 0.8x_{k-1}$
0	0	1	0
1	0.2	1.2	0.8
2	0.4	$1.2(1.2) + 0.4(0.8) = 1.76 \approx 1.8$	$1.2(0.8) + 0.8(1.2) = 1.92 \approx 1.9$
3	0.6	$1.2(1.8) + 0.4(1.9) = 2.92 \approx 2.9$	$1.2(1.9) + 0.8(1.8) = 3.72 \approx 3.7$
4	0.8	$1.2(2.9) + 0.4(3.7) = 4.96 \approx 5.0$	$1.2(3.7) + 0.8(2.9) = 6.76 \approx 6.8$
5	1	$1.2(5.0) + 0.4(6.8) = 8.72 \approx 8.7$	$1.2(6.8) + 0.8(5.0) = 12.16 \approx 12.2$

25. $f(x) = ax^2 + bx + c$.
$f'(x) = 2ax + b$.
Newton's formula:
$$x_n = x_{n-1} - \frac{f(x_{n-1})}{f'(x_{n-1})} = x_{n-1} - \frac{(ax_{n-1}^2 + bx_{n-1} + c)}{2ax_{n-1} + b}$$
Thus,
$$x_n = \frac{ax_{n-1}^2 - c}{2ax_{n-1} + b}.$$

26. $f(x) = \dfrac{10x^2}{1 + x^2}$

x	-2	-1	0	1	2
$f(x)$	8	5	0	5	8

The divided difference table is:

x_k	y_k	1st D.D.	2nd D.D.	3rd D.D.	4th D.D.
-2	8				
		-3			
-1	5		-1		
		-5		2	
0	0		5		-1
		5		-2	
1	5		-1		
		3			
2	8				

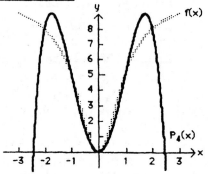

Thus, the interpolating polynomial is:

$$p(x) = 8 - 3(x + 2) - (x + 2)(x + 1)$$
$$+ 2(x + 2)(x + 1)x$$
$$- (x + 2)(x + 1)x(x - 1)$$

Simplifying p, we have
$$p(x) = 6x^2 - x^4.$$

The graphs of f and p are shown at the right.

27. The exact value of the integral $\displaystyle\int_0^2 x^4\,dx$ is:

$$\int_0^2 x^4\,dx = \frac{x^5}{5}\bigg|_0^2 = \frac{32}{5} = 6.4$$

We now calculate T_n, $\text{Err}(T_n)$, S_n, and $\text{Err}(S_n)$ for (A) $n = 4$ and (B) $n = 8$.

(A) $a = 0$, $b = 2$, $n = 4$, $f(x) = x^4$, and $\Delta x = \dfrac{2 - 0}{4} = \dfrac{1}{2} = 0.5$.

$$T_4 = \frac{\Delta x}{2}[f(0) + 2f(0.5) + 2f(1) + 2f(1.5) + f(2)]$$

$$= \frac{\frac{1}{2}}{2}[0 + 0.125 + 2 + 10.125 + 16]$$

$$= \frac{1}{4}(28.250) = 7.0625 \approx 7.063$$

$$S_4 = \frac{\Delta x}{3}[f(0) + 4f(0.5) + 2f(1) + 4f(1.5) + f(2)]$$

$$= \frac{\frac{1}{2}}{3}[0 + 0.250 + 2 + 20.250 + 16]$$

$$= \frac{1}{6}(38.5) = 6.416667 \approx 6.417$$

Now, $\text{Err}(T_4) = \int_0^2 x^4 dx - T_4 = 6.4 - 7.063 = -0.663$

and $\text{Err}(S_4) = \int_0^2 x^4 dx - S_4 = 6.4 - 6.417 = -0.017.$

(B) $a = 0$, $b = 2$, $n = 8$, $f(x) = x^4$, and $\Delta x = \dfrac{2 - 0}{8} = \dfrac{1}{4} = 0.25.$

$$T_8 = \frac{\Delta x}{2}[f(0) + 2f(0.25) + 2f(0.5) + \cdots + 2f(1.75) + f(2)]$$

$$= \frac{\frac{1}{4}}{2}[0 + 0.0078125 + 0.125 + 0.6328125 + 2 + 4.8828125$$

$$+ 10.125 + 18.7578125 + 16]$$

$$= \frac{1}{8}(52.53125) = 6.56640625 \approx 6.566$$

$$S_8 = \frac{\Delta x}{3}[f(0) + 4f(0.25) + 2f(0.5) + \cdots + 4f(1.75) + f(2)]$$

$$= \frac{\frac{1}{4}}{3}[0 + 0.015625 + 0.125 + 1.265625 + 2 + 9.765625$$

$$+ 10.125 + 37.515625 + 16]$$

$$= \frac{1}{12}(76.8125) = 6.40104167 \approx 6.401$$

Now, $\text{Err}(T_8) = \int_0^2 x^4 dx - T_8 = 6.4 - 6.566 = -0.166$

and $\text{Err}(S_8) = \int_0^2 x^4 dx - S_8 = 6.4 - 6.401 = -0.001.$

Table:

n	T_n	$\text{Err}(T_n)$	S_n	$\text{Err}(S_n)$
4	7.063	−0.663	6.417	−0.017
8	6.566	−0.166	6.401	−0.001

28. $y' = 2y - 10x + 1$; $y(0) = 1.$

(A) Let $x_0 = 0$, $y_0 = 1$, $\Delta x = 0.2$, and $f(x, y) = 2y - 10x + 1.$
Euler's formula for y_k is:

$$y_k = y_{k-1} + f(x_{k-1}, y_{k-1})\Delta x$$
$$= y_{k-1} + (2y_{k-1} - 10x_{k-1} + 1)(0.2)$$
$$= 1.4y_{k-1} - 2x_{k-1} + 0.2$$

The approximate values are:

k	x_k	$y_k = 1.4y_{k-1} - 2x_{k-1} + 0.2$
0	0	1
1	0.2	$(1.4)(1) - 2(0) + 0.2 = 1.6$
2	0.4	$(1.4)(1.6) - 2(0.2) + 0.2 = 2.04$
3	0.6	$(1.4)(2.04) - 2(0.4) + 0.2 = 2.256 \approx 2.26$
4	0.8	$(1.4)(2.256) - 2(0.6) + 0.2 = 2.1584 \approx 2.16$
5	1	$(1.4)(2.1584) - 2(0.8) + 0.2 = 1.62176 \approx 1.62$

(B) Let $x_0 = 0$, $y_0 = 1$, $\Delta x = 0.1$, and $f(x, y) = 2y - 10x + 1$.
Euler's formula for y_k is:

$$y_k = y_{k-1} + (2y_{k-1} - 10x_{k-1} + 1)(0.1)$$
$$= 1.2y_{k-1} - x_{k-1} + 0.1$$

The approximate values are:

k	x_k	$y_k = 1.2y_{k-1} - x_{k-1} + 0.1$
0	0	1
1	0.1	$(1.2)(1) - 0 + 0.1 = 1.3$
2	0.2	$(1.2)(1.3) - 0.1 + 0.1 = 1.56$
3	0.3	$(1.2)(1.56) - 0.2 + 0.1 = 1.772 \approx 1.77$
4	0.4	$(1.2)(1.772) - 0.3 + 0.1 = 1.9264 \approx 1.93$
5	0.5	$(1.2)(1.9264) - 0.4 + 0.1 = 2.01168 \approx 2.01$
6	0.6	$(1.2)(2.01168) - 0.5 + 0.1 = 2.014016 \approx 2.01$
7	0.7	$(1.2)(2.014016) - 0.6 + 0.1 = 1.916819 \approx 1.92$
8	0.8	$(1.2)(1.916819) - 0.7 + 0.1 = 1.700183 \approx 1.70$
9	0.9	$(1.2)(1.700183) - 0.8 + 0.1 = 1.340220 \approx 1.34$
10	1	$(1.2)(1.340220) - 0.9 + 0.1 = 0.808264 \approx 0.81$

The exact solution is
$$y = -e^{2x} + 5x + 2.$$

The graphs of the exact and
approximate solutions are shown
in the diagram at the right.

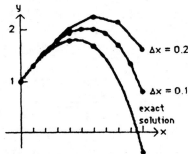

29. The break-even point occurs where $R(x) = C(x)$. That is,

$$2x + \frac{10x}{1 + x^2} = 10 + 0.5x \quad \text{or} \quad 1.5x + \frac{10x}{1 + x^2} - 10 = 0.$$

We apply Newton's method to $f(x) = 1.5x + \frac{10x}{1 + x^2} - 10$, $x \geq 1$. Now,

$$f'(x) = 1.5 + \frac{10 - 10x^2}{(1 + x^2)^2},$$

and

$$x_k = x_{k-1} - \frac{f(x_{k-1})}{f'(x_{k-1})} = x_{k-1} - \frac{\left[1.5x_{k-1} + \dfrac{10x_{k-1}}{1 + x_{k-1}^2} - 10\right]}{1.5 + \dfrac{10 - 10x_{k-1}^2}{(1 + x_{k-1}^2)^2}}$$

$$= x_{k-1} - \frac{\left[\dfrac{1.5x_{k-1} + 1.5x_{k-1}^3 + 10x_{k-1} - 10 - 10x_{k-1}^2}{1 + x_{k-1}^2}\right]}{\dfrac{1.5 + 3x_{k-1}^2 + 1.5x_{k-1}^4 + 10 - 10x_{k-1}^2}{(1 + x_{k-1}^2)^2}}$$

$$= x_{k-1} - \frac{(1.5x_{k-1}^3 - 10x_{k-1}^2 + 11.5x_{k-1} - 10)(1 + x_{k-1}^2)}{1.5x_{k-1}^4 - 7x_{k-1}^2 + 11.5}$$

Use the initial approximation $x_1 = 5$. Then, we have:

n	x_{k-1}	$f(x_{k-1})$	$f'(x_{k-1})$	$x_{k-1} - \dfrac{f(x_{k-1})}{f'(x_{k-1})}$
2	5	-0.5769231	1.1449704	5.503876
3	5.503876	0.0146538	1.2008604	5.4916733
4	5.4916733	0.0000073	1.1996605	5.4916672

Thus, the break-even point is (approximately) 5.491667.

30. The internal rate of return r is the solution of the equation

$$20,000 = \frac{8,000}{1 + r} + \frac{10,000}{(1 + r)^2} + \frac{9,000}{(1 + r)^3}$$

or $20 - \dfrac{8}{1 + r} - \dfrac{10}{(1 + r)^2} - \dfrac{9}{(1 + r)^3} = 0$

Let $x = 1 + r$ and $f(x) = 20 - 8x^{-1} - 10x^{-2} - 9x^{-3}$. Since r is an interest rate $0 < r < 1$ implying that $1 < x < 2$. Now, $f(1) = -7$ and $f(2) = 20 - 4 - \dfrac{5}{2} - \dfrac{9}{8} = \dfrac{99}{8} > 0$. Thus, f has a zero between $x = 1$ and $x = 2$. Moreover, since

$$f'(x) = 8x^{-2} + 20x^{-3} + 27x^{-4} > 0$$

for $x > 0$, f is increasing on $(0, \infty)$, and so f has exactly one positive zero.

By Newton's method:

$$x_n = x_{n-1} - \frac{f(x_{n-1})}{f'(x_{n-1})} = x_{n-1} - \frac{20 - 8x_{n-1}^{-1} - 10x_{n-1}^{-2} - 9x_{n-1}^{-3}}{8x_{n-1}^{-2} + 20x_{n-1}^{-3} + 27x_{n-1}^{-4}}$$

$$= x_{n-1} - \frac{20x_{n-1}^4 - 8x_{n-1}^3 - 10x_{n-1}^2 - 9x_{n-1}}{8x_{n-1}^2 + 20x_{n-1} + 27}$$

Letting $x_1 = 1$, we have:

n	x_n	$f(x_n)$	$f'(x_n)$
1	1	-7	55
2	1.127273	-1.249013	36.97781
3	1.16105	-0.0587959	33.57096
4	1.162802	0.0001440	33.40613
5	1.162806	0.0000005	33.40572

Thus, $f(x) \approx 0$ when $x = 1.1628$ (to four decimal places). Now, $r = x - 1$ $= 0.1628$ and the internal rate of return is 16.28% compounded annually.

31. Given

x	0	2	4	6
$R(x)$	0	44	112	108

The interpolating polynomial has the form
$$p_3(x) = a_0 + a_1 x + a_2 x(x - 2) + a_3 x(x - 2)(x - 4).$$

The divided difference table is:

x_k	y_k	1st D.D.	2nd D.D.	3rd D.D.
0	0			
		22		
2	44		3	
		34		-2
4	112		-9	
		-2		
6	108			

Thus, $p_3(x) = 22x + 3x(x - 2) - 2x(x - 2)(x - 4)$
$$= 15x^2 - 2x^3, \quad x \geq 0.$$
The approximate revenue if 3000 units are produced is
$$R(3) \approx p_3(3) = 15(3)^2 - 2(3)^3 = 81 \quad \text{or} \quad \$81,000.$$

To find the approximate production level that will maximize revenue, determine the maximum of $p_3(x)$.

$$p_3'(x) = 30x - 6x^2$$
Now,
$$30x - 6x^2 = 0$$
$$6x(5 - x) = 0$$
$$x = 0, \quad x = 5$$
$$p_3''(x) = 30 - 12x \quad \text{and} \quad p_3''(5) = 30 - 60 = -30 < 0$$
Thus, p_3 has a local maximum at $x = 5$, and the approximate production level that will maximize revenue is 5000 units.

32. Given the demand and supply functions
$$D(x) = \sqrt{144 - 4x^3} \quad \text{and} \quad S(x) = \sqrt{9 + x^3}.$$

To find the equilibrium price, set $D(x) = S(x)$ and solve for x:

$$\sqrt{144 - 4x^3} = \sqrt{9 + x^3}$$
$$144 - 4x^3 = 9 + x^3$$
$$5x^3 = 135$$
$$x^3 = 27$$
$$x = 3$$

The equilibrium price is
$$\bar{p} = D(3) = S(3) = \sqrt{36} = 6.$$

Now, consumer's surplus $= \displaystyle\int_0^3 [D(x) - \bar{p}]dx = \int_0^3 [\sqrt{144 - 4x^3} - 6]dx.$

Using Simpson's rule with $a = 0$, $b = 3$, $n = 4$, and $\Delta x = \dfrac{3 - 0}{4} = 0.75$,
we have:

$$\int_0^3 [\sqrt{144 - 4x^3} - 6]dx \sim S_4$$
$$= \frac{\Delta x}{3}[f(0) + 4f(0.75) + 2f(1.5) + 4f(2.25) + f(3)]$$
$$= \frac{0.75}{3}(6 + 23.7179212 + 10.8473193 + 15.6862697 + 0)$$
$$= 0.25(56.2515102) = 14.0628775$$

Thus, the consumer's surplus is (approximately) 14.06.

Producer's surplus $= \displaystyle\int_0^3 [\bar{p} - S(x)]dx = \int_0^3 [6 - \sqrt{9 + x^3}]dx$

and
$$\int_0^3 [6 - \sqrt{9 + x^3}]dx \sim S_4$$
$$= \frac{\Delta x}{3}[f(0) + 4f(0.75) + 2f(1.5) + 4f(2.25) + f(3)]$$
$$= \frac{0.75}{3}(3 + 11.7219708 + 4.9643736 + 5.93760813 + 0)$$
$$= 0.25(25.6239553) = 6.40598884$$

Thus, the producer's surplus is (approximately) 6.41.

33. Given the marginal revenue and marginal cost functions
$$R'(t) = \frac{8}{4 + t^2} \quad \text{and} \quad C'(t) = \frac{2t^2}{4 + t^2}$$

To find the useful life of the machine, set $R'(t) = C'(t)$ and solve for t:
$$\frac{8}{4 + t^2} = \frac{2t^2}{4 + t^2}$$
$$2t^2 = 8$$
$$t^2 = 4$$
$$t = 2 \quad \text{or} \quad -2$$

Thus, the useful life of the machine is two years.

The total profit is given by

$$\int_0^2 \left[\frac{8}{4 + t^2} - \frac{2t^2}{4 + t^2} \right] dt = \int_0^2 \frac{8 - 2t^2}{4 + t^2} \, dt.$$

Using Simpson's rule with $a = 0$, $b = 2$, $n = 4$, and $\Delta t = \frac{2 - 0}{4} = 0.5$, we have:

$$\int_0^2 \frac{8 - 2t^2}{4 + t^2} \, dt \approx S_4 = \frac{\Delta t}{3} [f(0) + 4f(0.5) + 2f(1) + 4f(1.5) + f(2)]$$

$$= \frac{0.5}{3} (2 + 7.05882353 + 2.4 + 2.24 + 0)$$

$$= \frac{1}{6} (13.69882353) = 2.283137255$$

Thus, the total profit is (approximately) $2300.

34. $\frac{ds}{dt} = 0.1\sqrt{s}(100 - \sqrt{s})$; $s(0) = 50$. Euler's formula for s_k, with $\Delta t = 1$, is:

$$s_k = s_{k-1} + f(t_{k-1}, s_{k-1})\Delta t$$
$$= s_{k-1} + 0.1\sqrt{s_{k-1}}(100 - \sqrt{s_{k-1}})(1)$$
$$= 0.9 s_{k-1} + 10\sqrt{s_{k-1}}$$

The approximate values are:

k	t_{k-1}	$s_k = 0.9 s_{k-1} + 10\sqrt{s_{k-1}}$
0	0	50
1	1	$(0.9)(50) + 10\sqrt{50} = 115.710678$
2	2	$(0.9)(115.710678) + 10\sqrt{115.710678} = 211.708508$
3	3	$(0.9)(211.708508) + 10\sqrt{211.708508} = 336.039722$
4	4	$(0.9)(336.039722) + 10\sqrt{336.039722} = 485.749613$
5	5	$(0.9)(485.749613) + 10\sqrt{485.749613} = 657.571932$

Thus, $s(5) \approx \$658,000$.

35. The graph of $L(t) = 100te^{-0.4t}$ is (approximately):

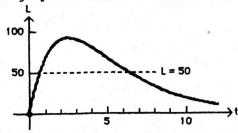

To find the time interval during which the hormone level is above 50 milligrams per milliliter, we must solve the equation:

$$L(t) = 50 \quad \text{or} \quad 100te^{-0.4t} = 50$$

We let $f(t) = 100te^{-0.4t} - 50$ and use Newton's method to approximate the zeros of f. From the graph, we will use initial approximations of $t_1 = 0.5$ and $t_1 = 5$, respectively.

$$f(t) = 100te^{-0.4t} - 50$$

$$f'(t) = 100e^{-0.4t} - 40te^{-0.4t}$$

$$t_n = t_{n-1} - \frac{f(t_{n-1})}{f'(t_{n-1})}$$

Near $t = 0.5$:

n	t_n	$f(t_n)$	$f'(t_n)$
1	0.5	−9.063462	65.498460
2	0.638377	−0.548478	57.683871
3	0.647885	−0.002439	57.171390
4	0.647928	0	57.169097

Near $t = 5$:

n	t_n	$f(t_n)$	$f'(t_n)$
1	5	17.667640	−13.533528
2	6.305472	0.622656	−12.220093
3	6.356423	0.002180	−12.134472
4	6.356603	0	−12.134164

Thus, $f(t) \approx 0$ when $t \approx 0.6$ and when $t \approx 6.4$. The hormone level is greater than 50 milligrams per milliliter when $0.6 < t < 6.4$.

36. The average blood pressure over the one-second interval is given by the definite integral

$$P = \frac{1}{1-0} \int_0^1 f(t)\,dt = \int_0^1 f(t)\,dt.$$

Now, letting $a = 0$, $b = 1$, $n = 5$, and $\Delta x = \frac{1-0}{5} = 0.2$, we have:

$$\int_0^1 f(t)\,dt \approx T_5 = \frac{\Delta x}{2}[f(0) + 2f(0.2) + 2f(0.4) + 2f(0.6) + 2f(0.8) + f(1)]$$

$$= \frac{0.2}{2}[80 + 2(60) + 2(110) + 2(130) + 2(100) + 70]$$

$$= 0.1(950) = 95$$

Thus, the average blood pressure over the one-second interval is (approximately) 95 torrs.

37. $\dfrac{dy}{dt} = y(0.9 - 0.05x); \quad y(0) = 50$

$\dfrac{dx}{dt} = x(0.005y - 0.2); \quad x(0) = 15$

Euler's formulas for y_k and x_k, with $\Delta t = 1$, are:

$$y_k = y_{k-1} + f(x_{k-1},\ y_{k-1})\Delta t$$

$$= y_{k-1} + y_{k-1}(0.9 - 0.05x_{k-1})(1)$$

$$= 1.9y_{k-1} - 0.05x_{k-1}y_{k-1}$$

and

$$x_k = x_{k-1} + g(x_{k-1}, y_{k-1})\Delta t$$
$$= x_{k-1} + x_{k-1}(0.005y_{k-1} - 0.2)(1)$$
$$= 0.8x_{k-1} + 0.005x_{k-1}y_{k-1}.$$

The approximate values of x_k and y_k are given by:

k	t_k	$y_k = 1.9y_{k-1} - 0.05x_{k-1}y_{k-1}$	$x_k = 0.8x_{k-1} + 0.005x_{k-1}y_{k-1}$
0	0	50	15
1	1	$1.9(50) - 0.05(15)(50) = 57.5$	$0.8(15) + 0.005(15)(50) = 15.75 \approx 15.8$
2	2	$1.9(57.5) - 0.05(15.8)(57.5)$ $= 63.825 \approx 63.8$	$0.8(15.8) + 0.005(57.5)(15.8)$ $= 17.1825 \approx 17.2$
3	3	$1.9(63.8) - 0.05(17.2)(63.8)$ $= 66.352 \approx 66.4$	$0.8(17.2) + 0.005(17.2)(63.8)$ $= 19.2468 \approx 19.2$
4	4	$1.9(66.4) - 0.05(19.2)(66.4)$ $= 62.322 \approx 62.4$	$0.8(19.2) + 0.005(19.2)(66.4) = 21.7$
5	5	$1.9(62.4) - 0.05(62.4)(21.7)$ $= 50.856 \approx 50.9$	$0.8(21.7) + 0.005(21.7)(62.4)$ $= 24.1304 \approx 24.1$

Thus, there are approximately 50,900 rabbits and 24,100 foxes.

38. The total number of components which a worker will assemble in the first four hours is given by

$$\int_0^4 N'(t)\,dt = \int_0^4 \frac{4t^2 + 4t + 15}{4t^2 + 4t + 5}\,dt.$$

Using Simpson's rule with $a = 0$, $b = 4$, $n = 4$, and $\Delta t = \frac{4 - 0}{4} = 1$, we have:

$$\int_0^4 \frac{4t^2 + 4t + 15}{4t^2 + 4t + 5}\,dt \approx S_4 = \frac{\Delta t}{3}[f(0) + 4f(1) + 2f(2) + 4f(3) + f(4)]$$

$$= \frac{1}{3}(3 + 7.07692308 + 2.68965517 + 4.7541698$$
$$+ 1.11764706)$$

$$= \frac{1}{3}(18.6389423) = 6.21298076$$

Thus, the number of components which a worker will assemble in the first four hours is six.

10 Probability & Calculus

Things to remember:

1. **PROBABILITY IN EQUALLY LIKELY SAMPLE SPACES**

   Assuming that each simple event in a sample space S is as likely to occur as another simple event, the probability of an arbitrary event E in S is given by

   $$P(E) = \frac{\text{Number of elements in } E}{\text{Number of elements in } S} = \frac{n(E)}{n(S)}$$

2. **RANDOM VARIABLE**

   A random variable is a function that assigns a numerical value to each simple event in a sample space S.

3. **PROBABILITY DISTRIBUTION OF A RANDOM VARIABLE**

   A probability function $P(X = x) = p(x)$ is a PROBABILITY DISTRIBUTION OF THE RANDOM VARIABLE X if

   (a) $0 \le P(x) \le 1$, $x \in \{x_1, x_2, \ldots, x_n\}$,

   (b) $P(x_1) + P(x_2) + \cdots + P(x_n) = 1$, where $\{x_1, x_2, \ldots, x_n\}$ are the (range) values of X.

4. **EXPECTED VALUE OF A RANDOM VARIABLE** X: Given the probability distribution for the random variable X:

x_i	x_1	x_2	$\cdots$	x_m
P_i	P_1	P_2	$\cdots$	P_m

   where $p_i = P(x_i)$, we define the EXPECTED VALUE OF X, denoted by $E(X)$, by the formula

   $$\mu = E(X) = x_1 P_1 + x_2 P_2 + \cdots + x_m P_m.$$

   Expected value is also referred to as the ARITHMETIC AVERAGE or MEAN.

5. STANDARD DEVIATION OF A RANDOM VARIABLE X:

Given the probability distribution for the random variable X:

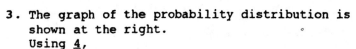

x_i	x_1	x_2	$\cdots$	x_m
P_i	P_1	P_2	$\cdots$	P_m

and the mean

$$\mu = x_1 P_1 + x_2 P_2 + \cdots + x_m P_m.$$

we define the VARIANCE OF X, denoted by $V(X)$, by the formula

$$V(X) = (x_1 - \mu)^2 P_1 + (x_2 - \mu)^2 P_2 + \cdots + (x_m - \mu)^2 P_m$$

and the STANDARD DEVIATION OF X, denoted by σ, be the formula

$$\sigma = \sqrt{V(X)}.$$

---

1. The graph of the probability distribution is shown at the right. Using $\underline{4}$,

$\mu = x_1 P_1 + x_2 P_2 + \cdots + x_m P_m$
$\quad = -2(.1) + (-1)(.2) + 0(.4) + 1(.2) + 2(.1)$
$\quad = 0$

$V(X)$ = variance of X
$\quad = (x_1 - \mu)^2 P_1 + (x_2 - \mu)^2 P_2 + \cdots$
$\qquad\qquad + (x_m - \mu)^2 P_m$
$\quad = (-2 - 0)^2(.1) + (-1 - 0)^2(.2)$
$\qquad + (0 - 0)^2(.4) + (1 - 0)^2(.2)$
$\qquad + (2 - 0)^2(.1)$
$\quad = 1.2$

Thus, $\sigma = \sqrt{V(X)} = \sqrt{1.2} = 1.0954451$.

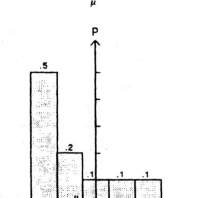

3. The graph of the probability distribution is shown at the right.
Using $\underline{4}$,

$\mu = -2(.5) + (-1)(.2) + 0(.1) + 1(.1)$
$\qquad\qquad\qquad\qquad\qquad + 2(.1)$
$\quad = -.9$

$V(X)$ = variance of X
$\quad = (-2 - (-.9))^2(.5) + (-1 - (-.9))^2(.2)$
$\qquad + (0 - (-.9))^2(.1) + (1 - (-.9))^2(.1)$
$\qquad + (2 - (-.9))^2(.1)$
$\quad = 1.89$

Thus, $\sigma = \sqrt{V(X)} = \sqrt{1.89} = 1.3747727$.

5. $S = \{1, 2, 3, 4, 5, 6, 7, 8, 9, 10\}$ (One simple event for each number)

7. Let Event A = Obtaining an even number

$$A = \{2, 4, 6, 8, 10\}$$

Probability of A = $P(A) = \dfrac{N(A)}{N(S)} = \dfrac{5}{10} = .5$

[Note: $N(A) = 5$ and $N(S) = 10$.]

9. The probability distribution for X is

x_i	1	2	3	4	5	6	7	8	9	10
p_i	$\frac{1}{10}$	$\frac{1}{10}$	$\frac{1}{10}$	$\frac{1}{10}$	$\frac{1}{10}$	$\frac{1}{10}$	$\frac{1}{10}$	$\frac{1}{10}$	$\frac{1}{10}$	$\frac{1}{10}$

Hence,

$$E(X) = 1\left(\frac{1}{10}\right) + 2\left(\frac{1}{10}\right) + 3\left(\frac{1}{10}\right) + 4\left(\frac{1}{10}\right) + 5\left(\frac{1}{10}\right) + 6\left(\frac{1}{10}\right) + 7\left(\frac{1}{10}\right) + 8\left(\frac{1}{10}\right)$$

$$+ 9\left(\frac{1}{10}\right) + 10\left(\frac{1}{10}\right)$$

$$= \frac{55}{10} = 5.5$$

11.

Event	Number of heads, x_i	Probability, p_i
TT	0	$\frac{1}{4}$
HT TH	1	$\frac{2}{4}$
HH	2	$\frac{1}{4}$

Hence,

$$E(X) = 0\left(\frac{1}{4}\right) + 1\left(\frac{2}{4}\right) + 2\left(\frac{1}{4}\right) = 1.$$

13. The probability distribution is as follows:

Event	Number of heads, x_i	Probability, p_i
TTTT	0	$\frac{1}{16}$
HTTT THTT TTHT TTTH	1	$\frac{4}{16}$
HHTT HTHT TTHH THTH THHT HTTH	2	$\frac{6}{16}$
THHH HTHH HHTH HHHT	3	$\frac{4}{16}$
HHHH	4	$\frac{1}{16}$

The graph of this probability distribution is shown above.

15. Let Event B = Obtaining an even number of heads. Then
    Event B = {TTTT, HHTT, HTHT, TTHH, THTH, THHT, HTTH, HHHH},
    and $P(B) = \dfrac{N(B)}{N(S)} = \dfrac{8}{16} = \dfrac{1}{2}$

17. Refer to Problem 13 and solve:
    $$E(X) = 0\left(\dfrac{1}{16}\right) + 1\left(\dfrac{4}{16}\right) + 2\left(\dfrac{6}{16}\right) + 3\left(\dfrac{4}{16}\right) + 4\left(\dfrac{1}{16}\right) = \dfrac{32}{16} = 2$$

19. Represent a simple event by an ordered pair (a, b). The first number in the ordered pair represents the number observed on the first die, and the second number represents the number observed on the second die. The probability distribution, then, is given as follows:

Events	Sum, x_i	Probability, p_i
(1, 1)	2	$\dfrac{1}{36}$
(1, 2), (2, 1)	3	$\dfrac{2}{36}$
(1, 3), (2, 2), (3, 1)	4	$\dfrac{3}{36}$
(4, 1), (3, 2), (2, 3), (1, 4)	5	$\dfrac{4}{36}$
(5, 1), (4, 2), (3, 3), (2, 4), (1, 5)	6	$\dfrac{5}{36}$
(6, 1), (5, 2), (4, 3), (3, 4), (2, 5), (1, 6)	7	$\dfrac{6}{36}$
(6, 2), (5, 3), (4, 4), (3, 5), (2, 6)	8	$\dfrac{5}{36}$
(6, 3), (5, 4), (4, 5), (3, 6)	9	$\dfrac{4}{36}$
(6, 4), (5, 5), (4, 6)	10	$\dfrac{3}{36}$
(6, 5), (5, 6)	11	$\dfrac{2}{36}$
(6, 6)	12	$\dfrac{1}{36}$

The graph of this probability distribution of X is shown below.

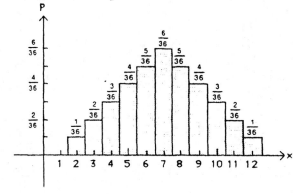

21. Let Event A be the sum is less than 6.

Event A includes $\{(1, 1), (1, 2), (2, 1), (1, 3), (2, 2), (3, 1), (4, 1), (3, 2), (2, 3), (1, 4)\}$.

Thus, $P(A) = \dfrac{N(A)}{N(S)} = \dfrac{10}{36} = \dfrac{5}{18}$.

23. Refer to Problem 19 and solve:

$$E(X) = 2\left(\frac{1}{36}\right) + 3\left(\frac{2}{36}\right) + 4\left(\frac{3}{36}\right) + 5\left(\frac{4}{36}\right) + 6\left(\frac{5}{36}\right) + 7\left(\frac{6}{36}\right) + 8\left(\frac{5}{36}\right) + 9\left(\frac{4}{36}\right) + 10\left(\frac{3}{36}\right)$$
$$+ 11\left(\frac{2}{36}\right) + 12\left(\frac{1}{36}\right)$$

$$= \frac{252}{36} = 7.$$

25.

Number on die	Net gain, x_i	Probability, p_i
1	-3	$\frac{1}{6}$
2	-2	$\frac{1}{6}$
3	-1	$\frac{1}{6}$
4	0	$\frac{1}{6}$
5	1	$\frac{1}{6}$
6	2	$\frac{1}{6}$

Hence,

$$E(X) = (-3)\left(\frac{1}{6}\right) + (-2)\left(\frac{1}{6}\right) + (-1)\left(\frac{1}{6}\right) + 0\left(\frac{1}{6}\right) + 1\left(\frac{1}{6}\right) + 2\left(\frac{1}{6}\right) = -\frac{1}{2} \quad \text{or} \quad -\$0.50.$$

27. Refer to Problem 11 and solve:

Number of heads	Net gain, x_i	Probability, p_i
0	-6	$\frac{1}{4}$
1	1	$\frac{2}{4}$
2	3	$\frac{1}{4}$

Hence,

$$E(X) = (-6)\left(\frac{1}{4}\right) + 1\left(\frac{2}{4}\right) + 3\left(\frac{1}{4}\right) = -\frac{1}{4} \quad \text{or} \quad -\$0.25.$$

29.

Event	Net gain, x_i	Probability, p_i
Won	\$35	$\frac{1}{38}$
Lost	-\$1	$\frac{37}{38}$

Thus,

$$E(X) = 35\left(\frac{1}{38}\right) + (-1)\left(\frac{37}{38}\right) = -\frac{2}{38} = -\$0.05263158 \approx -\$0.05$$

31. (A) P(Having winning ticket) $= \dfrac{5}{1000} = .005$

Thus, the payoff table is

x_i	$4950	-$50
p_i	.005	.995

(B) The expected value of X is:
$E(X) = 4950(.005) - 50(.995)$
$= 24.75 - 49.75 = -25$ or $-$25$

33. The payoff table is as follows:

Gain x_i	$4850	-$150
p_i	.01	.99

[<u>Note</u>: 5000 - 150 = 4850, the gain with a probability of .01 if stolen.]

Hence, $E(X) = 4850(.01) - 150(.99) = -100

35. The payoff table for site A is as follows:

x_i	30 million	-3 million
p_i	.2	.8

Hence, $E(X) = 30(.2) - 3(.8)$
$= 6 - 2.4$
$= 3.6 million

The payoff table for site B is as follows:

x_i	70 million	-4 million
p_i	.1	.9

Hence, $E(X) = 70(.1) + (-4)(.9)$
$= 7 - 3.6$
$= 3.4 million

The company should choose site A with $E(X) = 3.6 million.

37. Using <u>4</u>,
$E(X) = 0(.12) + 1(.36) + 2(.38) + 3(.14) = 1.54$

39. Action A_1: $E(X) = 10(.3) + 5(.2) + 0(.5) = 4.00
Action A_2: $E(X) = 15(.3) + 3(.1) + 0(.6) = 4.80
Action A_2 is the better choice.

EXERCISE 10-2

Things to remember:

<u>1</u>. BERNOULLI TRIALS

A sequence of experiments is called a SEQUENCE OF BERNOULLI TRIALS, or a BINOMIAL EXPERIMENT if:

(a) Each trial has only two possible outcomes: success S or failure F.

(b) The probability of success $P(S) = p$ for each trial is constant; the probability of failure $P(F) = q = 1 - p$; $p + q = 1$.

(c) All trials are independent.

2. BINOMIAL FORMULA

For n a natural number,
$$(a + b)^n = C_{n,0}a^n + C_{n,1}a^{n-1}b + C_{n,2}a^{n-2}b^2 + \cdots + C_{n,n}b^n$$
where
$$C_{n,r} = \frac{n!}{r!(n - r)!} \qquad n \geq r \geq 0$$

3. BINOMIAL DISTRIBUTION

$P(X_n = x) = P(x \text{ successes in } n \text{ trials})$
$$= C_{n,x}p^x q^{n-x} \qquad x \in \{0, 1, 2, \ldots, n\}$$

where p is the probability of success and q is the probability of failure on each trial.

Informally, write $P(x)$ in place of $P(X_n = x)$.

4. MEAN AND STANDARD DEVIATION

The MEAN μ and STANDARD DEVIATION σ of the random variable associated with a binomial distribution are given by:

$$\text{Mean:} \quad \mu = np$$
$$\text{Standard deviation:} \quad \sigma = \sqrt{npq}$$

---

1. $p = \frac{1}{2}$

$q = 1 - \frac{1}{2} = \frac{1}{2}$

$C_{3,2}\left(\frac{1}{2}\right)^2\left(\frac{1}{2}\right)^{3-2} = \frac{3!}{2!1!} \cdot \frac{1}{8}$

$\qquad\qquad = \frac{3}{8} = .375$

3. $p = \frac{1}{2}$

$q = 1 - \frac{1}{2} = \frac{1}{2}$

$C_{3,0}\left(\frac{1}{2}\right)^0\left(\frac{1}{2}\right)^{3-0} = \frac{3!}{0!3!} \cdot \frac{1}{8}$

$\qquad\qquad = \frac{1}{8} = .125$

5. $p = .4$
  $q = 1 - .4 = .6$

$C_{5,3}(.4)^3(.6)^{5-3} = \frac{5!}{3!2!}(.4)^3(.6)^2$

$\qquad\qquad = 10(.064)(.36) = .2304$

7. $p = $ probability of getting heads $= \frac{1}{2}$

$q = $ probability of getting tails $= \frac{1}{2}$

$x = 2, \ n = 3$

$P(2) = C_{3,2}\left(\frac{1}{2}\right)^2\left(\frac{1}{2}\right)^{3-2} = \frac{3!}{2!1!} \cdot \frac{1}{8} = \frac{3}{8} = .375$

9. $p = \frac{1}{2}, \ q = \frac{1}{2}, \ x = 0, \ n = 3$

$P(0) = C_{3,0}\left(\frac{1}{2}\right)^0\left(\frac{1}{2}\right)^{3-0} = \frac{3!}{0!3!} \cdot \frac{1}{8} = \frac{1}{8} = .125$

11. $P(\text{at least 2 heads}) = P(x \geq 2) = P(2) + P(3)$
$$= C_{3,2}\left(\tfrac{1}{2}\right)^2\left(\tfrac{1}{2}\right)^{3-2} + C_{3,3}\left(\tfrac{1}{2}\right)^3\left(\tfrac{1}{2}\right)^{3-3}$$
$$= \frac{3!}{2!1!} \cdot \frac{1}{8} + \frac{3!}{3!0!} \cdot \frac{1}{8} = \frac{3}{8} + \frac{1}{8} = .5$$

13. $P(x) = C_{2,x}(.3)^x(.7)^{2-x}$

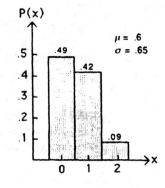

x	0	1	2
$P(x)$	.49	.42	.09

The histogram for this distribution is shown at the right.

Mean = np = 2(.3) = .6   (using 4)

Standard deviation = $\sigma = \sqrt{npq}$ (using 4)
$$= \sqrt{2(.3)(.7)}$$
$$\approx .65$$

15. $P(x) = C_{4,x}(.5)^x(.5)^{4-x}$

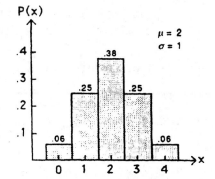

x	$P(x)$
0	.06
1	.25
2	.38
3	.25
4	.06

The histogram for this distribution is shown at the right.

$\mu = np = 4 \times .5 = 2$

$\sigma = \sqrt{npq} = \sqrt{4 \times .5 \times .5} = 1$

17. Let p = probability of getting a "2" in one trial = $\frac{1}{6}$,

and q = probability of not getting a "2" in one trial = $\frac{5}{6}$.

$n = 4$, $x = 3$
$$P(3) = C_{4,3}\left(\tfrac{1}{6}\right)^3\left(\tfrac{5}{6}\right)^{4-3} = \frac{4!}{3!1!}\left(\tfrac{1}{6}\right)^3\left(\tfrac{5}{6}\right) \approx .0154$$

19. Let p = probability of getting a "1" = $\frac{1}{6}$,

and q = probability of not getting a "1" = $\frac{5}{6}$.

$n = 4$, $x = 0$
$$P(0) = C_{4,0}\left(\tfrac{1}{6}\right)^0\left(\tfrac{5}{6}\right)^{4-0} = \frac{4!}{0!4!}\left(\tfrac{5}{6}\right)^4 \approx .482$$

21. Let p = probability of getting a "6" = $\frac{1}{6}$,

and q = probability of not getting a "6" = $\frac{5}{6}$.

It is actually easier to compute the probability of the complement event, $P(x < 1)$:

$$P(x \geq 1) = 1 - P(x < 1) = 1 - P(0)$$
$$= 1 - C_{4,0}\left(\frac{1}{6}\right)^0\left(\frac{5}{6}\right)^4 = 1 - .4822 \approx .518$$

23. $p = .35$, $q = 1 - .35 = .65$, $n = 4$

(A) The probability of getting exactly two hits is given by:
$$P(x = 2) = C_{4,2}(.35)^2(.65)^2 \approx .311$$

(B) The probability of getting at least two hits is given by:
$$P(x \geq 2) = P(2) + P(3) + P(4)$$
$$= C_{4,2}(.35)^2(.65)^2 + C_{4,3}(.35)^3(.65) + C_{4,4}(.35)^4$$
$$= .3105 + .1115 + .0150 \approx .437$$

25. $P(x) = C_{6,x}(.4)^x(.6)^{6-x}$

x	$P(x)$
0	.05
1	.19
2	.31
3	.28
4	.14
5	.04
6	.004

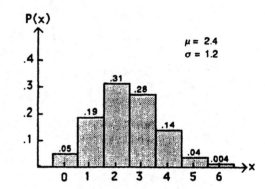

The histogram for this distribution is shown at the right.

$\mu = np = 6 \times .4 = 2.4$

$\sigma = \sqrt{npq} = \sqrt{6 \times .4 \times .6} = 1.2$

27. $P(x) = C_{8,x}(.3)^x(.7)^{8-x}$

x	$P(x)$
0	.06
1	.20
2	.30
3	.25
4	.14
5	.05
6	.01
7	.0012
8	.0001

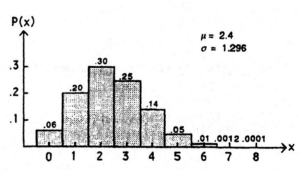

The histogram for this distribution is shown above.

$\mu = np = 8 \times .3 = 2.4$

$\sigma = \sqrt{npq} = \sqrt{8 \times .3 \times .7} \approx 1.296$

29. Let p = probability of getting heads = $\frac{3}{4}$,

and q = probability of not getting heads = $\frac{1}{4}$.

$n = 5$, $x = 5$

The probability of getting all heads $P(5) = C_{5,5}\left(\frac{3}{4}\right)^5\left(\frac{1}{4}\right)^0 = .2373$.

The probability of getting all tails is the same as the probability of getting no heads. Thus,

$P(0) = C_{5,0}\left(\frac{3}{4}\right)^0\left(\frac{1}{4}\right)^5 = .00098$

Therefore,

P(all heads or all tails) = $P(5) + P(0)$ = .2373 + .00098
$$= .23828 \approx .238$$

31. (A) Let p = probability of completing the program = .7,
and q = probability of not completing the program = .3.

$n = 7$, $x = 5$
$P(5) = C_{7,5}(.7)^5(.3)^2 = 21(.1681)(.09) = .318$

(B) $P(x \geq 5) = P(5) + P(6) + P(7)$
$$= .318 + C_{7,6}(.7)^6(.3) + C_{7,7}(.7)^7(.3)^0$$
$$= .318 + 7(.1176)(.3) + 1(.0824)(1)$$
$$= .3180 + .2471 + .0824 \approx .647$$

33. Let p = probability that an item is defective = .06,
and q = probability that an item is not defective = .94.

$n = 10$

$P(x > 2) = 1 - P[x \leq 2] = 1 - [P(2) + P(1) + P(0)]$
$$= 1 - [C_{10,2}(.06)^2(.94)^8 + C_{10,1}(.06)^1(.94)^9 + C_{10,0}(.06)^0(.94)^{10}]$$
$$= 1 - [.0988 + .3438 + .5386] = 1 - .9812 \approx .0188$$

A day's output will be inspected with a probability of .0188.

35. (A) $p = .05$, $q = .95$, $n = 6$

The following function defines the distribution:
$P(x) = C_{6,x}(.05)^x(.95)^{6-x}$

(B) The table shown on the following page is obtained by using the distribution function in part (A).

x	$P(x)$
0	.735
1	.232
2	.031
3	.002
4	.0001
5	.000
6	.000

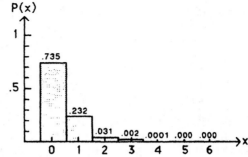

(C) The histogram for the distribution in part (B) is shown above.

(D) $\mu = np = 6 \times .05 = .30$

$\sigma = \sqrt{npq} = \sqrt{6 \times (.05) \times (.95)} = .53$

37. Let p = probability of detecting TB = .8,
and q = probability of not detecting TB = .2.

$n = 4$

The probability that at least one of the specialists will detect TB is:

$P(x \geq 1) = 1 - P(x < 1) = 1 - P(0)$
$= 1 - C_{4,0}(.8)^0(.2)^4$
$= 1 - .0016 = .9984 \sim .998$

39. Let p = probability of having a child with brown eyes = .75,
and q = probability of not having a child with brown eyes (i.e., with blue eyes) = .25.

$n = 5$

(A) $x = 0$ (all blue-eyed children, i.e., no brown-eyed children)
$P(0) = C_{5,0}(.75)^0(.25)^5 = .00098 \sim .001$

(B) $x = 3$
$P(3) = C_{5,3}(.75)^3(.25)^2 \sim .264$

(C) $x \geq 3$
$P(x \geq 3) = P(3) + P(4) + P(5)$
$\sim .264 + C_{5,4}(.75)^4(.25)^1 + C_{5,5}(.75)^5(.25)^0$
$\sim .2640 + .3955 + .2373$
$= .8968 \sim .897$

41. (A) $p = .6$, $q = .4$, $n = 6$

The following function defines the distribution:
$P(x) = C_{6,x}(.6)^x(.4)^{6-x}$

(B) The table shown on the following page is obtained by using the distribution function in part (A).

x	P(x)
0	.004
1	.037
2	.138
3	.276
4	.311
5	.187
6	.047

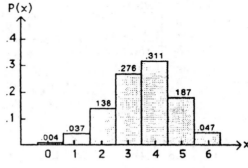

(C) The histogram for the distribution in part (B) is shown at the right.

(D) $\mu = np = 6(.6) = 3.6$

$\sigma = \sqrt{npq} = \sqrt{6 \times .4 \times .6} = 1.2$

43. Let p = probability of getting the right answer to a question = $\frac{1}{5}$, and q = probability of not getting the right answer to a question = $\frac{4}{5}$. $n = 10$, $x \geq 7$

$P(x \geq 7) = P(7) + P(8) + P(9) + P(10)$

$= C_{10,7}\left(\frac{1}{5}\right)^7\left(\frac{4}{5}\right)^3 + C_{10,8}\left(\frac{1}{5}\right)^8\left(\frac{4}{5}\right)^2 + C_{10,9}\left(\frac{1}{5}\right)^9\left(\frac{4}{5}\right) + C_{10,10}\left(\frac{1}{5}\right)^{10}$

$\approx .000864$

45. (A) p = probability of answer being correct by guessing = $\frac{1}{5}$ = .2, $q = .8$, $n = 5$

The following function defines the distribution:
$P(x) = C_{5,x}(.2)^x(.8)^{5-x}$

(B) The following table is obtained by using the distribution function in part (A):

x	P(x)
0	.328
1	.410
2	.205
3	.051
4	.006
5	.000

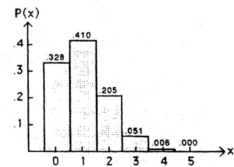

(C) The histogram for part (B) is shown at the right.

(D) $\mu = np = 5 \times .2 = 1.0$

$\sigma = \sqrt{npq} = \sqrt{5 \times .2 \times .8} \approx .894$

47. Let p = probability of a divorce within 20 years = .60, and q = probability of no divorce within 20 years = .40.

$n = 6$

(A) $P(x = 0) = C_{6,0}(.60)^0(.40)^6 \approx .0041$

(B) $P(x = 6) = C_{6,6}(.60)^6(.40)^0 \approx .0467$

(C) $P(x = 2) = C_{6,2}(.60)^2(.40)^4 \approx .138$

(D) $P(x \geq 2) = 1 - P(x < 2) = 1 - [P(0) + P(1)]$
$$= 1 - [.0041 + C_{6,1}(.60)^1(.40)^5]$$
$$\approx 1 - [.0041 + .0369]$$
$$= .959$$

EXERCISE 10-3

Things to remember:

1. **POISSON APPROXIMATION TO THE BINOMIAL DISTRIBUTION**

For n large and p small, and $\lambda = np$

$$C_{n,x}p^xq^{n-x} \approx \frac{\lambda^x}{x!}e^{-\lambda}, \quad x \in \{0, 1, 2, \ldots, n\}$$

RULE OF THUMB: Excellent approximations can be obtained when $n \geq 100$ and $np \leq 10$

2. **POISSON DISTRIBUTION WITH MEAN AND STANDARD DEVIATION**

$P(X = x) = P(x$ occurrences per unit of measure$) = P(x)$
$$= \frac{\lambda^x}{x!}e^{-\lambda} \quad x \in \{0, 1, 2, \ldots\}$$

Mean: $\mu = \lambda$

Standard Deviation: $\sigma = \sqrt{\lambda}$

Informally we write $P(x)$ in place of $P(X = x)$

---

1. $P(0) = \frac{4^0}{0!}e^{-4} = e^{-4} \approx .0183$

3. $P(2) = \frac{(.25)^2}{2!}e^{-.25} \approx \frac{.0625}{2}(.7788) = .0243$

5. $P(X < 3) = P(0) + P(1) + P(2)$
$$= \frac{2^0}{0!}e^{-2} + \frac{2^1}{1!}e^{-2} + \frac{2^2}{2!}e^{-2}$$
$$= e^{-2}(1 + 2 + 2) \approx 5(.1353) = .6767$$

7. $P(X \geq 3) = 1 - [P(0) + P(1) + P(2)]$

$$= 1 - e^{-2}\left(\frac{2^0}{0!} + \frac{2^1}{1!} + \frac{2^2}{2!}\right)$$

$$= 1 - 5e^{-2} \approx .3233$$

9. Binomial: $P(3) = C_{200,3}(.01)^3(.99)^{197}$

$$= \frac{200!}{3!197!}(.01)^3(.99)^{197}$$

$$= \frac{200 \cdot 199 \cdot 198}{6}(.000001)(.1381)$$

$$\approx .1814$$

Poisson: $\lambda = 200(.01) = 2$

$$P(3) = \frac{2^3}{3!}e^{-2}$$

$$\approx \frac{8}{6}(.1353) = .1804$$

11. Binomial: $P(3) = C_{10,000,3}(.00005)^3(.99995)^{9,997}$

$$= \frac{10,000!}{3!9,997!}(.00005)^3(.99995)^{9,997}$$

$$\approx \frac{10^4(9.999 \times 10^3)(9.998 \times 10^3)(1.25 \times 10^{-13})(.6066)}{6}$$

$$\approx .0126$$

Poisson: $\lambda = 10,000(.00005) = .5$

$$P(3) = \frac{(.5)^3}{3!}e^{-.5}$$

$$\approx (.0208)(.6065) \approx .0126$$

13. $n = 108$, $p = \frac{1}{36}$. Thus, $\lambda = np = 108\left(\frac{1}{36}\right) = 3$

(A) $P(0) = \frac{3^0}{0!}e^{-3} = e^{-3} \approx .0498$

(B) $P(5) = \frac{3^5}{5!}e^{-3} = \frac{243}{120}e^{-3} \approx .1008$

15. $P(0) = \frac{\left(\frac{N}{2500}\right)^0}{0!}e^{-N/2500} = .01$

$$e^{-N/2500} = .01$$

$$\frac{-N}{2500} = \ln(.01)$$

$$-N = 2500 \ln(.01) \approx -11,513$$

$$\text{or} \quad N = 11,513$$

17. $p = \frac{5}{1000} = .005$, $n = 100$

Thus, $\lambda = 100(.005) = .5$

(A) $P(0) = \frac{(.5)^0}{0!}e^{-.5} = e^{-.5} \approx .6065$

(B) $P(0 \le X \le 2) = P(0) + P(1) + P(2)$

$$P(1) = \frac{(.5)^1}{1!} e^{-.5} = .5e^{-.5} \approx .3033$$

$$P(2) = \frac{(.5)^2}{2!} e^{-.5} = .125e^{-.5} \approx .0758$$

Thus, $P(X \le 2) \approx .6065 + .3033 + .0758 = .9856$

(C) $P(X > 2) = 1 - P(0 \le X \le 2)$
$$\approx 1 - .9856 = .0144$$

19. The three conditions of a Poisson random variable are met. There are three 8-hour workshifts per day and $7 \cdot 3 = 21$ shifts per week. Thus, the average number of births per 8-hour shift is: $\frac{21}{21} = 1 = \lambda$

(A) $P(0) = \frac{1^0}{0!} e^{-1} = e^{-1} \approx .3679$

(B) $P(4) = \frac{1^4}{4!} e^{-1} = \frac{1}{24} e^{-1} \approx .0153$

(C) $P(X \ge 4) = 1 - [P(0) + P(1) + P(2) + P(3)]$

Now, $P(1) = \frac{1^1}{1!} e^{-1}$, $P(2) = \frac{1^2}{2!} e^{-1}$, $P(3) = \frac{1^3}{3!} e^{-1}$

so $P(X \ge 4) = 1 - e^{-1} \left[\frac{1^0}{0!} + \frac{1^1}{1!} + \frac{1^2}{2!} + \frac{1^3}{3!} \right]$

$$= 1 - e^{-1} \left[1 + 1 + \frac{1}{2} + \frac{1}{6} \right]$$

$$= 1 - e^{-1} \left(\frac{16}{6} \right) \approx .0190$$

21. Average number of flaws per square yard of carpet is: $\frac{3}{10} = .3 = \lambda$

(A) $P(X > 1) = 1 - P(X \le 1) = 1 - [P(0) + P(1)]$

Now, $P(0) = \frac{(.3)^0}{0!} e^{-.3} = e^{-.3}$

$$P(1) = \frac{(.3)^1}{1!} e^{-.3} = .3e^{-.3}$$

Thus, $P(X > 1) = 1 - (e^{-.3} + 3e^{-.3})$
$$= 1 - e^{-.3}(1.3) \approx .0369$$

23. The three conditions of a Poisson random variable are met. The computer is down $\frac{2}{5} = .4$ times per day. Thus, $\lambda = .4$

(A) $P(0) = \frac{(.4)^0}{0!} e^{-.4} = e^{-.4} \approx .6703$

(B) $P(2) = \frac{(.4)^2}{2!} e^{-.4} = \frac{.16}{2} e^{-.4} \approx .0536$

(C) $P(X > 1) = 1 - P(0 \le X \le 1)$
$$= 1 - [P(0) + P(1)]$$
$$= 1 - \left[\frac{(.4)^0}{0!} e^{-.4} + \frac{(.4)^1}{1!} e^{-.4} \right]$$
$$= 1 - e^{-.4}[1 + .4] \approx .0616$$

25. On the average, there will be 2 typesetting errors per 30 pages. Thus, $\lambda = 2$.

(A) $P(0) = \frac{2^0}{0!}e^{-2} = e^{-2} \approx .1353$

(B) $P(0 \le X \le 4) = P(0) + P(1) + P(2) + P(3) + P(4)$

$$= e^{-2}\left[\frac{2^0}{0!} + \frac{2^1}{1!} + \frac{2^2}{2!} + \frac{2^3}{3!} + \frac{2^4}{4!}\right]$$

$$= e^{-2}\left[1 + 2 + 2 + \frac{8}{6} + \frac{16}{24}\right]$$

$$= e^{-2}(7) \approx .9473$$

(C) $P(X > 4) = 1 - P(0 \le X \le 4)$

$$\approx 1 - .9473 = .0527$$

27. Given $p = .04$, $n = 200$. Thus, $\lambda = np = 200(.04) = 8$

(A) $P(2) = \frac{8^2}{2!}e^{-8} = 32e^{-8} \approx .0107$

(B) $P(0 \le X \le 2) = P(0) + P(1) + P(2)$

$$= e^{-8}\left[\frac{8^0}{0!} + \frac{8^1}{1!} + \frac{8^2}{2!}\right]$$

$$= e^{-8}[1 + 8 + 32]$$

$$= 41e^{-8} \approx .0138$$

29. The average number of organisms per drop is $\frac{300,000}{100,000} = 3$. Thus, $\lambda = 3$.

(A) $P(0) = \frac{3^0}{0!}e^{-3} = e^{-3} \approx .0498$

(B) Let N be the number of organisms per liter. Then $\frac{N}{100,000} = \lambda$ is the (average) number of organisms per drop. We want to find N such that

$$P(0) = .01 = \frac{\left(\frac{N}{100,000}\right)^0}{0!}e^{-N/100,000} = e^{-N/100,000}$$

Taking the natural log of both sides of this equation, we have

$$\frac{-N}{100,000} = \ln(.01)$$

$$-N = 100,000\ \ln(.01) \approx -460,517$$

Thus, $N = 461,000$ per liter, rounded to the nearest thousand.

31. The three conditions of a Poisson random variable are met. The average number of boats per day is $5 = \lambda$.

(A) $P(0) = \frac{5^0}{0!}e^{-5} = e^{-5} \approx .0067$

(B) $P(4 \le X \le 6) = P(4) + P(5) + P(6)$

$$= e^{-5}\left[\frac{5^4}{4!} + \frac{5^5}{5!} + \frac{5^6}{6!}\right]$$

$$= 5^4 e^{-5}\left[\frac{1}{24} + \frac{5}{120} + \frac{25}{720}\right]$$

$$= 5^4 e^{-5}\left(\frac{85}{720}\right)$$

$$\approx .4972$$

(C) $P(0 \le X < 3) = P(0) + P(1) + P(2)$

$$= e^{-5}\left[\frac{5^0}{0!} + \frac{5^1}{1!} + \frac{5^2}{2!}\right]$$

$$= e^{-5}\left(1 + 5 + \frac{25}{2}\right) = e^{-5}\left(\frac{37}{2}\right)$$

$$\approx .1247$$

33. The three conditions of a Poisson random variable are met. The average number of patients per hour during the midnight to 6AM shift is $\frac{18}{6} = 3$. Thus, $\lambda = 3$.

(A) $P(0 \le X \le 5) = P(0) + P(1) + P(2) + P(3) + P(4) + P(5)$

$$= e^{-3}\left[\frac{3^0}{0!} + \frac{3^1}{1!} + \frac{3^2}{2!} + \frac{3^3}{3!} + \frac{3^4}{4!} + \frac{3^5}{5!}\right]$$

$$= e^{-3}\left(1 + 3 + \frac{9}{2} + \frac{9}{2} + \frac{27}{8} + \frac{81}{40}\right)$$

$$= e^{-3}\left(13 + \frac{216}{40}\right)$$

$$\approx .9161$$

(B) $P(X > 5) = 1 - P(0 \le X \le 5)$

$$\approx 1 - .9161 = .0839$$

(C) On the average, 6 patients arrive per 2 hour period. Thus, $\lambda = 6$.

$$P(0 \le X \le 2) = e^{-6}[P(0) + P(1) + P(2)]$$

$$= e^{-6}\left[\frac{6^0}{0!} + \frac{6^1}{1!} + \frac{6^2}{2!}\right]$$

$$= e^{-6}(1 + 6 + 18) = e^{-6}(25)$$

$$\approx .0620$$

EXERCISE 10-4

Things to remember:

1. CONTINUOUS RANDOM VARIBLE

   A CONTINUOUS RANDOM VARIABLE is a variable whose set of possible values (range) is an interval of real numbers. This interval may be open or closed, and it may be bounded or unbounded.

2. PROBABILITY DENSITY FUNCTION

   The function $f(x)$ is a PROBABILITY DENSITY FUNCTION for a continuous random variable X if:

   (a) $f(x) \ge 0$ for all $x \in (-\infty, \infty)$

(b) $\displaystyle\int_{-\infty}^{\infty} f(x)\,dx = 1$

(c) The probability that x lies in the interval $[c,\ d]$ is given by
$$P(c \le X \le d) = \int_{c}^{d} f(x)\,dx.$$

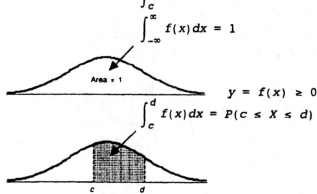

$$\int_{-\infty}^{\infty} f(x)\,dx = 1$$

Area = 1

$$y = f(x) \ge 0$$

$$\int_{c}^{d} f(x)\,dx = P(c \le X \le d)$$

Range of $X = (-\infty,\ \infty) =$ Domain of f.

3. CUMULATIVE PROBABILITY DISTRIBUTION FUNCTION

If f is a probability density function, then the associated cumulative probability distribution function F is defined by
$$F(x) = P(X \le x) = \int_{-\infty}^{x} f(t)\,dt.$$

Furthermore,
$$P(c \le X \le d) = F(d) - F(c),$$

where F is an antiderivative of f, that is, $F' = f$.

4. PROPERTIES OF CUMULATIVE PROBABILITY DISTRIBUTION FUNCTIONS

If f is a probability density function and
$$F(x) = \int_{-\infty}^{x} f(t)\,dt$$

is the associated cumulative probability distribution function, then:

(a) $F'(x) = f(x)$ wherever f is continuous.

(b) $0 \le F(x) \le 1,\ -\infty < x < \infty$.

(c) $F(x)$ is nondecreasing on $(-\infty,\ \infty)$.

1. The graph of $f(x)$ is shown at the right. From the graph we see that $f(x) \geq 0$ for $x \in (-\infty, \infty)$.

$$\int_{-\infty}^{\infty} f(x)\,dx = \int_0^4 \frac{1}{8}x\,dx$$
$$= \frac{1}{8} \cdot \frac{x^2}{2}\Big|_0^4$$
$$= \frac{1}{16}(16 - 0)$$
$$= 1$$

x	$f(x)$
0	0
1	$\frac{1}{8}$
4	$\frac{1}{2}$
$x > 4$	0

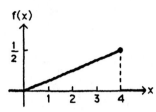

3. (A) Using 2(c),

$$P(1 < X < 3) = \int_1^3 \frac{1}{8}x\,dx = \frac{1}{8} \cdot \frac{x^2}{2}\Big|_1^3$$
$$= \frac{1}{16}(9 - 1) = \frac{8}{16} = \frac{1}{2}.$$

The graph is shown at the right.

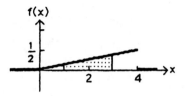

(B) $P(X \leq 2) = \int_{-\infty}^2 \frac{1}{8}x\,dx = \int_0^2 \frac{1}{8}x\,dx$ [since $f(x) = 0$ for $x \leq 0$]

$$= \frac{1}{8} \cdot \frac{x^2}{2}\Big|_0^2 = \frac{1}{16}(4) = \frac{1}{4}.$$

The graph is shown at the right.

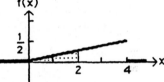

(C) $P(X > 3) = \int_3^\infty \frac{1}{8}x\,dx = \int_3^4 \frac{1}{8}x\,dx$ [since $f(x) = 0$ for $x > 4$]

$$= \frac{1}{8} \cdot \frac{x^2}{2}\Big|_3^4 = \frac{1}{16}(16 - 9) = \frac{7}{16}.$$

The graph is shown at the right.

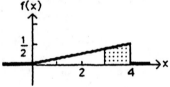

5. (A) $P(X = 1) = \int_1^1 f(x)\,dx = 0$

(B) $P(X > 5) = \int_5^\infty f(x)\,dx = \int_5^\infty 0\,dx = 0$ [$f(x) = 0$ for $x > 4$]

(C) $P(X < 5) = \int_{-\infty}^5 f(x)\,dx = \int_0^4 \frac{1}{8}x\,dx$ [$f(x) = 0$ when $x < 0$ and when $x > 4$]

$$= \frac{1}{8} \cdot \frac{x^2}{2}\Big|_0^4 = \frac{1}{16}(16) = 1.$$

7. If $x < 0$, then
$$F(x) = \int_{-\infty}^x f(t)\,dt = \int_{-\infty}^x 0\,dt = 0$$

If $0 \leq x \leq 4$, then
$$F(x) = \int_{-\infty}^x f(t)\,dt = \int_{-\infty}^0 f(t)\,dt + \int_0^x f(t)\,dt = 0 + \int_0^x \frac{1}{8}t\,dt = \frac{1}{16}t^2\Big|_0^x = \frac{1}{16}x^2.$$

If $x > 4$, then

$$F(x) = \int_{-\infty}^{x} f(t)\,dt = \int_{-\infty}^{0} f(t)\,dt + \int_{0}^{4} f(t)\,dt + \int_{4}^{x} f(t)\,dt$$

$$= 0 + \int_{0}^{4} \frac{1}{8} t\,dt + 0 = \frac{1}{16} t^2 \Big|_{0}^{4} = \frac{1}{16}(16 - 0) = 1.$$

Thus, the cumulative probability distribution function is:

$$F(x) = \begin{cases} 0 & x < 0 \\ \frac{1}{16} x^2 & 0 \le x \le 4 \\ 1 & x > 4 \end{cases}$$

The graph of $F(x)$ is shown at the right.

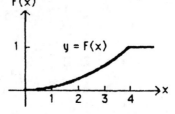

9. Using $\underline{3}$ and the cumulative probability distribution function F from Problem 7:

(A) $P(2 \le X \le 4) = F(4) - F(2)$

$\qquad = \frac{1}{16}(4)^2 - \frac{1}{16}(2)^2$

$\qquad = 1 - \frac{1}{4} = \frac{3}{4}$

(B) $P(0 < X < 2) = F(2) - F(0)$

$\qquad = \frac{1}{16}(2)^2 - 0$

$\qquad = \frac{1}{4}$

11. From Problem 7:

(A) $P(0 \le X \le x) = F(x) - F(0) = \frac{1}{16} x^2 - 0 = \frac{1}{16} x^2$

Now $\frac{1}{16} x^2 = \frac{1}{4}$

$\qquad x^2 = 4$

Since $x \ge 0$, the solution is $x = 2$.

(B) $P(0 \le X \le x) = F(x) - F(0) = \frac{1}{9}$ implies $\frac{1}{16} x^2 = \frac{1}{9}$

$\qquad\qquad\qquad\qquad\qquad\qquad\qquad\qquad x^2 = \frac{16}{9}$

Since $x \ge 0$, the solution is $x = \frac{4}{3}$.

13. From the graph of $f(x)$ shown below, we see that $f(x) \ge 0$ for $x \in (-\infty, \infty)$.

x	$f(x)$
0	2
2	$\frac{2}{27}$
4	$\frac{2}{125}$
$x < 0$	0

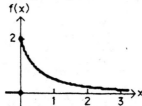

Also,

$$\int_{-\infty}^{\infty} f(x)\,dx = \int_{0}^{\infty} \frac{2}{(1 + x)^3}\,dx = \lim_{R \to \infty} \int_{0}^{R} \frac{2}{(1 + x)^3}\,dx$$

$$= \lim_{R \to \infty} \left(-\frac{1}{(1 + x)^2} \right) \Big|_{0}^{R} = -\lim_{R \to \infty} \left(\frac{1}{(1 + R)^2} - 1 \right) = -(0 - 1) = 1.$$

15. (A) $P(1 \le X \le 4) = \int_1^4 \frac{2}{(1+x)^3}\,dx = \frac{-1}{(1+x)^2}\Big|_1^4 = \frac{-1}{(1+4)^2} - \frac{-1}{(1+1)^2}$

$$= \frac{-1}{25} + \frac{1}{4} = \frac{21}{100} = .21$$

(B) $P(X > 3) = \int_3^\infty \frac{2}{(1+x)^3}\,dx$

Now, $1 = \int_{-\infty}^\infty \frac{2}{(1+x)^3}\,dx = \int_{-\infty}^3 \frac{2}{(1+x)^3}\,dx + \int_3^\infty \frac{2}{(1+x)^3}\,dx,$

so $\int_3^\infty \frac{2}{(1+x)^3}\,dx = 1 - \int_{-\infty}^3 \frac{2}{(1+x)^3}\,dx = 1 - \int_0^3 \frac{2}{(1+x)^3}\,dx,$

since $f(x) = 0$ for $x < 0$. Thus,

$$\int_3^\infty \frac{2}{(1+x)^3}\,dx = 1 - \left(\frac{-1}{(1+x)^2}\Big|_0^3\right) = 1 - \left(-\frac{1}{16} + 1\right) = \frac{1}{16}.$$

(C) $P(X \le 2) = \int_{-\infty}^2 \frac{2}{(1+x)^3}\,dx = \int_0^2 \frac{2}{(1+x)^3}\,dx = \frac{-1}{(1+x)^2}\Big|_0^2 = -\frac{1}{9} + 1 = \frac{8}{9}$

17. If $x < 0$, then
$$F(x) = \int_{-\infty}^x f(t)\,dt = \int_{-\infty}^x 0\,dt = 0.$$

If $x \ge 0$, then
$$F(x) = \int_{-\infty}^x f(t)\,dt = \int_{-\infty}^0 f(t)\,dt + \int_0^x f(t)\,dt = 0 + \int_0^x \frac{2}{(1+t)^3}\,dt$$

$$= \left(-\frac{1}{(1+t)^2}\right)\Big|_0^x = -\frac{1}{(1+x)^2} + 1 \quad \text{or} \quad 1 - \frac{1}{(1+x)^2}.$$

Thus, the cumulative probability distribution function is given by:

$$F(x) = \begin{cases} 0 & x < 0 \\ 1 - \dfrac{1}{(1+x)^2} & x \ge 0 \end{cases}$$

The graph of $F(x)$ is shown at the right.

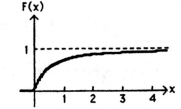

19. From Problem 17,

$$F(x) = \begin{cases} 0 & x < 0 \\ 1 - \dfrac{1}{(1+x)^2} & x \ge 0 \end{cases}$$

and $P(0 \le X \le x) = F(x) - F(0) = 1 - \dfrac{1}{(1+x)^2}.$

(A) Set $P(0 \le X \le x) = \dfrac{3}{4}$ and solve for x.

$$1 - \frac{1}{(1+x)^2} = \frac{3}{4}$$

$$\frac{1}{(1+x)^2} = \frac{1}{4}$$

$$(1+x)^2 = 4$$

Since $x \ge 0$, we have $1 + x = 2$, so $x = 1$.

(B) $1 = P(X \le x) + P(X > x)$. Therefore,

$$P(X > x) = 1 - P(X \le x) = 1 - F(x) = 1 - \left(1 - \frac{1}{(1 + x)^2}\right) = \frac{1}{(1 + x)^2}.$$

Set $P(X > x) = \frac{1}{16}$ and solve for x.

$$\frac{1}{(1 + x)^2} = \frac{1}{16}$$
$$(1 + x)^2 = 16$$
$$1 + x = 4$$
$$x = 3$$

21. $f(x) = \begin{cases} \frac{3}{2}x - \frac{3}{4}x^2 & 0 \le x \le 2 \\ 0 & \text{otherwise} \end{cases}$

If $x < 0$, then

$$F(x) = \int_{-\infty}^{x} f(t)\,dt = \int_{-\infty}^{x} 0 \, dt = 0.$$

If $0 \le x \le 2$, then

$$F(x) = \int_{-\infty}^{x} f(t)\,dt = \int_{-\infty}^{0} f(t)\,dt + \int_{0}^{x} f(t)\,dt = 0 + \int_{0}^{x} \left(\frac{3}{2}t - \frac{3}{4}t^2\right)dt$$

$$= \left(\frac{3}{2} \cdot \frac{t^2}{2} - \frac{3}{4} \cdot \frac{t^3}{3}\right)\Big|_0^x = \left(\frac{3}{4}t^2 - \frac{1}{4}t^3\right)\Big|_0^x = \frac{3}{4}x^2 - \frac{1}{4}x^3.$$

If $x > 2$, then

$$F(x) = \int_{-\infty}^{x} f(t)\,dt = \int_{-\infty}^{0} f(t)\,dt + \int_{0}^{2} f(t)\,dt + \int_{2}^{x} f(t)\,dt$$

$$= 0 + \int_{0}^{2} \left(\frac{3}{2}t - \frac{3}{4}t^2\right)dt + 0 = \left(\frac{3}{4}t^2 - \frac{1}{4}t^3\right)\Big|_0^2 = \frac{3}{4}(2)^2 - \frac{1}{4}(2)^3 = 1$$

Thus, the cumulative probability distribution function is:

$$F(x) = \begin{cases} 0 & x < 0 \\ \frac{3}{4}x^2 - \frac{1}{4}x^3 & 0 \le x \le 2 \\ 1 & x > 2 \end{cases}$$

The graphs of $F(x)$ and $f(x)$ are as follows:

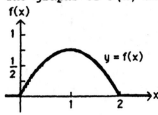
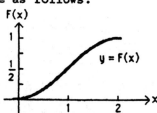

23. $f(x) = \begin{cases} \frac{1}{2} + \frac{1}{2}x^3 & -1 \le x \le 1 \\ 0 & \text{otherwise} \end{cases}$

If $x < -1$, then

$$F(x) = \int_{-\infty}^{x} f(t)\,dt = \int_{-\infty}^{x} 0 \, dt = 0$$

If $-1 \le x \le 1$, then

$$F(x) = \int_{-\infty}^{x} f(t)\,dt = \int_{-\infty}^{-1} f(t)\,dt + \int_{-1}^{x} f(t)\,dt = 0 + \int_{-1}^{x} \left(\frac{1}{2} + \frac{1}{2}t^3\right) dt$$

$$= \left(\frac{1}{2}t + \frac{1}{8}t^4\right)\Big|_{-1}^{x} = \frac{1}{2}x + \frac{1}{8}x^4 - \left(-\frac{1}{2} + \frac{1}{8}\right)$$

$$= \frac{3}{8} + \frac{1}{2}x + \frac{1}{8}x^4$$

If $x > 1$, then

$$F(x) = \int_{-\infty}^{x} f(t)\,dt = \int_{-\infty}^{-1} f(t)\,dt + \int_{-1}^{1} f(t)\,dt + \int_{1}^{x} f(t)\,dt$$

$$= 0 + \int_{-1}^{1} \left(\frac{1}{2} + \frac{1}{2}t^3\right) dt + 0$$

$$= \left(\frac{1}{2}t + \frac{1}{8}t^4\right)\Big|_{-1}^{1} = \left(\frac{1}{2} + \frac{1}{8}\right) - \left(-\frac{1}{2} + \frac{1}{8}\right)$$

$$= 1$$

Thus, the cumulative probability distribution function is:

$$F(x) = \begin{cases} 0 & x < -1 \\ \frac{3}{8} + \frac{1}{2}x + \frac{1}{8}x^4 & -1 \le x \le 1 \\ 1 & x > 1 \end{cases}$$

The graphs of $f(x)$ and $F(x)$ are:

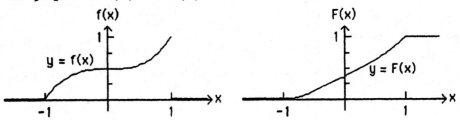

25. The graphs of

$$F(x) = \begin{cases} 0 & x < 0 \\ \frac{3}{4}x^2 - \frac{1}{4}x^3 & 0 \le x \le 2 \\ 1 & x > 2 \end{cases} \qquad \text{and} \quad y = 0.2 \text{ are shown below.}$$

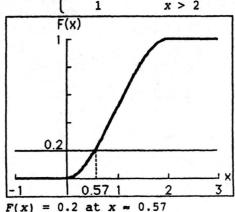

$F(x) = 0.2$ at $x \approx 0.57$

27. The graphs of

$$F(x) = \begin{cases} 0 & x < -1 \\ \dfrac{3}{8} + \dfrac{1}{2}x + \dfrac{1}{8}x^4 & -1 \le x \le 1 \\ 1 & x > 1 \end{cases} \quad \text{and} \quad y = 0.6 \text{ are shown below.}$$

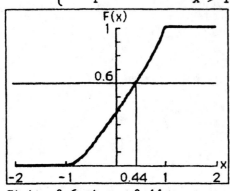

$F(x) = 0.6$ at $x = 0.44$

29. Given $f(x) = \begin{cases} \ln x & 1 \le x \le e \\ 0 & \text{otherwise} \end{cases}$

First, we find $F(x)$:

If $x < 1$, then

$$F(x) = \int_{-\infty}^{x} f(t)\,dt = \int_{-\infty}^{x} 0\ dt = 0.$$

If $1 \le x \le e$, then

$$F(x) = \int_{-\infty}^{x} f(t)\,dt = \int_{-\infty}^{1} f(t)\,dt + \int_{1}^{x} f(t)\,dt$$

$$= 0 + \int_{1}^{x} \ln t\ dt$$

$$= (\ln t)t \Big|_{1}^{x} - \int_{1}^{x} t \cdot \frac{1}{t}\,dt \qquad \text{(integration by parts)}$$

$$= (x \ln x - 0) - t \Big|_{1}^{x} \qquad \left[\underline{\text{Note}}: u = \ln t,\ dv = dt, \atop du = (1/t)dt,\ v = t.\right]$$

$$= x \ln x - (x - 1) = x \ln x - x + 1.$$

If $x > e$, then

$$F(x) = \int_{-\infty}^{x} f(t)\,dt = \int_{-\infty}^{1} f(t)\,dt + \int_{1}^{e} f(t)\,dt + \int_{e}^{x} f(t)\,dt$$

$$= 0 + \int_{1}^{e} \ln t\ dt + 0$$

$$= ((\ln t)t - t)\Big|_{1}^{e} \qquad \text{(integration by parts)}$$

$$= ((\ln e)e - e) - (0 - 1) = 0 + 1 = 1.$$

Thus, the function $F(x)$ is given by:

$$F(x) = \begin{cases} 0 & x < 1 \\ x \ln x - x + 1 & 1 \le x \le e \\ 1 & x > e \end{cases}$$

Finally,

$$\begin{aligned} P(1 \le X \le 2) &= F(2) - F(1) \\ &= 2 \ln 2 - 2 + 1 - (\ln 1 - 1 + 1) \\ &= 2 \ln 2 - 1 \approx .3863 \end{aligned}$$

31. Given $f(x) = \begin{cases} xe^{-x} & x \ge 0 \\ 0 & \text{otherwise} \end{cases}$

First, we find $F(x)$:

If $x < 0$, then

$$F(x) = \int_{-\infty}^{x} f(t)\,dt = \int_{-\infty}^{x} 0\ dt = 0.$$

If $x \ge 0$, then

$$F(x) = \int_{-\infty}^{x} f(t)\,dt = \int_{-\infty}^{0} f(t)\,dt + \int_{0}^{x} f(t)\,dt = 0 + \int_{0}^{x} te^{-t}\,dt$$

$$= -te^{-t}\Big|_{0}^{x} + \int_{0}^{x} e^{-t}\,dt \qquad \text{(integration by parts: } u = t,\ dv = e^{-t}dt, \\ du = dt,\ v = -e^{-t})$$

$$= (-xe^{-x} - 0) - e^{-t}\Big|_{0}^{x} = -xe^{-x} - e^{-x} + e^{0} = 1 - xe^{-x} - e^{-x}.$$

Thus, the cumulative probability distribution function is:

$$F(x) = \begin{cases} 1 - xe^{-x} - e^{-x} & x \ge 0 \\ 0 & \text{otherwise} \end{cases}$$

Now, we have

$$P(X \ge 1) = 1 - F(1) = 1 - (1 - e^{-1} - e^{-1}) = 2e^{-1} \approx .7358.$$

33. The relationship between $f(x)$ and $F(x)$ is $F'(x) = f(x)$. Thus, if

$$F(x) = \begin{cases} 0 & x < 0 \\ x^2 & 0 \le x \le 1 \\ 1 & x > 1 \end{cases}$$

then

$$f(x) = \begin{cases} 0 & x < 0 \\ 2x & 0 \le x \le 1 \\ 0 & x > 1 \end{cases} \quad \text{or} \quad f(x) = \begin{cases} 2x & 0 \le x \le 1 \\ 0 & \text{otherwise} \end{cases}$$

35. $F(x) = \begin{cases} 0 & x < 0 \\ 6x^2 - 8x^3 + 3x^4 & 0 \le x \le 1 \\ 1 & x > 1 \end{cases}$

Thus,

$$f(x) = \begin{cases} 0 & x < 0 \\ 12x - 24x^2 + 12x^3 & 0 \le x \le 1 \\ 0 & \text{otherwise} \end{cases} \qquad [\underline{\text{Note}}: f(x) = F'(x).]$$

or

$$f(x) = \begin{cases} 12x(1 - 2x + x^2) & 0 \le x \le 1 \\ 0 & \text{otherwise} \end{cases}$$

37. Given $f(x) = \begin{cases} x & 0 \le x \le 1 \\ 2 - x & 1 < x \le 2 \\ 0 & \text{otherwise} \end{cases}$

If $x < 0$, then

$$F(x) = \int_{-\infty}^{x} f(t)\,dt = \int_{-\infty}^{x} 0\,dt = 0.$$

If $0 \le x \le 1$, then

$$F(x) = \int_{-\infty}^{x} f(t)\,dt = \int_{-\infty}^{0} f(t)\,dt + \int_{0}^{x} f(t)\,dt = 0 + \int_{0}^{x} t\,dt = \frac{1}{2}t^2 \Big|_{0}^{x} = \frac{1}{2}x^2.$$

If $1 < x \le 2$, then

$$F(x) = \int_{-\infty}^{x} f(t)\,dt = \int_{-\infty}^{0} f(t)\,dt + \int_{0}^{1} f(t)\,dt + \int_{1}^{x} f(t)\,dt$$

$$= 0 + \int_{0}^{1} t\,dt + \int_{1}^{x} (2 - t)\,dt = \frac{1}{2}t^2 \Big|_{0}^{1} + \left(2t - \frac{1}{2}t^2\right)\Big|_{1}^{x}$$

$$= \frac{1}{2} + \left(2x - \frac{1}{2}x^2\right) - \left(2 - \frac{1}{2}\right) = \frac{1}{2} + 2x - \frac{1}{2}x^2 - \frac{3}{2} = 2x - \frac{1}{2}x^2 - 1.$$

If $x > 2$, then

$$F(x) = \int_{-\infty}^{x} f(t)\,dt = \int_{-\infty}^{0} f(t)\,dt + \int_{0}^{1} f(t)\,dt + \int_{1}^{2} f(t)\,dt + \int_{2}^{x} f(t)\,dt$$

$$= 0 + \int_{0}^{1} t\,dt + \int_{1}^{2} (2 - t)\,dt + 0 = \frac{1}{2}t^2 \Big|_{0}^{1} + \left(2t - \frac{1}{2}t^2\right)\Big|_{1}^{2}$$

$$= \frac{1}{2} + \left[\left(4 - \frac{1}{2} \cdot 4\right) - \left(2 - \frac{1}{2}\right)\right] = 1.$$

Thus, $F(x)$ is given by:

$$F(x) = \begin{cases} 0 & x < 0 \\ \frac{1}{2}x^2 & 0 \le x \le 1 \\ 2x - \frac{1}{2}x^2 - 1 & 1 < x \le 2 \\ 1 & x > 2 \end{cases}$$

39. $f(x) = \begin{cases} .2 - .02x & 0 \le x \le 10 \\ 0 & \text{otherwise} \end{cases}$

(A) $P(X \le 8) = \int_{-\infty}^{8} f(x)\,dx = \int_{0}^{8} f(x)\,dx = \int_{0}^{8} (.2 - .02x)\,dx$

$$= \left(.2x - \frac{.02x^2}{2}\right)\Big|_{0}^{8} = .2(8) - .01(8)^2 = 1.6 - .64 = .96$$

(B) $P(X > 5) = \int_{5}^{\infty} f(x)\,dx = \int_{5}^{10} f(x)\,dx = \int_{5}^{10} (.2 - .02x)\,dx$

$$= \left(.2x - \frac{.02x^2}{2}\right)\Big|_{5}^{10} = [.2(10) - .01(10)^2] - [.2(5) - .01(5)^2]$$

$$= 2 - 1 - (1 - .25) = .25$$

41. (A) $P(0 \le X \le 1) = \int_0^1 f(x)\,dx = \int_0^1 \frac{1}{10} e^{-x/10}\,dx$

$$= \frac{1}{10}\int_0^1 e^{-x/10}\,dx = \frac{1}{10} \cdot \frac{e^{-x/10}}{-\frac{1}{10}}\Big|_0^1$$

$$= -(e^{-1/10} - 1) = 1 - e^{-1/10} \approx .0952$$

(B) $P(X > 4) = \int_4^\infty \frac{1}{10} e^{-x/10}\,dx = \lim_{R \to \infty} \frac{1}{10}\int_4^R e^{-x/10}\,dx = \lim_{R \to \infty}\left(-e^{-x/10}\Big|_4^R\right)$

$$= -\lim_{R \to \infty}(e^{-R/10} - e^{-4/10}) = -(0 - e^{-2/5}) = e^{-2/5} \approx .6703$$

43. (A) $P(X > 4) = \int_4^{10} f(x)\,dx$ [<u>Note</u>: 4 stands for 4000.]

$$= \int_4^{10} .003x\sqrt{100 - x^2}\,dx$$

$$= \frac{-.003}{2}\int_4^{10}(100 - x^2)^{1/2}(-2x)\,dx \quad [\underline{\text{Note}}: d(100 - x^2) = -2x\,dx.]$$

$$= -.0015 \cdot \frac{2}{3}(100 - x^2)^{3/2}\Big|_4^{10} = -\frac{1}{1000}(100 - x^2)^{3/2}\Big|_4^{10}$$

$$= -\frac{1}{1000}(0 - (84)^{3/2})$$

$$= \frac{(84)^{3/2}}{1000} \approx .7699$$

(B) $P(0 \le x \le 8) = \int_0^8 f(x)\,dx = \int_0^8 .003x\sqrt{100 - x^2}\,dx$

$$= -\frac{1}{1000}(100 - x^2)^{3/2}\Big|_0^8 \quad \text{[refer to part (A)]}$$

$$= -\frac{1}{1000}\left[(100 - 64)^{3/2} - (100)^{3/2}\right]$$

$$= -\frac{1}{1000}(36^{3/2} - 100^{3/2}) = \frac{-1}{1000}(216 - 1000) = .784$$

(C) We must solve the following for x:

$$\int_0^x f(t)\,dt = .9$$

$$\int_0^x .003t\sqrt{100 - t^2}\,dt = .9$$

$$-\frac{1}{1000}(100 - t^2)^{3/2}\Big|_0^x = .9 \quad \text{[refer to part (A)]}$$

$$(100 - t^2)^{3/2}\Big|_0^x = -900$$

$$(100 - x^2)^{3/2} - (100)^{3/2} = -900$$

$$(100 - x^2)^{3/2} - 1000 = -900$$

$$(100 - x^2)^{3/2} = 100$$

$$100 - x^2 = 100^{2/3}$$

$$x^2 = 100 - 100^{2/3}$$
$$x = \sqrt{100 - 100^{2/3}} \approx 8.858 \quad \text{or} \quad 8858 \text{ pounds}$$

45. (A) $P(7 \leq X) = \int_7^\infty f(x)\,dx = \int_7^{10} f(x)\,dx + \int_{10}^\infty f(x)\,dx$

$$= \int_7^{10} \frac{1}{5000}(10x^3 - x^4)\,dx + \int_{10}^\infty 0\,dx = \frac{1}{5000}\left(\frac{10}{4}x^4 - \frac{x^5}{5}\right)\Big|_7^{10} + 0$$

$$= \frac{1}{5000}\left(\left[\frac{5}{2}(10)^4 - \frac{1}{5}(10)^5\right] - \left[\frac{5}{2}(7)^4 - \frac{1}{5}(7)^5\right]\right) \approx .47178$$

(B) $P(X \leq 5) = \int_{-\infty}^5 f(x)\,dx = \int_{-\infty}^0 f(x)\,dx + \int_0^5 f(x)\,dx$

$$= \int_{-\infty}^0 0\,dx + \int_0^5 \frac{1}{5000}(10x^3 - x^4)\,dx = 0 + \frac{1}{5000}\left(\frac{5}{2}x^4 - \frac{1}{5}x^5\right)\Big|_0^5$$

$$= \frac{1}{5000}\left[\frac{5}{2}(5)^4 - \frac{1}{5}(5)^5\right] = \frac{3}{16} = .1875$$

47. (A) $P(X \leq 20) = \int_{-\infty}^{20} f(x)\,dx = \int_0^{20} \frac{800x}{(400 + x^2)^2}\,dx = 400\int_0^{20} \frac{2x}{(400 + x^2)^2}\,dx$

$$= \frac{-400}{400 + x^2}\Big|_0^{20} = \frac{-400}{800} + \frac{400}{400} = .5$$

(B) $P(X > 15) = \int_{15}^\infty f(x)\,dx = 1 - \int_{-\infty}^{15} f(x)\,dx = 1 - \int_0^{15} \frac{800x}{(400 + x^2)^2}\,dx$

$$= 1 - \left(\frac{-400}{400 + x^2}\right)\Big|_0^{15} = 1 + \frac{400}{625} - 1 = .64$$

(C) We must solve the following for x:

$$\int_0^x f(t)\,dt = .8$$

$$\int_0^x \frac{800t}{(400 + t^2)^2}\,dt = .8$$

$$\frac{-400}{400 + t^2}\Big|_0^x = .8$$

$$\frac{-400}{400 + x^2} + 1 = .8$$

$$\frac{-400}{400 + x^2} = -.2$$

$$-400 = -80 - .2x^2$$

$$.2x^2 = 320$$

$$x^2 = 1600$$

$$x = 40 \text{ days}$$

49. (A) $P(X \geq 30) = \int_{30}^{\infty} f(x)\,dx = 1 - \int_{-\infty}^{30} f(x)\,dx = 1 - \int_{0}^{30} \frac{1}{20} e^{-x/20}\,dx$

$\qquad = 1 + e^{-x/20}\Big|_{0}^{30} = 1 + e^{-30/20} - 1 = e^{-3/2} \approx .223$

(B) $P(X \geq 80) = \int_{80}^{\infty} f(x)\,dx = 1 - \int_{-\infty}^{80} f(x)\,dx = 1 - \int_{0}^{80} \frac{1}{20} e^{-x/20}\,dx$

$\qquad = 1 + e^{-x/20}\Big|_{0}^{80} = 1 + e^{-80/20} - 1 = e^{-4} \approx .018$

EXERCISE 10-5

Things to remember:

1. **EXPECTED VALUE AND STANDARD DEVIATION FOR A CONTINUOUS RANDOM VARIABLE**

    Let $f(x)$ be the probability density function for a continuous random variable X. The EXPECTED VALUE, or MEAN, of X is

    $$\mu = E(X) = \int_{-\infty}^{\infty} xf(x)\,dx.$$

    The VARIANCE is

    $$V(X) = \int_{-\infty}^{\infty} (x - \mu)^2 f(x)\,dx,$$

    and the STANDARD DEVIATION is

    $$\sigma = \sqrt{V(X)}.$$

2. **ALTERNATE FORMULA FOR VARIANCE:**

    $$V(X) = \int_{-\infty}^{\infty} x^2 f(x)\,dx - \mu^2$$

3. If x_m is the median, then it must satisfy

    $$F(x_m) = P(X \leq x_m) = \frac{1}{2}.$$

---

1. Using 1,

$$\mu = E(X) = \int_{-\infty}^{\infty} xf(x)\,dx = \int_0^2 x \cdot \frac{1}{2}x\,dx = \frac{1}{2} \cdot \frac{x^3}{3}\Big|_0^2 = \frac{1}{6}(2^3) = \frac{8}{6} \text{ or } \frac{4}{3} \approx 1.333.$$

$$V(X) = \int_{-\infty}^{\infty} (x - \mu)^2 f(x)\,dx = \int_0^2 \left(x - \frac{4}{3}\right)^2 \frac{1}{2}x\,dx = \frac{1}{2}\int_0^2 \left(x^2 - \frac{8}{3}x + \frac{16}{9}\right)x\,dx$$

$$= \frac{1}{2}\int_0^2 \left(x^3 - \frac{8}{3}x^2 + \frac{16}{9}x\right)dx = \frac{1}{2}\left(\frac{x^4}{4} - \frac{8}{9}x^3 + \frac{16}{18}x^2\right)\Big|_0^2$$

$$= \frac{1}{2}\left(\frac{16}{4} - \frac{64}{9} + \frac{32}{9}\right) = \frac{4}{18} = \frac{2}{9} \approx .222.$$

Thus, the standard deviation is $\sigma = \sqrt{V(X)} = \sqrt{\frac{2}{9}} = \frac{\sqrt{2}}{3} \approx .471.$

3. Using 1,

$$\mu = E(X) = \int_{-\infty}^{\infty} xf(x)\,dx = \int_2^5 \frac{1}{3}x\,dx = \frac{1}{6}x^2\Big|_2^5 = \frac{25}{6} - \frac{4}{6} = \frac{7}{2} = 3.5$$

Using 2,

$$V(X) = \int_{-\infty}^{\infty} x^2 f(x)\,dx - \mu^2 = \int_2^5 \frac{1}{3}x^2\,dx - \frac{49}{4} = \frac{1}{9}x^3\Big|_2^5 - \frac{49}{4}$$

$$= \frac{125}{9} - \frac{8}{9} - \frac{49}{4} = \frac{3}{4} = .75$$

Thus, $\sigma = \sqrt{V(X)} = \sqrt{\frac{3}{4}} = \frac{\sqrt{3}}{2} \approx .866.$

5. $\mu = E(X) = \int_{-\infty}^{\infty} xf(x)\,dx = \int_1^2 x(4 - 2x)\,dx = \int_1^2 (4x - 2x^2)\,dx = \left(2x^2 - \frac{2}{3}x^3\right)\Big|_1^2$

$$= 8 - \frac{16}{3} - \left(2 - \frac{2}{3}\right) = \frac{4}{3} \approx 1.333$$

Using 2,

$$V(X) = \int_{-\infty}^{\infty} x^2 f(x)\,dx - \mu^2 = \int_1^2 x^2(4 - 2x)\,dx - \frac{16}{9} = \int_1^2 (4x^2 - 2x^3)\,dx - \frac{16}{9}$$

$$= \left(\frac{4}{3}x^3 - \frac{1}{2}x^4\right)\Big|_1^2 - \frac{16}{9} = \frac{32}{3} - 8 - \left(\frac{4}{3} - \frac{1}{2}\right) - \frac{16}{9} = \frac{1}{18}$$

Thus, $\sigma = \sqrt{V(X)} = \sqrt{\frac{1}{18}} \approx .236.$

7. Step 1: Find the cumulative probability distribution function.

If $x < 0$, then $F(x) = 0$. If $0 \le x \le 1$, then

$$F(x) = \int_{-\infty}^x f(t)\,dt = \int_0^x 2t\,dt = t^2\Big|_0^x = x^2.$$

If $x > 1$, then

$$F(x) = \int_{-\infty}^{x} f(t)\,dt = \int_{-\infty}^{0} f(t)\,dt + \int_{0}^{1} f(t)\,dt + \int_{1}^{x} f(t)\,dt$$

$$= 0 + \int_{0}^{1} 2t\,dt + 0 = t^2 \Big|_{0}^{1} = 1.$$

Thus, $F(x) = \begin{cases} 0 & \text{if } x < 0 \\ x^2 & \text{if } 0 \le x \le 1 \\ 1 & \text{if } x > 1 \end{cases}$

Step 2: Solve the equation $P(X \le x_m) = \frac{1}{2}$ for x_m, where x_m is the median.

$$F(x_m) = P(X \le x_m) = \frac{1}{2}$$

$$x_m^2 = \frac{1}{2}$$

$$x_m^2 = \frac{1}{\sqrt{2}} \approx .707$$

9. **Step 1**: Find the cumulative probability distribution function.

If $x < 2$, then $F(x) = 0$. If $2 \le x \le 4$, then

$$F(x) = \int_{-\infty}^{x} f(t)\,dt = \int_{2}^{x} \frac{1}{6} t\,dt = \frac{1}{12} t^2 \Big|_{2}^{x} = \frac{x^2}{12} - \frac{1}{3}.$$

If $x > 4$, then

$$F(x) = \int_{-\infty}^{x} f(t)\,dt = \int_{-\infty}^{2} f(t)\,dt + \int_{2}^{4} f(t)\,dt + \int_{4}^{x} f(t)\,dt$$

$$= 0 + \int_{2}^{4} \frac{1}{6} t\,dt + 0 = \frac{1}{12} t^2 \Big|_{2}^{4} = 1.$$

Thus, $F(x) = \begin{cases} 0 & \text{if } x < 2 \\ \dfrac{x^2}{12} - \dfrac{1}{3} & \text{if } 2 \le x \le 4 \\ 1 & \text{if } x > 4 \end{cases}$

Step 2: Solve the equation $P(X \le x_m) = \frac{1}{2}$ for x_m.

$$F(x_m) = P(X \le x_m) = \frac{1}{2}$$

$$\frac{x_m^2}{12} - \frac{1}{3} = \frac{1}{2}$$

$$\frac{x_m^2}{12} = \frac{5}{6}$$

$$x_m^2 = 10$$

$$x_m = \sqrt{10} \approx 3.162$$

11. **Step 1**: Find the cumulative probability distribution function.

If $x < 0$, then $F(x) = 0$. If $0 \le x \le 4$, then

$$F(x) = \int_{-\infty}^{x} f(t)\,dt = \int_{0}^{x} \left(\frac{1}{2} - \frac{1}{8} t \right) dt = \left(\frac{1}{2} t - \frac{1}{16} t^2 \right) \Big|_{0}^{x} = \frac{1}{2} x - \frac{1}{16} x^2.$$

If $x > 4$, then

$$F(x) = \int_{-\infty}^{x} f(t)\,dt = \int_{-\infty}^{0} f(t)\,dt + \int_{0}^{4} f(t)\,dt + \int_{4}^{x} f(t)\,dt$$

$$= 0 + \int_{0}^{4}\left(\frac{1}{2} - \frac{1}{8}t\right)dt + 0$$

$$= \left(\frac{1}{2}t - \frac{1}{16}t^2\right)\Big|_{0}^{4} = 2 - 1 = 1$$

Thus, $F(x) = \begin{cases} 0 & \text{if } x < 0 \\ \frac{1}{2}x - \frac{1}{16}x^2 & \text{if } 0 \le x \le 4 \\ 1 & \text{if } x > 4 \end{cases}$

Step 2: Solve the equation $P(X \le x_m) = \frac{1}{2}$ for x_m.

$$F(x_m) = P(X \le x_m) = \frac{1}{2}$$

$$\frac{1}{2}x_m - \frac{1}{16}x_m^2 = \frac{1}{2}$$

$$x_m^2 - 8x_m + 8 = 0$$

Now, the roots of the quadratic equation are

$$\frac{8 \pm \sqrt{64 - 32}}{2} = 4 \pm 2\sqrt{2}.$$

Since x_m must lie in the interval $[0, 4]$, $x_m = 4 - 2\sqrt{2} \approx 1.172$.

13. $\mu = E(X) = \displaystyle\int_{-\infty}^{\infty} x f(x)\,dx = \int_{1}^{\infty} x \cdot \frac{4}{x^5}\,dx = \int_{1}^{\infty} \frac{4}{x^4}\,dx = \lim_{R \to \infty}\int_{1}^{R} \frac{4}{x^4}\,dx$

$$= \lim_{R \to \infty}\left(-\frac{4}{3x^3}\right)\Big|_{1}^{R} = \lim_{R \to \infty}\left(-\frac{4}{3R^3} + \frac{4}{3}\right) = \frac{4}{3}$$

$V(X) = \displaystyle\int_{-\infty}^{\infty} x^2 f(x)\,dx - \mu^2 = \int_{1}^{\infty} x^2 \cdot \frac{4}{x^5}\,dx - \frac{16}{9} = \int_{1}^{\infty} \frac{4}{x^3}\,dx - \frac{16}{9}$

$$= \lim_{R \to \infty}\int_{1}^{R} \frac{4}{x^3}\,dx - \frac{16}{9} = \lim_{R \to \infty}\left(-\frac{2}{x^2}\right)\Big|_{1}^{R} - \frac{16}{9} = \lim_{R \to \infty}\left(-\frac{2}{R^2} + 2\right) - \frac{16}{9} = \frac{2}{9}$$

$\sigma = \sqrt{V(X)} = \sqrt{\frac{2}{9}} = \frac{\sqrt{2}}{3} \approx .471$

15. $\mu = E(X) = \displaystyle\int_{-\infty}^{\infty} x f(x)\,dx = \int_{2}^{\infty} x \cdot \frac{64}{x^5}\,dx = \int_{2}^{\infty} \frac{64}{x^4}\,dx = \lim_{R \to \infty}\int_{2}^{R} \frac{64}{x^4}\,dx$

$$= \lim_{R \to \infty}\left(\frac{-64}{3x^3}\right)\Big|_{2}^{R} = \lim_{R \to \infty}\left(\frac{-64}{3R^3} + \frac{64}{24}\right) = \frac{8}{3} \approx 2.667$$

$V(X) = \displaystyle\int_{-\infty}^{\infty} x^2 f(x)\,dx - \mu^2 = \int_{2}^{\infty} x^2 \cdot \frac{64}{x^5}\,dx - \frac{64}{9} = \int_{2}^{\infty} \frac{64}{x^3}\,dx - \frac{64}{9}$

$$= \lim_{R \to \infty}\int_{2}^{R} \frac{64}{x^3}\,dx - \frac{64}{9} = \lim_{R \to \infty}\left(\frac{-32}{x^2}\right)\Big|_{2}^{R} - \frac{64}{9} = \lim_{R \to \infty}\left(\frac{-32}{R^2} + 8\right) - \frac{64}{9} = \frac{8}{9}$$

$\sigma = \sqrt{V(X)} = \sqrt{\frac{8}{9}} = \frac{2\sqrt{2}}{3} \approx .943$

17. **Step 1**: Find the cumulative probability distribution function.

If $x < 1$, then $F(x) = 0$. If $1 \leq x \leq e$, then

$$F(x) = \int_{-\infty}^{x} f(t)\,dt = \int_{-\infty}^{1} f(t)\,dt + \int_{1}^{x} f(t)\,dt$$

$$= 0 + \int_{1}^{x} \frac{1}{t}\,dt = \ln t \Big|_{1}^{x} = \ln x - \ln 1 = \ln x.$$

If $x > e$, then $F(x) = \int_{-\infty}^{x} f(t)\,dt = \int_{-\infty}^{1} f(t)\,dt + \int_{1}^{e} f(t)\,dt + \int_{e}^{x} f(t)\,dt$

$$= 0 + \int_{1}^{e} \frac{1}{t}\,dt + 0 = \ln t \Big|_{1}^{e} = \ln e - \ln 1 = 1.$$

Thus, $F(x) = \begin{cases} 0 & x < 1 \\ \ln x & 1 \leq x \leq e \\ 1 & x > e \end{cases}$

Step 2: Solve the equation $P(X \leq x_m) = \frac{1}{2}$ for x_m.

$$F(x_m) = P(X \leq x_m) = \frac{1}{2}$$

$$\ln x_m = \frac{1}{2} \qquad (1 \leq x \leq e)$$

Thus, the median $x_m = e^{1/2} \approx 1.649$.

19. **Step 1**: Find the cumulative probabilty distribution function.

If $x < 0$, then $F(x) = 0$. If $0 \leq x \leq 2$, then

$$F(x) = \int_{-\infty}^{x} f(t)\,dt = \int_{0}^{x} \frac{4}{(2 + t)^2}\,dt = \frac{-4}{2 + t}\Big|_{0}^{x} = \frac{-4}{2 + x} + 2.$$

If $x > 2$, then

$$F(x) = \int_{-\infty}^{x} f(t)\,dt = \int_{-\infty}^{0} f(t)\,dt + \int_{0}^{2} f(t)\,dt + \int_{2}^{x} f(t)\,dt$$

$$= 0 + \int_{0}^{2} \frac{4}{(2 + t)^2}\,dt + 0 = \frac{-4}{2 + t}\Big|_{0}^{2} = -1 + 2 = 1$$

Thus, $F(x) = \begin{cases} 0 & \text{if } x < 0 \\ \dfrac{-4}{2 + x} + 2 & \text{if } 0 \leq x \leq 2 \\ 1 & \text{if } x > 2 \end{cases}$

Step 2: Solve the equation $P(X \leq x_m) = \frac{1}{2}$ for x_m.

$$F(x_m) = P(X \leq x_m) = \frac{1}{2}$$

$$\frac{-4}{2 + x_m} + 2 = \frac{1}{2}$$

$$\frac{-4}{2 + x_m} = \frac{-3}{2}$$

$$-6 - 3x_m = -8$$

$$x_m = \frac{2}{3}$$

21. **Step 1**: Find $F(x)$.

If $x < 0$, then $F(x) = 0$. If $x \geq 0$, then

$$F(x) = \int_{-\infty}^{x} f(t)\,dt = \int_{-\infty}^{0} f(t)\,dt + \int_{0}^{x} f(t)\,dt = 0 + \int_{0}^{x} \frac{1}{(1+t)^2}\,dt$$

$$= -\frac{1}{(1+t)}\Big|_{0}^{x} = -\left(\frac{1}{1+x} - 1\right) = 1 - \frac{1}{1+x} = \frac{x}{1+x}.$$

Thus,

$$F(x) = \begin{cases} 0 & x < 0 \\ \dfrac{x}{1+x} & x \geq 0 \end{cases}$$

Step 2: Solve $P(X \leq x_m) = \frac{1}{2}$ for x_m.

$$F(x_m) = P(X \leq x_m) = \frac{1}{2}$$

$$\frac{x_m}{1+x_m} = \frac{1}{2} \qquad (x \geq 0)$$

$$2x_m = 1 + x_m$$

Thus, the median $x_m = 1$.

23. **Step 1**: Find $F(x)$.

If $x < 0$, then $F(x) = 0$. If $x \geq 0$, then

$$F(x) = \int_{-\infty}^{x} f(t)\,dt = \int_{-\infty}^{0} f(t)\,dt + \int_{0}^{x} f(t)\,dt = 0 + \int_{0}^{x} 2e^{-2t}\,dt$$

$$= -e^{-2t}\Big|_{0}^{x} = -e^{-2x} + 1$$

Thus, $F(x) = \begin{cases} 0 & \text{if } x < 0 \\ 1 - e^{-2x} & \text{if } x \geq 0 \end{cases}$

Step 2: Solve $P(X \leq x_m) = \frac{1}{2}$ for x_m.

$$F(x_m) = P(X \leq x_m) = \frac{1}{2}$$

$$1 - e^{-2x_m} = \frac{1}{2}$$

$$e^{-2x_m} = \frac{1}{2}$$

$$-2x_m = \ln\frac{1}{2} = -\ln 2$$

$$x_m = \frac{\ln 2}{2} \approx .347$$

25. Since f is a probability density function,

$$\int_{-\infty}^{\infty} f(x)\,dx = 1 \quad \text{and} \quad \int_{-\infty}^{\infty} xf(x)\,dx = \mu, \text{ the mean.}$$

Now,

$$\int_{-\infty}^{\infty} (ax + b)f(x)\,dx = \int_{-\infty}^{\infty} axf(x)\,dx + \int_{-\infty}^{\infty} bf(x)\,dx$$

$$= a\int_{-\infty}^{\infty} xf(x)\,dx + b\int_{-\infty}^{\infty} f(x)\,dx = a\mu + b.$$

27. **Step 1**: Find $F(x)$.

If $x < 0$, then $F(x) = 0$. If $0 \leq x \leq 2$, then

$$F(x) = \int_{-\infty}^{x} f(t)\,dt = \int_{-\infty}^{0} f(t)\,dt + \int_{0}^{x} f(t)\,dt$$

$$= 0 + \frac{1}{2}\int_{0}^{x} t\,dt = \frac{1}{4}t^2 \Big|_{0}^{x} = \frac{1}{4}x^2.$$

If $x > 2$, then

$$F(x) = \int_{-\infty}^{x} f(t)\,dt = \int_{-\infty}^{0} f(t)\,dt + \int_{0}^{2} f(t)\,dt + \int_{2}^{x} f(t)\,dt$$

$$= 0 + \frac{1}{2}\int_{0}^{2} t\,dt + 0 = \frac{1}{4}t^2 \Big|_{0}^{2} = 1.$$

Thus,

$$F(x) = \begin{cases} 0 & x < 0 \\ \frac{1}{4}x^2 & 0 \leq x \leq 2 \\ 1 & x > 2 \end{cases}$$

Step 2: In order to find the quartile point x_1, we solve the following for x_1:

$$F(x_1) = P(X \leq x_1) = \frac{1}{4}$$

$$\frac{1}{4}x_1^2 = \frac{1}{4}$$

$$x_1^2 = 1$$

$$x_1 = 1$$

For the quartile point x_2 (or x_m), we solve the following for x_2:

$$F(x_2) = P(X \leq x_2) = \frac{1}{2}$$

$$\frac{1}{4}x_2^2 = \frac{1}{2}$$

$$x_2^2 = 2$$

$$x_2 = \sqrt{2} \approx 1.414$$

For the quartile point x_3, we solve the following for x_3:

$$F(x_3) = P(X \leq x_3) = \frac{3}{4}$$

$$\frac{1}{4}x_3^2 = \frac{3}{4}$$

$$x_3^2 = 3$$

$$x_3 = \sqrt{3} \approx 1.732$$

29. Step 1: Find $F(x)$.

If $x < 0$, then $F(x) = 0$. If $x \geq 0$, then

$$F(x) = \int_{-\infty}^{x} f(t)\,dt = \int_{-\infty}^{0} f(t)\,dt + \int_{0}^{x} f(t)\,dt = 0 + \int_{0}^{x} \frac{3}{(3+t)^2}\,dt$$

$$= \frac{-3}{3+t}\Big|_{0}^{x} = \frac{-3}{3+x} + 1.$$

Thus, $F(x) = \begin{cases} 0 & \text{if } x < 0 \\ 1 - \dfrac{3}{3+x} & \text{if } x \geq 0 \end{cases}$

Step 2: For the quartile point x_1, we solve:

$$F(x_1) = P(X \leq x_1) = \frac{1}{4}$$

$$1 - \frac{3}{3+x_1} = \frac{1}{4}$$

$$-\frac{3}{3+x_1} = -\frac{3}{4}$$

$$3 + x_1 = 4$$

$$x_1 = 1$$

For the quartile point x_2, we solve:

$$F(x_2) = P(X \leq x_2) = \frac{1}{2}$$

$$1 - \frac{3}{3+x_2} = \frac{1}{2}$$

$$-\frac{3}{3+x_2} = -\frac{1}{2}$$

$$3 + x_2 = 6$$

$$x_2 = 3$$

For the quartile point x_3, we solve:

$$F(x_3) = P(X \leq x_3) = \frac{3}{4}$$

$$1 - \frac{3}{3+x_3} = \frac{3}{4}$$

$$-\frac{3}{3+x_3} = -\frac{1}{4}$$

$$3 + x_3 = 12$$

$$x_3 = 9$$

31. Given $f(x) = \begin{cases} 4x - 4x^3 & 0 \leq x \leq 1 \\ 0 & \text{otherwise} \end{cases}$

Step 1. Find $F(x)$.

If $x < 0$, then $F(x) = 0$. If $0 \leq x \leq 1$, then

$$F(x) = \int_{-\infty}^{x} f(t)\,dt = \int_{-\infty}^{0} f(t)\,dt + \int_{0}^{x} f(t)\,dt$$

$$= 0 + \int_{0}^{x} (4t - 4t^3)\,dt = (2t^2 - t^4)\Big|_{0}^{x}$$

$$= 2x^2 - x^4$$

If $x > 1$, then

$$F(x) = \int_{-\infty}^{x} f(t)\,dt = \int_{-\infty}^{0} f(t)\,dt + \int_{0}^{1} f(t)\,dt + \int_{1}^{x} f(t)\,dt$$

$$= 0 + \int_{0}^{1} (4t - 4t^3)\,dt + 0 = (2t^2 - t^4)\Big|_{0}^{1} = 1$$

Thus, $F(x) = \begin{cases} 0 & x < 0 \\ 2x^2 - x^4 & 0 \le x \le 1 \\ 1 & x > 1 \end{cases}$

Step 2. Solve the equation $F(x_m) = \frac{1}{2}$ for x_m. The graphs of F and $y = \frac{1}{2}$ are shown below.

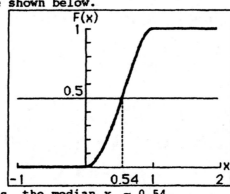

Thus, the median $x_m \sim 0.54$.

33. Given $f(x) = \begin{cases} \ln x & 1 \le x \le e \\ 0 & \text{otherwise} \end{cases}$

From Problem 29, Exercise 12-4,

$$F(x) = \begin{cases} 0 & x < 1 \\ x \ln x - x + 1 & 1 \le x \le e \\ 1 & x > e \end{cases}$$

To find x_m we solve the equation $F(x_m) = \frac{1}{2}$ for x_m. The graphs of F and $y = \frac{1}{2}$ are shown below.

Thus, the median $x_m \sim 2.16$.

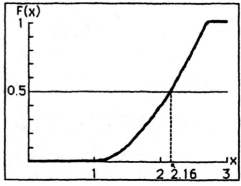

35. (A) The contractor's expected profit is given by:

$$E(X) = \int_{-\infty}^{\infty} xf(x)\,dx = \int_{6}^{10} x \cdot \frac{1}{8}(10 - x)\,dx = \frac{1}{8}\int_{6}^{10}(10x - x^2)\,dx$$

$$= \frac{1}{8}\left(\frac{10}{2}x^2 - \frac{x^3}{3}\right)\Big|_{6}^{10} = \frac{1}{8}\left[\left(5 \cdot 10^2 - \frac{1}{3} \cdot 10^3\right) - \left(5 \cdot 6^2 - \frac{1}{3} \cdot 6^3\right)\right]$$

$$= \frac{1}{8}\left(\frac{500}{3} - 108\right) = \frac{1}{8}\left(\frac{176}{3}\right) = \frac{22}{3} \approx 7.333 \quad \text{or} \quad \$7333$$

(B) <u>Step 1</u>: Find $F(x)$.

If $x < 6$, then $F(x) = 0$. If $6 \le x \le 10$, then

$$F(x) = \int_{-\infty}^{x} f(t)\,dt = \int_{-\infty}^{6} f(t)\,dt + \int_{6}^{x} f(t)\,dt = 0 + \frac{1}{8}\int_{6}^{x}(10 - t)\,dt$$

$$= \frac{1}{8}\left(10t - \frac{t^2}{2}\right)\Big|_{6}^{x} = \frac{1}{8}\left[\left(10x - \frac{x^2}{2}\right) - \left(60 - \frac{36}{2}\right)\right] = \frac{1}{8}\left(10x - \frac{x^2}{2} - 42\right).$$

If $x > 10$, then

$$F(x) = \int_{-\infty}^{x} f(t)\,dt = \int_{-\infty}^{6} f(t)\,dt + \int_{6}^{10} f(t)\,dt + \int_{10}^{x} f(t)\,dt$$

$$= 0 + \frac{1}{8}\int_{6}^{10}(10 - t)\,dt + 0 = \frac{1}{8}\left(10t - \frac{t^2}{2}\right)\Big|_{6}^{10}$$

$$= \frac{1}{8}\left[(100 - 50) - (60 - 18)\right] = 1.$$

Thus,

$$F(x) = \begin{cases} 0 & x < 6 \\ \frac{1}{8}\left(10x - \frac{x^2}{2} - 42\right) & 6 \le x \le 10 \\ 1 & x > 10 \end{cases}$$

<u>Step 2</u>: To find the median profit, x_m, we solve the following:

$$F(x_m) = P(X \le x_m) = \frac{1}{2}$$

$$\frac{1}{8}\left(10x_m - \frac{x_m^2}{2} - 42\right) = \frac{1}{2}$$

$$10x_m - \frac{x_m^2}{2} - 42 = 4$$

$$x_m^2 - 20x_m + 92 = 0$$

$$x_m = \frac{20 \pm \sqrt{20^2 - 4(92)}}{2} \quad \text{(using the quadratic formula)}$$

$$= \frac{20 \pm \sqrt{32}}{2} = 10 \pm 2\sqrt{2}$$

Since x_m lies in the interval $[6, 10]$, $x_m = 10 - 2\sqrt{2} \approx \$7.172$ thousand, or $\$7,172$.

37. Step 1: Find $F(x)$.

If $x < 0$, then $F(x) = 0$. If $x \geq 0$, then

$$F(x) = \int_{-\infty}^{x} f(t)\,dt = \int_{-\infty}^{0} f(t)\,dt + \int_{0}^{x} f(t)\,dt = 0 + \int_{0}^{x} \frac{1}{3} e^{-t/3}\,dt$$

$$= -e^{-t/3}\Big|_{0}^{x} = -e^{-x/3} + 1.$$

Thus, $F(x) = \begin{cases} 0 & \text{if } x < 0 \\ 1 - e^{-x/3} & \text{if } x \geq 0 \end{cases}$

Step 2: Solve $P(X \leq x_m) = \frac{1}{2}$ for x_m.

$$F(x_m) = P(X \leq x_m) = \frac{1}{2}$$

$$1 - e^{-x_m/3} = \frac{1}{2}$$

$$e^{-x_m/3} = \frac{1}{2}$$

$$\frac{-x_m}{3} = \ln \frac{1}{2} = -\ln 2$$

$$x_m = 3 \ln 2 \approx 2.079 \text{ minutes}$$

39. The expected daily consumption is given by:

$$E(X) = \int_{-\infty}^{\infty} x f(x)\,dx = \int_{-\infty}^{\infty} \frac{x}{(1 + x^2)^{3/2}}\,dx$$

$$= \lim_{R \to \infty} \int_{0}^{R} \frac{x}{(1 + x^2)^{3/2}}\,dx \quad \left[\text{Note: If } u = 1 + x^2, \text{ then } \frac{du}{2} = x\,dx \text{ and}\right.$$

$$\int \frac{x}{(1 + x^2)^{3/2}}\,dx = \frac{1}{2}\int \frac{du}{u^{3/2}} = \frac{1}{2} \cdot \frac{-2}{u^{1/2}}$$

$$= -\frac{1}{(1 + x^2)^{1/2}} \cdot \Big]$$

$$= -\lim_{R \to \infty} \frac{1}{(1 + x^2)^{1/2}}\Big|_{0}^{R} = -\lim_{R \to \infty}\left(\frac{1}{(1 + R^2)^{1/2}} - \frac{1}{1}\right) = 1 \text{ or } 1 \text{ million gallons}$$

41. Mean life expectancy is given by:

$$E(X) = \mu = \int_{-\infty}^{\infty} x f(x)\,dx = \frac{1}{5000}\int_{0}^{10} x(10x^3 - x^4)\,dx = \frac{1}{5000}\left(10 \cdot \frac{x^5}{5} - \frac{x^6}{6}\right)\Big|_{0}^{10}$$

$$= \frac{1}{5000}\left(2 \cdot 10^5 - \frac{1}{6} \cdot 10^6 - 0\right) = \frac{1}{5000}\left(\frac{1}{3} \cdot 10^5\right) = \frac{20}{3} \approx 6.7 \text{ minutes}$$

43. Step 1: Find $F(x)$.

If $x < 0$, $F(x) = 0$. If $x \geq 0$, then

$$F(x) = \int_{-\infty}^{x} f(t)\,dt = \int_{-\infty}^{0} f(t)\,dt + \int_{0}^{x} f(t)\,dt = 0 + \int_{0}^{x} \frac{800t}{(400 + t^2)^2}\,dt$$

$$= \frac{-400}{400 + t^2}\Big|_{0}^{x} = \frac{-400}{400 + x^2} + 1.$$

Thus, $F(x) = \begin{cases} 0 & \text{if } x < 0 \\ 1 - \dfrac{400}{400 + x^2} & \text{if } x \geq 0 \end{cases}$

<u>Step 2</u>: Solve $P(X \leq x_m) = \dfrac{1}{2}$ for x_m.

$$1 - \frac{400}{400 + x_m^2} = \frac{1}{2}$$

$$\frac{-400}{400 + x_m^2} = \frac{-1}{2}$$

$$400 + x_m^2 = 800$$

$$x_m^2 = 400$$

$$x_m = 20 \text{ days}$$

45. The expected number of hours to learn the task is given by:

$$E(X) = \mu = \int_{-\infty}^{\infty} x f(x)\,dx = \int_{0}^{3} x\left(\frac{4}{9}x^2 - \frac{4}{27}x^3\right)dx = \left(\frac{4}{9}\cdot\frac{x^4}{4} - \frac{4}{27}\cdot\frac{x^5}{5}\right)\bigg|_0^3$$

$$= \frac{1}{9}(3^4) - \frac{4}{3^3(5)}(3^5) = 9 - \frac{36}{5} = \frac{9}{5} = 1.8 \text{ hours}$$

EXERCISE 10-6

Things to remember:

1.   UNIFORM PROBABILITY DENSITY FUNCTION

   (a) Probability density function:

   $$f(x) = \begin{cases} \dfrac{1}{b - a} & a \leq x \leq b \\ 0 & \text{otherwise} \end{cases}$$

   (b) Cumulative probability distribution:

   $$F(x) = \begin{cases} 0 & x < a \\ \dfrac{x - a}{b - a} & a \leq x \leq b \\ 1 & x > b \end{cases}$$

   (c) Mean: $\mu = \dfrac{1}{2}(a + b)$

   (d) Median: $x_m = \dfrac{1}{2}(a + b)$

   (e) Standard deviation: $\sigma = \dfrac{1}{\sqrt{12}}(b - a)$

2. **BETA PROBABILITY DENSITY FUNCTION**

(a) $f(x) = \begin{cases} (\beta + 1)(\beta + 2)x^{\beta}(1 - x) & 0 \leq x \leq 1 \\ 0 & \text{otherwise} \end{cases}$

where $\beta \geq 0$

(b) $F(x) = \begin{cases} 0 & x < 0 \\ (\beta + 2)x^{\beta+1} - (\beta + 1)x^{\beta+2} & 0 \leq x \leq 1 \\ 1 & x > 1 \end{cases}$

(c) Mean: $\mu = \dfrac{\beta + 1}{\beta + 3}$

(d) Standard deviation: $\sigma = \sqrt{\dfrac{2(\beta + 1)}{(\beta + 4)(\beta + 3)^2}}$

3. **EXPONENTIAL PROBABIILTY DENSITY FUNCTION**

(a) $f(x) = \begin{cases} \dfrac{1}{\lambda} e^{-x/\lambda} & x \geq 0 \\ 0 & \text{otherwise} \end{cases}$

(b) $F(x) = \begin{cases} 1 - e^{-x/\lambda} & x \geq 0 \\ 0 & \text{otherwise} \end{cases}$

(c) Mean: $\mu = \lambda$

(d) Median: $x_m = \lambda \ln 2$

(e) Standard deviation: $\sigma = \lambda$

---

1. Using 1(a) with $[a, b] = [0, 2]$, we have:

$f(x) = \begin{cases} \dfrac{1}{2 - 0} & 0 \leq x \leq 2 \\ 0 & \text{otherwise} \end{cases} = \begin{cases} \dfrac{1}{2} & 0 \leq x \leq 2 \\ 0 & \text{otherwise} \end{cases}$

Using 1(b) with $[a, b] = [0, 2]$, we have:

$F(x) = \begin{cases} 0 & x < 0 \\ \dfrac{x - 0}{2 - 0} & 0 \leq x \leq 2 \\ 1 & x > 2 \end{cases} = \begin{cases} 0 & x < 0 \\ \dfrac{x}{2} & 0 \leq x \leq 2 \\ 1 & x > 2 \end{cases}$

3. Using 2(a) with $\beta = 3$, we have:

$f(x) = \begin{cases} (3 + 1)(3 + 2)x^3(1 - x) & 0 \leq x \leq 1 \\ 0 & \text{otherwise} \end{cases} = \begin{cases} 20x^3(1 - x) & 0 \leq x \leq 1 \\ 0 & \text{otherwise} \end{cases}$

Using 2(b) with ß = 3, we have:

$$F(x) = \begin{cases} 0 & x < 0 \\ (3 + 2)x^{3+1} - (3 + 1)x^{3+2} & 0 \le x \le 1 \\ 1 & x > 1 \end{cases} = \begin{cases} 0 & x < 0 \\ 5x^4 - 4x^5 & 0 \le x \le 1 \\ 1 & x > 1 \end{cases}$$

5. Using 3(a) with $\lambda = \frac{1}{2}$, we have:

$$f(x) = \begin{cases} \dfrac{1}{1/2} e^{-x/(1/2)} & x \ge 0 \\ 0 & \text{otherwise} \end{cases} = \begin{cases} 2e^{-2x} & x \ge 0 \\ 0 & \text{otherwise} \end{cases}$$

Using 3(b) with $\lambda = \frac{1}{2}$, we have:

$$F(x) = \begin{cases} 1 - e^{-x/(1/2)} & x \ge 0 \\ 0 & \text{otherwise} \end{cases} = \begin{cases} 1 - e^{-2x} & x \ge 0 \\ 0 & \text{otherwise} \end{cases}$$

7. Using 1(c), (d), (e), with $[a, b] = [1, 5]$, we have:

Mean: $\mu = \frac{1}{2}(a + b) = \frac{1}{2}(1 + 5) = 3$

Median: $x_m = \frac{1}{2}(a + b) = \frac{1}{2}(1 + 6) = 3$

Standard deviation: $\sigma = \dfrac{1}{\sqrt{12}}(b - a) = \dfrac{1}{\sqrt{12}}(5 - 1) = \dfrac{4}{\sqrt{12}} = \dfrac{2}{\sqrt{3}} \approx 1.155$

9. Using 3(c), (d), (e), with $\lambda = 5$, we have:

Mean: $\mu = 5$

Median: $x_m = 5 \ln 2 \approx 3.466$

Standard deviation: $\sigma = 5$

11. Using 2(c), (d), with $ß = \frac{1}{2}$, we have:

Mean: $\mu = \dfrac{ß + 1}{ß + 3} = \dfrac{\frac{1}{2} + 1}{\frac{1}{2} + 3} = \dfrac{\frac{3}{2}}{\frac{7}{2}} = \dfrac{3}{7}$

Standard deviation: $\sigma = \sqrt{\dfrac{2(ß + 1)}{(ß + 4)(ß + 3)^2}} = \sqrt{\dfrac{2\left(\frac{1}{2} + 1\right)}{\left(\frac{1}{2} + 4\right)\left(\frac{1}{2} + 3\right)^2}} = \sqrt{\dfrac{3}{\frac{9}{2} \cdot \frac{49}{4}}}$

$$= \sqrt{\dfrac{8}{147}} \approx .233$$

13. X is uniformly distributed on $[0, 4]$. The probability density function is

$$f(x) = \begin{cases} \dfrac{1}{4} & 0 \le x \le 4 \\ 0 & \text{otherwise} \end{cases}$$

and the mean is

$$\mu = \frac{1}{2}(0 + 4) = 2.$$

Thus, $P(X \le 2) = \displaystyle\int_0^2 f(x)\,dx = \int_0^2 \frac{1}{4}\,dx = \frac{1}{4}x \Big|_0^2 = \frac{1}{2}.$

15. X is a beta random variable with $\beta = 0$. Then
$$f(x) = \begin{cases} 1(2)x^0(1-x) & 0 \le x \le 1 \\ 0 & \text{otherwise} \end{cases} = \begin{cases} 2(1-x) & 0 \le x \le 1 \\ 0 & \text{otherwise} \end{cases}$$
and the mean is
$$\mu = \frac{0+1}{0+3} = \frac{1}{3}.$$
Thus, $P\left(X \le \frac{1}{3}\right) = \displaystyle\int_0^{1/3} f(x)\,dx = \int_0^{1/3} 2(1-x)\,dx = (2x - x^2)\Big|_0^{1/3}$
$$= \frac{2}{3} - \frac{1}{9} = \frac{5}{9}.$$

17. X is an exponential random variable with $\mu = 1$. Then
$$f(x) = \begin{cases} e^{-x} & x \ge 0 \\ 0 & \text{otherwise} \end{cases}$$
and the mean is
$$\mu = 1.$$
Thus, $P(X \le 1) = \displaystyle\int_0^1 e^{-x}\,dx = -e^{-x}\Big|_0^1 = -e^{-1} + 1 = 1 - e^{-1} \approx .632.$

19. X is uniformly distributed on $[-5, 5]$. The mean is
$$\mu = \frac{1}{2}(-5 + 5) = 0$$
and the standard deviation is
$$\sigma = \frac{1}{\sqrt{12}}[5 - (-5)] = \frac{10}{\sqrt{12}} = \frac{5}{\sqrt{3}} \approx 2.887.$$
Also,
$$f(x) = \begin{cases} \dfrac{1}{10} & -5 \le x \le 5 \\ 0 & \text{otherwise} \end{cases}$$
Thus, $P(\mu - \sigma \le X \le \mu + \sigma) = P\left(\dfrac{-5}{\sqrt{3}} \le X \le \dfrac{5}{\sqrt{3}}\right) = \displaystyle\int_{-5/\sqrt{3}}^{5/\sqrt{3}} f(x)\,dx = \int_{-5/\sqrt{3}}^{5/\sqrt{3}} \frac{1}{10}\,dx$
$$= \frac{1}{10}x\Big|_{-5\sqrt{3}}^{5/\sqrt{3}} = \frac{1}{10}\left(\frac{5}{\sqrt{3}}\right) - \frac{1}{10}\left(\frac{-5}{\sqrt{3}}\right) = \frac{1}{\sqrt{3}} \approx .577.$$

21. X is an exponential random variable with median $x_m = 6 \ln 2$. Since $x_m = \lambda \ln 2$, we have $\lambda = 6$. Thus, mean $\mu = 6$ and standard deviation $\sigma = 6$. Also,
$$f(x) = \begin{cases} \dfrac{1}{6}e^{-x/6} & x \ge 0 \\ 0 & \text{otherwise} \end{cases}$$
Now, $P(\mu - \sigma \le X \le \mu + \sigma) = P(0 \le X \le 12) = \displaystyle\int_0^{12} f(x)\,dx = \int_0^{12} \frac{1}{6}e^{-x/6}\,dx$
$$= -e^{-x/6}\Big|_0^{12} = -e^{-2} + 1 \approx .865.$$

23. X is a beta random variable with mean $\mu = \frac{3}{5}$. Thus,

$$\frac{\beta + 1}{\beta + 3} = \frac{3}{5}$$

$$5\beta + 5 = 3\beta + 9$$

$$2\beta = 4$$

$$\beta = 2$$

Now, $f(x) = \begin{cases} 12x^2(1 - x) & 0 \le x \le 1 \\ 0 & \text{otherwise} \end{cases}$

and $P(X \le \mu) = P\left(X \le \frac{3}{5}\right) = \int_0^{3/5} f(x)\,dx = \int_0^{3/5} 12x^2(1 - x)\,dx$

$$= \int_0^{3/5} (12x^2 - 12x^3)\,dx = (4x^3 - 3x^4)\Big|_0^{3/5} = 4\left(\frac{3}{5}\right)^3 - 3\left(\frac{3}{5}\right)^4$$

$$= \left(\frac{3}{5}\right)^3\left[4 - \frac{9}{5}\right] = \frac{297}{625} \approx .475.$$

25. From Section 12-5,

$$\mu = \int_{-\infty}^{\infty} xf(x)\,dx,$$

where

$$f(x) = \begin{cases} \dfrac{1}{b - a} & a \le x \le b \\ 0 & \text{otherwise} \end{cases}$$

Thus,

$$\mu = \int_a^b x\left(\frac{1}{b - a}\right)dx = \frac{1}{b - a}\int_a^b x\,dx = \frac{1}{b - a} \cdot \frac{x^2}{2}\Big|_a^b = \frac{1}{b - a}\left(\frac{b^2}{2} - \frac{a^2}{2}\right)$$

$$= \frac{1}{b - a} \cdot \frac{1}{2}(b - a)(b + a) = \frac{a + b}{2}.$$

27. $\displaystyle\int_{-\infty}^{\infty} x^2 f(x)\,dx = \int_a^b x^2\left(\frac{1}{b - a}\right)dx = \frac{1}{b - a} \cdot \frac{x^3}{3}\Big|_a^b = \frac{1}{3} \cdot \frac{1}{b - a}(b^3 - a^3)$

$$= \frac{1}{3} \cdot \frac{1}{b - a}(b - a)(b^2 + ab + a^2) = \frac{1}{3}(b^2 + ab + a^2)$$

29. For $\beta = 2$, the cumulative probability distribution is:

$$F(x) = \begin{cases} 0 & x < 0 \\ 4x^3 - 3x^4 & 0 \le x \le 1 \\ 1 & x > 1 \end{cases}$$

To find the median x_m, we solve the equation $F(x_m) = \frac{1}{2}$ for x_m.

The graphs of F and $y = \frac{1}{2}$ are shown at the right.

Thus, the median $x_m \approx 0.61$.

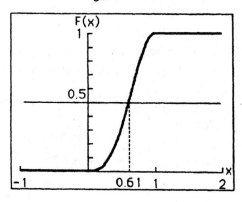

31. For $\beta = 4$, the cumulative probability distribution is:

$$F(x) = \begin{cases} 0 & x < 0 \\ 6x^5 - 5x^6 & 0 \leq x \leq 1 \\ 1 & x > 1 \end{cases}$$

To find the median x_m, we solve the equation $F(x_m) = \frac{1}{2}$ for x_m. The graphs of F and $y = \frac{1}{2}$ are shown below:

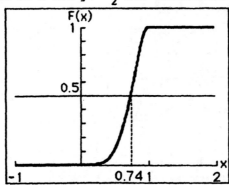

Thus, the median $x_m \approx 0.74$.

33. Using the uniform cumulative probability distribution function:

$$\begin{aligned} P(25 \leq X \leq 40) &= F(40) - F(25) \\ &= \frac{40 - 0}{40 - 0} - \frac{25 - 0}{40 - 0} \quad \text{[\underline{Note}: } a = 0, \ b = 40.\text{]} \\ &= 1 - \frac{25}{40} = \frac{15}{40} = \frac{3}{8} = .375 \end{aligned}$$

35. X is a beta random variable with $\beta = 2$.

(A) $\mu = E(X) = \frac{\beta + 1}{\beta + 3} = \frac{3}{5} = .6$ or 60%.

(B) $P(X \geq .8) = \displaystyle\int_{.8}^{\infty} f(x)\,dx = 1 - \int_{-\infty}^{.8} f(x)\,dx = 1 - F(.8),$

where F is the cumulative probability distribution

$$F(x) = \begin{cases} 0 & x < 0 \\ 4x^3 - 3x^4 & 0 \leq x \leq 1 \\ 1 & x > 1 \end{cases}$$

Thus, $P(X \geq .8) = 1 - [4(.8)^3 - 3(.8)^4]$
$$= 1 + 3(.8)^4 - 4(.8)^3 \approx .1808.$$

37. (A) $\mu = 50\% = .5$. Also $\mu = \frac{\beta + 1}{\beta + 3}$. Thus,

$$.5 = \frac{\beta + 1}{\beta + 3}$$
$$.5\beta + 1.5 = \beta + 1$$
$$\beta = 1$$

(B) $P(0 \leq X \leq .75) = F(.75) - F(0)$
$$= [(1 + 2)(.75)^{1+1} - (1 + 1)(.75)^{1+2}] - 0$$
$$= 3\left(\frac{3}{4}\right)^2 - 2\left(\frac{3}{4}\right)^3 = \frac{27}{16} - \frac{27}{32} = \frac{27}{32} \approx .844$$

39. We are given that $\mu = 3$. Also $\lambda = \mu$. Thus, $\lambda = 3$, and we have:
$$P(0 \leq X \leq 2) = F(2) - F(0) = (1 - e^{-2/3}) - (1 - e^0)$$
$$= 1 - e^{-2/3} \approx .487$$

41. X is an exponential random variable and the median $x_m = 2$. Since $x_m = \lambda \ln 2$, we have $2 = \lambda \ln 2$ or $\lambda = \frac{2}{\ln 2}$. Now $P(X \leq 1) = F(1)$, where F is the cumulative probability distribution:
$$F(x) = \begin{cases} 1 - e^{-x/\lambda} & x \geq 0 \\ 0 & \text{otherwise} \end{cases}$$

Setting $\lambda = \frac{2}{\ln 2}$, we have
$$F(x) = \begin{cases} 1 - e^{-(x \ln 2)/2} & x \geq 0 \\ 0 & \text{otherwise} \end{cases}$$

Thus, $P(X \leq 1) = 1 - e^{-(\ln 2)/2} = 1 - e^{-(1/2)\ln 2}$
$$= 1 - e^{\ln (2)^{-1/2}}$$
$$= 1 - 2^{-1/2}$$
$$= 1 - \frac{1}{\sqrt{2}} \approx .293.$$

43. (A) $E(X) = \mu = \frac{\beta + 1}{\beta + 3} = \frac{.2 + 1}{.2 + 3} = \frac{1.2}{3.2} = \frac{3}{8} = 37.5\%$ of vitamin D per serving

(B) $P(.5 \leq X \leq 1) = F(1) - F(.5)$
$$= [(.2 + 2)(1)^{.2+1} - (.2 + 1)(1)^{.2+2}]$$
$$- [(.2 + 2)(.5)^{.2+1} - (.2 + 1)(.5)^{.2+2}]$$
$$= 1 - [(2.2)(.5)^{1.2} - (1.2)(.5)^{2.2}] \approx .304$$

45. X is a beta random with mean $\mu = .95$.

(A) β satisfies $\frac{\beta + 1}{\beta + 3} = \mu = .95$. Thus, $\beta + 1 = .95\beta + 2.85$
$$.05\beta = 1.85$$
$$\beta = 37$$

(B) $P(X \geq .9) = 1 - F(.9)$, where F is the cumulative probability distribution. Therefore
$$P(X \geq .9) = 1 - [39(.9)^{38} - 38(.9)^{39}]$$
$$= 1 - 39(.9)^{38} + 38(.9)^{39} \approx .912.$$

47. (A) We are given that
$$P(0 \leq X \leq 1) = .3 = F(1) - F(0) = 1 - e^{-1/\lambda} - (1 - e^0).$$
Thus,
$$1 - e^{-1/\lambda} = .3$$
$$e^{-1/\lambda} = .7$$

$$-\frac{1}{\lambda} = \ln(.7)$$

$$\lambda = -\frac{1}{\ln(.7)}$$

But $E(X) = \mu = \lambda = -\frac{1}{\ln(.7)} \approx 2.8$ years.

(B) $P(X \geq 2.8) = \int_{2.8}^{\infty} f(x)\,dx = \lim_{R \to \infty} \int_{2.8}^{R} \frac{1}{\lambda} e^{-x/\lambda}\,dx$

$$= \lim_{R \to \infty} \int_{2.8}^{R} \frac{1}{2.8} e^{-x/2.8}\,dx = \lim_{R \to \infty} \frac{1}{2.8} (-2.8 e^{-x/2.8}) \Big|_{2.8}^{R}$$

$$= \lim_{R \to \infty} (-e^{-R/2.8} + e^{-2.8/2.8})$$

$$= e^{-1} \approx .368$$

49. (A) $E(X) = \mu = \frac{\beta + 1}{\beta + 3} = \frac{17 + 1}{17 + 3} = \frac{18}{20} = .90$ or 90%.

(B) $P(X \geq .95) = 1 - F(.95)$
$$= 1 - [(17 + 2)(.95)^{17+1} - (17 + 1)(.95)^{17+2}]$$
$$= 1 - 19(.95)^{18} + 18(.95)^{19} \approx .245$$

$$\left[\underline{\text{Note}}: P(X \geq .95) = P(.95 \leq X \leq 1) = \int_{.95}^{1} f(x)\,dx. \right]$$

51. X is an exponential random variable with mean $\mu = 2$ (minutes). Thus, $\lambda = 2$ and

$$P(X \geq 5) = \int_{5}^{\infty} f(x)\,dx = \int_{5}^{\infty} \frac{1}{2} e^{-x/2}\,dx = \lim_{R \to \infty} \int_{5}^{R} \frac{1}{2} e^{-x/2}\,dx = \lim_{R \to \infty} (-e^{-x/2}) \Big|_{5}^{R}$$

$$= \lim_{R \to \infty} (-e^{-R/5} + e^{-5/2}) = e^{-5/2} = e^{-2.5} \approx .082.$$

EXERCISE 10-7

Things to remember:

<u>1</u>. NORMAL PROBABILITY DENSITY FUNCTION

$$f(x) = \frac{1}{\sigma \sqrt{2\pi}} e^{-(x-\mu)^2/2\sigma^2}, \quad \sigma > 0$$

Mean: μ
Median: μ
Standard Deviation: σ

The graph of f is symmetric with respect to the line $x = \mu$.

<u>2</u>. The normal random variable Z with mean $\mu = 0$ and standard deviation $\sigma = 1$ is called the STANDARD NORMAL RANDOM VARIABLE and the graph of its probability density function is called the STANDARD NORMAL CURVE.

3. If X is a normal random variable with mean μ and standard deviation σ, Z is the standard random variable, and

$$z_i = \frac{x_i - \mu}{\sigma}, \; i = 1, 2,$$

then $P(x_1 \le X \le x_2) = P(z_1 \le Z \le z_2)$
$P(x_1 \le X) = P(z_1 \le Z)$
$P(X \le x_2) = P(Z \le z_2)$

4. "RULE-OF-THUMB TEST" FOR APPROXIMATING A BINOMIAL DISTRIBUTION

Use a normal distribution to approximate a binomial distribution only if the interval $[\mu - 3\sigma, \; \mu + 3\sigma]$ lies entirely in the interval from 0 to n.

---

1. From Table III in the text, the area under the standard normal curve between $z = 0$ and $z = 1$ is $A = .3413$.

3. The standard normal curve is symmetric with respect to the line $x = 0$. Thus, the area under the curve between $z = 0$ and $z = -3$ is the same as the area between $z = 0$ and $z = 3$. $A = .4987$.

5. From Table III, for $z = .9$, $A = .3159$.

7. From Table III, for $z = 2.47$, $A = .4932$.

9. By Theorem 4, $z = \dfrac{65 - 60}{10} = 1.5$ 11. $z = \dfrac{83 - 50}{10} = 3.3$

From Table III, we have the area corresponding to $z = 1.5$ is .4332.

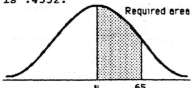

From Table III, the area corresponding to $z = 3.3$ is .4995.

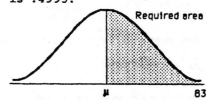

13. $z = \dfrac{45 - 50}{10} = -.5$ 15. $z = \dfrac{42 - 50}{10} = -.8$

From Table III, the area corresponding to $z = .5$ is .1915.

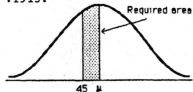

From Table III, the area corresponding to $z = .8$ is .2981.

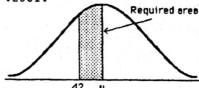

17.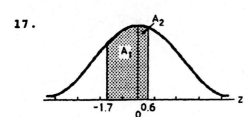

$P(-1.7 \leq Z \leq .6) = A_1 + A_2$
For area A_1, let $z = 1.7$. Thus,
$A_1 = .4554$. For area A_2, $z = .6$ and
$A_2 = .2257$. Thus,
$P(-1.7 \leq Z \leq .6) = .6811$.

19.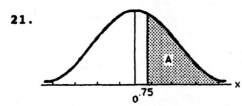

$P(.45 \leq Z \leq 2.25) = $ area A.
Let A_1 be the area of the region over the
interval [0, .45] and let A_2 be the area
of the region over the interval [0, 2.25].
Then $A_1 = .1736$ and $A_2 = .4878$. Thus,
$P(.45 \leq Z \leq 2.25) = $ area $A = A_2 - A_1 = .3142$.

21.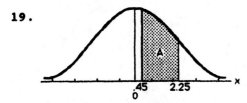

$P(Z \geq .75) = $ area A.
Let $A_1 = $ area of the region over the
interval $(-\infty, 0]$ and $A_2 = $ area of the
region over the interval [0, .75].
Then $A_1 = .5$ and $A_2 = .2734$. Now area
$A = 1 - (A_1 + A_2) = 1 - .7734 = .2266$.
Thus,
$P(Z \geq .75) = .2266$.

23.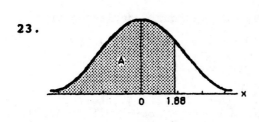

$P(Z \leq 1.88) = $ area A.
Let $A_1 = $ area of the region over the
interval $(-\infty, 0]$ and let $A_2 = $ the area of
the region over the interval [0, 1.88].
Then $A_1 = .5$ and $A_2 = .4699$. Now
$A = A_1 + A_2 = .9699$. Thus,
$P(Z \leq 1.88) = .9699$.

25. $\mu = 70$, $\sigma = 8$

z (for $x = 60$) $= \dfrac{60 - 70}{8} = -1.25$

z (for $x = 80$) $= \dfrac{80 - 70}{8} = 1.25$

Area $A_1 = .3944$. Area $A_2 = .3944$.
Total area $= A = A_1 + A_2 = .7888$.

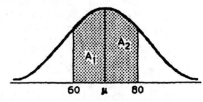

27. $\mu = 70$, $\sigma = 8$

z (for $x = 62$) $= \dfrac{62 - 70}{8} = -1.00$

z (for $x = 74$) $= \dfrac{74 - 70}{8} = .5$

Area $A_1 = .3413$. Area $A_2 = .1915$.
Total area $= A = A_1 + A_2 = .5328$.

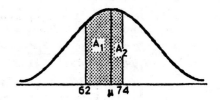

29. $\mu = 70$, $\sigma = 8$

z (for $x = 88$) $= \dfrac{88 - 70}{8} = 2.25$

Required area $= .5 - \begin{array}{l}\text{(area corresponding to} \\ z = 2.25)\end{array}$

$= .5 - .4878$

$= .0122$

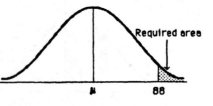

Required area

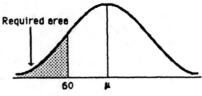

31. $\mu = 70$, $\sigma = 8$

z (for $x = 60$) $= \dfrac{60 - 70}{8} = -1.25$

Required area $= .5 - \begin{array}{l}\text{(area corresponding to} \\ z = 1.25)\end{array}$

$= .5 - .3944$

$= .1056$

33. With $n = 15$, $p = .7$, and $q = .3$, the mean and standard deviation of the binomial distribution are:

$\mu = np = 10.5$

$\sigma = \sqrt{npq} = \sqrt{(15)(.7)(.3)} \approx 1.8$

$[\mu - 3\sigma, \mu + 3\sigma] = [5.1, 15.9]$

Since this interval is not contained in the interval $[0, 15]$, the normal distribution should not be used to approximate the binomial distribution.

35. With $n = 15$, $p = .4$, and $q = .6$, the mean and standard deviation of the binomial distribution are:

$\mu = np = 15(.4) = 6$

$\sigma = \sqrt{npq} = \sqrt{15(.4)(.6)} \approx 1.9$

$[\mu - 3\sigma, \mu + 3\sigma] = [.3, 11.7]$

Since this interval is contained in the interval $[0, 15]$, the normal distribution *is* a suitable approximation for the binomial distribution.

37. With $n = 100$, $p = .05$, and $q = .95$, the mean and standard deviation of the binomial distribution are:

$\mu = np = 100(.05) = 5$

$\sigma = \sqrt{npq} = \sqrt{100(.05)(.95)} \approx 2.2$

$[\mu - 3\sigma, \mu + 3\sigma] = [-1.6, 11.6]$

Since this interval is not contained in the interval $[0, 100]$, the normal distribution is *not* a suitable approximation for the binomial distribution.

39. With $n = 500$, $p = .05$, and $q = .95$, the mean and standard deviation of the binomial distribution are:

$\mu = np = 500(.05) = 25$

$\sigma = \sqrt{npq} = \sqrt{500(.05)(.95)} \approx 4.9$

$[\mu - 3\sigma, \mu + 3\sigma] = [10.3, 39.7]$

Since this interval is contained in the interval $[0, 500]$, the normal distribution *is* a suitable approximation for the binomial distribution.

In *Problems 41–47*, $\mu = 500(.4) = 200$, and $\sigma = \sqrt{npq} = \sqrt{500(.4)(.6)} \approx 10.95$.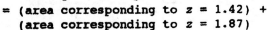
The intervals are adjusted as in Examples 33 and 34.

41. z (for $x = 184.5$) $= \dfrac{184.5 - 200}{10.95} \approx -1.42$

z (for $x = 220.5$) $= \dfrac{220.5 - 200}{10.95} \approx 1.87$

Thus, the probability that the number of successes will be between 185 and 220
= area A_1 + area A_2
= (area corresponding to $z = 1.42$) + (area corresponding to $z = 1.87$)
= .4222 + .4693
= .8915
$\approx$ .89

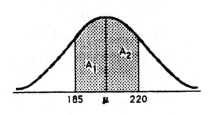

43. z (for $x = 209.5$) $= \dfrac{209.5 - 200}{10.95} \approx .87$

z (for $x = 220.5$) $= \dfrac{220.5 - 200}{10.95} \approx 1.87$

Thus, the probability that the number of successes will be between 210 and 220
= area A
= (area corresponding to $z = 1.87$) − (area corresponding to $z = .87$)
= .4693 − .3078
= .1615
$\approx$ .16

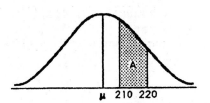

45. z (for $x = 224.5$) $= \dfrac{224.5 - 200}{10.95} \approx 2.24$

The probability that the number of successes will be 225 or more
= area A
= .5 − (area corresponding to $z = 2.24$)
= .5 − .4875
= .0125
$\approx$ .01

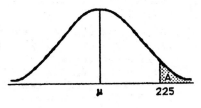

47. z (for $x = 175.5$) $= \dfrac{175.5 - 200}{10.95} \approx -2.24$

The probability that the number of successes will be 175 or less
= area A
= .5 − (area corresponding to $z = 2.24$)
= .5 − .4875
= .0125
$\approx$ .01

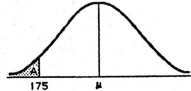

49. Let $f(x) = \dfrac{1}{5\sqrt{2\pi}} e^{-(x-\mu)^2/50}$

The graphs of f with:
(A) $\mu = 10$,
(B) $\mu = 15$, and
(C) $\mu = 20$, and
x range = $[-10, 40]$,
y range = $[0, 0.1]$
are shown at the right.

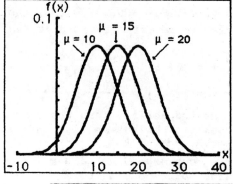

51. Let $f(x) = \dfrac{1}{\sigma\sqrt{2\pi}} e^{-(x-20)^2/2\sigma^2}$

The graphs of f with:
(A) $\sigma = 2$, and
(B) $\sigma = 4$, and
x range = $[0, 40]$,
y range = $[0, 0.2]$
are shown at the right.

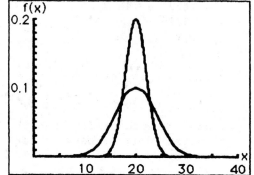

53. $\mu = 200{,}000$, $\sigma = 20{,}000$, $x \geq 240{,}000$

z (for $x = 240{,}000$) $= \dfrac{240{,}000 - 200{,}000}{20{,}000} = 2.0$

Fraction of the salesmen who would be expected to make annual sales of $240,000 or more

$= \text{Area } A_1$

$= .5 - (\text{area between } \mu \text{ and } 240{,}000)$
$= .5 - .4772$
$= .0228$

Thus, the percentage of salesmen expected to make annual sales of $240,000 or more is 2.28%.

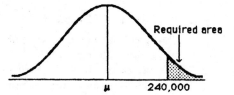

55. $x = 105$, $x = 95$, $\mu = 100$, $\sigma = 2$

z (for $x = 105$) $= \dfrac{105 - 100}{2} = 2.5$

z (for $x = 95$) $= \dfrac{95 - 100}{2} = -2.5$

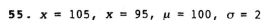

Fraction of parts to be rejected $= \text{Area } A_1 + A_2$

$= 1 - 2(\text{area corresponding to } z = 2.5)$
$= 1 - 2(.4938)$
$= .0124$

Thus, the percentage of parts to be rejected is 1.24%.

586

57. With $n = 40$, $p = .6$, and $q = .4$, the mean and standard deviation of the binomial distribution are:

$\mu = np = 40(.6) = 24$

$\sigma = \sqrt{npq} = \sqrt{40(.6)(.4)} \approx 3.10$

z (for $x = 15.5$) $= \dfrac{15.5 - 24}{3.1} = -2.74$

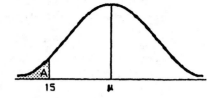

The probability that 15 or fewer households use the product

= area A

= .5 − (area corresponding to $z = 2.74$)

= .5 − .4969

= .0031

Either a rare event has occurred, e.g., the sample was not random, or the company's claim is false.

59. $\mu = 240$, $\sigma = 20$

8 days = 192 hours = x

z (for $x = 192$) $= \dfrac{192 - 240}{20} = -2.4$

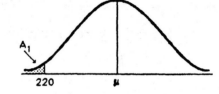

Fraction of people having this incision who would heal in 192 hours or less = Area A_1

= .5 − (area corresponding to $z = 2.4$)

= .5 − .4918

= .0082

Thus, the percentage of people who would heal in 8 days or less is 0.82%.

61. $p = .25$, $q = .75$, $n = 1000$

$\mu = np = (1000)(.25) = 250$

$\sigma = \sqrt{npq} = \sqrt{1000 \times .25 \times .75}$

$\approx 13.693 \approx 13.69$

$x = 220.5$ or less

z (for $x = 220.5$) $= \dfrac{220.5 - 250}{13.69} \approx -2.15$

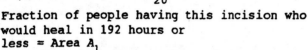

Probability that 220.5 or less will have two girls = Area A_1

= .5 − (area corresponding to $z = 2.15$)

= .5 − .4842

= .0158

63. $\mu = 500$, $\sigma = 100$, $x = 700$ or more

z (for $x = 700$) $= \dfrac{700 - 500}{100} = 2$

Fraction of students who should score 700 or more = Area A_1

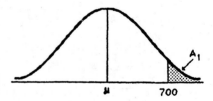

= .5 − (area corresponding to $z = 2$)

= .5 − .4722

= .0228

Thus, 2.28% should score 700 or more.

65. $\mu = 70$, $\sigma = 8$

We compute x_1, x_2, x_3, and x_4 corresponding to z_1, z_2, z_3, and z_4, respectively. The area between μ and x_3 is .2.

Hence, from the table, $z_3 = .52$ (approximately). Thus, we have:

$$.52 = \frac{x_3 - 70}{8}$$

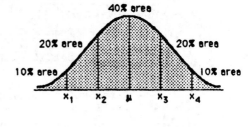

$$x_3 - 70 = 4.16 \left[\underline{\text{Note}}: z = \frac{x - \mu}{\sigma}.\right] \approx 4.2$$

and $x_3 = 74.2$.

Also, $x_2 = 70 - 4.2 = 65.8$

The area between μ and x_4 is .4. Hence, from the table, $z_4 = 1.28$ (approximately). Therefore:

$$1.28 = \frac{x_4 - 70}{8}$$

$x_4 - 70 = 10.24 \approx 10.2$

and $x_4 = 70 + 10.2 = 80.2$.

Also, $x_1 = 70 - 10.2 = 59.8$.

Thus, we have $x_1 = 59.8$, $x_2 = 65.8$, $x_3 = 74.2$, $x_4 = 80.2$. So, A's = 80.2 or greater, B's = 74.2 to 80.2, C's = 65.8 to 74.2, D's = 59.8 to 65.8, and F's = 59.8 or lower.

EXERCISE 10-8   CHAPTER REVIEW

1. Sample space = $S = \{1, 2, 3, 4\}$
Probability distribution:

x_i	p_i
1	$\frac{1}{8}$
2	$\frac{2}{8}$
3	$\frac{3}{8}$
4	$\frac{2}{8}$

2. Event A: Spinner stops on an even number.

$$P(A) = P(2) + P(4)$$
$$= \frac{2}{8} + \frac{2}{8} = \frac{4}{8} = .5$$

3. $E(X) = x_1 p_1 + x_2 p_2 + x_3 p_3 + x_4 p_4$

$$= 1 \cdot \frac{1}{8} + 2 \cdot \frac{2}{8} + 3 \cdot \frac{3}{8} + 4 \cdot \frac{2}{8} \quad \text{(refer to Problem 1)}$$

$$= \frac{22}{8} = \frac{11}{4} = 2.75$$

$$V(X) = (1 - 2.75)^2 \cdot \frac{1}{8} + (2 - 2.75)^2 \cdot \frac{2}{8} + (3 - 2.75)^2 \cdot \frac{3}{8} + (4 - 2.75)^2 \cdot \frac{2}{8}$$

$$= \frac{15}{16} = .9375$$

$$\sigma = \sqrt{V(X)} = \sqrt{\frac{15}{16}} = \frac{\sqrt{15}}{4} \approx .9682$$

4. This is a Bernoulli experiment with $p = q = \frac{1}{2}$, and $n = 6$

$$P(\text{exactly 2 heads}) = C_{6,2}\left(\frac{1}{2}\right)^2\left(\frac{1}{2}\right)^6 = \frac{8!}{2!6!}\left(\frac{1}{2}\right)^8$$
$$= \frac{28}{256} = \frac{7}{64}$$

5. (A) $P(x) = C_{3,x}(.4)^x(.6)^{3-x}$ (B) $\mu = np = 3(.4) = 1.2$

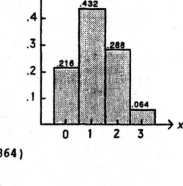

$$\sigma = \sqrt{npq} = \sqrt{3 \times .4 \times .6} \approx .85$$

x	$P(x)$
0	.216
1	.432
2	.288
3	.064

The histogram for this distribution is shown at the right.

6. $n = 500$, $p = .004$

Binomial: $P(3) = C_{500,3}(.004)^3(.996)^{497}$

$$= \frac{500!}{3!497!}(.004)^3(.996)^{497}$$
$$\approx \frac{500 \cdot 499 \cdot 498}{6}(6.4 \times 10^{-8})(.1364)$$
$$\approx .1808$$

Poisson: $\lambda = 500(.004) = 2$

$$P(3) = \frac{2^3}{3!}e^{-2} = \frac{8}{6}e^{-2} \approx .1804$$

7. $\lambda = \mu = 4$

$$P(0 \leq X \leq 1) = P(0) + P(1)$$
$$= e^{-4}\left(\frac{4^0}{0!} + \frac{4^1}{1!}\right) = e^{-4}(5) \approx .0916$$

$$P(X > 2) = 1 - P(0 \leq X \leq 2)$$
$$= 1 - [P(0) + P(1) + P(2)]$$
$$= 1 - e^{-4}\left(\frac{4^0}{0!} + \frac{4^1}{1!} + \frac{4^2}{2!}\right)$$
$$= 1 - e^{-4}(13) \approx .7619$$

8. $P(0 \leq X \leq 1) = \int_0^1 \left(1 - \frac{1}{2}x\right)dx$

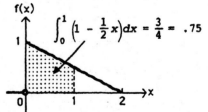

$$= \left(x - \frac{1}{4}x^2\right)\Big|_0^1$$
$$= 1 - \frac{1}{4} = .75$$

The graph of the function is given at the right.

9. $\mu = E(X) = \int_{-\infty}^{\infty} xf(x)\,dx = \int_0^2 x\left(1 - \frac{1}{2}x\right)dx = \int_0^2 \left(x - \frac{1}{2}x^2\right)dx$

$= \left(\frac{x^2}{2} - \frac{1}{6}x^3\right)\Big|_0^2 = 2 - \frac{8}{6} = \frac{2}{3} \approx .6667$

$V(X) = \int_{-\infty}^{\infty} x^2 f(x)\,dx - \mu^2 = \int_0^2 x^2\left(1 - \frac{1}{2}x\right)dx - \left(\frac{2}{3}\right)^2$

$= \int_0^2 \left(x^2 - \frac{1}{2}x^3\right)dx - \frac{4}{9} = \left(\frac{x^3}{3} - \frac{1}{8}x^4\right)\Big|_0^2 - \frac{4}{9}$

$= \frac{8}{3} - \frac{16}{8} - \frac{4}{9} = \frac{16}{72} = \frac{2}{9} \approx .2222$

$\sigma = \sqrt{V(X)} = \sqrt{\frac{2}{9}} = \frac{\sqrt{2}}{3} \approx .4714$

10. When $x < 0$, then $F(x) = 0$. When $0 \le x \le 2$,

$F(x) = \int_{-\infty}^{x} f(t)\,dt = \int_{-\infty}^{0} f(t)\,dt + \int_0^x f(t)\,dt = 0 + \int_0^x \left(1 - \frac{1}{2}t\right)dt$

$= \left(t - \frac{1}{4}t^2\right)\Big|_0^x = x - \frac{1}{4}x^2.$

When $x > 2$,

$F(x) = \int_{-\infty}^{x} f(t)\,dt = \int_{-\infty}^{0} f(t)\,dt + \int_0^2 f(t)\,dt + \int_2^x f(t)\,dt$

$= 0 + \int_0^2 \left(1 - \frac{1}{2}t\right)dt + 0 = \left(t - \frac{1}{4}t^2\right)\Big|_0^2 = 2 - \frac{1}{4}\cdot 4 = 1.$

Thus,

$$F(x) = \begin{cases} 0 & x < 0 \\ x - \frac{1}{4}x^2 & 0 \le x \le 2 \\ 1 & x > 2 \end{cases}$$

The graph of $F(x)$ is shown at the right.

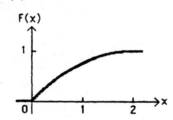

11. We must solve the following for x_m:

$F(x_m) = P(X \le x_m) = \frac{1}{2}$

$x_m - \frac{1}{4}x_m^2 = \frac{1}{2}$ (refer to Problem 10)

$x_m^2 - 4x_m + 2 = 0$

$x_m = \frac{4 \pm \sqrt{16 - 4(2)}}{2} = \frac{4 \pm \sqrt{8}}{2}$

$x_m = 2 \pm \sqrt{2}$

Thus, the median is $x = 2 - \sqrt{2} \approx .5858$.

12.

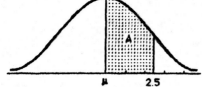

$P(0 \leq Z \leq 2.5) =$ area A
$= .4938$ (from Table III).

13. $\mu = 100$, $\sigma = 10$, $x = 118$.

$z = \dfrac{118 - 100}{10} = 1.8$

$P(100 \leq X \leq 118) = P(0 \leq Z \leq 1.8) =$ area of region over the interval $[0, 1.8]$
$= .4641$ (from Table I).

14. (A) $P(x) = C_{6,x}(.5)^x(.5)^{6-x}$

x	$P(x)$
0	.016
1	.094
2	.234
3	.313
4	.234
5	.094
6	.016

The histogram for this
distribution is shown
at the right.

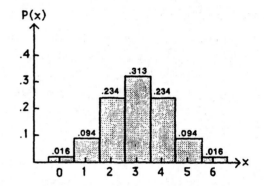

(B) Mean $= \mu = np = 6 \times .5 = 3$

Standard deviation $= \sigma = \sqrt{npq} = \sqrt{6 \times .5 \times .5} \approx 1.225$

15. $n = 117$, $p = \dfrac{1}{13}$. Thus, $\lambda = \dfrac{117}{13} = 9$

$P(5) = \dfrac{9^5}{5!}e^{-9} = \dfrac{59,049}{120}e^{-9} \approx .0607$

16. $P(1 \leq X \leq 4) = \displaystyle\int_1^4 \frac{5}{2}x^{-7/2}\,dx$

$= \dfrac{5}{2}\left(-\dfrac{2}{5}\right)x^{-5/2}\Big|_1^4$

$= -[(4)^{-5/2} - (1)^{-5/2}]$

$= -\left(\dfrac{1}{32} - 1\right) = \dfrac{31}{32}$

$\approx .9688$

The graph is shown at the right.

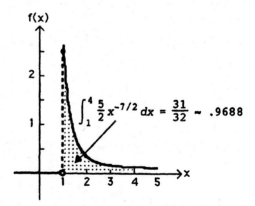

$\displaystyle\int_1^4 \frac{5}{2}x^{-7/2}\,dx = \frac{31}{32} \approx .9688$

17. $\mu = E(X) = \int_{-\infty}^{\infty} x f(x)\,dx = \int_{1}^{\infty} x \cdot \frac{5}{2} x^{-7/2}\,dx$

$\qquad = \lim_{R\to\infty} \int_{1}^{R} \frac{5}{2} x^{-5/2}\,dx = \lim_{R\to\infty}\left(\frac{5}{2}\left(-\frac{2}{3}\right) x^{-3/2}\Big|_{1}^{R}\right)$

$\qquad = -\frac{5}{3} \lim_{R\to\infty}(R^{-3/2} - 1^{-3/2}) = -\frac{5}{3}(-1) = \frac{5}{3} \approx 1.667$

$\quad V(X) = \int_{-\infty}^{\infty} x^2 f(x)\,dx - \mu^2 = \int_{1}^{\infty} x^2 \cdot \frac{5}{2} x^{-7/2}\,dx - \left(\frac{5}{3}\right)^2$

$\qquad = \lim_{R\to\infty} \int_{1}^{R} \frac{5}{2} x^{-3/2}\,dx - \frac{25}{9} = \lim_{R\to\infty}\left(\frac{5}{2}(-2)x^{-1/2}\Big|_{1}^{R}\right) - \frac{25}{9}$

$\qquad = -5 \lim_{R\to\infty}[R^{-1/2} - (1)^{-1/2}] - \frac{25}{9} = -5(-1) - \frac{25}{9} = 5 - \frac{25}{9} = \frac{20}{9} \approx 2.222$

$\quad \sigma = \sqrt{V(X)} = \sqrt{\frac{20}{9}} = \frac{2}{3}\sqrt{5} \approx 1.491$

18. When $x < 1$, $F(x) = 0$. When $x \geq 1$,

$\quad F(x) = \int_{-\infty}^{x} f(t)\,dt = \int_{-\infty}^{1} f(t)\,dt + \int_{1}^{x} f(t)\,dt = 0 + \int_{1}^{x} \frac{5}{2} t^{-7/2}\,dt$

$\qquad = \frac{5}{2}\left(-\frac{2}{5}\right) t^{-5/2}\Big|_{1}^{x} = -(x^{-5/2} - 1^{-5/2}) = 1 - x^{-5/2}.$

Thus,

$\quad F(x) = \begin{cases} 1 - x^{-5/2} & x \geq 1 \\ 0 & \text{otherwise} \end{cases}$

The graph of $F(x)$ is shown at the right.

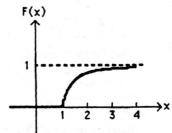

19. We must solve the following for x_m:

$\quad F(x_m) = P(X \leq x_m) = \frac{1}{2}$

$\qquad 1 - x_m^{-5/2} = \frac{1}{2}$ (refer to Problem 18)

$\qquad\qquad x_m^{-5/2} = \frac{1}{2}$

$\qquad\qquad \frac{1}{x_m^{-5/2}} = \frac{1}{2}$

$\qquad\qquad x_m^{-5/2} = 2$ (square both sides)

$\qquad\qquad x_m^{-5/2} = 4$

$\qquad\qquad\quad x_m = (4)^{1/5}$

$\qquad\qquad\quad x_m = 2^{2/5} \approx 1.32$

20. $f(x) = \begin{cases} (\beta + 1)(\beta + 2)x^{\beta}(1 - x) & 0 \leq x \leq 1 \\ 0 & \text{otherwise} \end{cases}$

Since $\beta = 5$, we have:

$f(x) = \begin{cases} (5 + 1)(5 + 2)x^5(1 - x) & 0 \leq x \leq 1 \\ 0 & \text{otherwise} \end{cases}$

$= \begin{cases} 42x^5(1 - x) & 0 \leq x \leq 1 \\ 0 & \text{otherwise} \end{cases}$

The graph of $f(x)$ is shown at the right.

21. $P\left(\dfrac{1}{4} \leq X \leq \dfrac{3}{4}\right) = \displaystyle\int_{1/4}^{3/4} f(x)\,dx = \int_{.25}^{.75} 42x^5(1 - x)\,dx = 42\left(\dfrac{x^6}{6} - \dfrac{x^7}{7}\right)\Big|_{.25}^{.75}$

$= 42\left[\left(\dfrac{(.75)^6}{6} - \dfrac{(.75)^7}{7}\right) - \left(\dfrac{(.25)^6}{6} - \dfrac{(.25)^7}{7}\right)\right] \approx .4436$

22. $F(x) = \begin{cases} 0 & x < 0 \\ (\beta + 2)x^{\beta+1} - (\beta + 1)x^{\beta+2} & 0 \leq x \leq 1 \\ 1 & x > 1 \end{cases}$

$= \begin{cases} 0 & x < 0 \\ (5 + 2)x^{5+1} - (5 + 1)x^{5+2} & 0 \leq x \leq 1 \qquad (\beta = 5) \\ 1 & x > 1 \end{cases}$

$= \begin{cases} 0 & x < 0 \\ 7x^6 - 6x^7 & 0 \leq x \leq 1 \\ 1 & x > 1 \end{cases}$

The graph of $F(x)$ is shown at the right.

23. $\mu = \dfrac{\beta + 1}{\beta + 3} = \dfrac{5 + 1}{5 + 3} \qquad (\beta = 5)$

$= \dfrac{6}{8} = \dfrac{3}{4} = .75$

$\sigma = \sqrt{\dfrac{2(\beta + 1)}{(\beta + 4)(\beta + 3)^2}} = \sqrt{\dfrac{2(5 + 1)}{(5 + 4)(5 + 3)^2}}$

$= \sqrt{\dfrac{12}{9(64)}} = \sqrt{\dfrac{3}{144}} = \dfrac{\sqrt{3}}{12} \approx .1443$

24. $P(4 \leq X) = \displaystyle\int_4^{\infty} f(x)\,dx = e^{-2} \qquad \text{(Solve for } \lambda.\text{)}$

$= \displaystyle\int_4^{\infty} \dfrac{1}{\lambda} e^{-x/\lambda}\,dx = \lim_{R \to \infty} \dfrac{1}{\lambda} \int_4^R e^{-x/\lambda}\,dx = e^{-2}$

$= \lim_{R \to \infty} \dfrac{1}{\lambda} -\lambda e^{-x/\lambda} \Big|_4^R = -\lim_{R \to \infty} (e^{-R/\lambda} - e^{-4/\lambda}) = e^{-2}$

$= e^{-4/\lambda} = e^{-2}$

Thus, we have $-\dfrac{4}{\lambda} = -2$

$$\lambda = 2.$$

The probability density function, with $\lambda = 2$, is:

$$f(x) = \begin{cases} \dfrac{1}{\lambda} e^{-x/\lambda} & x \geq 0 \\ 0 & \text{otherwise} \end{cases} = \begin{cases} \dfrac{1}{2} e^{-x/2} & x \geq 0 \\ 0 & \text{otherwise} \end{cases}$$

25. $P(0 \leq X \leq 2) = \displaystyle\int_0^2 f(x)\,dx = \int_0^2 \dfrac{1}{2} e^{-x/2}\,dx$ (refer to Problem 24)

$$= \dfrac{1}{2}(-2e^{-x/2})\Big|_0^2 = -(e^{-2/2} - e^0)$$

$$= -(e^{-1} - 1) \text{ or } (1 - e^{-1}) \approx .6321$$

26. $F(x) = \begin{cases} 1 - e^{-x/\lambda} & x \geq 0 \\ 0 & \text{otherwise} \end{cases} = \begin{cases} 1 - e^{-x/2} & x \geq 0 \\ 0 & \text{otherwise} \end{cases}$ [Note: $\lambda = 2$.]

27. $\mu = \lambda = 2$

$\sigma = \lambda = 2$

$x_m = \lambda \ln 2 = 2 \ln 2$

28. $p = .6$, $q = .4$, $n = 1000$

$\mu = np = 1000 \times .6 = 600$

$\sigma = \sqrt{npq} = \sqrt{1000 \times .6 \times .4} = \sqrt{240}$

≈ 15.49

29. The mean μ and the standard deviation σ for the binomial distribution are:

$\mu = np = 1000 \times .6 = 600$

$\sigma = \sqrt{npq} = \sqrt{1000 \times .6 \times .4} \approx 15.49 \approx 15.5$

Now, we approximate the binomial distribution with a normal distribution.

z (for $x = 550$) $= \dfrac{549.5 - 600}{15.5} = -3.26$

z (for $x = 650$) $= \dfrac{650.5 - 600}{15.5} = 3.26$

The probability of obtaining successes between 550 and 650 = Area A

$= 2(\text{area corresponding to } z = 3.24)$

$= 2(.4994)$

$= .9988 \approx .999$

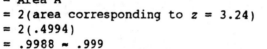
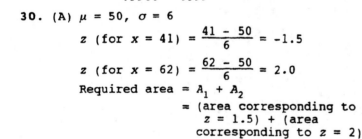

30. (A) $\mu = 50$, $\sigma = 6$

z (for $x = 41$) $= \dfrac{41 - 50}{6} = -1.5$

z (for $x = 62$) $= \dfrac{62 - 50}{6} = 2.0$

Required area $= A_1 + A_2$

$= (\text{area corresponding to } z = 1.5) + (\text{area corresponding to } z = 2)$

$= .4332 + .4772$

$= .9104$

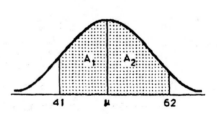

(B) z (for $x = 59$) $= \dfrac{59 - 50}{6} = 1.5$

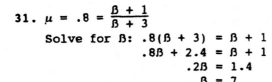

Required area $= .5 - \begin{array}{l}\text{(area corresponding to}\\ z = 1.5)\end{array}$

$= .5 - .4332$

$= .0668$

31. $\mu = .8 = \dfrac{\beta + 1}{\beta + 3}$

Solve for β: $\quad .8(\beta + 3) = \beta + 1$

$.8\beta + 2.4 = \beta + 1$

$.2\beta = 1.4$

$\beta = 7$

32. $\mu = \displaystyle\int_0^\infty x f(x)\, dx = \int_0^\infty \dfrac{50x}{(x+5)^3}\, dx$

$= \displaystyle\lim_{R\to\infty} \int_0^R \dfrac{50x}{(x+5)^3}\, dx = 50 \lim_{R\to\infty} \int_0^R \left[\dfrac{1}{(x+5)^2} - \dfrac{5}{(x+5)^3} \right] dx$

$= 50 \displaystyle\lim_{R\to\infty} \left(-\dfrac{1}{(x+5)} + \dfrac{5}{2} \cdot \dfrac{1}{(x+5)^2} \right) \Bigg|_0^R$

$= 50 \displaystyle\lim_{R\to\infty} \left[\left(-\dfrac{1}{(R+5)} + \dfrac{5}{2} \cdot \dfrac{1}{(R+5)^2} \right) - \left(-\dfrac{1}{5} + \dfrac{5}{2} \cdot \dfrac{1}{25} \right) \right]$

$= 50 \left(\dfrac{1}{5} - \dfrac{1}{10} \right) = 50 \left(\dfrac{1}{10} \right) = 5$

Now find the cumulative probability distribution function.
When $x < 0$, $F(x) = 0$. When $x \geq 0$, we have:

$F(x) = \displaystyle\int_{-\infty}^x f(t)\, dt = \int_{-\infty}^0 f(t)\, dt + \int_0^x f(t)\, dt = 0 + \int_0^x \dfrac{50}{(t+5)^3}\, dt$

$= -\dfrac{50}{2} \left(\dfrac{1}{(t+5)^2} \right) \Bigg|_0^x = -25 \left(\dfrac{1}{(x+5)^2} - \dfrac{1}{25} \right) = 1 - \dfrac{25}{(x+5)^2}$

Thus, $F(x) = \begin{cases} 1 - \dfrac{25}{(x+5)^2} & x \geq 0 \\ 0 & \text{otherwise} \end{cases}$

Next, to find the median, x_m, we must solve the following for x_m:

$F(x_m) = P(X \leq x_m) = \dfrac{1}{2}$

$1 - \dfrac{25}{(x_m + 5)^2} = \dfrac{1}{2}$

$\dfrac{25}{(x_m + 5)^2} = \dfrac{1}{2}$

$(x_m + 5)^2 = 50$

$x_m + 5 = \sqrt{50}$

$x_m + 5 = 5\sqrt{2}$

Therefore, the median, x_m, equals $5\sqrt{2} - 5 \approx 2.071$.

33. $\displaystyle\int_{-\infty}^{\infty} (ax^2 + bx + c)f(x) = a\int_{-\infty}^{\infty} x^2 f(x)\,dx + b\int_{-\infty}^{\infty} xf(x)\,dx + c\int_{-\infty}^{\infty} f(x)\,dx$

$$= a(\sigma^2 + \mu^2) + b\mu + c,$$

since $\displaystyle\int_{-\infty}^{\infty} x^2 f(x)\,dx = \sigma^2 + \mu^2$, $\displaystyle\int_{-\infty}^{\infty} xf(x)\,dx = \mu$, and $\displaystyle\int_{-\infty}^{\infty} f(x)\,dx = 1$.

34. Let p = probability that an item is defective = .06, and q = probability that an item is not defective = .94. $n = 10$.

$P(X > 2) = 1 - P[X \le 2] = 1 - [P(2) + P(1) + P(0)]$

$\quad = 1 - C_{10,2}(.06)^2(.94)^8 + C_{10,1}(.06)^1(.94)^9 + C_{10,0}(.06)^0(.94)^{10}$

$\quad = 1 - [.0988 + .3438 + .5386] = 1 - .9812 \approx .0188$.

A day's output will be inspected with a probability of .0188.

35. The three conditions of a Poisson random variable are met. The average number of times per week that the press breaks down is $\dfrac{26}{52} = .5$. Thus, $\lambda = .5$

(A) $P(0) = \dfrac{(.5)^0}{0!} e^{-.5} = e^{-.5} \approx .6065$ (B) $P(1) = \dfrac{(.5)^1}{1!} e^{-.5} = .5e^{-.5} \approx .3033$

(C) $P(X > 2) = 1 - P(0 \le X \le 2)$

$\quad = 1 - [P(0) + P(1) + P(2)]$

$\quad = 1 - e^{-.5}\left[\dfrac{(.5)^0}{0!} + \dfrac{(.5)^1}{1!} + \dfrac{(.5)^2}{2!}\right]$

$\quad = 1 - e^{-.5}(1 + .5 + .125)$

$\quad = 1 - e^{-.5}(1.625)$

$\quad \approx .0144$

36. (A) $P(X \le 50) = \displaystyle\int_0^{50} f(x)\,dx = \dfrac{1}{50}\int_0^{50} (1 - .01x)\,dx = \dfrac{1}{50}(x - .005x^2)\Big|_0^{50}$

$\quad = \dfrac{1}{50}(50 - .005 \cdot 50^2) = 1 - .25 = .75$

(B) Solve the following for x:

$\displaystyle\int_0^x f(t)\,dt = .96$ (x = number of pounds of popcorn)

$\dfrac{1}{50}\displaystyle\int_0^x (1 - .01t)\,dt = .96$

$\dfrac{1}{50}(t - .005t^2)\Big|_0^x = .96$

$\dfrac{1}{50}(x - .005x^2) = .96$

$x - .005x^2 = 48$

$5x^2 - 1000x + 48{,}000 = 0$

$x^2 - 200x + 9600 = 0$

$(x - 80)(x - 120) = 0$

$x = 80$ or $x = 120$

Thus, 80 pounds of popcorn must be on hand at the beginning of the week.

37. $f(x) = \begin{cases} (\beta + 1)(\beta + 2)x^{\beta}(1 - x) & 0 \leq x \leq 1 \\ 0 & \text{otherwise} \end{cases}$

Thus, $f(x)$, with $\beta = 1$, is given by:

$f(x) = \begin{cases} (1 + 1)(1 + 2)x(1 - x) & 0 \leq x \leq 1 \\ 0 & \text{otherwise} \end{cases}$

$ = \begin{cases} 6x(1 - x) & 0 \leq x \leq 1 \\ 0 & \text{otherwise} \end{cases}$

(A) $P(X \geq .2) = \int_{.2}^{1} f(x)\,dx = \int_{.2}^{1} 6x(1 - x)\,dx = 6\left(\frac{1}{2}x^2 - \frac{1}{3}x^3\right)\Big|_{.2}^{1}$

$= 6\left[\left(\frac{1}{2} - \frac{1}{3}\right) - \left(\frac{.04}{2} - \frac{.008}{3}\right)\right] = 6\left(\frac{.96}{2} - \frac{.992}{3}\right)$

$= 2.88 - 1.984 = .896$

(B) $\mu = E(X) = \frac{\beta + 1}{\beta + 3} \quad (\beta = 1)$

$= \frac{1 + 1}{1 + 3} = \frac{2}{4} = .5 \text{ or } 50\%$

38. Mean failure time $= \mu = 4000$. As an exponential density function, it is expressed by $\lambda = \mu = 4000$. Thus,

$f(x) = \begin{cases} \frac{1}{\lambda}e^{-x/\lambda} = \frac{1}{4000}e^{-x/4000} & x \geq 0 \\ 0 & \text{otherwise} \end{cases}$

The cumulative distribution function is given by:

$F(x) = \begin{cases} 1 - e^{-x/\lambda} \\ 0 \end{cases} = \begin{cases} 1 - e^{-x/4000} & x \geq 0 \\ 0 & \text{otherwise} \end{cases}$

(A) $P(X \geq 4000) = \int_{4000}^{\infty} f(x)\,dx = 1 - F(4000)$

$= 1 - (1 - e^{-4000/4000}) = e^{-1} = .3679$

(B) $P(0 \leq X \leq 1000) = \int_{0}^{1000} f(x)\,dx = F(1000) - F(0)$

$= (1 - e^{-1000/4000}) - (1 - e^{0}) = 1 - e^{-.25} \approx .2212$

39. The three conditions of a Poisson random variable are met. The average number of phone calls per minute is $\frac{120}{60} = 2$. Thus, $\lambda = 2$

(A) $P(4) = \frac{2^4}{4!}e^{-2} = \frac{16}{24}e^{-2} = \frac{2}{3}e^{-2} \approx .0902$

(B) Let X be the exponential random variable that represents the length of time between calls (in seconds). Since there are 2 calls per minute, the average length of time between calls is 30 seconds, $\mu = \lambda = 30$. Thus, the probability density function for X is

$$f(x) = \begin{cases} \dfrac{1}{30}\,e^{-x/30} & x \geq 0 \\ 0 & \text{otherwise} \end{cases}$$

and

$$F(x) = \begin{cases} 1 - e^{-x/30} & x \geq 0 \\ 0 & \text{otherwise} \end{cases}$$

Now
$$\begin{aligned} P(X \geq 45) &= 1 - F(45) \\ &= 1 - (1 - e^{-45/30}) \\ &= e^{-45/30} \approx .2231 \end{aligned}$$

40. $\mu = 35{,}000$, $\sigma = 5{,}000$

z (for $x = 25{,}000$) $= \dfrac{25{,}000 - 35{,}000}{5{,}000} = -2$

Required probability = area A

$\qquad\qquad\qquad\quad = .5 -$ area A_1

$\qquad\qquad\qquad\quad = .5 - .4772$

$\qquad\qquad\qquad\quad = .0228$

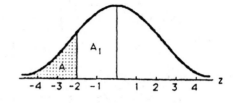

41. $\mu = 100$, $\sigma = 10$

(A) z (for $x = 91.5$) $= \dfrac{91.5 - 100}{10} = -.85$

$\quad z$ (for $x = 108$) $= \dfrac{108.5 - 100}{10} = .85$

The probability of an applicant scoring between 92 and 108

$\qquad =$ area A

$\qquad = 2 \cdot$ area A_1

$\qquad = 2$(area corresponding to $z = .85$)

$\qquad = 2(.3023) = .6046$

Thus, the percentage of applicants scoring between 92 and 108 is 60.46%.

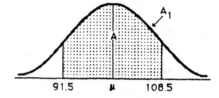

(B) z (for $x = 114.5$) $= \dfrac{114.5 - 100}{10} = 1.45$

The probability of an applicant scoring 115 or higher

$\qquad =$ area A

$\qquad = .5 -$ (area corresponding to $z = 1.45$)

$\qquad = .5 - .4265$

$\qquad = .0735$

Thus, the percentage of applicants scoring 115 or higher is 7.35%.

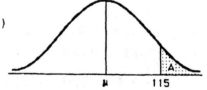

42. Based on the publisher's claim, the probability that a person selected at random reads the newspaper is: $p = .7$.

Thus, the probability that a randomly selected person does not read the newspaper is: $q = .3$.

(A) With $n = 200$,
the mean $\mu = 200(.7) = 140$,
and standard deviation $\sigma = \sqrt{200(.7)(.3)} = \sqrt{42} \approx 6.48$.

(B) $[\mu - 3\sigma, \ \mu + 3\sigma] = [120.76, \ 159.24]$ and the interval lies entirely in the interval $[0, 200]$. Thus, the normal distribution *does* provide an adequate approximation to the binomial distribution.

(C) z (for $x = 129.5$) $= \dfrac{129.5 - 140}{6.48} = \dfrac{-10.5}{6.48} = -1.62$

z (for $x = 155.5$) $= \dfrac{155.5 - 140}{6.48} = \dfrac{15.5}{6.48} = 2.39$

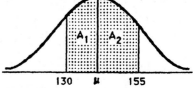

The probability of finding between 130 and 155 readers in the sample
= area A_1 + area A_2
= (area corresponding to $z = 1.62$) +
  (area corresponding to $z = 2.39$)
= $.4474 + .4916$
= $.9390$

(D) z (for $x = 125.5$) $= \dfrac{125.5 - 140}{6.48} = \dfrac{-14.5}{6.48} = -2.24$

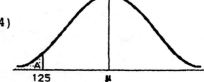

The probability of finding fewer than 125 readers in the sample
= area A
= $.5$ - (area corresponding to $z = 2.24$)
= $.5 - .4875$
= $.0125$

43. (A) Probability that the drug is usable after five months is:
$$P(X > 5) = \int_5^\infty f(x)\,dx = \int_5^\infty \frac{10}{(x + 10)^2}\,dx = \lim_{R \to \infty} \int_5^R \frac{10}{(x + 10)^2}\,dx$$

$$= \lim_{R \to \infty} 10\left(-\frac{1}{x + 10}\right)\Big|_5^R = -10 \lim_{R \to \infty} \left(\frac{1}{R + 10} - \frac{1}{5 + 10}\right)$$

$$= -10\left(-\frac{1}{15}\right) = \frac{2}{3} \approx .6667$$

(B) In order to find the median, x_m, we must solve the following for x_m:
$$P(X \le x_m) = \int_0^{x_m} f(x)\,dx = \frac{1}{2}$$

$$\int_0^{x_m} \frac{10}{(x + 10)^2}\,dx = \frac{1}{2}$$

$$-\frac{10}{(x + 10)}\Big|_0^{x_m} = \frac{1}{2}$$

$$-\left(\frac{10}{x_m + 10} - 1\right) = \frac{1}{2}$$

$$-\frac{10}{x_m + 10} + 1 = \frac{1}{2}$$

599

$$-\frac{10}{x_m + 10} = -\frac{1}{2}$$

$$x_m + 10 = 20$$

$$x_m = 10 \text{ months}$$

44. $f(x) = \begin{cases} \dfrac{1}{\lambda}e^{-x/\lambda} & x \geq 0 \\ 0 & \text{otherwise} \end{cases}$

$$P(X > 1) = \frac{1}{\lambda}\int_1^\infty e^{-x/\lambda}\,dx = e^{-2} \quad \text{(Given)}$$

Thus, $\quad \dfrac{1}{\lambda}\lim_{R\to\infty}\displaystyle\int_1^R e^{-x/\lambda}\,dx = e^{-2}$

$$\frac{1}{\lambda}(-\lambda)\lim_{R\to\infty}(e^{-x/\lambda})\Big|_1^R = e^{-2}$$

$$-1\cdot\lim_{R\to\infty}(e^{-R/\lambda} - e^{-1/\lambda}) = e^{-2}$$

$$e^{-1/\lambda} = e^{-2}$$

Thus, $\qquad\qquad -\dfrac{1}{\lambda} = -2$

$$\lambda = \frac{1}{2}$$

Therefore, $f(x)$, with $\lambda = \dfrac{1}{2}$, is given by $f(x) = \begin{cases} 2e^{-2x} & x \geq 0 \\ 0 & \text{otherwise} \end{cases}$

(A) $P(X > 2) = \displaystyle\int_2^\infty f(x)\,dx = \int_2^\infty 2e^{-2x}\,dx = 2\lim_{R\to\infty}\int_2^R e^{-2x}\,dx$

$$= 2\lim_{R\to\infty}\left(-\frac{1}{2}e^{-2x}\Big|_2^R\right) = -\lim_{R\to\infty}(e^{-2R} - e^{-4}) = -(-e^{-4}) = e^{-4} \approx .0183$$

(B) Mean life expectancy:

$$\mu = \int_0^\infty xf(x)\,dx = \int_0^\infty x\cdot 2e^{-2x}\,dx$$

$$= 2\lim_{R\to\infty}\int_0^R xe^{-2x}\,dx \quad \text{(integration by parts; } u = x,\ dv = e^{-2x}\,dx)$$

$$= 2\lim_{R\to\infty}\left[x\left(-\frac{1}{2}e^{-2x}\right)\Big|_0^R + \frac{1}{2}\int_0^R e^{-2x}\,dx\right] = 2\lim_{R\to\infty}\left(-\frac{1}{2}xe^{-2x} - \frac{1}{4}e^{-2x}\right)\Big|_0^R$$

$$= -2\lim_{R\to\infty}\left[\left(\frac{1}{2}Re^{-2R} + \frac{1}{4}e^{-2R}\right) - \left(0 + \frac{1}{4}\right)\right]$$

$$= -2\left(-\frac{1}{4}\right) = \frac{1}{2} \text{ or } .5 \text{ month } or\ \mu = \lambda = \frac{1}{2}$$

45. Let p = probability drug will cause side effects = .25
and q = probability drug will not cause side effects = .75.
$n = 100$.
By the "Rule of Thumb Test," $\mu = 100(.25) = 25$ and
$\sigma = \sqrt{100(.25)(.75)} \approx 4.22$.
Now, $z = \dfrac{29.5 - 25}{4.33} \approx 1.04$

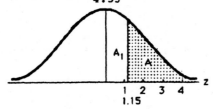

Required probability = area A
$= .5 - \text{area } A_1$
$= .5 - .3508$
$= .1492$

46. Given $\mu = \lambda = 3$.

(A) $P(0) = \dfrac{3^0}{0!} e^{-3} = e^{-3} \approx .0498$

(B) $P(1) = \dfrac{3^1}{1!} e^{-3} = 3e^{-3} \approx .1494$

(C) $P(X > 3) = 1 - P(0 \le X \le 3)$
$\qquad\qquad = 1 - [P(0) + P(1) + P(2) + P(3)]$
$\qquad\qquad = 1 - e^{-3}\left[\dfrac{3^0}{0!} + \dfrac{3^1}{1!} + \dfrac{3^2}{2!} + \dfrac{3^3}{3!}\right]$
$\qquad\qquad = 1 - e^{-3}\left[1 + 3 + \dfrac{9}{2} + \dfrac{9}{2}\right] = 1 - e^{-3}(13)$
$\qquad\qquad \approx .3528$

47. Given that the mean score = μ = .75. However, in a beta distribution,
we have:
$\mu = \dfrac{\beta + 1}{\beta + 3} = .75$ (Solve for β.)
$\qquad \beta + 1 = .75(\beta + 3)$
$\qquad\quad .25\beta = 1.25$
$\qquad\qquad \beta = 5$

Thus, the cumulative probability distribution function, with $\beta = 5$, is
given by:
$$F(x) = \begin{cases} 0 & x < 0 \\ (\beta + 2)x^{\beta+1} - (\beta + 1)x^{\beta+2} & 0 \le x \le 1 \\ 1 & x > 1 \end{cases}$$
$$\quad = \begin{cases} 0 & x < 0 \\ (5 + 2)x^{5+1} - (5 + 1)x^{5+2} & 0 \le x \le 1 \\ 1 & x > 1 \end{cases}$$

601

$$= \begin{cases} 0 & x < 0 \\ 7x^6 - 6x^7 & 0 \le x \le 1 \\ 1 & x > 1 \end{cases}$$

Thus,

$$P(X > .5) = F(1) - F(.5) = F(1) - F\left(\frac{1}{2}\right)$$

$$= \left[7(1)^6 - 6(1)^7 - 7\left(\frac{1}{2}\right)^6 + 6\left(\frac{1}{2}\right)^7 \right]$$

$$= 1 - \left(\frac{1}{2}\right)^6 (7 - 3) = 1 - \frac{4}{2^6} = 1 - \frac{1}{2^4} = 1 - \frac{1}{16} = \frac{15}{16} = .9375$$

48. $\mu = 108$, $\sigma = 12$.

$$z \text{ (for } x = 134.5) = \frac{134.5 - 108}{12} = \frac{26.5}{12} = 2.21$$

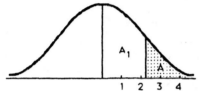

Required probability = area A
    = .5 - area A_1
    = .5 - .4864
    = .0136

49. The three conditions of a Poisson random variable are met. The average number of vehicles which arrive at the intersection per second (from 4:00PM to 5:00PM) is $\frac{2880}{3600} = .8$. Thus, $\lambda = .8$.

(A) $P(0) = \frac{(.8)^0}{0!} e^{-.8} = e^{-.8} \approx .4493$

(B) $P(1) = \frac{(.8)^1}{1!} e^{-.8} = .8e^{-.8} \approx .3595$

(C) $P(X \ge 5) = 1 - P(0 \le X \le 4) = 1 - [P(0) + P(1) + P(2) + P(3) + P(4)]$

$$= 1 - e^{-.8}\left[\frac{(.8)^0}{0!} + \frac{(.8)^1}{1!} + \frac{(.8)^2}{2!} + \frac{(.8)^3}{3!} + \frac{(.8)^4}{4!} \right]$$

$$= 1 - e^{-.8}[1 + .8 + .32 + .0853 + .0171]$$

$$\approx .0014$$

11 Linear Programming

Things to remember:

1. A line divides the plane into two sets called HALF-PLANES. A vertical line divides the plane into LEFT and RIGHT HALF-PLANES; a nonvertical line divides the plane into UPPER and LOWER HALF-PLANES. In either case, the dividing line is called the BOUNDARY LINE of each half-plane.

2. The graph of the linear inequality

   $Ax + By < C$ or $Ax + By > C$

   with $B \neq 0$ is either the upper half-plane or the lower half-plane (but not both) determined by the line $Ax + By = C$.
   If $B = 0$, the graph of

   $Ax < C$ or $Ax > C$

   is either the right half-plane or the left half-plane (but not both) determined by the vertical line $Ax = C$.

3. For strict inequalities ("<" or ">"), the line is not included in the graph. For weak inequalities ("≤" or "≥"), the line is included in the graph.

4. PROCEDURE FOR GRAPHING LINEAR INEQUALITIES
   (a) First graph $Ax + By = C$ as a broken line if equality is not included in the original statement or as a solid line if equality is included.
   (b) Choose a test point anywhere in the plane not on the line [the origin (0, 0) often requires the least computation] and substitute the coordinates into the inequality.
   (c) The graph of the original inequality includes the half-plane containing the test point if the inequality is satisfied by that point or the half-plane not containing the test point if the inequality is not satisfied by that point.

5. To solve a system of linear inequalities graphically, graph each inequality in the system and then take the intersection of all the graphs. The resulting graph is called the SOLUTION REGION, or FEASIBLE REGION.

6. A CORNER POINT of a solution region is a point in the solution region that is the intersection of two boundary lines.

7. The solution region of a system of linear inequalities is BOUNDED if it can be enclosed within a circle; if it cannot be enclosed within a circle, then it is UNBOUNDED.

1. $y \le x - 1$

Graph $y = x - 1$ as a solid line.

Test point $(0, 0)$:

$0 \le 0 - 1$

$0 \le -1$

The inequality is false. Thus, the graph is the half-plane below the line $y = x - 1$, including the line.

x	y
0	-1
1	0

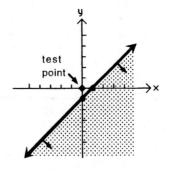

3. $3x - 2y > 6$

Graph $3x - 2y = 6$ as a broken line.

Test point $(0, 0)$:

$3 \cdot 0 - 2 \cdot 0 > 6$

$0 > 6$

The inequality is false. Thus, the graph is the half-plane below the line $3x - 2y = 6$, not including the line.

x	y
0	-3
2	0

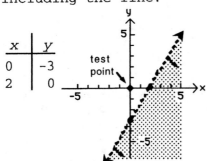

5. $x \ge -4$

Graph $x = -4$ [the vertical line through $(-4, 0)$] as a solid line.

Test point $(0, 0)$:

$0 \ge -4$

The inequality is true. Thus, the graph is the half-plane to the right of the line $x = -4$, including the line.

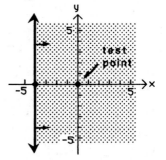

7. $6x + 4y \ge 24$

Graph the line $6x + 4y = 24$ as a solid line.

Test point $(0, 0)$:

$6 \cdot 0 + 4 \cdot 0 \ge 24$

$0 \ge 24$

The inequality is false. Thus, the graph is the half-plane above the line, including the line.

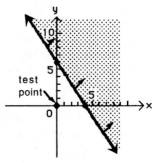

9. $5x \le -2y$ or $5x + 2y \le 0$

Graph the line $5x + 2y = 0$ as a solid line. Since the line passes through the origin $(0, 0)$, we use $(1, 0)$ as a test point:

$5 \cdot 1 + 2 \cdot 0 \le 0$

$5 \le 0$

This inequality is false. Thus, the graph is the half-plane below the line $5x + 2y = 0$, including the line.

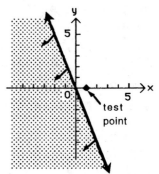

604

11. (A) Graph $2x + 3y = 18$ as a broken line
   Test point $(0, 0)$:
$$2 \cdot 0 + 3 \cdot 0 < 18$$
$$0 < 18$$

The inequality is true. Thus, the graph is
the half-plane below the line $2x + 3y = 18$,
not including the line.

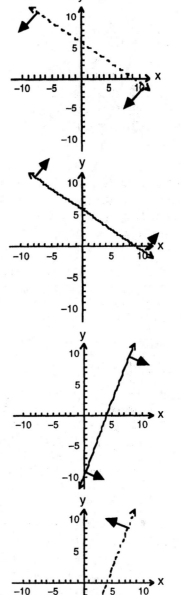

(B) The set of points that do not satisfy the
inequality is the half-plane above the line,
including the line.

13. (A) Graph $5x - 2y = 20$ as a solid line
   Test point $(0, 0)$:
$$5 \cdot 0 - 2 \cdot 0 \geq 20$$
$$0 \geq 20$$

This inequality is false. Thus, the graph is
the half-plane below the line $5x - 2y = 20$,
including the line.

(B) The set of points that do not satisfy the
inequality is the half-plane above the line,
not including the line.

15. The graph of $x + 2y \leq 8$ is the half-plane below the line $x + 2y = 8$
   [e.g., $(0, 0)$ satisfies the inequality]. The graph of $3x - 2y \geq 0$ is
   the half-plane below the line $3x - 2y = 0$ [e.g., $(1, 0)$ satisfies the
   inequality]. The intersection of these two regions is region IV.

17. The graph of $x + 2y \geq 8$ is the half-plane above the line $x + 2y = 8$
   [e.g., $(0, 0)$ does not satisfy the inequality]. The graph of $3x - 2y \geq$
   0 is the half-plane below the line $3x - 2y = 0$ [e.g., $(1, 0)$ satisfies
   the inequality]. The intersection of these two regions is region I.

19. The graphs of the inequalities $3x + y \geq 6$ and $x \leq 4$ are:

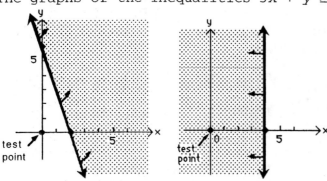

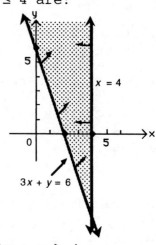

The intersection of these regions (drawn on the same coordinate plane) is shown in the graph at the right.

21. The graphs of the inequalities $x - 2y \leq 12$ and $2x + y \geq 4$ are:

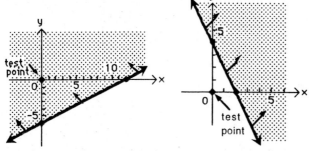

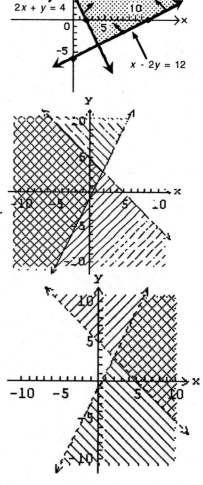

The intersection of these regions (drawn on the same coordinate plane) is shown in the graph at the right.

23. $x + y \leq 5$
$2x - y \leq 1$

(A) The graph of $x + y \leq 5$ is the half-plane below the line $x + y = 5$, including the line. The graph of $2x - y \leq 1$ is the half-plane above the line $y = 2x - 1$, including the line. The solution set of the system is the double-shaded region.

(B) The set of points that do not satisfy $x + y \leq 5$ is the half-plane above the line $x + y = 5$, not including the line. The set of points that do not satisfy $2x - y \leq 1$ is the half-plane below the line $2x - y = 1$, not including the line. The solution set of the system is the unshaded region.

25. $2x + y \geq 4$
$3x - y \leq 7$

(A) The graph of $2x + y \geq 4$ is the half-plane above the line $2x + y = 4$, including the line. The graph of $3x - y \leq 7$ is the half-plane above the line $3x - y = 7$, including the line. The solution set of the system is the double-shaded region.

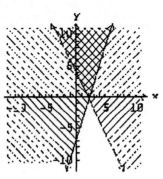

(B) The set of points that do not satisfy $2x + y \geq 4$ is the half-plane below the line $2x + y = 4$, not including the line. The set of points that do not satisfy $3x - y \leq 7$ is the set of points below the line $3x - y = 7$, not including the region. The solution set of the system is the unshaded region.

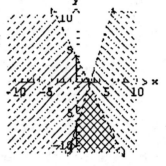

27. The graph of $x + 3y \leq 18$ is the region below the line $x + 3y = 18$ and the graph of $2x + y \geq 16$ is the region above the line $2x + y = 16$. The graph of $x \geq 0$, $y \geq 0$ is the first quadrant. The intersection of these regions is region IV. The corner points are $(8, 0)$, $(18, 0)$, and $(6, 4)$.

29. The graph of $x + 3y \geq 18$ is the region above the line $x + 3y = 18$ and the graph of $2x + y \geq 16$ is the region above the line $2x + y = 16$. The graph of $x \geq 0$, $y \geq 0$ is the first quadrant. The intersection of these regions is region I. The corner points are $(0, 16)$, $(6, 4)$, and $(18, 0)$.

31. The graphs of the inequalities are shown at the right. The solution region is indicated by the shaded region. The solution region is *bounded*.

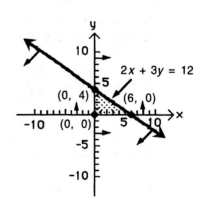

The corner points of the solution region are:

$(0, 0)$, the intersection of $x = 0$, $y = 0$;
$(0, 4)$, the intersection of $x = 0$, $2x + 3y = 12$;
$(6, 0)$, the intersection of $y = 0$, $2x + 3y = 12$.

33. The graphs of the inequalities are shown at the right. The solution region is shaded. The solution region is *bounded*.

The corner points of the solution region are:

$(0, 0)$, the intersection of $x = 0$, $y = 0$;
$(0, 4)$, the intersection of $x = 0$, $x + 2y = 8$;
$(4, 2)$, the intersection of $x + 2y = 8$, $2x + y = 10$;
$(5, 0)$, the intersection of $y = 0$, $2x + y = 10$.

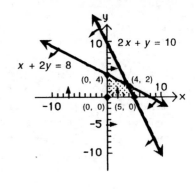

35. The graphs of the inequalities are shown at the right. The solution region is shaded. The solution region is *unbounded*.

The corner points of the solution region are:

$(0, 10)$, the intersection of $x = 0$, $2x + y = 10$;
$(4, 2)$, the intersection of $x + 2y = 8$, $2x + y = 10$;
$(8, 0)$, the intersection of $y = 0$, $x + 2y = 8$.

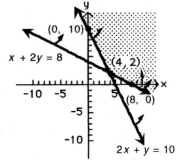

37. The graphs of the inequalities are shown at the right. The solution is indicated by the shaded region. The solution region is *bounded*.

The corner points of the solution region are:

$(0, 0)$, the intersection of $x = 0$, $y = 0$,
$(0, 6)$, the intersection of $x = 0$, $x + 2y = 12$;
$(2, 5)$, the intersection of $x + 2y = 12$, $x + y = 7$;
$(3, 4)$, the intersection of $x + y = 7$, $2x + y = 10$;
$(5, 0)$, the intersection of $y = 0$, $2x + y = 10$.

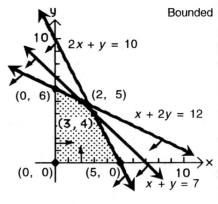

Note that the point of intersection of the lines $2x + y = 10$, $x + 2y = 12$ is not a corner point because it is not in the solution region.

39. The graphs of the inequalities are shown at the right. The solution is indicated by the shaded region, which is *unbounded*.

The corner points are:

$(0, 16)$, the intersection of $x = 0$, $2x + y = 16$;
$(4, 8)$, the intersection of $2x + y = 16$, $x + y = 12$;
$(10, 2)$, the intersection of $x + y = 12$, $x + 2y = 14$;
$(14, 0)$, the intersection of $y = 0$, $x + 2y = 14$.

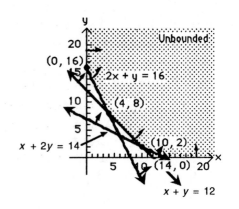

The intersection of $x + 2y = 14$, $2x + y = 16$ is not a corner point because it is not in the solution region.

608

41. The graphs of the inequalities are shown at the right. The solution is indicated by the shaded region, which is *bounded*.

The corner points are (8, 6), (4, 7), and (9, 3).

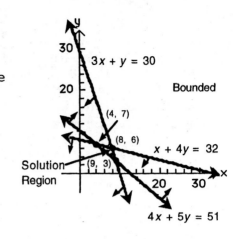

43. The graphs of the inequalities are shown at the right. The system of inequalities does not have a solution because the intersection of the graphs is empty.

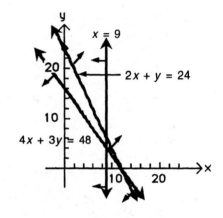

45. The graphs of the inequalities are shown at the right. The solution is indicated by the shaded region, which is *unbounded*.

The corner points are (0, 0), (4, 4), and (8, 12).

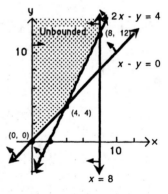

47. The graphs of the inequalities are shown at the right. The solution is indicated by the shaded region, which is *bounded*.

The corner points are (2, 1), (3, 6), (5, 4), and (5, 2).

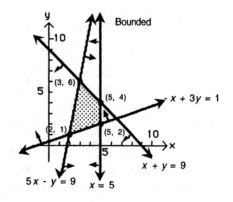

49. The graphs of the inequalities are shown at the right. The solution is indicated by the shaded region, which is *bounded*. The corner points are (1.16, 5.32), (2.17, 6.56), and (6.2, 1.6).

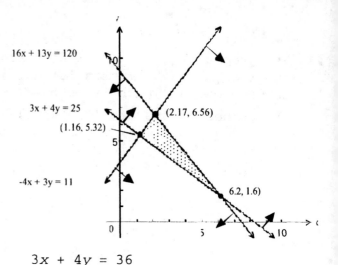

51. (A)

$3x + 4y = 36$		$3x + 4y = 36$
$3x + 2y = 30$ subtract		$x = 0$
$2y = 6$		$4y = 36$
$y = 3$		$y = 9$
$x = 8$		

intersection point: (8, 3)   intersection point: (0, 9)

$3x + 4y = 36$ $3x + 2y = 30$
$y = 0$ $x = 0$
$3x = 36$ $2y = 30$
$x = 12$ $y = 15$

intersection point: (12, 0)   intersection point: (0, 15)

$3x + 2y = 30$ $x = 0$
$y = 0$ $y = 0$
$3x = 30$
$x = 10$

intersection point: (10, 0)   intersection point: (0, 0)

(B) The corner points are: (8, 3), (0, 9), (10, 0), (0, 0);
(0, 15) does not satisfy $3x + 4y \leq 36$,
(12, 0) does not satisfy $3x + 2y \leq 30$.

53. Let x = the number of trick skis and y = the number of slalom skis produced per day. The information is summarized in the following table.

| | Hours per ski | | |
	Trick ski	Slalom ski	Maximum labor-hours per day available
Fabrication	6 hrs	4 hrs	108 hrs
Finishing	1 hr	1 hr	24 hrs

We have the following inequalities:

$6x + 4y \leq 108$ for fabrication
$x + y \leq 24$ for finishing

Also, $x \geq 0$ and $y \geq 0$.

The graphs of these inequalities are shown at the right. The shaded region indicates the set of feasible solutions.

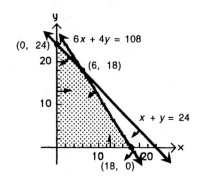

55. (A) If x is the number of trick skis and y is the number of slalom skis per day, then the profit per day is given by
$$P(x, y) = 50x + 60y$$
All the production schedules in the feasible region that lie on the graph of the line
$$50x + 60y = 1,100$$
will provide a profit of $1,100.

(B) There are many possible choices. For example, producing 5 trick skis and 15 slalom skis per day will produce a profit of
$$P(5, 15) = 50(5) + 60(15) = 1,150$$
All the production schedules in the feasible region that lie on the graph of $50x + 60y = 1,150$ will provide a profit of $1,150.

57. Let x = the number of cubic yards of mix A and y = the number of cubic yards of mix B. The information is summarized in the following table:

| | Amount of substance per cubic yard | | Minimum monthly requirement |
	Mix A	Mix B	
Phosphoric acid	20 lbs	10 lbs	460 lbs
Nitrogen	30 lbs	30 lbs	960 lbs
Potash	5 lbs	10 lbs	220 lbs

We have the following inequalities:

$20x + 10y \geq 460$
$30x + 30y \geq 960$
$5x + 10y \geq 220$

Also, $x \geq 0$ and $y \geq 0$.

The graphs of these inequalities are shown at the right. The shaded region indicates the set of feasible solutions.

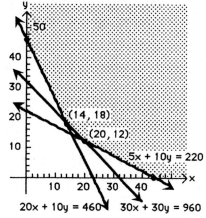

59. Let x = the number of mice used and y = the number of rats used. The information is summarized in the following table.

	Mice	Rats	Maximum time available per day
Box A	10 min	20 min	800 min
Box B	20 min	10 min	640 min

We have the following inequalities:

$10x + 20y \leq 800$ for box A
$20x + 10y \leq 640$ for box B

Also, $x \geq 0$ and $y \geq 0$.

The graphs of these inequalities are shown at the right. The shaded region indicates the set of feasible solutions.

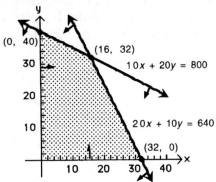

EXERCISE 11-2

Things to remember:

1. A LINEAR PROGRAMMING PROBLEM is a problem that is concerned with finding the OPTIMAL VALUE (maximum or minimum value) of a linear OBJECTIVE FUNCTION of the form

$$z = c_1 x_1 + c_2 x_2 + \cdots + c_n x_n,$$

where the DECISION VARIABLES x_1, x_2, ..., x_n are subject to PROBLEM CONSTRAINTS in the form of linear inequalities and equations. In addition, the decision variables must satisfy the NONNEGATIVE CONSTRAINTS $x_i \geq 0$, for i = 1, 2, ..., n. The set of points satisfying both the problem constraints and the nonnegative constraints is called the FEASIBLE REGION for the problem. Any point in the feasible region that produces the optimal value of the objective function over the feasible region is called an OPTIMAL SOLUTION.

2. PROCEDURE: CONSTRUCTING THE MATHEMATICAL MODEL FOR AN APPLIED LINEAR PROGRAMMING PROBLEM

   a. Introduce decision variables

   b. Summarize relevant material in table form, relating the decision variables with the columns in the table, if possible.

   c. Determine the objective and write a linear objective function.

   d. Write problem constraints using linear equations and/or inequalities.

   e. Write non-negative constraints.

3. FUNDAMENTAL THEOREM OF LINEAR PROGRAMMING

If the optimal value of the objective function in a linear programming problem exists, then that value must occur at one (or more) of the corner points of the feasible region.

4. EXISTENCE OF SOLUTIONS

(A) If the feasible region for a linear programming problem is bounded, then both the maximum value and the minimum value of the objective function always exist.

(B) If the feasible region is unbounded, and the coefficients of the objective function are positive, then the minimum value of the objective function exists, but the maximum value does not.

(C) If the feasible region is empty (that is, there are no points that satisfy all the constraints), then both the maximum value and the minimum value of the objective function do not exist.

5. PROCEDURE: GEOMETRIC SOLUTION OF A LINEAR PROGRAMMING PROBLEM WITH TWO DECISION VARIABLES.

Step 1. Graph the feasible region. Then, if according to 4 an optimal solution exists, find the coordinates of each corner point.

Step 2. Construct a CORNER POINT TABLE listing the value of the objective function at each corner point.

Step 3. Determine the optimal solution(s) from the table in Step (2).

Step 4. For an applied problem, interpret the optimal solution(s) in terms of the original problem.

1.

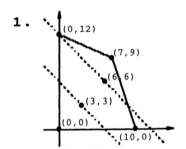

From the figure:
   maximum profit $P = 16$ at $x_1 = 7$, $x_2 = 9$.

Step (2): Evaluate the objective function at each corner point.

Corner Point	$P = x_1 + x_2$
(0, 0)	0
(0, 12)	12
(7, 9)	16
(10, 0)	10

Step (3): Determine the optimal solution from Step (2).
   The maximum value of P is 16 at (7, 9).

3.

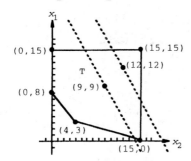

From the figure:
maximum profit $P = 84$ at $x_1 = 0$, $x_2 = 12$; at $x_1 = 7$, $x_2 = 9$; and at every point on the line segment joining $(0, 12)$ and $(7, 9)$.

Step (2): Evaluate the objective function at each corner point.

Corner Point	$P = 3x_1 + 7x_2$
(0, 0)	0
(0, 12)	84
(7, 9)	84
(10, 0)	30

Step (3): Determine the optimal solution from Step (2).
The maximum value of P is 84 at $(0, 12)$ *and* $(7, 9)$. This is a multiple optimal solution.

5. $C = 7x_1 + 4x_2$

From the figure:
minimum cost $C = 32$ at $x_1 = 0$, $x_2 = 8$.

Step (2): Evaluate the objective function at each corner point.

Corner Point	$C = 7x_1 + 4x_2$
(15, 15)	165
(0, 15)	60
(0, 8)	32
(4, 3)	40
(15, 0)	105

Step (3): Determine the optimal solution from Step (2).
The minimum value of C is 32 at $x_1 = 0$, $x_2 = 8$.

7. $C = 3x_1 + 8x_2$

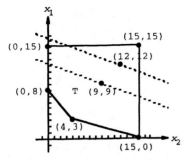

From the figure:
    minimum cost $C = 36$ at $x_1 = 4$, $x_2 = 3$.

<u>Step (2)</u>: Evaluate the objective function at each corner point.

Corner Point	$C = 3x_1 + 8x_2$
(15, 15)	165
(0, 15)	120
(0, 8)	64
(4, 3)	36
(15, 0)	45

<u>Step (3)</u>: Determine the optimal solution from Step (2).
       The minimum value of C is 36 at $x_1 = 4$, $x_2 = 3$.

9. <u>Step (1)</u>: Graph the feasible region and find the corner points.

The feasible region S is the solution set of the given inequalities. This region is indicated by the shading in the graph at the right.

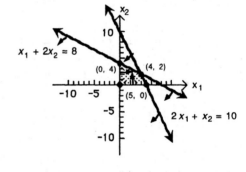

The corner points are (0, 0), (0, 4), (4, 2), and (5, 0).

Since S is bounded, it follows from <u>4</u>(a) that P has a maximum value

<u>Step (2)</u>: Evaluate the objective function at each corner point.
       The value of P at each corner point is given in the following table.

Corner Point	$P = 5x_1 + 5x_2$
(0, 0)	$P = 5(0) + 5(0) = 0$
(0, 4)	$P = 5(0) + 5(4) = 20$
(4, 2)	$P = 5(4) + 5(2) = 30$
(5, 0)	$P = 5(5) + 5(0) = 25$

<u>Step (3)</u>: Determine the optimal solution.
       The maximum value of P is 30 at $x_1 = 4$, $x_2 = 2$.

11. <u>Step (1)</u>: Graph the feasible region and find the corner points.

The feasible region S is the solution set of the given inequalities. This region is indicated by the shading in the graph at the right.

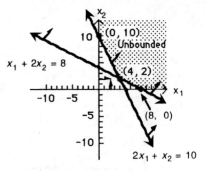

The corner points are $(0, 10)$, $(4, 2)$, and $(8, 0)$.

Since S is unbounded and $a = 2 > 0$, $b = 3 > 0$, it follows from <u>4</u>(b) that P has a minimum value but not a maximum value.

<u>Step (2)</u>: Evaluate the objective function at each corner point.
The value of P at each corner point is given in the following table:

Corner Point	$z = 2x_1 + 3x_2$
$(0, 10)$	$z = 2(0) + 3(10) = 30$
$(4, 2)$	$z = 2(4) + 3(2) = 14$
$(8, 0)$	$z = 2(8) + 3(0) = 16$

<u>Step (3)</u>: Determine the optimal solutions.
The minimum occurs at $x_1 = 4$, $x_2 = 2$, and the minimum value is $z = 14$; z does not have a maximum value.

13. <u>Step (1)</u>: Graph the feasible region and find the corner points.

The feasible region S is the solution set of the given inequalities. This region is indicated by the shading in the graph at the right.

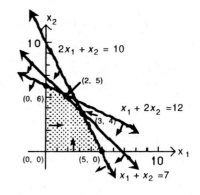

The corner points are $(0, 0)$, $(0, 6)$, $(2, 5)$, $(3, 4)$, and $(5, 0)$.

Since S is bounded, it follows from <u>4</u>(a) that P has a maximum value.

<u>Step (2)</u>: Evaluate the objective function at each corner point.
The value of P at each corner point is:

Corner Point	$P = 30x_1 + 40x_2$
$(0, 0)$	$P = 30(0) + 40(0) = 0$
$(0, 6)$	$P = 30(0) + 40(6) = 240$
$(2, 5)$	$P = 30(2) + 40(5) = 260$
$(3, 4)$	$P = 30(3) + 40(4) = 250$
$(5, 0)$	$P = 30(5) + 40(0) = 150$

<u>Step (3)</u>: Determine the optimal solution.
The maximum occurs at $x_1 = 2$, $x_2 = 5$, and the maximum value is $P = 260$.

15. <u>Step (1)</u>: Graph the feasible region and find the corner points.

The feasible region S is the solution set of the given inequalities. This region is indicated by the shading in the graph at the right.

The corner points are $(0, 16)$, $(4, 8)$, $(10, 2)$, and $(14, 0)$.

Since S is unbounded and $a = 10 > 0$, $b = 30 > 0$, it follows from <u>4</u>(b) that z has a minimum value but not a maximum value.

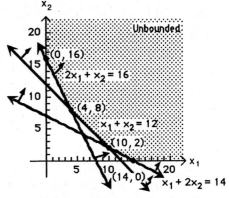

<u>Step (2)</u>: Evaluate the objective function at each corner point.
The value of z at each corner point is:

Corner Point	$z = 10x_1 + 30x_2$
$(0, 16)$	$z = 10(0) + 30(16) = 480$
$(4, 8)$	$z = 10(4) + 30(8) = 280$
$(10, 2)$	$z = 10(10) + 30(2) = 160$
$(14, 0)$	$z = 10(14) + 30(0) = 140$

<u>Step (3)</u>: Determine the optimal solution.
The minimum occurs at $x_1 = 14$, $x_2 = 0$, and the minimum value is $z = 140$; z does not have a maximum value.

17. <u>Step (1)</u>: Graph the feasible region and find the corner points.

The feasible region S is the solution set of the given inequalities, and is indicated by the shading in the graph at the right.

The corner points are $(0, 2)$, $(0, 9)$, $(2, 6)$, $(5, 0)$, and $(2, 0)$.

Since S is bounded, it follows from <u>4</u>(a) that P has a maximum value and a minimum value.

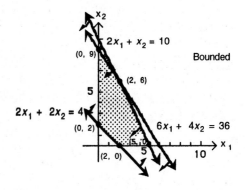

<u>Step (2)</u>: Evaluate the objective function at each corner point.
The value of P at each corner point is given in the following table:

Corner Point	$P = 30x_1 + 10x_2$
$(0, 2)$	$P = 30(0) + 10(2) = 20$
$(0, 9)$	$P = 30(0) + 10(9) = 90$
$(2, 6)$	$P = 30(2) + 10(6) = 120$
$(5, 0)$	$P = 30(5) + 10(0) = 150$
$(2, 0)$	$P = 30(2) + 10(0) = 60$

<u>Step (3)</u>: Determine the optimal solutions.
The maximum occurs at $x_1 = 5$, $x_2 = 0$, and the maximum value is $P = 150$; the minimum occurs at $x_1 = 0$, $x_2 = 2$, and the minimum value is $P = 20$.

19. Step (1): Graph the feasible region and find the corner points.

The feasible region S is the solution set of the given inequalities. As indicated, the feasible region is empty. Thus, by 4(c), there are no optimal solutions.

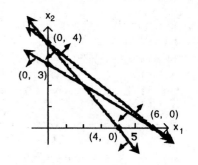

21. Step (1): Graph the feasible region and find the corner points.

The feasible region S is the solution set of the given inequalities, and is indicated by the shading in the graph at the right.

The corner points are $(3, 8)$, $(8, 10)$, and $(12, 2)$.

Since S is bounded, it follows from 4(a) that P has a maximum value and a minimum value.

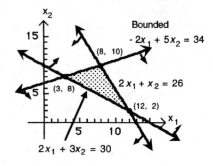

Step (2): Evaluate the objective function at each corner point. The value of P at each corner point is:

Corner Point	$P = 20x_1 + 10x_2$
$(3, 8)$	$P = 20(3) + 10(8) = 140$
$(8, 10)$	$P = 20(8) + 10(10) = 260$
$(12, 2)$	$P = 20(12) + 10(2) = 260$

Step (3): Determine the optimal solutions.
The minimum occurs at $x_1 = 3$, $x_2 = 8$, and the minimum value is $P = 140$; the maximum occurs at $x_1 = 8$, $x_2 = 10$, at $x_1 = 12$, $x_2 = 2$, and at any point along the line segment joining $(8, 10)$ and $(12, 2)$. The maximum value is $P = 260$.

23. Step (1): Graph the feasible region and find the corner points. The feasible region S is the set of solutions of the given inequalities, and is indicated by the shading in the graph at the right.

The corner points are $(0, 0)$, $(0, 800)$, $(400, 600)$, $(600, 450)$, and $(900, 0)$. Since S is bounded, it follows from 4(a) that P has a maximum value.

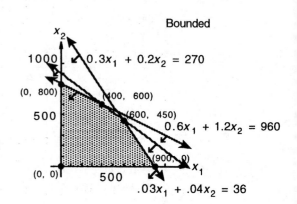

Step (2): Evaluate the objective function at each corner point.
The value of P at each corner point is:

Corner Point	$P = 20x_1 + 30x_2$
$(0, 0)$	$P = 20(0) + 30(0) = 0$
$(0, 800)$	$P = 20(0) + 30(800) = 24,000$
$(400, 600)$	$P = 20(400) + 30(600) = 26,000$
$(600, 450)$	$P = 20(600) + 30(450) = 25,500$
$(900, 0)$	$P = 20(900) + 30(0) = 18,000$

Step (3): Determine the optimal solution.
The maximum occurs at $x_1 = 400$, $x_2 = 600$, and the maximum value is $P = 26,000$.

25. $\ell_1: 275x_1 + 322x_2 = 3,381$
$\ell_2: 350x_1 + 340x_2 = 3,762$
$\ell_3: 425x_1 + 306x_2 = 4,114.$

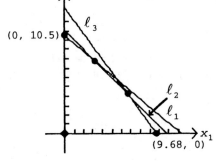

Step (1): Graph the feasible region and find the corner points.
The feasible region S is the solution set of the given inequalities, and is indicated by the shading in the graph at the right.
The corner points are $(0, 0)$, $(0, 10.5)$, $(3.22, 7.75)$, $(6.62, 4.25)$, $(9.68, 0)$.

Step (2): Evaluate the objective function at each corner point.
The value of P at each corner point is

Corner Point	$P = 525x_1 + 478x_2$
$(0, 0)$	$P = 525(0) + 478(0) = 0$
$(0, 10.5)$	$P = 525(0) + 478(10.5) = 5,019$
$(3.22, 7.75)$	$P = 525(3.22) + 478(7.75) = 5,395$
$(6.62, 4.25)$	$P = 525(6.62) + 478(4.25) = 5,507$
$(9.68, 0)$	$P = 525(9.68) + 478(0) = 5,082$

Step (3): Determine the optimal solution.
The maximum occurs at $x_1 = 6.62$, $x_2 = 4.25$, and the maximum value is $P = 5,507$.

27. Minimize and maximize $z = x_1 - x_2$
Subject to
$$x_1 - 2x_2 \leq 0$$
$$2x_1 - x_2 \leq 6$$
$$x_1, x_2 \geq 0$$

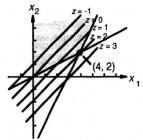

The feasible region and several values of the objective function are shown in the figure.

The points $(0, 0)$ and $(4, 2)$ are the corner points; $z = x_1 - x_2$ does not have a minimum value. Its maximum value is 2 at $(4, 2)$.

29. The value of $P = ax_1 + bx_2$, $a > 0$, $b > 0$, at each corner point is:

Corner Point	P
O: (0, 0)	$P = a(0) + b(0) = 0$
A: (0, 5)	$P = a(0) + b(5) = 5b$
B: (4, 3)	$P = a(4) + b(3) = 4a + 3b$
C: (5, 0)	$P = a(5) + b(0) = 5a$

(A) For the maximum value of P to occur at A only, we must have $5b > 4a + 3b$ and $5b > 5a$. Solving the first inequality, we get $2b > 4a$ or $b > 2a$; from the second inequality, we get $b > a$. Therefore, we must have $b > 2a$ or $2a < b$ in order for P to have its maximum value at A only.

(B) For the maximum value of P to occur at B only, we must have $4a + 3b > 5b$ and $4a + 3b > 5a$. Solving this pair of inequalities, we get $4a > 2b$ and $3b > a$, which is the same as $\frac{a}{3} < b < 2a$.

(C) For the maximum value of P to occur at C only, we must have $5a > 4a + 3b$ and $5a > 5b$. This pair of inequalities implies that $a > 3b$ or $b < \frac{a}{3}$.

(D) For the maximum value of P to occur at both A and B, we must have $5b = 4a + 3b$ or $b = 2a$.

(E) For the maximum value of P to occur at both B and C, we must have $4a + 3b = 5a$ or $b = \frac{a}{3}$.

31. (A) Construct the mathematical model

　a. Decision variables:
　　Let x_1 = Number of trick skis
　　　x_2 = Number of slalom skis

　b. Relevant material in table form:

	Trick ski	Slalom ski	Labor-hours available
Fabricating	6	4	108
Finishing	1	1	24
Profit	$40/ski	$30/ski	

　c. Objective function:
　　Maximize profit $P = 40x_1 + 30x_2$

　d. Problem constraints:
　　　$6x_1 + 4x_2 \leq 108$　　[Fabricating constraint]
　　　$x_1 + x_2 \leq 24$　　[Finishing constraint]

　e. Non-negativity constraints
　　　$x_1 \geq 0$, $x_2 \geq 0$

The mathematical model for this problem is:

$$\text{Maximize } P = 40x_1 + 30x_2$$
$$\text{Subject to: } 6x_1 + 4x_2 \leq 108$$
$$x_1 + x_2 \leq 24$$
$$x_1 \geq 0, \ x_2 \geq 0$$

Step (1): Graph the feasible region and find the corner points.

The feasible region S is the solution set of the given system of inequalities, and is indicated by the shading in the graph below.

The corner points are $(0, 0)$, $(0, 24)$, $(6, 18)$, and $(18, 0)$.

Since S is bounded, P has a maximum value by $\underline{4}$(a).

Step (2): Evaluate the objective function at each corner point. The value of P at each corner point is:

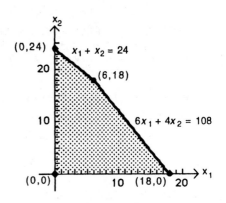

Corner Point	$P = 40x_1 + 30x_2$
$(0, 0)$	$P = 40(0) + 30(0) = 0$
$(0, 24)$	$P = 40(0) + 30(24) = 720$
$(6, 18)$	$P = 40(6) + 30(18) = 780$
$(18, 0)$	$P = 40(18) + 30(0) = 720$

Step (3): Determine the optimal solution. The maximum occurs when $x_1 = 6$ (trick skis) and $x_2 = 18$ (slalom skis) are produced. The maximum profit is $P = \$780$.

(B)

Corner Point	$P = 40x_1 + 25x_2$
$(0, 0)$	$P = 40(0) + 25(0) = 0$
$(0, 24)$	$P = 40(0) + 25(24) = 600$
$(6, 18)$	$P = 40(6) + 25(18) = 690$
$(18, 0)$	$P = 40(18) + 25(0) = 720$

The maximum profit decreases to $720 when 18 trick skis and no slalom skis are produced.

(C)

Corner Point	$P = 40x_1 + 45x_2$
$(0, 0)$	$P = 40(0) + 45(0) = 0$
$(0, 24)$	$P = 40(0) + 45(24) = 1080$
$(6, 18)$	$P = 40(6) + 45(18) = 1050$
$(18, 0)$	$P = 40(18) + 45(0) = 720$

The maximum profit increases to $1,080 when no trick skis and 24 slalom skis are produced.

33. (A) Construct the mathematical model

    a. Decision variables:

        Let x_1 = Number of days to operate Plant A

            x_2 = Number of days to operate Plant B

    b. Relevant material in table form:

	Plant A	Plant B	Amount required
Tables	20	25	200
Chairs	60	60	500
Cost/day	$1000	$900	

    c. Objective function:

        Minimize the cost $C = 1000x_1 + 900x_2$

    d. Problem constraints:

        $20x_1 + 25x_2 \geq 200$ [Table constraint]

        $60x_1 + 60x_2 \geq 500$ [Chair constraint]

    e. Non-negativity constraints

        $x_1 \geq 0,\ x_2 \geq 0$

    The mathematical model for this problem is:

            Minimize $C = 1000x_1 + 900x_2$

          Subject to: $20x_1 + 25x_2 \geq 200$

                    $60x_1 + 50x_2 \geq 500$

                    $x_1 \geq 0,\ x_2 \geq 0$

<u>Step (1)</u>: Graph the feasible region and find the corner points.

    The feasible region S is the solution set of the system of inequalities, and is indicated by the shading in the graph shown below.

    The corner points are (0, 10), (5, 4), and (10, 0).

    Since S is unbounded and $a = 1000 > 0$, $b = 900 > 0$, C has a minimum value by <u>4</u>(b).

<u>Step (2)</u>: Evaluate the objective function at each corner point.

The value of C at each corner point is:

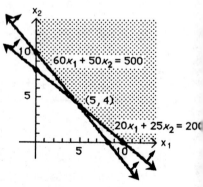

Corner Point	$C = 1000x_1 + 900x_2$
(0, 10)	$C = 1000(0) + 900(10) = 9{,}000$
(5, 4)	$C = 1000(5) + 900(4) = 8{,}600$
(10, 0)	$C = 1000(10) + 900(0) = 10{,}000$

<u>Step (3)</u>: Determine the optimal solution.

The minimum occurs when $x_1 = 5$ and $x_2 = 4$.

That is, Plant A should be operated five days and Plant B should be operated four days. The minimum cost is $C = \$8600$.

Corner Point | $C = 600x_1 + 900x_2$

Corner Point	$C = 600x_1 + 900x_2$
(0, 10)	$C = 600(0) + 900(10) = 9000$
(5, 4)	$C = 600(5) + 900(4) = 6600$
(10, 0)	$C = 600(10) + 900(0) = 6000$

The minimum cost decreases to \$6,000 per day when Plant A is operated 10 days and Plant B is operated 0 days.

(C) Corner Point | $C = 1000x_1 + 800x_2$

Corner Point	$C = 1000x_1 + 800x_2$
(0, 10)	$C = 600(0) + 800(10) = 8,000$
(5, 4)	$C = 1000(5) + 800(4) = 8,200$
(10, 0)	$C = 1000(10) + 800(0) = 10,000$

The minimum cost decreases to \$8,000 per day when Plant A is operated 0 days and Plant B is operated 10 days.

35. (A) Construct the mathematical model

  a. Decision variables:
     Let x_1 = Number of buses
         x_2 = Number of vans

  b. Relevant material in table form:

	Buses	Vans	Number to accomodate
Students	40	8	400
Chaperones	3	1	36
Rental cost	\$1200/bus	\$100/van	

  c. Objective function:
     Minimize the cost $C = 1200x_1 + 100x_2$

  d. Problem constraints:
     $40x_1 + 8x_2 \geq 400$ [Student constraint]
     $3x_1 + x_2 \leq 36$ [Chaperone constraint]

  e. Non-negative constraints
     $x_1 \geq 0$, $x_2 \geq 0$

  The mathematical model for this problem is:
       Minimize $C = 1200x_1 + 100x_2$
       Subject to: $40x_1 + 8x_2 \geq 400$
                   $3x_1 + x_2 \leq 36$
                   $x_1 \geq 0$, $x_2 \geq 0$

<u>Step (1)</u>: Graph the feasible region and find the corner points.

The feasible region S is the solution set of the system of inequalities, and is indicated by the shading in the graph at the right.

The corner points are (10, 0), (7, 15), and (12, 0).

Since S is bounded, C has a minimum value by <u>4</u>(a).

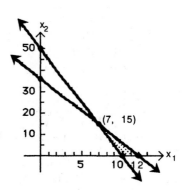

Step (2): Evaluate the objective function at each corner point. The value of C at each corner point is:

Corner Point	$C = 1200x_1 + 100x_2$
(10, 0)	$C = 1200(10) + 100(0) = 12,000$
(7, 15)	$C = 1200(7) + 100(15) = 9,900$
(12, 0)	$C = 1200(12) + 100(0) = 14,400$

Step (3): Determine the optimal solution.
The minimum occurs when $x_1 = 7$ and $x_2 = 15$. That is, the officers should rent 7 buses and 15 vans at the minimum cost of $9900.

37. (A) Construct the mathematical model
   a. Decision variables:
      Let x_1 = Amount invested in the CD
          x_2 = Amount invested in the mutual fund

   c. Objective function:
      Maximize the return $P = 0.05x_1 + 0.09x_2$

   d. Problem constraints:
   $$x_1 + x_2 \leq 60,000 \qquad \text{[Amount available constraint]}$$
   $$x_2 \geq 10,000 \qquad \text{[Mutual fund constraint]}$$
   $$x_1 \geq 2x_2 \qquad \text{[Investor constraint]}$$

   e. Non-negative constraints
   $$x_1 \geq 0, \ x_2 \geq 0$$

The mathematical model for this problem is
Maximize $P = 0.05x_1 + 0.09x_2$
Subject to $x_1 + x_2 \leq 60,000$
                   $x_2 \geq 10,000$
                   $x_1 \geq 2x_2$
        $x_1, \ x_2 \geq 0$

The feasible region S is the solution set of the system of inequalities and is indicated by the shading in the graph.

The corner points are (20,000, 10,000), (40,000, 20,000) and (50,000, 10,000).

Since S is bounded, P has a maximum value by 4<u>a</u>.

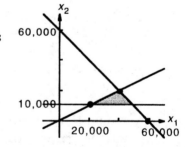

The value of P at each corner point is given in the table below.

Corner Point	$P = x_1 + x_2$
(20,000, 10,000)	$P = 0.05(20,000) + 0.09(10,000) = 1900$
(40,000, 20,000)	$P = 0.05(40,000) + 0.09(20,000) = 3800$
(50,000, 10,000)	$P = 0.05(50,000) + 0.09(10,000) = 3400$

Thus, the maximum return is $3,800 when $40,000 is invested in the CD and $20,000 is invested in the mutual fund.

39. Construct the mathematical model

     a. Decision variables:

        Let x_1 = Number of gallons produced by old process

            x_2 = Number of gallons produced by new process

     b. Relevant material in table form:

	Grams/gallon old process	Grams/gallon new process	Maximum allowed
Sulfur dioxide	20	5	16,000
Particulate	40	20	30,000
Profit	60¢/gal	20¢/gal	

     c. Objective function:

        Maximize the profit function $P = 60x_1 + 20x_2$

     d. Problem constraints:

        $20x_1 + 5x_2 \leq 16,000$ [Sulfur dioxide constraint]

        $40x_1 + 20x_2 \leq 30,000$ [Particulate constraint]

     e. Non-negative constraints

        $x_1 \geq 0,\ x_2 \geq 0$

     The mathematical model for this problem is:

$$\text{Maximize } P = 60x_1 + 20x_2$$
$$\text{Subject to: } 20x_1 + 5x_2 \leq 16,000$$
$$40x_1 + 20x_2 \leq 30,000$$
$$x_1 \geq 0,\ x_2 \geq 0$$

<u>Step (1)</u>: Graph the feasible region and find the corner points.

The feasible region S is the solution set of the given inequalities, and is indicated by the shading in the graph at the right.

The corner points are $(0, 0)$, $(0, 1500)$, and $(750, 0)$.

Since S is bounded, P has a maximum value by <u>4</u>(a).

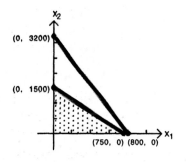

<u>Step (2)</u>: Evaluate the objective function at each corner point.

    The value of P at each corner point is:

Corner Point	$P = 60x_1 + 20x_2$
(0, 0)	$P = 60(0) + 20(0) = 0$ (cents)
(0, 1500)	$P = 60(0) + 20(1500) = 30,000$ (cents)
(750, 0)	$P = 60(750) + 20(0) = 45,000$ (cents)

<u>Step (3)</u>: The maximum profit is $450 when 750 gallons are produced using the old process exclusively.

(B) The mathematical model for this problem is:
Maximize $P = 60x_1 + 20x_2$
Subject to: $20x_1 + 5x_2 \leq 11,500$
$40x_1 + 20x_2 \leq 30,000$

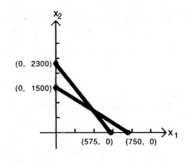

The feasible region S for this problem is indicated by the shading in the graph at the right.

The corner points are $(0, 0)$, $(0, 1500)$, $(400, 700)$, and $(575, 0)$.

The value P at each corner point is:

Corner Point	$P = 60x_1 + 20x_2$
$(0, 0)$	$P = 60(0) + 20(0) = 0$
$(0, 1500)$	$P = 60(0) + 20(1,500) = 30,000$
$(400, 700)$	$P = 60(400) + 20(700) = 38,000$
$(575, 0)$	$P = 60(575) + 20(0) = 34,500$

The maximum profit is $380 when 400 gallons are produced using the old process and 700 gallons using the new process.

(C) The mathematical model for this problem is:
Maximize $P = 60x_1 + 20x_2$
Subject to: $20x_1 + 5x_2 \leq 7,200$
$40x_1 + 20x_2 \leq 30,000$

The feasible region S for this problem is indicated by the shading in the graph at the right. The corner points are $(0, 0)$, $(0, 1440)$, and $(360, 0)$.
The value of P at each corner point is:

Corner Point	$P = 60x_1 + 20x_2$
$(0, 0)$	$P = 60(0) + 20(0) = 0$
$(0, 1440)$	$P = 60(0) + 20(1,440) = 28,800$
$(360, 0)$	$P = 60(360) + 20(0) = 21,600$

The maximum profit is $288 when 1,440 gallons are produced by the new process exclusively.

41. Construct the mathematical model
a. Decision variables:
Let x_1 = Number of bags of Brand A
x_2 = Number of bags of Brand B

b. Relevant material in table form:

	Brand A	Brand B	Amounts
Phosphoric acid	4	4	1000
Chlorine	2	1	400
Nitrogen	8 lbs.	3 lbs.	

c. Objective function:
   Maximize the amount of nitrogen $N = 8x_1 + 3x_2$

d. Problem constraints:
   $4x_1 + 4x_2 \geq 1,000$ [Phosphoric acid constraint]
   $2x_1 + x_2 \leq 400$ [Chlorine constraint]

e. Non-negative constraints
   $x_1 \geq 0, \; x_2 \geq 0$

(A) The mathematical model for this problem is:
Maximize $N = 8x_1 + 3x_2$
Subject to: $4x_1 + 4x_2 \geq 1000$
$2x_1 + x_2 \leq 400$
$x_1 \geq 0, \; x_2 \geq 0$

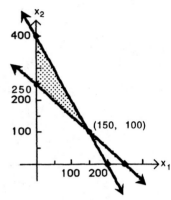

The feasible region S is the solution
set of the system of inequalities, and is
indicated by the shading in the graph at the
right. The corner points are $(0, 250)$,
$(0, 400)$, and $(150, 100)$.
Since S is bounded, N has a maximum value by 4(a).
The value of N at each corner point is given in the table below:

Corner Point	$N = 8x_1 + 3x_2$
$(0, 250)$	$N = 8(0) + 3(250) = 750$
$(150, 100)$	$N = 8(150) + 3(100) = 1500$
$(0, 400)$	$N = 8(0) + 3(400) = 1200$

Thus, the maximum occurs when $x_1 = 150$ and $x_2 = 100$. That is, the
grower should use 150 bags of Brand A and 100 bags of Brand B. The
maximum number of pounds of nitrogen is 1500.

(B) The mathematical model for this problem is:
Minimize $N = 8x_1 + 3x_2$
Subject to: $4x_1 + 4x_2 \geq 1000$
$2x_1 + x_2 \leq 400$
$x_1 \geq 0, \; x_2 \geq 0$

The feasible region S and the corner points are the same as in part
(A). Thus, the minimum occurs when $x_1 = 0$ and $x_2 = 250$. That is,
the grower should use 0 bags of Brand A and 250 bags of Brand B.
The minimum number of pounds of nitrogen is 750.

43. Construct the mathematical model

a. Decision variables:

Let x_1 = Number of cubic yards of mix A

x_2 = Number of cubic yards of mix B

b. Relevant material in table form:

	Amount per Cubic Yard (in pounds)		Minimum monthly requirement
	Mix A	Mix B	
Phosphoric acid	20	10	460
Nitrogen	30	30	960
Potash	5	10	220
Cost/cubic yd.	$30	$35	

c. Objective function:

Minimize the cost $C = 30x_1 + 35x_2$

d. Problem constraints:

$20x_1 + 10x_2 \geq 460$ [Phosphoric acid constraint]

$30x_1 + 30x_2 \geq 960$ [Nitrogen constraint]

$5x_1 + 10x_2 \geq 220$ [Potash constraint]

e. Non-negative constraints

$x_1 \geq 0, \ x_2 \geq 0$

The mathematical model for this problem is:

Minimize $C = 30x_1 + 35x_2$

Subject to: $20x_1 + 10x_2 \geq 460$

$30x_1 + 30x_2 \geq 960$

$5x_1 + 10x_2 \geq 220$

$x_1 \geq 0, \ x_2 \geq 0$

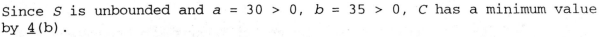

The feasible region S is the solution set of the given inequalities and is indicated by the shading in the graph at the right.

The corner points are $(0, 46)$, $(14, 18)$, $(20, 12)$, and $(44, 0)$.

Since S is unbounded and $a = 30 > 0$, $b = 35 > 0$, C has a minimum value by 4(b).

The value of C at each corner point is:

Corner Point	$C = 30x_1 + 35x_2$
$(0, 46)$	$C = 30(0) + 35(46) = 1610$
$(14, 18)$	$C = 30(14) + 35(18) = 1050$
$(20, 12)$	$C = 30(20) + 35(12) = 1020$
$(44, 0)$	$C = 30(44) + 35(0) = 1320$

Thus, the minimum occurs when the amount of mix A used is 20 cubic yards and the amount of mix B used is 12 cubic yards. The minimum cost is $C = \$1020$.

45. Construct the mathematical model

    a. Decision variables:

       Let x_1 = Number of mice used

          x_2 = Number of rats used

    c. Objective function:

       Maximize the number of mice and rats used $P = x_1 + x_2$

    d. Problem constraints:

       $10x_1 + 20x_2 \leq 800$ [Box A constraint]

       $20x_1 + 10x_2 \leq 640$ [Box B constraint]

    e. Non-negative constraints

       $x_1 \geq 0, \ x_2 \geq 0$

The mathematical model for this problem is:

Maximize $P = x_1 + x_2$

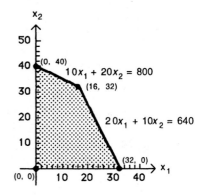

Subject to: $10x_1 + 20x_2 \leq 800$

             $20x_1 + 10x_2 \leq 640$

             $x_1 \geq 0, \ x_2 \geq 0$

The feasible region S is the solution set of
the given inequalities, and is indicated by
the shading in the graph at the right.
The corner points are $(0, 0)$, $(0, 40)$,
$(16, 32)$, and $(32, 0)$.

Since S is bounded, P has a maximum value by <u>4</u>(a).

The value of P at each corner point is:

Corner Point	$P = x_1 + x_2$
$(0, 0)$	$P = 0 + 0 = 0$
$(0, 40)$	$P = 0 + 40 = 40$
$(16, 32)$	$P = 16 + 32 = 48$
$(32, 0)$	$P = 32 + 0 = 32$

Thus, the maximum occurs when the number of mice used is 16 and the
number of rats used is 32. The maximum number of mice and rats that can
be used is 48.

EXERCISE 11-3

Things to remember:

<u>1</u>. STANDARD MAXIMIZATION PROBLEM IN STANDARD FORM

    A linear programming problem is said to be a STANDARD
    MAXIMIZATION PROBLEM IN STANDARD FORM if its mathematical model
    is of the form:

       Maximize $P = c_1x_1 + c_2x_2 + \cdots + c_nx_n$

       Subject to problem constraints of the form:

       $a_1x_1 + a_2x_2 + \cdots + a_nx_n \leq b, \quad b \geq 0$

       with nonnegative constraints:

       $x_1, \ x_2, \ \ldots, \ x_n \geq 0$.

[<u>Note</u>: The coefficients of the objective function can be any real numbers.]

2. SLACK VARIABLES

Given a linear programming problem. SLACK VARIABLES are nonnegative quantities that are introduced to convert problem constraint inequalities into equations.

3. BASIC VARIABLES AND NONBASIC VARIABLES; BASIC SOLUTIONS AND BASIC FEASIBLE SOLUTIONS

Given a system of linear equations associated with a linear programming problem. (Such a system will always have more variables than equations.)

The variables are divided into two (mutually exclusive) groups, called BASIC VARIABLES and NONBASIC VARIABLES, as follows: Basic variables are selected arbitrarily with the one restriction that there be as many basic variables as there are equations. The remaining variables are called nonbasic variables.

A solution found by setting the nonbasic variables equal to zero and solving for the basic variables is called a BASIC SOLUTION. If a basic solution has no negative values, it is a BASIC FEASIBLE SOLUTION.

4. FUNDAMENTAL THEOREM OF LINEAR PROGRAMMING

If the optimal value of the objective function in a linear programming problem exists, then that value must occur at one (or more) of the basic feasible solutions.

---

1. (A) Since there are 2 problem constraints, 2 slack variables are introduced.

(B) Since there are two equations (from the two problem constraints) and three decision variables, there are two basic variables and three nonbasic variables.

(C) There will be two linear equations and two variables.

3. (A) There are 5 constraint equations; the number of equations is the same as the number of slack variables.

(B) There are 4 decision variables since there are 9 variables altogether, and 5 of them are slack variables.

(C) There are 5 basic variables and 4 nonbasic variables; the number of basic variables equals the number of equations.

(D) Five linear equations with 5 variables.

5.

	Nonbasic	Basic	Feasible?
(A)	x_1, x_2	s_1, s_2	Yes, all values are nonnegative.
(B)	x_1, s_1	x_2, s_2	Yes, all values are nonnegative.
(C)	x_1, s_2	x_2, s_1	No, $s_1 = -12 < 0$.
(D)	x_2, s_1	x_1, s_2	No, $s_2 = -12 < 0$.
(E)	x_2, s_2	x_1, s_1	Yes, all values are nonnegative.
(F)	s_1, s_2	x_1, x_2	Yes, all values are nonnegative.

Evaluate z at each basic feasible solution; the maximum value of $z = 2x_1 + 3x_2$ is 24 at $x_1 = 0$, $x_2 = 8$; at $x_1 = 6$, $x_2 = 4$; at every point of the line segment joining $(0, 8)$ and $(6, 4)$.

7.

	x_1	x_2	s_1	s_2	Feasible?
(A)	0	0	50	40	Yes, all values are nonnegative.
(B)	0	50	0	-60	No, $s_2 = -60 < 0$.
(C)	0	20	30	0	Yes, all values are nonnegative.
(D)	25	0	0	15	Yes, all values are nonnegative.
(E)	40	0	-30	0	No, $s_1 = -30 < 0$.
(F)	20	10	0	0	Yes, all values are nonnegative.

9.

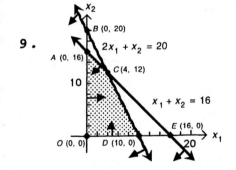

Introduce slack variables s_1 and s_2 to obtain the system of equations:

$$x_1 + x_2 + s_1 \qquad = 16$$
$$2x_1 + x_2 \qquad + s_2 = 20$$

x_1	x_2	s_1	s_2	Intersection Point	Feasible?
0	0	16	20	O	Yes
0	16	0	4	A	Yes
0	20	-4	0	B	No, $s_1 = -4 < 0$
16	0	0	-12	E	No, $s_2 = -12 < 0$
10	0	6	0	D	Yes
4	12	0	0	C	Yes

11.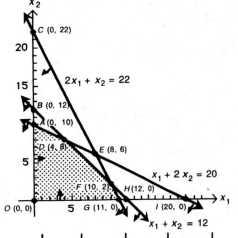

Introduce slack variables s_1, s_2, and s_3 to obtain the system of equations:

$$2x_1 + x_2 + s_1 \qquad\qquad = 22$$
$$x_1 + x_2 \qquad + s_2 \qquad = 12$$
$$x_1 + 2x_2 \qquad\qquad + s_3 = 20$$

x_1	x_2	s_1	s_2	s_3	Intersection Point	Feasible?
0	0	22	12	20	O	Yes
0	22	0	-10	-24	C	No
0	12	10	0	-4	B	No
0	10	12	2	0	A	Yes
11	0	0	1	9	G	Yes
12	0	-2	0	8	H	No
20	0	-18	-8	0	I	No
10	2	0	0	6	F	Yes
8	6	0	-2	0	E	No
4	8	6	0	0	D	Yes

EXERCISE 11-4

Things to remember:

<u>1.</u>   PROCEDURE: SELECTING BASIC AND NONBASIC VARIABLES FOR THE SIMPLEX PROCESS
Given a simplex tableau.

   (a) Determine the number of basic and the number of nonbasic variables. These numbers do not change during the simplex process.

   (b) SELECTING BASIC VARIABLES: A variable can be selected as a basic variable only if it corresponds to a column in the tableau that has exactly one nonzero element (usually 1) and the nonzero element in the column is not in the same row as the nonzero element in the column of another basic variable. (This procedure always selects P as a basic variable, since the P column never changes during the simplex process.)

(c) SELECTING NONBASIC VARIABLES: After the basic variables are selected in Step (b), the remaining variables are selected as the nonbasic variables. (The tableau columns under the nonbasic variables will usually contain more than one nonzero element.)

2. PROCEDURE: SELECTING THE PIVOT ELEMENT

(a) Locate the most negative indicator in the bottom row of the tableau to the left of the P column (the negative number with the largest absolute value). The column containing this element is the PIVOT COLUMN. If there is a tie for the most negative, choose either.

(b) Divide each POSITIVE element in the pivot column above the dashed line into the corresponding element in the last column. The PIVOT ROW is the row corresponding to the smallest quotient. If there is a tie for the smallest quotient, choose either. If the pivot column above the dashed line has no positive elements, then there is no solution and we stop.

(c) The PIVOT (or PIVOT ELEMENT) is the element in the intersection of the pivot column and pivot row. [Note: The pivot element is always positive and is never in the bottom row.]

[Remember: The entering variable is at the top of the pivot column and the exiting variable is at the left of the pivot row.]

3. PROCEDURE: PERFORMING THE PIVOT OPERATION

A PIVOT OPERATION or PIVOTING consists of performing row operations as follows:

(a) Multiply the pivot row by the reciprocal of the pivot element to transform the pivot element into a 1. (If the pivot element is already a 1, omit this step.)

(b) Add multiples of the pivot row to other rows in the tableau to transform all other nonzero elements in the pivot column into 0's.

[Note: Rows are not to be interchanged while performing a pivot operation. The only way the (positive) pivot element can be transformed into 1 (if it is not a 1 already) is for the pivot row to be multiplied by the reciprocal of the pivot element.]

4. SIMPLEX ALGORITHM FOR STANDARD MAXIMIZATION PROBLEMS

Problem constraints are of the ≤ form with nonnegative constants on the right hand side. The coefficients of the objective function can be any real numbers.

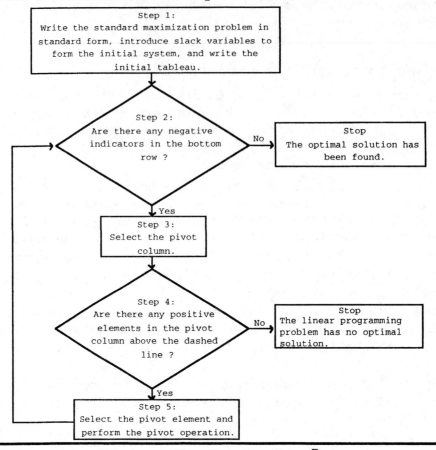

1. Given the simplex tableau:

$$
\begin{array}{ccccc}
x_1 & x_2 & s_1 & s_2 & P \\
\end{array}
$$
$$
\left[
\begin{array}{ccccc|c}
2 & 1 & 0 & 3 & 0 & 12 \\
3 & 0 & 1 & -2 & 0 & 15 \\
\hline
-4 & 0 & 0 & 4 & 1 & 20
\end{array}
\right]
$$

which corresponds to the system of equations:

$$
\text{(I)} \quad
\begin{cases}
2x_1 + x_2 \quad\quad\; + 3s_2 \quad\quad\;\; = 12 \\
3x_1 \quad\quad + s_1 - 2s_2 \quad\quad\; = 15 \\
-4x_1 \quad\quad\quad\quad + 4s_2 + P = 20
\end{cases}
$$

(A) The basic variables are x_2, s_1, and P, and the nonbasic variables are x_1 and s_2.

(B) The corresponding basic feasible solution is found by setting the nonbasic variables equal to 0 in system (I). This yields:

$$x_1 = 0, \; x_2 = 12, \; s_1 = 15, \; s_2 = 0, \; P = 20$$

(C) An additional pivot is required, since the last row of the tableau has a negative indicator, the -4 in the first column.

634

3. Given the simplex tableau:

$$\begin{array}{ccccccc} x_1 & x_2 & x_3 & s_1 & s_2 & s_3 & P \\ \end{array}$$

$$\left[\begin{array}{ccccccc|c} -2 & 0 & 1 & 3 & 1 & 0 & 0 & 5 \\ 0 & 1 & 0 & -2 & 0 & 0 & 0 & 15 \\ -1 & 0 & 0 & 4 & 1 & 1 & 0 & 12 \\ \hline -4 & 0 & 0 & 2 & 4 & 0 & 1 & 45 \end{array}\right]$$

which corresponds to the system of equations:

$$(\text{I}) \quad \begin{cases} -2x_1 & + x_3 + 3s_1 + s_2 & = 5 \\ x_2 & - 2s_1 & = 15 \\ -x_1 & + 4s_1 + s_2 + s_3 & = 12 \\ -4x_1 & + 2s_1 + 4s_2 & + P = 45 \end{cases}$$

(A) The basic variables are x_2, x_3, s_3, and P, and the nonbasic variables are x_1, s_1, and s_2.

(B) The corresponding basic feasible solution is found by setting the nonbasic variables equal to 0 in system (I). This yields:
$x_1 = 0$, $x_2 = 15$, $x_3 = 5$, $s_1 = 0$, $s_2 = 0$, $s_3 = 12$, $P = 45$

(C) Since the last row of the tableau has a negative indicator, the -4 in the first column, an additional pivot should be required. However, since there are no positive elements in the pivot column (the first column), the problem has *no solution*.

5. Given the simplex tableau:

$$\begin{array}{ccccc} x_1 & x_2 & s_1 & s_2 & P \\ \end{array}$$

$$\left[\begin{array}{ccccc|c} 1 & 4 & 1 & 0 & 0 & 4 \\ 3 & 5 & 0 & 1 & 0 & 24 \\ \hline -8 & -5 & 0 & 0 & 1 & 0 \end{array}\right]$$

The most negative indicator is -8 in the first column. Thus, the first column is the pivot column. Now, $\dfrac{4}{1} = 4$ and $\dfrac{24}{3} = 8$. Thus, the first row is the pivot row and the pivot element is the element in the first row, first column. These are indicated in the following tableau.

Enter

$$\begin{array}{cccccc} & x_1 & x_2 & s_1 & s_2 & P \\ \end{array}$$

$$\text{Exit } \begin{array}{c} s_1 \\ s_2 \\ P \end{array} \left[\begin{array}{ccccc|c} ① & 4 & 1 & 0 & 0 & 4 \\ 3 & 5 & 0 & 1 & 0 & 24 \\ \hline -8 & -5 & 0 & 0 & 1 & 0 \end{array}\right] \begin{array}{l} \frac{4}{1} = 4 \text{ (minimum)} \\ \frac{24}{3} = 8 \end{array}$$

$$\left[\begin{array}{ccccc|c} ① & 4 & 1 & 0 & 0 & 4 \\ 3 & 5 & 0 & 1 & 0 & 24 \\ \hline -8 & -5 & 0 & 0 & 1 & 0 \end{array}\right] \sim \left[\begin{array}{ccccc|c} 1 & 4 & 1 & 0 & 0 & 4 \\ 0 & -7 & -3 & 1 & 0 & 12 \\ \hline 0 & 27 & 8 & 0 & 1 & 32 \end{array}\right]$$

$$(-3)R_1 + R_2 \rightarrow R_2$$
$$8R_1 + R_3 \rightarrow R_3$$

7. Given the simplex tableau:

$$
\begin{array}{cccccc}
x_1 & x_2 & s_1 & s_2 & s_3 & P \\
\end{array}
$$

$$
\left[\begin{array}{cccccc|c}
2 & 1 & 1 & 0 & 0 & 0 & 4 \\
3 & 0 & 1 & 1 & 0 & 0 & 8 \\
0 & 0 & 2 & 0 & 1 & 0 & 2 \\
\hline
-4 & 0 & -3 & 0 & 0 & 1 & 5
\end{array}\right]
$$

The most negative indicator is -4. Thus, the first column is the pivot column. Now, $\dfrac{4}{2} = 2$, $\dfrac{8}{3} = 2\dfrac{2}{3}$. Thus, the first row is the pivot row, and the pivot element is the element in the first row, first column. These are indicated in the tableau.

$$
\begin{array}{r}
\text{Enter} \\
\end{array}
$$

$$
\begin{array}{cccccccc}
& x_1 & x_2 & s_1 & s_2 & s_3 & P & \\
\text{Exit } x_2 & \left(2\right) & 1 & 1 & 0 & 0 & 0 & 4 \\
s_2 & 3 & 0 & 1 & 1 & 0 & 0 & 8 \\
s_3 & 0 & 0 & 2 & 0 & 1 & 0 & 2 \\
P & -4 & 0 & -3 & 0 & 0 & 1 & 5 \\
\end{array}
$$

$\dfrac{4}{2} = 2$ (minimum)

$\dfrac{8}{3} = 2\dfrac{2}{3}$

$$
\left[\begin{array}{cccccc|c}
\left(2\right) & 1 & 1 & 0 & 0 & 0 & 4 \\
3 & 0 & 1 & 1 & 0 & 0 & 8 \\
0 & 0 & 2 & 0 & 1 & 0 & 2 \\
\hline
-4 & 0 & -3 & 0 & 0 & 1 & 5
\end{array}\right]
\sim
\left[\begin{array}{cccccc|c}
\left(1\right) & \frac{1}{2} & \frac{1}{2} & 0 & 0 & 0 & 2 \\
3 & 0 & 1 & 1 & 0 & 0 & 8 \\
0 & 0 & 2 & 0 & 1 & 0 & 2 \\
\hline
-4 & 0 & -3 & 0 & 0 & 1 & 5
\end{array}\right]
$$

$$
\begin{array}{cccccc}
x_1 & x_2 & s_1 & s_2 & s_3 & P \\
\end{array}
$$

$\dfrac{1}{2}R_1 \rightarrow R_1$

$(-3)R_1 + R_2 \rightarrow R_2, \quad 4R_1 + R_4 \rightarrow R_4$

$$
\sim
\left[\begin{array}{cccccc|c}
1 & \frac{1}{2} & \frac{1}{2} & 0 & 0 & 0 & 2 \\
0 & -\frac{3}{2} & -\frac{1}{2} & 1 & 0 & 0 & 2 \\
0 & 0 & 2 & 0 & 1 & 0 & 2 \\
\hline
0 & 2 & -1 & 0 & 0 & 1 & 13
\end{array}\right]
$$

9. (A) Introduce slack variables s_1 and s_2 to obtain:

Maximize $P = 15x_1 + 10x_2$

Subject to:
$$
\begin{aligned}
2x_1 + x_2 + s_1 \quad\quad &= 10 \\
x_1 + 3x_2 \quad\quad + s_2 &= 10 \\
x_1,\ x_2,\ s_1,\ s_2 &\geq 0
\end{aligned}
$$

This system can be written in initial form:

$$
\begin{aligned}
2x_1 + x_2 + s_1 \quad\quad\quad\quad &= 10 \\
x_1 + 3x_2 \quad + s_2 \quad\quad &= 10 \\
-15x_1 - 10x_2 \quad\quad\quad + P &= 0 \\
x_1,\ x_2,\ s_1,\ s_2 &\geq 0
\end{aligned}
$$

(B) The simplex tableau for this problem is:

$$
\begin{array}{c}
\text{Exit} \\
\\
\\
\end{array}
\begin{array}{c}
s_1 \\
s_2 \\
P
\end{array}
\overset{\text{Enter}}{\underset{}{
\begin{array}{ccccc}
x_1 & x_2 & s_1 & s_2 & P
\end{array}}}
\left[
\begin{array}{ccccc|c}
\textcircled{2} & 1 & 1 & 0 & 0 & 10 \\
1 & 3 & 0 & 1 & 0 & 10 \\
\hline
-15 & -10 & 0 & 0 & 1 & 0
\end{array}
\right]
\begin{array}{l}
\frac{10}{2} = 5 \ (\text{minimum}) \\[4pt]
\frac{10}{1} = 10 \\
\end{array}
$$

Column 1 is the pivot column (-15 is the most negative indicator). Row 1 is the pivot row (5 is the smallest positive quotient). Thus, the pivot element is the circled 2.

(C) We use the simplex method as outlined above. The pivot elements are circled.

$$
\begin{array}{c}
s_1 \\
s_2 \\
P
\end{array}
\begin{array}{ccccc}
x_1 & x_2 & s_1 & s_2 & P
\end{array}
\left[
\begin{array}{ccccc|c}
\textcircled{2} & 1 & 1 & 0 & 0 & 10 \\
1 & 3 & 0 & 1 & 0 & 10 \\
\hline
-15 & -10 & 0 & 0 & 1 & 0
\end{array}
\right]
\sim
\left[
\begin{array}{ccccc|c}
\textcircled{1} & \frac{1}{2} & \frac{1}{2} & 0 & 0 & 5 \\
1 & 3 & 0 & 1 & 0 & 10 \\
\hline
-15 & -10 & 0 & 0 & 1 & 0
\end{array}
\right]
\sim
$$

$$
\frac{1}{2}R_1 \rightarrow R_1
$$
$$
(-1)R_1 + R_2 \rightarrow R_2
$$
$$
15R_1 + R_3 \rightarrow R_3
$$

$$
\sim
\left[
\begin{array}{ccccc|c}
1 & \frac{1}{2} & \frac{1}{2} & 0 & 0 & 5 \\
0 & \textcircled{\tfrac{5}{2}} & -\frac{1}{2} & 1 & 0 & 5 \\
\hline
0 & -\frac{5}{2} & \frac{15}{2} & 0 & 1 & 75
\end{array}
\right]
\sim
\left[
\begin{array}{ccccc|c}
1 & \frac{1}{2} & \frac{1}{2} & 0 & 0 & 5 \\
0 & \textcircled{1} & -\frac{1}{5} & \frac{2}{5} & 0 & 2 \\
\hline
0 & -\frac{5}{2} & \frac{15}{2} & 0 & 1 & 75
\end{array}
\right]
$$

$$
\frac{2}{5}R_2 \rightarrow R_2
$$
$$
\left(-\frac{1}{2}\right)R_2 + R_1 \rightarrow R_1
$$
$$
\left(\frac{5}{2}\right)R_2 + R_3 \rightarrow R_3
$$

$$
\sim
\begin{array}{c}
x_1 \\
x_2 \\
P
\end{array}
\begin{array}{ccccc}
x_1 & x_2 & s_1 & s_2 & P
\end{array}
\left[
\begin{array}{ccccc|c}
1 & 0 & \frac{3}{5} & -\frac{1}{5} & 0 & 4 \\
0 & 1 & -\frac{1}{5} & \frac{2}{5} & 0 & 2 \\
\hline
0 & 0 & 7 & 1 & 1 & 80
\end{array}
\right]
$$

All elements in the last row are nonnegative. Thus, max $P = 80$ at $x_1 = 4$, $x_2 = 2$, $s_1 = 0$, $s_2 = 0$.

11. (A) Introduce slack variables s_1 and s_2 to obtain:

Maximize $P = 30x_1 + x_2$
Subject to: $2x_1 + x_2 + s_1 = 10$
$x_1 + 3x_2 + s_2 = 10$
$x_1, \ x_2, \ s_1, \ s_2 \geq 0$

This system can be written in the initial form:

$$
\begin{aligned}
2x_1 + x_2 + s_1 &= 10 \\
x_1 + 3x_2 + s_2 &= 10 \\
-30x_1 - x_2 + P &= 0
\end{aligned}
$$

(B) The simplex tableau for this problem is:

$$
\begin{array}{c}
\quad\quad\quad\quad \text{Enter} \\
\quad\quad x_1 \quad x_2 \quad s_1 \quad s_2 \quad P
\end{array}
$$

$$
\begin{array}{cc}
\text{Exit} \; s_1 \\
s_2 \\
P
\end{array}
\left[
\begin{array}{ccccc|c}
② & 1 & 1 & 0 & 0 & 10 \\
1 & 3 & 0 & 1 & 0 & 10 \\
\hline
-30 & -1 & 0 & 0 & 1 & 0
\end{array}
\right]
\begin{array}{l}
\dfrac{10}{2} = 5 \;(\text{minimum}) \\[2mm]
\dfrac{10}{1} = 10
\end{array}
$$

$$
\begin{array}{c}
\uparrow \\
\text{pivot} \\
\text{column}
\end{array}
$$

(C)

$$
\begin{array}{c}
x_1 \quad x_2 \quad s_1 \quad s_2 \quad P
\end{array}
$$

$$
\begin{array}{c}
s_1 \\
s_2 \\
P
\end{array}
\left[
\begin{array}{ccccc|c}
② & 1 & 1 & 0 & 0 & 10 \\
1 & 3 & 0 & 1 & 0 & 10 \\
\hline
-30 & -1 & 0 & 0 & 1 & 0
\end{array}
\right]
\sim
\left[
\begin{array}{ccccc|c}
① & \frac{1}{2} & \frac{1}{2} & 0 & 0 & 5 \\
1 & 3 & 0 & 1 & 0 & 10 \\
\hline
-30 & -1 & 0 & 0 & 1 & 0
\end{array}
\right]
$$

$$
\tfrac{1}{2} R_1 \rightarrow R_1
$$

$$
(-1) R_1 + R_2 \rightarrow R_2
$$

$$
30 R_1 + R_3 \rightarrow R_3
$$

$$
\begin{array}{c}
x_1 \quad x_2 \quad s_1 \quad s_2 \quad P
\end{array}
$$

$$
\sim
\begin{array}{c}
x_1 \\
s_2 \\
P
\end{array}
\left[
\begin{array}{ccccc|c}
1 & \frac{1}{2} & \frac{1}{2} & 0 & 0 & 5 \\
0 & \frac{5}{2} & -\frac{1}{2} & 1 & 0 & 5 \\
\hline
0 & 14 & 15 & 0 & 1 & 150
\end{array}
\right]
$$

All the elements in the last row are nonnegative. Thus, max $P = 150$ at $x_1 = 5$, $x_2 = 0$, $s_1 = 0$, $s_2 = 5$.

13. The simplex tableau for this problem is:

$$
\begin{array}{c}
\quad\quad\quad\quad\quad \text{Enter} \\
\quad x_1 \quad x_2 \quad s_1 \quad s_2 \quad s_3 \quad P
\end{array}
$$

$$
\begin{array}{c}
s_1 \\
s_2 \\
\text{pivot} \rightarrow s_3 \\
\text{row} \\
\text{Exit}
\end{array}
\left[
\begin{array}{cccccc|c}
2 & 1 & 1 & 0 & 0 & 0 & 10 \\
1 & 1 & 0 & 1 & 0 & 0 & 7 \\
1 & ② & 0 & 0 & 1 & 0 & 12 \\
\hline
-30 & -40 & 0 & 0 & 0 & 1 & 0
\end{array}
\right]
\begin{array}{l}
10 \\
7 \\
\dfrac{12}{2} = 6 \;(\text{minimum})
\end{array}
$$

[Note: The pivot elements have been circled.]

$$
\begin{array}{c}
\uparrow \\
\text{pivot} \\
\text{column}
\end{array}
\quad \tfrac{1}{2} R_3 \rightarrow R_3
$$

$$
\sim
\left[
\begin{array}{cccccc|c}
2 & 1 & 1 & 0 & 0 & 0 & 10 \\
1 & 1 & 0 & 1 & 0 & 0 & 7 \\
\frac{1}{2} & ① & 0 & 0 & \frac{1}{2} & 0 & 6 \\
\hline
-30 & -40 & 0 & 0 & 0 & 1 & 0
\end{array}
\right]
$$

$$
(-1) R_3 + R_1 \rightarrow R_1, \quad (-1) R_3 + R_2 \rightarrow R_2, \quad \text{and} \quad 40 R_3 + R_4 \rightarrow R_4
$$

$$\begin{array}{c} \text{pivot} \rightarrow \\ \text{row} \end{array} \sim \begin{bmatrix} \frac{3}{2} & 0 & 1 & 0 & -\frac{1}{2} & 0 & 4 \\ \boxed{\frac{1}{2}} & 0 & 0 & 1 & -\frac{1}{2} & 0 & 1 \\ \frac{1}{2} & 1 & 0 & 0 & \frac{1}{2} & 0 & 6 \\ \hdashline -10 & 0 & 0 & 0 & 20 & 1 & 240 \end{bmatrix} \begin{array}{l} \frac{4}{3/2} = \frac{8}{3} \\ \frac{1}{1/2} = 2 \text{ (minimum)} \\ \frac{6}{1/2} = 12 \end{array}$$

$$\begin{array}{c} \uparrow \\ \text{pivot} \\ \text{column} \end{array} \quad 2R_2 \rightarrow R_2$$

$$\sim \begin{bmatrix} \frac{3}{2} & 0 & 1 & 0 & -\frac{1}{2} & 0 & 4 \\ \boxed{1} & 0 & 0 & 2 & -1 & 0 & 2 \\ \frac{1}{2} & 1 & 0 & 0 & \frac{1}{2} & 0 & 6 \\ \hdashline -10 & 0 & 0 & 0 & 20 & 1 & 240 \end{bmatrix}$$

$$\left(-\frac{3}{2}\right)R_2 + R_1 \rightarrow R_1, \quad \left(-\frac{1}{2}\right)R_2 + R_3 \rightarrow R_3, \quad \text{and} \quad 10R_2 + R_4 \rightarrow R_4$$

$$\begin{array}{c} \\ s_1 \\ \sim \quad x_1 \\ x_2 \\ \\ \end{array} \begin{array}{cccccc} x_1 & x_2 & s_1 & s_2 & s_3 & P \\ \end{array} \\ \begin{bmatrix} 0 & 0 & 1 & -3 & 1 & 0 & 1 \\ 1 & 0 & 0 & 2 & -1 & 0 & 2 \\ 0 & 1 & 0 & -1 & 1 & 0 & 5 \\ \hdashline 0 & 0 & 0 & 20 & 10 & 1 & 260 \end{bmatrix}$$

Optimal solution: max $P = 260$ at $x_1 = 2$, $x_2 = 5$, $s_1 = 1$, $s_2 = 0$, $s_3 = 0$.

15. The simplex tableau for this problem is:

$$\begin{array}{c} \\ \text{pivot} \\ \text{row} \rightarrow \\ \\ \\ \end{array} \begin{array}{c} \\ \text{Exit} \\ s_1 \\ s_2 \\ s_3 \\ P \end{array} \begin{array}{cccccc} & \overset{\text{Enter}}{\downarrow} & & & & \\ x_1 & x_2 & s_1 & s_2 & s_3 & P \\ \end{array} \\ \begin{bmatrix} -2 & \boxed{1} & 1 & 0 & 0 & 0 & 2 \\ -1 & 1 & 0 & 1 & 0 & 0 & 5 \\ 0 & 1 & 0 & 0 & 1 & 0 & 6 \\ \hdashline -2 & -3 & 0 & 0 & 0 & 1 & 0 \end{bmatrix} \begin{array}{l} \frac{2}{1} = 2 \text{ (minimum)} \\ \frac{5}{1} = 5 \\ \frac{6}{1} = 6 \end{array}$$

$$\begin{array}{c} \uparrow \\ \text{pivot} \\ \text{column} \end{array} \quad (-1)R_1 + R_2 \rightarrow R_2, \quad (-1)R_1 + R_3 \rightarrow R_3, \quad \text{and} \quad 3R_1 + R_4 \rightarrow R_4$$

$$\begin{array}{c} \\ \\ \text{pivot} \sim \\ \text{row} \rightarrow \\ \\ \end{array} \begin{bmatrix} -2 & 1 & 1 & 0 & 0 & 0 & 2 \\ 1 & 0 & -1 & 1 & 0 & 0 & 3 \\ \boxed{2} & 0 & -1 & 0 & 1 & 0 & 4 \\ \hdashline -8 & 0 & 3 & 0 & 0 & 1 & 6 \end{bmatrix} \begin{array}{l} \\ \frac{3}{1} = 3 \\ \frac{4}{2} = 2 \text{ (minimum)} \end{array}$$

$$\begin{array}{c} \uparrow \\ \text{pivot} \\ \text{column} \end{array} \quad \frac{1}{2}R_3 \rightarrow R_3$$

$$\sim \begin{bmatrix} -2 & 1 & 1 & 0 & 0 & 0 & 2 \\ 1 & 0 & -1 & 1 & 0 & 0 & 3 \\ ① & 0 & -\tfrac{1}{2} & 0 & \tfrac{1}{2} & 0 & 2 \\ \hdashline -8 & 0 & 3 & 0 & 0 & 1 & 6 \end{bmatrix}$$

$2R_3 + R_1 \rightarrow R_1,\ (-1)R_3 + R_2 \rightarrow R_2,$

and $8R_3 + R_4 \rightarrow R_4$

$$\begin{array}{cccccc} x_1 & x_2 & s_1 & s_2 & s_3 & P \end{array}$$
$$\sim \begin{bmatrix} 0 & 1 & 0 & 0 & 1 & 0 & 6 \\ 0 & 0 & -\tfrac{1}{2} & 1 & -\tfrac{1}{2} & 0 & 1 \\ 1 & 0 & -\tfrac{1}{2} & 0 & \tfrac{1}{2} & 0 & 2 \\ \hdashline 0 & 0 & -1 & 0 & 4 & 1 & 22 \end{bmatrix}$$

↑

pivot
column

Since there are no positive elements in the pivot column (above the dashed line), we conclude that there is no solution.

17. The simplex tableau for this problem is:

$$\begin{array}{cccccc} x_1 & x_2 & s_1 & s_2 & s_3 & P \end{array}$$

$$\begin{array}{c} \text{pivot} \rightarrow s_1 \\ \text{row} \\ s_2 \\ \\ s_3 \\ \\ P \end{array} \begin{bmatrix} -1 & ① & 1 & 0 & 0 & 0 & 2 \\ -1 & 3 & 0 & 1 & 0 & 0 & 12 \\ 1 & -4 & 0 & 0 & 1 & 0 & 4 \\ \hdashline 1 & -2 & 0 & 0 & 0 & 1 & 0 \end{bmatrix} \begin{array}{l} \tfrac{2}{1} = 2 \text{ (minimum)} \\[6pt] \tfrac{12}{3} = 4 \\[30pt] \end{array}$$

↑

pivot   pivot $(-3)R_1 + R_2 \rightarrow R_2,\ 4R_1 + R_3 \rightarrow R_3,$ and $2R_1 + R_4 \rightarrow R_4$
column

$$\begin{array}{c} \\ \text{pivot} \rightarrow \\ \text{row} \\ \sim \\ \\ \\ \end{array} \begin{bmatrix} -1 & 1 & 1 & 0 & 0 & 0 & 2 \\ ② & 0 & -3 & 1 & 0 & 0 & 6 \\ -3 & 0 & 4 & 0 & 1 & 0 & 12 \\ \hdashline -1 & 0 & 2 & 0 & 0 & 1 & 4 \end{bmatrix} \begin{array}{l} \\ \tfrac{6}{2} = 3 \leftarrow \text{pivot row} \\[6pt] [\underline{\text{Note}}\text{: We only use the} \\ \textit{positive} \text{ elements above} \\ \text{the dashed line in the} \\ \text{pivot column.]} \end{array}$$

↑

pivot $\tfrac{1}{2}R_2 \rightarrow R_2$
column

$$\sim \begin{bmatrix} -1 & 1 & 1 & 0 & 0 & 0 & 2 \\ ① & 0 & -\tfrac{3}{2} & \tfrac{1}{2} & 0 & 0 & 3 \\ -3 & 0 & 4 & 0 & 1 & 0 & 12 \\ \hdashline -1 & 0 & 2 & 0 & 0 & 1 & 4 \end{bmatrix}$$

$R_2 + R_1 \rightarrow R_1,\ 3R_2 + R_3 \rightarrow R_3,$

and $R_2 + R_4 \rightarrow R_4$

$$\begin{array}{cccccc} x_1 & x_2 & s_1 & s_2 & s_3 & P \end{array}$$
$$\sim \begin{array}{c} x_2 \\ x_1 \\ s_3 \\ \\ \end{array} \begin{bmatrix} 0 & 1 & -\tfrac{1}{2} & \tfrac{1}{2} & 0 & 0 & 5 \\ 1 & 0 & -\tfrac{3}{2} & \tfrac{1}{2} & 0 & 0 & 3 \\ 0 & 0 & -\tfrac{1}{2} & \tfrac{3}{2} & 1 & 0 & 21 \\ \hdashline 0 & 0 & \tfrac{1}{2} & \tfrac{1}{2} & 0 & 1 & 7 \end{bmatrix}$$

Optimal solution: max $P = 7$ at $x_1 = 3$, $x_2 = 5$, $s_1 = 0$, $s_2 = 0$, $s_3 = 21$.

19. The simplex tableau for this problem is:

$$
\begin{array}{c}
\text{pivot} \to s_1 \\
\text{row} \quad\;\; s_2 \\
P
\end{array}
\begin{array}{ccccccc}
x_1 & x_2 & x_3 & s_1 & s_2 & P \\
\end{array}
$$

$$
\begin{array}{c}
\text{pivot} \to s_1 \\
\text{row} \;\; s_2 \\
\;\;\; P
\end{array}
\left[
\begin{array}{cccccc|c}
① & 1 & -1 & 1 & 0 & 0 & 10 \\
2 & 4 & 3 & 0 & 1 & 0 & 30 \\
\hdashline
-5 & -2 & 1 & 0 & 0 & 1 & 0
\end{array}
\right]
\begin{array}{l}
\dfrac{10}{1} = 10 \text{ (minimum)} \\[2mm]
\dfrac{30}{2} = 15
\end{array}
$$

pivot column $(-2)R_1 + R_2 \to R_2,\;\; 5R_1 + R_3 \to R_3$

$$
\sim
\left[
\begin{array}{cccccc|c}
1 & 1 & -1 & 1 & 0 & 0 & 10 \\
0 & 2 & ⑤ & -2 & 1 & 0 & 10 \\
\hdashline
0 & 3 & -4 & 5 & 0 & 1 & 50
\end{array}
\right]
\sim
\left[
\begin{array}{cccccc|c}
1 & 1 & -1 & 1 & 0 & 0 & 10 \\
0 & \frac{2}{5} & ① & -\frac{2}{5} & \frac{1}{5} & 0 & 2 \\
\hdashline
0 & 3 & -4 & 5 & 0 & 1 & 50
\end{array}
\right]
$$

$\dfrac{1}{5}R_2 \to R_2$ $R_2 + R_1 \to R_1,\;\; 4R_2 + R_3 \to R_3$

$$
\begin{array}{c}
x_1 \\
\sim \;\; x_3 \\
P
\end{array}
\left[
\begin{array}{cccccc|c}
x_1 & x_2 & x_3 & s_1 & s_2 & P \\
1 & \frac{7}{5} & 0 & \frac{3}{5} & \frac{1}{5} & 0 & 12 \\
0 & \frac{2}{5} & 1 & -\frac{2}{5} & \frac{1}{5} & 0 & 2 \\
\hdashline
0 & \frac{23}{5} & 0 & \frac{17}{5} & \frac{4}{5} & 1 & 58
\end{array}
\right]
$$

Optimal solution: max $P = 58$ at $x_1 = 12,\; x_2 = 0,\; x_3 = 2,\; s_1 = 0,\; s_2 = 0$.

21. The simplex tableau for this problem is:

$$
\begin{array}{ccccccc}
& x_1 & x_2 & x_3 & s_1 & s_2 & P \\
\end{array}
$$

$$
\begin{array}{c}
s_1 \\
\text{pivot} \to s_2 \\
\text{row} \;\;\;\; P
\end{array}
\left[
\begin{array}{cccccc|c}
1 & 0 & 1 & 1 & 0 & 0 & 4 \\
0 & 1 & ① & 0 & 1 & 0 & 3 \\
\hdashline
-2 & -3 & -4 & 0 & 0 & 1 & 0
\end{array}
\right]
\begin{array}{l}
\dfrac{4}{1} = 4 \\[2mm]
\dfrac{3}{1} = 3 \text{ (minimum)}
\end{array}
$$

pivot column $(-1)R_2 + R_1 \to R_1,\;\; 4R_2 + R_3 \to R_3$

$$
\sim
\left[
\begin{array}{cccccc|c}
① & -1 & 0 & 1 & -1 & 0 & 1 \\
0 & 1 & 1 & 0 & 1 & 0 & 3 \\
\hdashline
-2 & 1 & 0 & 0 & 4 & 1 & 12
\end{array}
\right]
\sim
\left[
\begin{array}{cccccc|c}
1 & -1 & 0 & 1 & -1 & 0 & 1 \\
0 & ① & 1 & 0 & 1 & 0 & 3 \\
\hdashline
0 & -1 & 0 & 2 & 2 & 1 & 14
\end{array}
\right]
$$

$2R_1 + R_3 \to R_3$ $R_2 + R_1 \to R_1$ and $R_2 + R_3 \to R_3$

$$
\begin{array}{ccccccc}
x_1 & x_2 & x_3 & s_1 & s_2 & P \\
\end{array}
$$

$$
\sim
\left[
\begin{array}{cccccc|c}
1 & 0 & 1 & 1 & 0 & 0 & 4 \\
0 & 1 & 1 & 0 & 1 & 0 & 3 \\
\hdashline
0 & 0 & 1 & 2 & 3 & 1 & 17
\end{array}
\right]
$$

Optimal solution: max $P = 17$ at $x_1 = 4,\; x_2 = 3,\; x_3 = 0,\; s_1 = 0,\; s_2 = 0$.

23. The simplex tableau for this problem is:

$$
\begin{array}{c}
\\
\text{pivot} \rightarrow \\
\text{row}
\end{array}
\begin{array}{c}
s_1 \\
s_2 \\
s_3 \\
\\
\end{array}
\left[
\begin{array}{ccccccc|c}
x_1 & x_2 & x_3 & s_1 & s_2 & s_3 & P & \\
3 & 2 & 5 & 1 & 0 & 0 & 0 & 23 \\
② & 1 & 1 & 0 & 1 & 0 & 0 & 8 \\
1 & 1 & 2 & 0 & 0 & 1 & 0 & 7 \\
\hline
-4 & -3 & -2 & 0 & 0 & 0 & 1 & 0
\end{array}
\right]
\begin{array}{l}
\frac{23}{3} = 7\frac{2}{3} \\
\frac{8}{2} = 4 \text{ (minimum)} \\
\frac{7}{1} = 7 \\
\\
\end{array}
$$

$$
\begin{array}{c}
\text{pivot} \\
\text{column}
\end{array} \quad \frac{1}{2}R_2 \rightarrow R_2
$$

$$
\sim
\left[
\begin{array}{ccccccc|c}
3 & 2 & 5 & 1 & 0 & 0 & 0 & 23 \\
① & \frac{1}{2} & \frac{1}{2} & 0 & \frac{1}{2} & 0 & 0 & 4 \\
1 & 1 & 2 & 0 & 0 & 1 & 0 & 7 \\
\hline
-4 & -3 & -2 & 0 & 0 & 0 & 1 & 0
\end{array}
\right]
\sim
\left[
\begin{array}{ccccccc|c}
0 & \frac{1}{2} & \frac{7}{2} & 1 & -\frac{3}{2} & 0 & 0 & 11 \\
1 & \frac{1}{2} & \frac{1}{2} & 0 & \frac{1}{2} & 0 & 0 & 4 \\
0 & ⑫ & \frac{3}{2} & 0 & -\frac{1}{2} & 1 & 0 & 3 \\
\hline
0 & -1 & 0 & 0 & 2 & 0 & 1 & 16
\end{array}
\right]
$$

$(-3)R_2 + R_1 \rightarrow R_1$, $\ (-1)\ R_2 + R_3 \rightarrow R_3$, and $\quad 2R_3 \rightarrow R_3$
$4R_2 + R_4 \rightarrow R_4$

$$
\sim
\left[
\begin{array}{ccccccc|c}
0 & \frac{1}{2} & \frac{7}{2} & 1 & -\frac{3}{2} & 0 & 0 & 11 \\
1 & \frac{1}{2} & \frac{1}{2} & 0 & \frac{1}{2} & 0 & 0 & 4 \\
0 & ① & 3 & 0 & -1 & 2 & 0 & 6 \\
\hline
0 & -1 & 0 & 0 & 2 & 0 & 1 & 16
\end{array}
\right]
\sim
\begin{array}{c}
s_1 \\
x_1 \\
x_2 \\
\\
P
\end{array}
\left[
\begin{array}{ccccccc|c}
x_1 & x_2 & x_3 & s_1 & s_2 & s_3 & P & \\
0 & 0 & 2 & 1 & -1 & -1 & 0 & 8 \\
1 & 0 & -1 & 0 & 1 & -1 & 0 & 1 \\
0 & 1 & 3 & 0 & -1 & 2 & 0 & 6 \\
\hline
0 & 0 & 3 & 0 & 1 & 2 & 1 & 22
\end{array}
\right]
$$

$\left(-\dfrac{1}{2}\right)R_3 + R_1 \rightarrow R_1$, $\left(-\dfrac{1}{2}\right)R_3 + R_2 \rightarrow R_2$, and

$R_3 + R_4 \rightarrow R_4$

Optimal solution: max $P = 22$ at $x_1 = 1$, $x_2 = 6$, $x_3 = 0$, $s_1 = 8$, $s_2 = 0$, $s_3 = 0$.

25. Multiply the first problem constraint by $\dfrac{10}{6}$, the second by 100, and the third by 10 to clear the fractions. Then, the simplex tableau for this problem is:

$$
\begin{array}{c}
s_1 \\
s_2 \\
s_3 \\
P
\end{array}
\left[
\begin{array}{cccccc|c}
x_1 & x_2 & s_1 & s_2 & s_3 & P & \\
1 & ② & 1 & 0 & 0 & 0 & 1,600 \\
3 & 4 & 0 & 1 & 0 & 0 & 3,600 \\
3 & 2 & 0 & 0 & 1 & 0 & 2,700 \\
\hline
-20 & -30 & 0 & 0 & 0 & 1 & 0
\end{array}
\right]
\begin{array}{l}
\dfrac{1,600}{2} = 800 \\
\dfrac{3,600}{4} = 900 \\
\dfrac{2,700}{2} = 1,350 \\
\\
\end{array}
$$

$\dfrac{1}{2}R_1 \rightarrow R_1$

$$\sim \begin{bmatrix} \frac{1}{2} & ① & \frac{1}{2} & 0 & 0 & 0 & 800 \\ 3 & 4 & 0 & 1 & 0 & 0 & 3,600 \\ 3 & 2 & 0 & 0 & 1 & 0 & 2,700 \\ \hdashline -20 & -30 & 0 & 0 & 0 & 1 & 0 \end{bmatrix}$$

$(-4)R_1 + R_2 \rightarrow R_2, \quad (-2)R_1 + R_3 \rightarrow R_3, \quad \text{and} \quad 30R_1 + R_4 \rightarrow R_4$

$$\sim \begin{bmatrix} \frac{1}{2} & 1 & \frac{1}{2} & 0 & 0 & 0 & 800 \\ ① & 0 & -2 & 1 & 0 & 0 & 400 \\ 2 & 0 & -1 & 0 & 1 & 0 & 1,100 \\ \hdashline -5 & 0 & 15 & 0 & 0 & 1 & 24,000 \end{bmatrix} \quad \begin{array}{l} \dfrac{800}{1/2} = 1,600 \\[6pt] \dfrac{400}{1} = 400 \\[6pt] \dfrac{1,100}{2} = 550 \end{array}$$

$\left(-\dfrac{1}{2}\right)R_2 + R_1 \rightarrow R_1, \quad (-2)R_2 + R_3 \rightarrow R_3, \quad \text{and} \quad 5R_2 + R_4 \rightarrow R_4$

$$\sim \begin{array}{c} \\ x_2 \\ x_1 \\ s_3 \\ P \end{array} \begin{array}{cccccc} x_1 & x_2 & s_1 & s_2 & s_3 & P \\ \end{array}$$

$$\sim \begin{array}{c} x_2 \\ x_1 \\ s_3 \\ \\ P \end{array} \left[\begin{array}{cccccc|c} 0 & 1 & \frac{3}{2} & -\frac{1}{2} & 0 & 0 & 600 \\ 1 & 0 & -2 & 1 & 0 & 0 & 400 \\ 0 & 0 & 3 & -2 & 1 & 0 & 300 \\ \hdashline 0 & 0 & 5 & 5 & 0 & 1 & 26,000 \end{array} \right]$$

Optimal solution: max $P = 26,000$ at $x_1 = 400$, $x_2 = 600$, $s_1 = 0$, $s_2 = 0$, $s_3 = 300$.

27. The simplex tableau for this problem is:

$$\begin{array}{c} \\ s_1 \\ s_2 \\ s_3 \\ P \end{array} \begin{array}{ccccccc} x_1 & x_2 & x_3 & s_1 & s_2 & s_3 & P \\ \end{array}$$

$$\begin{array}{c} s_1 \\ s_2 \\ s_3 \\ \\ P \end{array} \left[\begin{array}{ccccccc|c} 2 & 2 & ⑧ & 1 & 0 & 0 & 0 & 600 \\ 1 & 3 & 2 & 0 & 1 & 0 & 0 & 600 \\ 3 & 2 & 1 & 0 & 0 & 1 & 0 & 400 \\ \hdashline -1 & -2 & -3 & 0 & 0 & 0 & 1 & 0 \end{array} \right] \quad \begin{array}{l} \dfrac{600}{8} = 75 \\[6pt] \dfrac{600}{2} = 300 \\[6pt] \dfrac{400}{1} = 400 \end{array}$$

$\dfrac{1}{8}R_1 \rightarrow R_1$

$$\sim \begin{bmatrix} \frac{1}{4} & \frac{1}{4} & ① & \frac{1}{8} & 0 & 0 & 0 & 75 \\ 1 & 3 & 2 & 0 & 1 & 0 & 0 & 600 \\ 3 & 2 & 1 & 0 & 0 & 1 & 0 & 400 \\ \hdashline -1 & -2 & -3 & 0 & 0 & 0 & 1 & 0 \end{bmatrix}$$

$(-2)R_1 + R_2 \rightarrow R_2, \quad (-1)R_1 + R_3 \rightarrow R_3, \quad \text{and} \quad 3R_1 + R_4 \rightarrow R_4$

$$\sim \begin{bmatrix} \frac{1}{4} & \frac{1}{4} & 1 & \frac{1}{8} & 0 & 0 & 0 & 75 \\ \frac{1}{2} & \boxed{\frac{5}{2}} & 0 & -\frac{1}{4} & 1 & 0 & 0 & 450 \\ \frac{11}{4} & \frac{7}{4} & 0 & -\frac{1}{8} & 0 & 1 & 0 & 325 \\ \hline -\frac{1}{4} & -\frac{5}{4} & 0 & \frac{3}{8} & 0 & 0 & 1 & 225 \end{bmatrix} \begin{matrix} \frac{75}{1/4} = 300 \\[4pt] \frac{450}{5/2} = 180 \\[4pt] \frac{325}{7/4} = 185.71 \end{matrix}$$

$$\frac{2}{5}R_2 \rightarrow R_2$$

$$\sim \begin{bmatrix} \frac{1}{4} & \frac{1}{4} & 1 & \frac{1}{8} & 0 & 0 & 0 & 75 \\ \frac{1}{5} & \boxed{1} & 0 & -\frac{1}{10} & \frac{2}{5} & 0 & 0 & 180 \\ \frac{11}{4} & \frac{7}{4} & 0 & -\frac{1}{8} & 0 & 1 & 0 & 325 \\ \hline -\frac{1}{4} & -\frac{5}{4} & 0 & \frac{3}{8} & 0 & 0 & 1 & 225 \end{bmatrix}$$

$$\left(-\frac{1}{4}\right)R_2 + R_1 \rightarrow R_1, \quad \left(-\frac{7}{4}\right)R_2 + R_3 \rightarrow R_3, \quad \text{and} \quad \frac{5}{4}R_2 + R_4 \rightarrow R_4$$

$$\begin{array}{c} \\ x_3 \\ x_2 \\ s_3 \\ P \end{array} \sim \begin{array}{c} \begin{matrix} x_1 & x_2 & x_3 & s_1 & s_2 & s_3 & P \end{matrix} \\ \begin{bmatrix} \frac{1}{5} & 0 & 1 & \frac{3}{20} & -\frac{1}{10} & 0 & 0 & 30 \\ \frac{1}{5} & 1 & 0 & -\frac{1}{10} & \frac{2}{5} & 0 & 0 & 180 \\ \frac{12}{5} & 0 & 0 & \frac{1}{20} & -\frac{7}{10} & 1 & 0 & 10 \\ \hline 0 & 0 & 0 & \frac{1}{4} & \frac{1}{2} & 0 & 1 & 450 \end{bmatrix} \end{array}$$

Optimal solution: max $P = 450$ at $x_1 = 0$, $x_2 = 180$, $x_3 = 30$, $s_1 = 0$, $s_2 = 0$, $s_3 = 10$.

29. The simplex tableau for this problem is:

$$\begin{array}{c} \\ s_1 \\ s_2 \\ s_3 \\ s_4 \\ P \end{array} \begin{array}{c} \begin{matrix} x_1 & x_2 & s_1 & s_2 & s_3 & s_4 & P \end{matrix} \\ \begin{bmatrix} 1 & 2 & 1 & 0 & 0 & 0 & 0 & 40 \\ 1 & 3 & 0 & 1 & 0 & 0 & 0 & 48 \\ 1 & 4 & 0 & 0 & 1 & 0 & 0 & 60 \\ 0 & \boxed{1} & 0 & 0 & 0 & 1 & 0 & 14 \\ \hline -2 & -5 & 0 & 0 & 0 & 0 & 1 & 0 \end{bmatrix} \end{array} \begin{matrix} \frac{40}{2} = 20 \\[4pt] \frac{48}{3} = 16 \\[4pt] \frac{60}{4} = 15 \\[4pt] \frac{14}{1} = 14 \end{matrix}$$

$$(-2)R_4 + R_1 \rightarrow R_1, \quad (-3)R_4 + R_2 \rightarrow R_2, \quad (-4)R_4 + R_3 \rightarrow R_3,$$
$$\text{and } 5R_4 + R_5 \rightarrow R_5$$

$$
\sim
\begin{bmatrix}
1 & 0 & 1 & 0 & 0 & -2 & 0 & 12 \\
1 & 0 & 0 & 1 & 0 & -3 & 0 & 6 \\
① & 0 & 0 & 0 & 1 & -4 & 0 & 4 \\
0 & 1 & 0 & 0 & 0 & 1 & 0 & 14 \\
\hdashline
-2 & 0 & 0 & 0 & 0 & 5 & 1 & 70
\end{bmatrix}
\begin{array}{l}
\frac{12}{1} = 12 \\[4pt]
\frac{6}{1} = 6 \\[4pt]
\frac{4}{1} = 4 \\[4pt]
\\
\end{array}
$$

$(-1)R_3 + R_1 \to R_1$, $(-1)R_3 + R_2 \to R_2$, and $2R_3 + R_5 \to R_5$

$$
\sim
\begin{bmatrix}
0 & 0 & 1 & 0 & -1 & 2 & 0 & 8 \\
0 & 0 & 0 & 1 & -1 & ① & 0 & 2 \\
1 & 0 & 0 & 0 & 1 & -4 & 0 & 4 \\
0 & 1 & 0 & 0 & 0 & 1 & 0 & 14 \\
\hdashline
0 & 0 & 0 & 0 & 2 & -3 & 1 & 78
\end{bmatrix}
\begin{array}{l}
\frac{8}{2} = 4 \\[4pt]
\frac{2}{1} = 2 \\[4pt]
\\
\frac{14}{1} = 14 \\[4pt]
\\
\end{array}
$$

$(-2)R_2 + R_1 \to R_1$, $4R_2 + R_3 \to R_3$, $(-1)R_2 + R_4 \to R_4$,

and $3R_2 + R_5 \to R_5$

$$
\sim
\begin{bmatrix}
0 & 0 & 1 & -2 & ① & 0 & 0 & 4 \\
0 & 0 & 0 & 1 & -1 & 1 & 0 & 2 \\
1 & 0 & 0 & 4 & -3 & 0 & 0 & 12 \\
0 & 1 & 0 & -1 & 1 & 0 & 0 & 12 \\
\hdashline
0 & 0 & 0 & 3 & -1 & 0 & 1 & 84
\end{bmatrix}
\begin{array}{l}
\frac{4}{1} = 4 \\[4pt]
\\
\\
\frac{12}{1} = 12 \\[4pt]
\\
\end{array}
$$

$R_1 + R_2 \to R_2$, $3R_1 + R_3 \to R_3$, $(-1)R_1 + R_4 \to R_4$, and $R_1 + R_5 \to R_5$

$$
\sim
\begin{array}{c}
\\ s_3 \\ s_4 \\ x_1 \\ x_2 \\ \\ P
\end{array}
\begin{array}{c}
\begin{array}{ccccccc}
x_1 & x_2 & s_1 & s_2 & s_3 & s_4 & P
\end{array} \\
\begin{bmatrix}
0 & 0 & 1 & -2 & 1 & 0 & 0 & 4 \\
0 & 0 & 1 & -1 & 0 & 1 & 0 & 6 \\
1 & 0 & 3 & -2 & 0 & 0 & 0 & 24 \\
0 & 1 & -1 & 1 & 0 & 0 & 0 & 8 \\
\hdashline
0 & 0 & 1 & 1 & 0 & 0 & 1 & 88
\end{bmatrix}
\end{array}
$$

Optimal solution: max $P = 88$ at $x_1 = 24$, $x_2 = 8$, $s_1 = 0$, $s_2 = 0$, $s_3 = 4$, $s_4 = 6$.

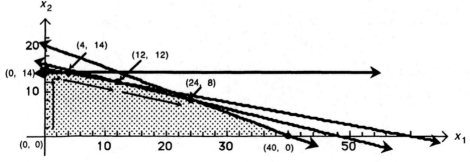

645

Simplex Method:
The simplex tableau for this problem is:

$$
\begin{array}{c}
\\ s_1 \\ s_2
\end{array}
\begin{array}{cccccc}
x_1 & x_2 & s_1 & s_2 & P & \\
\end{array}
$$

$$
\begin{array}{cc}
 & \begin{array}{ccccc} x_1 & x_2 & s_1 & s_2 & P \end{array}\\
\begin{array}{c} \\ s_1 \\ s_2 \end{array} & \left[\begin{array}{ccccc|c}
-2 & \textcircled{1} & 1 & 0 & 0 & 4 \\
0 & 1 & 0 & 1 & 0 & 10 \\ \hdashline
-2 & -3 & 0 & 0 & 1 & 0
\end{array}\right]
\begin{array}{l} \\ \frac{4}{1}=4 \\ \frac{10}{1}=10 \end{array}
\end{array}
$$

$$(-1)R_1 + R_2 \to R_2, \quad 3R_1 + R_3 \to R_3$$

$$
\sim \left[\begin{array}{ccccc|c}
-2 & 1 & 0 & 0 & 0 & 4 \\
\textcircled{2} & 0 & -1 & 1 & 0 & 6 \\ \hdashline
-8 & 0 & 3 & 0 & 1 & 12
\end{array}\right]
\begin{array}{l} \\ \frac{6}{2}=3 \\ \end{array}
$$

$$\frac{1}{2}R_2 \to R_2$$

$$
\sim \left[\begin{array}{ccccc|c}
-2 & 1 & 0 & 0 & 0 & 4 \\
\textcircled{1} & 0 & -\frac{1}{2} & \frac{1}{2} & 0 & 3 \\ \hdashline
-8 & 0 & 3 & 0 & 1 & 12
\end{array}\right]
$$

$$2R_2 + R_1 \to R_1, \quad 8R_2 + R_3 \to R_3$$

$$
\sim \left[\begin{array}{ccccc|c}
0 & 1 & -1 & 1 & 0 & 10 \\
1 & 0 & -\frac{1}{2} & \frac{1}{2} & 0 & 3 \\ \hdashline
0 & 0 & -1 & 4 & 1 & 36
\end{array}\right]
$$

No positive elements in the pivot column; no optimal solution exists.

Geometric Method:
Step (1): Graph the feasible region and find the corner points. The feasible region S is the solution set of the inequalities. This region is indicated by the shading in the graph at the right.

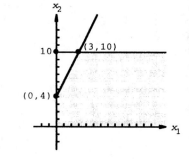

The corner points are $(0, 0)$, $(0, 4)$, and $(3, 10)$.

Since S is unbounded and the coefficients of the objective function are positive, P does not have a maximum value.

33. The simplex tableau for this problem is:

$$
\begin{array}{cc}
 & \begin{array}{cccccc} x_1 & x_2 & s_1 & s_2 & s_3 & P \end{array}\\
\begin{array}{c} s_1 \\ \\ s_2 \\ \\ s_3 \\ P \end{array} & \left[\begin{array}{cccccc|c}
2 & 1 & 1 & 0 & 0 & 0 & 16 \\
1 & 0 & 0 & 1 & 0 & 0 & 6 \\
0 & 1 & 0 & 0 & 1 & 0 & 10 \\ \hdashline
-1 & -1 & 0 & 0 & 0 & 1 & 0
\end{array}\right]
\end{array}
$$

(A) Solution using the first column as the pivot column

$$
\begin{array}{cccccc}
x_1 & x_2 & s_1 & s_2 & s_3 & P
\end{array}
$$

$$
\left[\begin{array}{cccccc|c}
2 & 1 & 1 & 0 & 0 & 0 & 16 \\
\textcircled{1} & 0 & 0 & 1 & 0 & 0 & 6 \\
0 & 1 & 0 & 0 & 1 & 0 & 10 \\
\hline
-1 & -1 & 0 & 0 & 0 & 1 & 0
\end{array}\right]
\begin{array}{l}
\dfrac{16}{2} = 8 \\[2mm]
\dfrac{6}{1} = 6
\end{array}
$$

$(-2)R_2 + R_1 \rightarrow R_1, \quad R_2 + R_4 \rightarrow R_4$

$$
\sim
\left[\begin{array}{cccccc|c}
0 & \textcircled{1} & 1 & -2 & 0 & 0 & 4 \\
1 & 0 & 0 & 1 & 0 & 0 & 6 \\
0 & 1 & 0 & 0 & 1 & 0 & 10 \\
\hline
0 & -1 & 0 & 1 & 0 & 1 & 6
\end{array}\right]
\begin{array}{l}
\dfrac{4}{1} = 4 \\[4mm]
\dfrac{10}{1} = 10
\end{array}
$$

$(-1)R_1 + R_3 \rightarrow R_3, \quad R_1 + R_4 \rightarrow R_4$

$$
\sim
\left[\begin{array}{cccccc|c}
0 & 1 & 1 & -2 & 0 & 0 & 4 \\
1 & 0 & 0 & 1 & 0 & 0 & 6 \\
0 & 0 & -1 & \textcircled{2} & 1 & 0 & 6 \\
\hline
0 & 0 & 1 & -1 & 0 & 1 & 10
\end{array}\right]
\begin{array}{l}
\dfrac{6}{1} = 6 \\[2mm]
\dfrac{6}{2} = 3
\end{array}
$$

$\dfrac{1}{2}R_3 \rightarrow R_3$

$$
\sim
\left[\begin{array}{cccccc|c}
0 & 1 & 1 & -2 & 0 & 0 & 4 \\
1 & 0 & 0 & 1 & 0 & 0 & 6 \\
0 & 0 & -\frac{1}{2} & 1 & \frac{1}{2} & 0 & 3 \\
\hline
0 & 0 & 1 & -1 & 0 & 1 & 10
\end{array}\right]
$$

$2R_3 + R_1 \rightarrow R_1, \quad (-1)R_3 + R_2 \rightarrow R_2, \quad R_3 + R_4 \rightarrow R_4$

$$
\begin{array}{c}
 \\
x_2 \\
x_1 \\
s_2 \\
P
\end{array}
\begin{array}{cccccc}
x_1 & x_2 & s_1 & s_2 & s_3 & P
\end{array}
$$

$$
\sim
\left[\begin{array}{cccccc|c}
0 & 1 & 0 & 0 & 1 & 0 & 10 \\
1 & 0 & \frac{1}{2} & 0 & -\frac{1}{2} & 0 & 3 \\
0 & 0 & -\frac{1}{2} & 1 & \frac{1}{2} & 0 & 3 \\
\hline
0 & 0 & \frac{1}{2} & 0 & \frac{1}{2} & 1 & 13
\end{array}\right]
$$

Optimal solution: max $P = 13$ at $x_1 = 3$, $x_2 = 10$, $s_1 = 0$, $s_2 = 3$, $s_3 = 0$

(B) Solution using the second column as the pivot column

$$
\begin{array}{c}
\begin{array}{cccccc}
\ \ x_1 & x_2 & s_1 & s_2 & s_3 & P
\end{array}\\
\begin{array}{c}
s_1\\ s_2\\ s_3\\ P
\end{array}
\left[
\begin{array}{cccccc|c}
2 & 1 & 1 & 0 & 0 & 0 & 16\\
1 & 0 & 0 & 1 & 0 & 0 & 6\\
0 & \text{①} & 0 & 0 & 1 & 0 & 10\\
\hdashline
-1 & -1 & 0 & 0 & 0 & 1 & 0
\end{array}
\right]
\begin{array}{l}
\frac{16}{1} = 16\\[6pt]\\[2pt]
\frac{10}{1} = 10
\end{array}
\end{array}
$$

$$(-1)R_3 + R_1 \to R_1, \quad R_3 + R_4 \to R_4$$

$$
\sim
\left[
\begin{array}{cccccc|c}
\text{②} & 0 & 1 & 0 & -1 & 0 & 6\\
1 & 0 & 0 & 1 & 0 & 0 & 6\\
0 & 1 & 0 & 0 & 1 & 0 & 10\\
\hdashline
-1 & 0 & 0 & 0 & 1 & 1 & 10
\end{array}
\right]
\begin{array}{l}
\frac{6}{2} = 3\\[6pt]
\frac{6}{1} = 6
\end{array}
$$

$$\tfrac{1}{2}R_1 \to R_1$$

$$
\sim
\left[
\begin{array}{cccccc|c}
1 & 0 & \frac{1}{2} & 0 & -\frac{1}{2} & 0 & 3\\
1 & 0 & 0 & 1 & 0 & 0 & 6\\
0 & 1 & 0 & 0 & 1 & 0 & 10\\
\hdashline
-1 & 0 & 0 & 0 & 1 & 1 & 10
\end{array}
\right]
$$

$$(-1)R_1 + R_2 \to R_2, \quad R_1 + R_4 \to R_4$$

$$
\begin{array}{c}
\begin{array}{cccccc}
\ \ x_1 & x_2 & s_1 & s_2 & s_3 & P
\end{array}\\
\begin{array}{c}
x_1\\ s_2\\ x_2\\ P
\end{array}
\sim
\left[
\begin{array}{cccccc|c}
1 & 0 & \frac{1}{2} & 0 & -\frac{1}{2} & 0 & 3\\
0 & 0 & -\frac{1}{2} & 1 & \frac{1}{2} & 0 & 3\\
0 & \text{①} & 0 & 0 & 1 & 0 & 10\\
\hdashline
0 & 0 & \frac{1}{2} & 0 & \frac{1}{2} & 1 & 13
\end{array}
\right]
\end{array}
$$

Choosing either solution produces
the *same* optimal solution.

Optimal solution: max $P = 13$ at $x_1 = 3$, $x_2 = 10$, $s_1 = 0$,
$s_2 = 3$, $s_3 = 0$

35. The simplex tableau for this problem is:

$$
\begin{array}{c}
\begin{array}{cccccc}
\ \ x_1 & x_2 & x_3 & s_1 & s_2 & P
\end{array}\\
\begin{array}{c}
s_1\\ s_2\\ P
\end{array}
\left[
\begin{array}{cccccc|c}
1 & 1 & 2 & 1 & 0 & 0 & 20\\
2 & 1 & 4 & 0 & 1 & 0 & 32\\
\hdashline
-3 & -3 & -2 & 0 & 0 & 1 & 0
\end{array}
\right]
\end{array}
$$

(A) Solution using the first column as the pivot column

$$\begin{array}{cccccc} x_1 & x_2 & x_3 & s_1 & s_2 & P \end{array}$$

$$\left[\begin{array}{cccccc|c} 1 & 1 & 2 & 1 & 0 & 0 & 20 \\ ② & 1 & 4 & 0 & 1 & 0 & 32 \\ \hdashline -3 & -3 & -2 & 0 & 0 & 1 & 0 \end{array}\right] \begin{array}{l} \frac{20}{1} = 20 \\ \frac{32}{2} = 16 \end{array}$$

$$\frac{1}{2}R_2 \to R_2$$

$$\sim \left[\begin{array}{cccccc|c} 1 & 1 & 2 & 1 & 0 & 0 & 20 \\ 1 & \frac{1}{2} & 2 & 0 & \frac{1}{2} & 0 & 16 \\ \hdashline -3 & -3 & -2 & 0 & 0 & 1 & 0 \end{array}\right]$$

$$(-1)R_2 + R_1 \to R_1, \quad 3R_2 + R_3 \to R_3$$

$$\sim \left[\begin{array}{cccccc|c} 0 & ①/② & 0 & 1 & -\frac{1}{2} & 0 & 4 \\ 1 & \frac{1}{2} & 2 & 0 & \frac{1}{2} & 0 & 16 \\ \hdashline 0 & -\frac{3}{2} & 4 & 0 & \frac{3}{2} & 1 & 48 \end{array}\right] \begin{array}{l} \frac{4}{1/2} = 8 \\ \frac{16}{1/2} = 32 \end{array}$$

$$2R_1 \to R_1$$

$$\sim \left[\begin{array}{cccccc|c} 0 & 1 & 0 & 2 & -1 & 0 & 8 \\ 1 & \frac{1}{2} & 2 & 0 & \frac{1}{2} & 0 & 16 \\ \hdashline 0 & -\frac{3}{2} & 4 & 0 & \frac{3}{2} & 1 & 48 \end{array}\right]$$

$$\left(-\frac{1}{2}\right)R_1 + R_2 \to R_2, \quad \frac{3}{2}R_1 + R_3 \to R_3$$

$$\begin{array}{cccccc} & x_1 & x_2 & x_3 & s_1 & s_2 & P \end{array}$$

$$\sim \begin{array}{c} x_2 \\ x_1 \\ P \end{array} \left[\begin{array}{cccccc|c} 0 & 1 & 0 & 2 & -1 & 0 & 8 \\ 1 & 0 & 2 & -1 & 1 & 0 & 12 \\ \hdashline 0 & 0 & 4 & 3 & 0 & 1 & 60 \end{array}\right]$$

Optimal solution: max $P = 60$ at $x_1 = 12$, $x_2 = 8$, $x_3 = 0$, $s_1 = 0$, $s_2 = 0$

(B) Solution using the second column as the pivot column

$$\begin{array}{cccccc} & x_1 & x_2 & x_3 & s_1 & s_2 & P \end{array}$$

$$\begin{array}{c} s_1 \\ s_2 \\ P \end{array} \left[\begin{array}{cccccc|c} 1 & ① & 2 & 1 & 0 & 0 & 20 \\ 2 & 1 & 4 & 0 & 1 & 0 & 32 \\ \hdashline -3 & -3 & -2 & 0 & 0 & 1 & 0 \end{array}\right] \begin{array}{l} \frac{20}{1} = 20 \\ \frac{32}{1} = 32 \end{array}$$

$$(-1)R_1 + R_2 \to R_2, \quad 3R_1 + R_3 \to R_3$$

$$\begin{array}{c} \\ x_2 \\ \sim \quad s_2 \\ P \end{array} \begin{array}{cccccc} x_1 & x_2 & x_3 & s_1 & s_2 & P \\ \left[\begin{array}{cccccc|c} 1 & 1 & 2 & 1 & 0 & 0 & 20 \\ 1 & 0 & 2 & -1 & 1 & 0 & 12 \\ \hline 0 & 0 & 4 & 3 & 0 & 1 & 60 \end{array}\right] \end{array}$$

Optimal solution: max $P = 60$
at $x_1 = 0$, $x_2 = 20$, $x_3 = 0$,
$s_1 = 0$, $s_2 = 12$

The maximum value of P is 60. Since the optimal solution is obtained at two corner points, (12, 8, 0) and (0, 20, 0), every point on the line segment connecting these points is also an optimal solution.

37. Let x_1 = the number of A components
x_2 = the number of B components
x_3 = the number of C components
The mathematical model for this problem is:
Maximize $P = 7x_1 + 8x_2 + 10x_3$
Subject to $\quad 2x_1 + 3x_2 + 2x_3 \le 1000$
$\qquad\qquad x_1 + x_2 + 2x_3 \le 800$
$\qquad\qquad x_1, \ x_2, \ x_3 \ge 0$

We introduce slack variables s_1, s_2 to obtain the equivalent form:
$$2x_1 + 3x_2 + 2x_3 + s_1 \qquad\qquad = 1000$$
$$x_1 + x_2 + 2x_3 \qquad + s_2 \qquad = 800$$
$$-7x_1 - 8x_2 - 10x_3 \qquad\qquad + P = \quad 0$$

The simplex tableau for this problem is:

$$\begin{array}{c} \\ s_1 \\ s_2 \\ P \end{array} \begin{array}{cccccc} x_1 & x_2 & x_3 & s_1 & s_2 & P \\ \left[\begin{array}{cccccc|c} 2 & 3 & 2 & 1 & 0 & 0 & 1000 \\ 1 & 1 & ② & 0 & 1 & 0 & 800 \\ \hline -7 & -8 & -10 & 0 & 0 & 1 & 0 \end{array}\right] \end{array} \begin{array}{l} \frac{1000}{2} = 500 \\[4pt] \frac{800}{2} = 400 \end{array}$$

$$\frac{1}{2}R_2 \to R_2$$

$$\sim \left[\begin{array}{cccccc|c} 2 & 3 & 2 & 1 & 0 & 0 & 1000 \\ \frac{1}{2} & \frac{1}{2} & ① & 0 & \frac{1}{2} & 0 & 400 \\ \hline -7 & -8 & -10 & 0 & 0 & 1 & 0 \end{array}\right]$$

$$(-2)R_2 + R_1 \to R_1, \quad 10R_2 + R_3 \to R_3$$

$$\sim \left[\begin{array}{cccccc|c} 1 & ② & 0 & 1 & -1 & 0 & 200 \\ \frac{1}{2} & \frac{1}{2} & 1 & 0 & \frac{1}{2} & 0 & 400 \\ \hline -2 & -3 & 0 & 0 & 5 & 1 & 4000 \end{array}\right] \begin{array}{l} \frac{200}{2} = 100 \\[4pt] \frac{400}{1/2} = 800 \end{array}$$

$$\frac{1}{2}R_1 \to R_1$$

$$\sim \begin{bmatrix} \frac{1}{2} & \textcircled{1} & 0 & \frac{1}{2} & -\frac{1}{2} & 0 & | & 100 \\ \frac{1}{2} & \frac{1}{2} & 1 & 0 & \frac{1}{2} & 0 & | & 400 \\ \hdashline -2 & -3 & 0 & 0 & 5 & 1 & | & 4000 \end{bmatrix}$$

$$\left(-\frac{1}{2}\right)R_1 + R_2 \rightarrow R_2, \quad 3R_1 + R_3 \rightarrow R_3$$

$$\sim \begin{bmatrix} \textcircled{\frac{1}{2}} & 1 & 0 & \frac{1}{2} & -\frac{1}{2} & 0 & | & 100 \\ \frac{1}{4} & 0 & 1 & -\frac{1}{4} & \frac{3}{4} & 0 & | & 350 \\ \hdashline -\frac{1}{2} & 0 & 0 & \frac{3}{2} & \frac{7}{2} & 1 & | & 4300 \end{bmatrix} \begin{matrix} \frac{100}{1/2} = 200 \\ \frac{350}{1/4} = 1400 \end{matrix}$$

$$2R_1 \rightarrow R_1$$

$$\sim \begin{bmatrix} 1 & 2 & 0 & 1 & -1 & 0 & | & 200 \\ \frac{1}{4} & 0 & 1 & -\frac{1}{4} & \frac{3}{4} & 0 & | & 350 \\ \hdashline -\frac{1}{2} & 0 & 0 & \frac{3}{2} & \frac{7}{2} & 1 & | & 4300 \end{bmatrix}$$

$$\left(-\frac{1}{4}\right)R_1 + R_2 \rightarrow R_2, \quad \frac{1}{2}R_1 + R_3 \rightarrow R_3$$

$$\sim \begin{matrix} & \begin{matrix} x_1 & x_2 & x_3 & s_1 & s_2 & P \end{matrix} \\ \begin{matrix} x_1 \\ x_3 \\ P \end{matrix} & \begin{bmatrix} 1 & 2 & 0 & 1 & -1 & 0 & | & 200 \\ 0 & -\frac{1}{2} & 1 & -\frac{1}{2} & 1 & 0 & | & 300 \\ \hdashline 0 & 1 & 0 & 2 & 3 & 1 & | & 4400 \end{bmatrix} \end{matrix}$$

Optimal solution: the maximum profit is $4400 when 200 A components, 0 B components and 300 C components are manufactured.

39. Let x_1 = the amount invested in government bonds,

x_2 = the amount invested in mutual funds,

and x_3 = the amount invested in money market funds.

The mathematical model for this problem is:

Maximize $P = .08x_1 + .13x_2 + .15x_3$

Subject to: $x_1 + x_2 + x_3 \leq 100,000$

$x_2 + x_3 \leq x_1$

$x_1, x_2, x_3 \geq 0$

We introduce slack variables s_1 and s_2 to obtain the equivalent form:

$$\begin{aligned} x_1 + x_2 + x_3 + s_1 &= 100,000 \\ -x_1 + x_2 + x_3 + s_2 &= 0 \\ -.08x_1 - .13x_2 - .15x_3 + P &= 0 \end{aligned}$$

The simplex tableau for this problem is:

$$
\begin{array}{c}
 \\
s_1 \\
s_2 \\
P
\end{array}
\begin{array}{c}
\begin{array}{cccccc}
x_1 & x_2 & x_3 & s_1 & s_2 & P
\end{array} \\
\left[\begin{array}{cccccc|c}
1 & 1 & 1 & 1 & 0 & 0 & 100,000 \\
-1 & 1 & \boxed{1} & 0 & 1 & 0 & 0 \\
\hline
-.08 & -.13 & -.15 & 0 & 0 & 1 & 0
\end{array}\right]
\end{array}
\begin{array}{c}
\dfrac{100,000}{1} = 100,000
\end{array}
$$

$(-1)R_2 + R_1 \rightarrow R_1$ and $.15R_2 + R_3 \rightarrow R_3$

$$
\sim
\left[\begin{array}{cccccc|c}
\boxed{2} & 0 & 0 & 1 & -1 & 0 & 100,000 \\
-1 & 1 & 1 & 0 & 1 & 0 & 0 \\
\hline
-.23 & .02 & 0 & 0 & .15 & 1 & 0
\end{array}\right]
\sim
\left[\begin{array}{cccccc|c}
\boxed{1} & 0 & 0 & \frac{1}{2} & -\frac{1}{2} & 0 & 50,000 \\
-1 & 1 & 1 & 0 & 1 & 0 & 0 \\
\hline
-.23 & .02 & 0 & 0 & .15 & 1 & 0
\end{array}\right]
$$

$$\frac{1}{2}R_1 \rightarrow R_1 \qquad\qquad\qquad R_1 + R_2 \rightarrow R_2 \text{ and } .23R_1 + R_3 \rightarrow R_3$$

$$
\begin{array}{c}
 \\
x_1 \\
x_2 \\
P
\end{array}
\begin{array}{c}
\begin{array}{cccccc}
x_1 & x_2 & x_3 & s_1 & s_2 & P
\end{array} \\
\sim\left[\begin{array}{cccccc|c}
1 & 0 & 0 & \frac{1}{2} & -\frac{1}{2} & 0 & 50,000 \\
0 & 1 & 1 & \frac{1}{2} & \frac{1}{2} & 0 & 50,000 \\
\hline
0 & .02 & 0 & .115 & .035 & 1 & 11,500
\end{array}\right]
\end{array}
$$

Optimal solution: the maximum return is \$11,500 when $x_1 =$ \$50,000 is invested in government bonds, $x_2 = \$0$ is invested in mutual funds, and $x_3 = \$50,000$ is invested in money market funds.

41. Let x_1 = the number of daytime ads,
x_2 = the number of prime-time ads,
and x_3 = the number of late-night ads.

The mathematical model for this problem is:
Maximize $P = 14,000x_1 + 24,000x_2 + 18,000x_3$
Subject to: $1000x_1 + 2000x_2 + 1500x_3 \leq 20,000$
$x_1 + x_2 + x_3 \leq 15$
$x_1,\ x_2,\ x_3 \geq 0$

We introduce slack variables to obtain the following initial form:
$$1000x_1 + 2000x_2 + 1500x_3 + s_1 = 20,000$$
$$x_1 + x_2 + x_3 + s_2 = 15$$
$$-14,000x_1 - 24,000x_2 - 18,000x_3 + P = 0$$

The simplex tableau for this problem is:

$$
\begin{array}{c}
 \\
s_1 \\
s_2 \\
P
\end{array}
\begin{array}{c}
\begin{array}{cccccc}
x_1 & x_2 & x_3 & s_1 & s_2 & P
\end{array} \\
\left[\begin{array}{cccccc|c}
1000 & \boxed{2000} & 1500 & 1 & 0 & 0 & 20,000 \\
1 & 1 & 1 & 0 & 1 & 0 & 15 \\
\hline
-14,000 & -24,000 & -18,000 & 0 & 0 & 1 & 0
\end{array}\right]
\end{array}
\begin{array}{c}
\dfrac{20,000}{2000} = 10 \\[2ex]
\dfrac{15}{1} = 15
\end{array}
$$

$$\frac{1}{2000}R_1 \rightarrow R_1$$

$$\sim \begin{bmatrix} \frac{1}{2} & \boxed{1} & \frac{3}{4} & \frac{1}{2000} & 0 & 0 & | & 10 \\ 1 & 1 & 1 & 0 & 1 & 0 & | & 15 \\ \hline -14,000 & -24,000 & -18,000 & 0 & 0 & 1 & | & 0 \end{bmatrix}$$

$(-1)R_1 + R_2 \to R_2, \quad 24,000R_1 + R_3 \to R_3$

$$\sim \begin{bmatrix} \frac{1}{2} & 1 & \frac{3}{4} & \frac{1}{2000} & 0 & 0 & | & 10 \\ \boxed{\frac{1}{2}} & 0 & \frac{1}{4} & -\frac{1}{2000} & 1 & 0 & | & 5 \\ \hline -2000 & 0 & 0 & 12 & 0 & 1 & | & 240,000 \end{bmatrix}$$

$2R_2 \to R_2$

$$\sim \begin{bmatrix} \frac{1}{2} & 1 & \frac{3}{4} & \frac{1}{2000} & 0 & 0 & | & 10 \\ \boxed{1} & 0 & \frac{1}{2} & -\frac{1}{1000} & 2 & 0 & | & 10 \\ \hline -2000 & 0 & 0 & 12 & 0 & 1 & | & 240,000 \end{bmatrix}$$

$\left(-\frac{1}{2}\right)R_2 + R_1 \to R_c, \quad 2000R_2 + R_3 \to R_3$

$$\sim \begin{array}{c} \\ x_2 \\ x_1 \\ P \end{array} \begin{array}{cccccc} x_1 & x_2 & x_3 & s_1 & s_2 & P \end{array}$$

	x_1	x_2	x_3	s_1	s_2	P		
x_2	0	1	$\frac{1}{2}$	$\frac{1}{1000}$	-1	0		5
x_1	1	0	$\frac{1}{2}$	$-\frac{1}{1000}$	2	0		10
P	0	0	1000	10	4000	1		260,000

Optimal solution: maximum number of potential customers is 260,000 when $x_1 = 10$ daytime ads, $x_2 = 5$ prime-time ads, and $x_3 = 0$ late-night ads are placed.

43. Let x_1 = the number of colonial houses,

x_2 = the number of split-level houses,

and x_3 = the number of ranch-style houses.

(A) The mathematical model for this problem is:

Maximize $P = 20,000x_1 + 18,000x_2 + 24,000x_3$

Subject to:
$$\frac{1}{2}x_1 + \frac{1}{2}x_2 + x_3 \le 30$$
$$60,000x_1 + 60,000x_2 + 80,000x_3 \le 3,200,000$$
$$4,000x_1 + 3,000x_2 + 4,000x_3 \le 180,000$$
$$x_1,\ x_2,\ x_3 \ge 0$$

We simplify the inequalities and then introduce slack variables to obtain the initial form:

$$\frac{1}{2}x_1 + \frac{1}{2}x_2 + x_3 + s_1 \qquad\qquad = 30$$
$$6x_1 + 6x_2 + 8x_3 + s_2 \qquad\quad = 320$$
$$4x_1 + 3x_2 + 4x_3 \qquad\quad + s_3 \quad = 180$$
$$-20{,}000x_1 - 18{,}000x_2 - 24{,}000x_3 \qquad\qquad\quad + P = 0$$

[Note: This simplification will change the interpretation of the slack variables.]

The simplex tableau for this problem is:

$$
\begin{array}{c}
\\ s_1 \\ s_2 \\ s_3 \\ P
\end{array}
\begin{array}{c}
x_1 \quad\ x_2 \quad\ x_3 \ \ s_1 \ s_2 \ s_3 \ \ P \\
\left[\begin{array}{ccccccc|c}
\frac{1}{2} & \frac{1}{2} & \textcircled{1} & 1 & 0 & 0 & 0 & 30 \\
6 & 6 & 8 & 0 & 1 & 0 & 0 & 320 \\
4 & 3 & 4 & 0 & 0 & 1 & 0 & 180 \\
\hline
-20{,}000 & -18{,}000 & -24{,}000 & 0 & 0 & 0 & 1 & 0
\end{array}\right]
\end{array}
\begin{array}{l}
\frac{30}{1} = 30 \\[4pt]
\frac{320}{8} = 40 \\[4pt]
\frac{180}{4} = 45
\end{array}
$$

$$(-8)R_1 + R_2 \to R_2, \quad (-4)R_1 + R_3 \to R_3, \quad 24{,}000R_1 + R_4 \to R_4$$

$$
\sim
\left[\begin{array}{ccccccc|c}
\frac{1}{2} & \frac{1}{2} & 1 & 1 & 0 & 0 & 0 & 30 \\
2 & 2 & 0 & -8 & 1 & 0 & 0 & 80 \\
\textcircled{2} & 1 & 0 & -4 & 0 & 1 & 0 & 60 \\
\hline
-8000 & -6000 & 0 & 24{,}000 & 0 & 0 & 1 & 720{,}000
\end{array}\right]
$$

$$\frac{1}{2}R_3 \to R_3$$

$$
\sim
\left[\begin{array}{ccccccc|c}
\frac{1}{2} & \frac{1}{2} & 1 & 1 & 0 & 0 & 0 & 30 \\
2 & 2 & 0 & -8 & 1 & 0 & 0 & 80 \\
\textcircled{1} & \frac{1}{2} & 0 & -2 & 0 & \frac{1}{2} & 0 & 30 \\
\hline
-8000 & -6000 & 0 & 24{,}000 & 0 & 0 & 1 & 720{,}000
\end{array}\right]
$$

$$\left(-\frac{1}{2}\right)R_3 + R_1 \to R_1, \quad (-2)R_3 + R_2 \to R_2, \quad 8000R_3 + R_4 \to R_4$$

$$
\sim
\left[\begin{array}{ccccccc|c}
0 & \frac{1}{4} & 1 & 2 & 0 & -\frac{1}{4} & 0 & 15 \\
0 & \textcircled{1} & 0 & -4 & 1 & -1 & 0 & 20 \\
1 & \frac{1}{2} & 0 & -2 & 0 & \frac{1}{2} & 0 & 30 \\
\hline
0 & -2000 & 0 & 8000 & 0 & 4000 & 1 & 960{,}000
\end{array}\right]
$$

$$\left(-\frac{1}{4}\right)R_2 + R_1 \to R_1, \quad \left(-\frac{1}{2}\right)R_2 + R_3 \to R_3, \quad 2000R_2 + R_4 \to R_4$$

$$\begin{array}{c} \\ x_3 \\ x_2 \\ \sim \; x_1 \\ \\ P \end{array} \begin{array}{ccccccc} x_1 & x_2 & x_3 & s_1 & s_2 & s_3 & P \end{array}$$

	x_1	x_2	x_3	s_1	s_2	s_3	P	
x_3	0	0	1	3	$-\frac{1}{4}$	0	0	10
x_2	0	1	0	-4	1	-1	0	20
x_1	1	0	0	0	$-\frac{1}{2}$	1	0	20
P	0	0	0	0	2000	2000	1	1,000,000

Optimal solution: maximum profit is $1,000,000 when $x_1 = 20$ colonial houses, $x_2 = 20$ split-level houses, and $x_3 = 10$ ranch-style houses are built.

(B) The mathematical model for this problem is:
Maximize $P = 17,000x_1 + 18,000x_2 + 24,000x_3$

Subject to:
$$\frac{1}{2}x_1 + \frac{1}{2}x_2 + x_3 \le 30$$
$$60,000x_1 + 60,000x_2 + 80,000x_3 \le 3,200,000$$
$$4,000x_1 + 3,000x_2 + 4,000x_3 \le 180,000$$

Following the solution in part (A), we obtain the simplex tableau:

	x_1	x_2	x_3	s_1	s_2	s_3	P		
s_1	$\frac{1}{2}$	$\frac{1}{2}$	①	1	0	0	0	30	$\frac{30}{1} = 30$
s_2	6	6	8	0	1	0	0	320	$\frac{320}{8} = 40$
s_3	4	3	4	0	0	1	0	180	$\frac{180}{4} = 45$
P	-17,000	-18,000	-24,000	0	0	0	1	0	

$$(-8)R_1 + R_2 \to R_2, \quad (-4)R_1 + R_3 \to R_3, \quad 24,000R_1 + R_4 \to R_4$$

	$\frac{1}{2}$	$\frac{1}{2}$	1	1	0	0	0	30	$\frac{30}{1/2} = 60$
	2	②	0	-8	1	0	0	80	$\frac{80}{2} = 40$
$\sim$	2	1	0	-4	0	1	0	60	$\frac{60}{1} = 60$
	-5000	-6000	0	24,000	0	0	1	720,000	

$$\frac{1}{2}R_2 \to R_2$$

	$\frac{1}{2}$	$\frac{1}{2}$	1	1	0	0	0	30
	1	①	0	-4	$\frac{1}{2}$	0	0	40
$\sim$	2	1	0	-4	0	1	0	60
	-5000	-6000	0	24,000	0	0	1	720,000

$$\left(-\frac{1}{2}\right)R_2 + R_1 \to R_1, \quad (-1)R_2 + R_3 \to R_3, \quad 6,000R_2 + R_4 \to R_4$$

$$
\begin{array}{c} \\ x_3 \\ x_2 \\ \sim \quad s_3 \\ \\ P \end{array}
\begin{array}{ccc}
\quad x_1 & x_2 & x_3 & s_1 & s_2 & s_3 & P \\
\left[\begin{array}{ccccccc}
0 & 0 & 1 & 3 & -\frac{1}{4} & 0 & 0 \\
1 & 1 & 0 & -4 & \frac{1}{2} & 0 & 0 \\
1 & 0 & 0 & 0 & -\frac{1}{2} & 1 & 0 \\
\hline
1000 & 0 & 0 & 0 & 3000 & 0 & 1
\end{array}\right.
& \left|\begin{array}{c}
10 \\
40 \\
20 \\
\hline
960,000
\end{array}\right]
\end{array}
$$

Optimal solution: maximum profit is \$960,000 when $x_1 = 0$ colonial houses, $x_2 = 40$ split level houses and $x_3 = 10$ ranch houses are built. In this case, $s_3 = 20$ (thousand) labor hours are not used.

(C) The mathematical model for this problem is:

Maximize $P = 25,000x_1 + 18,000x_2 + 24,000x_3$

Subject to:
$$\frac{1}{2}x_1 + \frac{1}{2}x_2 + x_3 \leq 30$$
$$60,000x_1 + 60,000x_2 + 80,000x_3 \leq 3,200,000$$
$$4,000x_1 + 3,000x_2 + 4,000x_3 \leq 180,000$$

Following the solutions in parts (A) and (B), we obtain the simplex tableau:

$$
\begin{array}{c} \\ s_1 \\ s_2 \\ s_3 \\ \\ P \end{array}
\begin{array}{ccc}
\quad x_1 & x_2 & x_3 & s_1 & s_2 & s_3 & P \\
\left[\begin{array}{ccccccc}
\frac{1}{2} & \frac{1}{2} & 1 & 1 & 0 & 0 & 0 \\
6 & 6 & 8 & 0 & 1 & 0 & 0 \\
④ & 3 & 4 & 0 & 0 & 1 & 0 \\
\hline
-25,000 & -18,000 & -24,000 & 0 & 0 & 0 & 1
\end{array}\right.
& \left|\begin{array}{c}
30 \\
320 \\
180 \\
\hline
0
\end{array}\right]
& \begin{array}{l}
\frac{30}{1/2} = 60 \\[4pt]
\frac{320}{6} = 53.33 \\[4pt]
\frac{180}{4} = 45 \\[4pt]
\end{array}
\end{array}
$$

$$\frac{1}{4}R_3 \to R_3$$

$$
\sim
\left[\begin{array}{ccccccc}
\frac{1}{2} & \frac{1}{2} & 1 & 1 & 0 & 0 & 0 \\
6 & 6 & 8 & 0 & 1 & 0 & 0 \\
① & \frac{3}{4} & 1 & 0 & 0 & \frac{1}{4} & 0 \\
\hline
-25,000 & -18,000 & -24,000 & 0 & 0 & 0 & 1
\end{array}\right.
\left|\begin{array}{c}
30 \\
320 \\
45 \\
\hline
0
\end{array}\right]
$$

$$\left(-\frac{1}{2}\right)R_3 + R_1 \to R_1, \quad -6R_3 + R_2 \to R_2, \quad 25,000R_3 + R_4 \to R_4$$

$$
\begin{array}{c} \\ s_1 \\ s_2 \\ \sim \quad x_1 \\ \\ P \end{array}
\begin{array}{ccc}
\quad x_1 & x_2 & x_3 & s_1 & s_2 & s_3 & P \\
\left[\begin{array}{ccccccc}
0 & \frac{1}{8} & \frac{1}{2} & 1 & 0 & -\frac{1}{8} & 0 \\
0 & \frac{3}{2} & 2 & 0 & 1 & \frac{3}{2} & 0 \\
1 & \frac{3}{4} & 1 & 0 & 0 & \frac{1}{4} & 0 \\
\hline
0 & 750 & 1000 & 0 & 0 & 6250 & 1
\end{array}\right.
& \left|\begin{array}{c}
7.5 \\
50 \\
45 \\
\hline
1,125,000
\end{array}\right]
\end{array}
$$

Optimal solution: maximum profit is \$1,125,000 when $x_1 = 45$ colonial houses, $x_2 = 0$ split level houses and $x_3 = 0$ ranch houses are built. In this case, $s_1 = 7.5$ acres of land, and $s_2 = 50(10,000) = \$500,000$ of capital are not used.

45. Let x_1 = the number of boxes of Assortment I,
x_2 = the number of boxes of Assortment II,
and x_3 = the number of boxes of Assortment III.

(A) The profit per box of Assortment I is:
$$9.40 - [4(0.20) + 4(0.25) + 12(0.30)] = \$4.00$$
The profit per box of Assortment II is:
$$7.60 - [12(0.20) + 4(0.25) + 4(0.30)] = \$3.00$$
The profit per box of Assortment III is:
$$11.00 - [8(0.20) + 8(0.25) + 8(0.30)] = \$5.00$$
The mathematical model for this problem is:

Maximize $P = 4x_1 + 3x_2 + 5x_3$

Subject to:
$$4x_1 + 12x_2 + 8x_3 \le 4800$$
$$4x_1 + 4x_2 + 8x_3 \le 4000$$
$$12x_1 + 4x_2 + 8x_3 \le 5600$$
$$x_1,\ x_2,\ x_3 \ge 0$$

We introduce slack variables to obtain the initial form:
$$4x_1 + 12x_2 + 8x_3 + s_1 = 4800$$
$$4x_1 + 4x_2 + 8x_3 + s_2 = 4000$$
$$12x_1 + 4x_2 + 8x_3 + s_3 = 5600$$
$$-4x_1 - 3x_2 - 5x_3 + P = 0$$

$$
\begin{array}{c}
\\
s_1 \\
s_2 \\
s_3 \\
P
\end{array}
\begin{array}{c}
\begin{array}{ccccccc}
x_1 & x_2 & x_3 & s_1 & s_2 & s_3 & P
\end{array} \\
\left[
\begin{array}{ccccccc|c}
4 & 12 & 8 & 1 & 0 & 0 & 0 & 4800 \\
4 & 4 & \boxed{8} & 0 & 1 & 0 & 0 & 4000 \\
12 & 4 & 8 & 0 & 0 & 1 & 0 & 5600 \\
\hline
-4 & -3 & -5 & 0 & 0 & 0 & 1 & 0
\end{array}
\right]
\end{array}
\begin{array}{l}
\frac{4800}{8} = 600 \\[4pt]
\frac{4000}{8} = 500 \\[4pt]
\frac{5600}{8} = 700 \\[4pt]

\end{array}
$$

$$\tfrac{1}{8}R_2 \to R_2$$

$$
\sim
\left[
\begin{array}{ccccccc|c}
4 & 12 & 8 & 1 & 0 & 0 & 0 & 4800 \\
\frac{1}{2} & \frac{1}{2} & \boxed{1} & 0 & \frac{1}{8} & 0 & 0 & 500 \\
12 & 4 & 8 & 0 & 0 & 1 & 0 & 5600 \\
\hline
-4 & -3 & -5 & 0 & 0 & 0 & 1 & 0
\end{array}
\right]
\sim
\left[
\begin{array}{ccccccc|c}
0 & 8 & 0 & 1 & -1 & 0 & 0 & 800 \\
\frac{1}{2} & \frac{1}{2} & 1 & 0 & \frac{1}{8} & 0 & 0 & 500 \\
\boxed{8} & 0 & 0 & 0 & -1 & 1 & 0 & 1600 \\
\hline
-\frac{3}{2} & -\frac{1}{2} & 0 & 0 & \frac{5}{8} & 0 & 1 & 2500
\end{array}
\right]
$$

$$(-8)R_2 + R_1 \to R_1,\quad (-8)R_2 + R_3 \to R_3,\qquad \tfrac{1}{8}R_3 \to R_3$$
$$5R_2 + R_4 \to R_4$$

$$
\sim
\left[
\begin{array}{ccccccc|c}
0 & 8 & 0 & 1 & -1 & 0 & 0 & 800 \\
\frac{1}{2} & \frac{1}{2} & 1 & 0 & \frac{1}{8} & 0 & 0 & 500 \\
\boxed{1} & 0 & 0 & 0 & -\frac{1}{8} & \frac{1}{8} & 0 & 200 \\
\hline
-\frac{3}{2} & -\frac{1}{2} & 0 & 0 & \frac{5}{8} & 0 & 1 & 2500
\end{array}
\right]
\sim
\left[
\begin{array}{ccccccc|c}
0 & \boxed{8} & 0 & 1 & -1 & 0 & 0 & 800 \\
0 & \frac{1}{2} & 1 & 0 & \frac{3}{16} & -\frac{1}{16} & 0 & 400 \\
1 & 0 & 0 & 0 & -\frac{1}{8} & \frac{1}{8} & 0 & 200 \\
\hline
0 & -\frac{1}{2} & 0 & 0 & \frac{7}{16} & \frac{3}{16} & 1 & 2800
\end{array}
\right]
$$

$$\left(-\tfrac{1}{2}\right)R_3 + R_2 \to R_2,\quad \tfrac{3}{2}R_3 + R_4 \to R_4,\qquad \tfrac{1}{8}R_1 \to R_1$$

$$\sim \begin{bmatrix} 0 & \textcircled{1} & 0 & \frac{1}{8} & -\frac{1}{8} & 0 & 0 & | & 100 \\ 0 & \frac{1}{2} & 1 & 0 & \frac{3}{16} & -\frac{1}{16} & 0 & | & 400 \\ 1 & 0 & 0 & 0 & -\frac{1}{8} & \frac{1}{8} & 0 & | & 200 \\ \hdashline 0 & -\frac{1}{2} & 0 & 0 & \frac{7}{16} & \frac{3}{16} & 1 & | & 2800 \end{bmatrix} \sim$$

$$\begin{array}{ccccccc} x_1 & x_2 & x_3 & s_1 & s_2 & s_3 & P \end{array}$$
$$\begin{bmatrix} 0 & 1 & 0 & \frac{1}{8} & -\frac{1}{8} & 0 & 0 & | & 100 \\ 0 & 0 & 1 & -\frac{1}{16} & \frac{1}{4} & -\frac{1}{16} & 0 & | & 350 \\ 1 & 0 & 0 & 0 & -\frac{1}{8} & \frac{1}{8} & 0 & | & 200 \\ \hdashline 0 & 0 & 0 & \frac{1}{16} & \frac{3}{8} & \frac{3}{16} & 1 & | & 2850 \end{bmatrix}$$

$$\left(-\frac{1}{2}\right)R_1 + R_2 \rightarrow R_2, \quad \frac{1}{8}R_1 + R_4 \rightarrow R_4$$

Optimal solution: maximum profit is $2850 when 200 boxes of Assortment I, 100 boxes of Assortment II, and 350 boxes of Assortment III are made.

(B) The mathematical model for this problem is:

Maximize $P = 4x_1 + 3x_2 + 5x_3$

Subject to:
$$\begin{aligned} 4x_1 + 12x_2 + 8x_3 &\le 4800 \\ 4x_1 + 4x_2 + 8x_3 &\le 5000 \\ 12x_1 + 4x_2 + 8x_3 &\le 5600 \end{aligned}$$

Following the solution in part (A), we obtain the simplex tableau:

$$\begin{array}{c} \\ s_1 \\ s_2 \\ s_3 \\ \\ P \end{array} \begin{array}{ccccccc} x_1 & x_2 & x_3 & s_1 & s_2 & s_3 & P \end{array}$$

$$\begin{bmatrix} 4 & 12 & \textcircled{8} & 1 & 0 & 0 & 0 & | & 4800 \\ 4 & 4 & 8 & 0 & 1 & 0 & 0 & | & 5000 \\ 12 & 4 & 8 & 0 & 0 & 1 & 0 & | & 5600 \\ \hdashline -4 & -3 & -5 & 0 & 0 & 0 & 1 & | & 0 \end{bmatrix} \quad \begin{array}{l} \frac{4800}{8} = 600 \\ \frac{5000}{8} = 625 \\ \frac{5600}{8} = 700 \end{array}$$

$$\frac{1}{8}R_1 \rightarrow R_1$$

$$\sim \begin{bmatrix} \frac{1}{2} & \frac{3}{2} & \textcircled{1} & \frac{1}{8} & 0 & 0 & 0 & | & 600 \\ 4 & 4 & 8 & 0 & 1 & 0 & 0 & | & 5000 \\ 12 & 4 & 8 & 0 & 0 & 1 & 0 & | & 5600 \\ \hdashline -4 & -3 & -5 & 0 & 0 & 0 & 1 & | & 0 \end{bmatrix}$$

$$(-8)R_1 + R_2 \rightarrow R_2, \quad (-8)R_1 + R_3 \rightarrow R_3, \quad 5R_1 + R_4 \rightarrow R_4$$

$$\sim \begin{bmatrix} \frac{1}{2} & \frac{3}{2} & 1 & \frac{1}{8} & 0 & 0 & 0 & | & 600 \\ 0 & -8 & 0 & -1 & 1 & 0 & 0 & | & 200 \\ \textcircled{8} & -8 & 0 & -1 & 0 & 1 & 0 & | & 800 \\ \hdashline -\frac{3}{2} & \frac{9}{2} & 0 & \frac{5}{8} & 0 & 0 & 1 & | & 3000 \end{bmatrix} \quad \begin{array}{l} \frac{600}{1/2} = 1200 \\ \\ \frac{800}{8} = 100 \end{array}$$

$$\frac{1}{8}R_3 \rightarrow R_3$$

$$\sim \begin{bmatrix} \frac{1}{2} & \frac{3}{2} & 1 & \frac{1}{8} & 0 & 0 & 0 & 600 \\ 0 & -8 & 0 & -1 & 1 & 0 & 0 & 200 \\ \textcircled{1} & -1 & 0 & -\frac{1}{8} & 0 & \frac{1}{8} & 0 & 100 \\ \hdashline -\frac{3}{2} & \frac{9}{2} & 0 & \frac{5}{8} & 0 & 0 & 1 & 3000 \end{bmatrix}$$

$$\left(-\frac{1}{2}\right)R_3 + R_1 \rightarrow R_1, \quad \left(\frac{3}{2}\right)R_3 + R_4 \rightarrow R_4$$

$$\begin{array}{c} \\ x_3 \\ s_2 \\ \sim \quad x_1 \\ \\ P \end{array} \begin{array}{c} \begin{array}{ccccccc} x_1 & x_2 & x_3 & s_1 & s_2 & s_3 & P \end{array} \\ \begin{bmatrix} 0 & 2 & 1 & \frac{3}{16} & 0 & -\frac{1}{16} & 0 & 550 \\ 0 & -8 & 0 & -1 & 1 & 0 & 0 & 200 \\ 1 & -1 & 0 & -\frac{1}{8} & 0 & \frac{1}{8} & 0 & 100 \\ \hdashline 0 & 3 & 0 & \frac{7}{16} & 0 & \frac{3}{16} & 1 & 3150 \end{bmatrix} \end{array}$$

Optimal solution: maximum profit is \$3,150 when $x_1 = 100$ boxes of assortment I, $x_2 = 0$ boxes of assortment II, and $x_3 = 550$ boxes of assortment III are produced. In this case, $s_2 = 200$ fruit-filled candies are not used.

(C) The mathematical model for this problem is:

Maximize $P = 4x_1 + 3x_2 + 5x_3$

Subject to:
$$\begin{aligned} 4x_1 + 12x_2 + 8x_3 &\leq 6000 \\ 4x_1 + 4x_2 + 8x_3 &\leq 6000 \\ 12x_1 + 4x_2 + 8x_3 &\leq 5600 \end{aligned}$$

Following the solutions in parts (A) and (B), we obtain the simplex tableau:

$$\begin{array}{c} \\ s_1 \\ s_2 \\ s_3 \\ \\ P \end{array} \begin{array}{c} \begin{array}{ccccccc} x_1 & x_2 & x_3 & s_1 & s_2 & s_3 & P \end{array} \\ \begin{bmatrix} 4 & 12 & 8 & 1 & 0 & 0 & 0 & 6000 \\ 4 & 4 & 8 & 0 & 1 & 0 & 0 & 6000 \\ 12 & 4 & \textcircled{8} & 0 & 0 & 1 & 0 & 5600 \\ \hdashline -4 & -3 & -5 & 0 & 0 & 0 & 1 & 0 \end{bmatrix} \end{array} \begin{array}{l} \frac{6000}{8} = 750 \\[6pt] \frac{6000}{8} = 750 \\[6pt] \frac{5600}{8} = 700 \end{array}$$

$$\frac{1}{8}R_3 \rightarrow R_3$$

$$\sim \begin{bmatrix} 4 & 12 & 8 & 1 & 0 & 0 & 0 & 6000 \\ 4 & 4 & 8 & 0 & 1 & 0 & 0 & 6000 \\ \frac{3}{2} & \frac{1}{2} & 1 & 0 & 0 & \frac{1}{8} & 0 & 700 \\ \hdashline -4 & -3 & -5 & 0 & 0 & 0 & 1 & 0 \end{bmatrix}$$

$$(-8)R_3 + R_1 \rightarrow R_1, \quad (-8)R_3 + R_2 \rightarrow R_2, \quad 5R_3 + R_4 \rightarrow R_4$$

659

$$\sim \begin{bmatrix} -8 & \circled{8} & 0 & 1 & 0 & -1 & 0 & 400 \\ -8 & 0 & 0 & 0 & 1 & -1 & 0 & 400 \\ \frac{3}{2} & \frac{1}{2} & 1 & 0 & 0 & \frac{1}{8} & 0 & 700 \\ \hdashline \frac{7}{2} & -\frac{1}{2} & 0 & 0 & 0 & \frac{5}{8} & 1 & 3500 \end{bmatrix} \begin{array}{l} \frac{400}{8} = 50 \\ \\ \frac{700}{1/2} = 1400 \end{array}$$

$$\frac{1}{8}R_1 \rightarrow R_1$$

$$\sim \begin{bmatrix} -1 & \circled{1} & 0 & \frac{1}{8} & 0 & -\frac{1}{8} & 0 & 50 \\ -8 & 0 & 0 & 0 & 1 & -1 & 0 & 400 \\ \frac{3}{2} & \frac{1}{2} & 1 & 0 & 0 & \frac{1}{8} & 0 & 700 \\ \hdashline \frac{7}{2} & -\frac{1}{2} & 0 & 0 & 0 & \frac{5}{8} & 1 & 3500 \end{bmatrix}$$

$$\left(-\frac{1}{2}\right)R_1 + R_3 \rightarrow R_3, \quad \frac{1}{2}R_1 + R_4 \rightarrow R_4$$

$$\begin{array}{c} \\ x_2 \\ s_2 \\ x_3 \\ \\ P \end{array} \overset{\begin{array}{ccccccc} x_1 & x_2 & x_3 & s_1 & s_2 & s_3 & P \end{array}}{\sim \begin{bmatrix} -1 & 1 & 0 & \frac{1}{8} & 0 & -\frac{1}{8} & 0 & 50 \\ -8 & 0 & 0 & 0 & 1 & -1 & 0 & 400 \\ 2 & 0 & 1 & -\frac{1}{16} & 0 & \frac{3}{16} & 0 & 675 \\ \hdashline 3 & 0 & 0 & \frac{1}{16} & 0 & \frac{9}{16} & 1 & 3525 \end{bmatrix}}$$

Optimal solution: maximum profit is \$3,525 when $x_1 = 0$ boxes of assortment I, $x_2 = 50$ boxes of assortment II, and $x_3 = 675$ boxes of assortment III are produced. In this case, $s_2 = 400$ fruit-filled candies are not used.

47. Let x_1 = the number of grams of food A,
x_2 = the number of grams of food B,
and x_3 = the number of grams of food C.

The mathematical model for this problem is:
Maximize $P = 3x_1 + 4x_2 + 5x_3$
Subject to: $x_1 + 3x_2 + 2x_3 \le 30$
$2x_1 + x_2 + 2x_3 \le 24$
$x_1, x_2, x_3 \ge 0$

We introduce slack variables s_1 and s_2 to obtain the initial form:

$$\begin{aligned} x_1 + 3x_2 + 2x_3 + s_1 \qquad\qquad &= 30 \\ 2x_1 + x_2 + 2x_3 \qquad + s_2 \qquad &= 24 \\ -3x_1 - 4x_2 - 5x_3 \qquad\qquad + P &= 0 \end{aligned}$$

The simplex tableau for this problem is:

$$\begin{array}{c} \\ s_1 \\ s_2 \\ P \end{array} \begin{array}{cccccc} x_1 & x_2 & x_3 & s_1 & s_2 & P \\ \left[\begin{array}{cccccc|c} 1 & 3 & 2 & 1 & 0 & 0 & 30 \\ 2 & 1 & \boxed{2} & 0 & 1 & 0 & 24 \\ \hdashline -3 & -4 & -5 & 0 & 0 & 1 & 0 \end{array}\right] \end{array} \begin{array}{l} \frac{30}{2} = 15 \\[4pt] \frac{24}{2} = 12 \end{array}$$

$$\frac{1}{2}R_2 \to R_2$$

$$\sim \left[\begin{array}{cccccc|c} 1 & 3 & 2 & 1 & 0 & 0 & 30 \\ 1 & \frac{1}{2} & \boxed{1} & 0 & \frac{1}{2} & 0 & 12 \\ \hdashline -3 & -4 & -5 & 0 & 0 & 1 & 0 \end{array}\right] \quad \sim \left[\begin{array}{cccccc|c} -1 & \boxed{2} & 0 & 1 & -1 & 0 & 6 \\ 1 & \frac{1}{2} & 1 & 0 & \frac{1}{2} & 0 & 12 \\ \hdashline 2 & -\frac{3}{2} & 0 & 0 & \frac{5}{2} & 1 & 60 \end{array}\right] \begin{array}{l} \frac{6}{2} = 3 \\[4pt] \frac{12}{1/2} = 24 \end{array}$$

$$(-2)R_2 + R_1 \to R_1, \quad 5R_2 + R_3 \to R_3 \qquad\qquad \frac{1}{2}R_1 \to R_1$$

$$\sim \left[\begin{array}{cccccc|c} -\frac{1}{2} & \boxed{1} & 0 & \frac{1}{2} & -\frac{1}{2} & 0 & 3 \\ 1 & \frac{1}{2} & 1 & 0 & \frac{1}{2} & 0 & 12 \\ \hdashline 2 & -\frac{3}{2} & 0 & 0 & \frac{5}{2} & 1 & 60 \end{array}\right] \quad \begin{array}{c} \\ x_2 \\ x_3 \\ P \end{array}\sim \begin{array}{cccccc} x_1 & x_2 & x_3 & s_1 & s_2 & P \\ \left[\begin{array}{cccccc|c} -\frac{1}{2} & 1 & 0 & \frac{1}{2} & -\frac{1}{2} & 0 & 3 \\ \frac{5}{4} & 0 & 1 & -\frac{1}{4} & \frac{3}{4} & 0 & \frac{21}{2} \\ \hdashline \frac{5}{4} & 0 & 0 & \frac{3}{4} & \frac{7}{4} & 1 & \frac{129}{2} \end{array}\right] \end{array}$$

$$\left(-\frac{1}{2}\right)R_1 + R_2 \to R_2, \quad \frac{3}{2}R_1 + R_3 \to R_3$$

Optimal solution: the maximum amount of protein is 64.5 units when $x_1 = 0$ grams of food A, $x_2 = 3$ grams of food B and $x_3 = 10.5$ grams of food C are used.

49. Let x_1 = the number of undergraduate students,
$\quad\quad x_2$ = the number of graduate students,
and x_3 = the number of faculty members.

The mathematical model for this problem is:
Maximize $P = 18x_1 + 25x_2 + 30x_3$
Subject to: $\quad x_1 + \quad x_2 + \quad x_3 \le 20$
$\quad\quad\quad\quad 100x_1 + 150x_2 + 200x_3 \le 3200$
$\quad\quad\quad\quad\quad\quad x_1, \; x_2, \; x_3 \ge 0$

Divide the second inequality by 50 to simplify the arithmetic. Then introduce slack variables s_1 and s_2 to obtain the initial form.

$$x_1 + \quad x_2 + \quad x_3 + s_1 \quad\quad\quad = 20$$
$$2x_1 + \quad 3x_2 + \quad 4x_3 \quad\quad + s_2 \quad\quad = 64$$
$$-18x_1 - 25x_2 - 30x_3 \quad\quad\quad\quad + P = 0$$

The simplex tableau for this problem is:

$$
\begin{array}{c}
\begin{array}{cccccc} x_1 & x_2 & x_3 & s_1 & s_2 & P \end{array} \\
\begin{array}{c} s_1 \\ s_2 \\ P \end{array}
\left[\begin{array}{cccccc|c}
1 & 1 & 1 & 1 & 0 & 0 & 20 \\
2 & 3 & ④ & 0 & 1 & 0 & 64 \\
\hline
-18 & -25 & -30 & 0 & 0 & 1 & 0
\end{array}\right]
\begin{array}{l} \frac{20}{1} = 20 \\[4pt] \frac{64}{4} = 16 \end{array}
\end{array}
$$

$$\tfrac{1}{4}\, R_2 \to R_2$$

$$
\sim
\left[\begin{array}{cccccc|c}
1 & 1 & 1 & 1 & 0 & 0 & 20 \\
\frac{1}{2} & \frac{3}{4} & ① & 0 & \frac{1}{4} & 0 & 16 \\
\hline
-18 & -25 & -30 & 0 & 0 & 1 & 0
\end{array}\right]
\quad \sim
\left[\begin{array}{cccccc|c}
⑫ \frac{1}{2} & \frac{1}{4} & 0 & 1 & -\frac{1}{4} & 0 & 4 \\
\frac{1}{2} & \frac{3}{4} & 1 & 0 & \frac{1}{4} & 0 & 16 \\
\hline
-3 & -\frac{5}{2} & 0 & 0 & \frac{15}{2} & 1 & 480
\end{array}\right]
\begin{array}{l} \frac{4}{1/2} = 8 \\[4pt] \frac{16}{1/2} = 32 \end{array}
$$

$$(-1)R_2 + R_1 \to R_1, \quad 30R_2 + R_3 \to R_3 \qquad\qquad 2R_1 \to R_1$$

$$
\sim
\left[\begin{array}{cccccc|c}
① & \frac{1}{2} & 0 & 2 & -\frac{1}{2} & 0 & 8 \\
\frac{1}{2} & \frac{3}{4} & 1 & 0 & \frac{1}{4} & 0 & 16 \\
\hline
-3 & -\frac{5}{2} & 0 & 0 & \frac{15}{2} & 1 & 480
\end{array}\right]
\quad \sim
\left[\begin{array}{cccccc|c}
1 & ⑫ \frac{1}{2} & 0 & 2 & -\frac{1}{2} & 0 & 8 \\
0 & \frac{1}{2} & 1 & -1 & \frac{1}{2} & 0 & 12 \\
\hline
0 & -1 & 0 & 6 & 6 & 1 & 504
\end{array}\right]
\begin{array}{l} \frac{8}{1/2} = 16 \\[4pt] \frac{12}{1/2} = 24 \end{array}
$$

$$\left(-\tfrac{1}{2}\right) R_1 + R_2 \to R_2, \quad 3R_1 + R_3 \to R_3 \qquad\qquad 2R_1 \to R_1$$

$$
\begin{array}{c}
\\
\sim
\left[\begin{array}{cccccc|c}
2 & 1 & 0 & 4 & -1 & 0 & 16 \\
0 & \frac{1}{2} & 1 & -1 & \frac{1}{2} & 0 & 12 \\
\hline
0 & -1 & 0 & 6 & 6 & 1 & 504
\end{array}\right]
\end{array}
\quad
\begin{array}{c}
\begin{array}{cccccc} x_1 & x_2 & x_3 & s_1 & s_2 & P \end{array}\\
\begin{array}{c} x_2 \\ x_3 \\ P \end{array}
\sim
\left[\begin{array}{cccccc|c}
2 & 1 & 0 & 4 & -1 & 0 & 16 \\
-1 & 0 & 1 & -3 & 1 & 0 & 4 \\
\hline
2 & 0 & 0 & 10 & 5 & 1 & 520
\end{array}\right]
\end{array}
$$

$$\left(-\tfrac{1}{2}\right) R_1 + R_2 \to R_2, \quad R_1 + R_3 \to R_3$$

Optimal solution: the maximum number of interviews is 520 when $x_1 = 0$ undergraduates, $x_2 = 16$ graduate students, and $x_3 = 4$ faculty members are hired.